ESSENTIALS OF HUMAN ANATOMY & PHYSIOLOGY

ELAINE N. MARIEB, R.N., Ph.D.,

Holyoke Community College

NINTH EDITION

PEARSON

Benjamin Cummings

San Francisco Boston   New York
Cape Town Hong Kong London Madrid Mexico City
Montreal Munich Paris Singapore Sydney Tokyo Toronto

Senior Acquisitions Editor: Deirdre Espinoza
Project Editor: Sabrina Larson
Managing Editor: Wendy Earl
Production Supervisor: Janet Vail
Development Editor: Irene Nunes
Editorial Assistant: Shannon Cutt
Cover and Text Design: Yvo Riezebos Design
Copy Editor: Sally Peyrefitte
Proofreader: Martha Ghent

Indexer: Karen Hollister
Art Coordinator: Bettina Borer
Photo Researcher: Clare Maxwell
Director, Image Resource Center: Melinda Patelli
Image Rights and Permissions Manager: Zina Arabia
Senior Manufacturing Buyer: Stacey Weinberger
Marketing Manager: Gordon Lee
Compositor: Aptara Corporation

Cover Image: Veer/Canopy Photography/Le Studio.

Photo and illustration credits follow the Appendices.

Library of Congress Cataloging-in-Publication Data

Marieb, Elaine Nicpon
  Essentials of human anatomy & physiology/Elaine N. Marieb.–9th ed.
    p.; cm.
  Includes index.
  ISBN-13: 978-0-321-51353-3
  ISBN-10: 0-321-51353-3
  1. Human physiology, 2. Human anatomy
[DNLM: 1. Anatomy. 2. Physiological Processes. 3. Physiology. QS 4 M334e 2009] I. Title:
Essentials of human anatomy and physiology. II. Title.
  QP34.5.M455 2009
  612—dc22

                                                    2007041750

ISBN: 0-321-51353-3 (Student edition)
ISBN: 978-0-321-51353-3 (Student edition)
ISBN: 0-321-53189-2 (Professional copy)
ISBN: 978-0-321-53189-6 (Professional copy)
ISBN: 0-136-00165-3 (NASTA)
ISBN: 978-0-136-00165-2 (NASTA)
4 5 6 7 8 9 10—DOR—12 11 10 09

www.aw-bc.com

Preface to the Student

This book is written with you, the student, in mind. Human anatomy and physiology is more than just interesting—it is fascinating. To help get you involved in the study of this subject, a number of special features are incorporated throughout the book.

The *informal writing style* invites you to learn more about anatomy and physiology without intimidation. We want you to enjoy reading this book.

Topic boxes and *tables* are designed with you in mind. The topic boxes present scientific information that can be applied to your daily life. When reading the topic boxes, you will probably find yourself saying, "I didn't know that," or "Now I understand why. . . ." The tables are summaries of important information in the text. You should be able to use the tables when studying for an exam or reviewing an important topic.

Important terms are defined within the text as they are introduced and are listed at the ends of the chapters. An extensive *glossary* is provided at the back of the book to help you review these terms.

Phonetic spellings are provided for many of these important terms, especially those that are likely to be unfamiliar to you. To read these, you will need to remember the following rules:

1. Accent marks follow stressed syllables. The primary stress is shown by ', and the secondary stress by ".

2. Unless otherwise noted, assume that vowels at the ends of syllables are long and vowels followed by consonants are short. Exceptions to this rule are indicated by a bar (ˉ) over the vowel, which indicates a long vowel, or a breve sign (˘) over the vowel, indicating that the vowel is short.

For example, the phonetic spelling of "thrombophlebitis" is *throm″ bo-flĕ-bi′ tis*. The next-to-the-last syllable (*bi′*) receives the greatest stress, and the first syllable (*throm″*) gets the secondary stress. The vowel in the second syllable comes at the end of the syllable and is long. The vowel that comes at the end of the third syllable is short because it has a breve sign.

Any exam causes anxiety. Exams in anatomy and physiology are no exception. To help you better prepare for an exam or comprehend the material you have just read, extensive *summaries, review questions,* and *clinical problems* ("Critical Thinking & Clinical Application Questions") are found at the ends of the chapters. The *Systems in Sync* feature, which accompanies each system, will also be very helpful in your preparations because it lays out very simply the most important ways body systems interact with each other.

The art program is designed to help you learn the different structures and functions of the human body. All figures are referred to within the text discussion. The best way to make use of the extensive art program is to carefully study each illustration when it is discussed in the text.

Be sure to check out The Anatomy & Physiology Place, at www.anatomyandphysiology.com. You'll find an array of quizzes, activities, and other features to help you make the grade in A&P. To help you better understand physiological concepts, combine your reading of the text with your use of the *Essentials of InterActive Physiology*® CD-ROM packaged with your text. And remember—in every chapter summary you'll find handy references to the CD-ROM **IP** and The Anatomy & Physiology Place **WEB** to help you on specific topics.

I hope that you enjoy *Essentials of Human Anatomy and Physiology* and that this book makes learning A&P a fun and rewarding process. Write to me and let me know how you fare in your A&P course.

Elaine N. Marieb

Benjamin Cummings
1301 Sansome Street
San Francisco, CA 94111

There are only a couple of textbooks that have helped me change the way I teach. From the first time I opened the fourth edition of Elaine Marieb's book, I knew it was going to help my students be more successful.

The best feature of the ninth edition of *Essentials of Human Anatomy & Physiology* is Marieb's consistent and coherent philosophy. In this text, no concept is more important than homeostasis. A good teacher always wants his or her students to see the bigger picture and this text provides many opportunities to relate homeostasis to other concepts. Features such as Homeostatic Imbalance and Systems in Sync are easy ways to help students connect concepts to prior experience and stimulate interest in the material.

Whether you primarily use a lecture/discussion approach or an inquiry approach in your teaching, the objective checklist found at the beginning of each chapter will help you create the standards for your course. The tight integration of the textbook with the anatomyandphysiology.com website, the Media Manager, and the *Essentials of InterActive Physiology* CD make it easy to create different kinds of lessons for each unit based on your teaching style. Creating differentiated assessments is also easy to do. You won't have to spend a lot of time modifying test questions to fit your classes—the questions available in the chapter and test bank are appropriate for the typical high school level student.

Many students take Anatomy and Physiology because they have an interest in a medical career. So part of my job is to expose them to the range of career possibilities available in medicine and related fields other than doctor or nurse. In my course, I bring in guest speakers who do unique jobs, but that approach is limited. The career feature in each chapter provides my students with a chance to explore many careers they might not have considered. Because all of the career features are supported by an extensive website, students can find out everything about a career, from education requirements to expected salary.

This ninth edition of *Essentials of Human Anatomy & Physiology* continues to set the standard for Anatomy and Physiology texts.

John Murnan

Etowah High School
Woodstock, GA

PREFACE TO THE TEACHER

With the ninth edition of *Essentials of Human Anatomy & Physiology* in our hands, I would like to take this opportunity to thank my loyal users and those who have provided constructive criticism to me over the past 20-plus years. My vision for this book is that it speaks the language of the health science student. I have found over the years that using a straightforward, unintimidating writing style is the best way to help students with a limited background in the sciences grasp the fundamental concepts of human anatomy and the inner workings of the body, and you will find that this edition continues in that tradition. I have updated the book thoroughly (see page x for a list of specific chapter-by-chapter changes) and included timely topics, such as immunology and clinical advances, so that the explanations are both accurate and current. The following pages describe the ninth edition of *Essentials of Human Anatomy & Physiology* in more detail.

Organization

As before, extensive reviews by anatomy and physiology instructors helped me decide on a particular presentation. My choice was to remain with a sequence of topics that encourages learning. The first chapter orients students to the new world of learning in which they become immersed in anatomical terminology, names of major body areas, and brief overviews of functions that must be performed to sustain life.

Chemistry, cells, tissues, and the first organ system (skin) are treated in succession. Most students find that the skin is an interesting system, and thus the transition to the organ system discussions is easily accomplished. Subsequent chapters include systems requiring a good deal of anatomical terminology (for example, skeletal, muscular, and nervous systems). Each organ system is approached from simple to increasingly complex levels. Building on an understanding of the concepts, rather than rote memorization, is emphasized.

Organizational Flexibility and Hallmark Writing Style

A good textbook meets the needs of both instructors and students. Because every instructor has a personal style and philosophic approach to teaching and course organization, I have written each chapter to allow flexibility in topic presentation. In the ninth edition, text material is offered up in smaller bites. More section heads have been added to focus student reading. All chapters are self contained; hence an instructor may choose a chapter sequence that is personally preferred.

The content of this edition continues to present a balance of anatomical and physiological concepts. Discussions of diseases and dysfunctions appear where they enhance and reinforce an understanding of normal human structure and function. The writing style is intentionally informal, and complex topics are explained consistently by the use of analogies to foster, rather than discourage, student interest. In instances requiring more than the usual amount of memorization of terminology and facts, the material is presented in both a text discussion and tabular form to reinforce learning. New terminology is set in boldface or italic type, followed by phonetic pronunciation. Terms are defined within the text and again in the glossary.

The kidneys, which maintain the purity and constancy of our internal fluids, are perfect examples of homeostatic organs. Much like sanitation workers who keep a city's water supply drinkable and dispose of its waste, the kidneys are usually unappreciated until there is a malfunction and "internal garbage" piles up. Every day, the kidneys filter gallons of fluid from the bloodstream. They then process this filtrate, allowing wastes and excess ions to leave the body in urine while returning needed substances to the blood in just the right proportions. Although the lungs and the skin also play roles in excretion, the kidneys bear the major responsibility for eliminating nitrogenous (nitrogen-containing) wastes, toxins, and drugs from the body.

Disposing of wastes and excess ions is only one part of the work of the kidneys. As they perform these excretory functions, they also regulate

Meaningful analogies and jargon-free explanations. Drawing on her own unique experience as an A&P professor and former nursing student, Marieb presents anatomy and physiology as a "story" that can be more easily understood and remembered.

STUDY TOOLS TO STIMULATE LEARNING

Several pedagogical devices are used to ensure that students learn important terminology and concepts. In addition to the illustrated tables and Did You Get It? questions highlighted below, each chapter begins with student objectives. A summary of text contents and review questions appear at the end of each chapter. New to this edition is Appendix D, where you can find the answers to end-of-chapter multiple choice review questions, as well as answers to the new Did You Get It? questions. Additionally, a list of word roots, prefixes, and suffixes is included in Appendix A.

Illustrated tables
summarize complex information and serve as a "one-stop shopping" study tool.

important disorders resulting from hypo- or hypersecretion of glucagon are known.

▶ DID YOU GET IT?

13. What hormone stimulates the kidneys to reabsorb more sodium?

14. Mrs. Bellamy's husband has suffered a heart attack and is hospitalized. Would you expect her blood glucose levels to be elevated, normal, or lower than normal? Why?

15. Which group of hormones produced by the adrenal cortex has some of the same effects as the ovaries and the testes?

16. Insulin and glucagon are both pancreatic hormones. Which stimulates cellular uptake of glucose?

For answers, see Appendix D.

NEW! Did You Get It? concept check questions follow major sections within each chapter, and serve to reinforce students' understanding of the main concepts of the section. These will also serve as a self-test for students to assess their progess in learning the chapter's concepts. Answers appear in Appendix D.

TABLE 6.1	Comparison of Skeletal, Cardiac, and Smooth Muscles		
Characteristic	**Skeletal**	**Cardiac**	**Smooth**
Body location	Attached to bones or, for some facial muscles, to skin	Walls of the heart	Mostly in walls of hollow visceral organs (other than the heart)
Cell shape and appearance	Single, very long, cylindrical, multinucleate cells with very obvious striations	Branching chains of cells; uninucleate, striations; intercalated discs	Single, fusiform, uninucleate; no striations
Connective tissue components	Epimysium, perimysium, and endomysium	Endomysium attached to the fibrous skeleton of the heart	Endomysium
Regulation of	Voluntary; via nervous controls	Involuntary; the heart has a pacemaker; also nervous system controls; hormones	Involuntary; nervous system controls; hormones, chemicals, stretch
	Fast	Slow	Very slow
		Yes	Yes, in some

PEDAGOGICALLY DRIVEN ART

Revisions to the Art Program

Several new pieces of art were added in this edition and many figures were reconceptualized or modernized. Keeping in mind that automatic learning is very important in studying and learning a subject like A&P, I continued to pay close attention to maintaining a uniform style and consistent use of color in recurring structures across chapters. Special attention was given to the labeling of each illustration to ensure that it is consistent with the discussion in the accompanying text.

All of the bone art has been completely rerendered by professional medical illustrators based on extensive rounds of feedback and accuracy checking, resulting in incredibly realistic, textured, and detailed bone figures. Each piece of muscle art was also rerendered to reflect in realistic detail the rich colors and texture of actual muscle.

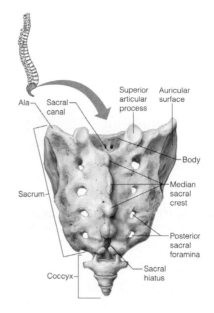

FIGURE 5.19 **Sacrum and coccyx, posterior view.**

REVISED! Incredibly realistic, three-dimensional bone art

REVISED! Systems in Sync art
This feature summarizes in simple form for the student the "must know" information about the interactions that occur between the system being studied and all other body systems. This approach, provided for each body system, helps to emphasize that the body is a dynamic composite of interdependent parts. All of the Systems in Sync figures have been rerendered to showcase more realistic, dynamic presentations of the integration of different body systems. In addition, the body system titles have been colorized, making these stunning figures easier than ever to navigate.

FIGURE 6.16 **Muscles of the anterior trunk, shoulder, and arm. (a)** Muscles crossing the shoulder joint, causing movements of the arm. The platysma of the neck is removed. **(b)** Muscles of the abdominal wall. Portions of the superficial muscles of the right side of the abdomen are cut away to reveal the deeper muscles.

REVISED! Muscle art presents a more realistic view of muscles

FEATURES TO CAPTURE STUDENT INTEREST

A Closer Look

All of the A Closer Look boxes have been updated to capture student interest with new advances in science and intriguing topics. Thoroughly updated subjects include topics such as contraception (p.574), obesity (p.508), and AIDS (p.432).

A CLOSER LOOK

TATTOOS

Tattos are made by using a needle to deposit pigment in the dermis. Tattooing is an ancient practice believed to have originated around 10,000 years ago. These days, tattoos are symbols of club membership for some men (street gangs, the military, fraternities); other people view them as symbols of individuality. In recent years, more women have acquired tattoos as a means of expression and for cosmetic purposes: permanent eyeliner

to be used over seven to nine treatments spaced about a month apart, each costing $75 to $150. The cost in pain is roughly equal to getting tattooed in the first place. Nonetheless, tattoo removal across the United States is skyrocketing.

Tattoos present some other risks. The FDA has some regulations

" Tattoo

focus on CAREERS

CERTIFIED SURGICAL TECHNOLOGIST

Surgical technologists use their knowledge of anatomy to assist surgeons in the operating room.

Ask Nathan Williams what it takes to be a good surgical technologist, and he will list several key qualities. "Attention to detail is crucial," he says. "You have to be methodical,

and surgical tools and technologies to facilitate a physician's performance in the operating room.

Says Williams, "My primary job is to maintain the sterility of the operating room environment. I start the day by setting up a sterile field—that is, I carefully open sealed surgical instruments and lay them out in an orderly fashion to prepare for each procedure. I try to anticipate everything the surgeon will need during that operation. Everything remains sterile until the end of the procedure, when I assist the patient onto a stretcher. After that, I sort out instruments for decontamination and remove my surgical gown and gloves. If this sterile environment is compromised, it can have devastating effects because the pa-

body, I have to be s only the smooth ty ceps with teeth cou nal organs."

Surgical technolo plete an accredited usually 9 to 12 mor cluding at least 90(

" I'n

surgeon'

eyes and

This is w

traini

Focus on Careers

This feature, which utilizes interviews with working professionals in allied health fields (such as LPN, phlebotomist, dental hygienist, and others), introduces students to several careers that rely to a substantial extent on a background in human anatomy and physiology. This feature may help students to validate their professional career choices or perhaps suggest new options they haven't yet considered.

EMPHASIS ON CLINICAL APPLICATIONS AND CRITICAL THINKING

l function is

 CRITICAL THINKING AND CLINICAL APPLICATION QUESTIONS

crine systems **(b)** the way in lls, and **(c)** the

24. A woman with excessive body hair and a deep voice shows the outward symptoms of which hormonal dysfunction?

NEW! Critical Thinking & Clinical Application Questions

This unique feature ends each chapter by asking questions that help students apply the knowledge they've gained to clinical situations.

Clinical examples with an emphasis on homeostasis

Because the normal and most desirable condition of the body is homeostasis, or maintenance of a stable internal environment, the concept of homeostasis is introduced early (Chapter 1) and is then emphasized throughout the book. Also stressed is the understanding that loss of homeostasis leads to pathology or disease–temporary or permanent. Thus, pathological conditions are introduced and integrated with the text material as appropriate to clarify normal functioning, not as an end in themselves. The normal functional process is always explained first. The chosen clinical examples are those seen most often by people working in the allied health fields and are intended to familiarize students with the possible consequences when body structures are damaged or functional processes diverge from normal pathways. In each case, the disease conditions are highlighted by the symbol of a seesaw that has been tipped off balance to remind students that disease is a loss of homeostasis.

HOMEOSTATIC IMBALANCE

If untreated, both deficits and excesses of GH may result in structural abnormalities. Hyposecretion of GH during childhood leads to **pituitary dwarfism** (Figure 9.5). Body proportions are fairly normal, but the person as a whole is a living miniature (with a maximum adult height of 4 feet). Hypersecretion during

Developmental Aspects of the Muscular System

In the developing embryo, the muscular system is laid down in segments (much like the structural plan of an earthworm), and then each segment is invaded by nerves. The m

Developmental aspects and aging

Each chapter ends with a section on developmental aspects. The section presents the formation of that system in the embryo and follows the changes that occur through old age. Important health problems unique to that system are introduced, and emphasis is placed on problems that accompany the aging process. Because many healthcare workers are involved in the care of elderly people, this emphasis will be valuable to today's student.

Figure legend questions accompany selected figures and

prod the student to interpret the concepts or illustrated processes or to make predictions about "what's next." They have proven their value and are retained for this edition.

What is the meaning of epi? Of mys? How do these word roots relate to the role and position of the epimysium?

- Blood vessel
- Perimysium
- Epimysium
- Muscle fiber (cell)

CHAPTER-BY-CHAPTER CHANGES

This edition has been thoroughly updated. Specific chapter-by-chapter changes include:

Chapter 1: The Human Body: An Orientation
- All new Figure 1.2, rerendered body systems figures
- New terms added to body landmarks
- New section added: Open Body Cavities

Chapter 2: Basic Chemistry
- Expanded discussion of forms of energy
- New Figure 2.4, Properties of a compound
- New Table 2.4, Factors Increasing the Rate of Chemical Reactions
- New figure questions for Figures 2.8 and 2.15
- New discussions on direction of chemical reactions and fatty acid chains and fats

Chapter 3: Cells and Tissues
- New figure question for Figure 3.2
- Expanded Figure 3.10, Diffusion through the plasma membrane

Chapter 4: Skin and Body Membranes
- Updated discussion of integumentary system
- Updated rules for recognizing melanoma
- New photomicrographs for Figure 4.6, Photomicrographs of cutaneous glands

Chapter 5: The Skeletal System
- All new bone art
- New Figure 5.5, Photo of the C-shaped spine typical of a newborn
- New Table 5.3, Summary of Joint Classes
- Expanded explanation of the bones of the arm and pelvic girdle

Chapter 6: The Muscular System
- All new muscle art
- New entry in Table 6.1 on connective tissue components, with art
- New entry in Table 6.4 on quadratus lumborum

Chapter 7: The Nervous Systems
- Updated discussion of cerebral cortex
- New photomicrograph in Figure 7.4, Structure of a motor neuron
- New Figure 7.15, Frontal section of the brain showing commissural fibers running between the cerebrum and the lower CNS
- New Figure 7.19, Hydrocephalus in a newborn (photo)
- New Figure 7.22, Schematic of ascending (sensory) and descending (motor) pathways between the brain and the spinal cord
- Updated information in Table 7.2, Spinal Nerve Plexuses
- Added adipose tissue as a target organ/system to Table 7.3, Effects of the Sympathetic and Parasympathetic Divisions of the Autonomic Nervous System

Chapter 8: Special Senses
- New Figure 8.1, Surface anatomy of the eye (photo)
- New discussion of the pigmented and neural layers of the eye
- Updated discussion of the external ear and internal ear, taste buds
- Updated homeostatic imbalance sections on hearing and equilibrium deficits

Chapter 9: The Endocrine System
- New section heads on endocrine gland stimuli
- New Figure 9.5, Disorders of pituitary growth hormone (photos)
- New photo for Closer Look box on potential uses for growth hormone
- New Figure 9.11, Microscopic structure of the adrenal gland
- Added resistin to hormones in Table 9.2, Hormones Produced by Organs Other than the Major Endocrine Organs

Chapter 10: Blood
- Updated discussion of the components of blood, albumin, and granulocytes
- New mnemonic for listing WBCs in order of relative abundance in the blood
- Added column in Table 10.3, ABO Blood Groups, for Native American statistics on % of different blood types compared to other groups
- All new material for Closer Look box on artificial blood substitutes

Chapter 11: The Cardiovascular System
- New discussion of the coverings of the heart
- New Figure 11.4, Anatomical differences in right and left ventricles
- New flowchart for Figure 11.7, influence of selected factors on cardiac output; new flowchart for Figure 11.21, summary of factors causing an increase in arterial blood pressure
- New Figure 11.15, The basic scheme of the hepatic portal system and associated vessels
- Updated Closer Look box on atherosclerosis, including two new photos
- New Figure 11.23, Bulk fluid flow across capillary walls

Chapter 12: The Lymphatic System and Body Defenses
- Updated Table 12.3, Function of Cells and Molecules Involved in Immunity
- Immune response cells style updated in figures to be more realistic

Chapter 13: The Respiratory System
- New discussion of respiration mechanisms
- Reorganized Figure 13.12, Breathing control centers, sensory inputs, and effector nerves

Chapter 14: The Digestive System and Body Metabolism
- New part (d) for Figure 14.14 showing cardioesophageal sphincter relaxed
- Updated Closer Look box on peptic ulcers, with new statistics, new discussion of treatments, and new additional photo of ulcer–causing bacteria
- Intestinal gastrin added to Table 14.1, Hormones and Hormonelike Products That Act in Digestion
- New discussion of colon contractions
- New Figure 14.17, USDA Food Guide Pyramid, with new discussion
- Updated Closer Look box on obesity, with new discussion of weight-loss drugs and supplements, and different diets, with updated statistics and a new photo

Chapter 15: The Urinary System
- Updated Closer Look box on renal failure, with new statistics and warning signs of kidney trouble, new discussion of transplants
- New Figure 15.9, The continuous mixing of body fluids
- Added discussion of plasma circulation and the thirst mechanism

Chapter 16: The Reproductive System
- Added discussion on metabolic effects of estrogen
- Expanded discussion of breast cancer homeostatic imbalance, with new discussion of heredity defects, genetic roots, and risk factors, with statistics
- New Figure 16.17, Photo of the seven–week embryo
- Updated Closer Look on contraception, with new discussion of methods on the market

MEDIA SUPPLEMENTS

Most of the teacher supplements and resources for this book are available electronically for download on the Instructor Resource Center (IRC). Please go to PHSchool.com/advanced and click "Online Teacher Supplements" for directions. You will be required to complete a one time registration subject to verification before being emailed access information to download materials.

NEW! Media Manager 2.0 CD-ROMs

New for this edition, this cross-platform set of CD-ROMs organizes all instructor media resources into one convenient and easy-to-use digital library of resources. The Media Manager includes all the figures and tables from the text in both JPEG and PowerPoint® format, which can be downloaded individually or in complete chapter sets. Select figures also appear as Label Edit Art, with fully customizable labels and leaders, as well as Step Edit Art, which breaks down complex physiological processes into step-by-step presentations. There are over 40 additional animations, as well as PowerPoint lecture presentation slides, clicker questions, the Instructor Guide and Test Bank in Microsoft Word, *Essentials of Inter-Active Physiology*® (IP for EHAP) slides, a new interactive "quiz show" that can be used during lecture to promote student interaction, and other valuable tools that help instructors create memorable presentations effortlessly. Instructors can search through the material, add assets to a shopping cart, and easily download them to their computers.

Updated and Expanded *Essentials of InterActive Physiology* (IP)

An award-winning, dynamic, and highly effective learning tool. This CD-ROM features activities specifically selected from the IP software for your one-semester course, with a new module on the digestive system. Also included are animations, tutorials, and quizzes. Icons with references to Essentials of IP tutorials appear in the chapter summaries of the text to help students integrate book coverage and media. This CD-ROM is included in the back of the text. A replacement CD (ISBN 0131357840) is available for purchase.

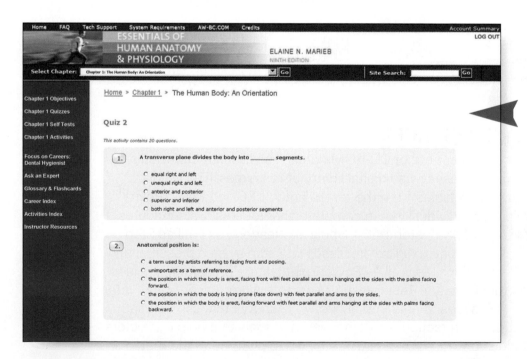

The Anatomy & Physiology Place Website

This redesigned and updated, open-access website includes learning activities, self tests, quizzes, case studies, and more for every chapter.

ADDITIONAL SUPPLEMENTS

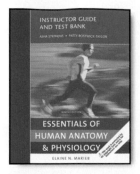

Updated and Expanded Instructor Guide/ Test Bank

The Instructor Guide has been revised to support each chapter in the ninth edition. Expanded lecture outlines, updated references, and new teaching tips make this guide a useful tool for instructors. The improved test bank now includes over 1500 questions (including many new and updated questions) in multiple formats with page references to the text, and difficulty ratings. There are two computerized test bank options available for this text. An **ExamView** version has been developed especially for high school users, and allows instructors to edit and customize tests. In addition, a TestGen version is available. Both are available for purchase.

Essentials of Human Anatomy & Physiology Laboratory Manual, **Fourth**

Edition by Elaine N. Marieb. This best-selling lab manual offers 27 concise, activity based lab exercises that explore basic concepts in anatomy and physiology. It includes a four-color histology atlas, an overview of safety in the lab, and a microscope exercise. Each lab is presented with learning objectives, exceptionally cogent summaries of key concepts, and meaningful activities that build students' observational laboratory skills. Available for purchase.

Transparency Acetates

The high-quality acetate package includes all illustrations (excluding photographs), approximately 275 images, from the text. They are easy to use and to read in any lecture setting. Available for purchase.

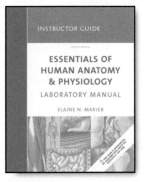

Instructor Guide to *Essentials of Human Anatomy & Physiology Laboratory Manual,* Fourth Edition

This useful guide includes detailed directions for setting up the laboratory, comments on the exercises, and answers to questions that appear in the laboratory manual. It includes an answer key, multimedia resources, and hints for lab preparation and presentation. Available for purchase.

Anatomy & Physiology Coloring Workbook: A Complete Study Guide, Ninth Edition

by Elaine N. Marieb. This excellent standalone workbook promotes learning with a variety of visual and written exercises, combining the best features and activities of both a study guide and a coloring book. Available for purchase.

ACKNOWLEDGMENTS

Many people contributed to my efforts in the creation of this ninth edition. In addition to the hundreds of college reviewers who critiqued this text, we would like to acknowledge the following high school teachers who reviewed content: Laura S. Cox, Woodstock High School, Woodstock, GA; Jeanne M. Dietrich, Clay High School, South Bend, IN; Jodi Hall, Cherokee High School, Canton, GA; Waynette Helms, Lassiter High School, Marietta, GA; Hyden Henry, Bergen Catholic High School, Oradell, NJ; Jennifer Kinsey, North Forsyth High School, Cumming, GA; John A. Murnan, Etowah High School, Woodstock, GA.

Elaine N. Marieb
Benjamin Cummings, San Francisco

Contents

1 THE HUMAN BODY: AN ORIENTATION 1

An Overview of Anatomy and Physiology 2

Anatomy 2

Physiology 2

Relationship between Anatomy and Physiology 2

Levels of Structural Organization 3

From Atoms to Organisms 3

Organ System Overview 4
Integumentary System • Skeletal System • Muscular System • Nervous System • Endocrine System • Cardiovascular System • Lymphatic System • Respiratory System • Digestive System • Urinary System • Reproductive System

Maintaining Life 10

Necessary Life Functions 10
Maintaining Boundaries • Movement • Responsiveness • Digestion • Metabolism • Excretion • Reproduction • Growth

Survival Needs 11

Homeostasis 12

Homeostatic Control Mechanisms 12
Homeostatic Imbalance

The Language of Anatomy 15

Anatomical Position 15

Directional Terms 15

Regional Terms 16
Anterior Body Landmarks • Posterior Body Landmarks

Body Planes and Sections 17

Body Cavities 17
Dorsal Body Cavity • Ventral Body Cavity

SUMMARY 22

REVIEW QUESTIONS 23

CRITICAL THINKING AND CLINICAL APPLICATION QUESTIONS 25

Focus on Careers Dental Hygienist 14

A Closer Look Medical Imaging: Illuminating the Body 8

2 BASIC CHEMISTRY 26

Concepts of Matter and Energy 27

Matter 27

Energy 27
Forms of Energy • Energy Form Conversions

Composition of Matter 29

Elements and Atoms 29

Atomic Structure 29
Planetary and Orbital Models of an Atom

Identifying Elements 31
Atomic Number • Atomic Mass • Atomic Weight and Isotopes

Molecules and Compounds 34

Chemical Bonds and Chemical Reactions 35

Bond Formation 35
Role of Electrons • Types of Chemical Bonds

Patterns of Chemical Reactions 40
Synthesis Reactions • Decomposition Reactions • Exchange Reactions • Factors Influencing the Rate of Chemical Reactions

Chapter 2, continued

Biochemistry: The Chemical Composition of Living Matter 41

Inorganic Compounds 42
Water • Salts • Acids and Bases

Organic Compounds 45
Carbohydrates • Lipids • Proteins • Nucleic Acids • Adenosine Triphosphate (ATP)

SUMMARY 58

REVIEW QUESTIONS 61

CRITICAL THINKING AND CLINICAL APPLICATION QUESTIONS 63

Focus on Careers Food Technologist 53

A Closer Look DNA Fingerprinting: Cracking Our Genetic "Barcode" 57

3 CELLS AND TISSUES 64

PART I: CELLS 65

Overview of the Cellular Basis of Life 65

Anatomy of a Generalized Cell 66

The Nucleus 67
Nuclear Envelope • Nucleoli • Chromatin

The Plasma Membrane 67
Specializations of the Plasma Membrane

The Cytoplasm 69
Cytoplasmic Organelles

Cell Diversity 74

Cell Physiology 76

Membrane Transport 76
Passive Transport Processes: Diffusion and Filtration • Active Transport Processes

Cell Division 83
Preparations: DNA Replication • Events of Cell Division

Protein Synthesis 86
Genes: The Blueprint for Protein Structure • The Role of RNA • Transcription • Translation

PART II: BODY TISSUES 88

Epithelial Tissue 88

Special Characteristics of Epithelium 89

Classification of Epithelium 89
Simple Epithelia • Stratified Epithelia • Glandular Epithelium

Connective Tissue 93

Common Characteristics of Connective Tissue 93

Extracellular Matrix 93

Types of Connective Tissue 94
Bone • Cartilage • Dense Connective Tissue • Loose Connective Tissue • Blood

Muscle Tissue 98

Types of Muscle Tissue 98
Skeletal Muscle • Cardiac Muscle • Smooth Muscle

Nervous Tissue 98

Tissue Repair (Wound Healing) 100

PART III: DEVELOPMENTAL ASPECTS OF CELLS AND TISSUES 101

SUMMARY 104

REVIEW QUESTIONS 106

CRITICAL THINKING AND CLINICAL APPLICATION QUESTIONS 108

A Closer Look IV Therapy and Cellular "Tonics" 80

A Closer Look Cancer—The Intimate Enemy 102

4 SKIN AND BODY MEMBRANES 109

Classification of Body Membranes 110

Epithelial Membranes 110
Cutaneous Membrane • Mucous Membranes • Serous Membranes

Connective Tissues Membranes 112

Integumentary System (Skin) 114

Functions of the Integumentary System 114

Structure of the Skin 115
Epidermis • Dermis

Skin Color 118

Appendages of the Skin 119
Cutaneous Glands • Hair and Hair Follicles • Nails

Homeostatic Imbalances of Skin 123
Infections and Allergies • Burns • Skin Cancer

Developmental Aspects of Skin and Body Membranes 127

SUMMARY 130

REVIEW QUESTIONS 131

CRITICAL THINKING AND CLINICAL APPLICATION QUESTIONS 132

A Closer Look Tattoos 113

Focus on Careers Medical Transcriptionist 128

Systems in Sync 129

5 THE SKELETAL SYSTEM 133

Bones: An Overview 134

Functions of the Bones 134

Classification of Bones 135

Structure of a Long Bone 135
Gross Anatomy • Microscopic Anatomy

Bone Formation, Growth, and Remodeling 140

Bone Fractures 142

Axial Skeleton 145

Skull 145
Cranium • Facial Bones • The Hyoid Bone • Fetal Skull

Vertebral Column (Spine) 150
Cervical Vertebrae • Thoracic Vertebrae • Lumbar Vertebrae • Sacrum • Coccyx

Thoracic Cage 157
Sternum • Ribs

Appendicular Skeleton 158

Bones of the Shoulder Girdle 158

Bones of the Upper Limbs 160
Arm • Forearm • Hand

Bones of the Pelvic Girdle 162

Bones of the Lower Limbs 164
Thigh • Leg • Foot

Joints 166

Fibrous Joints 168

Cartilaginous Joints 168

Synovial Joints 168

Type of Synovial Joints Based on Shape 170

Developmental Aspects of the Skeleton 174

SUMMARY 178

REVIEW QUESTIONS 179

CRITICAL THINKING AND CLINICAL APPLICATION QUESTIONS 181

A Closer Look Protect Your Back—It's the Only One You've Got! 152

Chapter 5, continued

A Closer Look   Them Bones, Them Bones
Goin' to Walk Around—
Clinical Advances in Bone
Repair   167

Systems in Sync   177

THE MUSCULAR SYSTEM 182

Overview of Muscle Tissues   183

Muscle Types   183
Skeletal Muscle • Smooth Muscle • Cardiac Muscle

Muscle Functions   187
Producing Movement • Maintaining Posture
• Stabilizing Joints • Generating Heat

Microscopic Anatomy of Skeletal Muscle   187

Skeletal Muscle Activity   189

Stimulation and Contraction of Single
Skeletal Muscle Cells   189
The Nerve Stimulus and the Action Potential
• Mechanism of Muscle Contraction: The Sliding
Filament Theory

Contraction of a Skeletal Muscle
as a Whole   194
Graded Responses • Providing Energy for Muscle
Contraction • Muscle Fatigue and Oxygen Deficit
• Types of Muscle Contractions—Isotonic and
Isometric • Muscle Tone • Effect of Exercise on
Muscles

Muscle Movements, Types, and Names   198

Types of Body Movements   198
Special Movements

Interactions of Skeletal Muscles
in the Body   202

Naming Skeletal Muscles   202

Arrangement of Fasicles   204

Gross Anatomy of Skeletal Muscles   206

Head and Neck Muscles   206
Facial Muscles • Chewing Muscles • Neck Muscles

Trunk Muscles   207
Anterior Muscles • Posterior Muscles

Muscles of the Upper Limb   210
Muscles of the Humerus That Act on the Forearm

Muscles of the Lower Limb   211
Muscles Causing Movement at the Hip Joint
• Muscles Causing Movement at the Knee Joint
• Muscles Causing Movement at the Ankle and Foot

Developmental Aspects of the Muscular System   221

SUMMARY   223

REVIEW QUESTIONS   224

CRITICAL THINKING AND CLINICAL
APPLICATION QUESTIONS   226

A Closer Look   Are Athletes Looking
Good and Doing Better
with Anabolic
Steroids? 203

Focus on Careers   Massage Therapist 220

Systems in Sync   222

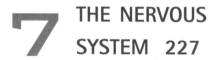

THE NERVOUS SYSTEM 227

Organization of the Nervous System   229

Structural Classification   229

Functional Classification   229

Nervous Tissue: Structure and Function   230

Supporting Cells   230

Neurons   232
Anatomy • Classification • Physiology

Central Nervous System   242

Functional Anatomy of the Brain   242
Cerebral Hemispheres • Diencephalon • Brain-Stem
• Cerebellum

Protection of the Central Nervous
System   248
Meninges • Cerebrospinal Fluid • The Blood-Brain
Barrier

Brain Dysfunctions   252
Traumatic Brain Injuries

Spinal Cord   255
Gray Matter of the Spinal Cord and Spinal Roots
• White Matter of the Spinal Cord

Peripheral Nervous System   258

Structure of a Nerve   258

Cranial Nerves   258

Spinal Nerves and Nerve Plexuses   262

Autonomic Nervous System   262
Somatic and Autonomic Nervous Systems Compared
• Anatomy of the Parasympathetic Division
• Anatomy of the Sympathetic Division • Autonomic
Functioning

Developmental Aspects of
the Nervous System   272

SUMMARY   275

REVIEW QUESTIONS   277

CRITICAL THINKING AND CLINICAL
APPLICATION QUESTIONS   279

A Closer Look   Alzheimer's, Parkinson's and
Huntington's—The Terrible
Three   253

A Closer Look   Tracking Down CNS
Problems   271

Systems in Sync   274

8 SPECIAL SENSES   280

PART I: THE EYE AND VISION   281

Anatomy of the Eye   281

External and Accessory Structures   281

Internal Structures: The Eyeball   283
Layers Forming the Wall of the Eyeball • Lens

Pathway of Light through the Eye
and Light Refraction   290

Visual Fields and Visual Pathways
to the Brain   290

Eye Reflexes   291

PART II: THE EAR: HEARING
AND BALANCE   294

Anatomy of the Ear   294

External (Outer) Ear   294

Middle Ear   294

Internal (Inner) Ear   295

Mechanisms of Equilibrium   296

Static Equilibrium   296

Dynamic Equilibrium   297

Mechanism of Hearing   298

Hearing and Equilibrium Deficits   300

PART III: CHEMICAL SENSES:
TASTE AND SMELL   301

Olfactory Receptors and the Sense
of Smell   301

Taste Buds and the Sense of Taste   302

Chapter 8, continued

PART IV: DEVELOPMENTAL ASPECTS OF THE SPECIAL SENSES   303

SUMMARY   305

REVIEW QUESTIONS   307

CRITICAL THINKING AND CLINICAL APPLICATION QUESTIONS   308

A Closer Look   Visual Pigments—The Actual Photoreceptors   287

A Closer Look   If I Can't See Things Far Away, Am I Nearsighted or Farsighted?   292

9   THE ENDOCRINE SYSTEM   309

The Endocrine System and Hormone Function—An Overview   310

The Chemistry of Hormones   310

Mechanisms of Hormone Action   311
Direct Gene Activation • Second-Messenger System

Control of Hormone Release   311
Endocrine Gland Stimuli

The Major Endocrine Organs   313

Pituitary Gland   314
Hormones of the Anterior Pituitary • Pituitary-Hypothalamus Relationship • Hormones of the Posterior Pituitary

Thyroid Gland   319

Parathyroid Glands   321

Adrenal Glands   322
Hormones of the Adrenal Cortex • Hormones of the Adrenal Medulla

Pancreatic Islets   326

Pineal Gland   329

Thymus Gland   329

Gonads   329
Hormones of the Ovaries • Hormones of the Testes

Other Hormone-Producing Tissues and Organs   332

Placenta   332

Developmental Aspects of the Endocrine System   332

SUMMARY   335

REVIEW QUESTIONS   337

CRITICAL THINKING AND CLINICAL APPLICATION QUESTIONS   338

A Closer Look   Potential Uses for Growth Hormone   317

Systems in Sync   334

10   BLOOD   339

Composition and Functions of Blood   340

Components   340

Physical Characteristics and Volume   340

Plasma   340

Formed Elements   342
Erythrocytes • Leukocytes • Platelets

Hematopoiesis (Blood Cell Formation)   347
Formation of Red Blood Cells • Formation of White Blood Cells and Platelets

Hemostasis   349

Disorders of Hemostasis   350

Blood Groups and Transfusions   351

Human Blood Groups   351

Blood Typing   354

Developmental Aspects of Blood 354

SUMMARY   357

REVIEW QUESTIONS   358

CRITICAL THINKING AND CLINICAL
APPLICATION QUESTIONS   359

Focus on Careers   Phlebotomy
                   Technician 352

A Closer Look   Concocting Blood: Artificial
                Blood Substitutes 355

11 THE CARDIOVASCULAR SYSTEM 360

The Heart 362

Anatomy of the Heart   362
Location and Size • Coverings and Wall • Chambers
and Associated Great Vessels • Valves • Cardiac
Circulation

Physiology of the Heart   368
Intrinsic Conduction System of the Heart: Setting
the Basic Rhythm • Cardiac Cycle and Heart
Sounds • Cardiac Output

Blood Vessels 374

Microscopic Anatomy of Blood
Vessels   374
Tunics • Structural Differences in Arteries, Veins,
and Capillaries

Gross Anatomy of Blood Vessels   378
Major Arteries of the Systemic Circulation • Major
Veins of the Systemic Circulation • Special
Circulations

Physiology of Circulation   387
Arterial Pulse • Blood Pressure • Capillary Exchange
of Gases and Nutrients • Fluid Movements at
Capillary Beds

Developmental Aspects of the
Cardiovascular System   395

SUMMARY   397

REVIEW QUESTIONS   399

CRITICAL THINKING AND CLINICAL
APPLICATION QUESTIONS   401

A Closer Look   Electrocardiography: (Don't)
                Be Still My Heart 370

Focus on Careers   Certified Surgical
                   Technologist (CST) 382

A Closer Look   Atherosclerosis? Get Out the
                Cardiovascular Drāno 392

Systems in Sync   396

12 THE LYMPHATIC SYSTEM AND BODY DEFENSES 402

PART I: THE LYMPHATIC
SYSTEM   403

Lymphatic Vessels 403

Lymph Nodes 405

Other Lymphoid Organs 407

PART II: BODY DEFENSES   408

Innate Body Defenses 409

Surface Membrane Barriers   409

Internal Defenses: Cells
and Chemicals   396
Phagocytes • Natural Killer Cells • Inflammatory
Response • Antimicrobial Proteins • Fever

Adaptive Body Defenses 415

Antigens   416

Cells of the Adaptive Defense System:
An Overview   416
Lymphocytes • Macrophages

Chapter 12, continued

Humoral (Antibody-Mediated) Immune
Response   418
Active and Passive Humoral Immunity • Antibodies

Cellular (Cell-Mediated) Immune
Response   425

Organ Transplants and Rejection   427

Disorders of Immunity   429

PART III: DEVELOPMENTAL ASPECTS
OF THE LYMPHATIC SYSTEM AND
BODY DEFENSES   431

SUMMARY   435

REVIEW QUESTIONS   437

CRITICAL THINKING AND CLINICAL
APPLICATION QUESTIONS   438

A Closer Look   AIDS: The Modern Day
Plague   432

Systems in Sync   434

13 THE RESPIRATORY SYSTEM 440

**Functional Anatomy of the Respiratory
System   441**

The Nose   441

Pharynx   443

Larynx   444

Trachea   444

Main Bronchi   445

Lungs   445
The Respiratory Membrane

Respiratory Physiology   448

Mechanics of Breathing   449
Inspiration • Expiration • Nonrespiratory Air
Movements

Respiratory Volumes and Capacities   452

Respiratory Sounds   453

External Respiration, Gas Transport,
and Internal Respiration   453
External Respiration • Gas Transport in the
Blood • Internal Respiration

Control of Respiration   456
Neural Regulation: Setting the Basic Rhythm • Non-Neural
Factors Influencing Respiratory Rate and Depth

Respiratory Disorders   460

**Developmental Aspects of the
Respiratory System   461**

SUMMARY   465

REVIEW QUESTIONS   466

CRITICAL THINKING AND CLINICAL
APPLICATION QUESTIONS   467

A Closer Look   Lung Cancer: The Facts
Behind the Smoke
Screen   458

Focus on Careers   Licensed Practical
Nurse (LPN)   462

Systems in Sync   463

14 THE DIGESTIVE SYSTEM AND BODY METABOLISM 468

PART I: ANATOMY AND
PHYSIOLOGY OF THE DIGESTIVE
SYSTEM   469

Anatomy of the Digestive System   469

Organs of the Alimentary Canal   470
Mouth • Pharynx • Esophagus • Stomach • Small
Intestine • Large Intestine

Accessory Digestive Organs   479
Teeth • Salivary Glands • Pancreas • Liver and Gallbladder

Functions of the Digestive System 481

Overview of Gastrointestinal Processes and Controls   481

Activities Occurring in the Mouth, Pharynx, and Esophagus   485
Food Ingestion and Breakdown • Food Propulsion—Swallowing and Peristalsis

Activities of the Stomach   485
Food Breakdown • Food Propulsion

Activities of the Small Intestine   489
Food Breakdown and Absorption • Food Propulsion

Activities of the Large Intestine   492
Food Breakdown and Absorption • Propulsion of the Residue and Defecation

PART II: NUTRITION AND METABOLISM   493

Nutrition 493

Dietary Sources of the Major Nutrients   494
Carbohydrates • Lipids • Proteins • Vitamins • Minerals

Metabolism   495

Carbohydrate, Fat, and Protein Metabolism in Body Cells   496
Carbohydrate Metabolism • Fat Metabolism • Protein Metabolism

The Central Role of the Liver in Metabolism   500
General Metabolic Functions • Cholesterol Metabolism and Transport

Body Energy Balance   502
Regulation of Food Intake • Metabolic Rate and Body Heat Production • Body Temperature Regulation

PART III: DEVELOPMENTAL ASPECTS OF THE DIGESTIVE SYSTEM AND METABOLISM   506

SUMMARY   512
REVIEW QUESTIONS   514

CRITICAL THINKING AND CLINICAL APPLICATION QUESTIONS   516

A Closer Look   Peptic Ulcers: "Something Is Eating at Me"   488

A Closer Look   Obesity: Magical Solution Wanted   508

Systems in Sync   511

15 THE URINARY SYSTEM 517

Kidneys 518

Location and Structure   518
Blood Supply

Nephrons and Urine Formation   521
Nephrons • Urine Formation • Characteristics of Urine

Ureters, Urinary Bladder, and Urethra 528

Ureters   528

Urinary Bladder   528

Urethra   529

Micturition   530

Fluid, Electrolyte, and Acid Base Balance 531

Maintaining Water and Electrolyte Balance of Blood   531
Body Fluids and Fluid Compartments • The Link between Water and Salt • Regulation of Water Intake and Output

Maintaining Acid Base Balance of Blood   535
Blood Buffers • Respiratory System Controls • Renal Mechanisms

Developmental Aspects of the Urinary System 538

➤

Chapter 15, continued

SUMMARY   540

REVIEW QUESTIONS   541

CRITICAL THINKING AND CLINICAL
APPLICATION QUESTIONS   542

A Closer Look   Renal Failure and the
Artificial Kidney   526

Systems in Sync   539

16   THE REPRODUCTIVE SYSTEM   544

Anatomy of the Male Reproductive System   546

Testes   546

Duct System   546
Epididymis • Ductus Deferens • Urethra

Accessory Glands and Semen   548
Seminal Vesicles • Prostate • Bulbourethral
Glands • Semen

External Genitalia   549

Male Reproductive Functions   550

Spermatogenesis   550

Testosterone Production   552

Anatomy of the Female Reproductive System   553

Ovaries   553

Duct System   554
Uterine (Fallopian) Tubes • Uterus • Vagina

External Genitalia   556

Female Reproductive Functions and Cycles   557

Oogenesis and the Ovarian Cycle   557

Uterine (Menstrual) Cycle   559

Hormone Production by the Ovaries   561

Mammary Glands   561

Survey of Pregnancy and Embryonic Development   563

Accomplishing Fertilization   563

Events of Embryonic and Fetal
Development   565

Effects of Pregnancy on the Mother   566
Anatomical Changes • Physiological Changes

Childbirth   569
Initiation of Labor • Stages of Labor

Developmental Aspects of the Reproductive System   571

SUMMARY   578

REVIEW QUESTIONS   580

CRITICAL THINKING AND CLINICAL
APPLICATION QUESTIONS   581

Focus on Careers   Doula   572

A Closer Look   Contraception: Preventing
Pregnancy   574

Systems in Sync   577

Appendixes

Appendix A: Word Roots, Prefixes, and
Suffixes   583

Appendix B: Periodic Table of the
Elements   586

Appendix C: Key Information about
Vitamins and Many Essential
Minerals   587

Appendix D: Answers to Did You Get It?
and Multiple Choice Review
Questions   589

Photographic and Art Credits   597

Glossary   598

Index   609

The Human Body: An Orientation

YOUR GOALS

After completing this chapter, you will have mastered the objectives listed below.

OBJECTIVE CHECKLIST

An Overview of Anatomy and Physiology (pp. 2–3)

➤ Define *anatomy* and *physiology*.

➤ Explain how anatomy and physiology are related.

Levels of Structural Organization (pp. 3–7, 10)

➤ Name the levels of structural organization that make up the human body, and explain how they are related.

➤ Name the organ systems of the body, and briefly state the major functions of each system.

➤ Classify by organ system all organs discussed.

➤ Identify the organs shown on a diagram or a dissectible torso.

Maintaining Life (pp. 10–12)
- ➤ List functions that humans must perform to maintain life.
- ➤ List the survival needs of the human body.

Homeostasis (pp. 12–13, 15)
- ➤ Define *homeostasis*, and explain its importance.
- ➤ Define *negative feedback*, and describe its role in maintaining homeostasis and normal body function.

The Language of Anatomy (pp. 15–22)
- ➤ Verbally describe or demonstrate the anatomical position.
- ➤ Use proper anatomical terminology to describe body directions, surfaces, and body planes.
- ➤ Locate the major body cavities, and list the chief organs in each cavity.

An Overview of Anatomy and Physiology

Most of us are naturally curious about our bodies; we want to know what makes us tick. This curiosity is even seen in infants, who can keep themselves happy for a long time staring at their own hands or pulling their mother's nose. Older children wonder where food goes when they swallow it, and some believe that they will grow a watermelon in their belly if they swallow the seeds. They scream loudly when approached by medical personnel (fearing shots that sting), but they like to play doctor. Adults become upset when their hearts pound, when they have uncontrollable hot flashes, or when they cannot keep their weight down.

Anatomy and physiology, subdivisions of biology, explore many of these topics as they describe how our bodies are put together and how they work.

Anatomy

Anatomy (ah-nat′o-me) is the study of the structure and shape of the body and its parts and their relationships to one another. Whenever we look at our own body or study large body structures such as the heart or bones, we are observing *gross anatomy;* that is, we are studying large, easily observable structures. Indeed, the term *anatomy,* derived from the Greek words meaning to cut (*tomy*) apart (*ana*), is related most closely to gross anatomical studies because in such studies preserved animals or their organs are dissected (cut up) to be examined. *Microscopic anatomy,* in contrast, is the study of body structures that are too small to be seen with the naked eye. The cells and tissues of the body can only be seen through a microscope.

Physiology

Physiology (fiz″e-ol′o-je) is the study of how the body and its parts work or function (*physio* = nature; *ology* = the study of). Like anatomy, physiology has many subdivisions. For example, *neurophysiology* explains the workings of the nervous system, and *cardiac physiology* studies the function of the heart, which acts as a muscular pump to keep blood flowing throughout the body.

Relationship between Anatomy and Physiology

Anatomy and physiology are always related. The parts of your body form a well-organized unit, and each of those parts has a job to do to make the body operate as a whole. Structure determines what functions can take place. For example, the lungs are not muscular chambers like the heart and cannot pump blood through the body, but because the walls of their air sacs are very thin, they *can* exchange gases and provide oxygen to the body. The intimate relationship between anatomy and physiology is stressed throughout this book to make your learning meaningful.

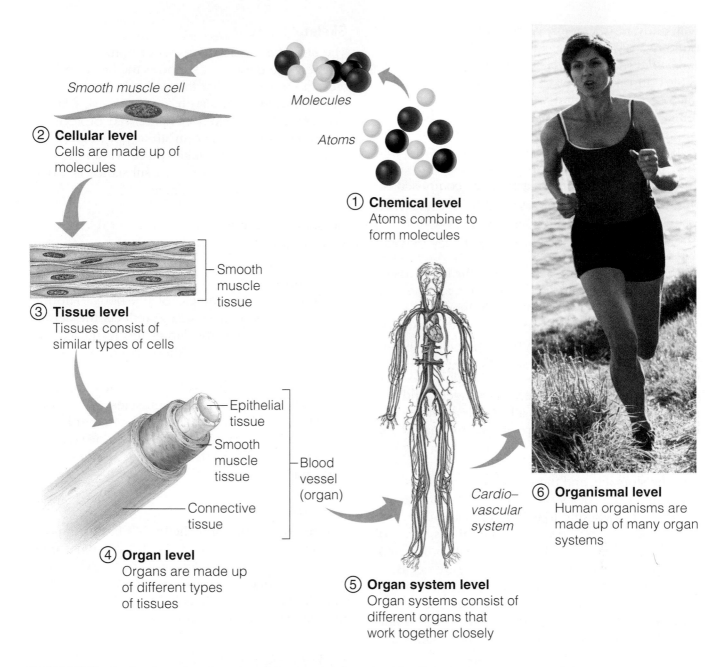

Smooth muscle cell

Molecules

Atoms

② **Cellular level**
Cells are made up of
molecules

① **Chemical level**
Atoms combine to
form molecules

—Smooth
muscle
tissue

③ **Tissue level**
Tissues consist of
similar types of cells

—Epithelial
tissue

—Smooth
muscle
tissue

—Blood
vessel
(organ)

—Connective
tissue

④ **Organ level**
Organs are made up
of different types
of tissues

*Cardio–
vascular
system*

⑥ **Organismal level**
Human organisms are
made up of many organ
systems

⑤ **Organ system level**
Organ systems consist of
different organs that
work together closely

FIGURE 1.1   Levels of structural organization. In this diagram, components of the cardiovascular system illustrate the various levels of structural organization in a human being.

▶ DID YOU GET IT?

1. Why would you have a hard time learning and understanding physiology if you did not also understand anatomy?

For the answer, see Appendix D.

Levels of Structural Organization

From Atoms to Organisms

The human body exhibits many levels of structural complexity (Figure 1.1). The simplest level of the structural ladder is the *chemical level*, which we will study in Chapter 2. At this level, **atoms,** tiny building blocks of matter, combine to form *molecules* such as water, sugar, and proteins. Molecules, in turn, associate in specific ways to form microscopic **cells,** the smallest units of all living things. The *cellular level* is examined in Chapter 3. All cells have some common functions, but individual cells vary widely in size and shape, reflecting their particular functions in the body.

The simplest living creatures are composed of single cells, but in complex organisms such as trees or human beings, the structural ladder continues on to the *tissue level.* **Tissues** consist of groups of similar cells that have a common function. As we will discuss in Chapter 3, each of the four basic tissue types (epithelial, connective, muscular, and neural) plays a definite but different role in the body.

An **organ** is a structure composed of two or more tissue types that performs a specific function for the body. At the *organ level* of organization, extremely complex functions become possible. For example, the small intestine, which digests and absorbs food, is composed of all four tissue types. An **organ system** is a group of organs that work together to accomplish a common purpose. For example, the digestive system includes the esophagus, the stomach, and the small and large intestines (to name a few of its organs). Each organ has its own job. By working together, all of these organs keep food moving through the digestive system so that it is properly broken down and absorbed into the blood, providing fuel for all the body's cells.

In all, 11 organ systems make up the living body, or the **organism,** which represents the highest level of structural organization, the *organismal level.* The major organs of each of the systems are shown in Figure 1.2. Refer to the figure as you read through the following descriptions of the organ systems.

Organ System Overview

Integumentary System

The **integumentary** (in-teg″u-men′tar-e) **system** is the external covering of the body, or the skin. It waterproofs the body and cushions and protects the deeper tissues from injury. It also excretes salts and urea in perspiration and helps regulate body temperature. Temperature, pressure, and pain receptors located in the skin alert us to what is happening at the body surface.

Skeletal System

The **skeletal system** consists of bones, cartilages, ligaments, and joints. It supports the body and provides a framework that the skeletal muscles use to cause movement. It also has a protective function (for example, the skull encloses and protects the brain). *Hematopoiesis* (hem″ah-to-poi-e′sis), or formation of blood cells, takes place within the cavities of the skeleton. The hard substance of bones acts as a storehouse for minerals.

Muscular System

The muscles of the body have only one function—to *contract,* or shorten. When this happens, movement occurs. Hence, muscles can be viewed as the "machines" of the body. The mobility of the body as a whole reflects the activity of *skeletal muscles,* the large, fleshy muscles attached to bones. When these contract, you are able to stand erect, walk, leap, grasp, throw a ball, or smile. The skeletal muscles form the **muscular system.** These muscles are distinct from the muscles of the heart and of other hollow organs, which move fluids (blood, urine) or other substances (such as food) along definite pathways within the body.

Nervous System

The **nervous system** is the body's fast-acting control system. It consists of the brain, spinal cord, nerves, and sensory receptors. The body must be able to respond to irritants or stimuli coming from outside the body (such as light, sound, or changes in temperature) and from inside the body (such as decreases in oxygen or stretching of tissue). The sensory receptors detect these changes and send messages (via electrical signals called *nerve impulses*) to the central nervous system (brain and spinal cord) so that it is constantly informed about what is going on. The central nervous system then assesses this information and responds by activating the appropriate body effectors (muscles or glands).

F I G U R E 1 . 2   **The body's organ systems.** The structural components of each organ system are illustrated in the diagrammatic views. The major functions of the organ systems are listed beneath each illustration.

(a) Integumentary System

Forms the external body covering; protects deeper tissue from injury; synthesizes vitamin D; location of cutaneous (pain, pressure, etc.) receptors and sweat and oil glands.

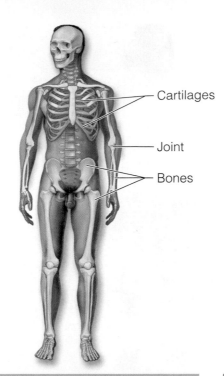

Cartilages

Joint

Bones

(b) Skeletal System

Protects and supports body organs; provides a framework the muscles use to cause movement; blood cells are formed within bones; stores minerals.

Skeletal muscles

(c) Muscular System

Allows manipulation of the environment, locomotion, and facial expression; maintains posture; produces heat.

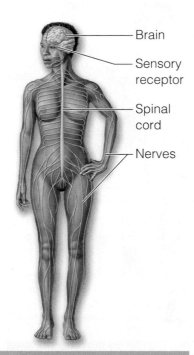

Brain

Sensory receptor

Spinal cord

Nerves

(d) Nervous System

Fast-acting control system of the body; responds to internal and external changes by activating appropriate muscles and glands.

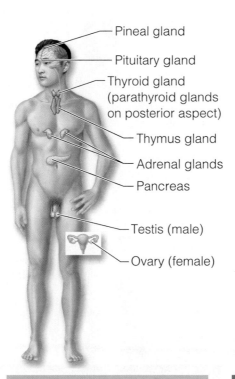

Pineal gland

Pituitary gland

Thyroid gland (parathyroid glands on posterior aspect)

Thymus gland

Adrenal glands

Pancreas

Testis (male)

Ovary (female)

(e) Endocrine System

Glands secrete hormones that regulate processes such as growth, reproduction, and nutrient use (metabolism) by body cells.

Heart

Blood vessels

(f) Cardiovascular System

Blood vessels transport blood, which carries oxygen, carbon dioxide, nutrients, wastes, etc.; the heart pumps blood.

(Continues on page 6)

1

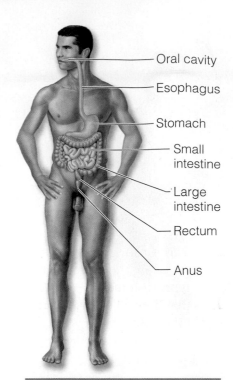

Thoracic duct

Lymph nodes

Lymphatic vessels

Nasal cavity

Pharynx

Larynx

Trachea

Bronchus

Left lung

Oral cavity

Esophagus

Stomach

Small intestine

Large intestine

Rectum

Anus

(g) Lymphatic System

Picks up fluid leaked from blood vessels and returns it to blood; disposes of debris in the lymphatic stream; houses white blood cells involved in immunity.

(h) Respiratory System

Keeps blood constantly supplied with oxygen and removes carbon dioxide; the gaseous exchanges occur through the walls of the air sacs of the lungs.

(i) Digestive System

Breaks food down into absorbable units that enter the blood for distribution to body cells; indigestible foodstuffs are eliminated as feces.

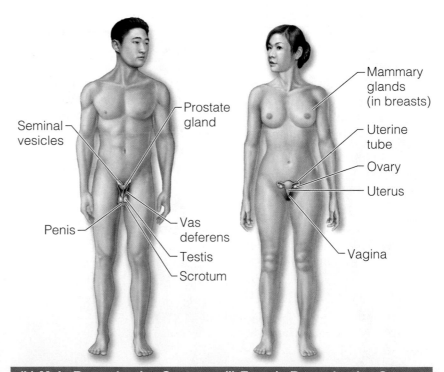

Kidney

Ureter

Urinary bladder

Urethra

Seminal vesicles

Prostate gland

Penis

Vas deferens

Testis

Scrotum

Mammary glands (in breasts)

Uterine tube

Ovary

Uterus

Vagina

(j) Urinary System

Eliminates nitrogenous wastes from the body; regulates water, electrolyte, and acid-base balance of the blood.

(k) Male Reproductive System   (l) Female Reproductive System

Overall function of the reproductive system is production of offspring. Testes produce sperm and male sex hormone; ducts and glands aid in delivery of viable sperm to the female reproductive tract. Ovaries produce eggs and female sex hormones; remaining structures serve as sites for fertilization and development of the fetus. Mammary glands of female breast produce milk to nourish the newborn.

FIGURE 1.2 *(continued)* **The body's organ systems.**

Endocrine System

Like the nervous system, the **endocrine** (en'do-krin) **system** controls body activities, but it acts much more slowly. The endocrine glands produce chemical molecules called *hormones* and release them into the blood to travel to relatively distant target organs.

The endocrine glands include the pituitary, thyroid, parathyroids, adrenals, thymus, pancreas, pineal, ovaries (in the female), and testes (in the male). The endocrine glands are not connected anatomically in the same way that parts of the other organ systems are. What they have in common is that they all secrete hormones, which regulate other structures. The body functions controlled by hormones are many and varied, involving every cell in the body. Growth, reproduction, and food use by cells are all controlled (at least in part) by hormones.

Cardiovascular System

The primary organs of the **cardiovascular system** are the heart and blood vessels. Using blood as the transporting fluid, the cardiovascular system carries oxygen, nutrients, hormones, and other substances to and from the tissue cells where exchanges are made. White blood cells and chemicals in the blood help to protect the body from such foreign invaders as bacteria, toxins, and tumor cells. The heart acts as the blood pump, propelling blood out of its chambers into the blood vessels to be transported to all body tissues.

Lymphatic System

The role of the **lymphatic system** complements that of the cardiovascular system. Its organs include lymphatic vessels, lymph nodes, and other lymphoid organs such as the spleen and tonsils. The lymphatic vessels return fluid leaked from the blood back to the blood vessels so that blood can be kept continuously circulating through the body. The lymph nodes and other lymphoid organs help to cleanse the blood and house cells involved in immunity.

Respiratory System

The job of the **respiratory system** is to keep the body constantly supplied with oxygen and to remove carbon dioxide. The respiratory system consists of the nasal passages, pharynx, larynx, trachea, bronchi, and lungs. Within the lungs are tiny air sacs. It is through the thin walls of these air sacs that gases are transported to and from the blood.

Digestive System

The **digestive system** is basically a tube running through the body from mouth to anus. The organs of the digestive system include the oral cavity (mouth), esophagus, stomach, small and large intestines, and rectum. Their role is to break down food and deliver the products to the blood for dispersal to the body cells. The undigested food that remains in the tract leaves the body through the anus as feces. The breakdown activities that begin in the mouth are completed in the small intestine. From that point on, the major function of the digestive system is to reclaim water. The liver is considered a digestive organ because the bile it produces helps to break down fats. The pancreas, which delivers digestive enzymes to the small intestine, also is functionally a digestive organ.

Urinary System

The body produces wastes as by-products of its normal functions, and these wastes must be disposed of. One type of waste contains nitrogen (examples are urea and uric acid), which results when the body cells break down proteins and nucleic acids. The **urinary system** removes the nitrogen-containing wastes from the blood and flushes them from the body in urine. This system, often called the *excretory system,* is composed of the kidneys, ureters, bladder, and urethra. Other important functions of this system include maintaining the body's water and salt (electrolyte) balance and regulating the acid-base balance of the blood.

Reproductive System

The **reproductive system** exists primarily to produce offspring. The testes of the male produce sperm. Other male reproductive system structures are the scrotum, penis, accessory glands, and the duct system, which carries sperm to the outside of the body. The ovaries of the female produce eggs, or ova; the female duct system consists of the uterine tubes, uterus, and vagina. The uterus provides the site for the development of the fetus (immature infant) once fertilization has occurred.

MEDICAL IMAGING: ILLUMINATING THE BODY

By bombarding the body with energy, new scanning techniques can reveal the structure of internal organs and wring out information about the private and, until now, secret working of their molecules. These new imaging techniques are changing the face of medical diagnosis.

Until about 50 years ago, the magical but murky X ray was the only means of peering into a living body. What X rays did and still do best was visualize hard, bony structures and locate abnormally dense structures (tumors, tuberculosis nodules) in the lungs. The 1950s saw the birth of nuclear medicine, which uses radioisotopes to scan the body, and ultrasound techniques. In the 1970s, CT, PET, and MRI scanning techniques were introduced.

The best known of new imaging devices is *computed tomography (CT)* (formerly called *computerized axial tomography, or CAT*) a refined version of X ray. A CT scanner confines its beam to a thin slice of the body, about as thick as a dime, and ends the confusion resulting from images of overlapping structures seen in conventional X-ray images. As the patient is slowly moved through the doughnut-shaped CT machine, its X-ray tube rotates around the body. Different tissues absorb the radiation in varying amounts. The device's computer translates this information into a detailed, cross-sectional picture of the body region scanned; see photo (a). CT scans are at the forefront in evaluating most problems that affect the brain and abdomen, and their clarity has all but eliminated exploratory surgery. Special ultrafast CT scanners have produced a technique called *dynamic spatial reconstruction (DSR)*, which provides three-dimensional images of body organs from any angle.

> " *New imaging techniques are changing the face of medical diagnosis.* "

It also allows their movements and changes in their internal volumes to be observed at normal speed, in slow motion, and at a specific moment in time. The greatest value of DSR has been to visualize the heart beating and blood flowing through blood vessels. This allows medical personnel to assess heart defects, constricted blood vessels, and the status of coronary bypass grafts.

Another computer-assisted X-ray technique is *digital subtraction angiography (DSA)* (*angiography* = vessel pictures). This technique provides an unobstructed view of diseased blood vessels; see photo (b). Conventional radiographs are taken before and after a contrast medium is injected into an artery. Then the computer subtracts the "before" image from the "after" image, eliminating all traces of body structures that obscure the vessel. DSA is often used to identify blockages in the arteries that supply the heart wall and the brain; see photo (b).

Just as the X ray spawned "new technologies," so did nuclear medicine in the form of *positron emission tomography (PET)*. PET excels in observing metabolic processes. The patient is given an injection of short-lived radioisotopes that have been tagged to biological molecules (such as glucose) and then positioned in the PET scanner. As the radioisotopes are absorbed by the most active brain cells, high-energy gamma rays are produced. The computer analyzes the gamma emission and produces a picture of the brain's biochemical activity in vivid colors. PET's greatest clinical value has been its ability to provide insights into brain activity in people affected by mental illness, Alzheimer's disease, and epilepsy. One of its most exciting uses is to determine which areas of the healthy brain are most active during certain tasks (speaking, listening to music, and so on).

Ultrasound imaging, or *ultrasonography*, has some distinct advantages over the approaches described so far. The equipment is inexpensive, and it employs high-frequency sound waves (ultrasound) as its energy source. Ultrasound, unlike ionizing forms of radiation, has no harmful effects on living tissues (as far as we know). The body is probed with pulses of sound waves, which cause echoes when reflected and scattered by body tissues. The echoes are analyzed by computer to construct visual images of body organs of interest. Because of its safety, ultrasound is the imaging technique of choice for obstetrics, that is, for determining fetal age and position and locating the placenta. Because sound waves have very low penetrating power and are rapidly scattered in air, sonography is of little value for looking at air-filled structures (the lungs) or those surrounded by bone (the brain and spinal cord).

Another technique that depends on nonionizing radiation is *magnetic resonance imaging (MRI)*, which uses magnetic fields up to 60,000 times stronger than the Earth's to pry information from the body's tissues. The patient lies in a chamber within a huge magnet. Hydrogen molecules spin like tops in the magnetic field, and their energy is enhanced by radio waves. When the radio waves are turned off, the energy is released and translated by the computer into a visual image. MRI is immensely popular because it can do many things a CT scan cannot. Dense structures do not show up in MRI, so bones of the skull and/or vertebral column do not impair the view of *soft tissues* such as the brain. MRI is also particularly good at detecting degenerative disease of various kinds. Multiple sclerosis plaques, for example, do not show up well in CT scans but are dazzlingly clear in MRI scans. MRI studies are also being used to investigate

(a)

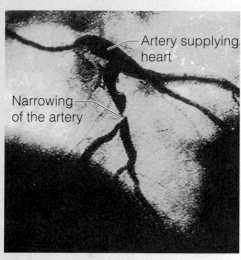

Artery supplying heart

Narrowing of the artery

(b)

Two different methods for illuminating the body. (a) CT scan showing a brain tumor (oval area on right side of brain). **(b)** DSA image of arteries supplying the heart.

how brain development and behavior change with growth or experience.

A newer variation of MRI called *magnetic resonance spectroscopy (MRS)* maps the distribution of elements other than hydrogen to reveal more about how disease changes body chemistry. In 1992, MRI technology leaped forward with the development of the *functional MRI*, which allows tracking of blood flow into the brain in real time. Until then, matching thoughts, deeds, and disease to corresponding brain activity had been the sole domain of PET. Because functional MRI does not require injections of tracer elements, it provides another, perhaps more desirable, alternative. Despite its advantages, the powerful magnets of the clanging MRI present some thorny problems. For example they can

"suck" metal objects, such as implanted pacemakers and loose tooth fillings, through the body. Also, there is no convincing evidence that such magnetic fields are risk free.

As you can see, modern medical science has many remarkable tools at its disposal. CT and PET scans account for about 25 percent of all imaging. Ultrasonography, because of its safety and low cost, is the most widespread of the new techniques. Conventional X rays remain the workhorse of diagnostic imaging techniques and still account for more than half of all imaging currently done.

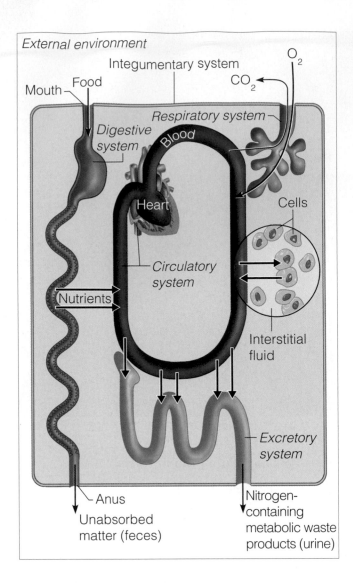

External environment

Integumentary system

O_2

CO_2

Mouth — Food

Respiratory system

Digestive system

Blood

Heart

Cells

Circulatory system

Nutrients

Interstitial fluid

Excretory system

Anus

Unabsorbed matter (feces)

Nitrogen-containing metabolic waste products (urine)

FIGURE 1.3   Examples of selected interrelationships among body organ systems. The integumentary system protects the body as a whole from the external environment. The digestive and respiratory systems, in contact with the external environment, take in nutrients and oxygen, respectively, which the blood then distributes to all body cells. The urinary and respiratory systems eliminate metabolic wastes from the body.

▶**DID YOU GET IT?**

2. At which level of structural organization is the stomach? At which level is a glucose molecule?

3. Which organ system includes the trachea, lungs, nasal cavity, and bronchi?

For answers, see Appendix D.

Maintaining Life
Necessary Life Functions

Now that we have introduced the structural levels composing the human body, a question naturally follows: What does this highly organized human body do? Like all complex animals, human beings maintain their boundaries, move, respond to environmental changes, take in and digest nutrients, carry out metabolism, dispose of wastes, reproduce themselves, and grow. We will discuss each of these necessary life functions briefly here and in more detail in later chapters.

Organ systems do not work in isolation; instead, they work together to promote the well-being of the entire body. Because this theme will be emphasized throughout this book, it is worthwhile to identify the most important organ systems contributing to each of the necessary life functions (Figure 1.3). Also, as you read through this material, you may want to refer back to the more detailed descriptions of the organ systems provided on pp. 4 through 7 and in Figure 1.2.

Maintaining Boundaries

Every living organism must be able to maintain its boundaries so that its "inside" remains distinct from its "outside." Every cell of the human body is surrounded by an external membrane that contains its contents and allows needed substances in while generally preventing entry of potentially damaging or unnecessary substances. The body as a whole is also enclosed by the integumentary system, or skin. The integumentary system protects internal organs from drying out (which would be fatal), from bacteria, and from the damaging effects of heat, sunlight, and an unbelievable number of chemical substances in the external environment.

Movement

Movement includes all the activities promoted by the muscular system, such as propelling ourselves from one place to another (by walking, swimming, and so forth) and manipulating the external environment with our fingers. The skeletal system provides the bones that the muscles pull on as they work. Movement also occurs when substances such as blood, foodstuffs, and urine are propelled through the internal organs of the cardiovascular, digestive, and urinary systems, respectively.

Responsiveness

Responsiveness, or **irritability,** is the ability to sense changes (stimuli) in the environment and then to react to them. For example, if you cut your hand on broken glass, you involuntarily pull your hand away from the painful stimulus (the broken glass). You do not need to think about it—it just happens! Likewise, when the amount of carbon dioxide in your blood rises to dangerously high levels, your breathing rate speeds up to blow off the excess carbon dioxide.

Because nerve cells are highly irritable and can communicate rapidly with each other via electrical impulses, the nervous system bears the major responsibility for responsiveness. However, all body cells are irritable to some extent.

Digestion

Digestion is the process of breaking down ingested food into simple molecules that can then be absorbed into the blood. The nutrient-rich blood is then distributed to all body cells by the cardiovascular system. In a simple, one-celled organism such as an amoeba, the cell itself is the "digestion factory," but in the complex, multicellular human body, the digestive system performs this function for the entire body.

Metabolism

Metabolism is a broad term that refers to all chemical reactions that occur within body cells. It includes breaking down complex substances into simpler building blocks, making larger structures from smaller ones, and using nutrients and oxygen to produce molecules of adenosine triphosphate (ATP), the energy-rich molecules that power cellular activities. Metabolism depends on the digestive and respiratory systems to make nutrients and oxygen available to the blood and on the cardiovascular system to distribute these needed substances throughout the body. Metabolism is regulated chiefly by hormones secreted by the glands of the endocrine system.

Excretion

Excretion is the process of removing *excreta* (ek-skre′tah), or wastes, from the body. If the body is to continue to operate as we expect it to, it must get rid of the nonuseful substances produced during digestion and metabolism. Several organ systems participate in excretion. For example, the digestive system rids the body of indigestible food residues in feces, and the urinary system disposes of nitrogen-containing metabolic wastes in urine.

Reproduction

Reproduction, the production of offspring, can occur on the cellular or organismal level. In cellular reproduction, the original cell divides, producing two identical daughter cells that may then be used for body growth or repair. Reproduction of the human organism, or making a whole new person, is the task of the organs of the reproductive system, which produce sperm and eggs. When a sperm unites with an egg, a fertilized egg forms, which then develops into a baby within the mother's body. The function of the reproductive system is regulated very precisely by hormones of the endocrine system.

Growth

Growth is an increase in size, usually accomplished by an increase in the number of cells. For growth to occur, cell-constructing activities must occur at a faster rate than cell-destroying ones.

Survival Needs

The goal of nearly all body systems is to maintain life. However, life is extraordinarily fragile and requires that several factors be available. These factors, which we will call *survival needs,* include nutrients (food), oxygen, water, and appropriate temperature and atmospheric pressure.

Nutrients, which the body takes in through food, contain the chemicals used for energy and cell building. Carbohydrates are the major energy-providing fuel for body cells. Proteins and, to a lesser extent, fats are essential for building cell structures. Fats also cushion body organs and provide reserve fuel. Minerals and vitamins are required for the chemical reactions that go on in cells and for oxygen transport in the blood.

All the nutrients in the world are useless unless *oxygen* is also available. Because the chemical reactions that release energy from foods require oxygen, human cells can survive for only a few minutes without it. Approximately 20 percent of the air we breathe is oxygen. It is made available to the blood and body cells by the cooperative efforts of the respiratory and cardiovascular systems.

Water accounts for 60 to 80 percent of body weight. It is the single most abundant chemical substance in the body and provides the fluid base for body secretions and excretions. Water is obtained chiefly from ingested foods or liquids and is lost from the body by evaporation from the lungs and skin and in body excretions.

For good health, *body temperature* must be maintained at around 37°C (98°F). As body temperature drops below this point, metabolic reactions become slower and slower and finally stop. When body temperature is too high, chemical reactions proceed too rapidly, and body proteins begin to break down. At either extreme, death occurs. Most body heat is generated by the activity of the skeletal muscles.

The force exerted on the surface of the body by the weight of air is referred to as *atmospheric pressure*. Breathing and the exchange of oxygen and carbon dioxide in the lungs depend on appropriate atmospheric pressure. At high altitudes, where the air is thin and atmospheric pressure is lower, gas exchange may be too low to support cellular metabolism.

The mere presence of these survival factors is not sufficient to maintain life. They must be present in appropriate amounts as well; excesses and deficits may be equally harmful. For example, the food ingested must be of high quality and in proper amounts; otherwise, nutritional disease, obesity, or starvation is likely.

> ▶ *DID YOU GET IT?*
>
> 4. In addition to being able to metabolize, grow, digest food, and excrete wastes, what other functions must an organism perform if it is to survive?
>
> 5. Oxygen is a survival need. Why is it so important?
>
> For answers, see Appendix D.

Homeostasis

When you really think about the fact that your body contains trillions of cells in nearly constant activity, and that remarkably little usually goes wrong with it, you begin to appreciate what a marvelous machine your body really is. The word **homeostasis** (ho″me-o-sta′sis) describes the body's ability to maintain relatively stable internal conditions even though the outside world is continuously changing. Although the literal translation of *homeostasis* is "unchanging" (*homeo* = the same; *stasis* = standing still), the term does not really mean an unchanging state. Instead, it indicates a *dynamic* state of equilibrium, or a balance in which internal conditions change and vary but always within relatively narrow limits.

In general, the body demonstrates homeostasis when its needs are being adequately met and it is functioning smoothly. Virtually every organ system plays a role in maintaining the constancy of the internal environment. Adequate blood levels of vital nutrients must be continuously present, and heart activity and blood pressure must be constantly monitored and adjusted so that the blood is propelled with adequate force to reach all body tissues. Additionally, wastes must not be allowed to accumulate, and body temperature must be precisely controlled.

Homeostatic Control Mechanisms

Communication within the body is essential for homeostasis and is accomplished chiefly by the nervous and endocrine systems, which use electrical signals delivered by nerves or bloodborne hormones, respectively, as information carriers. The details of how these two regulating systems operate are the subjects of later chapters, but the basic characteristics of the neural and hormonal control systems that promote homeostasis are explained here.

Regardless of the factor or event being regulated (this is called the *variable*), all homeostatic control mechanisms have at least three components (Figure 1.4). The first component is a **receptor.** Essentially, it is some type of sensor that monitors and responds to changes in the environment. It responds to such changes, called *stimuli,* by sending information (input) to the second element, the *control center.* Information flows from the receptor to the control center along the *afferent pathway.* (It may help to remember that information traveling along the *afferent* pathway *approaches* the control center.)

The **control center,** which determines the level (set point) at which a variable is to be maintained, analyzes the information it receives and then determines the appropriate response or course of action.

The third component is the **effector,** which provides the means for the control center's response

If this control system were regulating room temperature, what apparatus would be the effector?

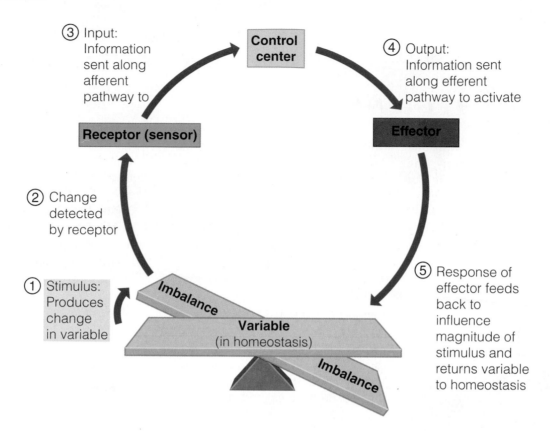

③ Input: Information sent along afferent pathway to

Control center

④ Output: Information sent along efferent pathway to activate

Receptor (sensor)

Effector

② Change detected by receptor

⑤ Response of effector feeds back to influence magnitude of stimulus and returns variable to homeostasis

① Stimulus: Produces change in variable

Imbalance

Variable (in homeostasis)

Imbalance

FIGURE 1.4   The elements of a homeostatic control system. Communication between the receptor, control center, and effector is essential for normal operation of the system.

(output) to the stimulus. Information flows from the control center to the effector along the *efferent pathway.* (*Efferent* information *exits* from the control center.) The results of the response then *feed back* to influence the stimulus, either by depressing it (negative feedback), so that the whole control mechanism is shut off; or by enhancing it (positive feedback), so that the reaction continues at an even faster rate.

Most homeostatic control mechanisms are **negative feedback mechanisms.** In such systems, the net effect of the response to the stimulus is to shut off the original stimulus or reduce its intensity. A good example of a nonbiological negative feedback system is a home heating system connected to a thermostat. In this situation, the thermostat contains both the receptor and the control center. If the thermostat is set at 20°C (68°F), the heating system (effector) will be trig-

gered ON when the house temperature drops below that setting. As the furnace produces heat, the air is warmed. When the temperature reaches 20°C or slightly higher, the thermostat sends a signal to shut off the furnace. Your body "thermostat," located in a part of your brain called the *hypothalamus,* operates in a similar way to regulate body temperature. Other negative feedback mechanisms regulate heart rate, blood pressure, breathing rate, and blood levels of glucose, oxygen, carbon dioxide, and minerals.

Positive feedback mechanisms are rare in the body because they tend to increase the original disturbance (stimulus) and to push the variable *farther* from its original value. Typically these mechanisms control infrequent events that occur explosively and do not require continuous adjustments. Blood clotting and the birth of a baby are the most familiar examples of positive feedback mechanisms.

A ‌The heat-generating furnace or oil burner.

focus on CAREERS

DENTAL HYGIENIST

Dental hygienists need thorough training in human anatomy and physiology to properly care for their patients.

Feel a bit nervous when getting your teeth cleaned? Many people do. But probably you'll feel better after you hear how well trained your dental hygienist is.

Dental hygienists are licensed oral health professionals who provide educational, clinical, and therapeutic

services to the public. Take Robin Mendica, a hygienist for 15 years, who holds an associate's degree in dental hygiene. Mendica's course work included training in whole-body anatomy and physiology, plus specialized classes focusing on head and neck anatomy. "We learned every nerve and blood vessel above the shoulders," she recalls. "This is important because dental hygienists can give injections of anesthetic for deep cleaning and root cleaning procedures. You have to know where

the nerves are to minimize pain and avoid injuries that could lead to facial paralysis."

When patients come into the office, Mendica conducts a preliminary examination: "I look at their dental X-ray films and their charts to remind myself of any problems or concerns they may have. Then I examine the mouth inside and check their teeth, tongue, crowns, and fillings for signs of tooth decay." Then Mendica polishes patients' teeth, removing stains, tartar, and plaque (a soft, sticky deposit of bacteria that leads to periodontal problems) in preparation for the dentist's examination.

Mendica plays an important role in alerting the dentist to symptoms of dental problems and other health conditions. "Untreated dental conditions can lead to trouble in other parts of the body; I've seen tooth abscesses spread into the sinuses and cause bad infections. People who have lost a lot of teeth can't chew food properly, and that can cause digestive problems. In school we also learned to recognize nodules, precancerous conditions, and oral cancer."

What does Mendica enjoy most about her work? "I love dealing with people. Every patient is different, and I love teaching them about good oral hygiene and motivating them to take care of their teeth." She tells of many patients she has helped, such as the man who tried to "glue" a rotten molar back in his mouth with bubble gum, or the hapless woman who attempted to brighten stained bridge work with white nail polish. "I consider patient education an important part of

my job, because I'm a big advocate of regular dental exams. Getting your teeth cleaned every six months is an investment in your lifelong health."

Dental hygiene education generally lasts two to four years beyond high school (or equivalent). Two-year programs offer a diploma, certificate, or associate's degree; four-year programs offer a bachelor's degree. Master's degrees are available for students interested in education, research, or administration.

> ❝ *We learned every nerve and blood vessel above the shoulders.* ❞

An accredited dental hygiene program requires supervised clinical instruction and courses in anatomy, physiology, chemistry, and microbiology. Dental hygienists must be licensed by the state in which they practice. State licensing requirements vary but usually include successful completion of a regional or state clinical board examination.

To learn more, contact the American Dental Hygienists Association (ADHA) at

444 N. Michigan Avenue
Suite 3400, Chicago, IL 60611
(312) 440-8900 or (800) 735-5121
http://www.adha.org

For additional information on this career, click the Focus on Careers link at www.anatomyandphysiology.com.

HOMEOSTATIC IMBALANCE

Homeostasis is so important that most disease can be regarded as a result of its disturbance, a condition called **homeostatic imbalance.** As we age, our body organs become less efficient, and our internal conditions become less and less stable. These events place us at an increasing risk for illness and produce the changes we associate with aging.

Examples of homeostatic imbalance will be provided throughout this book to enhance your understanding of normal physiological mechanisms. These homeostatic imbalance sections are preceded by the symbol to alert you that an abnormal condition is being described. ▲

►DID YOU GET IT?

6. When we say that the body demonstrates homeostasis, do we mean that conditions in the body are unchanging? Explain your answer.

7. When we begin to become dehydrated, we usually get thirsty, which causes us to drink liquids. Is the thirst sensation part of a negative or a positive feedback control system? Defend your choice.

For answers, see Appendix D.

The Language of Anatomy

Learning about the body is exciting, but our interest sometimes dwindles when we are faced with the terminology of anatomy and physiology. Let's face it. You can't just pick up an anatomy and physiology book and read it as though it were a novel. Unfortunately, confusion is inevitable without specialized terminology. For example, if you are looking at a ball, "above" always means the area over the top of the ball. Other directional terms can also be used consistently because the ball is a sphere. All sides and surfaces are equal. The human body, of course, has many protrusions and bends. Thus, the question becomes: Above what? To prevent misunderstanding, anatomists use a set of terms that allow body structures to be located and identified clearly with just a few words. This language of anatomy is presented and explained next.

Anatomical Position

To accurately describe body parts and position, we must have an initial reference point and use directional terms. To avoid confusion, it is always assumed that the body is in a standard position called the **anatomical position.** It is important to understand this position because most body terminology used in this book refers to this body positioning *regardless* of the position the body happens to be in. The face-front diagrams in Figure 1.5 and Table 1.1 (on page 18) illustrate the anatomical position. As you can see, the body is erect with the feet parallel and the arms hanging at the sides with the palms facing forward.

• Stand up and assume the anatomical position. Notice that it is similar to "standing at attention" but is less comfortable because the palms are held unnaturally forward (with thumbs pointing away from the body) rather than hanging cupped toward the thighs.

Directional Terms

Directional terms allow medical personnel and anatomists to explain exactly where one body structure is in relation to another. For example, we can describe the relationship between the ears and the nose informally by saying, "The ears are located on each side of the head to the right and left of the nose." Using anatomical terminology, this condenses to, "The ears are lateral to the nose." Using anatomical terminology saves a good deal of description and, once learned, is much clearer. Commonly used directional terms are defined and illustrated in Table 1.1 (p. 18). Although most of these terms are also used in everyday conversation, keep in mind that their anatomical meanings are very precise.

Before continuing, take a minute to check your understanding of what you have read in Table 1.1. Give the relationship between the following body parts using the correct anatomical terms.

The wrist is _____ to the hand.

The breastbone is _____ to the spine.

The brain is _____ to the spinal cord.

The thumb is _____ to the fingers. (Be careful here. Remember the anatomical position.)

Study this figure for a moment to answer these two questions. Where would you hurt if you (1) pulled a groin muscle or (2) cracked a bone in your olecranal area?

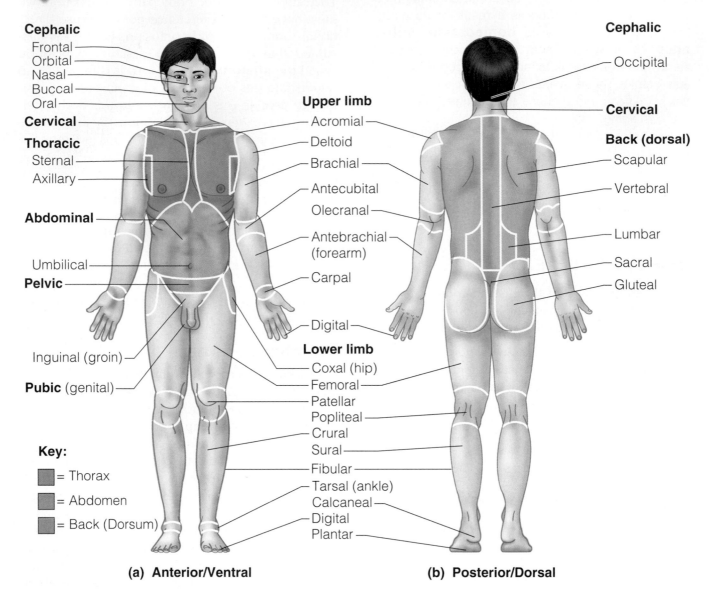

Cephalic
  Frontal
  Orbital
  Nasal
  Buccal
  Oral
Cervical
Thoracic
  Sternal
  Axillary
Abdominal
  Umbilical
Pelvic
  Inguinal (groin)
Pubic (genital)

Key:
■ = Thorax
■ = Abdomen
■ = Back (Dorsum)

Upper limb
  Acromial
  Deltoid
  Brachial
  Antecubital
  Olecranal
  Antebrachial (forearm)
  Carpal
  Digital
Lower limb
  Coxal (hip)
  Femoral
  Patellar
  Popliteal
  Crural
  Sural
  Fibular
  Tarsal (ankle)
  Calcaneal
  Digital
  Plantar

Cephalic
  Occipital
Cervical
Back (dorsal)
  Scapular
  Vertebral
  Lumbar
  Sacral
  Gluteal

(a) Anterior/Ventral

(b) Posterior/Dorsal

FIGURE 1.5 Regional terms: names of specific body areas. In **(b)** the heels are raised slightly to show the inferior plantar surface (sole) of the foot.

Regional Terms

There are many visible landmarks on the surface of the body. Once you know their proper anatomical names, you can be specific in referring to different regions of the body.

Anterior Body Landmarks

Look at Figure 1.5a to find the following body regions. Once you have identified all the anterior body landmarks, cover the labels that describe what the structures are. Then go through the list again, pointing out these areas on your own body.

- **abdominal** (ab-dom'ĭ-nal): anterior body trunk inferior to ribs
- **acromial** (ah-kro'me-ul): point of shoulder
- **antebrachial** (an″te-bra'ke-ul): forearm
- **antecubital** (an″te-ku'bĭ-tal): anterior surface of elbow

- **axillary** (ak′sĭ-lar″e): armpit
- **brachial** (bra′ke-al): arm
- **buccal** (buk′al): cheek area
- **carpal** (kar′pal): wrist
- **cervical** (ser′vĭ-kal): neck region
- **coxal** (kox′al): hip
- **crural** (kroo′ral): leg
- **deltoid** (del′toyd): curve of shoulder formed by large deltoid muscle
- **digital** (dij′ĭ-tal): fingers, toes
- **femoral** (fem′or-al): thigh
- **fibular** (fib′u-lar): lateral part of leg
- **frontal** (frun′-tal): forehead
- **inguinal** (in′gwĭ-nal): area where thigh meets body trunk; groin
- **nasal** (na′zul): nose area
- **oral** (o′ral): mouth
- **orbital** (or′bĭ-tal): eye area
- **patellar** (pah-tel′er): anterior knee
- **pelvic** (pel′vik): area overlying the pelvis anteriorly
- **pubic** (pu′bik): genital region
- **sternal** (ster′nul): breastbone area
- **tarsal** (tar′sal): ankle region
- **thoracic** (tho-ras′ik): chest
- **umbilical** (um-bil′ĭ-kal): navel

Posterior Body Landmarks

Identify the following body regions in Figure 1.5b, and then locate them on yourself without referring to this book.

- **calcaneal** (kal-ka′neul): heel of foot
- **cephalic** (seh-fă′lik): head
- **femoral** (fem′or-al): thigh
- **gluteal** (gloo′te-al): buttock
- **lumbar** (lum′bar): area of back between ribs and hips
- **occipital** (ok-sip′ĭ-tal): posterior surface of head
- **olecranal** (ol-eh-cra′nel): posterior surface of elbow
- **popliteal** (pop-lit′e-al): posterior knee area
- **sacral** (sa′krul): area between hips
- **scapular** (skap′u-lar): shoulder blade region

- **sural** (soo′ral): the posterior surface of lower leg; the calf
- **vertebral** (ver′tĕ-bral): area of spine

The **plantar** region, or the sole of the foot, actually on the inferior body surface, is illlustrated along with the posterior body landmarks in Figure 1.5b.

Body Planes and Sections

When preparing to look at the internal structures of the body, medical students make a **section,** or cut. When the section is made through the body wall or through an organ, it is made along an imaginary line called a **plane.** Because the body is three-dimensional, we can refer to three types of planes or sections that lie at right angles to one another (Figure 1.6).

A **sagittal** (saj′ĭ-tal) **section** is a cut along the lengthwise, or longitudinal, plane of the body, dividing the body into right and left parts. If the cut is down the median plane of the body and the right and left parts are equal in size, it is called a **median,** or **midsagittal, section.**

A **frontal section** is a cut along a lengthwise plane that divides the body (or an organ) into anterior and posterior parts. It is also called a **coronal** (ko-ro′nal) **section.**

A **transverse section** is a cut along a horizontal plane, dividing the body or organ into superior and inferior parts. It is also called a **cross section.**

Sectioning a body or one of its organs along different planes often results in very different views. For example, a transverse section of the body trunk at the level of the kidneys would show kidney structure in cross section very nicely; a frontal section of the body trunk would show a different view of kidney anatomy; and a midsagittal section would miss the kidneys completely. Information on body organ positioning that can be gained by taking magnetic resonance imaging (MRI) scans along different body planes is illustrated in Figure 1.6. (MRI scans are described further in the "A Closer Look" box on pp. 8–9).

Body Cavities

Anatomy and physiology textbooks typically describe two sets of internal body cavities, called the dorsal and ventral body cavities, that provide different degrees of protection to the organs within them

(Continues on page 20)

TABLE 1.1   Orientation and Directional Terms

Term	Definition	Illustration	Example
Superior (cranial or cephalad)	Toward the head end or upper part of a structure or the body; above		The forehead is superior to the nose.
Inferior (caudal)*	Away from the head end or toward the lower part of a structure or the body; below		The navel is inferior to the breastbone.
Ventral (anterior)†	Toward or at the front of the body; in front of		The breastbone is anterior to the spine.
Dorsal (posterior)†	Toward or at the backside of the body; behind		The heart is posterior to the breastbone.
Medial	Toward or at the midline of the body; on the inner side of		The heart is medial to the arm.
Lateral	Away from the midline of the body; on the outer side of		The arms are lateral to the chest.
Proximal	Close to the origin of the body part or the point of attachment of a limb to the body trunk		The elbow is proximal to the wrist (meaning that the elbow is closer to the shoulder or attachment point of the arm than the wrist is).
Distal	Farther from the origin of a body part or the point of attachment of a limb to the body trunk		The knee is distal to the thigh.
Superficial (external)	Toward or at the body surface		The skin is superficial to the skeleton.
Deep (internal)	Away from the body surface; more internal		The lungs are deep to the rib cage.

*The term *caudal*, literally "toward the tail," is synonymous with *inferior* only to the inferior end of the spine.
†*Ventral* and *anterior* are synonymous in humans; this is not the case in four-legged animals. *Ventral* refers to the "belly" of an animal and thus is the inferior surface of four-legged animals. Likewise, although the dorsal and posterior surfaces are the same in humans, the term *dorsal* refers to an animal's back. Thus, the dorsal surface of four-legged animals is their superior surface.

Which section type would separate the two eyes?

(a) Median (midsagittal)   **(b)** Frontal (coronal) plane   **(c)** Transverse plane

Vertebral column

Intestines

Rectum

Heart
Right lung
Left lung
Liver   Stomach   Spleen

Spinal cord
Aorta
Spleen
Liver
Subcutaneous fat layer
Stomach

FIGURE 1.6 **The anatomical position and planes of the body—median, frontal, and transverse with corresponding MRI scans.** Diagrams identifying body organs seen in the MRI scans are at the bottom.

A midsagittal section would separate the two eyes.

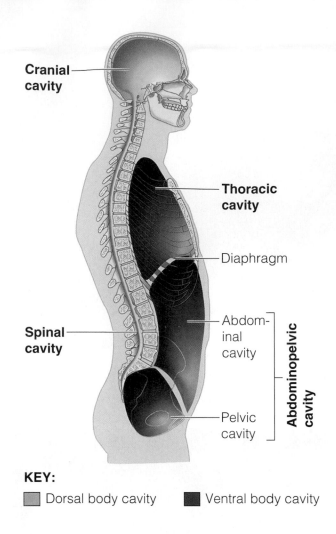

Cranial cavity

Thoracic cavity

Diaphragm

Abdom-inal cavity

Spinal cavity

Pelvic cavity

Abdominopelvic cavity

KEY:

☐ Dorsal body cavity   ■ Ventral body cavity

FIGURE 1.7   Body cavities. Notice the angular relationship between the abdominal and pelvic cavities.

(Figure 1.7). Because these cavities differ in their mode of embryological development and in their lining membranes, many anatomy reference books do not identify the dorsal, or neural, body cavity as an internal body cavity. However, the idea of two major sets of internal body cavities is a useful learning concept, so we will continue to use it here.

Dorsal Body Cavity

The **dorsal body cavity** has two subdivisions, which are continuous with each other. The **cranial cavity** is the space inside the bony skull. The brain is well protected because it occupies the cranial cavity. The **spinal cavity** extends from the cranial

cavity nearly to the end of the vertebral column. The spinal cord, which is a continuation of the brain, is protected by the vertebrae, which surround the spinal cavity.

Ventral Body Cavity

The **ventral body cavity** is much larger than the dorsal cavity. It contains all the structures within the chest and abdomen, that is, the visceral organs in those regions. Like the dorsal cavity, the ventral body cavity is subdivided. The superior **thoracic cavity** is separated from the rest of the ventral cavity by a dome-shaped muscle, the **diaphragm** (di'ah-fram). The organs in the thoracic cavity (lungs, heart, and others) are somewhat protected by the rib cage. A central region called the **mediastinum** (me"de-as-ti'num) separates the lungs into right and left cavities in the thoracic cavity. The mediastinum itself houses the heart, trachea, and other visceral organs.

The cavity inferior to the diaphragm is the **abdominopelvic** (ab-dom"ĭ-no-pel'vik) **cavity.** Some prefer to subdivide it into a superior **abdominal cavity,** containing the stomach, liver, intestines, and other organs, and an inferior **pelvic cavity,** with the reproductive organs, bladder, and rectum. However, there is no actual physical structure dividing the abdominopelvic cavity. If you look carefully at Figure 1.7, you will see that the pelvic cavity is not continuous with the abdominal cavity in a straight plane, but that it tips away from the abdominal cavity in the posterior direction.

HOMEOSTATIC IMBALANCE

When the body is subjected to physical trauma (as often happens in an automobile accident, for example), the most vulnerable abdominopelvic organs are those within the abdominal cavity. The reason is that the abdominal cavity walls are formed only of trunk muscles and are not reinforced by bone. The pelvic organs receive a somewhat greater degree of protection from the bony pelvis in which they reside. ▲

Because the abdominopelvic cavity is quite large and contains many organs, it helps to divide it up into smaller areas for study. A scheme commonly used by medical personnel divides the abdominopelvic cavity into four more or less equal regions called *quadrants*. The quadrants are

(a)

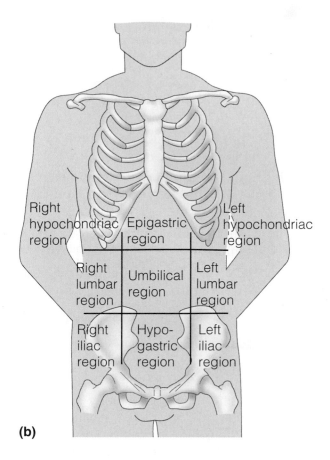

(b)

FIGURE 1.8   Abdominopelvic surface and cavity. (a) The four quadrants. **(b)** Nine regions delineated by four planes. The superior horizontal plane is at the inferior aspect of the ribs; the inferior horizontal plane is at the superior aspect of the hip bones, and the vertical planes are just medial to the nipples. **(c)** Anterior view of the ventral body cavity showing superficial organs.

then simply named according to their relative positions—that is, right upper quadrant (RUQ), right lower quadrant (RLQ), left upper quadrant (LUQ), and left lower quadrant (LLQ) (Figure 1.8a).

Another system, used mainly by anatomists, divides the abdominopelvic cavity into nine separate *regions* by four planes, as shown in Figure 1.8b. Although the names of the nine regions are unfamiliar to you now, with a little patience and study they will become easier to remember. As you locate these regions in the figure, notice the organs they contain by referring to Figure 1.8c.

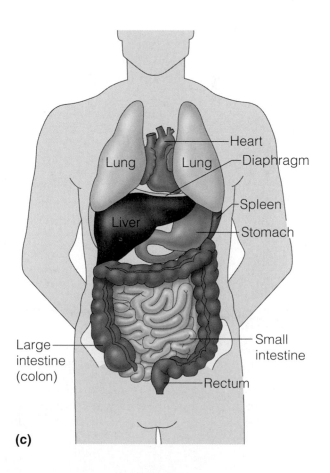

(c)

- The **umbilical region** is the centermost region, deep to and surrounding the umbilicus (navel).
- The **epigastric** (ep″ĭ-gas′trik) **region** is located superior to the umbilical region (*epi* = upon, above; *gastric* = stomach).
- The **hypogastric (pubic) region** is inferior to the umbilical region (*hypo* = below).
- The **right** and **left iliac,** or **inguinal, regions** are lateral to the hypogastric region (*iliac* = superior part of the hip bone).
- The **right** and **left lumbar regions** lie lateral to the umbilical region (*lumbus* = loin).
- The **right** and **left hypochondriac** (hi″po-kon′dre-ak) **regions** flank the epigastric region and contain the lower ribs (*chondro* = cartilage).

Open Body Cavities

In addition to the large closed body cavities, there are several smaller body cavities. Most of these are in the head and open to the body exterior. With the exception of the middle ear cavities, the body regions that house these cavities are all shown in Figure 1.5.

- **Oral and digestive cavities.** The oral cavity, commonly called the mouth, contains the teeth and tongue. This cavity is part of and continuous with the cavity of the digestive organs, which opens to the exterior at the anus.

- **Nasal cavity.** Located within and posterior to the nose, the nasal cavity is part of the respiratory system passageways.
- **Orbital cavities.** The orbital cavities (orbits) in the skull house the eyes and present them in an anterior position.
- **Middle ear cavities.** The middle ear cavities carved into the skull lie just medial to the eardrums. These cavities contain tiny bones that transmit sound vibrations to the hearing receptors in the inner ears.

▶ DID YOU GET IT?

8. Why is understanding the anatomical position important to an anatomy student?

9. The axillary and the acromial areas are both in the general area of the shoulder. To what specific body area does each of these terms apply?

10. Which kind of section would cut the brain into anterior and posterior parts?

11. If you wanted to separate the thoracic cavity from the abdominal cavity of a cadaver, which type of section would you make?

12. Of the spinal cord, small intestine, uterus, and heart, which are in the dorsal body cavity?

For answers, see Appendix D.

SUMMARY

Media study tools that provide additional review of key topics of Chapter 1 are referenced below.

  IP = *InterActive Physiology*
  WEB = The A&P Place

An Overview of Anatomy and Physiology (pp. 2–3)

1. Anatomy is the study of structure. Observation is used to see the sizes and relationships of body parts.

2. Physiology is the study of how a structure (which may be a cell, an organ, or an organ system) functions or works.

3. Structure determines what functions can occur; therefore, if the structure changes, the function must also change.

Levels of Structural Organization (pp. 3–7, 10)

1. There are six levels of structural organization. Atoms (at the chemical level) combine, forming the unit of life, the cell. Cells are grouped into tissues, which in turn are arranged in specific ways to form organs. A number of organs form an organ system that performs a specific function for the body (which no other organ system can do). Together, all of the organ systems form the organism, or living body.

  WEB Exercise: Chapter 1, Levels of Biological Organization.

2. For a description of organ systems naming the major organs and functions, see pp. 4–7.

Maintaining Life   (pp. 10–12)

1. To sustain life, an organism must be able to maintain its boundaries, move, respond to stimuli, digest nutrients and excrete wastes, carry on metabolism, reproduce itself, and grow.

2. Survival needs include food, oxygen, water, appropriate temperature, and normal atmospheric pressure. Extremes of any of these factors can be harmful.

Homeostasis   (pp. 12–13, 15)

1. Body functions interact to maintain homeostasis, or a relatively stable internal environment within the body. Homeostasis is necessary for survival and good health; its loss results in illness or disease.

2. All homeostatic control mechanisms have three components: (1) a receptor that responds to environmental changes, (2) a control center that assesses those changes and produces a response by activating (3) the effector.

3. Most homeostatic control systems are negative feedback systems, which act to reduce or stop the initial stimulus.

The Language of Anatomy   (pp. 15–22)

1. Anatomical terminology is relative and assumes that the body is in the anatomical position (erect, palms facing forward).

2. Directional terms

   a. Superior (cranial, cephalad): above something else, toward the head.

   b. Inferior (caudal): below something else, toward the tail.

   c. Ventral (anterior): toward the front of the body or structure.

   d. Dorsal (posterior): toward the rear or back of the body or structure.

   e. Medial: toward the midline of the body.

   f. Lateral: away from the midline of the body.

   g. Proximal: closer to the point of attachment.

   h. Distal: farther from the point of attachment.

   i. Superficial (external): at or close to the body surface.

   j. Deep (internal): below or away from the body surface.

3. Regional terms. Visible landmarks on the body surface may be used to specifically refer to a body part or area. See pp. 16 and 17 for terms referring to anterior and posterior surface anatomy.

WEB Exercise: Chapter 1, Anatomical Terminology: Orientation and Directional Terms.

4. Body planes and sections

   a. Sagittal section: separates the body longitudinally into right and left parts.

   b. Frontal (coronal) section: separates the body on a longitudinal plane into anterior and posterior parts.

   c. Transverse (cross) section: separates the body on a horizontal plane into superior and inferior parts.

WEB Exercise: Chapter 1, Body Planes.

5. Body cavities

   a. Dorsal: well protected by bone; has two subdivisions.

      (1) Cranial: contains the brain.

      (2) Spinal: contains the spinal cord.

   b. Ventral: less protected than dorsal cavity; has two subdivisions.

      (1) Thoracic: The superior cavity that extends inferiorly to the diaphragm; contains heart and lungs, which are protected by the rib cage.

      (2) Abdominopelvic: The cavity inferior to the diaphragm that contains the digestive, urinary, and reproductive organs. The abdominal portion is vulnerable because it is protected only by the trunk muscles. The pelvic portion is protected somewhat by the bony pelvis. The abdominopelvic cavity is often divided into four quadrants or nine regions (see Figure 1.8).

   c. Smaller open body cavities include the oral, nasal, orbital, and middle ear cavities.

WEB Exercise: Chapter 1, Dorsal and Ventral Cavities.

REVIEW QUESTIONS

Multiple Choice

More than one choice may apply.

1. Consider the following levels: (1) chemical; (2) tissue; (3) organ; (4) cellular; (5) organismal; (6) systemic. Which of the following choices has the levels listed in order of increasing complexity?

   a. 1, 2, 3, 4, 5, 6   d. 1, 4, 2, 3, 6, 5

   b. 1, 4, 2, 5, 3, 6   e. 4, 1, 3, 2, 6, 5

   c. 3, 1, 2, 4, 6, 5

2. Which of the following is (are) involved in maintaining homeostasis?

    a. Effector   d. Feedback

    b. Control center   e. Lack of change

    c. Receptor

3. Which is not essential to survival?

    a. Water   d. Atmospheric pressure

    b. Oxygen   e. Nutrients

    c. Gravity

4. Using the terms listed below, fill in the blank with the proper term.

    anterior   superior   medial   proximal   superfical
    posterior   inferior   lateral   distal   deep

    The heart is located _____ to the diaphragm.

    The muscles are _____ to the skin.

    The shoulder is _____ to the elbow.

    In anatomical position, the thumb is _____ to the index finger.

    The vertebral region is _____ to the scapular region.

    The gluteal region is located on the _____ surface of the body.

5. Match the proper anatomical term (column B) with the common name (column A) for the body regions listed below.

Column A	Column B
_____ buttocks	a. inguinal
_____ back	b. frontal
_____ shoulder blade	c. dorsal
_____ front of elbow	d. lumbar
_____ toes	e. gluteal
_____ groin	f. antecubital
_____ forehead	g. plantar
_____ lower back	h. digital
_____ sole of foot	i. scapular

6. Anatomical terms that apply to the backside of the body in the anatomical position include

    a. ventral and anterior.

    b. back and rear.

    c. posterior and dorsal.

    d. head and lateral.

7. A neurosurgeon orders a spinal tap for a patient. Into what body cavity will the needle be inserted?

    a. Ventral

    b. Thoracic

    c. Dorsal

    d. Cranial

    e. Pelvic

8. Which of the following groupings of the abdominopelvic regions is medial?

    a. Hypochondriac, hypogastric, umbilical

    b. Hypochondriac, lumbar, inguinal

    c. Hypogastric, umbilical, epigastric

    d. Lumbar, umbilical, iliac

    e. Iliac, umbilical, hypochondriac

Short Answer Essay

9. Define *anatomy* and *physiology*.

10. List the 11 organ systems of the body, briefly describe the function of each, and then name two organs in each system.

11. Explain the meaning of *homeostasis* as applied to the living organism.

12. What is the consequence of loss of homeostasis, or homeostatic imbalance?

13. Many body structures are symmetrical. Are the kidneys symmetrical? What about the stomach?

14. On what body surface is each of the following located: nose, calf of leg, ears, umbilicus, fingernails?

15. Which of the following organ systems—digestive, respiratory, reproductive, circulatory, urinary, or muscular—are found in *both* subdivisions of the ventral body cavity? Which are found in the thoracic cavity only? In the abdominopelvic cavity only?

CRITICAL THINKING AND CLINICAL APPLICATION QUESTIONS

16. A nurse informed John that she was about to take blood from his antecubital region. What part of his body was she referring to? Later, she came back and said that she was going to give him an antibiotic shot in the deltoid region. Did he take off his shirt or drop his pants to get the shot? Before John left the office, the nurse noticed that his left sural region was badly bruised. What part of his body was bruised?

17. How is the concept of homeostasis (or its loss) related to disease and aging? Provide examples to support your reasoning.

18. Jennie Dip fell off her motorcycle and tore a nerve in her axillary region. She also tore ligaments in her cervical and scapular regions and broke the only bone of her right brachial region. Explain where each of her injuries is located.

19. Mr. Petros is behaving abnormally, and doctors strongly suspect he has a brain tumor. Which medical imaging device—conventional X ray, DSA, PET, ultrasound, or MRT—would be best for precisely locating a tumor within the brain? Explain your choice.

20. Parathyroid hormone (PTH) is secreted in response to a drop in calcium levels in the blood. The secretion of PTH is regulated by a negative feedback mechanism. What can you expect to happen to calcium blood levels as increased amounts of PTH are secreted, and why?

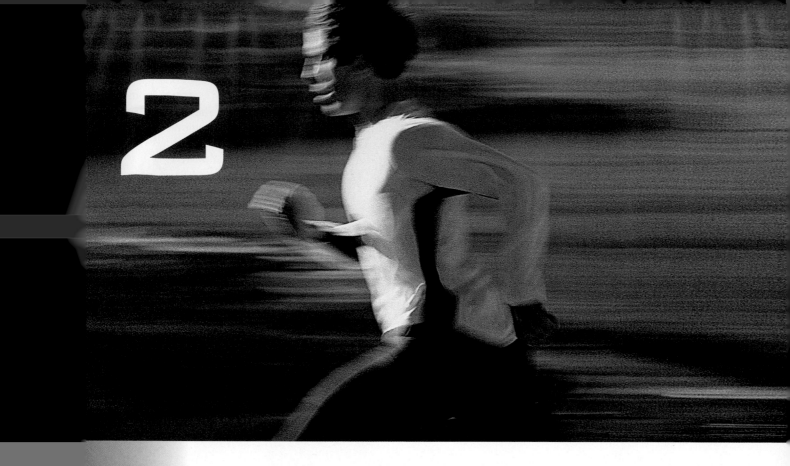

2

Basic Chemistry

YOUR GOALS

After completing this chapter, you will have mastered the objectives listed below.

OBJECTIVE CHECKLIST

Concepts of Matter and Energy   (pp. 27–28)

➤ Differentiate matter from energy.

➤ List the major energy forms, and provide one example of how each energy form is used in the body.

Composition of Matter   (pp. 29–34)

➤ Define *chemical element,* and list the four elements that form the bulk of body matter.

➤ Explain how elements and atoms are related.

➤ List the subatomic particles, and describe their relative masses, charges, and positions in the atom.

➤ Define *radioisotope,* and describe briefly how radioisotopes are used in the diagnosis and treatment of disease.

Molecules and Compounds   (pp. 34–35)

➤ Recognize that chemical reactions involve the interaction of electrons to make and break chemical bonds.

➤ Define *molecule,* and explain how molecules are related to compounds.

Chemical Bonds and Chemical Reactions (pp. 35–41)

➤ Differentiate ionic, polar covalent, and nonpolar covalent bonds, and describe the importance of hydrogen bonds.

➤ Contrast synthesis, decomposition, and exchange reactions.

Biochemistry: The Chemical Composition of Living Matter (pp. 41–58)

➤ Distinguish organic from inorganic compounds.

➤ Differentiate a salt, an acid, and a base.

➤ List several salts (or their ions) vitally important to body functioning.

➤ Explain the importance of water to body homeostasis, and provide several examples of the roles of water.

➤ Explain the concept of pH, and state the pH of blood.

➤ Compare and contrast carbohydrates, lipids, proteins, and nucleic acids in terms of their building blocks, structures, and functions in the body.

➤ Differentiate fibrous proteins from globular proteins.

➤ Compare and contrast the structure and functions of DNA and RNA.

➤ Define *enzyme,* and explain the role of enzymes.

➤ Explain the importance of ATP in the body.

Many short courses in anatomy and physiology lack the time to consider chemistry as a topic. So why include it here? The answer is simple. The food you eat and the medicines you take when you are ill are composed of chemicals. Indeed, your entire body is made up of chemicals—thousands of them—continuously interacting with one another at an incredible pace.

Although it is possible to study anatomy without much reference to chemistry, chemical reactions underlie all body processes—movement, digestion, the pumping of your heart, and even your thoughts. This chapter presents the basics of chemistry and biochemistry (the chemistry of living material), providing the background you will need to understand body functions.

Concepts of Matter and Energy

Matter

Matter is the "stuff" of the universe. With some exceptions, it can be seen, smelled, and felt. More precisely, matter is anything that occupies space and has mass (weight). Chemistry studies the na-

ture of matter—how its building blocks are put together and how they interact.

Matter exists in solid, liquid, and gaseous states. Examples of each state are found in the human body. *Solids,* such as bones and teeth, have a definite shape and volume. *Liquids* have a definite volume, but they conform to the shape of their container. Examples of body liquids are blood plasma and the interstitial fluid that bathes all body cells. *Gases* have neither a definite shape nor a definite volume. The air we breathe is composed of a mixture of gases.

Matter may be changed both physically and chemically. *Physical changes* do not alter the basic nature of a substance. Examples include changes in state, such as ice melting to become water and cutting food into smaller pieces. *Chemical changes* do alter the composition of the substance—often substantially. Fermenting grapes to make wine and the digestion of food in the body are examples of chemical changes.

Energy

In contrast to matter, **energy** is massless and does not take up space. It can be measured only by its effects on matter. Energy is commonly defined as the ability to do work or to put matter into motion. When energy is actually doing work (moving objects), it is referred to as **kinetic** (kĭ-neh'tik) **energy.** Kinetic energy is displayed in the constant movement of the tiniest particles of matter (atoms) as well as in larger objects, such as a bouncing ball. When energy is inactive or stored (as in the batteries of an unused toy), it is called **potential energy.** All forms of energy exhibit both kinetic and potential work capacities.

Actually, energy is a physics topic, but it is difficult to separate matter and energy. All living things are built of matter, and to grow and function they require a continuous supply of energy. Thus, matter is the substance, and energy is the mover of the substance. Because this is so, it is worth taking a brief detour to introduce the forms of energy the body uses as it does its work.

Forms of Energy

- **Chemical energy** is stored in the bonds of chemical substances. When the bonds are broken, the (potential) stored energy is unleashed and becomes kinetic energy (energy in action). For example, when gasoline molecules are broken apart in your automobile engine, the energy released powers your car. In like manner, all body activities are "run" by the chemical energy harvested from the foods we eat.

- **Electrical energy** results from the movement of charged particles. In your house, electrical energy is the flow of electrons along the wiring. In your body, an electrical current is generated when charged particles (called *ions*) move across cell membranes. The nervous system uses electrical currents called *nerve impulses* to transmit messages from one part of the body to another.

- **Mechanical energy** is energy *directly* involved in moving matter. When you ride a bicycle, your legs provide the mechanical energy that moves the pedals. We can take this example one step further back: As the muscles in your legs shorten, they pull on your bones, causing your limbs to move (so that you can pedal the bike).

- **Radiant energy** travels in waves; that is, it is the energy of the electromagnetic spectrum, which includes X rays, infrared radiation (heat energy), visible light, radio, and ultraviolet waves. Light energy, which stimulates the retinas of your eyes, is important in vision. Ultraviolet waves cause sunburn, but they also stimulate our bodies to make vitamin D.

Energy Form Conversions

With a few exceptions, energy is easily converted from one form to another. For example, chemical energy (from gasoline) that powers the motor of a speedboat is converted into the mechanical energy of the whirling propeller that allows the boat to skim across the water. In the body, chemical energy of foods is trapped in the bonds of a high-energy chemical called ATP (adenosine triphosphate), and ATP's energy may ultimately be transformed into the electrical energy of a nerve impulse or mechanical energy of shortening muscles.

Energy conversions are quite inefficient, and some of the initial energy supply is always "lost" to the environment as heat (thermal energy). It is not really lost, because energy cannot be created or destroyed, but the part given off as heat is *unusable.* You can easily demonstrate this principle by touching a lightbulb that has been lit for an hour or so. You will soon discover that some of the electrical energy reaching the bulb is producing heat instead of light. Likewise, all energy conversions that occur in the body liberate heat. It is this heat that makes us warm-blooded animals and contributes to our relatively high body temperature, which has an important influence on body functioning. For example, when matter is heated, its particles begin to move more quickly; that is, their kinetic energy (energy of motion) increases. This is important to the chemical reactions that occur in the body because, up to a point, the higher the temperature, the faster those reactions occur. We will learn more about this later.

▶ DID YOU GET IT?

1. Explain the difference between a chemical change and a physical change in a sample of matter, and give one example of each type of change.

2. Matter and energy—how are they interrelated?

3. What does it mean when we say that some energy is "lost" every time energy changes from one form to another in the body?

For answers, see Appendix D.

Composition of Matter

Elements and Atoms

All matter is composed of a limited number of substances called **elements,** unique substances that cannot be broken down into simpler substances by ordinary chemical methods. Examples of elements include many commonly known substances, such as oxygen, carbon, gold, copper, and iron.

So far, 112 elements are known with certainty, and numbers 113 through 118 are alleged. Ninety-two of these occur naturally; the rest are produced artificially in accelerator devices. Four elements—carbon, oxygen, hydrogen, and nitrogen—make up about 96 percent of body weight, but several others are present in small or trace amounts. A complete listing of the elements appears in the **periodic table,** an odd-shaped checkerboard that appears in Appendix B and in chemistry classrooms the world over. The most abundant elements found in the body and their major roles are listed in Table 2.1.

Each element is composed of more or less identical particles or building blocks called **atoms.** Because all elements are unique, the atoms of each element differ from those of all other elements. Each element is designated by a one- or two-letter chemical shorthand called an **atomic symbol.** In most cases, the atomic symbol is simply the first (or first two) letter(s) of the element's name. For example, C stands for carbon, O for oxygen, and Ca for calcium. In a few cases, the atomic symbol is taken from the Latin name for the element. For instance, sodium is indicated by Na (from the Latin word *natrium*).

Atomic Structure

The word *atom* comes from the Greek word meaning "incapable of being divided," and historically this idea of an atom was accepted as a scientific truth. According to this notion, you could theoretically divide a pure element, such as a block of gold, into smaller and smaller particles until you got down to the individual atoms, and then could subdivide no further. We now know that atoms, although indescribably small, are clusters of even smaller (subatomic) particles and that, under very special circumstances, atoms can be split into these smaller particles. Even so, the old idea of atomic indivisibility is still very appropriate, because an atom loses the unique properties of its element when it is split into its subparticles.

The atoms representing the 112-plus elements are composed of different numbers and proportions of three basic subatomic particles, which differ in their mass, electrical charge, and location within the atom (Table 2.2). **Protons (p^+)** have a positive charge, whereas **neutrons (n^0)** are uncharged, or neutral. Protons and neutrons are heavy particles and have approximately the same mass (1 atomic mass unit, or 1 amu). The tiny **electrons (e^-)** bear a negative charge equal in strength to the positive charge of the protons, but their mass is so small that it is usually designated as 0 amu.

The electrical charge of a particle is a measure of its ability to attract or repel other charged particles. Particles with the same type of charge (+ to + or − to −) repel each other, but particles with unlike charges (+ to −) attract each other. Neutral particles are neither attracted to nor repelled by charged particles.

Because all atoms are electrically neutral, the number of protons an atom has must be precisely balanced by its number of electrons (the + and − charges will then cancel the effect of each other). Thus, hydrogen has one proton and one electron, and iron has 26 protons and 26 electrons. For any atom, the number of protons and electrons is always equal. Atoms that have gained or lost electrons are called *ions,* as discussed shortly.

Planetary and Orbital Models of an Atom

The **planetary model** of an atom portrays the atom as a miniature solar system (Figure 2.1a) in which the protons and neutrons are clustered at the center of the atom in the atomic nucleus. Because the nucleus contains all the heavy particles, it is fantastically dense and positively charged. The tiny electrons orbit around the nucleus in fixed, generally circular orbits, like planets around the sun. But we can never determine the exact location of electrons at a particular time because they jump around following unknown paths. So, instead of speaking of specific orbits, chemists talk about *orbitals*—regions around the nucleus in which a given electron or electron pair is *likely* to be found most of the time. This more modern model of atomic structure, called the **orbital model,** has proved to be more useful in predicting the chemical

| TABLE 2.1 | Common Elements Making Up the Human Body |

Element	Atomic symbol	Percentage of body mass	Role
Major (96.1%)			
Oxygen	O	65.0	A major component of both organic and inorganic molecules; as a gas, essential to the oxidation of glucose and other food fuels, during which cellular energy (ATP) is produced.
Carbon	C	18.5	The primary elemental component of all organic molecules, including carbohydrates, lipids, proteins, and nucleic acids.
Hydrogen	H	9.5	A component of most organic molecules; in ionic form, influences the pH of body fluids.
Nitrogen	N	3.2	A component of proteins and nucleic acids (genetic material).
Lesser (3.9%)			
Calcium	Ca	1.5	Found as a salt in bones and teeth; in ionic form, required for muscle contraction, neural transmission, and blood clotting.
Phosphorus	P	1.0	Present as a salt, in combination with calcium, in bones and teeth; also present in nucleic acids and many proteins; forms part of the high-energy compound ATP.
Potassium	K	0.4	In its ionic form, the major intracellular cation; necessary for the conduction of nerve impulses and for muscle contraction.
Sulfur	S	0.3	A component of proteins (particularly contractile proteins of muscle).
Sodium	Na	0.2	As an ion, the major extracellular cation; important for water balance, conduction of nerve impulses, and muscle contraction.
Chlorine	Cl	0.2	In ionic form, a major extracellular anion.
Magnesium	Mg	0.1	Present in bone; also an important cofactor for enzyme activity in a number of metabolic reactions.
Iodine	I	0.1	Needed to make functional thyroid hormones.
Iron	Fe	0.1	A component of the functional hemoglobin molecule (which transports oxygen within red blood cells) and some enzymes.

Trace (less than 0.01%)*

Chromium (Cr), Cobalt (Co), Copper (Cu), Fluorine (F), Manganese (Mn), Molybdenum (Mo), Selenium (Se), Silicon (Si), Tin (Sn), Vanadium (V), Zinc (Zn)

*Referred to as the *trace elements* because they are required in very minute amounts; many are found as part of enzymes or are required for enzyme activation.

TABLE 2.2	Subatomic Particles		
Particle	**Position in atom**	**Mass (amu)**	**Charge**
Proton (p^+)	Nucleus	1	+
Neutron (n^0)	Nucleus	1	0
Electron (e^-)	Orbitals outside the nucleus	1/1800	−

behavior of atoms. As illustrated in Figure 2.1b, the orbital model depicts the general location of electrons outside the nucleus as a haze of negative charge referred to as the *electron cloud*. Regions where electrons are most likely to be found are shown by denser shading rather than by orbit lines. Regardless of which model is used, notice that the electrons have the run of nearly the entire volume of the atom and determine its chemical behavior (that is, its ability to bond with other atoms). Though now considered outdated, the planetary model is simple and easy to understand and use. Most of the descriptions of atomic structure in this book use that model.

Hydrogen is the simplest atom, with just one proton and one electron. You can visualize the spatial relationships within the hydrogen atom by imagining it enlarged until its diameter equals the length of a football field. In that case, the nucleus could be represented by a lead ball the size of a gumdrop in the exact center of the sphere and the lone electron pictured as a fly buzzing about unpredictably within the sphere. This mental picture should serve to remind you that most of the volume of an atom is empty space, and most of the mass is concentrated in the central nucleus.

Identifying Elements

All protons are alike, regardless of the atom being considered. The same is true of all neutrons and all electrons. So what determines the unique properties of each element? The answer is that atoms of different elements are composed of *different numbers* of protons, neutrons, and electrons.

The simplest and smallest atom, hydrogen, has one proton, one electron, and no neutrons (Figure 2.2). Next is the helium atom, with two protons,

Helium atom

2 protons (p^+)
2 neutrons (n^0)
2 electrons (e^-)

(a) Planetary model

Helium atom

2 protons (p^+)
2 neutrons (n^0)
2 electrons (e^-)

(b) Orbital model

KEY:

= Proton   = Electron
= Neutron   = Electron cloud

FIGURE 2.1   The structure of an atom. The dense central nucleus contains the protons and neutrons. **(a)** In the planetary model of atomic structure, the electrons move around the nucleus in fixed orbits. **(b)** In the orbital model electrons are shown as a cloud of negative charge.

two neutrons, and two orbiting electrons. Lithium follows with three protons, four neutrons, and three electrons. If this step-by-step listing of subatomic particles were continued, all known atoms could be described by adding one proton and one electron at each step. The number of neutrons is not as easy to pin down, but light atoms tend to have equal numbers of protons and neutrons, whereas in

KEY:
= Proton
= Neutron
= Electron

(a) Hydrogen (H)
$(1p^+; 0n^0; 1e^-)$

(b) Helium (He)
$(2p^+; 2n^0; 2e^-)$

(c) Lithium (Li)
$(3p^+; 4n^0; 3e^-)$

FIGURE 2.2   Atomic structure of the three smallest atoms.

larger atoms neutrons outnumber protons. However, all we really need to know to identify a particular element is its atomic number, mass number, and atomic weight. Taken together, these indicators provide a fairly complete picture of each element.

Atomic Number

Each element is given a number, called its **atomic number,** that is equal to the number of protons its atoms contain. Atoms of each element contain a different number of protons than the atoms of any other element; hence, its atomic number is unique. Because the number of protons is always equal to the number of electrons, the atomic number

indirectly also tells us the number of electrons that atom contains.

Atomic Mass

The **atomic mass** of any atom is the sum of the masses of all the protons and neutrons contained in its nucleus. (The mass of the electrons is so small that it is ignored.) Hydrogen has one bare proton and no neutrons in its nucleus; so its atomic number and atomic mass number are the same (1). Helium, with 2 protons and 2 neutrons, has a mass number of 4. The *atomic mass number* is written as a superscript to the left of the atomic symbol (see the examples in Figure 2.3).

Which of these isotopes is the heaviest?

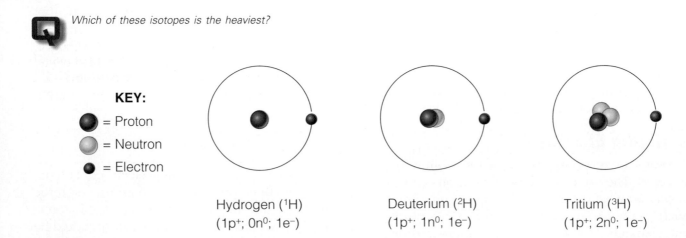

KEY:
= Proton
= Neutron
= Electron

Hydrogen (^{1}H)
$(1p^+; 0n^0; 1e^-)$

Deuterium (^{2}H)
$(1p^+; 1n^0; 1e^-)$

Tritium (^{3}H)
$(1p^+; 2n^0; 1e^-)$

FIGURE 2.3   Isotopes of hydrogen.

Tritium.

TABLE 2.3	Atomic Structures of the Most Abundant Elements in the Body				
Element	Symbol	Atomic number (# of p)	Mass number (# of p + n)	Atomic weight	Electrons in valence shell
Calcium	Ca	20	40	40.08	2
Carbon	C	6	12	12.011	4
Chlorine	Cl	17	35	35.453	7
Hydrogen	H	1	1	1.008	1
Iodine	I	53	127	126.905	7
Iron	Fe	26	56	55.847	2
Magnesium	Mg	12	24	24.305	2
Nitrogen	N	7	14	14.007	5
Oxygen	O	8	16	15.999	6
Phosphorus	P	15	31	30.974	5
Sodium	Na	11	23	22.99	1
Sulfur	S	16	32	32.064	6

Atomic Weight and Isotopes

At first glance, it would seem that the **atomic weight** of an atom should be equal to its atomic mass. This would be so if there were only one type of atom representing each element. However, the atoms of almost all elements exhibit two or more structural variations; these varieties are called **isotopes** (i′so-tōps). Isotopes have the same number of protons and electrons but vary in the number of *neutrons* they contain. Thus, the isotopes of an element have the same atomic number but have different atomic masses. Because all of an element's isotopes have the same number of electrons (and electrons determine bonding properties), their chemical properties are *exactly* the same. As a general rule, the atomic weight of any element is approximately equal to the mass number of its most abundant isotope. For example, as we said before, hydrogen has an atomic number of 1, but it also has isotopes with atomic masses of 1, 2, and 3 (Figure 2.3). Its atomic weight is 1.0079, which reveals that its lightest isotope is present in much greater amounts in our world than its ^2H or ^3H

forms. The atomic numbers, mass numbers, and atomic weights for elements commonly found in the body are provided in Table 2.3.

The heavier isotopes of certain atoms are unstable and tend to decompose to become more stable; such isotopes are called **radioisotopes.** The why of this process is very complex, but apparently the "glue" that holds the atomic nuclei together is weaker in the heavier isotopes. This process of spontaneous atomic decay is called **radioactivity** and can be compared to a tiny explosion. All types of radioactive decay involve the ejection of particles (*alpha* or *beta particles*) or electromagnetic energy (*gamma rays*) from the atom's nucleus and are damaging to living cells. Alpha emission has the least penetrating power; gamma radiation has the most. Contrary to what some believe, ionizing radiation does not damage the atoms in its path directly. Instead it sends electrons flying, like a bowling ball through pins, all along its path. It is these electrons that do the damage.

Radioisotopes are used in minute amounts to tag biological molecules so that they can be

Sodium (silvery metal)　　Chlorine (poisonous gas)　　Sodium chloride (table salt)

FIGURE 2.4　Properties of a compound differ from those of its atoms.

followed, or traced, through the body and are valuable tools for medical diagnosis and treatment. For example, PET scans, which use radioisotopes, are discussed in the "A Closer Look" box on pp. 8–9. Additionally, a radioisotope of iodine can be used to scan the thyroid gland of a patient suspected of having a thyroid tumor. Radium, cobalt, and certain other radioisotopes are used to destroy localized cancers.

 DID YOU GET IT?

4. Which four elements make up the bulk of living matter?

5. What is the relationship of an atom to an element?

6. An atom has 5 neutrons, 4 protons, and 4 electrons. What is its atomic number? What is its atomic mass number?

7. What name is given to an unstable atom that has either more or fewer neutrons than its typical number?

For answers, see Appendix D.

Molecules and Compounds

When two or more atoms combine chemically, **molecules** are formed. If two or more atoms of the same element bond together, a molecule of that element is produced. For example, when two hydrogen atoms bond, a molecule of hydrogen gas is formed:

$$H \text{ (atom)} + H \text{ (atom)} \rightarrow H_2 \text{ (molecule)}^*$$

In the example given, the *reactants* (the atoms taking part in the reaction) are indicated by their atomic symbols, and the composition of the *product* (the molecule formed) is indicated by a *molecular formula* that shows its atomic makeup. The chemical reaction is shown by writing a *chemical equation*.

When two or more *different* atoms bind together to form a molecule, the molecule is more specifically referred to as a molecule of a **compound.** For example, four hydrogen atoms and one carbon atom can interact chemically to form methane:

$$4H + C = CH_4 \text{ (methane)}$$

Thus, a molecule of methane is a compound, but a molecule of hydrogen gas is not—it is instead called molecular hydrogen.

It is important to understand that compounds always have properties quite different from those of the atoms making them up, and it would be next to impossible to determine the atoms making up a compound without analyzing it chemically. Sodium chloride is an excellent example of the difference in properties between a compound and its constituent atoms (Figure 2.4). Sodium is a silvery white metal, and chlorine in its molecular state is a

---

*Notice that when the number of atoms is written as a subscript, the subscript indicates that the atoms are joined by a chemical bond. Thus, 2H represents two unjoined atoms, but H_2 indicates that the two hydrogen atoms are bonded together to form a molecule.

poisonous green gas used to make bleach. However, sodium chloride is a white crystalline solid that we sprinkle on our food. Notice that just as an atom is the smallest particle of an element that still retains that element's properties, a molecule is the smallest particle of a compound that still retains the properties of that compound. If you break the bonds between the atoms of the compound, properties of the atoms, rather than those of the compound, will be exhibited.

 DID YOU GET IT?

8. What is the meaning of the term *molecule*?

9. How does a molecule of an element differ from a molecule of a compound?

For answers, see Appendix D.

Chemical Bonds and Chemical Reactions

Chemical reactions occur whenever atoms combine with or dissociate from other atoms. When atoms unite chemically, chemical bonds are formed.

Bond Formation

It is important to understand that a chemical bond is not an actual physical structure, like a pair of handcuffs linking two people together. Instead, it is an energy relationship that involves interactions between the electrons of the reacting atoms. Because this is so, we will devote a few words to the role electrons play in forming bonds.

Role of Electrons

As illustrated in Figure 2.2, electrons occupy orbits or generally fixed regions of space around the nucleus; these regions are also called **electron shells,** or **energy levels.** The maximum number of electron shells in any atom known so far is seven, and these are numbered 1 to 7 from the nucleus outward. The electrons closest to the nucleus are those most strongly attracted to its positive charge, and those farther away are less securely held. As a result, the more distant electrons are likely to interact with other atoms.

Perhaps this situation can be compared to the development of a child. During infancy and the toddler years, the child spends most of its time at home and is shaped and molded by the ideas and demands of its parents. However, when the child goes to school, it is increasingly influenced by friends and other adults, such as teachers and coaches. Thus, just as the child is more likely to become involved with "outsiders" as it roams farther from home, electrons are more influenced by other atoms as they get farther and farther away from the positive influence of the nucleus.

There is an upper limit to the number of electrons that each electron shell can hold. Shell 1, closest to the nucleus, is small and can accommodate only 2 electrons. Shell 2 holds a maximum of 8. Shell 3 can accommodate up to 18 electrons. Subsequent shells hold larger and larger numbers of electrons. In most (but not all) cases, the shells tend to be filled consecutively.

The only electrons that are important when considering bonding behavior are those in the atom's outermost shell. This shell is called the **valence shell,** and its electrons determine the chemical behavior of the atom. As a general rule, the electrons of inner shells do not take part in bonding.

When the valence shell of an atom contains 8 electrons, the atom is completely stable and is chemically inactive (inert). When the valence shell contains fewer than 8 electrons, an atom will tend to gain, lose, or share electrons with other atoms to reach a stable state. When any of these events occurs, chemical bonds are formed. Examples of chemically inert and reactive elements are shown in Figure 2.5.

The key to chemical reactivity is referred to as the *rule of eights;* that is, atoms interact in such a way that they will have 8 electrons in their valence shell. The first electron shell represents an exception to this rule, because it is "full" when it has 2 electrons. As you might guess, atoms must approach each other very closely for their electrons to interact—in fact, their outermost electron shells must overlap.

Types of Chemical Bonds

Ionic Bonds Ionic (i-on'ik) **bonds** form when electrons are completely transferred from one atom to another. Atoms are electrically neutral, but when they gain or lose electrons during bonding, their

Helium (He)
$(2p^+; 2n^0; 2e^-)$

Neon (Ne)
$(10p^+; 10n^0; 10e^-)$

**(a) Chemically inert elements
(valence shell complete)**

Hydrogen (H)
$(1p^+; 0n^0; 1e^-)$

Carbon (C)
$(6p^+; 6n^0; 6e^-)$

**(b) Chemically active elements
(valence shell incomplete)**

FIGURE 2.5 Chemically inert and reactive elements. (a) Helium and neon are chemically inert because in each case the outermost valence shell (energy level) is fully occupied by electrons. **(b)** Elements in which the valence shell is incomplete are chemically reactive and tend to interact with other atoms to gain, lose, or share electrons to fill their valence shells. (To simplify the diagrams, each atomic nucleus is shown as a circle with the atom's symbol in it; p's and n's not shown.)

Oxygen (O)
$(8p^+; 8n^0; 8e^-)$

Sodium (Na)
$(11p^+; 12n^0; 11e^-)$

positive and negative charges are no longer balanced, and charged particles, called **ions,** result. When an atom gains an electron, it acquires a net negative charge because it now has more electrons than protons. Negatively charged ions are more specifically called *anions.* When an atom loses an electron, it becomes a positively charged ion, a *cation,* because it now possesses more protons than electrons. (It may help you to remember that a cation is a positively charged ion by thinking of its "t" as a plus [+] sign.) Both anions and cations result when an ionic bond is formed. Because opposite charges attract, the newly created ions tend to stay close together.

The formation of sodium chloride (NaCl), common table salt, provides a good example of ionic bonding. As illustrated in Figure 2.6, sodium's valence shell contains only 1 electron and so is incomplete. However, if this single electron is "lost" to another atom, shell 2, which contains 8 electrons, becomes the valence shell; thus sodium becomes a cation (Na^+) and achieves stability. Chlorine needs only 1 electron to fill its valence shell, and it is much easier to gain 1 electron (forming Cl^-) than it is to try to "give away" 7. Thus, the ideal situation is for sodium to

donate its valence-shell electron to chlorine, and this is exactly what happens in the interaction between these two atoms. Sodium chloride and most other compounds formed by ionic bonding fall into the general category of chemicals called **salts.**

Covalent Bonds Electrons do not have to be completely lost or gained for atoms to become stable. Instead, they can be shared in such a way that each atom is able to fill its valence shell at least part of the time.

Molecules in which atoms share electrons are called *covalent molecules,* and their bonds are **covalent bonds** (*co* = with; *valent* = having power). For example, hydrogen, with its single electron, can become stable if it fills its valence shell (energy level 1) by sharing a pair of electrons—its own and one from another atom. As shown in Figure 2.7a on p. 38, a hydrogen atom can share an electron pair with another hydrogen atom to form a molecule of hydrogen gas. The shared electron pair orbits the whole molecule and satisfies the stability needs of both hydrogen atoms. Likewise, 2 oxygen atoms, each with 6 valence-shell electrons, can share 2 pairs of electrons

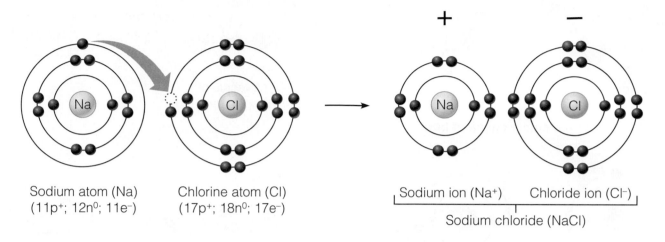

+   −

Sodium atom (Na)   Chlorine atom (Cl)
($11p^+$; $12n^0$; $11e^-$)   ($17p^+$; $18n^0$; $17e^-$)

Sodium ion (Na^+)   Chloride ion (Cl^-)
Sodium chloride (NaCl)

FIGURE 2.6   Formation of an ionic bond. Both sodium and chlorine atoms are chemically reactive because their valence shells are incompletely filled. Sodium gains stability by losing one electron, whereas chlorine becomes stable by gaining one electron. After electron transfer, sodium becomes a sodium ion (Na^+), and chlorine becomes a chloride ion (Cl^-). The oppositely charged ions attract each other.

(form double bonds) with each other (Figure 2.7b) to form a molecule of oxygen gas (O_2).

A hydrogen atom may also share its electron with an atom of a different element. Carbon has 4 valence-shell electrons but needs 8 to achieve stability. As shown in Figure 2.7c, when methane (CH_4) is formed, carbon shares 4 electron pairs with 4 hydrogen atoms (1 pair with each hydrogen atom). Because the shared electrons orbit and "belong to" the whole molecule, each atom has a full valence shell enough of the time to satisfy its stability needs.

In the covalent molecules described thus far, electrons have been shared *equally* between the atoms of the molecule. Such molecules are called *nonpolar covalently bonded molecules.* However, electrons are not shared equally in all cases. When covalent bonds are made, the molecule formed always has a definite three-dimensional shape. A molecule's shape plays a major role in determining just what other molecules (or atoms) it can interact with; the shape may also result in unequal electron-pair sharing. The following two examples illustrate this principle.

Carbon dioxide is formed when a carbon atom shares its 4 valence-shell electrons with 2 oxygen atoms. Oxygen is a very electron-hungry atom and attracts the shared electrons much more strongly than does carbon. However, because the carbon

dioxide molecule is linear (O=C=O), the electron-pulling power of one oxygen atom is offset by that of the other, like a tug-of-war at a standoff (Figure 2.8a). As a result, the electron pairs are shared equally and orbit the entire molecule, and carbon dioxide is a nonpolar molecule.

A water molecule is formed when 2 hydrogen atoms bind covalently to a single oxygen atom. Each hydrogen atom shares an electron pair with the oxygen atom, and again the oxygen has the stronger electron-attracting ability. But in this case, the molecule formed is V-shaped (H   H). The
                                                 \O/
two hydrogen atoms are located at one end of the molecule, and the oxygen atom is at the other (Figure 2.8b). Consequently, the electron pairs are not shared equally and spend more time in the vicinity of the oxygen atom, causing that end of the molecule to become slightly more negative (indicated by δ^-) and the hydrogen end to become slightly more positive (indicated by δ^+). In other words, a *polar molecule,* a molecule with two charged *poles,* is formed.

Polar molecules orient themselves toward other polar molecules or charged particles (ions, proteins, and others), and they play an important role in chemical reactions that occur in body cells. Because body tissues are 60 to 80 percent water, the fact that water is a polar molecule is particularly significant, as will be described shortly.

(a) Formation of a single covalent bond

(b) Formation of a double covalent bond

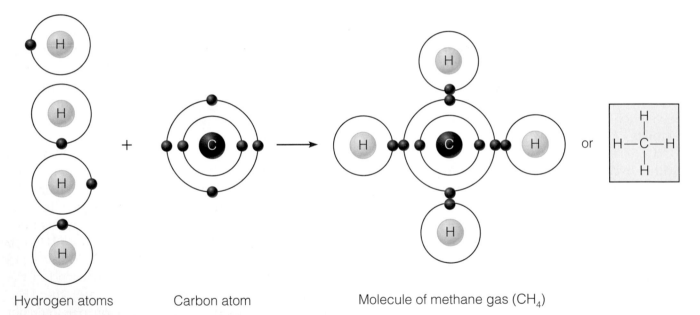

(c) Formation of four single covalent bonds

FIGURE 2.7 Formation of covalent bonds. (a) Formation of a single covalent bond between two hydrogen atoms to form a molecule of hydrogen gas. **(b)** Formation of a molecule of oxygen gas. Each oxygen atom shares two electron pairs with its partner; thus a double covalent bond is formed. **(c)** Formation of a molecule of methane. A carbon atom shares four electron pairs with four hydrogen atoms. In the diagrams of molecules shown in the colored boxes at the far right, each pair of shared electrons is indicated by a single line between the sharing atoms.

Which molecule—(a) or (b)—is a polar molecule?

O=C=O

(a) Carbon dioxide (CO₂)

δ^-

δ^+ δ^+

(b) Water (H₂O)

FIGURE 2.8 Molecular models illustrating the three-dimensional structure of carbon dioxide and water molecules.

Hydrogen Bonds **Hydrogen bonds** are extremely weak bonds formed when a hydrogen atom bound to one electron-hungry nitrogen or oxygen atom is attracted by another electron-hungry atom, and the hydrogen atom forms a "bridge" between them. Hydrogen bonding is common between water molecules (Figure 2.9a) and is reflected in water's surface tension. The surface tension of water causes it to "ball up," or form spheres, when it sits on a surface and allows some insects, such as water striders (Figure 2.9b), to walk on water as long as they tread lightly.

Hydrogen bonds are also important *intramolecular bonds;* that is, they help to bind different parts of the *same* molecule together into a special three-dimensional shape. These rather fragile bonds are very important in helping to maintain the structure of protein molecules, which are essential functional molecules and body-building materials.

(a)   **(b)**

FIGURE 2.9 Hydrogen bonding between polar water molecules. (a) The slightly positive ends (indicated by δ^+) of the water molecules become aligned with the slightly negative ends (indicated by δ^-) of other water molecules. **(b)** Water's high surface tension, a result of the combined strength of its hydrogen bonds, allows a water strider to walk on a pond without breaking the surface.

A *Water is a polar molecule.*

In all reactions shown, chemical bonds are being altered. What atomic subparticle is involved in these alterations?

Amino acids   Protein molecule

(a) Example of a synthesis reaction: amino acids are joined to form a protein molecule

Glycogen   Glucose molecules

(b) Example of a decomposition reaction: breakdown of glycogen to release glucose units

Glucose   Adenosine triphosphate (ATP)

Glucose phosphate   Adenosine diphosphate (ADP)

(c) Example of an exchange reaction: ATP transfers its terminal phosphate group to glucose to form glucose phosphate

FIGURE 2.10   Patterns of chemical reactions.
(a) In synthesis reactions, smaller particles are bonded together to form larger, more complex molecules. **(b)** Decomposition reactions involve the breaking of bonds. **(c)** In exchange reactions, bonds are both made and broken.

Patterns of Chemical Reactions

Chemical reactions involve the making or breaking of bonds between atoms. The total number of atoms remains the same, but the atoms appear in new combinations. Most chemical reactions have one of the three recognizable patterns described next.

Synthesis Reactions

Synthesis reactions occur when two or more atoms or molecules combine to form a larger, more complex molecule, which can be simply represented as

$$A + B \rightarrow AB$$

Synthesis reactions always involve bond formation. Because energy must be absorbed to make bonds, synthesis reactions are energy-absorbing reactions.

Synthesis reactions underlie all anabolic (constructive) activities that occur in body cells. They are particularly important for growth and for repair of worn-out or damaged tissues. As shown in Figure 2.10a, the formation of a protein molecule by the joining of amino acids into long chains is a synthesis reaction.

Decomposition Reactions

Decomposition reactions occur when a molecule is broken down into smaller molecules, atoms, or ions and can be indicated by

$$AB \rightarrow A + B$$

Essentially, decomposition reactions are synthesis reactions in reverse. Bonds are always broken, and the products of these reactions are smaller and simpler than the original molecules. As bonds are broken, chemical energy is released.

Decomposition reactions underlie all catabolic (destructive) processes that occur in body cells; that is, they are molecule-degrading reactions. Examples of decomposition reactions that occur in the body include the digestion of foods into their building blocks and the breakdown of glycogen (a large carbohydrate molecule stored in the liver) to release glucose (Figure 2.10b) when blood sugar levels start to decline.

Exchange Reactions

Exchange reactions involve both synthesis and decomposition reactions; bonds are both made and

Electrons.

TABLE 2.4	Factors Increasing the Rate of Chemical Reactions
Factor	**Mechanism to increase the number of collisions**
↑ temperature	↑ the kinetic energy of the molecules, which in turn move more rapidly and collide more forcefully.
↑ concentration of reacting particles	↑ the number of collisions because of increased numbers of reacting particles.
↓ particle size	Smaller particles have more kinetic energy and move faster than larger ones. Hence they take part in more collisions.
Presence of catalysts	↑ the amount of energy the molecules need to interact by holding the reactants in the proper positions to interact (see p. 52).

broken. During exchange reactions; a switch is made between molecule parts (changing partners, so to speak), and different molecules are made. Thus, an exchange reaction can be generally indicated as

$$AB + C \rightarrow AC + B \text{ and } AB + CD \rightarrow AD + CB$$

An exchange reaction occurs, for example, when ATP reacts with glucose and transfers its end phosphate group to glucose, forming glucose-phosphate (Figure 2.10c). At the same time, the ATP becomes ADP. This important reaction, which occurs whenever glucose enters a body cell, effectively traps the glucose fuel molecule inside the cell.

Regardless of the type of reaction occurring, most chemical reactions are reversible. If chemical bonds can be made, they can be broken and vice versa. Reversibility is indiated by a double arrow. When the arrows differ in length, the longer arrow indicates the more rapid reaction or the major direction in which the reaction is proceeding. For example, in the reaction

$$A + B \underset{\longleftarrow}{\overset{\longrightarrow}{\rightleftharpoons}} AB$$

the reaction going to the right is occurring more rapidly, and over time AB will accumulate while A and B will decrease in amount. If the arrows are of equal length, the reaction is at chemical equilibrium. Thus, in

$$A + B \rightleftharpoons AB$$

for each molecule of AB made, a molecule of AB is breaking down to release A and B.

Factors Influencing the Rate of Chemical Reactions

For atoms and molecules to react chemically, they must collide forcefully so that the electrons in their valence shells can interact. Bond making and breaking cannot occur long distance. Table 2.4 indicates several factors that influence the kinetic energy and, hence, the speed of the particles and the force of collisions.

 DID YOU GET IT?

10. How do ionic bonds differ from covalent bonds?

11. What kind of bond forms between water molecules?

12. What name is given to the type of chemical reaction in which a larger molecule is broken down into smaller molecules or atoms?

13. How can you indicate that a chemical reaction is reversible?

For answers, see Appendix D.

Biochemistry: The Chemical Composition of Living Matter

All chemicals found in the body fall into one of two major classes of molecules; they are either inorganic or organic compounds. The class of the compound is determined solely by the presence or absence of carbon. With a few so far unexplainable exceptions (such as carbon dioxide gas [CO_2] and carbon monoxide [CO]), **inorganic compounds** lack carbon and tend to be small, simple molecules. Examples of inorganic compounds found in the body are *water, salts,* and many (but not all) *acids* and *bases*. **Organic compounds** are carbon-containing compounds. The important organic compounds in the body are *carbohydrates, lipids, proteins,* and *nucleic acids.* All organic compounds are fairly (or very) large covalently bonded molecules.

Inorganic and organic compounds are equally essential for life. Trying to put a price tag on which is more valuable can be compared to trying to decide whether the ignition system or the engine is more essential to the operation of a car.

Inorganic Compounds

Water

Water is the most abundant inorganic compound in the body. It accounts for about two-thirds of body weight. Among the properties that make water so vital are the following:

1. **High heat capacity.** Water has a *high heat capacity;* that is, it absorbs and releases large amounts of heat before its temperature changes appreciably. Thus, it prevents the sudden changes in body temperature that might otherwise result from intense sun exposure, chilling winter winds, or internal events (such as vigorous muscle activity) that liberate large amounts of heat.

2. **Polarity/solvent properties.** Because of its polarity, water is an excellent solvent; indeed, it is often called the "universal solvent." A *solvent* is a liquid or gas in which smaller amounts of other substances, called *solutes* (which may be gases, liquids, or solids), can be dissolved or suspended. The resulting mixture is called a *solution* when the solute particles are exceedingly minute, and a *suspension* when the solute particles are fairly large. Translucent mixtures with solute particles of intermediate size are called *colloids.*

Small reactive chemicals—such as salts, acids, and bases—dissolve easily in water and become evenly distributed. Molecules cannot react chemically unless they are in solution, so virtually all chemical reactions that occur in the body depend on water's solvent properties.

Because nutrients, respiratory gases (oxygen and carbon dioxide), and wastes can dissolve in water, water can act as a transport and exchange medium in the body. For example, all these substances are carried from one part of the body to another in blood plasma and are exchanged between the blood and tissue cells by passing through interstitial fluid.

Specialized molecules that lubricate the body (such as mucus) also use water as their solvent, and synovial fluids "oil" the ends of bones as they move within joint cavities.

3. **Chemical reactivity.** Water is an important *reactant* in some types of chemical reactions. For example, to digest foods or break down biological molecules, water molecules are added to the bonds of the larger molecules. Such reactions are called *hydrolysis reactions,* a term that specifically recognizes this role of water (*hydro* = water; *lys* = splitting).

4. **Cushioning.** Water also serves a protective function. In the form of cerebrospinal fluid, water forms a cushion around the brain that helps to protect it from physical trauma. Amniotic fluid, which surrounds a developing fetus within the mother's body, plays a similar role in protecting the fetus.

Salts

A **salt** is an ionic compound containing cations other than H^+ and anions other than the hydroxyl ion (OH^-). Salts of many metal elements are commonly found in the body, but the most plentiful salts are those containing calcium and phosphorus, found chiefly in bones and teeth. When dissolved in body fluids, salts easily separate into their ions. This process, called *dissociation,* occurs rather easily because the ions have already been formed. All that remains is to pull the ions apart. This is accomplished by the polar water molecules, which orient themselves with their slightly negative ends toward the cations and their slightly positive ends toward the anions and thereby overcome the attraction between them (Figure 2.11).

Salts, both in their ionic forms and in combination with other elements, are vital to body func-

Ions in solution

Salt crystal

Na⁺

Na⁺

Cl⁻

Cl⁻

H δ^+
O   ⎤ Water
δ^- ⎦ molecule
H δ^+

FIGURE 2.11   Dissociation of a salt in water. The slightly negative ends of the water molecules (δ^-) are attracted to Na⁺, whereas the slightly positive ends of water molecules (δ^+) orient toward Cl⁻, causing the ions of the salt crystal to be pulled apart.

tioning. For example, sodium and potassium ions are essential for nerve impulses, and iron forms part of the hemoglobin molecule that transports oxygen within red blood cells.

Because ions are charged particles, all salts are **electrolytes**—substances that conduct an electrical current in solution. When ionic (or electrolyte) balance is severely disturbed, virtually nothing in the body works. The functions of the elements found in body salts are summarized in Table 2.1 (on p. 30).

Acids and Bases

Like salts, acids and bases are electrolytes. That is, they ionize and then dissociate in water and can then conduct an electrical current.

Characteristics of Acids   **Acids** have a sour taste and can dissolve many metals or "burn" a hole in your rug. But the most useful definition of an acid is that it is a substance that can release *hydrogen ions (H⁺)* in detectable amounts. Because a hydrogen ion is essentially a hydrogen nucleus (a "naked proton"), acids are also defined as **proton donors.**

When acids are dissolved in water, they release hydrogen ions and some anions. The anions are unimportant; it is the release of the protons that determines an acid's effects on the environment. The ionization of hydrochloric acid (an acid produced by stomach cells that aids digestion) is shown in the following equation:

$$HCl \rightarrow H^+ + Cl^-$$
(hydrochloric   (proton)   (anion)
acid)

Other acids found or produced in the body include acetic acid (the acidic component of vinegar) and carbonic acid.

Acids, such as hydrochloric acid, that ionize completely and liberate all their protons are called *strong acids*. Acids that ionize incompletely, as do acetic and carbonic acid, are called *weak acids*. For example, when carbonic acid dissolves in water, only some of its molecules ionize to liberate H⁺.

$$H_2CO_3 \rightarrow H^+ + HCO_3^- + H_2CO_3$$
(carbonic   (proton)   (anion)   (carbonic
acid)   acid)

Characteristics of Bases   **Bases** have a bitter taste, feel slippery, and are **proton acceptors.** The hydroxides are common inorganic bases. Like acids, the hydroxides ionize and dissociate in water; but in this case, the *hydroxyl ion (OH⁻)* and some cations are released. The ionization of sodium hydroxide (NaOH), commonly known as lye, is shown as

$$NaOH \rightarrow Na^+ + OH^-$$
(sodium   (cation)   (hydroxyl
hydroxide)   ion)

The hydroxyl ion is an avid proton (H⁺) seeker, and any base containing this ion is considered a strong base. By contrast, *bicarbonate ion (HCO₃⁻),* an important base in blood, is a fairly weak base.

Which ion is responsible for increased acidity?

Concentration in moles/liter

When acids and bases are mixed, they react with each other (in an exchange reaction) to form water and a salt:

$$HCl \; + \; NaOH \; \rightarrow \; H_2O \; + \; NaCl$$
(acid)   (base)   (water)   (salt)

This type of exchange reaction, in which an acid and a base interact, is more specifically called a **neutralization reaction.**

pH: Acid-Base Concentrations The relative concentration of hydrogen (and hydroxyl) ions in various body fluids is measured in concentration units called **pH** (pe-āch) units. The idea for a pH scale was devised in 1909 by a Danish biochemist (and part-time beer brewer) named Sørensen and is based on the number of protons in solution expressed in terms of moles per liter. (The *mole* is a concentration unit; its precise definition need not concern us here.) The pH scale runs from 0 to 14 (Figure 2.12), and each successive change of 1 pH unit represents a tenfold change in hydrogen-ion concentration.

At a pH of 7, the scale midpoint, the number of hydrogen ions exactly equals the number of hydroxyl ions, and the solution is neutral; that is, neither acidic nor basic. Solutions with a pH lower than 7 are acidic: the hydrogen ions outnumber the hydroxyl ions. A solution with a pH of 6 has 10 times as many hydrogen ions as a solution with a pH of 7, and a pH of 3 indicates a 10,000-fold ($10 \times 10 \times 10 \times 10$) increase in hydrogen-ion concentration. Solutions with a pH number higher than 7 are alkaline, or basic, and solutions with a pH of 8 and 12 (respectively) have 1/10 and 1/100,000 the number of hydrogen ions present in a solution with a pH of 7.

Living cells are extraordinarily sensitive to even slight changes in pH; and acid-base balance is carefully regulated by the kidneys, lungs, and a number of chemicals called **buffers,** which are present in body fluids. As described in some detail in Chapter 15, weak acids and weak bases are important components of the body's buffer systems, which act to maintain pH stability by taking up excess hydrogen or hydroxyl ions.

Because blood comes into close contact with nearly every body cell, regulation of blood pH is especially critical. Normally, blood pH varies in a narrow range, from 7.35 to 7.45. When blood pH changes more than a few tenths of a pH unit from these limits, death becomes a distinct possibility.

FIGURE 2.12 **The pH scale and pH values of representative substances.** The pH scale is based on the number of hydrogen ions in solution. The actual concentration (expressed in moles per liter) of hydrogen ions [H$^+$] and the corresponding hydroxyl ion concentration [OH$^-$] are indicated for each pH value noted. At a pH of 7, [H$^+$] = [OH$^-$], and the solution is neutral. A solution with a pH below 7 is acidic; above 7, basic or alkaline.

The hydrogen ion.

(a) Simple sugar (monosaccharide)   **(b)** Double sugar (disaccharide)

(c) Starch (polysaccharide)

FIGURE 2.13   Carbohydrates. (a) The generalized structure of a monosaccharide.
(b) and **(c)** The basic structures of a disaccharide and a polysaccharide, respectively.

Although there are hundreds of examples that could be given to illustrate this point, we will provide just one very important one: when blood pH begins to dip into the acid range, the amount of life-sustaining oxygen that the hemoglobin in blood can carry to body cells begins to fall rapidly to dangerously low levels. The approximate pH values of several body fluids and of a number of commonly ingested substances appear in Figure 2.12.

> ### ▶ DID YOU GET IT?

14. What property of water prevents rapid changes in body temperature?

15. Which is a proton donor—an acid or a base?

16. Is a pH of 11 acidic or basic?

17. Biochemistry is "wet" chemistry. What does this statement mean?

For answers, see Appendix D.

Organic Compounds

Carbohydrates

Carbohydrates, which include sugars and starches, contain carbon, hydrogen, and oxygen. With slight variations, the hydrogen and oxygen atoms appear in the same ratio as in water; that is, 2 hydrogen atoms to 1 oxygen atom. This is reflected in the word *carbohydrate,* which means "hydrated carbon," and in the molecular formulas of sugars. For example, glucose is $C_6H_{12}O_6$, and ribose is $C_5H_{10}O_5$.

Carbohydrates are classified according to size as monosaccharides, disaccharides, or polysaccharides. Because monosaccharides are joined to form the molecules of the other two groups, they are the structural units, or building blocks, of carbohydrates.

Monosaccharides **Monosaccharide** means one (*mono*) sugar (*saccharide*), and thus monosaccharides are also referred to as *simple sugars*. They are single-chain or single-ring structures, containing from 3 to 7 carbon atoms (Figure 2.13a).

The most important monosaccharides in the body are glucose, fructose, galactose, ribose, and deoxyribose. **Glucose,** also called *blood sugar,* is the universal cellular fuel. *Fructose* and *galactose* are converted to glucose for use by body cells. *Ribose* and *deoxyribose* form part of the structure of nucleic acids, another group of organic molecules.

Disaccharides **Disaccharides,** or *double sugars* (Figure 2.13b), are formed when two simple sugars are joined by a synthesis reaction known as **dehydration synthesis.** In this reaction, a water molecule is lost as the bond forms (Figure 2.14).

Some of the important disaccharides in the diet are *sucrose* (glucose-fructose), which is cane sugar; *lactose* (glucose-galactose), found in milk; and *maltose* (glucose-glucose), or malt sugar. Because the double sugars are too large to pass through cell membranes, they must be broken

Glucose   Fructose   Sucrose   Water

FIGURE 2.14   Dehydration synthesis and hydrolysis of a molecule of sucrose.
In the reaction going to the right (the dehydration synthesis reaction), glucose and fructose
are joined through a process that involves the removal of a water molecule at the bond site.
The resulting disaccharide is sucrose. Sucrose is broken down to its simple sugar units when
the reaction is reversed (goes to the left). In this hydrolysis reaction, a water molecule must
be added to the bond to release the monosaccharides.

down (digested) to their monosaccharide units to
be absorbed from the digestive tract into the
blood. This is accomplished by **hydrolysis.** As a
water molecule is added to each bond, the bond
is broken, and the simple sugar units are released
(see Figure 2.14).

Polysaccharides   Long, branching chains of linked
simple sugars are called **polysaccharides** (literally, "many sugars") (see Figure 2.13c). Because
they are large, insoluble molecules, they are ideal
storage products. Another consequence of their
large size is that they lack the sweetness of the
simple and double sugars.

Only two polysaccharides, starch and glycogen, are of major importance to the body. *Starch* is
the storage polysaccharide formed by plants. We
ingest it in the form of "starchy" foods, such as
grain products and root vegetables (potatoes and
carrots, for example). *Glycogen* is a slightly smaller,
but similar, polysaccharide found in animal tissues
(largely in the muscles and the liver). Like starch, it
is formed of linked glucose units.

Carbohydrates provide a ready, easily used
source of food energy for cells, and glucose is at
the top of the "cellular menu." When glucose is
oxidized (combined with oxygen) in a complex set
of chemical reactions, it is broken down into
carbon dioxide and water. Some of the energy
released as the glucose bonds are broken is trapped
in the bonds of high-energy ATP molecules, the energy "currency" of all body cells. If not immediately
needed for ATP synthesis, dietary carbohydrates are
converted to glycogen or fat and stored. Those of
us who have gained weight from eating too many

carbohydrate-rich snacks have a firsthand awareness of this conversion process!

Small amounts of carbohydrates are used for
structural purposes and represent 1 to 2 percent of
cell mass. Some sugars are found in our genes, and
others are attached to outer surfaces of cell membranes, where they act as road signs to guide cellular interactions.

Lipids

Lipids are a large and diverse group of organic
compounds (Table 2.5). They enter the body in
the form of fat-marbled meats, egg yolks, milk
products, and oils. The most abundant lipids in
the body are triglycerides, phospholipids, and
steroids. Like carbohydrates, all lipids contain
carbon, hydrogen, and oxygen atoms, but in
lipids, carbon and hydrogen atoms far outnumber oxygen atoms, as illustrated by the formula
for a typical fat named tristearin: $C_{57}H_{110}O_6$. Most
lipids are insoluble in water but readily dissolve
in other lipids and in organic solvents such as
alcohol and acetone.

Triglycerides   The **triglycerides** (tri-glis′er-īdz), or
neutral fats, are composed of two types of building blocks, **fatty acids** and **glycerol.** Their synthesis involves the attachment of three fatty acids to a
single glycerol molecule. The result is an E-shaped
molecule that resembles the tines of a fork (Figure
2.15a). Although the glycerol backbone is the same
in all neutral fats, the fatty acid chains vary; this
variation results in different kinds of neutral fats.

The length of a triglyceride's fatty acid chains
and their type of C—C bonds determine how solid

TABLE 2.5	Representative Lipids Found in the Body
Lipid type	**Location/function**
Neutral fats (Triglycerides)	Found in fat deposits (subcutaneous tissue and around organs); protect and insulate the body organs; the major source of stored energy in the body.
Phospholipids (Cephalin and others)	Found in cell membranes; participate in the transport of lipids in plasma; abundant in the brain and the nervous tissue in general, where they help to form insulating white matter.
Steroids	
Cholesterol	The basis of all body steroids.
Bile salts	A breakdown product of cholesterol; released by the liver into the digestive tract, where they aid in fat digestion and absorption.
Vitamin D	A fat-soluble vitamin produced in the skin on exposure to UV (ultraviolet) radiation; necessary for normal bone growth and function.
Sex hormones	Estrogen and progesterone (female hormones) and testosterone (a male hormone) produced from cholesterol; necessary for normal reproductive function; deficits result in sterility.
Corticosteroids (adrenal cortical hormones)	Cortisol, a glucocorticoid, is a long-term antistress hormone that is necessary for life; aldosterone helps regulate salt and water balance in body fluids by targeting the kidneys.
Other lipoid substances	
Fat-soluble vitamins	
A	Found in orange-pigmented vegetables (carrots) and fruits (tomatoes); part of the photoreceptor pigment involved in vision.
E	Taken in via plant products such as wheat germ and green leafy vegetables; may promote wound healing and contribute to fertility, but not proven in humans; an antioxidant; may help to neutralize free radicals (highly reactive particles believed to be involved in triggering some types of cancers).
K	Made available largely by the action of intestinal bacteria; also prevalent in a wide variety of foods; necessary for proper clotting of blood.
Prostaglandins	Derivatives of fatty acids found in cell membranes; various functions depending on the specific class, including stimulation of uterine contractions (thus inducing labor and abortions), regulation of blood pressure, and control of motility of the gastrointestinal tract; involved in inflammation.
Lipoproteins	Lipoid and protein-based substances that transport fatty acids and cholesterol in the bloodstream; major varieties are high-density lipoproteins (HDLs) and low-density lipoproteins (LDLs).

Triglycerides and phospholipids are similar. What is the major structural difference between them?

(a) Formation of a triglyceride

Glycerol   3 fatty acid chains   Triglyceride, or neutral fat   3 water molecules

Polar "head"

Nonpolar "tail"

Phosphorus-containing group (polar end)   Glycerol backbone   2 fatty acid chains (nonpolar end)

(b) Phospholipid molecule (phosphatidylcholine)

(c) Cholesterol

FIGURE 2.15 **Lipids. (a)** Triglycerides, or neutral fats, are synthesized by dehydration synthesis (three fatty acid chains are attached to a single glycerol molecule, and a water molecule is lost at each bond site). **(b)** Structure of a typical phospholipid molecule. Two fatty acid chains and a phosphorus-containing group are attached to the glycerol backbone. Notice that one fatty acid chain in (b) is unsaturated (has one or more double C=C bonds. **(c)** The generalized structure of cholesterol (the basis for all steroids made in the body).

They both have a glycerol backbone and fatty acid chains. However, triglycerides have three attached fatty acid chains and phospholipids have only two; the third is replaced by a phosphorous-containing group.

the molecule is at a given temperature. Fatty acid chains with only single covalent bonds between carbon atoms are referred to as **saturated.** Their fatty acid chains are straight (see Figure 2.15a) and, at room temperature, the molecules of a saturated fat pack closely together, forming a solid. Fatty acids that contain one or more double bonds between carbon atoms are said to be **unsaturated** (**monounsaturated** and **polyunsaturated,** respectively). The double and triple bonds cause the fatty acid chains to kink (Figure 2.15b) so that they cannot pack closely enough to solidify. Hence, triglycerides with short fatty acid chains or unsaturated fatty acids are oils (liquid at room temperature) and are typical of plant lipids. Examples include olive oil (rich in monounsaturated fats) and soybean and safflower oils, which contain a high percentage of polyunsaturated fatty acids. Longer fatty acid chains and more saturated fatty acids are common in animal fats, such as butterfat and the fat of meats, which are solid at room temperature. Of the two types of fatty acids, the unsaturated variety, especially olive oil, is said to be more "heart healthy."

Trans fats, common in many margarines and baked products, are oils that have been solidified by addition of hydrogen atoms at sites of double carbon bonds. They have recently been branded as increasing the risk of heart disease even more than the solid animal fats. In contrast, the **omega-3 fatty acids,** found naturally in cold-water fish, appear to decrease the risk of heart disease and some inflammatory diseases.

Triglycerides represent the body's most abundant and concentrated source of usable energy. When they are oxidized, they yield large amounts of energy. They are stored chiefly in fat deposits beneath the skin and around body organs, where they help insulate the body and protect deeper body tissues from heat loss and bumps.

Phospholipids **Phospholipids** (fos′fo-lip″idz) are similar to the triglycerides. They differ in that a phosphorus-containing group is always part of the molecule and takes the place of one of the fatty acid chains. Thus, phospholipids have two instead of three attached fatty acids (see Figure 2.15b).

Because the phosphorus-containing portion (the "head") bears an electrical charge, it gives phospholipids special chemical properties and polarity. For example, the charged region attracts and interacts with water and ions, but the fatty acid chains (the "tail") do not. The presence of phospholipids in cellular boundaries (membranes) allows cells to be selective about what may enter or leave.

Steroids **Steroids** are basically flat molecules formed of four interlocking rings (Figure 2.15c); thus, their structure differs quite a bit from that of fats. However, like fats, steroids are made largely of hydrogen and carbon atoms and are fat-soluble.

The single most important steroid molecule is **cholesterol.** We ingest cholesterol in animal products such as meat, eggs, and cheese, and some is made by the liver, regardless of dietary intake.

Cholesterol has earned bad press because of its role in arteriosclerosis, but it is essential for human life. Cholesterol is found in cell membranes and is the raw material of vitamin D, steroid hormones, and bile salts. Although steroid hormones are present in the body in only small quantities, they are vital to homeostasis. Without sex hormones, reproduction would be impossible, and a total lack of the corticosteroids produced by the adrenal glands is fatal.

Proteins

Proteins account for over 50 percent of the organic matter in the body, and they have the most varied functions of the organic molecules. Some are construction materials; others play vital roles in cell function. Like carbohydrates and lipids, all proteins contain carbon, oxygen, and hydrogen. In addition, they contain nitrogen and sometimes sulfur atoms as well.

The building blocks of proteins are small molecules called **amino** (ah-me′no) **acids.** About 20 common varieties of amino acids are found in proteins. All amino acids have an *amine group* (NH_2), which gives them basic properties, and an *acid group* (COOH), which allows them to act as acids. In fact, all amino acids are identical except for a single group of atoms called their *R-group* (Figure 2.16). Hence, it is differences in the R-groups that make each amino acid chemically unique. For example, an extra acid group (COOH) in the R-group makes the amino acid more acidic.

Amino acids are joined together in chains to form large, complex protein molecules that contain from 50 to thousands of amino acids. (Amino acid chains containing fewer than 50 amino acids are called *polypeptides.*) Because each type of amino acid has distinct properties, the sequence in which they are bound together produces proteins that vary

What is the importance of the R-groups (green here)?

(a) Generalized structure of all amino acids

(b) Glycine (the simplest amino acid)

(c) Aspartic acid (an acidic amino acid)

(d) Lysine (a basic amino acid)

(e) Cysteine (a sulfur-containing amino acid)

FIGURE 2.16   Amino acid structures. (a) Generalized structure of amino acids. All amino acids have both an amine (—NH$_2$) group and an acid (—COOH) group; they differ only in the atomic makeup of their R-groups (green). **(b)–(e)** Specific structures of four amino acids. The presence of sulfur (—SH) in the R-group of cysteine in (e) hints that this is an amino acid likely to take part in intramolecular bonding.

widely both in structure and function. To understand this more easily, think of the 20 amino acids as a 20-letter alphabet. The letters (amino acids) are used in specific combinations to form words (a protein). Just as a change in one letter of any word can produce a word with an entirely different meaning (flour → floor) or one that is nonsensical (flour → fluur), changes in kinds of amino acids (letters) or in their positions in the protein allow literally thousands of different protein molecules to be made. The structure of proteins is specified by our genes, as will be described in Chapter 3.

Fibrous and Globular Proteins   Based on their overall shape and structure, proteins are classed as either fibrous or globular proteins (Figure 2.17). The strandlike **fibrous proteins,** also called **structural proteins,** appear most often in body structures. They are very important in binding structures together and providing strength in certain body tissues. For example, *collagen* (kol'ah-jen) is found in bones, cartilage, and tendons and is the most abundant protein in the body. *Keratin* (ker'ah-tin) is the structural protein of hair and nails and the material that makes skin tough.

Globular proteins are mobile, generally spherical molecules that play crucial roles in virtually all biological processes. Because they *do things* rather than just form structures, they are also called **functional proteins.** As noted in Table 2.6, the scope of their activities is remarkable. Some (antibodies) help to provide immunity; others (hormones) help to regulate growth and development. Still others, called *enzymes* (en'zīmz), are biological catalysts that regulate essentially every chemical reaction that goes on within the body.

The fibrous structural proteins are exceptionally stable; the globular functional proteins are quite the opposite. Hydrogen bonds are critically important in maintaining their structure, but hydrogen bonds are fragile and are easily broken by heat and excesses of pH. When their three-dimensional structures are de-

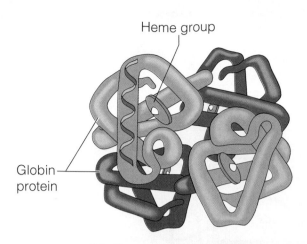

Heme group

Globin protein

(a) Triple helix of collagen (a fibrous or structural protein).

(b) Hemoglobin molecule composed of the protein globin and attached heme groups. (Globin is a globular or functional protein.)

FIGURE 2.17 **General structure of (a) a fibrous protein and (b) a globular protein.**

stroyed, the proteins are said to be *denatured* and can no longer perform their physiological roles. The reason is that their function depends on their specific structure—most importantly, on the presence of particular collections of atoms called **active sites** on their surface that "fit" and interact chemically with other molecules of complementary shape and charge (Figure 2.18). Hemoglobin becomes totally unable to bind and transport oxygen when blood pH becomes too acidic, as hinted earlier. Pepsin, a

TABLE 2.6	Representative Groups of Functional Proteins
Functional group	**Role(s) in the body**
Antibodies (immunoglobulins)	Highly specialized proteins that recognize, bind with, and inactivate bacteria, toxins, and some viruses; function in the immune response, which helps protect the body from "invading" foreign substances.
Hormones	Help to regulate growth and development. Examples include • Growth hormone—an anabolic hormone necessary for optimal growth. • Insulin—helps regulate blood sugar levels. • Nerve growth factor—guides the growth of neurons in the development of the nervous system.
Transport proteins	Hemoglobin transports oxygen in the blood; other transport proteins in the blood carry iron, cholesterol, or other substances.
Catalysts (enzymes)	Essential to virtually every biochemical reaction in the body; increase the rates of chemical reactions by at least a millionfold; in their absence (or destruction), biochemical reactions cease.

Substrate "fits" with active site

Active site

Enzyme (globular functional protein)

(a)

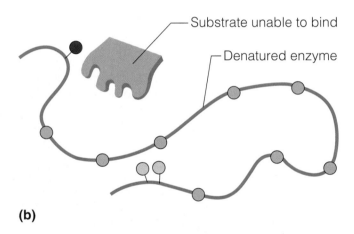

Substrate unable to bind

Denatured enzyme

(b)

FIGURE 2.18 Simple diagram illustrating denaturation of a functional protein molecule such as an enzyme. (a) The molecule's three-dimensional globular structure is maintained by intramolecular bonds. Atoms composing the active site of the enzyme are shown as stalked particles. The substrate, or molecule the enzyme acts on, has a corresponding binding site, and the two sites fit together very precisely. **(b)** Breaking the intramolecular bonds that maintain the three-dimensional structure of the enzyme results in a linear molecule, with the atoms of the former active site widely separated. Enzyme-substrate binding and catalysis can no longer occur.

A *The shape of the substrate and the enzyme's active site are complementary.*

protein-digesting enzyme, is inactivated by alkaline pH. In each case, the structure needed for function has been destroyed by the improper pH.

Except for enzymes, most important types of functional proteins are described with the organ system or functional process to which they are closely related. For instance, protein hormones are discussed in Chapter 9 (Endocrine System), hemoglobin is considered in Chapter 10 (Blood), and antibodies are described in Chapter 12 (The Lymphatic System and Body Defenses). However, enzymes are important in the functioning of all body cells, and so these incredibly complex molecules are considered here.

Enzymes and Enzyme Activity   **Enzymes** are functional proteins that act as biological catalysts. A **catalyst** is a substance that increases the rate of a chemical reaction without becoming part of the product or being changed itself. Enzymes accomplish this feat by binding to and "holding" the reacting molecules (the substrates) in the proper position for chemical interaction. While the substrates are bound to the enzyme's active site (see Figure 2.18a), they undergo structural changes that result in a new product. Once the reaction has occurred, the enzyme releases the product. Because enzymes are not changed in doing their job, they are reusable, and the cells need only small amounts of each enzyme.

Enzymes are capable of catalyzing millions of reactions each minute. However, they do more than just increase the speed of chemical reactions; they also determine just which reactions are possible at a particular time. No enzyme, no reaction! Enzymes can be compared to a bellows used to fan a sluggish fire into flaming activity. Without enzymes, biochemical reactions would occur far too slowly to sustain life.

Although there are hundreds of different kinds of enzymes in body cells, they are very specific in their activities, each controlling only one (or a small group of) chemical reaction(s) and acting only on specific molecules. Most enzymes are named according to that specific type of reaction they catalyze. There are "hydrolases," which add water; "oxidases," which cause oxidation; and so on. (In most cases, an enzyme can be recognized by the suffix **-ase** forming part of its name.)

Many enzymes are produced in an inactive form and must be activated in some way before they can function. In other cases, enzymes are inactivated immediately after they have performed

focus on CAREERS

FOOD TECHNOLOGIST

Food technologists regularly use chemistry to determine product stability and shelf life.

Have you ever picked a new product off the supermarket shelf and wondered how it was developed—how it got from an idea in someone's head to a product on the shelf? Anne Cristofano, a food technologist with a San Francisco Bay Area food and beverage product developer, is a central part of this process. Essential to her job is an understanding of basic chemistry and an ability to determine a product's pH and viscosity.

> ❝ *Knowledge of chemistry is essential in doing my job.* ❞

Anne's choice of occupation reflects her interest in both science *and* food. "I have a degree in Foods (a combination of culinary arts, food science, and nutrition) from California Polytechnic State University, which could have led me to a number of interesting occupations. I, however, am very interested in food! I like not only the culinary aspects—cooking and taking cooking classes—but also food science and product development. I love the challenge of creating a completely new product or making an existing product far superior."

"For example, at Mattson and Company, we developed a line of food entrées that are low in fat and sodium and fortified with essential vitamins for people with cardiovascular disease. We also have created products that are gluten-free, an area in which gluten-restricted consumers have few choices. I can't think of a more personally satisfying way to use my science and math background."

The terms *food science* and *food technology* often are used interchangeably, but the two disciplines are not identical. Food science studies the nature of foods, causes of food deterioration, principles underlying food processing, and the improvement of foods for the consuming public. Food technology applies food science to creating new foods and improving existing products. It applies basic science to preserve, process, package, and distribute safe, nutritious, and wholesome food to the consumer.

A new food or beverage begins as a concept, which is usually created by a marketing team, and then given to a food technologist to develop. "The criteria," Anne explains, "range from specific nutritional needs and consumer demands, for example, whether it must be kosher or natural, to processing constraints and cost; the list can go on and on. It is important to keep within the range of parameters I have been given to develop a great tasting, visually appealing product that goes easily from my benchtop to the manufacturing plant."

Undergraduate programs in Food Science and Technology prepare people for occupations in both the private and the public sectors, for example, the Food and Drug Administration and the Department of Agriculture. A search on the Web for "food science careers" reveals a wide range of career opportunities: nutritional science and education, sports nutrition, dietetics, and food management. One university's program will prepare you to become a "flavor chemist," which involves creating flavors "to improve the palatability of dog and cat foods." Other jobs range from assuring the

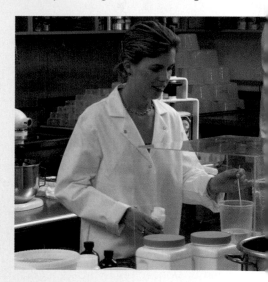

wholesomeness and safety of food to developing new food products and process methods.

For further information, contact the Institute of Food Technologists (IFT), at:

525 W. Van Buren, Suite 1000
Chicago, IL 60607
(312) 782-8424
http://www.ift.org

For additional information on this career, click the Focus on Careers link at www.anatomyandphysiology.com.

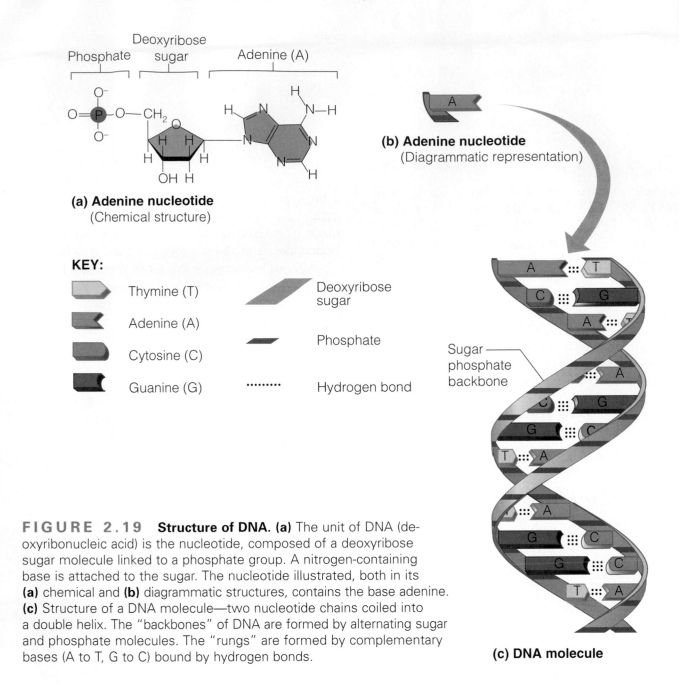

FIGURE 2.19   **Structure of DNA. (a)** The unit of DNA (deoxyribonucleic acid) is the nucleotide, composed of a deoxyribose sugar molecule linked to a phosphate group. A nitrogen-containing base is attached to the sugar. The nucleotide illustrated, both in its **(a)** chemical and **(b)** diagrammatic structures, contains the base adenine. **(c)** Structure of a DNA molecule—two nucleotide chains coiled into a double helix. The "backbones" of DNA are formed by alternating sugar and phosphate molecules. The "rungs" are formed by complementary bases (A to T, G to C) bound by hydrogen bonds.

their catalytic function. Both events are true of enzymes that promote blood clotting when a blood vessel has been damaged. If this were not so, large numbers of unneeded and potentially lethal blood clots would be formed.

Nucleic Acids

The role of **nucleic** (nu-kle′ik) **acids** is fundamental: they make up the genes, which provide the basic blueprint of life. They not only determine what type of organism you will be, but also direct your growth and development—and they do this largely by dictating protein structure. (Remember that enzymes, which catalyze all the chemical reactions that occur in the body, are proteins.)

Nucleic acids, composed of carbon, oxygen, hydrogen, nitrogen, and phosphorus atoms, are the largest biological molecules in the body. Their building blocks, the **nucleotides** (nu′kle-o-tīdz), are quite complex. Each consists of three basic parts: (1) a nitrogen-containing base, (2) a pentose (5-carbon) sugar, and (3) a phosphate group (Figure 2.19a and b).

The bases come in five varieties: *adenine* (A), *guanine* (G), *cytosine* (C), *thymine* (T), and *uracil* (U). A and G are large, two-ring bases, whereas the others are smaller, single-ring structures. The nucleotides are named according to the base they contain: A-containing bases are adenine nucleotides, C-containing bases are cytosine nucleotides, and so on.

The two major kinds of nucleic acid are **deoxyribonucleic** (de-ok″sĭ-ri″bo-nu-kle′ik) **acid (DNA)** and **ribonucleic acid (RNA).** DNA and RNA differ in many respects. DNA is the genetic material found within the cell nucleus (the control center of the cell). It has two fundamental roles: (1) It replicates itself exactly before a cell divides, thus ensuring that the genetic information in every body cell is identical. (2) It provides the instructions for building every protein in the body. For the most part, RNA is located outside the nucleus and can be considered the "molecular slave" of DNA; that is, RNA carries out the orders for protein synthesis issued by DNA.

Although both RNA and DNA are formed by the joining together of nucleotides, their final structures are different. As shown in Figure 2.19c, DNA is a long double chain of nucleotides. Its bases are A, G, T, and C, and its sugar is *deoxyribose*. Its two nucleotide chains are held together by hydrogen bonds between the bases, so that a ladderlike molecule is formed. Alternating sugar and phosphate molecules form the "uprights," or backbones, of the ladder, and each "rung" is formed by two joined bases (one base pair). Binding of the bases is very specific: A always binds to T, and G always binds to C. Thus, A and T are said to be *complementary bases,* as are C and G. A base sequence of ATGA on one nucleotide chain would necessarily be bonded to the complementary base sequence TACT on the other nucleotide strand. The whole molecule is then coiled into a spiral-staircaselike structure called a *double helix.*

Whereas DNA is double-stranded, RNA molecules are single nucleotide strands. The RNA bases are A, G, C, and U (U replaces the T found in DNA), and its sugar is *ribose* instead of deoxyribose. Three major varieties of RNA exist—*messenger, ribosomal,* and *transfer RNA*—and each has a specific role to play in carrying out DNA's instructions for building proteins. Messenger RNA carries the information for building the protein from the DNA genes to the ribosomes, the protein-synthesizing sites. Transfer RNA ferries amino acids to the ribosomes. Ribosomal RNA forms part of the ribosomes, where it oversees the translation of the message and the binding together of amino acids to form the proteins. Protein synthesis is described in greater detail in Chapter 3.

Adenosine Triphosphate (ATP)

The synthesis of **adenosine triphosphate** (ah-den′o-sēn tri-fos′fāt), or **ATP,** is all-important because it provides a form of chemical energy that is usable by all body cells. Without ATP, molecules cannot be made or broken down, cells cannot maintain their boundaries, and all life processes grind to a halt.

Although glucose is the most important fuel for body cells, none of the chemical energy contained in its bonds can be used directly to power cellular work. Instead, energy released as glucose is catabolized, and is captured and stored in the bonds of ATP molecules as small packets of energy.

Structurally, ATP is a modified nucleotide; it consists of an adenine base, ribose sugar, and three phosphate groups (Figure 2.20a). The phosphate groups are attached by unique chemical bonds called *high-energy phosphate bonds.* When these bonds are ruptured by hydrolysis, energy that can be used immediately by the cell to do work or power a particular activity—such as synthesizing proteins, transporting substances across its membrane, or, in the case of muscle cells, contracting—is liberated (Figure 2.20b). ATP can be compared to a tightly coiled spring that is ready to uncoil with tremendous energy when the "catch" is released. The consequence of cleavage of its terminal phosphate bond can be represented as follows:

$$\text{ATP} \quad \rightarrow \quad \text{ADP} \quad + \quad \textcircled{P} \quad + \quad \text{E}$$

(adenosine 　 (adenosine 　 (inorganic 　 (energy) triphosphate) 　 diphosphate) 　 phosphate)

As ATP is used to provide cellular energy, **adenosine diphosphate (ADP)** accumulates, and ATP supplies are replenished by oxidation of food fuels (Figure 2.21). Essentially the same amount of energy must be captured and used to reattach a phosphate group to ADP (that is, to reverse the reaction) as is liberated when the terminal phosphate is cleaved off.

(a) Adenosine triphosphate (ATP)

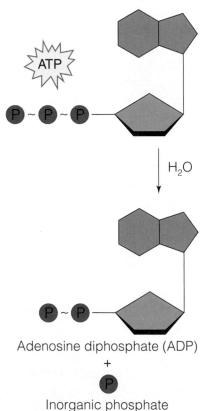

(b) Hydrolysis of ATP

FIGURE 2.20 **ATP—structure and hydroly-sis. (a)** The structure of ATP (adenosine triphosphate). **(b)** Hydrolysis of ATP to yield ADP (adenosine diphosphate) and inorganic phosphate. High-energy bonds are indicated by a red ~.

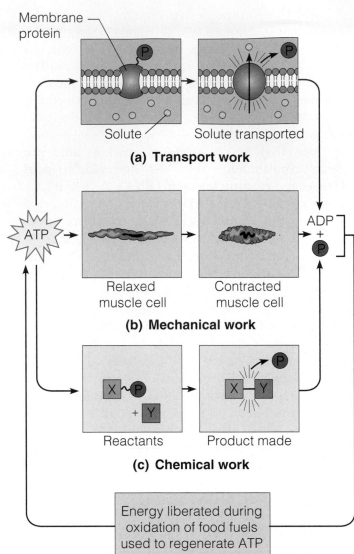

(a) Transport work

(b) Mechanical work

(c) Chemical work

Energy liberated during oxidation of food fuels used to regenerate ATP

FIGURE 2.21 **Three examples of how ATP drives cellular work.** The high-energy bonds of ATP release energy for use by the cell when they are broken. **(a)** ATP drives the transport of certain solutes (amino acids, for example) across cell membranes. **(b)** ATP activates contractile proteins in muscle cells so that the cells can shorten and perform mechanical work. **(c)** ATP provides the energy needed to drive energy-absorbing chemical reactions. ATP is regen-erated (phosphate is bound to ADP) as energy is released by the oxidation of food fuels and captured in the ADP–Ⓟ bond.

A CLOSER LOOK

DNA FINGERPRINTING: CRACKING OUR GENETIC "BARCODE"

The terrorist attacks on New York City's World Trade Center killed more than 3,000 people, their bodies buried in millions of tons of rubble. As weeks passed, it became clear that even if victims could be recovered from the wreckage, their bodies would probably be mangled, burned, or decomposed to a point where even family members would not recognize them.

In a situation like this, how can we identify individuals with any certainty? The New York Medical Examiner's Office turned to **DNA fingerprinting,** a technique for analyzing tiny samples of DNA taken from semen, skin, blood, or other body tissues. DNA fingerprinting is based on the fact that no two human beings, except for identical twins, possess identical sets of genetic material. In effect, DNA fingerprinting creates a unique genetic "barcode" that distinguishes each of us from all other humans. Let's see how it works.

Creating a DNA Profile

Recall that DNA contains four nucleotides—A, G, C, and T—that form complementary base pairs. In members of the same species, 99.9 percent of DNA is identical. This means that only 0.1 percent of your DNA differs from that of other humans—even close relatives, but this is enough to make you genetically unique. In a DNA string 3 billion units long, that 0.1 percent translates into

3 million variations that differ slightly from everyone else's. Unless you're an identical sibling, your set of DNA is yours alone. DNA fingerprinting involves analyzing an individual's DNA, mapping its unique pattern, and comparing it to other DNA profiles to determine whether there's a match.

A standard technique for creating a DNA profile focuses on 13 specific sites on our chromosomes where short segments of nuclear DNA are arranged in a repeating sequence. Although it is theoretically possible that unrelated people could show identical repeats at all 13 sites, the odds are less than 1 in 1 trillion.

Sometimes it can be difficult to obtain sufficient nuclear DNA for analysis. DNA samples recovered from crime scenes or disaster sites, for example, are frequently contaminated with dirt, fibers, and debris, or badly decomposed, limiting the amount of testable tissue. DNA retrieval can become a race against time as microbes, enzymes, insects, and environmental factors such as heat and humidity accelerate the process of decomposition.

Sorting and Identifying DNA

For DNA to be profiled, it must first be cut into manageable fragments by *restriction enzymes*, enzymes that recognize a specific base sequence and cleave the DNA at this location. This breaks down chromosomes into

DNA electrophoresis. A scientist looking at DNA fragments in an electrophoresis gel.

millions of pieces of different sizes that are then subjected to *gel electrophoresis*, which sorts the pieces by length. The DNA is placed on a gel

> **"DNA retrieval can become a race against time."**

and positioned in an electric field. The negatively charged fragments of DNA are attracted to the positively charged electrode and migrate toward it. Because the smaller pieces move more quickly than the larger pieces, the fragments end up sorted by size.

To locate a specific repeating sequence, researchers make a *DNA probe* with a complementary sequence and tag it with a radioactive compound. Because their sequences are complementary, the probe binds to the site; and when exposed to X-ray film, the image shows dark bands where the probe bound to the DNA.

A victim's DNA profile is then compared to known references to find one that matches. In the case of the World Trade Center attack, DNA references were obtained from victims' personal effects (such as toothbrushes and combs), entered into a computer, and sorted to find a match.

DNA Fingerprinting and Forensics

DNA fingerprinting has become a vital tool in forensic medicine (the application of medical knowledge to questions of law). For example, DNA fingerprinting is used to identify "John and Jane Does," unknown human remains. The U.S. military takes blood and saliva samples from every recruit so it can identify soldiers killed in the line of duty. DNA fingerprinting can also identify victims of mass disasters such as airplane crashes. The World Trade Center tragedy called for genetic analysis on an unprecedented scale.

DNA fingerprinting can prove that a suspect was actually at the scene of a crime. In the United States, some communities now require certain criminal offenders to provide DNA samples, which are classified and stored. DNA profiles can also establish innocence. At least 10 people in the United States have been released from death row after genetic evidence exonerated them.

DNA fingerprinting can also verify relationships in cases of disputed property, identify long-lost relatives, and establish paternity, even in paternity cases that are centuries old. For example, historians have fiercely debated whether Thomas Jefferson, our third president, fathered any children by his slave Sally Hemings. Modern DNA researchers entered the fray by profiling Jefferson's Y chromosome. A comparison of 19 genetic markers on the Jefferson Y chromosomes and those of Hemings' descendants found identical matches between the Jefferson line and Hemings' youngest son. Could it be chance? Hardly!

▶ DID YOU GET IT?

18. What are the structural units, or building blocks, of carbohydrates? Of proteins?

19. Which type of lipid molecule is found in large amounts in the fatty tissue beneath the skin? Which type of lipid is abundant in cellular membranes?

20. How do DNA and RNA differ from each other in the kinds of bases and sugars they contain?

21. What is the vital importance of ATP to body cells?

For answers, see Appendix D.

SUMMARY

Media study tools that provide additional review of key topics of Chapter 2 are referenced below.

 IP = *InterActive Physiology*
 WEB = *The A&P Place*

Concepts of Matter and Energy (pp. 27–28)

1. Matter
   a. Matter is anything that occupies space and has mass.
   b. Matter exists in three states: gaseous, liquid, and solid.

2. Energy

   a. Energy is the capacity to do work or to move matter. Energy has kinetic (active) and potential (stored) work capacities.

   b. Energy forms that are important in body function include chemical, electrical, mechanical, and radiant.

   c. Energy forms are interconvertible, but some energy is always unusable (lost as heat) in such transformations.

Composition of Matter   (pp. 29–34)

1. Elements and atoms

   a. Each element is a unique substance that cannot be decomposed into simpler substances by ordinary chemical methods. A total of 112 (to 118) elements exist; they differ from one another in their chemical and physical properties.

   b. Four elements (carbon, hydrogen, oxygen, and nitrogen) make up 96 percent of living matter. Several other elements are present in small or trace amounts.

   WEB Exercise: Chapter 2, Common Elements in Living Organisms.

   c. The building blocks of elements are atoms. Each atom is described by an atomic symbol consisting of one or two letters.

2. Atomic structure

   a. Atoms are composed of three subatomic particles: protons, electrons, and neutrons. Because all atoms are electrically neutral, the number of protons in any atom is equal to its number of electrons.

   b. The planetary model of the atom portrays all the mass of the atom (protons and neutrons) concentrated in a minute central nucleus. Electrons orbit the nucleus along specific orbits. The orbital model also locates protons and electrons in a central nucleus, but it depicts electrons as occupying areas of space called orbitals and forming an electron cloud of negative charge around the nucleus.

   WEB Exercise: Chapter 2, The Structure of Atoms.

   c. Each atom can be identified by an atomic number, which is equal to the number of protons contained in the atom's nucleus.

   d. The atomic mass number is equal to the sum of the protons and neutrons in the atom's nucleus.

   e. Isotopes are different atomic forms of the same element; they differ only in the number of neutrons in the nucleus. Many of the heavier isotopes are unstable and decompose to a more stable form by ejecting particles or energy from the nucleus, a phenomenon called radioactivity. Such radioisotopes are useful in medical diagnosis and treatment and in biochemical research.

   f. The atomic weight is approximately equal to the mass number of the most abundant isotope of any element.

Molecules and Compounds   (pp. 34–35)

1. A molecule is the smallest unit resulting from the binding of two or more atoms. If the atoms are different, a molecule of a compound is formed.

2. Compounds exhibit properties different from those of the atoms they comprise.

Chemical Bonds and Chemical Reactions (pp. 35–41)

1. Bond formation

   a. Chemical bonds are energy relationships. Electrons in the outermost energy level (valence shell) of the reacting atoms are active in the bonding.

   b. Atoms with a full valence shell (2 electrons in shell 1, or 8 in the subsequent shells) are chemically inactive. Those with an incomplete valence shell interact by losing, gaining, or sharing electrons to achieve stability (that is, to fill the valence shell).

   WEB Exercise: Chapter 2, Electron Arrangement.

   c. Ions are formed when valence-shell electrons are completely transferred from one atom to another. The oppositely charged ions thus formed attract each other, forming an ionic bond. Ionic bonds are common in salts.

   WEB Exercise: Chapter 2, Ionic Bonds.

   d. Covalent bonds involve the sharing of electron pairs between atoms. If the electrons are shared equally, the molecule is a nonpolar covalent molecule. If the electrons are not shared equally, the molecule is a polar covalent molecule. Polar molecules orient themselves toward charged particles and other molecules.

   WEB Exercise: Chapter 2, Covalent Bonds.

   e. Hydrogen bonds are fragile bonds that bind together water molecules or different parts of the same molecule (intramolecular bonds). They are common in large, complex organic molecules, such as proteins and nucleic acids.

2. Patterns of chemical reactions

   a. Chemical reactions involve the formation or breaking of chemical bonds. They are indicated by the writing of a chemical equation, which provides information about the atomic composition (formula) of the reactant(s) and product(s).

   b. Chemical reactions that result in larger, more complex molecules are synthesis reactions; they involve bond formation.

   c. In decomposition reactions, larger molecules are broken down into simpler molecules or atoms. Bonds are broken.

   d. Exchange reactions involve both the making and breaking of bonds. Atoms are replaced by other atoms.

   e. Regardless of the type of reaction, most chemical reactions are reversible. Reversibility is indicated by a double arrow.

3. Factors increasing the rate of chemical reactions

   a. For atoms to interact chemically, they must collide forcefully.

   b. Factors that affect the number or force of collisions include the temperature, concentration of the reactants, particle size, and catalysts.

Biochemistry: The Chemical Composition of Living Matter   (pp. 41–58)

1. Inorganic compounds

   a. Inorganic compounds making up living matter do not contain carbon (exceptions include CO_2 and CO). They include water, salts, and some acids and bases.

   WEB Exercise: Chapter 2, Characteristics of Acids, Bases, and Salts.

   b. Water is the single most abundant compound in the body. It acts as a universal solvent in which electrolytes (salts, acids, and bases) ionize and in which chemical reactions occur, and it is the basis of transport and lubricating fluids. It slowly absorbs and releases heat, thus helping to maintain homeostatic body temperature, and it protects certain body structures (such as the brain) by forming a watery cushion. Water is also a reactant in hydrolysis reactions.

   c. Salts in ionic form are involved in nerve transmission, muscle contraction, blood clotting, transport of oxygen by hemoglobin, cell permeability, metabolism, and many other reactions. Additionally, calcium salts (as bone salts) contribute to bone hardness.

   d. Acids are proton donors. When dissolved in water, they release hydrogen ions. Strong acids dissociate completely; weak acids dissociate incompletely.

   e. Bases are proton acceptors. The most important inorganic bases are hydroxides. Bicarbonate ions are important bases in the body. When bases and acids interact, neutralization occurs—that is, a salt and water are formed.

   f. The relative concentrations of hydrogen and hydroxyl ions in various body fluids is measured using a pH scale. Each change of one pH unit represents a tenfold change in hydrogen ion concentration. A pH of 7 is neutral (that is, the concentrations of hydrogen and hydroxyl ions are equal). A pH below 7 is acidic; a pH above 7 is alkaline (basic).

   g. Normal blood pH ranges from 7.35 to 7.45. Slight deviations outside this range can be fatal.

2. Organic compounds

   a. Organic compounds are the carbon-containing compounds that comprise living matter. Carbohydrates, lipids, proteins, and nucleic acids are examples. They all contain carbon, oxygen, and hydrogen. Proteins and nucleic acids also contain substantial amounts of nitrogen.

   b. Carbohydrates contain carbon, hydrogen, and oxygen in the general relationship $(CH_2O)_n$; their building blocks are monosaccharides. Monosaccharides include glucose, fructose, galactose, deoxyribose, and ribose. Disaccharides include sucrose, maltose, and lactose; and polysaccharides include starch and glycogen. Carbohydrates are ingested as sugars and starches. Carbohydrates, and in particular glucose, are the major energy source for the formation of ATP.

   c. Lipids include triglycerides (glycerol plus three fatty acid chains), phospholipids, and steroids (the most important of which is cholesterol). Triglycerides (neutral fats) are found primarily in adipose tissue, where they provide insulation and reserve body fuel. Phospholipids and cholesterol are found in all cell membranes. Cholesterol also forms the basis of certain hormones, bile salts, and vitamin D. Like carbohydrates, the lipids are degraded by hydrolysis and synthesized by dehydration synthesis.

   d. Proteins are constructed from building blocks called amino acids; 20 common types of amino acids are found in the body. Amino acid sequence determines the proteins constructed. Fibrous, or structural, proteins are the basic structural materials of the body. Globular proteins are also called functional proteins; examples of these include enzymes, some hormones, and hemoglobin. Disruption of the hydrogen bonds of functional proteins leads to their denaturation and inactivation.

e. Enzymes increase the rates of chemical reactions by combining specifically with the reactants and holding them in the proper position to interact. They do not become part of the product. Many enzymes are produced in an inactive form or are inactivated immediately after use.

f. Nucleic acids include deoxyribonucleic acid (DNA) and ribonucleic acid (RNA). The building unit of nucleic acids is the nucleotide; each nucleotide consists of a nitrogenous base, a sugar (ribose or deoxyribose), and a phosphate group. DNA (the "stuff" of the genes) maintains genetic heritage by replicating itself before cell division and contains the code-specifying protein structure. RNA acts in protein synthesis to ensure that instructions of the DNA are executed.

g. ATP (adenosine triphosphate) is the universal energy compound used by all cells of the body. When energy is liberated by the oxidation of glucose, some of that energy is captured in the high-energy phosphate bonds of ATP molecules and is stored for later use.

REVIEW QUESTIONS

Multiple Choice

More than one choice may apply.

1. Which of the following is (are) true concerning the atomic nucleus?
   a. Contains the mass of the atom.
   b. The negatively charged particles are here.
   c. Particles can be ejected.
   d. Contains particles that determine atomic number.
   e. Contains particles that interact with other atoms.

2. Pick out the correct match(es) of element and number of valence-shell electrons.
   a. Oxygen—6   d. Nitrogen—3
   b. Chlorine—8   e. Carbon—4
   c. Phosphorus—5

3. Important functions of water include which of the following?
   a. Provides cushioning
   b. Acts as a transport medium

c. Participates in chemical reactions
   d. Acts as a solvent for sugars, salts, and other solutes
   e. Reduces temperature fluctuations

4. Alkaline substances include
   a. gastric juice   d. orange juice
   b. water   e. ammonia
   c. blood

5. Glucose is to starch as
   a. a steroid is to a lipid.
   b. a nucleotide is to a nucleic acid.
   c. an amino acid is to a protein.
   d. a polypeptide is to an amino acid.

6. What lipid type is the foundation of cell membranes?
   a. Triglyceride   d. Phospholipid
   b. Steroid   e. Prostaglandin
   c. Vitamin D

7. Absence of which of the following nitrogen-containing bases would prevent protein synthesis?
   a. Adenine   d. Thymine
   b. Cytosine   e. Uracil
   c. Guanine

8. ATP is *not* associated with
   a. a basic nucleotide structure.
   b. high-energy phosphate bonds.
   c. deoxyribose.
   d. inorganic phosphate.
   e. reversible reactions.

9. The element essential for normal thyroid function is
   a. iodine.   d. selenium.
   b. iron.   e. zinc.
   c. copper.

Short Answer Essay

10. Why is a study of basic chemistry essential to understanding human physiology?

11. Matter occupies space and has mass. Explain how energy *must be* described in terms of these two factors. Then define energy.

12. Explain the relationship between kinetic and potential energy.

13. Identify the energy form in use in each of the following examples:
    a. Chewing food
    b. Vision (two types, please—think!)
    c. Bending the fingers to make a fist
    d. Breaking the bonds of ATP molecules to energize your muscle cells to make that fist

14. According to Greek history, a Greek scientist went running through the streets announcing that he had transformed lead into gold. Both lead and gold are elements. On the basis of what you know about the nature of elements, explain why his rejoicing was short-lived.

15. Name and provide the atomic symbols of the four elements that make up the bulk of all living matter. Which of these is found primarily in proteins and nucleic acids?

16. All atoms are neutral. Explain the basis of this fact.

17. Fill in the following table to fully describe an atom's subatomic particles.

Particle	Position in the atom	Charge	Mass
Proton			
Neutron			
Electron			

18. Define *radioactivity*. If an element has three isotopes, which of them (the lightest, the one with an intermediate mass, or the heaviest) is most likely to be a radioisotope, and why?

19. Define *molecule*.

20. Explain the basis of ionic bonding.

21. What are the hydrogen bonds, and how are they important in the body?

22. The two oxygen atoms forming molecules of oxygen gas that you breathe are joined by a polar covalent bond. Explain why this statement is true or false.

23. Oxygen and argon are both gases. Oxygen combines readily with other elements, but argon does not. What accounts for this difference?

24. Identify each of the following reactions as a synthesis, decomposition, or exchange reaction:

$$2Hg + O_2 \rightarrow 2HgO$$
$$Fe^{2+} + CuSO_4 \rightarrow FeSO_4 + Cu^{2+}$$
$$HCl + NaOH \rightarrow NaCl + H_2O$$
$$HNO_3 \rightarrow H^+ + NO_3^-$$

25. Distinguish between inorganic and organic compounds, and list the major categories of each in the body.

26. Salts, acids, and bases are electrolytes. What is an electrolyte?

27. Define *pH*. The pH range of blood is from 7.35 to 7.45. Circle the correct answer to complete the sentence: This is slightly (acidic / basic).

28. A pH of 3.3 is (1 / 10 / 100 / 1000) times more acidic than a pH of 4.3.

29. Define *monosaccharide, disaccharide,* and *polysaccharide*. Give at least two examples of each. What is the primary function of carbohydrates in the body?

30. What are the general structures of neutral fats, phospholipids, and steroids? Give one or two important uses of each of these lipid types in the body.

31. The building block of proteins is the amino acid. Draw a diagram of the structure of a generalized amino acid. What is the importance of the R-group?

32. Name the two protein classes based on structure and function in the body, and give two examples of each.

33. Define *enzyme*, and describe the mechanism of enzyme activity.

34. Virtually no chemical reaction can occur in the body in the absence of enzymes. How might excessively high body temperature interfere with enzyme activity?

35. What is the structural unit of nucleic acids? Name the two major classes of nucleic acid found in the body, and then compare and contrast them in terms of **(a)** general three-dimensional structure, and **(b)** relative functions.

36. What is ATP's central role in the body?

37. Explain why you can "stack" water slightly above the rim of a glass if you pour the water in very carefully.

38. Water is a precious natural resource in Florida, and it is said that supplies are dwindling. Desalinization (salt removal) of ocean water has been recommended as a solution to the problem. Why shouldn't we drink salt water?

CRITICAL THINKING AND CLINICAL APPLICATION QUESTIONS

39. A number of antibiotics act by binding to certain essential enzymes in the target bacteria. How might these antibiotics influence the chemical reaction controlled by the enzyme? What might be the effect on the bacteria? On the person taking the antibiotic prescription?

40. Mrs. Roberts, who is in a diabetic coma, has just been admitted to Noble Hospital. Her blood pH indicates that she is in severe acidosis, and the medical staff quickly institute measures to bring her blood pH back within normal limits. Note the normal pH of blood, and discuss why severe acidosis is a problem.

41. Evelyn is quite proud of her slender, model-like figure and boasts that she doesn't have an "ounce of excess body fat." Barbara, on the other hand, is grossly overweight. She complains of feeling hot most of the time, and on a hot day she is miserable. Evelyn generally feels chilled except on very hot days. Explain the relative sensitivity to environmental temperature of these two women on the basis of information you have been given in the Organic Compounds section of this chapter.

42. Pediatricians become concerned about the potential for brain damage when an infant's temperature approaches 105°F. Which class of organic molecules is most likely to be damaged by high temperature? Explain why.

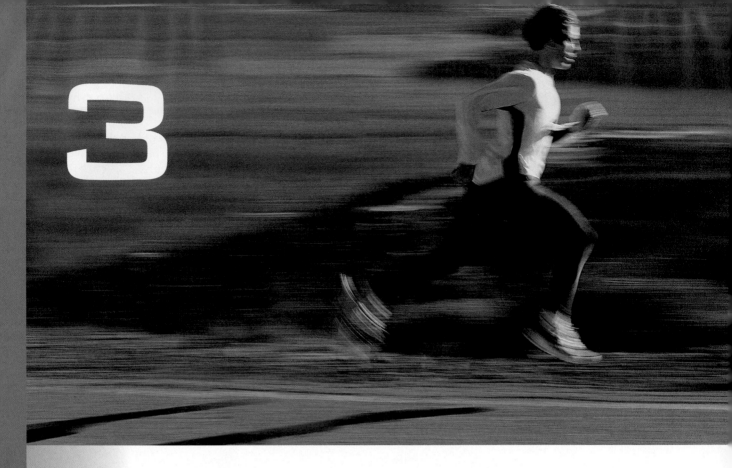

Cells and Tissues

YOUR GOALS

After completing this chapter, you will have a working knowledge of the functions of cells and tissues and will have mastered the objectives listed below.

FUNCTION PREVIEW

- Cells carry out all the chemical activities needed to sustain life.
- Tissues provide for a division of labor among body cells.

OBJECTIVE CHECKLIST

PART I: CELLS

Overview of the Cellular Basis of Life   (pp. 65–66)

➤ Name the four elements that make up the bulk of living matter, and list several trace elements.

Anatomy of a Generalized Cell   (pp. 66–76)

➤ Define *cell, organelle,* and *inclusion.*

➤ Identify on a cell model or diagram the three major cell regions (nucleus, cytoplasm, and plasma membrane).

➤ List the structures of the nucleus, and explain the function of chromatin and nucleoli.

➤ Identify the organelles on a cell model or describe them, and indicate the major function of each.

Cell Physiology   (pp. 76–88)

➤ Define *selective permeability, diffusion* (including *simple* and *facilitated diffusion* and *osmosis*), *active transport, passive transport, solute pumping, exocytosis, endocytosis, phagocytosis, pinocytosis, hypertonic, hypotonic,* and *isotonic.*

➤ Describe plasma membrane structure and explain how the various transport processes account for the directional movements of specific substances across the plasma membrane.

➤ Describe briefly the process of DNA replication and of mitosis. Explain the importance of mitotic cell division.

➤ Describe the roles of DNA and of the three major varieties of RNA in protein synthesis.

➤ Name some cell types, and relate their overall shape and internal structure to their special functions.

PART II: BODY TISSUES   (pp. 88–101)

➤ Name the four major tissue types and their chief subcategories. Explain how the four major tissue types differ structurally and functionally.

➤ Give the chief locations of the various tissue types in the body.

➤ Describe the process of tissue repair (wound healing).

PART III: DEVELOPMENTAL ASPECTS OF CELLS AND TISSUES
(pp. 101, 104)

➤ Define *neoplasm,* and distinguish between benign and malignant neoplasms.

➤ Explain the significance of the fact that some tissue types (muscle and nerve) are largely amitotic after the growth stages are over.

PART I: CELLS

In the late 1600s, Robert Hooke was looking through a crude microscope at some plant tissue—cork. He saw some cubelike structures that reminded him of the long rows of monk's rooms (or cells) at the monastery, so he named these structures **cells.** The living cells that had formed the cork were long since dead. However, the name stuck and is still used to describe the smallest unit, or the building block, of all living things, plants and animals alike. Whatever its form, however it behaves, the cell contains all the parts necessary to survive in a changing world. The human body has trillions of these microscopic building blocks.

Overview of the Cellular Basis of Life

Perhaps the most striking thing about a cell is its organization. If we chemically analyze cells, we find that they are made up primarily of four elements—carbon, oxygen, hydrogen, and nitrogen—plus much smaller amounts of several other elements. Although the four major elements build most of the cell's structure (which is largely protein), the trace elements are very important for certain cell functions. For example, calcium is needed for blood clotting (among other things), and iron is necessary to make hemoglobin, which carries oxygen in the blood. Iodine is required to make the thyroid hormone that controls metabolism. In their ionic form, many of the metals (such as calcium, sodium, and potassium) can carry an electrical charge; when they do they are called *electrolytes* (e-lek'tro-līts). Sodium and potassium ions are essential if nerve impulses are to be transmitted and muscles are to contract. (A more detailed account of body chemistry appears in Chapter 2.)

Strange as it may seem, especially when we feel our firm muscles, living cells are about 60 percent water, which is one of the reasons water is

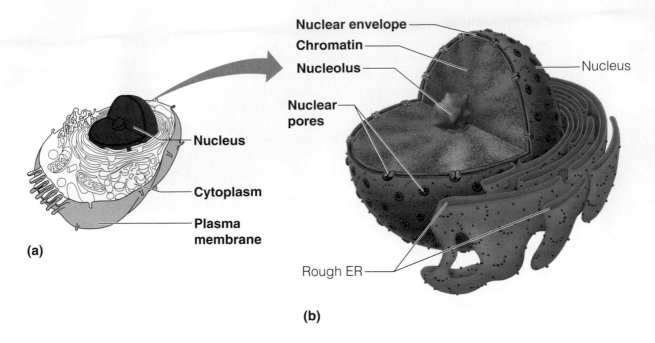

FIGURE 3.1 **Anatomy of the generalized animal cell nucleus.**
(a) Orientation diagram: The three main regions of the generalized cell.
(b) Structure of the nucleus.

essential for life. In addition to containing large amounts of water, all the body cells are constantly bathed in a dilute saltwater solution (something like seawater) called *interstitial fluid,* which is derived from the blood. All exchanges between cells and blood are made through this fluid.

Cells vary tremendously in length—ranging from 2 micrometers (1/12,000th of an inch) in the smallest cells to over a meter (3 feet) or more in the nerve cells that cause you to wiggle your toes. Furthermore, a cell's structure often reflects its function; this will become clear later in this chapter. Cells can have amazingly different shapes. Some are disk-shaped (red blood cells), some have threadlike extensions (nerve cells), others are like toothpicks pointed at each end (smooth muscle cells).

Cells also vary dramatically in the functions, or roles, they play in the body. For example, white blood cells wander freely through the body tissues and protect the body by destroying bacteria and other foreign substances. Some cells make hormones or chemicals that regulate other body cells. Still others take part in gas exchanges in the lungs or cleanse the blood (kidney tubule cells).

▶ *DID YOU GET IT?*

1. Hydrogen and nitrogen are two of the four elements that make up the bulk of cell structure. What are the other two?

2. Why are electrocytes, particularly Na$^+$ and K$^+$ ions, so important to body function?

For answers, see Appendix D.

Anatomy of a Generalized Cell

Although no one cell type is exactly like all others, cells *do* have the same basic parts, and there are certain functions common to *all* cells. Here we will talk about the **generalized cell,** which demonstrates these many typical features.

In general, all cells have three main regions or parts—a *nucleus* (nu′kle-us), *cytoplasm* (si′to-plazm″), and a *plasma membrane* (Figure 3.1a). The nucleus is usually located near the center of the cell. It is surrounded by the semifluid cytoplasm, which in turn is enclosed by the plasma membrane, which forms the outer cell boundary. (Figure 3.4 on p. 70

shows the more detailed structure of the generalized cell as revealed by the electron microscope.)

The Nucleus

Anything that works, works best when it is controlled. For cells, "headquarters," or the control center, is the gene-containing **nucleus** (*nucle* = kernal). The genetic material, or *deoxyribonucleic acid (DNA),* is much like a blueprint that contains all the instructions needed for building the whole body; so, as one might expect, human DNA differs from that of a frog. More specifically, DNA has the instructions for building *proteins.* DNA is also absolutely necessary for cell reproduction. A cell that has lost or ejected its nucleus (for whatever reason) is programmed only to die.

Although it is most often oval or spherical, the shape of the nucleus usually conforms to the shape of the cell. For example, if the cell is elongated, the nucleus is usually elongated as well. The nucleus has three recognizable regions or structures: the *nuclear envelope, nucleoli,* and *chromatin.*

Nuclear Envelope

The nucleus is bound by a double membrane barrier called the **nuclear envelope,** or **nuclear membrane** (see Figure 3.1b). Between the two membranes is a fluid-filled "moat," or space. At various points, the two layers of the nuclear envelope fuse, and **nuclear pores** penetrate through the fused regions. Like other cellular membranes, the nuclear envelope is selectively permeable, but substances pass through it much more freely than elsewhere because of its relatively large pores. The nuclear membrane encloses a jellylike fluid called *nucleoplasm* (nu'kle-o-plazm") in which other nuclear elements are suspended.

Nucleoli

The nucleus contains one or more small, dark-staining, essentially round bodies called **nucleoli** (nu-kle'o-li; "little nuclei"). Nucleoli are sites where ribosomes are assembled. The *ribosomes,* most of which eventually migrate into the cytoplasm, serve as the actual sites of protein synthesis, as described shortly.

Chromatin

When a cell is not dividing, its DNA is combined with protein and forms a loose network of bumpy threads called **chromatin** (kro'mah-tin) that is scattered throughout the nucleus. When a cell is dividing to form two daughter cells, the chromatin threads coil and condense to form dense, rodlike bodies called **chromosomes**—much the way a stretched spring becomes shorter and thicker when allowed to relax. The functions of DNA and the mechanism of cell division are discussed in the Cell Physiology section beginning on p. 76.

 DID YOU GET IT?

3. How would you explain the meaning of the term *generalized cell* to a classmate?

4. What is the general function of the cell nucleus?

5. What is the nuclear envelope?

For answers, see Appendix D.

The Plasma Membrane

The flexible **plasma membrane** is a fragile, transparent barrier that contains the cell contents and separates them from the surrounding environment. (The term *cell membrane* is often used instead, but because nearly all cellular organelles are composed of membranes, we will specifically refer to the cell's surface or outer limiting membrane as the plasma membrane.) Although the plasma membrane is important in defining the limits of the cell, it is much more than a passive envelope, or "baggie." As you will see, its unique structure allows it to play a dynamic role in many cellular activities.

The structure of the plasma membrane consists of two lipid (fat) layers arranged "tail to tail" in which protein molecules float (Figure 3.2). Most of the lipid portion is *phospholipids* (some with attached sugar groups), but a substantial amount of *cholesterol* is also found in plasma membranes. (The characteristics of these specialized lipids are described in Chapter 2.) The olive oil–like lipid bilayer forms the basic "fabric" of the membrane. The polar "heads" of the lollipop-shaped phospholipid molecules are *hydrophilic* ("water loving") and are attracted to water, the main component of both the intercellular and extracellular fluids, and so they lie on both the inner and outer surfaces of the membrane. Their nonpolar "tails," being *hydrophobic* ("water hating"), avoid water, and line up in the center of the membrane. The self-orienting property of the phospholipids allows biological membranes to reseal themselves quickly when

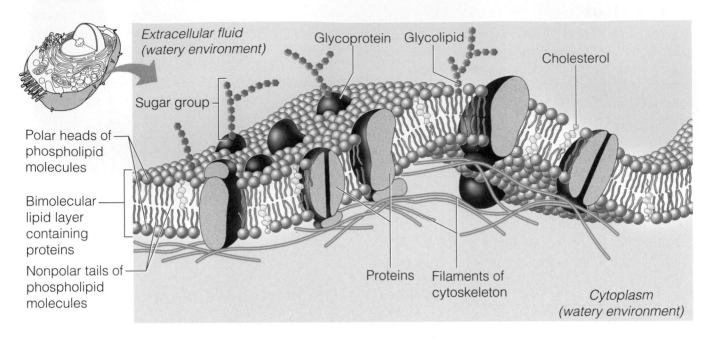

FIGURE 3.2 **Structure of the plasma membrane.**

torn. The hydrophobic makeup of the membrane interior makes the plasma membrane relatively impermeable to most water-soluble molecules. The cholesterol helps keep the membrane fluid.

The proteins scattered in the lipid bilayer are responsible for most of the specialized functions of the membrane. Some proteins are enzymes. Many of the proteins protruding from the cell exterior are receptors for hormones or other chemical messengers or are binding sites for anchoring the cell to fibers or to other structures inside or outside the cell. Most proteins that span the membrane are involved in transport functions. For example, some cluster together to form protein channels (tiny *pores*) through which water and small water-soluble molecules or ions can move; others act as *carriers* that bind to a substance and move it through the membrane. Branching sugar groups are attached to most of the proteins abutting the extracellular space. Such "sugar-proteins" are called *glycoproteins,* and because of their presence, the cell surface is a fuzzy, sticky, sugar-rich

area called the *glycocalyx* (gli-co-ka′liks). (You can think of your cells as being sugar-coated.) Among other things, these glycoproteins determine your blood type, act as receptors that certain bacteria, viruses, or toxins can bind to, and play a role in cell-to-cell interactions. Definite changes in glycoproteins occur in cells that are being transformed into cancer cells. (Cancer is discussed in "A Closer Look" on pp. 102–103.)

Specializations of the Plasma Membrane

Specializations of the plasma membrane—such as *microvilli* and *membrane junctions*—are commonly displayed by the (epithelial) cells that form the linings of hollow body organs, such as the small intestine (Figure 3.3). **Microvilli** (mi″kro-vil′i; "little shaggy hairs") are tiny fingerlike projections that greatly increase the cell's surface area for absorption so that the process occurs more quickly.

Membrane junctions vary structurally depending on their roles.

* **Tight junctions** are impermeable junctions that bind cells together into leakproof sheets that prevent substances from passing through the

extracellular space between cells. In tight junctions, adjacent plasma membranes fuse together tightly like a zipper. In the small intestine, for example, these junctions prevent digestive enzymes from seeping into the bloodstream.

- **Desmosomes** (des'mo-somz) are anchoring junctions that prevent cells subjected to mechanical stress (such as skin cells) from being pulled apart. Structurally, these junctions are buttonlike thickenings of adjacent plasma membranes (plaques), which are connected by fine protein filaments. Thicker protein filaments extend from the plaques inside the cells to the plaques on the cells' opposite sides, thus forming an internal system of strong guy wires.

- **Gap junctions,** commonly seen in the heart and between embryonic cells, function mainly to allow communication. Chemical molecules, such as nutrients or ions, can pass directly from one cell to another through them. In gap junctions, the neighboring cells are connected by **connexons,** which are hollow cylinders composed of proteins that span the entire width of the abutting membranes.

▶ DID YOU GET IT?

6. Why do phospholipids (which form the bulk of cell membranes) organize into a bilayer, tail to tail, in an aqueous environment?

7. The external faces of some membrane proteins have sugar groups attached to them. What are three roles these sugar-coated proteins play in the life of a cell?

8. What is the special function of gap junctions? Of tight junctions?

For answers, see Appendix D.

The Cytoplasm

The **cytoplasm** is the cellular material outside the nucleus and inside the plasma membrane. It is the site of most cellular activities, so you might think of the cytoplasm as the "factory area" of the cell. Although early scientists believed that the cytoplasm was a structureless gel, the electron microscope has revealed that it has three major elements: the *cytosol, organelles,* and *inclusions.* The **cytosol** is semitransparent fluid that suspends the other elements. Dissolved in the cytosol, which is largely

FIGURE 3.3 Cell junctions. An epithelial cell is shown joined to adjacent cells by the three common types of cell junctions: tight junctions, desmosomes, and gap junctions. Also illustrated are microvilli (seen projecting from the free cell surface).

water, are nutrients and a variety of other solutes (dissolved substances).

The **organelles** (or"gah-nelz'), described in detail shortly, are the metabolic machinery of the cell. Each type of organelle is specialized to carry out a specific function for the cell as a whole. Some synthesize proteins, others package those proteins, and so on.

Inclusions are chemical substances that may or may not be present, depending on the specific cell type. Most inclusions are stored nutrients or cell products. They include the lipid droplets common in fat cells, glycogen granules abundant in liver and muscle cells, pigments such as melanin in skin and hair cells, mucus and other secretory products, and various kinds of crystals.

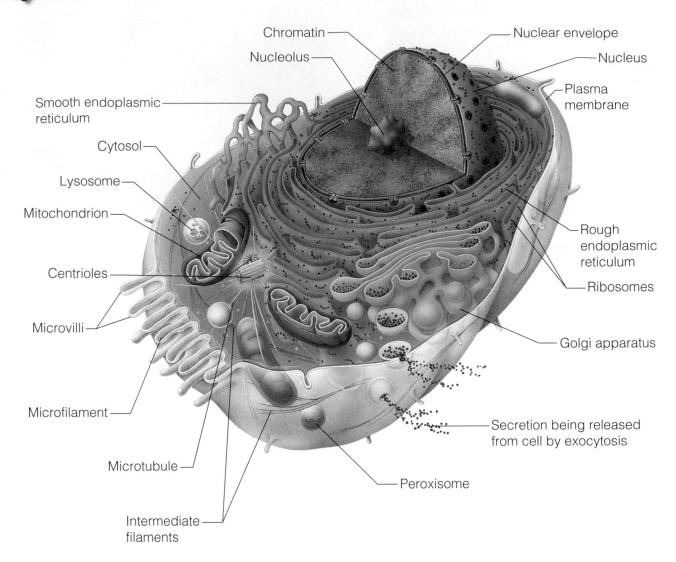

Chromatin ⎯ ⎯ Nuclear envelope

Nucleolus ⎯ ⎯ Nucleus

Smooth endoplasmic reticulum ⎯ ⎯ Plasma membrane

Cytosol ⎯

Lysosome ⎯

Mitochondrion ⎯ ⎯ Rough endoplasmic reticulum

Centrioles ⎯ ⎯ Ribosomes

Microvilli ⎯

⎯ Golgi apparatus

Microfilament ⎯

⎯ Secretion being released from cell by exocytosis

Microtubule ⎯ ⎯ Peroxisome

Intermediate filaments ⎯

FIGURE 3.4   Structure of the generalized cell. No cell is exactly like this one, but this generalized cell drawing illustrates features common to many human cells.

Cytoplasmic Organelles

The cytoplasmic organelles, literally "little organs," are specialized cellular compartments (Figure 3.4), each performing its own job to maintain the life of the cell. Many organelles are bounded by a membrane similar to the plasma membrane. The membrane boundaries of such organelles allow them to maintain an internal environment quite different from that of the surrounding cytosol. This compartmentalization is crucial to their ability to perform their specialized functions for the cell. Let us consider what goes on in each of the workshops of our cellular factory.

Mitochondria **Mitochondria** (mi″to-kon′dre-ah) are usually depicted as tiny threadlike (*mitos* = thread) or sausage-shaped organelles (see Figure 3.4), but in living cells they squirm, lengthen, and

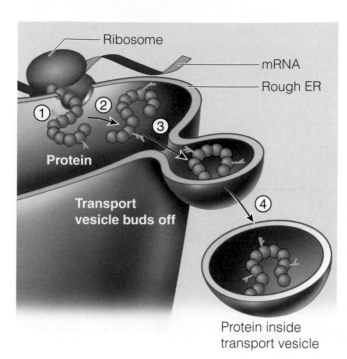

① As the protein is synthesized on the ribosome, it migrates into the rough ER cistern.

② In the cistern, the protein folds into its functional shape. Short sugar chains may be attached to the protein (forming a glycoprotein).

③ The protein is packaged in a tiny membranous sac called a transport vesicle.

④ The transport vesicle buds from the rough ER and travels to the Golgi apparatus for further processing or goes directly to the plasma membrane where its contents are secreted.

FIGURE 3.5   Synthesis and export of a protein by the rough ER.

change shape almost continuously. The mitochondrial wall consists of a double membrane, equal to *two* plasma membranes, placed side by side. The outer membrane is smooth and featureless, but the inner membrane has shelflike protrusions called *cristae* (kris′te; "crests"). Enzymes dissolved in the fluid within the mitochondria, as well as enzymes that form part of the cristae membranes, carry out the reactions in which oxygen is used to break down foods. As the foods are broken down, energy is released. Much of this energy escapes as heat, but some is captured and used to form *ATP molecules*. ATP provides the energy for all cellular work, and every living cell requires a constant supply of ATP for its many activities. Because the mitochondria supply most of this ATP, they are referred to as the "powerhouses" of the cell.

Metabolically "busy" cells, like liver and muscle cells, use huge amounts of ATP and have hundreds of mitochondria. By contrast, cells that are relatively inactive (an unfertilized egg, for instance) have just a few.

Ribosomes   Ribosomes (ri′bo-sōmz) are tiny, bilobed, dark bodies made of proteins and one variety of RNA called *ribosomal RNA*. Ribosomes are the actual sites of protein synthesis in the cell.

Some ribosomes float free in the cytoplasm, where they manufacture proteins that function in the cytoplasm. Others attach to membranes, and the whole ribosome-membrane combination is called the *rough endoplasmic reticulum.*

Endoplasmic Reticulum   The **endoplasmic reticulum** (en″do-plas′mik rĕ-tik′u-lum; "network within the cytoplasm") **(ER)** is a system of fluid-filled cisterns (tubules, or canals) that coil and twist through the cytoplasm. It accounts for about half of a cell's membranes. It serves as a minicirculatory system for the cell because it provides a network of channels for carrying substances (primarily proteins) from one part of the cell to another. There are two forms of ER; a particular cell may have both forms or only one, depending on its specific functions.

The **rough ER** is so called because it is studded with ribosomes. Because essentially all of the building materials of cellular membranes are formed either in it or on it, the rough ER can be thought of as the cell's membrane factory. The proteins made on its ribosomes migrate into the tubules of the rough ER, where they fold into their functional three-dimensional shapes and then are dispatched to other areas of the cell in **transport vesicles** (Figure 3.5). Rough ER is especially abundant in cells that make

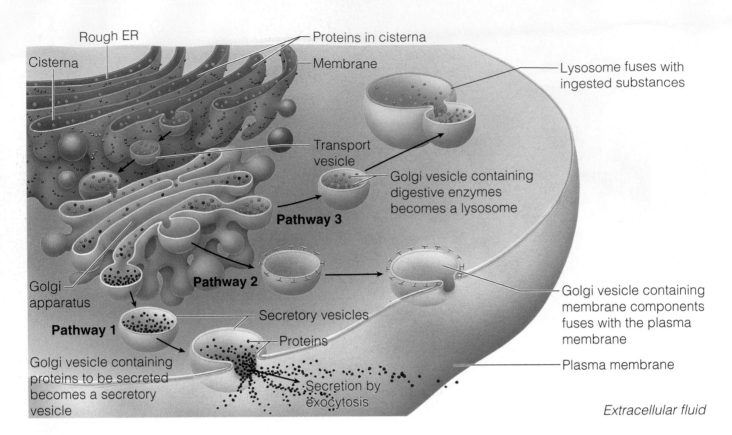

FIGURE 3.6   **Role of the Golgi apparatus in packaging the products of the rough ER.** Protein-containing transport vesicles pinch off the rough ER and migrate to fuse with the Golgi apparatus. As it passes through the Golgi apparatus, the protein product is sorted (and slightly modified). The product is then packaged within vesicles, which leave the Golgi apparatus and head for various destinations (pathways 1–3), as shown.

and export protein products—for example, pancreas cells, which produce digestive enzymes to be delivered to the small intestine. The enzymes that catalyze the synthesis of membrane lipids reside on the external face of the rough ER, where the needed building blocks are readily available.

Although the **smooth ER** communicates with the rough variety, it plays no role in protein synthesis. Instead it functions in lipid metabolism (cholesterol and fat synthesis and breakdown), and detoxification of drugs and pesticides. Hence it is not surprising that the liver cells are chock-full of smooth ER. So too are body cells that produce steroid-based hormones—for instance, cells of the male testes that manufacture testosterone.

Golgi Apparatus   The **Golgi** (gol′je) **apparatus** appears as a stack of flattened membranous sacs,

associated with swarms of tiny vesicles. It is generally found close to the nucleus and is the principal "traffic director" for cellular proteins. Its major function is to modify and package proteins (sent to it by the rough ER via transport vesicles) in specific ways, depending on their final destination (Figure 3.6).

As proteins "tagged" for export accumulate in the Golgi apparatus, the sacs swell. Then their swollen ends, filled with protein, pinch off and form **secretory vesicles** (ves′ĭ-kuls), which travel to the plasma membrane. When the vesicles reach the plasma membrane, they fuse with it, the membrane ruptures, and the contents of the sac are ejected to the outside of the cell (pathway 1 in Figure 3.6). Mucus is packaged this way, as are digestive enzymes made by pancreas cells.

In addition to its packaging-for-release functions, the Golgi apparatus pinches off sacs containing proteins and phospholipids destined for a "home" in the plasma membrane (pathway 2 in Figure 3.6) or other cellular membranes. It also packages hydrolytic enzymes into membranous sacs called *lysosomes* that remain in the cell (pathway 3 in Figure 3.6 and discussed next).

Lysosomes   Lysosomes (li′so-sōmz; "breakdown bodies"), which appear in different sizes, are membranous "bags" containing powerful digestive enzymes. Because lysosomal enzymes are capable of digesting worn-out or nonusable cell structures and most foreign substances that enter the cell, lysosomes function as the cell's demolition sites. Lysosomes are especially abundant in phagocytes, the cells that dispose of bacteria and cell debris. As described above, the enzymes they contain are formed by ribosomes and packaged by the Golgi apparatus.

HOMEOSTATIC IMBALANCE

The lysosomal membrane is ordinarily quite stable, but it becomes fragile when the cell is injured or deprived of oxygen and when excessive amounts of vitamin A are present. Lysosomal rupture results in self-digestion of the cell. ▲

Peroxisomes   Peroxisomes (per-ok′sih-sōmz) are membranous sacs containing powerful oxidase (ok′sĭ-dāz) enzymes that use molecular oxygen (O_2) to detoxify a number of harmful or poisonous substances, including alcohol and formaldehyde. However, their most important function is to "disarm" dangerous free radicals. **Free radicals** are highly reactive chemicals with unpaired electrons that can scramble the structure of proteins and nucleic acids. Although free radicals are normal byproducts of cellular metabolism, if allowed to accumulate, they can have devastating effects on cells. Peroxisomes convert free radicals to hydrogen peroxide (H_2O_2), a function indicated in their naming (*peroxisomes* = "peroxide bodies"). The enzyme *catalase* (kat′ah-lās) then converts excess hydrogen peroxide to water. Peroxisomes are especially numerous in liver and kidney cells, which are very active in detoxification.

Although peroxisomes look like small lysosomes (see Figure 3.4), they do not arise by budding from the Golgi apparatus. Instead, they appear to replicate themselves by simply pinching in half, as do mitochondria.

Cytoskeleton   An elaborate network of protein structures extends throughout the cytoplasm. This network, or **cytoskeleton,** acts as a cell's "bones and muscles" by furnishing an internal framework that determines cell shape, supports other organelles, and provides the machinery needed for intracellular transport and various types of cellular movements. From its largest to its smallest elements, the cytoskeleton is made up of microtubules, intermediate filaments, and microfilaments (Figures 3.4 and 3.7). Although there is some overlap in roles, generally speaking the strong, stable ropelike **intermediate filaments** help form desmosomes (see Figure 3.3) and provide internal guy wires to resist pulling forces on the cell. **Microfilaments** (such as *actin* and *myosin*) are most involved in cell motility and in producing changes in cell shape. You could say that cells move when they get their act(in) together. The tubelike **microtubules** determine the overall shape of a cell and the distribution of organelles. They are very important during cell division, as described on pp. 83–85.

Centrioles   The paired **centrioles** (sen′tre-ōlz) lie close to the nucleus (see Figure 3.4). They are rod-shaped bodies that lie at right angles to each other; internally they are made up of fine microtubules. Centrioles are best known for their role in generating microtubules, and during cell division, the centrioles direct the formation of the *mitotic spindle* (see Figure 3.15, p. 85).

In addition to the cell structures described above, some cells have projections called **cilia** (sil′e-ah; "eyelashes"), whiplike cellular extensions that move substances along the cell surface. For example, the ciliated cells of the respiratory system lining move mucus up and away from the lungs. Where cilia appear, there are usually many of them projecting from the exposed cell surface.

When a cell is about to make cilia, its centrioles multiply and then line up beneath the plasma membrane at the free cell surface. Microtubules then begin to "sprout" from the centrioles and put pressure on the membrane, forming the projections. If the projections formed by the centrioles are substantially longer, they are called **flagella** (flah-jel′ah). The only example of a flagellated cell in the human body is the sperm, which has a single propulsive flagellum called its *tail* (Figure 3.8g). *Notice that cilia propel other substances across a cell's surface, whereas a flagellum propels the cell itself.*

(a)

(b) **Microfilament**
Actin subunit
7 nm

(c) **Intermediate filament**
Fibrous subunits
10 nm

(d) **Microtubule**
Tubulin subunits
25 nm

FIGURE 3.7 The cytoskeleton. (a) In this light micrograph of the cytoskeleton of a nerve cell, the microtubules appear green; the microfilaments are blue. Intermediate filaments form most of the rest of the network. **(b–d)** Diagrammatic views of cytoskeletal elements.

▶ DID YOU GET IT?

9. How do the cytosol and the cytoplasm differ?

10. Which two organelles are sacs of enzymes and what is the function of each of these organelles?

11. Which organelle is the major site of ATP synthesis?

12. Name the three types of protein structures that make up the cytoskeleton. Which type helps form desmosomes? Which type is involved in cell motility?

For answers, see Appendix D.

Cell Diversity

So far in this chapter, we have focused on an average human cell. However, the trillions of cells in the human body are made up of some 200 different cell types that vary greatly in size, shape, and function. They include sphere-shaped fat cells, disk-shaped red blood cells, branching nerve cells, and cube-shaped cells of kidney tubules. Figure 3.8 illustrates how the shapes of cells and the relative numbers of the various organelles they contain relate to specialized cell functions. Let's take a look at some of these cell specialists.

1. **Cells that connect body parts:**

    • *Fibroblast.* The elongated shape of this cell lies along the cable-like fibers that it secretes. It has an abundant rough ER and a large Golgi apparatus to make and secrete the protein building blocks of these fibers.

    • *Erythrocyte (red blood cell).* This cell carries oxygen in the bloodstream. Its concave disk shape provides extra surface area for the uptake of oxygen and streamlines the cell so it flows easily through the bloodstream. So much oxygen-carrying pigment is packed in erythrocytes that all other organelles have been shed to make room.

2. **Cell that covers and lines body organs:**

    • *Epithelial cell.* The hexagonal shape of this cell is exactly like a "cell" in a honeycomb of a beehive. This shape allows epithelial cells to pack together in sheets. An epithelial cell has abundant intermediate filaments that resist tearing when the epithelium is rubbed or pulled.

3. **Cells that move organs and body parts:**
   - *Skeletal muscle and smooth muscle cells.* These cells are elongated and filled with abundant contractile filaments, so they can shorten forcefully and move the bones or change the size of internal organs.

4. **Cell that stores nutrients:**
   - *Fat cell.* The huge spherical shape of a fat cell is produced by a large lipid droplet in its cytoplasm.

5. **Cell that fights disease:**
   - *Macrophage (a phagocytic cell).* This cell extends long pseudopods ("false feet") to crawl through tissue to reach infection sites. The many lysosomes within the cell digest the infectious microorganisms it takes up.

6. **Cell that gathers information and controls body functions:**
   - *Nerve cell (neuron).* This cell has long processes for receiving messages and transmitting them to other structures in the body. The processes are covered with an extensive plasma membrane, and a plentiful rough ER is present to synthesize membrane components.

7. **Cells of reproduction:**
   - *Oocyte (female).* The largest cell in the body, this egg cell contains several copies of all organelles, for distribution to the daughter cells that arise when the fertilized egg divides to become an embryo.
   - *Sperm (male).* This cell is long and streamlined, built for swimming to the egg for fertilization. Its flagellum acts as a motile whip to propel the sperm.

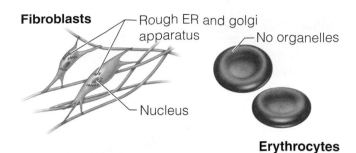

(a) Cells that connect body parts

(b) Cells that cover and line body organs

(c) Cells that move organs and body parts

(d) Cell that stores nutrients   **(e) Cell that fights disease**

(f) Cell that gathers information and controls body functions

(g) Cell of reproduction

FIGURE 3.8   Cell diversity. The shape of human cells and the relative abundances of their various organelles relate to their function in the body.

13. Name the two cell types involved in connecting body parts or regions.

14. What is the main function of a neuron?

For answers, see Appendix D.

Cell Physiology

As mentioned earlier, each of the cell's internal parts is designed to perform a specific function for the cell. Most cells have the ability to *metabolize* (use nutrients to build new cell material, break down substances, and make ATP), *digest foods, dispose of wastes, reproduce, grow, move,* and *respond to a stimulus* (irritability). Most of these functions are considered in detail in later chapters. For example, metabolism is covered in Chapter 14, and the ability to react to a stimulus is covered in Chapter 7. Here, we will consider only the functions of membrane transport (the means by which substances get through plasma membranes), protein synthesis, and cell reproduction (cell division).

Membrane Transport

The fluid environment on both sides of the plasma membrane is an example of a solution. It is important that you really understand solutions before we dive into an explanation of membrane transport. In the most basic sense, a **solution** is a homogeneous mixture of two or more components. Examples include the air we breathe (a mixture of gases), seawater (a mixture of water and salts), and rubbing alcohol (a mixture of water and alcohol). The substance present in the largest amount in a solution is called the **solvent** (or dissolving medium). Water is the body's chief solvent. Components or substances present in smaller amounts are called **solutes.** The solutes in a solution are so tiny; they do not settle out.

    Intracellular fluid (collectively, the nucleoplasm and the cytosol) is a solution containing small amounts of gases (oxygen and carbon dioxide), nutrients, and salts, dissolved in water. So too is **interstitial fluid,** the fluid that continuously bathes the exterior of our cells. Interstitial fluid can be thought of as a rich, nutritious, and rather unusual "soup." It contains thousands of ingredients, including nutrients (amino acids, sugars, fatty

acids, vitamins), regulatory substances such as hormones and neurotransmitters, salts, and waste products. To remain healthy, each cell must extract from this soup the exact amounts of the substances it needs at specific times and reject the rest.

    The plasma membrane is a selectively permeable barrier. **Selective permeability** means that a barrier allows some substances to pass through it while excluding others. Thus, it allows nutrients to enter the cell but keeps many undesirable substances out. At the same time, valuable cell proteins and other substances are kept within the cell, and wastes are allowed to pass out of it.

HOMEOSTATIC IMBALANCE

The property of selective permeability is typical only of healthy, unharmed cells. When a cell dies or is badly damaged, its plasma membrane can no longer be selective and becomes permeable to nearly everything. This phenomenon is evident when someone has been severely burned. Precious fluids, proteins, and ions "weep" (leak out) from the dead and damaged cells. ▲

Movement of substances through the plasma membrane happens in basically two ways—passively or actively. In **passive transport** processes, substances are transported across the membrane without any energy input from the cell. In **active transport** processes, the cell provides the metabolic energy (ATP) that drives the transport process.

Passive Transport Processes: Diffusion and Filtration

Diffusion (dĭ-fu′zhun) is an important means of passive membrane transport for every cell of the body. The other passive transport process, *filtration,* generally occurs only across capillary walls. Let us examine how these two types of passive transport differ.

Diffusion **Diffusion** is the process by which molecules (and ions) move away from a region where they are more concentrated (more numerous) to a region where they are less concentrated (fewer of them). All molecules possess *kinetic energy* (energy of motion), as described in Chapter 2, and as the molecules move about randomly at high speeds, they collide and change direction with each collision. The overall effect of this erratic movement is that molecules move *down* their **concentration gradient.** Because the driving force (source of energy) is the kinetic energy of the molecules themselves, the speed of diffusion is affected by the size of the molecules (the smaller the faster) and temperature (the warmer the faster).

An example should help you understand diffusion. Picture yourself pouring a cup of coffee and then adding a cube of sugar (but not stirring the cup). After you add the sugar, the phone rings, and you are called in to work. You never do get to drink the coffee. Upon returning that evening, you find that the coffee tastes sweet even though it was never stirred. The reason is that the sugar molecules moved around all day and eventually, as a result of their activity, became sufficiently distributed throughout the coffee to sweeten the entire cup. A laboratory example that might be familiar to some students is illustrated in Figure 3.9.

The hydrophobic core of the plasma membrane is a physical barrier to diffusion. However, molecules will diffuse through the plasma membrane if (1) they are small enough to pass through its pores (channels formed by membrane proteins), (2) they can dissolve in the fatty portion of the membrane, or (3) they are assisted by a membrane carrier. The unassisted diffusion of solutes through the plasma membrane (or any selectively permeable membrane) is called **simple diffusion** (Figure 3.10a). Solutes transported this way are either lipid-soluble (fats, fat-soluble vitamins, oxygen, carbon dioxide) or small enough to pass through the membrane pores (some small ions such as chloride ions, for example).

Diffusion of water through a selectively permeable membrane such as the plasma membrane is specifically called **osmosis** (oz-mo'sis). Because water is highly polar, it is repelled by the (nonpolar) lipid core of the plasma membrane, but it can and does pass easily through special pores called *aquaporins* ("water pores") created by the proteins in the membrane (Figure 3.10d). Osmosis into and out of cells is occurring all the time as water moves down its concentration gradient.

Still another example of diffusion is **facilitated diffusion.** Facilitated diffusion provides passage for certain needed substances (notably glucose) that are both lipid-insoluble and too large to pass through the membrane pores. Although facilitated diffusion follows the laws of diffusion—that is, the substances move down their own concentration

FIGURE 3.9   Diffusion. Particles in solution move continuously and collide constantly with other particles. As a result, particles tend to move away from areas where they are most highly concentrated and to become evenly distributed, as illustrated by the diffusion of dye molecules in a beaker of water.

gradient—a protein membrane channel is used (Figure 3.10c), or a protein molecule that acts as a carrier is needed as a transport vehicle (Figure 3.10b). Hence, some of the proteins in the plasma membrane form channels or act as carriers to move glucose and certain other solutes passively across the membrane and make it available for cell use.

Substances that pass into and out of cells by diffusion save the cell a great deal of energy. When you consider how vitally important water, glucose, and oxygen are to cells, it becomes apparent just how necessary these passive transport processes really are. Glucose and oxygen continually move into the cells (where they are in lower concentration because the cells keep using them up), and carbon dioxide (a waste product of cellular activity) continually moves out of the cells into the blood (where it is in lower concentration).

Filtration   **Filtration** is the process by which water and solutes are forced through a membrane (or capillary wall) by *fluid,* or *hydrostatic, pressure.* In the body, hydrostatic pressure is usually exerted by the blood. Like diffusion, filtration is a passive process, and a gradient is involved. In filtration, however, the gradient is a **pressure gradient** that actually pushes solute-containing fluid (*filtrate*) from the higher-pressure area to the lower-pressure area. Filtration is necessary for the kidneys to do their job properly. In the kidneys, water and small

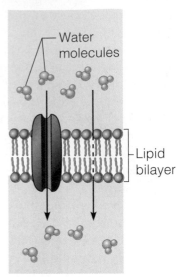

(a) Simple diffusion directly through the phospholipid bilayer

(b) Carrier-mediated facilitated diffusion via protein carrier specific for one chemical; binding of substrate causes shape change in transport protein

(c) Channel-mediated facilitated diffusion through a channel protein; mostly ions selected on basis of size and charge

(d) Osmosis, diffusion of water through a specific channel protein (aquaporin) or through the lipid bilayer

FIGURE 3.10   Diffusion through the plasma membrane. (a) In simple diffusion, fat-soluble molecules diffuse directly through the lipid bilayer of the plasma membrane, in which they can dissolve. **(b)** In facilitated diffusion using protein carriers, large, lipid-insoluble molecules (e.g., glucose) are moved across the membrane via a transport protein. **(c)** In facilitated diffusion via membrane channels, small polar or charged particles diffuse through membrane channels constructed by channel proteins. **(d)** In osmosis, water moves across the plasma membrane via specific channels (aquaporins) or diffuses directly through the lipid portion of the membrane.

solutes filter out of the capillaries into the kidney tubules because the blood pressure in the capillaries is greater than the fluid pressure in the tubules. Part of the filtrate formed in this way eventually becomes urine. Filtration is not very selective. For the most part, only blood cells and protein molecules too large to pass through the membrane pores are held back.

Active Transport Processes

Whenever a cell uses some of its ATP supply to move substances across the membrane, the process is referred to as *active*. Substances moved actively are

usually unable to pass in the desired direction by diffusion. They may be too large to pass through membrane channels, the membrane may lack special protein carriers for their transport, they may not be able to dissolve in the fat core, or they may have to move "uphill" *against* their concentration gradients. The two most important mechanisms of active membrane transport are active transport and vesicular transport.

Active Transport   Sometimes called *solute pumping*, **active transport** is similar to the carrier-mediated facilitated diffusion described earlier in that both processes require protein carriers that combine reversibly with the substances to be transported

 Carrier proteins or protein channels.

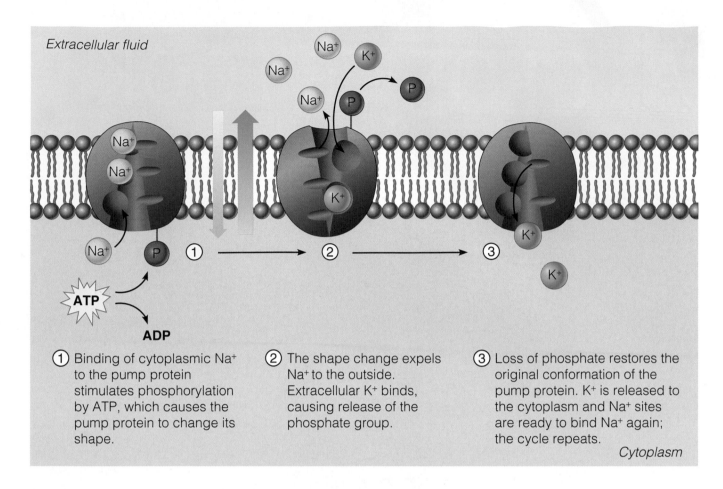

Extracellular fluid

1. Binding of cytoplasmic Na⁺ to the pump protein stimulates phosphorylation by ATP, which causes the pump protein to change its shape.

2. The shape change expels Na⁺ to the outside. Extracellular K⁺ binds, causing release of the phosphate group.

3. Loss of phosphate restores the original conformation of the pump protein. K⁺ is released to the cytoplasm and Na⁺ sites are ready to bind Na⁺ again; the cycle repeats.

Cytoplasm

FIGURE 3.11 Operation of the sodium-potassium pump, a solute pump. ATP provides the energy for a "pump" protein to move three sodium ions out of the cell and two potassium ions into the cell. Both ions are moved against their concentration gradients.

across the membrane. However, facilitated diffusion is driven by the kinetic energy of the diffusing molecules, whereas active transport uses ATP to energize its protein carriers, which are called **solute pumps.** Amino acids, some sugars, and most ions are transported by solute pumps, and in most cases these substances move *against* concentration (or electrical) gradients. This is opposite to the direction in which substances would naturally flow by diffusion, which explains the need for energy in the form of ATP. Amino acids are needed to build cellular proteins but are too large to pass through the membrane channels and are not lipid-soluble. The **sodium-potassium pump** that simultaneously carries sodium ions (Na⁺) out of and potassium ions into the cell is absolutely necessary for normal transmission of impulses by nerve cells

(Figure 3.11). There are more sodium ions outside the cells than inside, so they tend to remain in the cell unless the cell uses ATP to force, or "pump," them out. Likewise, there are relatively more potassium ions inside cells than in the interstitial (extracellular) fluid, and potassium ions that leak out of cells must be actively pumped back inside. Because each of the pumps in the plasma membrane transports only specific substances, active transport provides a way for the cell to be very selective in cases where substances cannot pass by diffusion. (No pump—no transport.)

Vesicular Transport   Some substances cannot get through the plasma membrane by passive transport or by active transport. **Vesicular transport,** which involves help from ATP, moves substances

A CLOSER LOOK

IV THERAPY AND CELLULAR "TONICS"

Why is it essential that medical personnel give only the proper *intravenous (IV)*, or into-the-vein, *solutions* to patients?

Consider that there is a steady traffic of small molecules across the plasma membrane. Although diffusion of solutes across the membrane is rather slow, osmosis, which moves water across the membrane, occurs very quickly. Anyone administering an IV must use the correct solution to protect the patient's cells from life-threatening dehydration or rupture due to rapid and excessive water entry.

The tendency of a solution to hold water or "pull" water into it is called osmotic pressure. Osmotic pressure is directly related to the concentration of solutes in the solution. The higher the solute concentration, the greater the osmotic pressure

and the greater the tendency of water to move into the solution. Many molecules, particularly proteins and some ions, are prevented from diffusing through the plasma mem-

> ## " *Cells placed in hypotonic solutions plump up rapidly.*"

brane. Consequently, any change in their concentration on one side of the membrane forces water to move from one side of the membrane to the other, causing cells to lose or gain

water. The ability of a solution to change the size and shape of cells by altering the amount of water they contain is called *tonicity* (ton-is'i-te; *ton* = strength).

Isotonic (i"so-ton'ik; "same tonicity") solutions (such as Ringer's lactate, 5 percent dextrose, and 0.9 percent saline) have the same solute and water concentrations as cells do. Isotonic solutions cause no visible changes in cells, and when such solutions are infused into the bloodstream, red blood cells (RBCs) retain their normal size and disclike shape (Photo a). As you might guess, interstitial fluid and most intravenous solutions are isotonic solutions.

If red blood cells are exposed to a *hypertonic* (hi"per-ton'ik) solution—a solution that contains more solutes, or dissolved substances, than there are inside the cells—the cells will

(a) RBC in isotonic solution

(b) RBC in hypertonic solution

(c) RBC in hypotonic solution

begin to shrink, or *crenate* (kre'nāt). This is because water is in higher concentration inside the cell than outside, so it follows its concentration gradient and leaves the cell (Photo b). Hypertonic solutions are sometimes given to patients who have *edema* (swelling of the feet and hands due to fluid retention). Such solutions draw water out of the tissue spaces into the bloodstream so that the kidneys can eliminate excess fluid.

When a solution contains fewer solutes (and therefore more water) than the cell does, it is said to be *hypotonic* (hi"po-ton'ik) to the cell. Cells placed in hypotonic solutions plump up rapidly as water rushes into them (Photo c). Distilled water represents the most extreme example of a hypotonic fluid. Because it contains no solutes at all, water will enter cells until they finally burst, or *lyse*. Hypotonic solutions are sometimes infused intravenously (slowly and with care) to rehydrate the tissues of extremely dehydrated patients. In less extreme cases, drinking hypotonic fluids usually does the trick. (Many fluids that we tend to drink regularly, such as tea, colas, and sport drinks, are hypotonic.)

into or out of cells without their actually crossing the plasma membrane. The two types of vesicular transport are *exocytosis* and *endocytosis*.

Exocytosis (ek"so-si-to'sis; "out of the cell") moves substances out of cells (Figure 3.12). It is the means by which cells actively secrete hormones, mucus, and other cell products or eject certain cellular wastes. The product to be released is first "packaged" (typically by the efforts of the Golgi apparatus) into a small membranous vesicle or sac. The sac migrates to the plasma membrane and fuses with it. The fused area then ruptures, spilling the sac contents out of the cell (also see Figure 3.6).

Endocytosis (en"do-si-to'sis; "into the cell") includes those ATP-requiring processes that take up, or engulf, extracellular substances by enclosing them in a small membranous vesicle (Figure

Extracellular fluid

Molecules to be secreted

Secretory vesicle

Cytoplasm

(a)

(b)

FIGURE 3.12 **Exocytosis. (a)** A secretory vesicle migrates to the plasma membrane, and the two membranes fuse. The fused site opens and releases the contents to the outside of the cell. **(b)** Electron micrograph of a vesicle in exocytosis (60,000×).

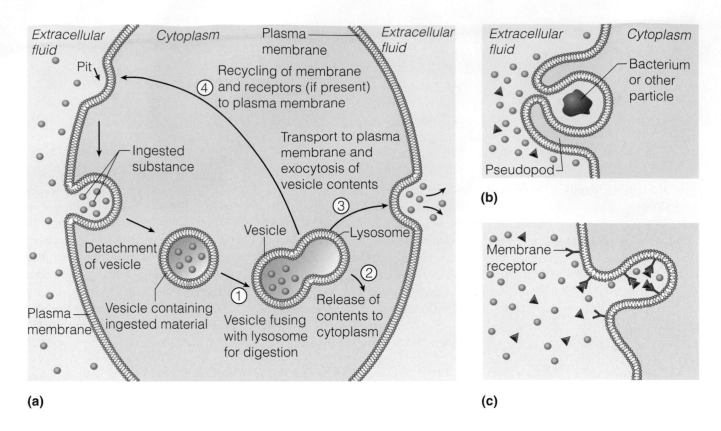

(a)

(b)

(c)

FIGURE 3.13 Events and types of endocytosis. (a) Sequence of events in endocytosis. Once the vesicle detaches from the plasma membrane, its contents may be digested within a lysosome and then released to the cytoplasm (its membrane components, and receptors if present, are recycled to the plasma membrane); or, alternatively, the vesicle may be transported across the cell intact and then released to the cell exterior by exocytosis. The type illustrated is pinocytosis. **(b)** Phagocytosis. **(c)** Receptor-mediated endocytosis.

3.13). Once the vesicle, or sac, is formed, it detaches from the plasma membrane and moves into the cytoplasm, where it fuses with a lysosome and its contents are digested (by lysosomal enzymes).

If the engulfed substances are relatively large particles such as bacteria or dead body cells, which are separated from the external environment by flowing cytoplasmic extensions called *pseudopods,* the endocytosis process is more specifically called **phagocytosis** (fag″o-si-to′sis), a term that means "cell eating" (Figure 3.13b). Certain white blood cells and other "professional" phagocytes of the body act as scavenger cells that police and protect the body by ingesting bacteria and other foreign debris. Hence, phagocytosis is a protective mechanism, not a means of getting nutrients.

If we say that cells can eat, we can also say that they can drink. In this form of endocytosis, called **pinocytosis** (pi″no-si-to′sis; "cell drinking"), the cell "gulps" droplets of extracellular fluid. The plasma membrane invaginates to form a tiny pit, and then its edges fuse around the droplet of extracellular fluid containing dissolved proteins or fats (Figure 3.13a). Unlike phagocytosis, pinocytosis is a routine activity of most cells. It is especially important in cells that function in absorption (for example, cells forming the lining of the small intestine).

Receptor-mediated endocytosis is the main cellular mechanism for taking up specific target molecules (Figure 3.13c). In this process, plasma membrane receptor proteins bind only with certain substances. Both the receptors and high concentrations of the attached target molecules are internalized in a vesicle, and then the contents of the vesicle are dealt with in one of the ways shown in Figure 3.13a. Although phagocytosis and pinocytosis are important, compared to receptor-mediated endocytosis, they are pretty unselective. Substances encytosed by receptor-mediated endocytosis include enzymes, some hormones, cholesterol, and iron. Unfortunately, flu viruses also use this route to enter and attack our cells.

▶ DID YOU GET IT?

15. What determines whether a membrane transport process is active or passive? How are concentration gradients involved in passive transport processes?

16. Which vesicular transport process moves large particles into the cell?

17. Which process is more selective—pinocytosis or receptor-mediated endocytosis?

For answers, see Appendix D.

Cell Division

The **cell life cycle** is the series of changes a cell goes through from the time it is formed until it divides. The cycle has two major periods: **interphase,** in which the cell grows and carries on its usual metabolic activities, and **cell division,** during which it reproduces itself. Although the term *interphase* leads one to believe that it is merely a resting time between the phases of cell division, this is not the case. During interphase, which is by far the longer phase of the cell cycle, the cell is very active and is resting *only* from division. A more accurate name for interphase would be *metabolic phase.*

Preparations: DNA Replication

The function of cell division is to produce more cells for growth and repair processes. Because it is essential that all body cells have the same genetic material, an important event *always precedes* cell division: the genetic material (the DNA molecules that form part of the chromatin) is duplicated exactly. This occurs toward the end of the cell's interphase period.

You will recall from Chapter 2 that DNA is a very complex molecule. It is composed of building blocks called *nucleotides,* each consisting of deoxyribose sugar, a phosphate group, and a nitrogen-containing base. Essentially DNA is a *double helix,* a ladderlike molecule that is coiled into a spiral staircase shape. The upright parts of the DNA "ladder" are alternating phosphate and sugar units, and the rungs of the ladder are made of pairs of nitrogen-containing bases.

The precise trigger for DNA synthesis is unknown, but once it starts, it continues until all the DNA has been replicated. The process begins as the DNA helix uncoils and gradually separates into its two nucleotide chains (Figure 3.14). Each nucleotide strand then serves as a *template,* or set of instructions, for building a new nucleotide strand.

Remember that nucleotides join in a *complementary* way: adenine (A) always bonds to thymine (T), and guanine (G) always bonds to cytosine (C). Hence, the order of the nucleotides on the template strand also determines the order on the new strand. For example, a TACTGC sequence on a template strand would bond to new nucleotides with the order ATGACG. The end result is that two DNA molecules are formed that are identical to the original DNA helix, and each consists of one old and one newly assembled nucleotide strand.

Events of Cell Division

In all cells other than bacteria and some cells of the reproductive system, cell division consists of two events. **Mitosis** (mi-to″sis), or division of the nucleus, occurs first. The second event is division of the cytoplasm, **cytokinesis** (si′to-kĭ-ne″sis), which begins when mitosis is nearly completed.

Mitosis   Mitosis results in the formation of two daughter nuclei with exactly the same genes as the mother nucleus. As explained above, DNA replication precedes mitosis, so that for a short time the cell nucleus contains a double dose of genes. When the nucleus divides, each *daughter cell* ends up with *exactly* the same genetic information as the original mother cell and the original fertilized egg from which it came.

The stages of mitosis, diagrammed in Figure 3.15, include the following events:

- **Prophase** (pro′faz). As cell division begins, the chromatin threads coil and shorten so that

Key:

= Adenine

= Thymine

= Cytosine

= Guanine

Old (template) strand

Newly synthesized strand

New strand forming

Old (template) strand

DNA of one chromatid

FIGURE 3.14 Replication of the DNA molecule during interphase. The DNA helix unwinds (center), and its nucleotide strands are separated. Each strand then acts as a template for building a new complementary strand. As a result, two helixes, each identical to the original DNA helix, are formed.

visible barlike bodies called **chromosomes** (*chromo* = colored; *soma* = body) appear. Because DNA has already been replicated, each chromosome is actually made up of two strands, each called a **chromatid** (kro′mah-tid), held together by a small buttonlike body called a **centromere** (sen′tro-mēr). The centrioles separate from each other and begin to move toward opposite sides of the cell, directing the assembly of a **mitotic spindle** (composed of microtubules) between them as they move. The spindle provides a scaffolding for the attachment and movement of the chromosomes during the later mitotic stages. By the end of prophase, the nuclear envelope and the nucleoli have broken down and disappeared, and the chromosomes have attached randomly to the spindle fibers by their centromeres.

- **Metaphase** (met′ah-faz). In this short stage, the chromosomes cluster and become aligned at the *metaphase plate* (the center of the spindle midway between the centrioles) so that a straight line of chromosomes is seen.

- **Anaphase** (an′ah-faz). During anaphase, the centromeres that have held the chromatids together split. The chromatids (now called chromosomes again) begin to move slowly apart, drawn toward opposite ends of the cell. The chromosomes seem to be pulled by their half-centromeres, with their "arms" dangling behind them. Anaphase is over when chromosome movement ends.

- **Telophase** (tel′o-faz). Telophase is essentially prophase in reverse. The chromosomes at opposite ends of the cell uncoil to become threadlike chromatin again. The spindle breaks down and disappears, a nuclear envelope forms around each chromatin mass, and nucleoli appear in each of the daughter nuclei.

Mitosis is basically the same in all animal cells. Depending on the type of tissue, it takes from 5 minutes to several hours to complete, but typically it lasts about 2 hours. Centriole replication is deferred until late interphase of the next cell cycle, when DNA replication begins before the onset of mitosis.

Cytokinesis Cytokinesis, or the division of the cytoplasm, usually begins during late anaphase and completes during telophase. A contractile ring made of microfilaments forms a **cleavage furrow** over the

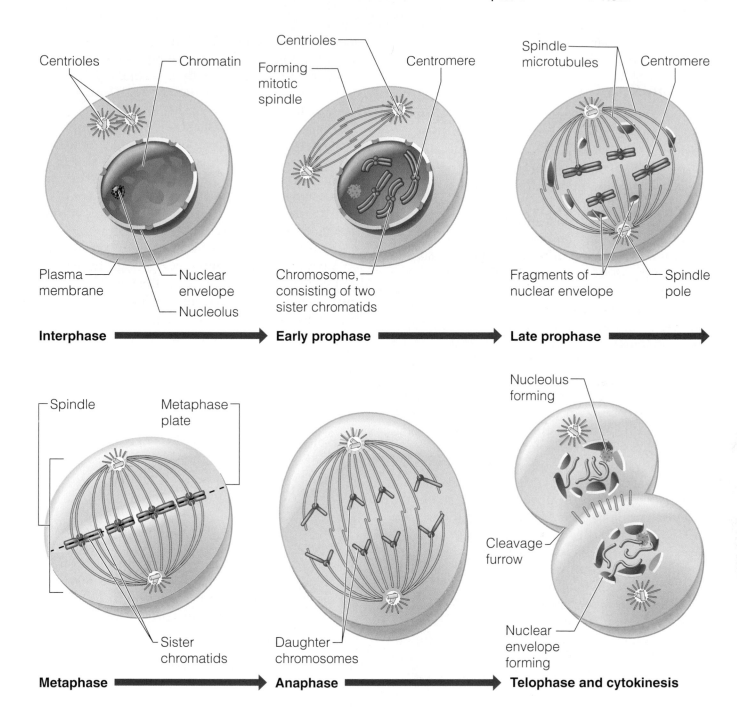

Centrioles — Chromatin

Centrioles
Forming mitotic spindle

Centrioles — Centromere

Spindle microtubules — Centromere

Plasma membrane — Nuclear envelope — Nucleolus

Chromosome, consisting of two sister chromatids

Fragments of nuclear envelope — Spindle pole

Interphase ➤   **Early prophase** ➤   **Late prophase** ➤

Spindle   Metaphase plate

Nucleolus forming

Cleavage furrow

Sister chromatids   Daughter chromosomes   Nuclear envelope forming

Metaphase ➤   **Anaphase** ➤   **Telophase and cytokinesis**

FIGURE 3.15   Stages of mitosis.

midline of the spindle, and it eventually squeezes or pinches the original cytoplasmic mass into two parts. Thus, at the end of cell division, two daughter cells exist. Each is smaller and has less cytoplasm than the mother cell, but it is genetically identical to it. The daughter cells grow and carry out normal cell activities until it is their turn to divide.

Mitosis and division of the cytoplasm usually go hand in hand, but in some cases the cytoplasm is not divided. This condition leads to the formation of *binucleate* (two nuclei) or *multinucleate* cells. This is fairly common in the liver.

As mentioned earlier, mitosis provides the "new" cells for body growth in youth and is necessary to repair body tissue all through life. Mitosis gone wild is the basis for tumors and cancers.

Protein Synthesis

Genes: The Blueprint for Protein Structure

In addition to replicating itself for cell division, DNA serves as the master blueprint for protein syntheses. Traditionally, a **gene** is defined as a DNA segment that carries the information for building one protein or polypeptide chain.

Proteins are key substances for all aspects of cell life. As described in Chapter 2, *fibrous (structural) proteins* are the major building materials for cells. Other proteins, the *globular (functional) proteins,* do things other than build structures. For example, all **enzymes,** biological catalysts that regulate chemical reactions in the cells, are functional proteins. The importance of enzymes cannot be overstated. Every chemical reaction that goes on in the body requires an enzyme. It follows that DNA regulates cell activities largely by specifying the structure of enzymes, which in turn control or direct the chemical reactions in which carbohydrates, fats, other proteins, and even DNA itself are made and broken down.

How does DNA bring about its miracles? It appears that DNA's information is encoded in the sequence of bases along each side of the ladder-like DNA molecules. Each sequence of *three* bases (a *triplet*) calls for a particular *amino acid* (Figure 3.16). (Amino acids are the building blocks of proteins that are joined during protein synthesis.) For example, a DNA base sequence of AAA specifies an amino acid called phenylalanine, whereas CCT calls for glycine. Just as different arrangements of notes on sheet music are played as different melodies, variations in the arrangements of A, C, T, and G in each gene allow cells to make all the different kinds of proteins needed. It has been estimated that a single gene has between 300 and 3,000 base pairs in sequence.

The Role of RNA

By itself, DNA is rather like a strip of magnetic recording tape; its information is not useful until it is decoded. Furthermore, most ribosomes—the manufacturing sites for proteins—are in the cytoplasm, but in interphase cells DNA never leaves the nucleus. Thus, DNA requires not only a decoder but also a messenger to achieve its task of specifying the structure of proteins to be built at the ribosomes. These messenger and decoder functions are carried out by a second type of nucleic acid, called **ribonucleic** (ri″bo-nu-kle′ik) **acid,** or **RNA.**

As you learned in Chapter 2, RNA differs from DNA in being single-stranded and in having ribose sugar instead of deoxyribose and a uracil (U) base instead of thymine (T). Three varieties of RNA play a special role in protein synthesis. **Transfer RNA (tRNA) molecules** are small cloverleaf-shaped molecules. **Ribosomal RNA (rRNA)** helps form the ribosomes, where proteins are built. **Messenger RNA (mRNA) molecules** are long, single nucleotide strands that resemble half of a DNA molecule and carry the "message" containing instructions for protein synthesis from the DNA gene in the nucleus to the ribosomes in the cytoplasm.

Protein synthesis involves two major phases: *transcription,* when complementary mRNA is made at the DNA gene, and *translation,* when the information carried in mRNA molecules is "decoded" and used to assemble proteins. These steps are summarized simply in Figure 3.16 and described in more detail next.

Transcription

The word *transcription* often refers to one of the jobs done by a secretary—converting notes from one form (shorthand notes or an audiotape recording) into another form (a typewritten letter, for example). In other words, the same information is transformed from one form or format to another. In cells, **transcription** involves the transfer of information from DNA's base sequence into the *complementary* base sequence of mRNA (Figure 3.16, step 1). Only DNA and mRNA are involved in transcription. Whereas each three-base sequence specifying a particular amino acid on the DNA gene is called a **triplet,** the corresponding three-base sequences on mRNA are called **codons.** The form is different, but the same information is being conveyed. Thus, if the (partial) sequence of DNA triplets is AAT-CGT-TCG, the related codons on mRNA would be UUA-GCA-AGC.

Translation

A translator takes words in one language and restates them in another language. In the **translation phase** of protein synthesis, the language of nucleic

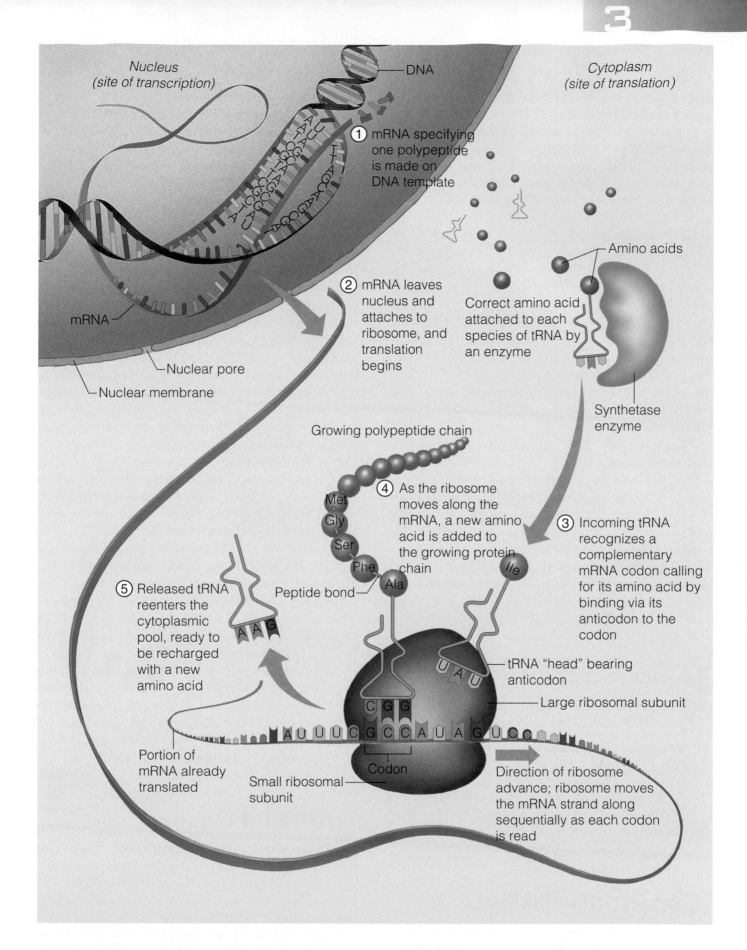

FIGURE 3.16 Protein synthesis. (①) Transcription. (②–⑤) Translation.

acids (base sequence) is "translated" into the language of proteins (amino acid sequence). Translation occurs in the cytoplasm and involves three major varieties of RNA. As illustrated in Figure 3.16, steps 2–5, translation consists of the following events. Once the mRNA attaches to the ribosome (step 2), tRNA comes into the picture. Its job is to transfer, or ferry, amino acids to the ribosome, where they are bound together by enzymes in the exact sequence specified by the gene (and its mRNA). There are about 45 common types of tRNAs, each capable of carrying one of the 20 or so common types of amino acid to the protein synthesis sites. But that is not the only job of the tiny tRNAs. They also have to recognize the mRNA codons "calling for" the amino acid they are toting. They can do this because they have a special three-base sequence called an **anticodon** on their "head" that can bind to the complementary codons (step 3).

Once the first tRNA has maneuvered itself into the correct position at the beginning of the mRNA message, the ribosome moves the mRNA strand along, bringing the next codon into position to be read by another tRNA. As amino acids are brought to their proper positions along the length of mRNA, they are joined together by enzymes (step 4). As an amino acid bonds to the chain, its tRNA is released and moves away from the ribosome to pick up another amino acid (step 5). When the last codon (the termination, or "stop," codon) is read, the protein is released.

▶ DID YOU GET IT?

18. How do the terms *template strand* and *complementary* relate to DNA synthesis?

19. What results if cytokinesis does not happen?

20. What is the role of mRNA in protein synthesis?

21. What are the two stages of protein synthesis, and in which stage are proteins actually synthesized?

For answers, see Appendix D.

PART II: BODY TISSUES

The human body, complex as it is, starts out as a single cell, the fertilized egg, which divides almost endlessly. The millions of cells that result become specialized for particular functions. Some become muscle cells, others the transparent lens of the eye, still others skin cells, and so on. Thus, there is a division of labor in the body, with certain groups of highly specialized cells performing functions that benefit the organism as a whole.

Cell specialization carries with it certain hazards. When a small group of cells is indispensable, its loss can disable or even destroy the body. For example, the action of the heart depends on a very specialized cell group in the heart muscle that controls its contractions. If those particular cells are damaged or stop functioning, the heart will no longer work efficiently, and the whole body will suffer or die from lack of oxygen.

Groups of cells that are similar in structure and function are called **tissues.** The four primary tissue types—epithelium, connective tissue, nervous tissue, and muscle—interweave to form the fabric of the body. If we had to assign a single term to each primary tissue type that would best describe its overall role, the terms would most likely be *covering* (epithelium), *support* (connective), *movement* (muscle), and *control* (nervous). However, these terms reflect only a tiny fraction of the functions that each of these tissues performs.

As explained in Chapter 1, tissues are organized into *organs* such as the heart, kidneys, and lungs. Most organs contain several tissue types, and the arrangement of the tissues determines each organ's structure and what it is able to do. Thus, a study of tissues should be helpful in your later study of the body's organs and how they work.

For now, we want to become familiar with the major similarities and differences in the primary tissues. Because epithelium and some types of connective tissue will not be considered again, they are emphasized more in this section than are muscle, nervous tissues, and bone (a connective tissue), which are covered in more depth in later chapters.

Epithelial Tissue

Epithelial tissue, or **epithelium** (ep"ĭ-the'le-um; *epithe* = laid on, covering) is the *lining, covering,* and *glandular tissue* of the body. Glandular epithelium forms various glands in the body. Covering and lining epithelium covers all free body surfaces and contains versatile cells. One type forms the outer layer of the skin. Others dip into the body to line its cavities. Because epithelium forms the boundaries that separate us from the out-side world, nearly all substances that the body gives off or receives must pass through epithelium.

Epithelial functions include *protection, absorption, filtration,* and *secretion.* For example, the epithelium of the skin protects against bacterial and chemical damage, and the epithelium lining the respiratory tract has cilia, which sweep dust and other debris away from the lungs. Epithelium specialized to absorb substances lines some digestive system organs such as the stomach and small intestine, which absorb food nutrients into the body. In the kidneys, epithelium both absorbs and filters. Secretion is a specialty of the glands, which produce such substances as perspiration, oil, digestive enzymes, and mucus.

Special Characteristics of Epithelium

Epithelium generally has the characteristics listed below:

- Except for glandular epithelium (described on p. 93), epithelial cells fit closely together to form continuous sheets. Neighboring cells are bound together at many points by specialized cell junctions, including desmosomes and tight junctions (see p. 69).

- The membranes always have one free (unattached) surface or edge. This so-called **apical surface** is exposed to the body's exterior or to the cavity of an internal organ. The exposed surfaces of some epithelia are slick and smooth, but others exhibit cell surface modifications, such as microvilli or cilia.

- The lower surface of an epithelium rests on a **basement membrane,** a structureless material secreted by both the epithelial cells and the connective tissue cells that abut the epithelium.

- Epithelial tissues have no blood supply of their own (that is, they are *avascular*) and depend on diffusion from the capillaries in the underlying connective tissue for food and oxygen.

- If well nourished, epithelial cells regenerate themselves easily.

Classification of Epithelium

Each epithelium is given two names. The first indicates the relative number of cell layers it has (Figure 3.17a). The classifications by cell arrangement (layers) are **simple epithelium** (one layer of cells)

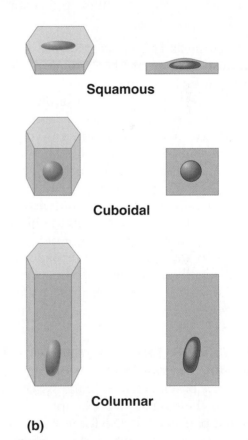

FIGURE 3.17   Classification of epithelia. **(a)** Classification on the basis of arrangement (layers). **(b)** Classification on the basis of cell shape; for each category, a whole cell is shown on the left and a longitudinal section is shown on the right.

and **stratified epithelium** (more than one cell layer). The second describes the shape of its cells (Figure 3.17b). There are *squamous* (skwa'mus) *cells,* flattened like fish scales (*squam* = scale), *cuboidal* (ku-boi'dal) *cells,* which are cube-shaped like dice, and *columnar cells,* shaped like columns. The terms describing the shape and arrangement are then combined to describe the epithelium fully. Stratified epithelia are named for the cells at the *free surface* of the epithelial membrane, not those resting on the basement membrane.

Simple Epithelia

The simple epithelia are most concerned with absorption, secretion, and filtration. Because simple epithelia are usually very thin, protection is not one of their specialties.

Simple Squamous Epithelium   **Simple squamous epithelium** is a single layer of thin squamous cells resting on a basement membrane. The cells fit closely together, much like floor tiles. This type of epithelium usually forms membranes where filtration or exchange of substances by rapid diffusion occurs. Simple squamous epithelium is in the air sacs of the lungs, where oxygen and carbon dioxide are exchanged (Figure 3.18a), and it forms the walls of capillaries, where nutrients and gases pass between the tissue cells and the blood in the capillaries. Simple squamous epithelium also forms **serous membranes,** or **serosae** (se-ro'se), the slick membranes that line the ventral body cavity and cover the organs in that cavity. The serous membranes are described in more detail in Chapter 4.

Simple Cuboidal Epithelium   **Simple cuboidal epithelium,** which is one layer of cuboidal cells resting on a basement membrane, is common in glands and their ducts (for example, the salivary glands and pancreas). It also forms the walls of the kidney tubules and covers the surface of the ovaries (Figure 3.18b).

Simple Columnar Epithelium   **Simple columnar epithelium** is made up of a single layer of tall cells that fit closely together. **Goblet cells,** which produce a lubricating mucus, are often seen in this type of epithelium. Simple columnar epithelium lines the entire length of the digestive tract from the stomach to the anus (Figure 3.18c). Epithelial membranes that line body cavities open to the body exterior are called **mucosae** (mu-ko'se) or **mucous membranes.**

Pseudostratified Columnar Epithelium   All of the cells of **pseudostratified** (soo"do-stra'ti-fid) **columnar epithelium** rest on a basement membrane. However, some of its cells are shorter than others, and their nuclei appear at different heights above the basement membrane. As a result, this epithelium gives the false (*pseudo*) impression that it is stratified; hence its name. Like simple columnar epithelium, this variety mainly functions in absorption and secretion. A ciliated variety (more precisely called *pseudostratified ciliated columnar epithelium*) lines most of the respiratory tract (Figure 3.18d). The mucus produced by the goblet cells in this epithelium traps dust and other debris, and the cilia propel the mucus upward and away from the lungs.

Stratified Epithelia

Stratified epithelia consist of two or more cell layers. Being considerably more durable than the simple epithelia, these epithelia function primarily to protect.

Stratified Squamous Epithelium   **Stratified squamous epithelium** is the most common stratified epithelium in the body. It usually consists of several layers of cells. The cells at the free edge are squamous cells, whereas those close to the basement membrane are cuboidal or columnar. Stratified squamous epithelium is found in sites that receive a good deal of abuse or friction, such as the esophagus, the mouth, and the outer portion of the skin (Figure 3.18e).

Stratified Cuboidal and Stratified Columnar Epithelia   **Stratified cuboidal epithelium** typically has just two cell layers with (at least) the surface cells being cuboidal in shape. The surface cells of **stratified columnar epithelium** are columnar cells, but its basal cells vary in size and shape. Both of these epithelia are fairly rare in the body, found mainly in the ducts of large glands. (Because the distribution of these two epithelia is extremely limited, they are not illustrated in Figure 3.18. They are described here only to provide a complete listing of the epithelial tissues.)

Transitional Epithelium   **Transitional epithelium** is a highly modified, stratified squamous epithelium

Nucleus of squamous epithelial cell

Basement membrane

Air sacs of lungs

Nuclei of squamous epithelial cells

(a) Diagram: Simple squamous

Photomicrograph: Simple squamous epithelium forming part of the alveolar (air sac) walls (100x).

Basement membrane

Nucleus of simple cuboidal epithelial cell

Simple cuboidal epithelial cells

Basement membrane

Connective tissue

(b) Diagram: Simple cuboidal

Photomicrograph: Simple cuboidal epithelium in kidney tubules (400x).

Nucleus of simple columnar epithelial cell

Basement membrane

Simple columnar epithelial cell

Basement membrane

(c) Diagram: Simple columnar

Photomicrograph: Simple columnar epithelium of the stomach lining (900x).

FIGURE 3.18   Types of epithelia and their common locations in the body. *(Continued on page 92.)*

Pseudo-
stratified
epithelial
layer

Basement
membrane

(d) Diagram: Pseudostratified (ciliated)
columnar

Cilia
Mucus of
goblet cell
Pseudo-
stratified
epithelial
layer
Basement
membrane
Connective
tissue

Photomicrograph: Pseudostratified
ciliated columnar epithelium lining
the human trachea (700x).

Stratified
squamous
epithelium

Basement
membrane

(e) Diagram: Stratified squamous

Nuclei

Stratified
squamous
epithelium

Basement
membrane
Connective
tissue

Photomicrograph: Stratified
squamous epithelium lining of
the esophagus (200x).

Transi-
tional
epithelium

Basement
membrane

(f) Diagram: Transitional

Basement
membrane

Transitional
epithelium

Connective
tissue

Photomicrograph: Transitional
epithelium lining of the bladder,
relaxed state (300x); note the rounded
appearance of the cells at the surface;
these cells flatten and elongate when
the bladder fills with urine.

FIGURE 3.18 *(continued)* **Types of epithelia and their
common locations in the body.**

that forms the lining of only a few organs—the urinary bladder, the ureters, and part of the urethra. *All* these organs are part of the urinary system and are subject to considerable stretching (Figure 3.18f). Cells of the basal layer are cuboidal or columnar; those at the free surface vary in appearance. When the organ is not stretched, the membrane is many-layered, and the superficial cells are rounded and domelike. When the organ is distended with urine, the epithelium thins, and the surface cells flatten and become squamouslike. This ability of transitional cells to slide past one another and change their shape (undergo "transitions") allows the ureter wall to stretch as a greater volume of urine flows through that tubelike organ. In the bladder, it allows more urine to be stored.

Glandular Epithelium

A **gland** consists of one or more cells that make and secrete a particular product. This product, called a **secretion,** typically contains protein molecules in an aqueous (water-based) fluid. The term *secretion* also indicates an active *process* in which the glandular cells obtain needed materials from the blood and use them to make their secretion, which they then discharge.

Two major types of glands develop from epithelial sheets. **Endocrine** (en′do-krin) **glands** lose their connection to the surface (duct); thus they are often called *ductless* glands. Their secretions (all hormones) diffuse directly into the blood vessels that weave through the glands. Examples of endocrine glands include the thyroid, adrenals, and pituitary.

Exocrine (ek′so-krin) **glands** retain their ducts, and their secretions empty through the ducts to the epithelial surface. Exocrine glands, which include the sweat and oil glands, liver, and pancreas, are both internal and external. They are discussed with the organ systems to which their products are related.

Connective Tissue

Connective tissue, as its name suggests, connects body parts. It is found everywhere in the body. It is the most abundant and widely distributed of the tissue types. Connective tissues perform many functions but they are primarily involved in *protecting, supporting,* and *binding together* other body tissues.

Common Characteristics of Connective Tissue

The characteristics of connective tissue include the following:

- **Variations in blood supply.** Most connective tissues are well *vascularized* (that is, they have a good blood supply), but there are exceptions. Tendons and ligaments have a poor blood supply, and cartilages are avascular. Consequently, all these structures heal very slowly when injured. (This is why some people say that, given a choice, they would rather have a broken bone than a torn ligament.)

- **Extracellular matrix.** Connective tissues are made up of many different types of cells plus varying amounts of a nonliving substance found outside the cells, called the extracellular matrix.

Extracellular Matrix

The **extracellular matrix** deserves a bit more explanation because it is what makes connective tissue so different from the other tissue types. The matrix, which is produced by the connective tissue cells and then secreted to their exterior, has two main elements, a structureless ground substance and fibers. The *ground substance* of the matrix is composed largely of water plus some adhesion proteins and large, charged polysaccharide molecules. The cell adhesion proteins serve as a glue that allows the connective tissue cells to attach themselves to the matrix fibers embedded in the ground substance. The charged polysaccharide molecules trap water as they intertwine. As the relative abundance of these polysaccharides increases, they cause the matrix to vary from fluid to gel-like to firm to rock-hard in its consistency. The ability of the ground substance to absorb large amounts of water allow it to serve as a water reservoir for the body.

Various types and amounts of fibers are deposited in the matrix and form part of it. These include collagen (white) fibers distinguished by their high tensile strength, elastic (yellow) fibers (the key characteristic of which is an ability to be stretched and then recoil), and reticular fibers (fine collagen fibers that form the internal "skeleton" of soft organs such as the spleen), depending on the connective tissue type. The building blocks, or *monomers,* of these fibers are made by the connective tissue cells and secreted into the ground substance in the extracellular space, where they join together to form the various fiber types.

Because of its extracellular matrix, connective tissue is able to form a soft packing tissue around other organs, to bear weight, and to withstand stretching and other abuses, such as abrasion, that no other tissue could endure. But there is variation. At one extreme, fat tissue is composed mostly of cells, and the matrix is soft. At the opposite extreme, bone and cartilage have very few cells and large amounts of hard matrix, which makes them extremely strong. Find the various types of connective tissues in Figure 3.19 as you read their descriptions, which follow.

Types of Connective Tissue

As noted above, all connective tissues consist of living cells surrounded by a matrix. Their major differences reflect fiber type and the number of fibers in the matrix. From most rigid to softest, the major connective tissue classes are *bone, cartilage, dense connective tissue, loose connective tissue,* and *blood.*

Bone

Bone, sometimes called *osseous* (os'e-us) *tissue,* is composed of bone cells sitting in cavities called *lacunae* (lah-ku'ne; "pits") and surrounded by layers of a very hard matrix that contains calcium salts in addition to large numbers of collagen fibers (Figure 3.19a). Because of its rocklike hardness, bone has an exceptional ability to protect and support other body organs (for example, the skull protects the brain).

Cartilage

Cartilage is less hard and more flexible than bone. It is found in only a few places in the body. Most widespread is **hyaline** (hi'ah-lin) **cartilage,** which has abundant collagen fibers hidden by a rubbery matrix with a glassy (*hyalin* = glass), blue-white appearance (Figure 3.19b). It forms the supporting structures of the larynx, or voice box, attaches the ribs to the breastbone, and covers the ends of many bones, where they form joints. The skeleton of a fetus is made largely of hyaline cartilage; but, by the time the baby is born, most of that cartilage has been replaced by bone.

Although hyaline cartilage is the most abundant type of cartilage in the body, there are others. Highly compressible **fibrocartilage** forms the cushionlike disks between the vertebrae of the spinal column (Figure 3.19c). **Elastic cartilage** is found where a structure with elasticity is desired. For example, it supports the external ear. (Elastic cartilage is not illustrated in Figure 3.19.)

(*Continues on page 97*)

(a) **Diagram:** Bone

Photomicrograph: Cross-sectional view of ground bone (250x).

FIGURE 3.19   Connective tissues and their common body locations.

(b) Diagram: Hyaline cartilage

Photomicrograph: Hyaline cartilage from the trachea (400x).

Labels: Chondrocyte (Cartilage cell); Lacunae; Chondrocyte in lacuna; Matrix

(c) Diagram: Fibrocartilage

Photomicrograph: Fibrocartilage of an intervertebral disc (200x).

Labels: Chondrocites in lacunae; Collagen fibers; Chondrocytes in lacunae; Collagen fiber

(d) Diagram: Dense fibrous

Photomicrograph: Dense fibrous connective tissue from a tendon (500x).

Labels: Ligament; Tendon; Collagen fibers; Nuclei of fibroblasts; Collagen fibers; Nuclei of fibroblasts

(Continues on page 96)

Mucosa epithelium

Lamina propria

Fibers of matrix

Nuclei of fibroblasts

(e) Diagram: Areolar

Elastic fibers

Collagen fibers

Fibroblast nuclei

Photomicrograph: Areolar connective tissue, a soft packaging tissue of the body (330x).

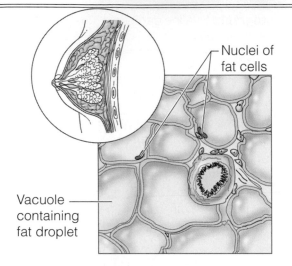

Nuclei of fat cells

Vacuole containing fat droplet

(f) Diagram: Adipose

Nuclei of fat cells

Vacuole containing fat droplet

Photomicrograph: Adipose tissue from the subcutaneous layer beneath the skin (330x).

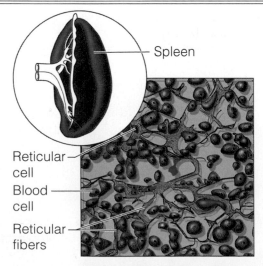

Spleen

Reticular cell

Blood cell

Reticular fibers

(g) Diagram: Reticular

White blood cell (lymphocyte)

Reticular fibers

Photomicrograph: Dark-staining network of reticular connective tissue (400x).

FIGURE 3.19 *(continued)* **Connective tissues and their common body locations.** (**e, f,** and **g** are subclasses of loose connective tissues.)

(h) Diagram: Blood

Photomicrograph: Smear of human blood (1300x)

FIGURE 3.19 *(continued)*

Dense Connective Tissue

Dense connective tissue, also called **dense fibrous tissue,** has collagen fibers as its main matrix element (Figure 3.19d). Crowded between the collagen fibers are rows of *fibroblasts* (fiber-forming cells) that manufacture the building blocks of the fibers. Dense connective tissue forms strong, ropelike structures such as tendons and ligaments. **Tendons** attach skeletal muscles to bones; **ligaments** connect bones to bones at joints. Ligaments are more stretchy and contain more elastic fibers than tendons. Dense connective tissue also makes up the lower layers of the skin (dermis), where it is arranged in sheets.

Loose Connective Tissue

Relatively speaking, **loose connective tissues** are softer and have more cells and fewer fibers than any other connective tissue type except blood.

Areolar Tissue **Areolar** (ah-re′o-lar) **tissue,** the most widely distributed connective tissue variety in the body, is a soft, pliable, "cobwebby" tissue that cushions and protects the body organs it wraps (Figure 3.19e). It functions as a universal packing tissue and connective tissue "glue" because it helps to hold the internal organs together and in their proper positions. A soft layer of areolar connective tissue called the *lamina propria* (lah′mĭ-nah pro′pre-ah) underlies all mucous membranes. Its

fluid matrix contains all types of fibers, which form a loose network. In fact, when viewed through a microscope, most of the matrix appears to be empty space, which explains the name of this tissue type (*areola* = small open space). Because of its loose and fluid nature, areolar connective tissue provides a reservoir of water and salts for the surrounding tissues, and essentially all body cells obtain their nutrients from and release their wastes into this "tissue fluid." When a body region is inflamed, the areolar tissue in the area soaks up the excess fluid like a sponge, and the area swells and becomes puffy, a condition called **edema.** Many types of *phagocytes* wander through this tissue, scavenging for bacteria, dead cells, and other debris, which they destroy.

Adipose Tissue **Adipose** (ad′ĭ-pŏs) **tissue** is commonly called *fat*. Basically, it is an areolar tissue in which fat cells predominate (Figure 3.19f). A glistening droplet of oil occupies most of a fat cell's volume and compresses the nucleus, displacing it to one side. Because the oil-containing region looks empty and the thin rim of cytoplasm containing the bulging nucleus looks like a ring with a seal, fat cells are sometimes called *signet ring cells.*

Adipose tissue forms the subcutaneous tissue beneath the skin, where it insulates the body and protects it from bumps and extremes of both heat and cold. Adipose tissue also protects some organs individually—the kidneys are surrounded by a capsule of fat, and adipose tissue cushions the eyeballs in their sockets. There are also fat "depots" in the body, such as the hips and breasts, where fat is stored and available for fuel if needed.

Reticular Connective Tissue **Reticular connective tissue** consists of a delicate network of interwoven reticular fibers associated with *reticular cells,* which resemble fibroblasts (Figure 3.19g). Reticular tissue is limited to certain sites: it forms the **stroma** (literally, "bed" or "mattress"), or internal framework, which can support many free blood cells (largely lymphocytes) in lymphoid organs such as lymph nodes, the spleen, and bone marrow.

Blood

Blood, or *vascular tissue,* is considered a connective tissue because it consists of *blood cells* surrounded by a nonliving, fluid matrix called *blood plasma* (Figure 3.19h). The "fibers" of blood are soluble protein molecules that become visible only during blood clotting. Still, we must recognize that blood is quite atypical as connective tissues go. Blood is the transport vehicle for the cardiovascular system, carrying nutrients, wastes, respiratory gases, and many other substances throughout the body. Blood is considered in detail in Chapter 10.

Muscle Tissue

Muscle tissues are highly specialized to *contract,* or *shorten,* to produce movement.

Types of Muscle Tissue

The three types of muscle tissue are illustrated in Figure 3.20. Notice their similarities and differences as you read through their descriptions.

Skeletal Muscle

Skeletal muscle tissue is packaged by connective tissue sheets into organs called *skeletal muscles,* which are attached to the skeleton. These muscles, which can be controlled *voluntarily* (or consciously), form the flesh of the body, the so-called muscular system (see Chapter 6). When the skeletal muscles contract, they pull on bones or skin. The result of their action is gross body movements or changes in our facial expressions. The cells of skeletal muscle are long, cylindrical, multinucleate, and they have obvious *striations* (stripes). Because skeletal muscle cells are elongated to provide a long axis for contraction, they are often called *muscle fibers.*

Cardiac Muscle

Cardiac muscle, covered in more detail in Chapter 11, is found only in the heart. As it contracts, the heart acts as a pump and propels blood through the blood vessels. Like skeletal muscle, cardiac muscle has striations, but cardiac cells are uninucleate, relatively short, branching cells that fit tightly together (like clasped fingers) at junctions called **intercalated disks.** These intercalated disks contain gap junctions that allow ions to pass freely from cell to cell, resulting in rapid conduction of the exciting electrical impulse across the heart. Cardiac muscle is under *involuntary control,* which means that we cannot consciously control the activity of the heart. (There are, however, rare individuals who claim they have such an ability.)

Smooth Muscle

Smooth, or **visceral, muscle** is so called because no striations are visible. The individual cells have a single nucleus and are spindle-shaped (pointed at each end). Smooth muscle is found in the walls of hollow organs such as the stomach, uterus, and blood vessels. As smooth muscle in its walls contracts, the cavity of an organ alternately becomes smaller (constricts on smooth muscle contraction) or enlarges (dilates on smooth muscle relaxation) so that substances are propelled through the organ along a specific pathway. Smooth muscle contracts much more slowly than the other two muscle types. *Peristalsis* (per"i-stal'sis), a wavelike motion that keeps food moving through the small intestine, is typical of its activity.

Nervous Tissue

When we think of **nervous tissue,** we think of cells called **neurons.** All neurons receive and conduct electrochemical impulses from one part of the body to another; thus, *irritability* and *conductivity* are their two major functional characteristics. The structure of neurons is unique (Figure 3.21). Their cytoplasm is drawn out into long processes (extensions), as much as 3 feet or more in the leg, which allows a single neuron to conduct an impulse over long distances in the body. Neurons, along with a special group of **supporting cells** that insulate, support, and protect the delicate neurons, make up the structures of the nervous system—the brain, spinal cord, and nerves.

Cell division typically yields two daughter cells, each with one nucleus. How is the multinuclear condition of skeletal muscle explained?

Nuclei

Part of muscle fiber

(a) Diagram: Skeletal muscle   **Photomicrograph:** Skeletal muscle (approx. 250x).

Intercalated discs

Nucleus

(b) Diagram: Cardiac muscle   **Photomicrograph:** Cardiac muscle (800x).

Smooth muscle cell

Nuclei

(c) Diagram: Smooth muscle   **Photomicrograph:** Sheet of smooth muscle (approx. 250x).

FIGURE 3.20   Types of muscle tissue and their common locations in the body.

Skeletal muscle cells repeatedly undergo mitosis unaccompanied by cytokinesis.

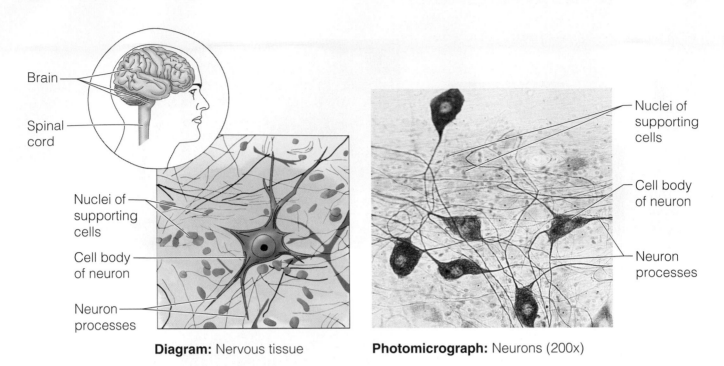

Diagram: Nervous tissue

Photomicrograph: Neurons (200x)

FIGURE 3.21 **Nervous tissue.** Neurons and supporting cells form the brain, spinal cord, and nerves.

Tissue Repair (Wound Healing)

The body has many techniques for protecting itself from uninvited guests or injury. Intact physical barriers such as the skin and mucous membranes, cilia, and the strong acid produced by stomach glands are just three examples of body defenses exerted at the local tissue level. When tissue injury does occur, it stimulates the body's inflammatory and immune responses, and the healing process begins almost immediately. Inflammation is a generalized (nonspecific) body response that attempts to prevent further injury. The immune response, in contrast, is extremely specific and mounts a vigorous attack against recognized invaders (bacteria, viruses, toxins). These protective responses are considered in detail in Chapter 12. Here we will concentrate on the process of tissue repair itself.

Tissue repair, or wound healing, occurs in two major ways: by regeneration and by fibrosis. **Regeneration** is the replacement of destroyed tissue by the same kind of cells, whereas **fibrosis** involves repair by dense (fibrous) connective tissue, that is, by the formation of *scar tissue*. Which occurs depends on (1) the type of tissue damaged

and (2) the severity of the injury. Generally speaking, clean cuts (incisions) heal much more successfully than ragged tears of the tissue.

Tissue injury sets a series of events into motion:

- **The capillaries become very permeable.** This allows fluid rich in clotting proteins and other substances to seep into the injured area from the bloodstream. Then leaked clotting proteins construct a clot, which stops the loss of blood, holds the edges of the wound together, and walls off the injured area, preventing bacteria or other harmful substances from spreading to surrounding tissues. Where the clot is exposed to air, it quickly dries and hardens, forming a scab.

- **Granulation tissue forms.** *Granulation tissue* is a delicate pink tissue composed largely of new capillaries that grow into the damaged area from undamaged blood vessels nearby. These capillaries are fragile and bleed freely, as when a scab is picked away from a skin wound. Granulation tissue also contains phagocytes that eventually dispose of the blood clot and connective tissue cells (fibroblasts) that synthesize the building blocks of collagen fibers (scar tissue) to permanently bridge the gap.

- **The surface epithelium regenerates.** As the surface epithelium begins to regenerate, it makes its way across the granulation tissue just beneath the scab. The scab soon detaches, and the final result is a fully regenerated surface epithelium that covers an underlying area of fibrosis (the scar). The scar is either invisible or visible as a thin white line, depending on the severity of the wound.

The ability of the different tissue types to regenerate varies widely. Epithelial tissues such as the skin epidermis and mucous membranes regenerate beautifully. So, too, do most of the fibrous connective tissues and bone. Skeletal muscle regenerates poorly, if at all, and cardiac muscle and nervous tissue within the brain and spinal cord are replaced largely by scar tissue.

HOMEOSTATIC IMBALANCE

Scar tissue is strong, but it lacks the flexibility of most normal tissues. Perhaps even more important is its inability to perform the normal functions of the tissue it replaces. Thus, if scar tissue forms in the wall of the bladder, heart, or another muscular organ, it may severely hamper the functioning of that organ. ▲

DID YOU GET IT?

22. What two criteria are used to classify epithelial tissues?

23. How do endocrine and exocrine glands differ in structure and function?

24. How do connective tissues differ significantly from other tissues?

25. Which of the three types of muscle tissue is striated? Which is voluntary?

For answers, see Appendix D.

PART III:
DEVELOPMENTAL ASPECTS OF CELLS AND TISSUES

We all begin life as a single cell, which divides thousands of times to form our multicellular embryonic body. Very early in embryonic development, the cells begin to specialize to form the primary tissues, and by birth, most organs are well formed and functioning. The body continues to grow and enlarge by forming new tissue throughout childhood and adolescence.

Cell division is extremely important during the body's growth period. Most cells (except neurons) undergo mitosis until the end of puberty, when adult body size is reached and overall body growth ends. After this time, only certain cells routinely divide (are mitotic)—for example, cells exposed to abrasion that continually wear away, such as skin and intestinal cells. Liver cells stop dividing; but they retain this ability should some of them die or become damaged and need to be replaced. Still other cell groups (for example, heart muscle and nervous tissue) almost completely lose their ability to divide when they are fully mature; that is, they become *amitotic* (am"ĭ-tot'ik). Amitotic tissues are severely handicapped by injury because the lost cells cannot be replaced by the same type of cells. This is why the heart of an individual who has had several severe heart attacks becomes weaker and weaker. Damaged cardiac muscle does not regenerate and is replaced by scar tissue that cannot contract, so the heart becomes less and less capable of acting as an efficient blood pump.

The aging process begins once maturity has been reached. (Some believe it begins at birth.) No one has been able to explain just *what* causes aging, but there have been many suggestions. Some believe it is a result of little "chemical insults," which occur continually through life—for example, the presence of toxic chemicals (such as alcohol, certain drugs, or carbon monoxide) in the blood, or the temporary absence of needed substances such as glucose or oxygen. Perhaps the effect of these chemical insults is cumulative and finally succeeds in upsetting the delicate chemical balance of the body cells. Others think that external physical factors such as radiation (X rays or ultraviolet waves) contribute to the aging process. Still another theory is that the aging "clock" is genetically programmed, or built into our genes. We all know of cases like the radiant woman of 50 who looks about 35 or the barely-out-of-adolescence man of 24 who looks 40. It appears that such traits can run in families.

There is no question that certain events are part of the aging process. For example, with age, epithelial membranes thin and are more easily damaged, and the skin loses its elasticity and

A CLOSER LOOK

CANCER—THE INTIMATE ENEMY

The word *cancer* elicits dread in nearly everyone. Why does cancer strike some and not others? Before attempting to answer that question, let's define some terms. An abnormal cell mass that develops when controls of the cell cycle and cell division malfunction is called a **neoplasm** ("new growth") or **tumor.** However, not all neoplasms are cancerous. **Benign** (be-nīn': "kindly") neoplasms are strictly local affairs. They tend to be surrounded by a capsule, grow slowly, and seldom kill their hosts if they are removed before they compress vital organs. In contrast, **malignant** ("bad") neoplasms (cancers) are nonencapsulated masses that grow more relentlessly and may become killers. Their cells resemble immature cells, and they invade their surroundings rather than pushing them aside, as reflected in the name *cancer,* from the Latin word for "crab." Whereas normal cells become fatally "homesick" and die when they lose contact with the surrounding matrix, malignant cells tend to break away from the parent mass and spread via the blood to distant parts of the body, where they form new masses. This last capability is called *metastasis* (mĕ-tas'tă-sis). Additionally, cancer cells consume an exceptional amount of the body's nutrients, leading to weight loss and tissue wasting that contributes to death.

What causes transformation—the changes that convert a normal cell into a cancerous one? It is well known that radiation, mechanical trauma, certain viral infections, and many chemicals (tobacco tars, saccharine) can act as **carcinogens** (cancer-causers). What all of these factors have in common is that they all cause *mutations*—changes in DNA

> ❝*The seeds of cancer do appear to be in our own genes.*❞

that alter the expression of certain genes. However, most carcinogens are eliminated by peroxisomal or lysosomal enzymes or the immune system. Furthermore, one mutation doesn't do it—apparently it takes a sequence of several genetic changes to change a normal cell to a full-fledged cancer cell. See figure (a).

Clues to the role of genes were provided by the discovery of *oncogenes* (cancer-causing [*onco* = tumor] genes), and then *proto-oncogenes*. Proto-oncogenes code for proteins that are needed for normal cell division and growth. However, many have fragile sites that break when they are exposed to carcinogens, and this event converts them into oncogenes. An example of a problem that might result from this conversion is the switching on of

dormant genes that allow cells to become invasive (an ability of embryonic cells—and cancer cells—but not normal adult cells). However, oncogenes have been discovered in only 15 to 20 percent of human cancers, so the more recent discovery of *tumor suppressor genes*, or anti-oncogenes, which work to suppress or prevent cancer, was not too surprising. The tumor suppressor genes (such as *p*53 and *p*16) aid DNA repair, put the "brakes" on cell division, help to inactivate carcinogens, or enhance the ability of the immune system to destroy cancer cells. When the tumor suppressor genes are damaged or changed in some way, the oncogenes are free to "do their thing." One of the best-understood of human cancers, colon cancer illustrates this principle; see figure (b). The first sign of colon cancer is a polyp (benign tumor), which forms when the division rate of apparently normal cells of the colon lining undergoes an unusual increase. In time, a malignant neoplasm makes its appearance at the site. In most cases, these changes parallel cellular changes at the DNA level and include activation of an oncogene and inactivation of two tumor suppressor genes. Whatever the precise genetic factor at work, the seeds of cancer do appear to be in our own genes. Thus, as you can see, cancer is an intimate enemy indeed.

Almost half of all Americans develop cancer in their lifetime, and a fifth of us will die of it. Cancer can arise

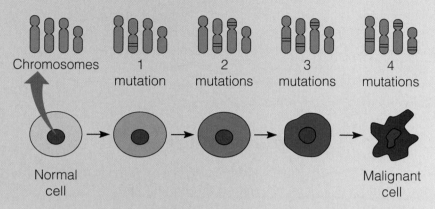

(a) Accumulation of mutations in the development of a cancer cell.

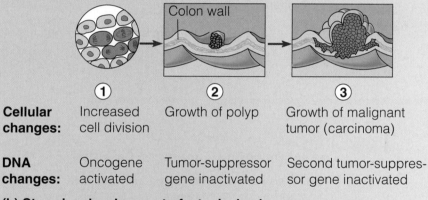

Cellular changes:	Increased cell division	Growth of polyp	Growth of malignant tumor (carcinoma)
DNA changes:	Oncogene activated	Tumor-suppressor gene inactivated	Second tumor-suppressor gene inactivated

(b) Stepwise development of a typical colon cancer.

from almost any cell type, but the most common cancers originate in the skin, lung, colon, breast, and male prostate gland. Although incidence of stomach and colon cancer is down, skin and lymphoid cancer rates are up.

Screening procedures, such as self-examination of one's breasts or testicles for lumps and checking fecal samples for blood, aid in early detection of cancers. Unfortunately, most cancers are diagnosed only after symptoms (pain, bloody discharge, lump, etc.) have already appeared. In this case the diagnostic method most used is the biopsy. In a biopsy, a sample of the primary tumor is removed surgically (or by scraping) and examined microscopically for structural changes typical of malignant cells. Increasingly, diagnosis is made by genetic or chemical analysis of the tissue samples, in which cancer cells are typed to determine which genes are switched on or off or which drugs will be most effective. MRI and CT scans can be used to detect large cancers.

The treatment of choice for either type of neoplasm is surgical removal. If surgery is not possible—as in cases where the cancer has spread widely or is inoperable—radiation and drugs (chemotherapy) are used. Anticancer drugs have unpleasant side effects because most target *all* rapidly dividing cells, including normal ones. The side effects include nausea, vomiting, and loss of hair. X rays, even if highly localized, also have side effects because, in passing through the body, they kill healthy cells that lie in their path as well as cancer cells.

Current cancer treatments—"cut, burn, and poison"—are recognized as crude and painful. Promising new methods focus on the following:

► Delivering radiation or anticancer drugs more precisely to the cancer (via monoclonal antibodies that respond to one type of protein on a cancer cell).

► Increasing the immune system's ability to fend off cancer.

► Starving tumors by cutting off their ability to attract a rich blood supply.

► Destroying cancer cells with viruses.

Additionally, a cancer vaccine is in clinical trials. As techniques for diagnosing and treating cancers become more and more specific, curing many types of cancer becomes increasingly probable.

103

begins to sag. The exocrine glands of the body (epithelial tissue) become less active, and we begin to "dry out" as less oil, mucus, and sweat are produced. Some endocrine glands produce decreasing amounts of hormones, and the body processes that they control (such as metabolism and reproduction) become less efficient or stop altogether.

Connective tissue structures also show changes with age. Bones become porous and weaken, and the repair of tissue injuries slows. Muscles begin to waste away. Although a poor diet may contribute to some of these changes, there is little doubt that decreased efficiency of the circulatory system, which reduces nutrient and oxygen delivery to body tissues, is a major factor.

Besides the tissue changes associated with aging, which accelerate in the later years of life, other modifications of cells and tissues may occur at any time. For example, when cells fail to honor normal controls on cell division and multiply wildly, an abnormal mass of proliferating cells, known as a **neoplasm** (ne′o-plazm″; "new growth"), results. Neoplasms may be benign or malignant (cancerous). See "A Closer Look," pp. 102–103, for more information on cancer.

However, not all increases in cell number involve neoplasms. Certain body tissues (or organs) may enlarge because there is some local irritant or condition that stimulates the cells. This response is called **hyperplasia** (hi″per-pla′ze-ah). For example, a woman's breasts enlarge during pregnancy in response to increased hormones; this is a normal but temporary situation that doesn't have to be treated. In contrast, **atrophy** (at′ro-fe), or decrease in size, can occur in an organ or body area that loses its normal stimulation. For example, muscles that are not used or that have lost their nerve supply begin to atrophy and waste away rapidly.

▶ DID YOU GET IT?

26. Which of the four types of tissue is most likely to remain mitotic throughout life?

27. What is a neoplasm?

28. How does the activity of endocrine glands change as the body ages?

For answers, see Appendix D.

SUMMARY

Media study tools that provide additional review of key topics of Chapter 3 are referenced below.

> **IP** = *InterActive Physiology*
> **WEB** = The A&P Place

PART I: CELLS (pp. 65–88)

Overview of the Cellular Basis of Life (pp. 65–66)

1. A cell is composed primarily of four elements—carbon, hydrogen, oxygen, and nitrogen—plus many trace elements. Living matter is over 60 percent water. The major building material of the cell is protein.

2. Cells vary in size from microscopic to over a meter in length. Shape often reflects function. For example, muscle cells have a long axis to allow shortening.

Anatomy of a Generalized Cell (pp. 66–76)

1. Cells have three major regions—nucleus, cytoplasm, and plasma membrane.

   a. The nucleus, or control center, directs cell activity and is necessary for reproduction. The nucleus contains genetic material (DNA), which carries instructions for synthesis of proteins.

   b. The plasma membrane limits and encloses the cytoplasm and acts as a selective barrier to the movement of substances into and out of the cell. It is composed of a lipid bilayer containing proteins. The water-impermeable lipid portion forms the basic membrane structure. The proteins (many of which are glycoproteins) act as enzymes or carriers in membrane transport, form membrane channels, provide receptor sites for hormones and other chemicals, or play a role in cellular recognition and interactions during development and immune reactions.

Specializations of the plasma membrane include microvilli (which increase the absorptive area) and cell junctions (desmosomes, tight junctions, and gap junctions).

WEB Exercise: Chapter 3, Structure of the Plasma Membrane.

c. The cytoplasm is where most cellular activities occur. Its fluid substance, the cytosol, contains inclusions, stored or inactive materials in the cytoplasm (fat globules, water vacuoles, crystals, and the like) and specialized bodies called organelles, each with a specific function. For example, mitochondria are sites of ATP synthesis, ribosomes are sites of protein synthesis, and the Golgi apparatus packages proteins for export from the cell. Lysosomes carry out intracellular digestion, and peroxisomes disarm dangerous chemicals in the cells. Cytoskeletal elements function in cellular support and motion. The centrioles play a role in cell division and form the bases of cilia and flagella.

WEB Exercise: Chapter 3, Parts of the Cell: Structure.

Cell Physiology   (pp. 76–88)

1. All cells exhibit irritability, digest foods, excrete wastes, and are able to reproduce, grow, move, and metabolize.

2. Transport of substances through the cell membrane:

   WEB Exercise: Chapter 3, Membrane Transport.

   a. Passive transport processes include diffusion and filtration.

      (1) Diffusion is the movement of a substance from an area of its higher concentration to an area of its lower concentration. It occurs because of kinetic energy of the molecules themselves. The diffusion of dissolved solutes through the plasma membrane is simple diffusion. The diffusion of water across the plasma membrane is osmosis. Diffusion that requires a protein channel or carrier is facilitated diffusion.

   WEB Exercise: Chapter 3, Passive Transport.

      (2) Filtration is the movement of substances through a membrane from an area of high hydrostatic pressure to an area of lower fluid pressure. In the body, the driving force of filtration is blood pressure.

   b. Active transport and vesicular transport use energy (ATP) provided by the cell.

      (1) In active transport, substances are moved across the membrane against an electrical or a concentration gradient by proteins called solute pumps. This accounts for the transport of amino acids, some sugars, and most ions.

      (2) The two types of ATP-activated vesicular transport are exocytosis and endocytosis. Exocytosis moves secretions and other substances out of cells; a membrane-bound vesicle fuses with the plasma membrane, ruptures, and ejects its contents to the cell exterior. Endocytosis, in which particles are taken up by enclosure in a plasma membrane sac, includes phagocytosis (uptake of solid particles), pinocytosis (uptake of fluids), and the highly selective receptor-mediated endocytosis. In the latter, membrane receptors bind with and internalize only selected target molecules.

3. Osmotic pressure, which reflects the solute concentration of a solution, determines whether cells gain or lose water. (Discussion in "A Closer Look" on pp. 80–81)

   a. Hypertonic solutions contain more solutes (and less water) than do cells. In these solutions, cells lose water by osmosis and crenate.

   b. Hypotonic solutions contain fewer solutes (and more water) than do the cells. In these solutions, cells swell and may rupture (lyse) as water rushes in by osmosis.

   c. Isotonic solutions, which have the same solute-to-solvent ratio as cells, cause no changes in cell size or shape.

4. Cell division has two phases, mitosis (nuclear division) and cytokinesis (division of the cytoplasm).

   a. Mitosis begins after DNA has been replicated (during interphase); it consists of four stages—prophase, metaphase, anaphase, and telophase. The result is two daughter nuclei, each identical to the mother nucleus.

   b. Cytokinesis usually begins during anaphase and progressively pinches the cytoplasm in half. Cytokinesis does not always occur; in such cases bi- or multinucleate cells result.

   c. Mitotic cell division provides an increased number of cells for growth and repair.

5. Protein synthesis involves both DNA (the genes) and RNA.

   a. A gene is a segment of DNA that carries the instructions for building one protein. The information is in the sequence of bases in the nucleotide strands. Each three-base sequence (triplet) specifies one amino acid in the protein.

b. Messenger RNA carries the instructions for protein synthesis from the DNA (gene) to the ribosomes. Transfer RNA transports amino acids to the ribosomes. Ribosomal RNA forms part of the ribosomal structure and helps coordinate the protein building process.

PART II: BODY TISSUES   (pp. 88–101)

1. Epithelium is the covering, lining, and glandular tissue. Its functions include protection, absorption, and secretion. Epithelia are named according to arrangement (simple, stratified) and cell shape (squamous, cuboidal, columnar).

2. Connective tissue is the supportive, protective, and binding tissue. It is characterized by the presence of a nonliving, extracellular matrix (ground substance plus fibers) produced and secreted by the cells; it varies in amount and consistency. Fat, ligaments and tendons, bones, and cartilage are all connective tissues or connective tissue structures.

    WEB Exercise: Chapter 3, Identifying Connective Tissue.

3. Muscle tissue is specialized to contract, or shorten, which causes movement. There are three types—skeletal (attached to the skeleton), cardiac (forms the heart), and smooth (in the walls of hollow organs).

4. Nervous tissue is composed of supporting cells and irritable cells called neurons, which are highly specialized to receive and transmit nerve impulses and supporting cells. Neurons are important in control of body processes. Nervous tissue is located in nervous system structures—brain, spinal cord, and nerves.

5. Tissue repair (wound healing) may involve regeneration, fibrosis, or both. In regeneration, the injured tissue is replaced by the same type of cells. In fibrosis, the wound is repaired with scar tissue. Epithelia and connective tissues regenerate well. Mature cardiac muscle and nervous tissue are repaired by fibrosis.

PART III: DEVELOPMENTAL ASPECTS OF CELLS AND TISSUES   (pp. 101, 104)

1. Growth through cell division continues through puberty. Cell populations exposed to friction (such as epithelium) replace lost cells throughout life. Connective tissue remains mitotic and forms repair (scar) tissue. With some exceptions, muscle tissue becomes amitotic by the end of puberty, and nervous tissue becomes amitotic shortly after birth. Amitotic tissues are severely handicapped by injury.

2. The cause of aging is unknown, but chemical and physical insults, as well as genetic programming, are suggested.

3. Neoplasms, both benign and cancerous, represent abnormal cell masses in which normal controls on cell division are not working. Hyperplasia (increase in size) of tissue or organ may occur when tissue is strongly stimulated or irritated. Atrophy (decrease in size) of a tissue or organ occurs when the organ is no longer stimulated normally.

REVIEW QUESTIONS

Multiple Choice

More than one choice may apply.

1. Which of the following would you expect to find in or on cells whose main function is absorption?

    a. Microvilli   c. Gap junctions

    b. Cilia   d. Secretory vesicles

2. Adult cell types you might expect to have gap junctions include

    a. skeletal muscle.   c. heart muscle.

    b. bone.   d. smooth muscle.

3. Which of the following are possible functions of the glycoproteins in the plasma membrane?

    a. Determination of blood groups

    b. Binding sites for toxins or bacteria

    c. Aiding the binding of sperm to egg

    d. Increasing the efficiency of absorption

4. A cell with abundant peroxisomes would most likely be involved in

    a. secretion.

    b. storage of glycogen.

    c. ATP manufacture.

    d. movement.

    e. detoxification activities.

5. A cell stimulated to increase its steroid production will have abundant

    a. ribosomes.   d. Golgi apparatus.

    b. rough ER.   e. secretory vesicles.

    c. smooth ER.

6. For diffusion to occur, there must be

    a. a selectively permeable membrane.

    b. equal amounts of solute.

    c. a concentration difference.

d. some sort of carrier system.

e. all of the above.

7. In which of the following tissue types might you expect to find goblet cells?

   a. Simple cuboidal   d. Stratified squamous

   b. Simple columnar   e. Transitional

   c. Simple squamous

8. An epithelium "built" to withstand friction is

   a. simple squamous.   d. simple columnar.

   b. stratified squamous.   e. pseudostratified.

   c. simple cuboidal.

9. What kind of connective tissue acts as a sponge, soaking up fluid when edema occurs?

   a. Areolar connective

   b. Adipose connective

   c. Dense irregular connective

   d. Reticular connective

   e. Vascular

10. What type of connective tissue prevents muscles from pulling away from bones during contraction?

   a. Dense connective   c. Elastic connective

   b. Areolar   d. Hyaline cartilage

11. Which of the following terms describe cardiac muscle?

   a. Striated   d. Involuntary

   b. Intercalated disks   e. Branching

   c. Multinucleated

12. Cancer is the same as

   a. all tumor.

   b. all neoplasms.

   c. all malignant neoplasms.

   d. benign tumors.

   e. AIDS.

13. Which of these processes involves specific membrane receptors?

   a. Phagocytosis

   b. Receptor-mediated endocytosis

   c. Exocytosis

   d. Pinocytosis

Short Answer Essay

14. Define *cell* and *organelle*.

15. Although cells have differences that reflect their special functions in the body, what functional abilities do *all* cells exhibit?

16. Describe the special function of DNA found in the nucleus. What nuclear structures contain DNA? Help to form ribosomes?

17. Describe the general structure and function of the plasma membrane.

18. Describe the general composition and function of the cytosol and inclusions of the cytoplasm.

19. Name the cellular organelles, and explain the function of each.

20. Define *diffusion, osmosis, simple diffusion, filtration, solute pumping, exocytosis, endocytosis, phagocytosis, pinocytosis,* and *receptor-mediated endocytosis.*

21. What two structural characteristics of cell membranes determine whether substances can pass through them passively? What determines whether or not a substance can be actively transported through the membrane?

22. Explain the effect of the following solutions on living cells: hypertonic, hypotonic, and isotonic.

23. Briefly describe the process of DNA replication.

24. Define *mitosis.* Why is mitosis important?

25. What is the role of the spindle in mitosis?

26. Why can an organ be permanently damaged if its cells are amitotic?

27. Describe the relative roles of DNA and RNA in protein synthesis.

28. Define *tissue.* List the four major types of tissue. Which of these types is most widely distributed in the body?

29. Describe the general characteristics of epithelial tissue. List the most important functions of epithelial tissues, and give examples of each.

30. Where is ciliated epithelium found, and what role does it play?

31. What are the general structural characteristics of connective tissues? What are the functions of connective tissues? How are their functions reflected in their structures?

32. Name a connective tissue with (1) a soft fluid matrix, and (2) a stony hard matrix.

33. What is the function of muscle tissue?

34. Tell where each of the three types of muscle tissue would be found in the body. What is meant by the statement, "Smooth muscles are involuntary in action"?

35. How does tissue healing by fibrosis differ from healing by regeneration? Which is more desirable and why?

36. Define *atrophy*.

CRITICAL THINKING AND CLINICAL APPLICATION QUESTIONS

37. Two examples of chemotherapeutic drugs (used to treat cancer) and their cellular actions are given below. Explain why each drug could be fatal to a cell.

    • Vincristine: damages the mitotic spindle.

    • Adriamycin: binds to DNA and blocks messenger RNA synthesis.

38. Hydrocortisone is an anti-inflammatory drug that stabilizes lysosomal membranes. Explain how this effect reduces cell damage and inflammation.

39. John has severely injured his knee during football practice. He is told that he has a torn knee cartilage and to expect that recovery and repair will take a long time. Why will it take a long time?

40. Three patients in an intensive care unit are examined by the resident doctor. One patient has brain damage from a stroke, another had a heart attack that severely damaged his heart muscle, and the third has a severely damaged liver (a gland) from a crushing injury in a car accident. All three patients have stabilized and will survive, but only one will have full functional recovery through regeneration. Which one and why?

41. Kareem had a nervous habit of chewing on the inner lining of his lip with his front teeth. The lip grew thicker and thicker from years of continual irritation. Kareem's dentist noticed his greatly thickened lip, then told him to have it checked to see if the thickening was a tumor. A biopsy revealed hyperplasia and scattered areas of dysplasia, but no evidence of neoplasia. What do these terms mean? Did Kareem have cancer of the mouth?

4

Skin and Body Membranes

YOUR GOALS

After completing this chapter, you will have a working knowledge of the functions of the skin and body membranes system and will have mastered the objectives listed below.

FUNCTION PREVIEW

- Body membranes line or cover, protect, and lubricate body surfaces.
- As the outermost boundary of the body, the skin protects against injuries of many types.

O B J E C T I V E   C H E C K L I S T

Classification of Body Membranes   (pp. 110–113)

➤ List the general functions of each membrane type—cutaneous, mucous, serous, and synovial—and give its location in the body.

➤ Compare the structure (tissue makeup) of the major membrane types.

The Integumentary System (Skin)   (pp. 113–127)

➤ List several important functions of the integumentary system, and explain how these functions are accomplished.

➤ When provided with a model or diagram of the skin, recognize and name the following skin structures: epidermis, dermis (papillary and reticular layers), hair and hair follicle, sebaceous gland, and sweat gland.

➤ Name the layers of the epidermis, and describe the characteristics of each.

➤ Describe the distribution and function of the epidermal derivatives—sebaceous glands, sweat glands, and hair.

➤ Name the factors that determine skin color, and describe the function of melanin.

➤ Differentiate first-, second-, and third-degree burns.

➤ Explain the importance of the "rule of nines."

➤ Summarize the characteristics of basal cell carcinoma, squamous cell carcinoma, and malignant melanoma.

Developmental Aspects of Skin and Body Membranes (p. 127)

➤ List several examples of integumentary system aging.

Body membranes cover surfaces, line body cavities, and form protective (and often lubricating) sheets around organs. They fall into two major groups: (1) *epithelial membranes,* which include the cutaneous, mucous, and serous membranes; and (2) *connective tissue membranes,* represented by synovial membranes. The cutaneous membrane, generally called the skin or integumentary system, will receive most of our attention in this chapter, but first we will consider the other body membranes.

Classification of Body Membranes

The two major categories of body membranes—epithelial and connective tissue—are classified in part according to their tissue makeup.

Epithelial Membranes

The **epithelial membranes,** also called *covering* and *lining membranes,* include the cutaneous membrane (skin), the mucous membranes, and the serous membranes (Figure 4.1). However, calling these membranes "epithelial" is not only misleading but also inaccurate. Although they all *do* contain an epithelial sheet, it is always combined with an underlying layer of connective tissue. Hence these membranes are actually simple organs. Because we will discuss the skin in some detail

shortly, we will list it here solely as a subcategory of the epithelial membranes.

Cutaneous Membrane

The **cutaneous** (ku-ta′ne-us) **membrane** is your skin. Its superficial epidermis is composed of a keratinizing stratified squamous epithelium. The underlying dermis is mostly dense (fibrous) connective tissue. Unlike the other epithelial membranes, the cutaneous membrane is exposed to air and is a *dry* membrane.

Mucous Membranes

A **mucous** (myu′kus) **membrane (mucosa)** is composed of epithelium (the type varies with the site) resting on a loose connective tissue membrane called a *lamina propria.* This membrane type lines all body cavities that open to the exterior, such as those of the hollow organs of the respiratory, digestive, urinary, and reproductive tracts (Figure 4.1b). Notice that the term *mucosa* refers only to the location of the epithelial membranes, *not* their cellular makeup, which varies. However, most mucosae contain either stratified squamous epithelium (as in the mouth and esophagus) or simple columnar epithelium (as in the rest of the digestive tract). In all cases, they are "wet," or moist, membranes that are almost continuously bathed in secretions or, in the case of the urinary mucosae, urine.

The epithelium of mucosae is often adapted for absorption or secretion. Although many mucosae

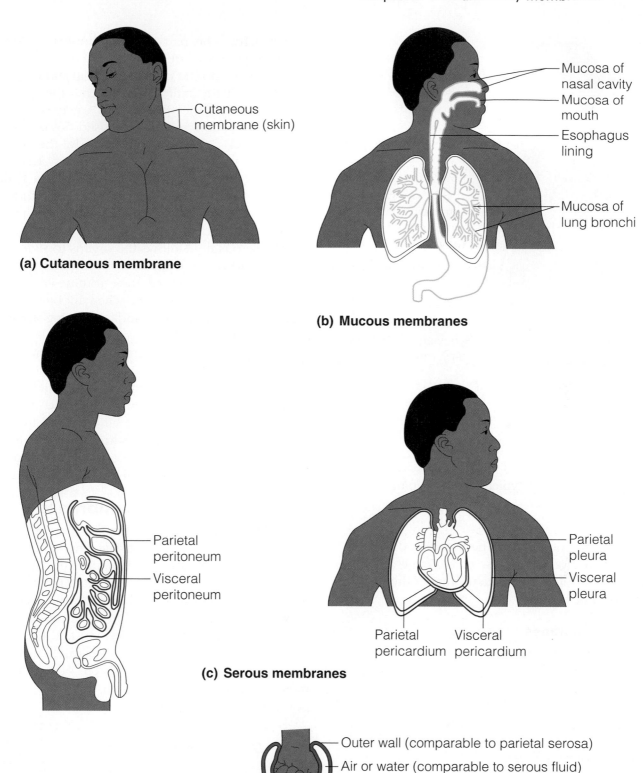

(a) Cutaneous membrane

(b) Mucous membranes

Mucosa of nasal cavity
Mucosa of mouth
Esophagus lining
Mucosa of lung bronchi

Cutaneous membrane (skin)

(c) Serous membranes

Parietal peritoneum
Visceral peritoneum

Parietal pleura
Visceral pleura

Parietal pericardium   Visceral pericardium

(d)

Outer wall (comparable to parietal serosa)
Air or water (comparable to serous fluid)
Inner wall (comparable to visceral serosa)

FIGURE 4.1   Classes of epithelial membranes. (a) Cutaneous membrane, or skin. **(b)** Mucous membranes (yellow) line body cavities that are open to the exterior. **(c)** Serous membranes (shown in red) line ventral body cavities that are closed to the exterior. **(d)** A fist thrust into a flaccid balloon demonstrates the relationship between the parietal and visceral serous membrane layers.

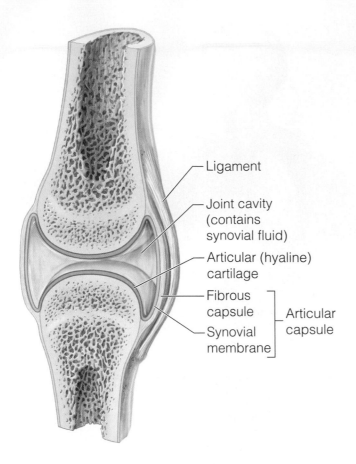

Ligament

Joint cavity (contains synovial fluid)

Articular (hyaline) cartilage

Fibrous capsule
Synovial membrane
} Articular capsule

FIGURE 4.2 **A typical synovial joint.**

secrete mucus, not all do. The mucosae of the respiratory and digestive tracts secrete large amounts of protective, lubricating mucus; that of the urinary tract does not.

Serous Membranes

A **serous membrane (serosa)** is composed of a layer of simple squamous epithelium resting on a thin layer of areolar connective tissue. In contrast to mucous membranes, which line open body cavities, serous membranes line body cavities that are closed to the exterior (except for the dorsal body cavity and joint cavities).

Serous membranes occur in pairs (Figure 4.1c). The *parietal* (pah-ri′e-tal: *parie* = wall) *layer* lines a specific portion of the wall of the ventral body cavity. It folds in on itself to form the *visceral* (vis′er-al) *layer,* which covers the outside of the organs in that cavity.

You can visualize the relationship between the serosal layers by pushing your fist into a limp balloon only partially filled with air or water

(Figure 4.1d). The part of the balloon that clings closely to your fist can be compared to the visceral serosa clinging to the organ's external surface. The outer wall of the balloon represents the parietal serosa that lines the walls of the cavity and that, unlike the balloon, is never exposed but is always fused to the cavity wall. In the body, the serous layers are separated not by air but by a scanty amount of thin, clear fluid, called **serous fluid,** which is secreted by both membranes. Although there is a potential space between the two membranes, they tend to lie very close to each other.

The serous fluid allows the organs to slide easily across the cavity walls and one another without friction as they carry out their routine functions. This is extremely important when mobile organs such as the pumping heart and a churning stomach are involved.

The specific names of the serous membranes depend on their locations. The serosa lining the abdominal cavity and covering its organs is the **peritoneum** (per″ĭ-to-ne′um). In the thorax, serous membranes isolate the lungs and heart from one another. The membrane surrounding the lungs (Figure 4.1c) is the **pleura** (ploo′rah); that around the heart is the **pericardium** (per″ĭ-kar′de-um).

Connective Tissue Membranes

Synovial (sĭ-no′ve-al) **membranes** are composed of soft areolar connective tissue and contain no epithelial cells at all. These membranes line the fibrous capsules surrounding joints (Figure 4.2), where they provide a smooth surface and secrete a lubricating fluid. They also line small sacs of connective tissue called *bursae* (ber′se) and the tube-like *tendon sheaths.* Both of these structures cushion organs moving against each other during muscle activity—such as the movement of a tendon across a bone's surface.

▶ *DID YOU GET IT?*

1. How do the body locations of serous and mucous membranes differ?

2. A scalpel penetrates the left lung and enters the heart. Name the six serous membrane layers the blade passes through as it moves from the body surface into the heart.

3. Where would you find a synovial membrane?

For answers, see Appendix D.

A CLOSER LOOK

TATTOOS

Tattos are made by using a needle to deposit pigment in the dermis. Tattooing is an ancient practice believed to have originated around 10,000 years ago. These days, tattoos are symbols of club membership for some men (street gangs, the military, fraternities); other people view them as symbols of individuality. In recent years, more women have acquired tattoos as a means of expression and for cosmetic purposes; permanent eyeliner and tattooed liplines now account for over 125,000 tattoos a year.

But what if a tattoo becomes unfashionable or the pigment migrates? Tattoo removal has been and still is a pain—both physically and financially. Until recently, once you had one, you were stuck with it, because attempts at removal—dermabrasion, cryosurgery (freezing), or applying caustic chemicals—left nasty scars. Using new laser-based technologies, dermatologists have no problem destroying the black or blue pigments in tattoos applied a generation ago, but newer, multicolored tattoos pose a larger problem. The multitude of pigments in tattoos today require several different lasers to be used over seven to nine treatments spaced about a month apart, each costing $75 to $150. The cost in pain is roughly equal to getting tattooed in the first place. Nonetheless, tattoo removal across the United States is skyrocketing.

Tattoos present some other risks. The FDA has some regulations

> **" Tattoo removal across the U.S. is skyrocketing."**

concerning the composition of tattoo pigments, but their safety is not well established. Indeed, studies of dyes collected from tattooing studios have been found to contain cancer-causing agents that could be activated during tattoo removal. Statutory regulations vary widely (from none to complete prohibition) from state to state. Still, in each case, needles are used and bleeding occurs, and practitioners' competence varies significantly. If the practitioner does not adhere to strict sterile procedures, tattooing can spread infections. The risk of hepatitis C infection (a chronic liver infection) is 15 times higher in people who have been tattooed than in those who have not. So if you're thinking about getting a tattoo, look into it carefully, and weigh your alternatives.

TABLE 4.1	Functions of the Integumentary System
Functions	**How accomplished**
Protects deeper tissues from	
• Mechanical damage (bumps)	Physical barrier contains keratin, which toughens cells; fat cells to cushion blows; and pressure receptors, which alert the nervous system to possible damage.
• Chemical damage (acids and bases)	Has relatively impermeable keratinized cells; contains pain receptors, which alert the nervous system to possible damage.
• Bacterial damage	Has an unbroken surface and "acid mantle" (skin secretions are acidic, and thus inhibit bacteria). Phagocytes ingest foreign substances and pathogens, preventing them from penetrating into deeper body tissues.
• Ultraviolet radiation (damaging effects of sunlight)	Melanin produced by melanocytes offers protection from UV damage.
• Thermal (heat or cold) damage	Contains heat/cold/pain receptors.
• Desiccation (drying out)	Contains a waterproofing glycolipid and keratin.
Aids in body heat loss or heat retention (controlled by the nervous system)	*Heat loss:* By activating sweat glands and by allowing blood to flush into skin capillary beds so that heat can radiate from the skin surface. *Heat retention:* By not allowing blood to flush into skin capillary beds.
Aids in excretion of urea and uric acid	Contained in perspiration produced by sweat glands.
Synthesizes vitamin D	Modified cholesterol molecules in skin converted to vitamin D by sunlight.

The Integumentary System (Skin)

Would you be enticed by an advertisement for a coat that is waterproof, stretchable, washable, and permanent-press, that invisibly repairs small cuts, rips, and burns, and that is guaranteed to last a lifetime with reasonable care? Sounds too good to be true, but you already have such a coat—your *cutaneous membrane,* or **skin.** The skin and its derivatives (sweat and oil glands, hair, and nails) serve a number of functions, mostly protective. Together, these organs are called the **integumentary** (in-teg"u-men'ta-re) **system.**

Functions of the Integumentary System

Also called the **integument** (in-teg'u-ment), which simply means "covering," the skin is much more than an external body covering. It is absolutely essential because it keeps water and other precious molecules in the body. It also keeps water (and other things) out. (This is why one can swim for hours without becoming waterlogged.) Structurally, the skin is a marvel. It is pliable yet tough, which allows it to take constant punishment from external agents. Without our skin, we would quickly fall prey to bacteria and perish from water and heat loss.

The integumentary system has many functions; most, but not all, are protective (Table 4.1). It insulates and cushions the deeper body organs and protects the entire body from mechanical damage (bumps and cuts), chemical damage (such as from acids and bases), thermal damage (heat and cold), ultraviolet radiation (in sunlight), and bacteria. The uppermost layer of the skin is full of **keratin** and is *cornified,* or hardened, to help prevent water loss from the body surface.

The skin's rich capillary network and sweat glands (both controlled by the nervous system) play an important role in regulating heat loss from the body surface. The skin acts as a mini-excretory system; urea, salts, and water are lost when we sweat. The skin also manufactures several proteins important to immunity and synthesizes vitamin D. (Modified cholesterol molecules located in the skin are converted to vitamin D by sunlight.) Finally, the *cutaneous sensory receptors,* which are actually part of the nervous system, are located in the skin. These tiny sensors, which include touch, pressure, temperature, and pain receptors, provide us with a great deal of information about our external environment. They alert us to bumps and the presence of tissue-damaging factors as well as to the feel of wind in our hair and a caress.

▶ DID YOU GET IT?

4. Explain the relationships between the words *skin, cutaneous membrane, integument,* and *integumentary system.*

5. What are three important functions of the integumentary system?

For answers, see Appendix D.

Structure of the Skin

The skin is composed of two kinds of tissue. The outer **epidermis** (ep″ĭ-der′mis) is made up of stratified squamous epithelium that is capable of *keratinizing* (ker′ah-tin-īz-ing), or becoming hard and tough. The underlying **dermis** is made up mostly of dense connective tissue. The epidermis and dermis are firmly connected. However, a burn or friction (such as the rubbing of a poorly fitting shoe) may cause them to separate, allowing interstitial fluid to accumulate in the cavity between the layers, which results in a *blister.*

Deep to the dermis is the **subcutaneous tissue,** or **hypodermis,** which essentially is adipose tissue.

Epidermis
• Stratum corneum
• Stratum lucidum
• Stratum granulosum
• Stratum spinosum
• Stratum basale

Dermis

FIGURE 4.3   The epidermis of thick skin (150×). From *Gray's Anatomy,* Henry Gray. Churchill Livingstone, UK.

It is not considered part of the skin, but it does anchor the skin to underlying organs. Subcutaneous tissue serves as a shock absorber and insulates the deeper tissues from extreme temperature changes occurring outside the body. It is also responsible for the curves that are more a part of a woman's anatomy than a man's. The main skin areas and structures are described next. As you read, locate the described areas or structures on Figures 4.3 and 4.4.

Epidermis

The epidermis is composed of up to five layers or *strata* (strah′tah; "bed sheets"). From the inside out these are the *stratum basale, spinosum, granulosum, lucidum,* and *corneum* (see Figure 4.3).

Like all other epithelial tissues, the epidermis is *avascular;* that is, it has no blood supply of its own. This explains why a man can shave daily and not bleed even though he cuts off many cell layers each time he shaves.

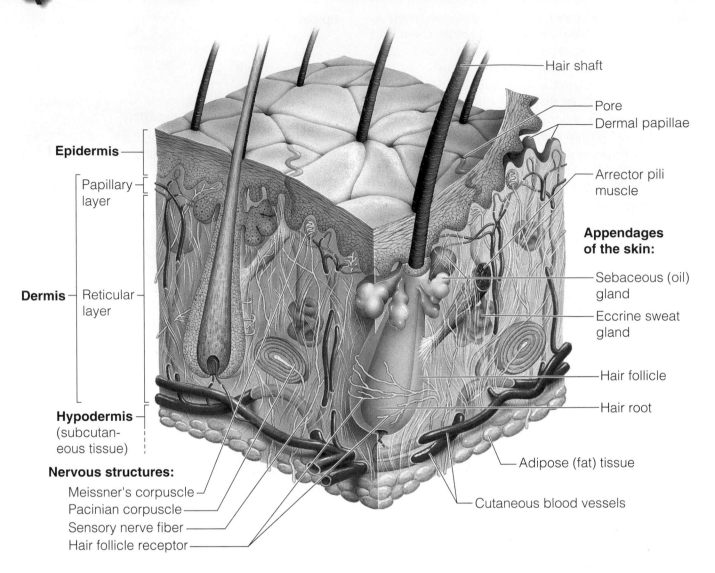

Hair shaft

Pore
Dermal papillae

Epidermis

Arrector pili
muscle

Papillary
layer

**Appendages
of the skin:**

Dermis — Reticular
layer

Sebaceous (oil)
gland

Eccrine sweat
gland

Hair follicle

Hair root

Hypodermis
(subcutan-
eous tissue)

Adipose (fat) tissue

Nervous structures:
Meissner's corpuscle
Pacinian corpuscle
Sensory nerve fiber
Hair follicle receptor

Cutaneous blood vessels

FIGURE 4.4 Skin structure. Three-dimensional view of the skin and underlying subcutaneous tissue. (Meissner's corpuscles are uncommon in hairy skin but are included here to show the entire group of cutaneous receptors.)

Most cells of the epidermis are **keratinocytes** (keratin cells), which produce keratin, the fibrous protein that makes the epidermis a tough protective layer. The deepest cell layer of the epidermis, the **stratum basale** (stra′tum bă-sah′le), lies closest to the dermis and is connected to it along a wavy borderline that resembles corrugated cardboard. This basal layer contains epidermal cells that re-

ceive the most adequate nourishment via diffusion of nutrients from the dermis. These cells are constantly undergoing cell division, and millions of new cells are produced daily; hence its alternate name, *stratum germinativum* (jer″min-ah-tiv′um; "germinating layer"). The daughter cells are pushed upward, away from the source of nutrition, to become part of the epidermal layers closer to the skin surface. As they move away from the dermis and become part of the more superficial layers,

Its fatty tissue.

the **stratum spinosum** and then the **stratum granulosum,** they become flatter and increasingly full of keratin (keratinized). Finally they die, forming the clear **stratum lucidum** (lu′sid-um). This latter epidermal layer is not present in all skin regions; it occurs only where the skin is hairless and extra thick, that is, on the palms of the hands and soles of the feet. The combination of accumulating keratin inside them, secreting a water-repellent glycolipid into the extracellular space, and their increasing distance from the blood supply (in the dermis) effectively dooms the stratum lucidum cells and the more superficial epidermal cells because they are unable to get adequate nutrients and oxygen.

The outermost layer, the **stratum corneum** (kor′ne-um), is 20 to 30 cell layers thick but it accounts for about three-quarters of the epidermal thickness. The shinglelike dead cell remnants, completely filled with keratin, are referred to as *cornified* or *horny cells* (*cornu* = horn). The common saying "Beauty is only skin deep" is especially interesting in light of the fact that nearly everything we see when we look at someone is dead! Keratin is an exceptionally tough protein. Its abundance in the stratum corneum allows that layer to provide a durable "overcoat" for the body, which protects deeper cells from the hostile external environment (air) and from water loss and helps the body resist biological, chemical, and physical assaults. The stratum corneum rubs and flakes off slowly and steadily as the *dandruff* familiar to everyone. The average person sheds about 18 kg (40 lb) of these flakes in a lifetime, providing a food source for the dust mites that inhabit our homes and bed linens. This layer is replaced by cells produced by the division of the deeper stratum basale cells. Indeed, we have a totally "new" epidermis every 25 to 45 days.

Melanin (mel′ah-nin), a pigment that ranges in color from yellow to brown to black, is produced by special spider-shaped cells called **melanocytes** (mel′ah-no-sītz), found chiefly in the stratum basale. When the skin is exposed to sunlight, which stimulates the melanocytes to produce more of the melanin pigment, tanning occurs. As the melanocytes produce melanin, it accumulates within them in membrane-bound granules called *melanosomes*. These granules then move to the ends of the spidery arms of the melanocytes, where they are taken up by nearby keratinocytes. Inside the keratinocytes, the melanin forms a pigment umbrella over the superficial, or "sunny," side of their nuclei that shields their genetic material (DNA) from the damaging effects of ultraviolet radiation in sunlight. *Freckles* and *moles* are seen where melanin is concentrated in one spot.

HOMEOSTATIC IMBALANCE

Despite melanin's protective effects, excessive sun exposure eventually damages the skin. It causes the elastic fibers to clump, leading to leathery skin. It also depresses the immune system. This may help to explain why many people infected with the **herpes simplex,** or *cold sore,* virus are more likely to have an eruption after sunbathing. Overexposure to the sun can also alter the DNA of skin cells, leading to skin cancer. Black people seldom have skin cancer, attesting to melanin's amazing effectiveness as a natural sunscreen. ▲

Dermis

The dermis is your "hide." It is a strong, stretchy envelope that helps to hold the body together. When you purchase leather goods (bags, belts, shoes, and the like), you are buying the treated dermis of animals.

The dense (fibrous) connective tissue making up the dermis consists of two major regions—the *papillary* and the *reticular* areas. Like the epidermis, the dermis varies in thickness. For example, it is particularly thick on the palms of the hands and soles of the feet but is quite thin on the eyelids.

The **papillary layer** is the upper dermal region. It is uneven and has peglike projections from its superior surface, called **dermal papillae** (pah-pil′e; *papill* = nipple), which indent the epidermis above. Many of the dermal papillae contain capillary loops, which furnish nutrients to the epidermis. Others house pain receptors (*free nerve endings*) and touch receptors called *Meissner's corpuscles* (mīs′nerz kor′puh-sulz). On the palms of the hands and soles of the feet, the papillae are arranged in definite patterns that form looped and whorled ridges on the epidermal surface that increase friction and enhance the gripping ability of the fingers and feet. Papillary patterns are genetically determined. The ridges of the fingertips are well provided with sweat pores and leave unique,

FIGURE 4.5   Photograph of a deep (stage III) decubitus ulcer.

identifying films of sweat called *fingerprints* on almost anything they touch.

The **reticular layer** is the deepest skin layer. It contains blood vessels, sweat and oil glands, and deep pressure receptors called *Pacinian* (pah-sin′e-an) *corpuscles* (see Figure 4.4). Phagocytes found here (and, in fact, throughout the dermis) act to prevent bacteria that have managed to get through the epidermis from penetrating any deeper into the body.

Both *collagen* and *elastic fibers* are found throughout the dermis. Collagen fibers are responsible for the toughness of the dermis; they also attract and bind water and thus help to keep the skin hydrated. Elastic fibers give the skin its elasticity when we are young. As we age, the number of collagen and elastic fibers decreases, and the subcutaneous tissue loses fat. As a result, the skin loses its elasticity and begins to sag and wrinkle.

The dermis is abundantly supplied with blood vessels that play a role in maintaining body temperature homeostasis. When body temperature is high, the capillaries of the dermis become engorged, or swollen, with heated blood, and the skin becomes reddened and warm. This allows body heat to radiate from the skin surface. If the environment is cool and body heat must be conserved, blood bypasses the dermis capillaries temporarily, allowing internal body temperature to stay high.

HOMEOSTATIC IMBALANCE

Any restriction of the normal blood supply to the skin results in cell death and, if severe or prolonged enough, skin ulcers. **Decubitus** (de-ku′bĭ-tus) **ulcers** (bedsores) occur in bedridden patients who are not turned regularly or who are dragged or pulled across the bed repeatedly. The weight of the body puts pressure on the skin, especially over bony projections. Because this pressure restricts the blood supply, the skin becomes pale or blanched at pressure points. At first, the skin reddens when pressure is released, but if the situation is not corrected, the cells begin to die, and small cracks or breaks in the skin appear at compressed sites. Permanent damage to the superficial blood vessels and tissue eventually results in degeneration and ulceration of the skin (Figure 4.5). ▲

The dermis also has a rich nerve supply. As mentioned earlier, many of the nerve endings have specialized receptor end-organs that send messages to the central nervous system for interpretation when they are stimulated by environmental factors (pressure, temperature, and the like). These cutaneous receptors are discussed in more detail in Chapter 7.

Skin Color

Three pigments contribute to skin color:

1. The amount and kind (yellow, reddish brown, or black) of *melanin* in the epidermis.

2. The amount of *carotene* deposited in the stratum corneum and subcutaneous tissue. (Carotene is an orange-yellow pigment plentiful in carrots and other orange, deep yellow, or leafy green vegetables.) The skin tends to take on a yellow-orange cast when the person eats large amounts of carotene-rich foods.

3. The amount of *oxygen-rich hemoglobin* (pigment in red blood cells) in the dermal blood vessels.

People who produce a lot of melanin have brown-toned skin. In light-skinned (Caucasian) people, who have less melanin, the crimson color of oxygen-rich hemoglobin in the dermal blood supply flushes through the transparent cell layers above and gives the skin a rosy glow.

HOMEOSTATIC IMBALANCE

When hemoglobin is poorly oxygenated, both the blood and the skin of Caucasians appear blue, a condition called **cyanosis** (si"ah-no'sis). Cyanosis is common during heart failure and severe breathing disorders. In black people, the skin does not appear cyanotic in the same situations because of the masking effects of melanin, but cyanosis is apparent in their mucous membranes and nail beds. ▲

Emotions also influence skin color, and many alterations in skin color signal certain disease states:

- *Redness, or erythema* (er"ĭ-the'mah). Reddened skin may indicate embarrassment (blushing), fever, hypertension, inflammation, or allergy.

- *Pallor, or blanching.* Under certain types of emotional stress (fear, anger, and others), some people become pale. Pale skin may also signify anemia, low blood pressure, or impaired blood flow into the area.

- *Jaundice (jon' dis) or a yellow cast.* An abnormal yellow skin tone usually signifies a liver disorder in which excess bile pigments are absorbed into the blood, circulated throughout the body, and deposited in body tissues.

- *Bruises or black-and-blue marks.* Black-and-blue marks reveal sites where blood has escaped from the circulation and has clotted in the tissue spaces. Such clotted blood masses are called *hematomas.* An unusual tendency to bruising may signify a deficiency of vitamin C in the diet or hemophilia (bleeder's disease).

▶ DID YOU GET IT?

6. What cell type is most abundant in the epidermis?

7. Which layer of the epidermis produces new epidermal cells?

8. Excess shedding of scales from the superficial layer of the skin of the scalp causes dandruff. What is the name of that skin layer?

9. What pigments determine skin color?

For answers, see Appendix D.

Appendages of the Skin

The **skin appendages** include cutaneous glands, hair and hair follicles, and nails (see Figure 4.4). Each of these appendages arises from the epidermis and plays a unique role in maintaining body homeostasis.

Cutaneous Glands

The cutaneous glands are all **exocrine glands** that release their secretions to the skin surface via ducts. They fall into two groups: *sebaceous glands* and *sweat glands.* As these glands are formed by the cells of the stratum basale, they push into the deeper skin regions and ultimately reside almost entirely in the dermis.

Sebaceous (Oil) Glands The **sebaceous** (seh-ba' shus) **glands,** or oil glands, are found all over the skin, except on the palms of the hands and the soles of the feet. Their ducts usually empty into a hair follicle (see Figures 4.4 and 4.6), but some open directly onto the skin surface.

The product of the sebaceous glands, **sebum** (se'bum; *seb* = grease), is a mixture of oily substances and fragmented cells. Sebum is a lubricant that keeps the skin soft and moist and prevents the hair from becoming brittle. Sebum also contains chemicals that *kill* bacteria, so it is important in preventing the bacteria present on the skin surface from invading the deeper skin regions. The sebaceous glands become very active when male sex hormones are produced in increased amounts (in both sexes) during adolescence. Thus, the skin tends to become oilier during this period of life.

⚖ HOMEOSTATIC IMBALANCE

If a sebaceous gland's duct is blocked by sebum, a **whitehead** appears on the skin surface. If the accumulated material oxidizes and dries, it darkens, forming a **blackhead. Acne** is an active infection of the sebaceous glands accompanied by pimples on the skin. It can be mild or extremely severe, leading to permanent scarring. **Seborrhea** (seb"o-re'ah; "fast-flowing sebum"), known as "cradle cap" in infants, is caused by overactivity of the sebaceous glands. It begins on the scalp as pink, raised lesions that gradually form a yellow to brown crust that sloughs off oily scales. Careful washing to remove the excessive oil often helps. ▲

Sweat Glands **Sweat glands,** also called **sudoriferous** (su"do-rif'er-us; *sudor* = sweat) **glands,** are widely distributed in the skin. Their number is staggering—more than 2.5 million per person. There are two types of sweat glands, *eccrine* and *apocrine.*

The **eccrine** (ek'rin) **glands** are far more numerous and are found all over the body. They

Which of these gland types can make your hair lank and oily?

(a) Sectioned sebaceous gland (160x)

(b) Sectioned eccrine gland (250x)

FIGURE 4.6   Photomicrographs of cutaneous glands.

produce **sweat,** a clear secretion that is primarily water plus some salts (sodium chloride), vitamin C, traces of metabolic wastes (ammonia, urea, uric acid), and lactic acid (a chemical that accumulates during vigorous muscle activity). Sweat is acidic (pH from 4 to 6), a characteristic that inhibits the growth of bacteria, which are always present on the skin surface. Typically, sweat reaches the skin surface via a duct that opens externally as a funnel-shaped *pore* (see Figures 4.4 and 4.6). Notice, however, that the facial "pores" commonly referred to when we talk about our complexion are *not* these sweat pores, but the external outlets of hair follicles.

The eccrine sweat glands are an important and highly efficient part of the body's heat-regulating equipment. They are supplied with nerve endings that cause them to secrete sweat when the external temperature or body temperature is high. When sweat evaporates off the skin surface, it carries large amounts of body heat with it. On a hot day, it is possible to lose up to 7 liters of body water in this way. The heat-regulating functions of the body are important—if internal temperature changes more than a few degrees from the normal 37°C (98.2°F), life-threatening changes occur in the body. Body temperature regulation is discussed in more detail in Chapter 14.

Apocrine (ap′o-krin) **glands** are largely confined to the axillary and genital areas of the body. They are usually larger than eccrine glands, and their ducts empty into hair follicles. Their secretion contains fatty acids and proteins, as well as all the substances present in eccrine secretion; consequently, it may have a milky or yellowish color. The secretion is odorless, but when bacteria that live on the skin use its proteins and fats as a source of nutrients for their growth, it takes on a musky, unpleasant odor.

Apocrine glands begin to function during puberty under the influence of *androgens* (male sex

The sebaceous glands, which produce oily secretions.

hormones). Although their secretion is produced almost continuously, apocrine glands play a minimal role in thermoregulation. Their precise function is not yet known, but they are activated by nerve fibers during pain and stress and during sexual foreplay.

Hair and Hair Follicles

There are millions of **hairs** scattered all over the body. But, other than serving a few minor protective functions—such as guarding the head against bumps, shielding the eyes (via eyelashes), and helping to keep foreign particles out of the respiratory tract (via nose hairs)—our body hair has lost much of its usefulness. Hair served early humans (and still serves hairy animals) by providing insulation in cold weather, but now we have other means of keeping warm.

Hairs A hair, produced by a *hair follicle,* is a flexible epithelial structure. That part of the hair enclosed in the follicle is called the *root.* The part projecting from the surface of the scalp or skin is called the *shaft* (Figure 4.7). A hair is formed by division of the well-nourished stratum basale epithelial cells in the **matrix** (growth zone) of the hair bulb at the inferior end of the follicle. As the daughter cells are pushed farther away from the growing region, they become keratinized and die. Thus the bulk of the hair shaft, like the bulk of the epidermis, is dead material and almost entirely protein.

Each hair consists of a central core called the *medulla* (me-dul'ah) surrounded by a bulky *cortex* layer. The cortex is, in turn, enclosed by an outermost *cuticle* formed by a single layer of cells that overlap one another like shingles on a roof. This arrangement of the cuticle cells helps to keep the hairs apart and keeps them from matting (see Figures 4.7b and 4.8). The cuticle is the most heavily keratinized region; it provides strength and helps keep the inner hair layers tightly compacted. Because it is most subject to abrasion, the cuticle tends to wear away at the tip of the shaft, allowing the keratin fibrils in the inner hair regions to frizz out, a phenomenon called "split ends." Hair pigment is made by melanocytes in the hair bulb, and varying amounts of different types of melanin (yellow, rust, brown, and black) combine to produce *all* varieties of hair color from pale blond to pitch black.

Hairs come in a variety of sizes and shapes. They are short and stiff in the eyebrows, long and

(b) Hair

(a)

(c)

FIGURE 4.7 Structure of a hair and hair follicle. (a) Longitudinal section of a hair within its follicle. **(b)** Enlarged longitudinal section of a hair. **(c)** Enlarged longitudinal view of the expanded hair bulb in the follicle showing the matrix, the region of actively dividing epithelial cells that produces the hair.

FIGURE 4.8 **Scanning electron micrograph showing a hair shaft emerging from a follicle at the skin surface.** Notice how the scalelike cells of the cuticle overlap one another (1300×).

flexible on the head, and usually nearly invisible almost everywhere else. When the hair shaft is oval, hair is smooth and silky and the person has wavy hair. When the shaft is flat and ribbonlike, the hair is curly or kinky. If it is perfectly round, the hair is straight and tends to be coarse. Hairs are found all over the body surface except the palms of the hands, soles of the feet, nipples, and lips. Humans are born with as many hair follicles as they will ever have, and hairs are among the fastest growing tissues in the body. Hormones account for the development of hairy regions—the scalp and, in the adult, the pubic and axillary (armpit) areas.

Hair Follicles **Hair follicles** are actually compound structures. The inner *epidermal sheath* is composed of epithelial tissue and forms the hair. The outer *dermal sheath* is actually dermal connective tissue. This dermal region supplies blood vessels to the epidermal portion and reinforces it. Its nipplelike *papilla* provides the blood supply to the matrix in the hair bulb.

Look carefully at the structure of the hair follicle at the front corner of Figure 4.4. Notice that it

is slanted. Small bands of smooth muscle cells—**arrector pili** (ah-rek′tor pi′li; "raiser of hair")—connect each side of the hair follicle to the dermal tissue. When these muscles contract (as when we are cold or frightened), the hair is pulled upright, dimpling the skin surface with "goose bumps." This action helps keep animals warm in winter by adding a layer of insulating air to the fur. It is especially dramatic in a scared cat, whose fur actually stands on end to make it look larger to scare off its enemy. However, this hair-raising phenomenon is not very useful to human beings.

Nails

A **nail** is a scalelike modification of the epidermis that corresponds to the hoof or claw of other animals. Each nail has a *free edge,* a *body* (visible attached portion), and a *root* (embedded in the skin). The borders of the nail are overlapped by skin folds, called *nail folds.* The thick proximal nail fold is commonly called the *cuticle* (Figure 4.9).

The stratum basale of the epidermis extends beneath the nail as the *nail bed.* Its thickened proximal area, called the *nail matrix,* is responsible for nail growth. As the nail cells are produced by the matrix, they become heavily keratinized and die. Thus, nails, like hairs, are mostly nonliving material.

Nails are transparent and nearly colorless, but they look pink because of the rich blood supply in the underlying dermis. The exception to this is the region over the thickened nail matrix that appears as a white crescent and is called the *lunula* (loo′nyu-luh; *lunul* = crescent). As noted earlier, when the supply of oxygen in the blood is low, the nail beds take on a cyanotic (blue) cast.

▶ DID YOU GET IT?

10. What are the three concentric regions of a hair shaft, from the outside in?

11. What is sebum?

12. How do secretions of apocrine glands differ from those of the eccrine sweat glands?

13. When a factory worker caught his finger in a machine, the entire nail, plus the nail matrix and bed, was torn off. Will his nail grow back? Why or why not?

For answers, see Appendix D.

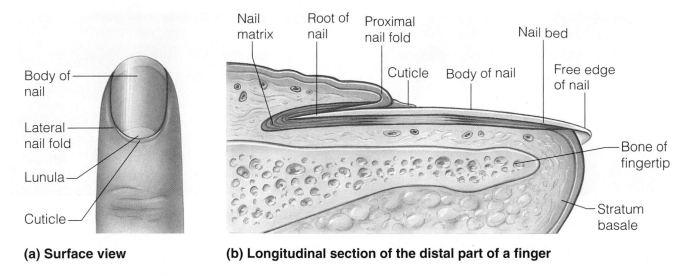

(a) Surface view   **(b) Longitudinal section of the distal part of a finger**

FIGURE 4.9   Structure of a nail.

Homeostatic Imbalances of Skin

It is difficult to scoff at anything that goes wrong with the skin because, when it rebels, it is quite a visible revolution. Loss of homeostasis in body cells and organs can reveal itself on the skin in ways that are sometimes almost unbelievable. The skin can develop more than 1000 different ailments. The most common skin disorders result from allergies or bacterial, viral, or fungal infections. Less common, but far more damaging, are burns and skin cancers. A number of the homeostatic imbalances of the skin are summarized briefly in the sections just below.

Infections and Allergies

- **Athlete's foot.** An itchy, red, peeling condition of the skin between the toes, resulting from fungus infection. Also called *tinea pedis*.
- **Boils and carbuncles** (kar′bun-kulz). Inflammation of hair follicles and sebaceous glands, common on the dorsal neck. Carbuncles are composite boils typically caused by bacterial infection (often *Staphylococcus aureus*).
- **Cold sores** (fever blisters). Small fluid-filled blisters that itch and sting, caused by a herpes simplex infection. The virus localizes in a cutaneous nerve, where it remains dormant until activated by emotional upset, fever, or UV radiation. Cold sores usually occur around the lips

and in the oral mucosa of the mouth (Figure 4.10a).

- **Contact dermatitis.** Itching, redness, and swelling of the skin, progressing to blistering. It is caused by exposure of the skin to chemicals (such as those in poison ivy) that provoke allergic responses in sensitive individuals.
- **Impetigo** (im-peh-ti′go; *impet* = an attack). Pink, water-filled, raised lesions (commonly around the mouth and nose) that develop a yellow crust and eventually rupture (Figure 4.10b). Caused by a highly contagious staphylococcus infection, impetigo is common in elementary school–aged children.
- **Psoriasis** (so-ri′ah-sis). A chronic condition, characterized by overproduction of skin cells that results in reddened epidermal lesions covered with dry, silvery scales that itch, burn, crack, and sometimes bleed (Figure 4.10c). When severe, psoriasis may be disfiguring. It is believed to be an autoimmune disorder in which the immune system attacks a person's own tissues. Attacks are often triggered by trauma, infection, hormonal changes, or stress.

Burns

The skin is only about as thick as a paper towel—not too impressive as organ systems go. And yet, when it is severely damaged, nearly every body system suffers. Metabolism accelerates or may be

(a) Cold sores   (b) Impetigo   (c) Psoriasis

FIGURE 4.10   Cutaneous lesions.

impaired, changes in the immune system occur, and the cardiovascular system may falter. Such severe damage can be caused by burns. A **burn** is tissue damage and cell death caused by intense heat, electricity, UV radiation (sunburn), or certain chemicals (such as acids).

There are few threats to skin more serious than burns. When the skin is burned and its cells are destroyed, two life-threatening problems result. First, the body loses its precious supply of fluids containing proteins and electrolytes as these seep from the burned surfaces. Dehydration and electrolyte imbalance follow and can lead to a shutdown of the kidneys and *circulatory shock* (inadequate circulation of blood caused by low blood volume). To save the patient, lost fluids must be replaced immediately. The volume of fluid lost can be estimated indirectly by determining how much of the body surface is burned (extent of burns), using the **rule of nines.** This method divides the body into 11 areas, each accounting for 9 percent of the total body surface area, plus an additional area surrounding the genitals (the perineum) representing 1 percent of body surface area (Figure 4.11a).

Later, infection becomes the most important threat and is the leading cause of death in burn victims. Burned skin is sterile for about 24 hours. But after that, *pathogens* (path'o-jenz) such as bacteria and fungi easily invade areas where the skin has been destroyed and multiply rapidly in the nutrient-rich environment of dead tissues. To make matters worse, the patient's immune system becomes depressed within one to two days after severe burn injury.

Burns are classified according to their severity (depth) as first-, second-, or third-degree burns (Figure 4.11b). In **first-degree burns,** only the epidermis is damaged. The area becomes red and swollen. Except for temporary discomfort, first-degree burns are not usually serious and generally heal in two to three days without any special attention. Sunburn is usually a first-degree burn.

Second-degree burns involve injury to the epidermis and the upper region of the dermis. The skin is red and painful, and *blisters* appear. Because sufficient numbers of epithelial cells are still present, regrowth (regeneration) of the epithelium can occur. Ordinarily, no permanent scars result if care is taken to prevent infection. First- and second-degree burns are referred to as **partial-thickness burns.**

Third-degree burns destroy the entire thickness of the skin, so these burns are also called **full-thickness burns.** The burned area appears blanched (gray-white) or blackened, and because the nerve endings in the area are destroyed, the burned area is not painful. In third-degree burns, regeneration is not possible, and skin grafting must be done to cover the underlying exposed tissues.

In general, burns are considered *critical* if any of the following conditions exists:

1. Over 25 percent of the body has second-degree burns,

2. Over 10 percent of the body has third-degree burns, or

3. There are third-degree burns of the face, hands, or feet.

Would you expect to see hair regeneration in an area that suffers third-degree burns? Why or why not?

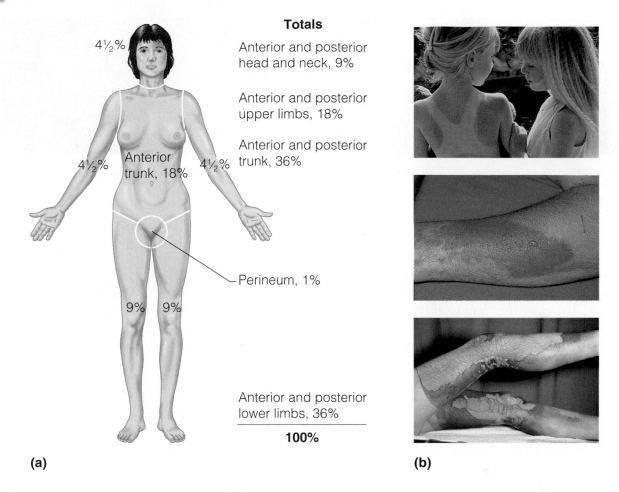

FIGURE 4.11   Burns. (a) Estimating the extent of burns using the rule of nines. The surface areas for the anterior body surface are indicated on the human figure. Total surface area (anterior and posterior body surfaces) is tabulated to the right of the figure. **(b)** Burns of increasing severity, from top to bottom: first-degree, second-degree, third-degree.

Facial burns are particularly dangerous because of the possibility of burns in respiratory passageways, which can swell and cause suffocation. Joint injuries are troublesome because the scar tissue that eventually forms can severely limit joint mobility.

Skin Cancer

Numerous types of neoplasms (tumors) arise in the skin. Most skin neoplasms are benign and do not spread (metastasize) to other body areas. (A *wart* caused by a virus is one such example.) However, some skin neoplasms are malignant, or cancerous, and they tend to invade other body areas. Indeed, skin cancer is the single most common type of cancer in humans. One in five Americans now develops skin cancer at some point in his or her life. The most important risk factor is overexposure to ultraviolet radiation in sunlight. Frequent irritation of the skin by infections, chemicals, or physical trauma also seems to be a predisposing factor.

Basal Cell Carcinoma   *Basal cell carcinoma* (kar″sĭ-no′mah) is the least malignant and most common skin cancer. Cells of the stratum basale, altered so

No, because third-degree burns destroy both the epidermis and dermis in that region.

(a) Basal cell carcinoma   **(b) Squamous cell carcinoma**   **(c) Melanoma**

FIGURE 4.12   Photographs of skin cancers.

that they cannot form keratin, no longer honor the boundary between epidermis and dermis. They proliferate, invading the dermis and subcutaneous tissue. The cancer lesions occur most often on sun-exposed areas of the face and appear as shiny, dome-shaped nodules that later develop a central ulcer with a "pearly" beaded edge (Figure 4.12a). Basal cell carcinoma is relatively slow-growing, and metastasis seldom occurs before it is noticed. Full cure is the rule in 99 percent of cases in which the lesion is removed surgically.

Squamous Cell Carcinoma   *Squamous cell carcinoma* arises from the cells of the stratum spinosum. The lesion appears as a scaly, reddened *papule* (small, rounded elevation) that gradually forms a shallow ulcer with a firm, raised border (Figure 4.12b). This variety of skin cancer appears most often on the scalp, ears, dorsum of the hands, and lower lip. It grows rapidly and metastasizes to adjacent lymph nodes if not removed. This epidermal cancer is also believed to be sun-induced. If it is caught early and removed surgically or by radiation therapy, the chance of complete cure is good.

Malignant Melanoma   *Malignant melanoma* (mel″-ah-no′mah) is a cancer of melanocytes. It accounts for only about 5 percent of skin cancers, but its incidence is increasing rapidly and it is often deadly. Melanoma can begin wherever there is pigment; most such cancers appear spontaneously, but some develop from pigmented moles. It arises

from accumulated DNA damage in a skin cell and usually appears as a spreading brown to black patch (Figure 4.12c) that metastasizes rapidly to surrounding lymph and blood vessels. The chance for survival is about 50 percent, and early detection helps. The American Cancer Society suggests that people who sunbathe frequently or attend tanning parlors examine their skin periodically for new moles or pigmented spots and apply the **ABCD rule** for recognizing melanoma:

(A) Asymmetry. The two sides of the pigmented spot or mole do not match.

(B) Border irregularity. The borders of the lesion are not smooth but exhibit indentations.

(C) Color. The pigmented spot contains areas of different colors (blacks, browns, tans, and sometimes blues and reds).

(D) Diameter. The spot is larger than 6 millimeters (mm) in diameter (the size of a pencil eraser).

Some experts have found that adding an **E,** for *elevation* above the skin surface, improves diagnosis. The usual therapy for malignant melanoma is wide surgical excision along with immunotherapy.

▶ DID YOU GET IT?

14. What are the two life-threatening consequences of a severe burn?

15. What are the criteria for classifying burns as first-, second-, or third-degree?

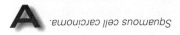

Squamous cell carcinoma.

16. What is the single most common risk factor for skin cancer?

17. Why do no skin cancers develop from stratum corneum cells?

For answers, see Appendix D.

Developmental Aspects of Skin and Body Membranes

During the fifth and sixth months of fetal development, the soon-to-be-born infant is covered with a downy type of hair called *lanugo* (lah-noo'go), but this hairy cloak has usually been shed by birth. When a baby is born, its skin is covered with *vernix caseosa* (ver'niks kah-se-o'sah). This white, cheesy-looking substance, produced by the sebaceous glands, protects the baby's skin while it is floating in its water-filled sac inside the mother. The newborn's skin is very thin, and blood vessels are easily seen through it. Commonly, there are accumulations in the sebaceous glands, which appear as small white spots called *milia* (mil'e-ah), on the baby's nose and forehead. These normally disappear by the third week after birth. As the baby grows, its skin becomes thicker and moist, and more subcutaneous fat is deposited.

During adolescence, the skin and hair become more oily as sebaceous glands are activated, and acne may appear. Acne usually subsides in early adulthood, and the skin reaches its optimal appearance when we are in our twenties and thirties. Then visible changes in the skin begin to appear as it is continually assaulted by abrasion, chemicals, wind, sun, and other irritants and as its pores become clogged with air pollutants and bacteria. As a result, pimples, scales, and various kinds of *dermatitis* (der"mah-ti'tis), or skin inflammation, become more common.

During old age, the amount of subcutaneous tissue decreases, leading to the intolerance to cold so common in older adults. The skin also becomes drier (because of decreased oil production), and as a result, it may become itchy and bothersome. Thinning of the skin, another result of the aging process, makes it more susceptible to bruising and other types of injuries. The decreasing elasticity of the skin, along with the loss of subcutaneous fat, allows bags to form under our eyes, and our jowls begin to sag. This loss of elasticity is speeded up by smoking and by sunlight, so two of the best things you can do for your skin are to stop smoking if you have that habit and to shield it from the sun by wearing sunscreens and protective clothing. In doing so, you will also be decreasing the chance of skin cancer. Although there is no way to avoid the aging of the skin, good nutrition, plenty of fluids, and cleanliness help delay the process.

Hair loses its luster as we age, and by age 50 the number of hair follicles has dropped by one-third and continues to decline, resulting in hair thinning and some degree of baldness, or *alopecia* (al"o-pe'she-ah), in most people. Many men become obviously bald as they age, a phenomenon called *male pattern baldness*. A bald man is not really hairless—he does have hairs in the bald area. But, because those hair follicles have begun to degenerate, the hairs are colorless and very tiny (and may not even emerge from the follicle). Such hairs are called *vellus* (*vell* = wool) hairs. Another phenomenon of aging is graying hair. Like balding, this is usually genetically controlled by a "delayed-action" gene. Once the gene takes effect, the amount of melanin deposited in the hair decreases or becomes entirely absent, which results in gray-to-white hair.

HOMEOSTATIC IMBALANCE

Certain events can cause hair to gray or fall out prematurely. For example, many people have claimed that they turned gray nearly overnight because of some emotional crisis in their life. In addition, we know that anxiety, protein-deficient diets, therapy with certain chemicals (chemotherapy), radiation, excessive vitamin A, and certain fungal diseases (ringworm) can cause both graying and hair loss. However, when the cause of these conditions is not genetic, hair loss is usually not permanent. ▲

DID YOU GET IT?

18. What change in aging skin accounts for wrinkles and cold intolerance in older adults?

For the answer, see Appendix D.

focus on CAREERS

MEDICAL TRANSCRIPTIONIST

"If you have a basic understanding of anatomy and medical terminology, you will be much more accurate at interpreting and transcribing what you hear."

Every time you consult a doctor or are hospitalized, records are kept to help healthcare professionals assess and monitor your condition. Medical transcriptionists play a key role in creating and maintaining these vital documents.

A medical transcriptionist is a medical language specialist who

interprets and transcribes notes dictated by physicians and other healthcare professionals. These reports, which cover all aspects of a patient's assessment, diagnosis, treatment, and outcome, become part of the person's confidential medical record. Medical transcriptionists work in hospitals, clinics, doctors' offices, transcription services, insurance companies, and home healthcare agencies.

What does it take to be a transcriptionist? "Certainly, you need a good

English background," says Pamela Shull, an experienced transcriptionist in San Jose, California. "Strong grammar, spelling, and punctuation skills are crucial. Physicians often dictate these records on the go, and a good transcriptionist must be able to edit the dictated material for grammar and clarity."

Knowledge of anatomy and physiology, however, is even more important. Notes Shull, "If you understand anatomy and medical terminology, you will be much more accurate at interpreting and transcribing what you hear. A hospital transcriptionist deals with terms from a wide variety of medical specialties—one dictation might be from a gynecologist, the next from an orthopedic surgeon, and the next from a pediatrician." This is why anatomy and physiology, medical terminology, and the study of disease processes make up most of the curriculum in medical transcription training programs.

All health professionals who treat a patient rely on these typed documents, so accurate transcription is vital: "I see the transcriptionist as a partner with physicians. We work with them to create excellent medical records, so patients will always be assured of receiving the best and most appropriate care possible."

Shull enjoys the variety of medical transcription work. "It's fascinating because you get to follow each patient's story, from the initial problem to diagnosis to treatment," she says. "You feel like you know these people. It's like watching a gripping television drama—only this is real life!"

Classes for medical transcription are offered through community colleges, proprietary schools, and home-study programs and vary in length from several months to two years. Accreditation procedures vary from state to state.

> **"** *Anatomy and physiology classes make up a large part of the curriculum in medical transcription training programs."*

The American Association for Medical Transcription (AAMT) recommends a two-year program that includes at least 240 hours of on-the-job training in a healthcare facility.

For more information, contact the AAMT:

100 Sycamore Avenue
Modesto, CA 95354
Telephone: (800) 982-2182 or
(209) 527-9620
http://www.aamt.org

For additional information on this career, click the Focus on Careers link at www.anatomyandphysiology.com.

SYSTEMS IN SYNC

HOMEOSTATIC RELATIONSHIPS BETWEEN THE
INTEGUMENTARY SYSTEM AND OTHER BODY SYSTEMS

Nervous System
- Skin protects nervous system organs; cutaneous sensory receptors located in skin
- Nervous system regulates diameter of blood vessels in skin; activates sweat glands, contributing to thermoregulation; interprets cutaneous sensation; activates arrector pili muscles

Endocrine System
- Skin protects endocrine organs
- Androgens produced by the endocrine system activate sebaceous glands and help regulate hair growth; estrogen helps maintain skin hydration

Respiratory System
- Skin protects respiratory organs
- Respiratory system furnishes oxygen to skin cells and removes carbon dioxide via gas exchange with blood

Lymphatic System/Immunity
- Skin protects lymphatic organs; prevents pathogen invasion
- Lymphatic system prevents edema by picking up excessive leaked fluid; immune system protects skin cells

Cardiovascular System
- Skin protects cardiovascular organs; prevents fluid loss from body surface; serves as blood reservoir
- Cardiovascular system transports oxygen and nutrients to skin and removes wastes from skin; provides substances needed by skin glands to make their secretions

Digestive System
- Skin protects digestive organs; provides vitamin D needed for calcium absorption
- Digestive system provides needed nutrients for the skin

Reproductive System
- Skin protects reproductive organs; highly modified sweat glands (mammary glands) produce milk. During pregnancy, skin stretches to accommodate growing fetus; changes in skin pigmentation may occur

Urinary System
- Skin protects urinary organs; excretes salts and some nitrogenous wastes in sweat
- Urinary system activates vitamin D made by keratinocytes; disposes of nitrogenous wastes of skin metabolism

Integumentary System (Skin)

Muscular System
- Skin protects muscles
- Active muscles generate large amounts of heat which increase blood flow to the skin and may promote activation of sweat glands of skin

Skeletal System
- Skin protects bones; skin synthesizes vitamin D bones need for normal calcium absorption and deposit of bone (calcium) salts which make bones hard
- Skeletal system provides support for the skin

SUMMARY

Media study tools that provide additional review of key topics of Chapter 4 are referenced below.

> **IP** = *InterActive Physiology*
> **WEB** = The A&P Place

Classification of Body Membranes (pp. 110–113)

1. Epithelial: Simple organs, epithelium and connective tissue components.
   a. Cutaneous (the skin): epidermis (stratified squamous epithelium) underlain by the dermis (dense connective tissue); protects body surface.
   b. Mucous: epithelial sheet underlain by a lamina propria (areolar connective tissue); lines body cavities open to the exterior.
   c. Serous: simple squamous epithelium resting on a scant connective tissue layer; lines the ventral body cavity.
2. Connective tissue: Synovial; lines joint cavities.

The Integumentary System (Skin) (pp. 113–127)

1. Skin functions include protecting the deeper tissue from chemicals, bacteria, bumps, and drying; regulating body temperature through radiation and sweating; and synthesizing defensive proteins and vitamin D. The cutaneous sensory receptors are located in the skin.
2. The epidermis, the more superficial part of the skin, is formed of stratified squamous keratinizing epithelium and is avascular. Moving from its superficial to deep region, its layers are the stratum corneum, stratum lucidum (in thick skin only), stratum granulosum, stratum spinosum, and stratum basale. Cells at its surface are dead and continually flake off. They are replaced by division of cells in the basal cell layer. As the cells move away from the basal layer, they accumulate keratin and die. Melanin, a pigment produced by melanocytes, protects the nuclei of epithelial cells from the damaging rays of the sun.
3. The dermis is composed of dense connective tissue. It is the site of blood vessels, nerves, and epidermal appendages. It has two regions, the papillary and reticular layers. The papillary layer has ridges, which press on the epidermis to produce fingerprints.
4. Skin appendages are formed from the epidermis but reside in the dermis.

a. Sebaceous glands produce an oily product (sebum), usually ducted into a hair follicle. Sebum keeps the skin and hair soft and contains bacteria-killing chemicals.

b. Sweat (sudoriferous) glands, under the control of the nervous system, produce sweat, which is ducted to the epithelial surface. These glands are part of the body's heat-regulating apparatus. There are two types: eccrine (the most numerous) and apocrine (their product includes fatty acids and proteins, which skin bacteria metabolize).

c. A hair is primarily dead keratinized cells and is produced by the matrix in the hair bulb. The root is enclosed in a sheath, the hair follicle.

d. Nails are hornlike derivatives of the epidermis. Like hair, nails are primarily dead keratinized cells.

WEB Exercise: Chapter 4, Structure of the Skin.

5. Most minor afflictions of the skin result from infections or allergic responses; more serious are burns and skin cancer. Because they interfere with skin's protective functions, burns represent a major threat to the body.

WEB Exercise: Chapter 4, Integumentary I Case Study.

a. Burns result in loss of body fluids and invasion of bacteria. The extent of burns is assessed by the rule of nines. The severity (depth) of burns is described as first-degree (epidermal damage only), second-degree (epidermal and some dermal injury), and third-degree (epidermis and dermis totally destroyed). Third-degree burns require skin grafting.

b. The most common cause of skin cancer is exposure to ultraviolet radiation. Cure of basal cell carcinoma and squamous cell carcinoma is complete if they are removed before metastasis. Malignant melanoma, a cancer of melanocytes, is still fairly rare but is fatal in about half the cases.

WEB Exercise: Chapter 4, Integumentary II Case Study; At the Clinic: Integumentary.

Developmental Aspects of Skin and Body Membranes (p. 127)

1. The skin is thick, resilient, and well hydrated in youth but loses its elasticity and thins as the person ages. Skin cancer is a major threat to skin exposed to excessive sunlight.

2. Balding and/or graying occurs with aging. Both are genetically determined, but other factors (drugs, emotional stress, and so on) can result in either.

REVIEW QUESTIONS

Multiple Choice

More than one choice may apply.

1. Select the one false statement about mucous and serous membranes.
   a. The epithelial type is the same in all serous membranes, but there are different epithelial types in different mucous membranes.
   b. Serous membranes line closed body cavities, whereas mucous membranes line body cavities open to the outside.
   c. Serous membranes always produce serous fluid, and mucous membranes always secrete mucus.
   d. Both membranes contain an epithelium plus a layer of loose connective tissue.

2. Serous membranes
   a. line the mouth.
   b. have parietal and visceral layers.
   c. consist of epidermis and dermis.
   d. have a connective tissue layer called the lamina propria.
   e. secrete a lubricating fluid.

3. Which is *not* a component of sweat?
   a. Water   d. Ammonia
   b. Sodium chloride e. Vitamin D
   c. Sebum

4. Which structure is *not* associated with a hair?
   a. Shaft   d. Matrix
   b. Cortex   e. Cuticle
   c. Lunula

5. In investigating the cause of thinning hair, which of the following questions needs to be asked?
   a. Is the diet deficient in proteins?
   b. Is the person taking megadoses of vitamin C?
   c. Has the person been exposed to excessive radiation?
   d. Has the person recently suffered severe emotional trauma?

6. Which structure is *not* associated with a nail?
   a. Nail bed   c. Nail folds
   b. Lunula   d. Nail follicle

7. Which one of the following is *not* associated with the production of perspiration?
   a. Sweat glands   d. Eccrine gland
   b. Sweat pores   e. Apocrine gland
   c. Arrector pili

8. Which of the following is not a skin structure?
   a. Pacinian corpuscle   c. Hair
   b. Dermal papilla   d. Nail

9. Match the structures on the right with their function listed on the left.

   ____ 1. Protection from ultraviolet radiation
   ____ 2. Insulation, energy storage
   ____ 3. Waterproofing and preventing water loss
   ____ 4. Temperature regulation
   ____ 5. Excretion of water, urea, and salts
   ____ 6. Produces the patterns for fingerprints

   a. Reticular layer of the dermis
   b. Dermal blood supply
   c. Papillary layer of the dermis
   d. Hypodermis
   e. Melanocytes
   f. Stratum corneum
   g. Eccrine sweat glands

Short Answer Essay

10. What is the name of the connective tissue membrane found lining the joint cavities?

11. From what types of damage does the skin protect the body?

12. Explain why we become tanned after sitting in the sun.

13. What is a decubitus ulcer? Why does it occur?

14. Name two different categories of skin secretions and the glands that manufacture them.

15. How does the skin help to regulate body temperature?

16. What is a blackhead?

17. What are arrector pili? What do they do?

18. Which skin cancer arises from the stratum spinosum cells?

19. Why does hair turn gray?

20. Name three changes that occur in the skin as one ages.

21. Is a bald man really hairless? Explain.

CRITICAL THINKING AND CLINICAL APPLICATION QUESTIONS

22. A nurse tells a doctor that a patient is cyanotic. What is cyanosis? What does its presence indicate?

23. Both newborn infants and aged individuals have very little subcutaneous tissue. How does this affect their sensitivity to cold environmental temperature?

24. A 40-year-old beachboy is complaining to you that his suntan made him popular when he was young—but now his face is all wrinkled, and he has several darkly pigmented moles that are growing rapidly and are as big as large coins. He shows you the moles, and immediately you think "ABCD." What does that mean, and why should he be concerned?

25. Martha, the mother of a 13-month-old infant, brings her child to the clinic because his skin has turned orange. Why does the pediatrician inquire about the child's diet?

26. The water of a swimming pool is hypotonic to our cells. Why do we not swell and pop when we go for a swim?

27. Mr. Bellazono, a fisherman in his late sixties, comes to the clinic to complain of small ulcers on both forearms as well as on his face and ears. Although he has had them for several years, he has not had any other problems. What is the likely diagnosis, and what is the likely cause?

28. Mr. Grayson is receiving a drug treatment transdermally (through the skin). Explain why drugs delivered by this route are fat-soluble rather than water-soluble.

29. Why does sunburned skin often peel in sheets?

30. Which type of injection would allow a drug to be absorbed more rapidly—intradermal or subcutaneous (a shallow injection *just* deep to the epidermis)? Why?

The Skeletal System

YOUR GOALS

After completing this chapter, you will have a working knowledge of the functions of the skeletal system and will have mastered the objectives listed below.

FUNCTION PREVIEW

• The skeletal system provides an internal framework for the body, protects organs by enclosure, and anchors skeletal muscles so that muscle contraction can cause movement.

OBJECTIVE CHECKLIST

Bones: An Overview (pp. 134–144)

▶ Identify the subdivisions of the skeleton as axial or appendicular.

▶ List at least three functions of the skeletal system.

▶ Name the four main classifications of bones.

▶ Identify the major anatomical areas of a long bone.

▶ Explain the role of bone salts and the organic matrix in making bone both hard and flexible.

▶ Describe briefly the process of bone formation in the fetus, and summarize the events of bone remodeling throughout life.

▶ Name and describe the various types of fractures.

Axial Skeleton (pp. 144–158)

➤ On a skull or diagram, identify and name the bones of the skull.

➤ Describe how the skull of a newborn infant (or fetus) differs from that of an adult, and explain the function of fontanels.

➤ Name the parts of a typical vertebra, and explain in general how the cervical, thoracic, and lumbar vertebrae differ from one another.

➤ Discuss the importance of the intervertebral discs and spinal curvatures.

➤ Explain how the abnormal spinal curvatures (scoliosis, lordosis, and kyphosis) differ from one another.

Appendicular Skeleton (pp. 158–166)

➤ Identify on a skeleton or diagram the bones of the shoulder and pelvic girdles and their attached limbs.

➤ Describe important differences between a male and female pelvis.

Joints (pp. 166–174)

➤ Name the three major categories of joints, and compare the amount of movement allowed by each.

Developmental Aspects of the Skeleton (pp. 174–176)

➤ Identify some of the causes of bone and joint problems throughout life.

Although the word *skeleton* comes from the Greek word meaning "dried-up body," our internal framework is so beautifully designed and engineered that it puts any modern skyscraper to shame. Strong, yet light, it is perfectly adapted for its functions of body protection and motion. Indeed, our skeleton is a tower of bones arranged so that we can stand upright and balance ourselves. No other animal has such relatively long legs (compared to the arms or forelimbs) or such a strange foot, and few have such remarkable grasping hands. Even though the infant's backbone is like an arch, it soon changes to the swayback, or **S**-shaped, structure that is required for the upright posture.

The skeleton is subdivided into two divisions: the **axial skeleton,** the bones that form the longitudinal axis of the body, and the **appendicular skeleton,** the bones of the limbs and girdles. In addition to bones, the **skeletal system** includes *joints, cartilages,* and *ligaments* (fibrous cords that bind the bones together at joints). The joints give the body flexibility and allow movement to occur.

Bones: An Overview

At one time or another, all of us have heard the expressions "bone tired," "dry as a bone," or "bag of bones"—pretty unflattering and inaccurate images of some of our most phenomenal organs. Our brains, not our bones, convey feelings of fatigue, and bones are far from dry. As for "bag of bones," they are indeed more obvious in some of us, but without them to form our internal skeleton, we would creep along the ground like slugs. Let's examine how our bones contribute to overall body homeostasis.

Functions of the Bones

Besides contributing to body shape and form, our bones perform several important body functions:

1. **Support.** Bones, the "steel girders" and "reinforced concrete" of the body, form the internal framework that supports the body and cradles its soft organs. The bones of the legs act as pillars to support the body trunk when we stand, and the rib cage supports the thoracic wall.

2. **Protection.** Bones protect soft body organs. For example, the fused bones of the skull provide a snug enclosure for the brain, allowing one to head a soccer ball without worrying about injuring the brain. The vertebrae surround the spinal cord, and the rib cage helps protect the vital organs of the thorax.

3. **Movement.** Skeletal muscles, attached to bones by tendons, use the bones as levers to move the body and its parts. As a result, we can walk, swim, throw a ball, and breathe. Before continuing, take a moment to imagine that your bones have turned to putty. What if you were running when this change took place? Now imagine your bones forming a rigid metal framework inside your body, somewhat like a system of plumbing pipes. What problems could you envision with this arrangement? These images should help you understand how well our skeletal system provides support and protection while allowing movement.

4. **Storage.** Fat is stored in the internal cavities of bones. Bone itself serves as a storehouse for minerals, the most important of which are calcium and phosphorus. A small amount of calcium in its ion form (Ca^{2+}) must be present in the blood at all times for the nervous system to transmit messages, for muscles to contract, and for blood to clot. Because most of the body's calcium is deposited in the bones as calcium salts, the bones are a convenient place to get more calcium ions for the blood as they are used up. Problems occur not only when there is too little calcium in the blood, but also when there is too much. Hormones control the movement of calcium to and from the bones and blood according to the needs of the body. Indeed, "deposits" and "withdrawals" of calcium (and other minerals) to and from bones go on almost all the time.

5. **Blood cell formation.** Blood cell formation, or hematopoiesis (hem″ah-to-poi-e′sis), occurs within the marrow cavities of certain bones.

Classification of Bones

The adult skeleton is composed of 206 bones. There are two basic types of osseous, or bone, tissue: **Compact bone** is dense and looks smooth and homogeneous. **Spongy bone** is composed of small needlelike pieces of bone and lots of open space.

Bones come in many sizes and shapes (Figure 5.1). For example, the tiny pisiform bone of the wrist is the size and shape of a pea, whereas the femur, or thigh bone, is nearly 2 feet long and has a large, ball-shaped head. The unique shape of each bone fulfills a particular need. Bones are classified according to shape into four groups: long, short, flat, and irregular (see Figure 5.1).

As their name suggests, **long bones** are typically longer than they are wide. As a rule they have a shaft with heads at both ends. Long bones are mostly compact bone. All the bones of the limbs, except the patella (kneecap) and the wrist and ankle bones, are long bones.

Short bones are generally cube-shaped and contain mostly spongy bone. The bones of the wrist and ankle are short bones. *Sesamoid* (ses′ah-moyd) *bones,* which form within tendons, are a special type of short bone. The best-known example is the patella.

Flat bones are thin, flattened, and usually curved. They have two thin layers of compact bone sandwiching a layer of spongy bone between them. Most bones of the skull, the ribs, and the sternum (breastbone) are flat bones.

Bones that do not fit one of the preceding categories are called **irregular bones.** The vertebrae, which make up the spinal column, and the hip bones fall into this group.

▶ DID YOU GET IT?

1. What is the relationship between muscle function and bones?

2. Where are most long bones found in the body?

For answers, see Appendix D.

Structure of a Long Bone
Gross Anatomy

The gross structure of a long bone is shown in Figure 5.2. The **diaphysis** (di-af′ĭ-sis), or shaft, makes up most of the bone's length and is composed of compact bone. The diaphysis is covered and protected by a fibrous connective tissue membrane, the **periosteum** (per-e-ŏs′te-um). Hundreds of connective tissue fibers, called **perforating,** or **Sharpey's, fibers** secure the periosteum to the underlying bone.

(a) Long bone
(humerus of arm)

(b) Short bone
(carpal of wrist)

(c) Flat bone
(sternum)

(d) Irregular bone
(vertebra)

FIGURE 5.1 **Classification of bones on the basis of shape.**

The **epiphyses** (ě-pif′ĭ-sēz) are the ends of the long bone. Each epiphysis consists of a thin layer of compact bone enclosing an area filled with spongy bone. **Articular cartilage,** instead of a periosteum, covers its external surface. Because the articular cartilage is glassy hyaline cartilage, it provides a smooth, slippery surface that decreases friction at joint surfaces.

In adult bones, there is a thin line of bony tissue spanning the epiphysis that looks a bit different from the rest of the bone in that area. This is the **epiphyseal line.** The epiphyseal line is a remnant of the **epiphyseal plate** (a flat plate of hyaline cartilage) seen in a young, growing bone. Epiphyseal plates cause the lengthwise growth of a long bone. By the end of puberty, when hormones inhibit long bone growth, epiphyseal

plates have been completely replaced by bone, leaving only the epiphyseal lines to mark their previous location.

In adults the cavity of the shaft is primarily a storage area for adipose (fat) tissue. It is called the **yellow marrow,** or **medullary, cavity.** However, in infants this area forms blood cells, and **red marrow** is found there. In adult bones, red marrow is confined to cavities in the spongy bone of flat bones and the epiphyses of some long bones.

Even when looking casually at bones, one can see that their surfaces are not smooth but scarred with bumps, holes, and ridges. These **bone markings,** described and illustrated in Table 5.1, reveal where muscles, tendons, and ligaments were attached and where blood vessels and nerves passed. There are two categories of bone markings:

FIGURE 5.2   The structure of a long bone (humerus).
(a) Anterior view with longitudinal section cut away at the proximal end.
(b) Pie-shaped, three-dimensional view of spongy bone and compact bone
of the epiphysis. **(c)** Cross section of the shaft (diaphysis). Note that the
external surface of the diaphysis is covered by a periosteum, but the
articular surface of the epiphysis (see b) is covered with hyaline cartilage.

(a) *projections,* or *processes,* which grow out from
the bone surface, and (b) *depressions,* or *cavities,*
which are indentations in the bone. You do not
have to learn these terms now, but they can help
you remember some of the specific markings on
bones to which you will be introduced later in this
chapter.

There is a little trick for remembering some of
the bone markings listed in the table: All the terms
beginning with **T** are projections. The terms beginning with **F** (except *facet*) are depressions.

Microscopic Anatomy

To the naked eye, spongy bone has a spiky, open
appearance, whereas compact bone appears to be
very dense. Looking at compact bone tissue
through a microscope, however, one can see that it
has a complex structure (Figure 5.3). It is riddled
with passageways carrying nerves, blood vessels,
and the like, which provide the living bone cells
with nutrients and a route for waste disposal. The
mature bone cells, **osteocytes** (os′te-o-sītz″), are

TABLE 5.1	Bone Markings

Name of bone marking	Description	Illustration

Projections That Are Sites of Muscle and Ligament Attachment

Tuberosity	Large, rounded projection; may be roughened
Crest	Narrow ridge of bone; usually prominent
Trochanter (tro-kan'ter)	Very large, blunt, irregularly shaped process (the only examples are on the femur)
Line	Narrow ridge of bone; less prominent than a crest
Tubercle (too'ber-kl)	Small, rounded projection or process
Epicondyle	Raised area on or above a condyle
Spine	Sharp, slender, often pointed projection
Process	Any bony prominence

Coxal bone

Femur of thigh

Vertebra

Projections That Help to Form Joints

Head	Bony expansion carried on a narrow neck
Facet	Smooth, nearly flat articular surface
Condyle (kon'dīl)	Rounded articular projection
Ramus (ra'mus)	Armlike bar of bone

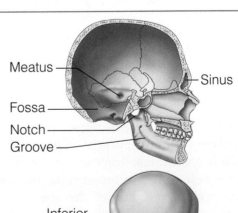

Rib

Mandible

Depressions and Openings Allowing Blood Vessels and Nerves to Pass

Meatus (me-a'tus)	Canal-like passageway
Sinus	Cavity within a bone, filled with air and lined with mucous membrane
Fossa (fos'ah)	Shallow, basinlike depression in a bone, often serving as an articular surface
Groove	Furrow
Fissure	Narrow, slitlike opening
Foramen (fo-ra'men)	Round or oval opening through a bone

Skull

Lamella

Osteocyte

Osteon
(Haversian system)

Lamellae

(b)

Canaliculus

Lacuna

Central
(Haversian) canal

Blood vessel continues
into medullary cavity
containing marrow

Spongy bone

Perforating
fibers

Compact
bone

Periosteal
blood vessel

Periosteum

(a)

Central (Haversian) canal

Perforating
(Volkmann's) canal

Blood vessel

Osteon

Lacuna

(c) Central
canal

Interstitial
lamellae

F I G U R E   5 . 3   Microscopic structure of compact bone. Diagram of a pie-shaped segment of compact bone. (The inset shows a more highly magnified view.) Notice the position of osteocytes in lacunae (cavities in the matrix).

found within the matrix in tiny cavities called **lacunae** (lah-ku'ne). The lacunae are arranged in concentric circles called **lamellae** (lah-mel'e) around **central (Haversian) canals.** Each complex consisting of central canal and matrix rings is called an **osteon,** or **Haversian system.** Central canals run lengthwise through the bony matrix, car-

rying blood vessels and nerves to all areas of the bone. Tiny canals, **canaliculi** (kan"ah-lik'u-li), radiate outward from the central canals to all lacunae. The canaliculi form a transportation system that connects all the bone cells to the nutrient supply through the hard bone matrix. Because of this elaborate network of canals, bone cells are well nourished in spite of the hardness of the matrix, and bone injuries heal quickly and well. The communication pathway from the outside of the bone to its interior (and the central canals) is completed by **perforating (Volkmann's) canals,** which run into the compact bone at right angles to the shaft.

Bone is one of the hardest materials in the body, and although relatively light in weight, it has a remarkable ability to resist tension and other forces acting on it. Nature has given us an extremely strong and exceptionally simple (almost crude) supporting system without giving up mobility. The calcium salts deposited in the matrix give bone its hardness, which resists compression. The organic parts (especially the collagen fibers) provide for bone's flexibility and great tensile strength.

DID YOU GET IT?

3. What is the anatomical name for the shaft of a long bone? For its ends?

4. How does the structure of compact bone differ from the structure of spongy bone when viewed with the naked eye?

For answers, see Appendix D.

Bone Formation, Growth, and Remodeling

The skeleton is formed from two of the strongest and most supportive tissues in the body—cartilage and bone. In embryos, the skeleton is primarily made of hyaline cartilage, but in the young child most of the cartilage has been replaced by bone. Cartilage remains only in isolated areas such as the bridge of the nose, parts of the ribs, and the joints.

Except for flat bones, which form on fibrous membranes, most bones develop using hyaline cartilage structures as their "models." Most simply, this process of bone formation, or **ossification** (os"ĭ-fĭ-ka'shun), involves two major phases (Figure 5.4a). First, the hyaline cartilage model is completely covered with bone matrix (a bone "collar") by bone-forming cells called **osteoblasts.** So, for a short period, the fetus has cartilage "bones" enclosed by "bony" bones. Then, the enclosed hyaline cartilage model is digested away, opening up a medullary cavity within the newly formed bone.

By birth or shortly after, most hyaline cartilage models have been converted to bone except for two regions—the articular cartilages (that cover the bone ends) and the epiphyseal plates. New cartilage is formed continuously on the external face of the articular cartilage and on the epiphyseal plate surface that faces the bone end (is farther away from the medullary cavity). At the same time, the old cartilage abutting the internal face of the articular cartilage and the medullary cavity is broken down and replaced by bony matrix (Figure 5.4b).

Growing bones also must widen as they lengthen. How do they widen? Simply, osteoblasts in the periosteum add bone tissue to the external face of the diaphysis as osteoclasts in the endosteum remove bone from the inner face of the diaphysis wall (see Figure 5.4b). Since these two processes occur at about the same rate, the circumference of the long bone expands and the bone widens. This process by which bones increase in diameter is called *appositional growth*. This process of long-bone growth is controlled by hormones, the most important of which are *growth hormone* and, during puberty, the *sex hormones*. It ends during adolescence, when the epiphyseal plates are completely converted to bone.

Many people mistakenly think that bones are lifeless structures that never change once long-bone growth has ended. Nothing could be further from the truth; bone is a dynamic and active tissue. Bones are remodeled continually in response to changes in two factors: (1) calcium levels in the blood and (2) the pull of gravity and muscles on the skeleton. How these factors influence bones is outlined next.

When blood calcium levels drop below homeostatic levels, the parathyroid glands (located in the throat) are stimulated to release parathyroid hormone (PTH) into the blood. PTH activates **osteoclasts,** giant bone-destroying cells in bones, to break down bone matrix and release calcium ions into the blood. When blood calcium levels are too high (*hypercalcemia* [hi"per-kal-se'me-ah]), calcium is deposited in bone matrix as hard calcium salts.

Bone remodeling is essential if bones are to retain normal proportions and strength during long-bone growth as the body increases in size and weight. It also accounts for the fact that bones become thicker and form large projections to increase their strength in areas where bulky muscles are

Q *(a) What specific cell types form the bone collar? (b) What do you think a long bone would look like at the end of adolescence if bone remodeling did not occur?*

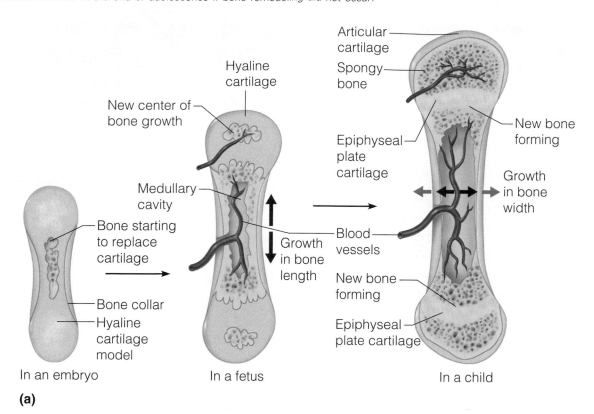

In an embryo | In a fetus | In a child

(a)

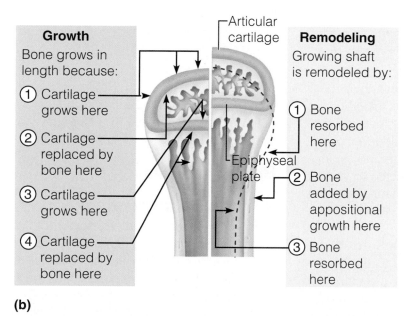

Growth
Bone grows in length because:

① Cartilage grows here

② Cartilage replaced by bone here

③ Cartilage grows here

④ Cartilage replaced by bone here

Articular cartilage

Epiphyseal plate

Remodeling
Growing shaft is remodeled by:

① Bone resorbed here

② Bone added by appositional growth here

③ Bone resorbed here

(b)

FIGURE 5.4 **Formation and growth of long bones. (a)** Stages of long-bone formation in an embryo, fetus, and young child. **(b)** The events indicated at the left depict the process of ossification that occurs at the articular cartilages and epiphyseal plates as the bone grows in length. The events indicated at the right reveal the process of appositional growth that occurs during long-bone growth to maintain proper bone proportions by enlarging long-bone diameter.

A *(a) Osteoblasts form the bone collar. (b) It would have a relatively short, slender shaft with elongated, clublike ends.*

TABLE 5.2	Common Types of Fractures		
Fracture type	**Illustration**	**Description**	**Comment**
Comminuted		Bone breaks into many fragments	Particularly common in older people, whose bones are more brittle
Compression		Bone is crushed	Common in porous bones (i.e., osteoporotic bones of older people)
Depressed		Broken bone portion is pressed inward	Typical of skull fracture
Impacted		Broken bone ends are forced into each other	Commonly occurs when one attempts to break a fall with outstretched arms
Spiral		Ragged break occurs when excessive twisting forces are applied to a bone	Common sports fracture
Greenstick		Bone breaks incompletely, much in the way a green twig breaks	Common in children, whose bones are more flexible than those of adults

attached. At such sites, osteoblasts lay down new matrix and become trapped within it. (Once they are trapped, they become osteocytes, or mature bone cells.) In contrast, the bones of bedridden or physically inactive people tend to lose mass and to atrophy because they are no longer subjected to stress.

These two controlling mechanisms—calcium uptake and release and bone remodeling—work together. PTH determines *when* (or *if*) bone is to be broken down or formed in response to the need for more or fewer calcium ions in the blood. The stresses of muscle pull and gravity acting on the skeleton determine *where* bone matrix is to be broken down or formed so that the skeleton can remain as strong and vital as possible.

HOMEOSTATIC IMBALANCE

Rickets is a disease of children in which the bones fail to calcify. As a result, the bones soften, and the weight-bearing bones of the legs show a definite bowing. Rickets is usually due to a lack of calcium in the diet or lack of vitamin D, which is needed to absorb calcium into the bloodstream. Rickets is not seen very often in the United States. Milk, bread, and other foods are fortified with vitamin D, and most children drink enough calcium-rich milk. However, it can happen in infants nursed by mothers who become vitamin D-deficient over the course of a long gray winter, and it remains a problem in some other parts of the world. ▲

Bone Fractures

HOMEOSTATIC IMBALANCE

For their relatively low mass, bones are amazingly strong. Consider, for example, the forces endured in touch football and professional hockey. Despite their remarkable strength, bones are susceptible to **fractures,** or breaks, all through life. During youth, most fractures result from exceptional trauma that twists or smashes the bones. Sports activities such as football, skating, and skiing jeopardize the bones, and automobile accidents certainly take their toll. In old age, bones thin and weaken, and fractures occur more often.

A fracture in which the bone breaks cleanly but does not penetrate the skin is a *closed* (or *simple*) *fracture.* When the broken bone ends penetrate through the skin, the fracture is *open* (or *compound*). Some of the many common types of fractures are illustrated and described in Table 5.2. ▲

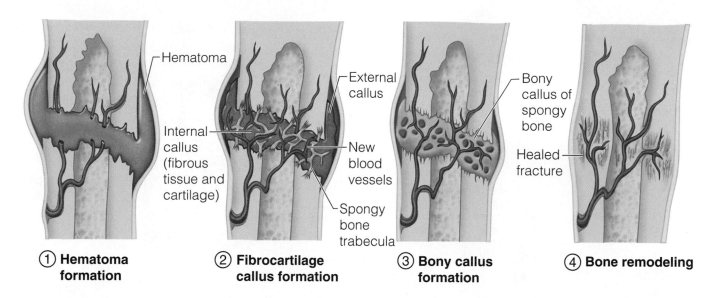

① **Hematoma formation**   ② **Fibrocartilage callus formation**   ③ **Bony callus formation**   ④ **Bone remodeling**

FIGURE 5.5   Stages in the healing of a bone fracture.

A fracture is treated by **reduction,** which is the realignment of the broken bone ends. In *closed reduction,* the bone ends are coaxed back into their normal position by the physician's hands. In *open reductions,* surgery is performed and the bone ends are secured together with pins or wires. After the broken bone is reduced, it is immobilized by a cast or traction to allow the healing process to begin. The healing time for a simple fracture is 6 to 8 weeks, but it is much longer for large bones and for the bones of older people (because of their poorer circulation).

The repair of bone fractures involves four major events (Figure 5.5):

1. **A hematoma forms.** Blood vessels are ruptured when the bone breaks. As a result, a blood-filled swelling called a **hematoma** (he-mah-to′mah) forms. Bone cells deprived of nutrition die.

2. **The break is splinted by a fibrocartilage callus.** As described in Chapter 3, an early event of tissue repair (and bone repair is no exception) is the growth of new capillaries (granulation tissue) into the clotted blood at the site of the damage and disposal of dead tissue by phagocytes. As this goes on, connective tissue cells of various types form a mass of repair tissue, the **fibrocartilage callus** (kal′us), that contains several elements—some cartilage matrix, some bony matrix, and collagen fibers—

and acts to "splint" the broken bone, closing the gap.

3. **The bony callus forms.** As more osteoblasts and osteoclasts migrate into the area and multiply, the fibrocartilage callus is gradually replaced by one made of spongy bone, the **bony callus.**

4. **Bone remodeling occurs.** Over the next few weeks to months, depending on the bone's size and site of the break, the bony callus is remodeled in response to the mechanical stresses placed on it, so that it forms a strong permanent "patch" at the fracture site.

▶ *DID YOU GET IT?*

5. Bones don't begin as bones. What do they begin as?

6. Which stimulus—PTH (a hormone) or mechanical forces acting on the skeleton—is more important in maintaining blood calcium levels than bone strength?

7. If osteoclasts in a long bone are more active than osteoblasts, what change in bone mass is likely to occur?

8. What is a fracture? What two fracture types are particularly common in older people?

For answers, see Appendix D.

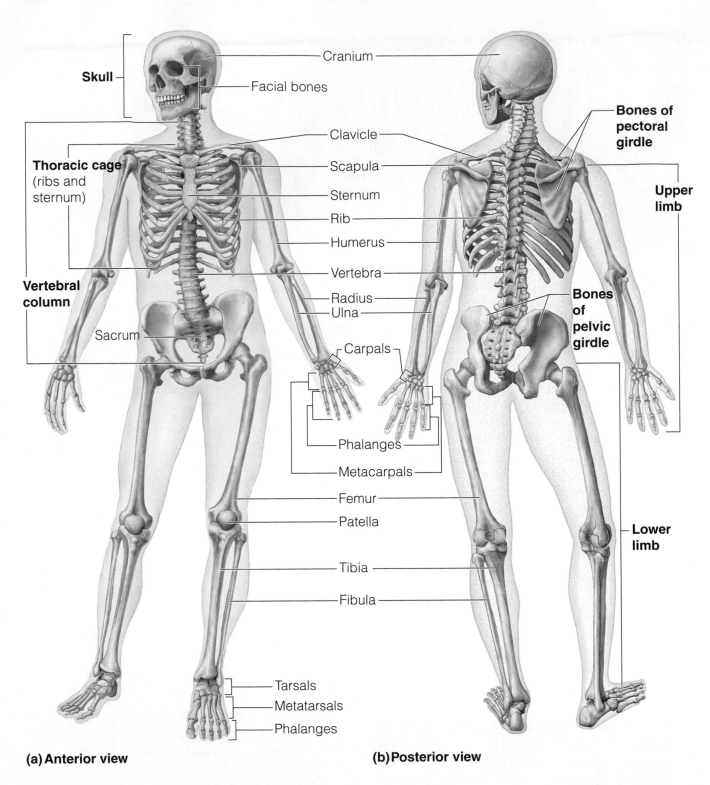

Skull
- Cranium
- Facial bones

Clavicle

Thoracic cage (ribs and sternum)
- Scapula
- Sternum
- Rib
- Humerus

Vertebral column
- Vertebra

Sacrum
- Radius
- Ulna

Carpals

Phalanges

Metacarpals

Femur

Patella

Tibia

Fibula

Tarsals

Metatarsals

Phalanges

Bones of pectoral girdle

Upper limb

Bones of pelvic girdle

Lower limb

(a) Anterior view

(b) Posterior view

FIGURE 5.6   The human skeleton. The bones of the axial skeleton are colored green. Bones of the appendicular skeleton are gold.

Axial Skeleton

As noted earlier, the skeleton is divided into two parts, the *axial* and *appendicular skeletons*. The axial skeleton, which forms the longitudinal axis of the body, is shown as the green portion of Figure 5.6. It can be divided into three parts—the *skull,* the *vertebral column,* and the *bony thorax.*

Skull

The **skull** is formed by two sets of bones. The **cranium** encloses and protects the fragile brain tissue. The **facial bones** hold the eyes in an anterior position and allow the facial muscles to show our feelings through smiles or frowns. All but one of the bones of the skull are joined together by *sutures,* which are interlocking, immovable joints. Only the mandible (jawbone) is attached to the rest of the skull by a freely movable joint.

Cranium

The boxlike cranium is composed of eight large flat bones. Except for two paired bones (the parietal and temporal), they are all single bones.

Frontal Bone   The frontal bone forms the forehead, the bony projections under the eyebrows, and the superior part of each eye's orbit (Figure 5.7).

Parietal Bones   The paired parietal bones form most of the superior and lateral walls of the cranium (see Figure 5.7). They meet in the midline of the skull at the **sagittal suture** and form the **coronal suture,** where they meet the frontal bone.

Temporal Bones   The temporal bones lie inferior to the parietal bones; they join them at the **squamous sutures.** Several important bone markings appear on the temporal bone (see Figure 5.7):

- The **external acoustic meatus** is a canal that leads to the eardrum and the middle ear. It is the route by which sound enters the ear.

- The **styloid process,** a sharp, needlelike projection, is just inferior to the external auditory meatus. Many neck muscles use the styloid process as an attachment point.

- The **zygomatic** (zi″go-mat′ik) **process** is a thin bridge of bone that joins with the cheekbone (zygomatic bone) anteriorly.

- The **mastoid** (mas′toid) **process,** which is full of air cavities (mastoid sinuses), is a rough projection posterior and inferior to the external acoustic meatus. It provides an attachment site for some muscles of the neck. The mastoid sinuses are so close to the middle ear—a high-risk spot for infections—that they may become infected too, a condition called *mastoiditis.* Also, this area is so close to the brain that mastoiditis may spread to the brain.

- The **jugular foramen,** at the junction of the occipital and temporal bones (Figures 5.8 and 5.9), allows passage of the jugular vein, the largest vein of the head, which drains the brain. Just anterior to it in the cranial cavity is the **internal acoustic meatus** (see Figure 5.8), which transmits cranial nerves VII and VIII (the facial and vestibulocochlear nerves). Anterior to the jugular foramen on the skull's inferior aspect is the **carotid canal** (see Figure 5.9), through which the internal carotid artery runs, supplying blood to most of the brain.

Occipital Bone   If you look at Figures 5.7, 5.8, and 5.9, you can see that the occipital (ok-sip′ĭ-tal) bone is the most posterior bone of the cranium. It forms the floor and back wall of the skull. The occipital bone joins the parietal bones anteriorly at the **lambdoid** (lam′doyd) **suture.** In the base of the occipital bone is a large opening, the **foramen magnum** (literally, "large hole"). The foramen magnum surrounds the lower part of the brain and allows the spinal cord to connect with the brain. Lateral to the foramen magnum on each side are the rockerlike **occipital condyles** (see Figure 5.9), which rest on the first vertebra of the spinal column.

Sphenoid Bone   The butterfly-shaped sphenoid (sfe′noid) bone spans the width of the skull and forms part of the floor of the cranial cavity (see Figure 5.8). In the midline of the sphenoid is a small depression, the **sella turcica** (sel′ah tur′sĭ-kah), or *Turk's saddle,* which forms a snug enclosure for the pituitary gland. The **foramen ovale,** a large oval opening in line with the posterior end of the sella turcica (Figure 5.9), allows fibers of cranial nerve V (the trigeminal nerve) to pass to the chewing muscles of the lower jaw (mandible). Parts of the sphenoid bone, seen exteriorly forming part of the eye orbits, have two important

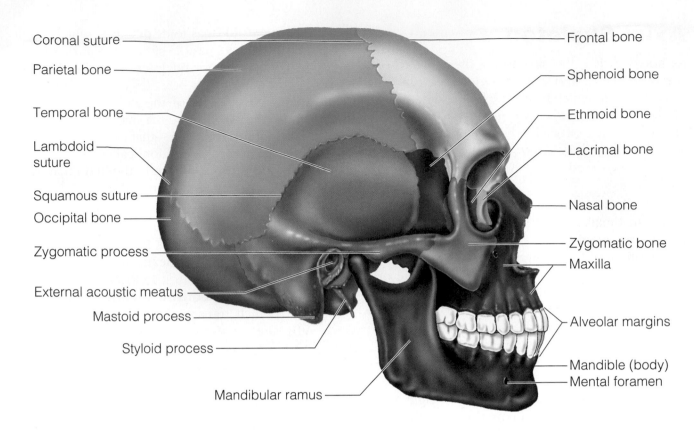

Coronal suture
Parietal bone
Temporal bone
Lambdoid suture
Squamous suture
Occipital bone
Zygomatic process
External acoustic meatus
Mastoid process
Styloid process
Mandibular ramus

Frontal bone
Sphenoid bone
Ethmoid bone
Lacrimal bone
Nasal bone
Zygomatic bone
Maxilla
Alveolar margins
Mandible (body)
Mental foramen

FIGURE 5.7   **Human skull, lateral view.**

Sphenoid bone
Temporal bone
Internal acoustic meatus
Parietal bone
Occipital bone
Foramen magnum

Frontal bone
Cribriform plate
Crista galli
Ethmoid bone
Optic canal
Sella turcica
Foramen ovale
Jugular foramen

FIGURE 5.8   **Human skull, superior view (top of cranium removed).**

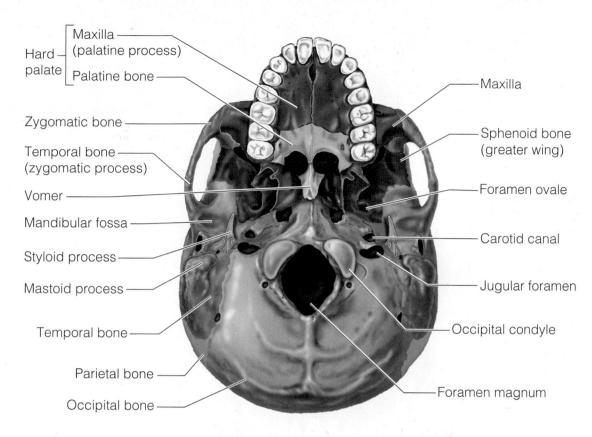

FIGURE 5.9   **Human skull, inferior view (mandible removed).**

openings, the **optic canal,** which allows the optic nerve to pass to the eye, and the slitlike **superior orbital fissure,** through which the cranial nerves controlling eye movements (III, IV, and VI) pass (see Figures 5.7 and 5.11). The central part of the sphenoid bone is riddled with air cavities, the **sphenoid sinuses** (Figure 5.10).

Ethmoid Bone   The ethmoid (eth'moid) bone is very irregularly shaped and lies anterior to the

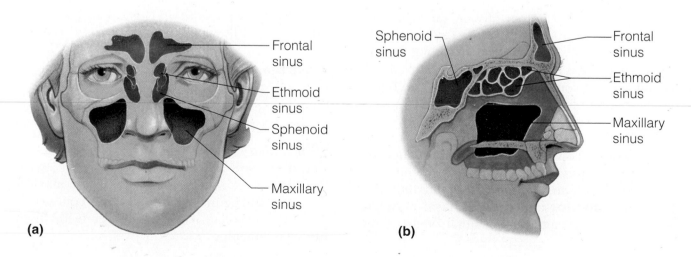

FIGURE 5.10   **Paranasal sinuses. (a)** Anterior view **(b)** Medial view.

Q *What bone articulates with every other facial bone?*

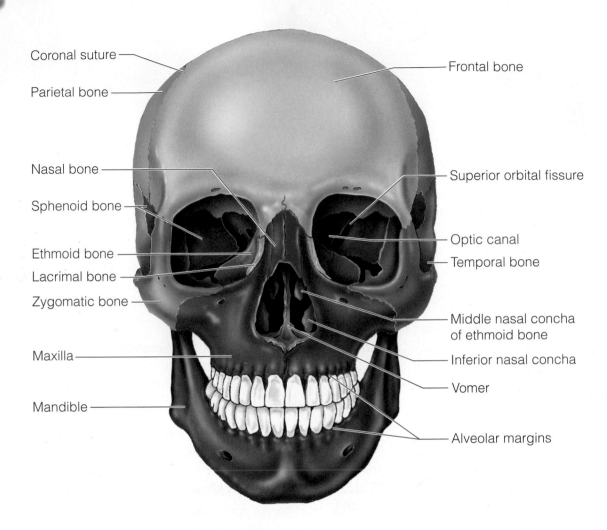

Coronal suture

Parietal bone

Nasal bone

Sphenoid bone

Ethmoid bone

Lacrimal bone

Zygomatic bone

Maxilla

Mandible

Frontal bone

Superior orbital fissure

Optic canal

Temporal bone

Middle nasal concha of ethmoid bone

Inferior nasal concha

Vomer

Alveolar margins

FIGURE 5.11 Human skull, anterior view.

sphenoid (Figure 5.11; see also Figures 5.7 and 5.8). It forms the roof of the nasal cavity and part of the medial walls of the orbits. Projecting from its superior surface is the **crista galli** (kris′tah gah′le), literally "cock's comb" (see Figure 5.8). The outermost covering of the brain attaches to this projection. On each side of the crista galli are many small holes. These holey areas, the **cribriform** (krib′rĭ-form) **plates,** allow nerve fibers carrying impulses from the olfactory (smell) receptors of the nose to reach the brain. Extensions of the ethmoid bone, the **superior** and **middle nasal conchae** (kong′ke), form part of the lateral walls of the

nasal cavity (see Figure 5.11) and increase the turbulence of air flowing through the nasal passages.

Facial Bones

Fourteen bones compose the face. Twelve are paired; only the mandible and vomer are single. Figures 5.7 and 5.11 show most of the facial bones.

■ *Maxillae* The two maxillae (mak-si′le), or **maxillary bones,** fuse to form the upper jaw. All facial bones except the mandible join the maxillae; thus they are the main, or "keystone," bones of the face. The maxillae carry the upper teeth in the **alveolar margin.**

Extensions of the maxillae called the **palatine** (pal'ah-tīn) **processes** form the anterior part of the hard palate of the mouth (see Figure 5.9). Like many other facial bones, the maxillae contain **sinuses,** which drain into the nasal passages (see Figure 5.10). These **paranasal sinuses,** whose naming reveals their position surrounding the nasal cavity, lighten the skull bones and amplify the sounds we make as we speak. They also cause many people a great deal of misery. Because the mucosa lining these sinuses is continuous with that in the nasal passages and throat, infections in these areas tend to migrate into the sinuses, causing *sinusitis*. Depending on which sinuses are infected, a headache or upper jaw pain is the usual result.

Palatine Bones   The paired palatine bones lie posterior to the palatine processes of the maxillae. They form the posterior part of the hard palate (see Figure 5.9). Failure of these or the palatine processes to fuse medially results in *cleft palate*.

Zygomatic Bones   The zygomatic bones are commonly referred to as the cheekbones. They also form a good-sized portion of the lateral walls of the orbits, or eye sockets.

Lacrimal Bones   The lacrimal (lak'rĭ-mal) bones are fingernail-sized bones forming part of the medial walls of each orbit. Each lacrimal bone has a groove that serves as a passageway for tears (*lacrima* = tear).

Nasal Bones   The small rectangular bones forming the bridge of the nose are the nasal bones. (The lower part of the skeleton of the nose is made up of cartilage.)

Vomer Bone   The single bone in the median line of the nasal cavity is the vomer. (*Vomer* means "plow," which refers to the bone's shape.) The vomer forms most of the bony nasal septum.

Inferior Nasal Conchae   The inferior nasal conchae are thin, curved bones projecting medially from the lateral walls of the nasal cavity. (As mentioned earlier, the superior and middle conchae are similar but are parts of the ethmoid bone.)

Mandible   The mandible, or lower jaw, is the largest and strongest bone of the face. It joins the temporal bones on each side of the face, forming the only freely movable joints in the skull. You can find these joints on yourself by placing your fingers

FIGURE 5.12   Anatomical location and structure of the hyoid bone. Anterior view.

— Greater horn
— Lesser horn
— Body

over your cheekbones and opening and closing your mouth. The horizontal part of the mandible (the *body*) forms the chin. Two upright bars of bone (the *rami*) extend from the body to connect the mandible with the temporal bone. The lower teeth lie in *alveoli* (sockets) in the **alveolar margin** at the superior edge of the mandibular body.

The Hyoid Bone

Though not really part of the skull, the **hyoid** (hi'oid) **bone** (Figure 5.12) is closely related to the mandible and temporal bones. The hyoid bone is unique in that it is the only bone of the body that does not articulate directly with any other bone. Instead, it is suspended in the midneck region about 2 cm (1 inch) above the larynx, where it is anchored by ligaments to the styloid processes of the temporal bones. Horseshoe-shaped, with a *body* and two pairs of *horns*, or *cornua*, the hyoid bone serves as a movable base for the tongue and as an attachment point for neck muscles that raise and lower the larynx when we swallow and speak.

Fetal Skull

The skull of a fetus or newborn infant is different in many ways from an adult skull (Figure 5.13). As Figure 5.13b illustrates, the infant's face is very small compared to the size of its cranium, but the skull as a whole is large compared to the infant's

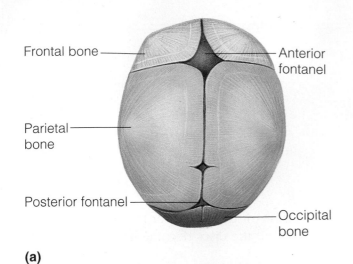

Frontal bone — Anterior fontanel

Parietal bone

Posterior fontanel — Occipital bone

(a)

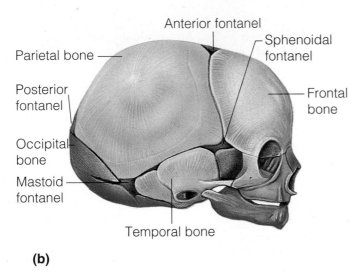

Anterior fontanel — Sphenoidal fontanel

Parietal bone —

Posterior fontanel —

Occipital bone — Frontal bone

Mastoid fontanel

Temporal bone

(b)

FIGURE 5.13 **The fetal skull. (a)** Superior view. **(b)** Lateral view.

total body length. The adult skull represents only one-eighth of the total body length, whereas that of a newborn infant is one-fourth as long as its entire body. When a baby is born, its skeleton is still unfinished. As noted earlier, some areas of hyaline cartilage still remain to be ossified, or converted to bone. In the newborn, the skull also has fibrous regions that have yet to be converted to bone. These fibrous membranes connecting the cranial bones are called **fontanels** (fon"tah-nelz′). The rhythm of the baby's pulse can be felt in these "soft spots," which explains their name (*fontanel* = little fountain). The largest fontanel is the diamond-shaped *anterior fontanel*. The fontanels allow the fetal

skull to be compressed slightly during birth. In addition, because they are flexible, they allow the infant's brain to grow during the later part of pregnancy and early infancy. This would not be possible if the cranial bones were fused in sutures as in the adult skull. The fontanels are gradually converted to bone during the early part of infancy and can no longer be felt by 22 to 24 months after birth.

▶ DID YOU GET IT?

9. What are the three main parts of the axial skeleton?

10. Johnny was vigorously exercising the only joints in the skull that are freely movable. What would you guess he was doing?

11. Which skull bone(s) form the "keystone of the face"?

12. Which bone has the cribriform plate and crista galli?

13. Which bones are connected by the coronal suture? By the sagittal suture?

For answers, see Appendix D.

Vertebral Column (Spine)

Serving as the axial support of the body, the **vertebral column,** or **spine,** extends from the skull, which it supports, to the pelvis, where it transmits the weight of the body to the lower limbs. Some people think of the vertebral column as a rigid supporting rod, but that picture is inaccurate. Instead, the spine is formed from 26 irregular bones connected and reinforced by ligaments in such a way that a flexible, curved structure results (Figure 5.14). Running through the central cavity of the vertebral column is the delicate spinal cord, which the vertebral column surrounds and protects.

Before birth, the spine consists of 33 separate bones called **vertebrae,** but 9 of these eventually fuse to form the two composite bones, the *sacrum* and the *coccyx,* that construct the inferior portion of the vertebral column. Of the 24 single bones, the 7 vertebrae of the neck are *cervical vertebrae,* the next 12 are the *thoracic vertebrae,* and the remaining 5 supporting the lower back are *lumbar vertebrae.*

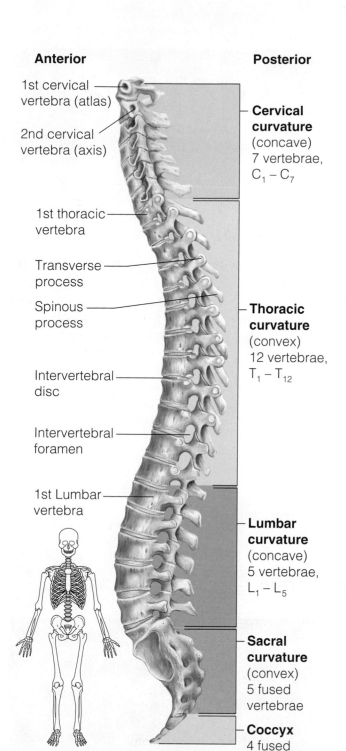

Anterior

1st cervical vertebra (atlas)

2nd cervical vertebra (axis)

1st thoracic vertebra

Transverse process

Spinous process

Intervertebral disc

Intervertebral foramen

1st Lumbar vertebra

Posterior

Cervical curvature
(concave)
7 vertebrae,
$C_1 - C_7$

Thoracic curvature
(convex)
12 vertebrae,
$T_1 - T_{12}$

Lumbar curvature
(concave)
5 vertebrae,
$L_1 - L_5$

Sacral curvature
(convex)
5 fused vertebrae

Coccyx
4 fused vertebrae

FIGURE 5.14   The vertebral column. Thin discs between the thoracic vertebrae allow great flexibility in the thoracic region; thick discs between the lumbar vertebrae reduce flexibility. Notice that the terms *convex* and *concave* refer to the curvature of the posterior aspect of the vertebral column.

• Remembering common meal times, 7 AM, 12 noon, and 5 PM, may help you to recall the number of bones in these three regions of the vertebral column.

The individual vertebrae are separated by pads of flexible fibrocartilage—**intervertebral discs**—that cushion the vertebrae and absorb shocks while allowing the spine flexibility. In a young person, the discs have a high water content (about 90 percent) and are spongy and compressible. But as a person ages, the water content of the discs decreases (as it does in other tissues throughout the body), and the discs become harder and less compressible.

HOMEOSTATIC IMBALANCE

Drying of the discs, along with a weakening of the ligaments of the vertebral column, predisposes older people to **herniated** ("slipped") **discs.** However, herniation also may result when the vertebral column is subjected to exceptional twisting forces. If the protruding disc presses on the spinal cord or the spinal nerves exiting from the cord, numbness and excruciating pain can result. ▲

The discs and the S-shaped structure of the vertebral column work together to prevent shock to the head when we walk or run. They also make the body trunk flexible. The spinal curvatures in the thoracic and sacral regions are referred to as **primary curvatures** because they are present when we are born. Together the two primary curvatures produce the C-shaped spine of the newborn baby (Figure 5.15). The curvatures in the

Text continues on p. 154

FIGURE 5.15   The C-shaped spine typical of a newborn.

A CLOSER LOOK

PROTECT YOUR BACK—IT'S THE ONLY ONE YOU'VE GOT!

Regular exercise is vital to keep the spine strong and to protect its beautifully proportioned structure. Unfortunately, most of us neglect our backs until pains and aches demand our attention. Next to sore throats and the common cold. Millions of U.S. citizens suffer from back pain, and back injuries account for a quarter of all disability insurance payments.

Although backache may be symptomatic of many ailments, from spinal tumor to kidney disease, over 80 percent of back problems result from weak muscles or are anxiety-related. This is not surprising; strong abdominal muscles and flexible back and hip muscles play a major role in reinforcing the spine's delicate architecture, and stress causes muscles to "knot." Tense muscles can aggravate a back problem even if they do not cause it. Obese individuals and those who rarely exercise are prime candidates for lower back pain. Indeed, some orthopedists (bone specialists) look upon back pain as an index of affluence. The more gadgets we accumulate to do our work for us, the more we can sit or lie down—and the more our muscles deteriorate. On the other side of the coin, people who work at jobs that require heavy lifting are also at risk for lower back pain if they do not lift properly.

As the saying goes, "An ounce of prevention is worth a pound of cure,"

and preventing back problems is better than attempting to treat agonizing back pain. Perhaps 70 to 80 percent of all cases of lower back pain are preventable with only 10 minutes of daily exercise, if proper body alignment and certain precautions are observed.

> " *Backaches are among the most common reasons for visits to the physician's office.*"

Here are a few well-documented guidelines for protecting your back.

1. Keep your weight down. Just a few extra pounds of weight, particularly the unbalanced weight of a protruding potbelly, exert a strain on the spine that is much greater than that of the weight itself. The protruding abdomen pulls

the body forward, forcing the back muscles to contract more strongly to counterbalance the weight. For example, 10 extra pounds located 10 inches anterior to the spine in the abdominal region force the back muscles to exert 50 extra pounds of force to counteract the 10-pound pulling force.

2. Wear high-heeled and negative-heeled shoes or boots infrequently, and avoid them altogether if you have back problems. Both change the alignment of the spine. High-heeled shoes tilt the pelvis forward and increase the stress on the abdominal and back muscles. Negative-heeled shoes tilt the pelvis backward,

Lowering the center of gravity by squatting.

making it difficult for you to transfer your weight during walking.

3. Maintain good posture. Keep your head and back aligned, with abdomen and buttocks tucked inward.

4. Lift heavy objects using proper body mechanics. Every object, including a human body, has a center of gravity around which its mass is equally distributed. In a standing adult, the center of gravity is inside the pelvis, slightly posterior to the anterior border of the joint between the sacrum and the fifth lumbar vertebra. A basic principle of body mechanics is the broader your base of support and the lower your center of gravity, the more stable you are. Applying this principle to lifting demands that you take a wider than normal stance (spread your feet apart slightly), and then bend your knees (rather than your back) to reach for and pick up the object (see the photograph on previous page). The weight is then transmitted to your stronger legs, sparing your more delicate spine. If you must move large objects, push rather than pull them.

5. Avoid sitting for prolonged periods. Sitting puts much more stress on the spine than standing: truck drivers have five times the normal risk for lower back problems and herniated discs. If you must sit for an extended time, resting your feet on a small stool (or the lowest desk drawer) will reduce the stress on your vertebral column.

6. Take 10 minutes a day to stretch your lower back extensor muscles and hip flexor muscles and to strengthen your abdominal muscles. (See instructions and photos **a–c**, which follow.) If you have a history of back problems, avoid any exercise that strains your lower back, including (1) sit-ups with straight legs, (2) double leg raises, and (3) lying on your abdomen and then raising your head, arms, and legs.

Dare to be different! Be good to your spine and you may well be saved from uttering that nearly universal complaint, "Oh, my aching back!"

(a) *Stretching the extensor muscles of the lower back.* Lie on back with knees bent and feet flat on the floor. Keeping your arms at your sides, raise one knee to the chest. Lower the foot to the floor with knee bent, and then slide the foot along the floor until the leg is fully extended. Rotate the leg gently from side to side.

Resume the starting position and repeat the exercise with the alternate leg. Repeat the entire exercise 5 to 6 times.

(b) *Stretching the flexor muscles of the hip.* Lie on back. Exhale as you bring both knees toward the chest. Then, while holding one knee to the chest, slide the opposite leg along the floor until it is fully extended. Attempt to touch the back of the knee (popliteal region) of the extended leg to the floor. Hold for a count of 6.

(a)

A CLOSER LOOK Protect Your Back *(continued)*

Resume the starting position and repeat the exercise with the alternate leg. Repeat the entire exercise 5 to 6 times.

(c) *Strengthening the abdominal muscles.* Lie on back with knees bent and feet flat on floor. Keeping your arms at your sides, raise one knee toward your chest. Exhale as you lift your head, attempting to touch your raised knee to your forehead. Count to 6. Resume the starting position, and roll your head gently from side to side. Inhale, and repeat the exercise with the alternate leg.

Repeat the entire exercise 8 to 10 times at the beginning; work up to 25 repetitions per day.

(b)

(c)

cervical and lumbar regions are referred to as **secondary curvatures** because they develop some time after birth. In adults, the secondary curvatures allow us to center our body weight on our lower limbs with minimum effort. The cervical curvature appears when a baby begins to raise its head, and the lumbar curvature develops when the baby begins to walk.

HOMEOSTATIC IMBALANCE

Why do they do "spine checks" in middle school? The answer is that they are looking for abnormal spinal curvatures. There are several types of abnormal spinal curvatures. Figure 5.16 shows three of these—**scoliosis** (sko"le-o'sis), **kyphosis** (ki-fo'sis), and **lordosis** (lor-do'sis). These abnormalities may be congenital (present at birth) or result from disease, poor posture, or unequal muscle pull on the spine. As you look at these diagrams, try to pinpoint how each of these conditions differs from the normal healthy spine. ▲

All vertebrae have a similar structural pattern (Figure 5.17). The common features of vertebrae include the following:

Scoliosis   Kyphosis   Lordosis

FIGURE 5.16 Abnormal spinal curvatures.

- **Body** or **centrum:** disclike, weight-bearing part of the vertebra facing anteriorly in the vertebral column.

- **Vertebral arch:** arch formed from the joining of all posterior extensions, the **laminae** and **pedicles,** from the vertebral body.

- **Vertebral foramen:** canal through which the spinal cord passes.

- **Transverse processes:** two lateral projections from the vertebral arch.

- **Spinous process:** single projection arising from the posterior aspect of the vertebral arch (actually the fused laminae).

- **Superior and inferior articular processes:** paired projections lateral to the vertebral foramen, allowing a vertebra to form joints with adjacent vertebrae (see also Figure 5.18).

In addition to the common features just described, vertebrae in the different regions of the spine have very specific structural characteristics. These unique regional characteristics of the vertebrae are described next.

Cervical Vertebrae

The seven **cervical vertebrae** (identified as C_1 to C_7) form the neck region of the spine. The first two vertebrae (*atlas* and *axis*) are different because they perform functions not shared by the other cervical vertebrae. As you can see in Figure 5.18a, the **atlas** (C_1) has no body. The superior surfaces of its transverse processes contain large depressions that receive the occipital condyles of the skull. This joint allows you to nod "yes." The **axis** (C_2) acts as a pivot for the rotation of the atlas (and skull) above. It has a large upright process, the **dens,** which acts as the pivot point. The joint between C_1 and C_2 allows you to rotate your head from side to side to indicate "no."

The "typical" cervical vertebrae (C_3 through C_7) are shown in Figure 5.18b. They are the smallest, lightest vertebrae, and most often their spinous processes are short and divided into two branches. The transverse processes of the cervical vertebrae contain foramina (openings) through which the vertebral arteries pass on their way to the brain above. Any time you see these foramina in a vertebra, you should know immediately that it is a cervical vertebra.

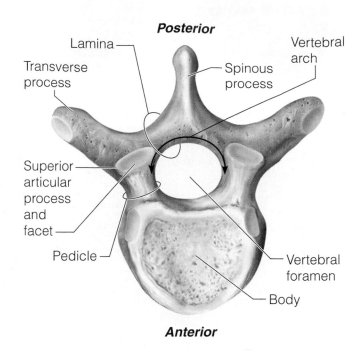

FIGURE 5.17   A typical vertebra, superior view. (Inferior articulating surfaces are not shown.)

Thoracic Vertebrae

The 12 **thoracic vertebrae** (T_1 to T_{12}) are all typical. They are larger than the cervical vertebrae and are distinguished by the fact that they are the only vertebrae to articulate with the ribs. As seen in Figure 5.18c, the body is somewhat heart-shaped and has two costal facets (articulating surfaces) on each side, which receive the heads of the ribs. The two transverse processes of each thoracic vertebra articulate with the nearby knoblike tubercles of the ribs. The spinous process is long and hooks sharply downward, causing the vertebra to look like a giraffe's head viewed from the side.

Lumbar Vertebrae

The five **lumbar vertebrae** (L_1 to L_5) have massive, blocklike bodies. Their short, hatchet-shaped spinous processes (Figure 5.18d) make them look like a moose head from the lateral aspect. Because most of the stress on the vertebral column occurs in the lumbar region, these are the sturdiest of the vertebrae.

Sacrum

The **sacrum** (sa′krum) is formed by the fusion of five vertebrae (Figure 5.19). Superiorly it articulates

(a) ATLAS AND AXIS

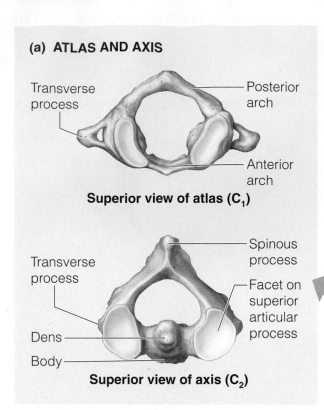

Transverse process

Posterior arch

Anterior arch

Superior view of atlas (C₁)

Transverse process

Spinous process

Facet on superior articular process

Dens

Body

Superior view of axis (C₂)

(b) TYPICAL CERVICAL VERTEBRAE

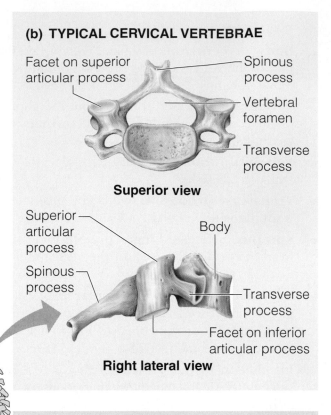

Facet on superior articular process

Spinous process

Vertebral foramen

Transverse process

Superior view

Superior articular process

Body

Spinous process

Transverse process

Facet on inferior articular process

Right lateral view

(c) THORACIC VERTEBRAE

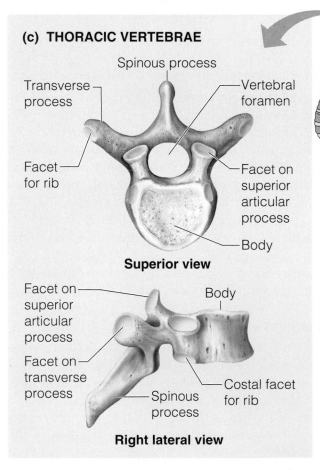

Transverse process

Spinous process

Vertebral foramen

Facet for rib

Facet on superior articular process

Body

Superior view

Facet on superior articular process

Body

Facet on transverse process

Costal facet for rib

Spinous process

Right lateral view

(d) LUMBAR VERTEBRAE

Spinous process

Transverse process

Vertebral foramen

Body

Facet on superior articular process

Superior view

Superior articular process

Body

Spinous process

Facet on inferior articular process

Right lateral view

F I G U R E   5.18   Regional characteristics of vertebrae.
(a) Superior views of the atlas and axis. (b) Typical cervical vertebrae.
(c) Thoracic vertebrae. (d) Lumbar vertebrae.

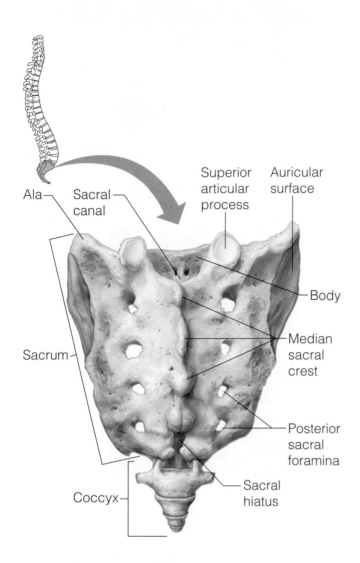

FIGURE 5.19   Sacrum and coccyx, posterior view.

with L_5, and inferiorly it connects with the coccyx. The winglike **alae** articulate laterally with the hip bones, forming the sacroiliac joints. The sacrum forms the posterior wall of the pelvis. Its posterior midline surface is roughened by the **median sacral crest,** the fused spinous processes of the sacral vertebrae. This is flanked laterally by the *posterior sacral foramina.* The vertebral canal continues inside the sacrum as the **sacral canal** and terminates in a large inferior opening called the **sacral hiatus.**

Coccyx

The **coccyx** is formed from the fusion of three to five tiny, irregularly shaped vertebrae (see Figure 5.19). It is the human "tailbone," a remnant of the tail that other vertebrate animals have.

Thoracic Cage

The sternum, ribs, and thoracic vertebrae make up the **bony thorax.** The bony thorax is routinely called the **thoracic cage** because it forms a protective, cone-shaped cage of slender bones around the organs of the thoracic cavity (heart, lungs, and major blood vessels). The bony thorax is shown in Figure 5.20.

Sternum

The **sternum** (breastbone) is a typical flat bone and the result of the fusion of three bones— the **manubrium** (mah-nu′bre-um), **body,** and **xiphoid** (zif′oid) **process.** It is attached to the first seven pairs of ribs.

The sternum has three important bony landmarks—the jugular notch, the sternal angle, and the xiphisternal joint.

- The **jugular notch** (concave upper border of the manubrium) can be palpated easily; generally it is at the level of the third thoracic vertebra.

- The **sternal angle** results where the manubrium and body meet at a slight angle to each other, so that a transverse ridge is formed at the level of the second ribs. It provides a handy reference point for counting ribs to locate the second intercostal space for listening to certain heart valves.

- The **xiphisternal** (zi′fe-ster″nal) **joint,** the point where the sternal body and xiphoid process fuse, lies at the level of the ninth thoracic vertebra.

Palpate your sternal angle and jugular notch.

Because the sternum is so close to the body surface, it is easy to obtain samples from it of blood-forming (hematopoietic) tissue for the diagnosis of suspected blood diseases. A needle is inserted into the marrow of the sternum, and the sample is withdrawn; this procedure is called a *sternal puncture.* Because the heart lies immediately posterior to the sternum, the physician must take extreme care not to penetrate through the sternum during this procedure.

Ribs

Twelve pairs of **ribs** form the walls of the bony thorax. (Contrary to popular misconception, men do *not* have one rib fewer than women!) All the ribs articulate with the vertebral column posteriorly and then curve downward and toward the anterior body surface. The **true ribs,** the first seven pairs, attach

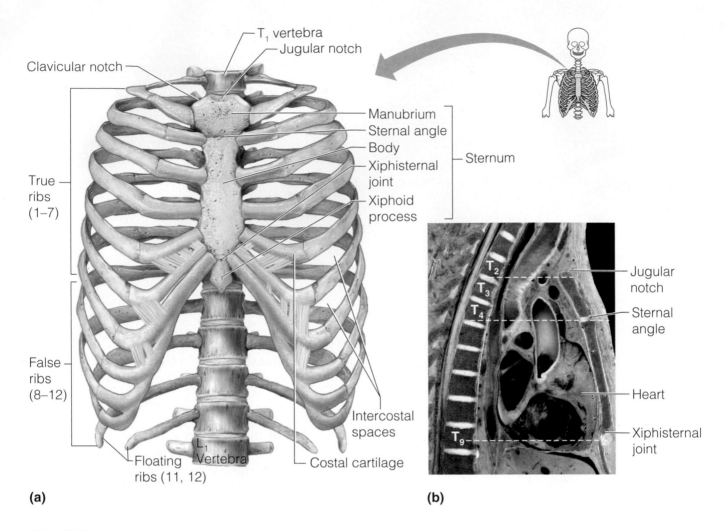

FIGURE 5.20 **The bony thorax (thoracic cage). (a)** Anterior view. **(b)** Midsagittal section through the thorax, showing the relationship of the key parts of the sternum to the vertebral column.

directly to the sternum by costal cartilages. **False ribs,** the next five pairs, either attach indirectly to the sternum or are not attached to the sternum at all. The last two pairs of false ribs lack the sternal attachments, so they are also called **floating ribs.**

The intercostal spaces (spaces between the ribs) are filled with the intercostal muscles that aid in breathing.

▶ *DID YOU GET IT?*

14. What are the five major regions of the vertebral column?

15. How can you distinguish a lumbar vertebra from a cervical vertebra?

16. What is a true rib? A false rib?

17. How would a complete fracture of the dens affect the mobility of the vertebral column?

For answers, see Appendix D.

Appendicular Skeleton

The *appendicular skeleton* is shaded gold in Figure 5.6. It is composed of 126 bones of the limbs (appendages) and the pectoral and pelvic girdles, which attach the limbs to the axial skeleton.

Bones of the Shoulder Girdle

Each **shoulder girdle,** or **pectoral girdle,** consists of two bones—a clavicle and a scapula (Figure 5.21).

The **clavicle** (klav′ĭ-kl), or *collarbone,* is a slender, doubly curved bone. It attaches to the

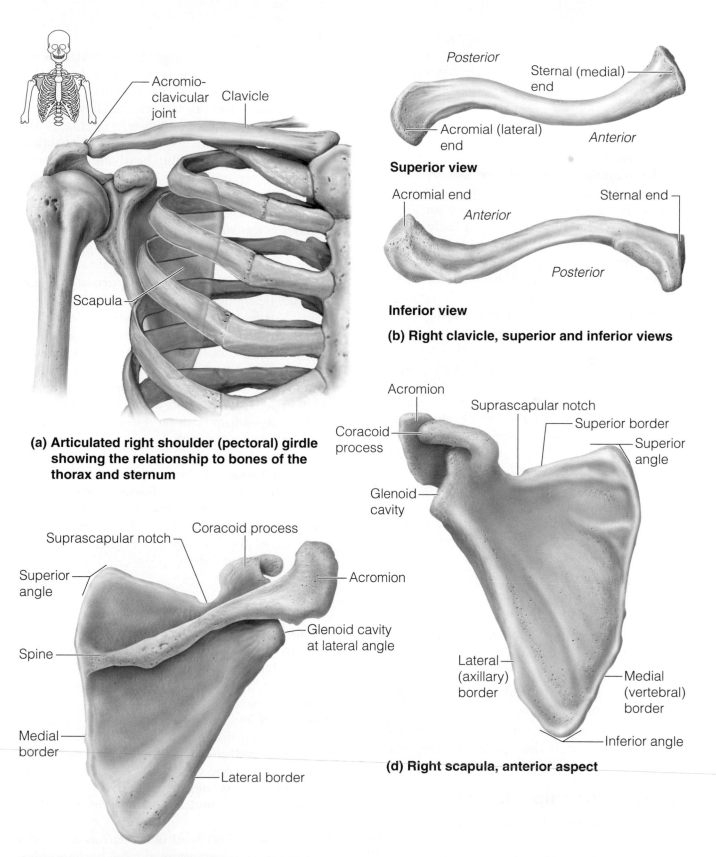

(a) Articulated right shoulder (pectoral) girdle showing the relationship to bones of the thorax and sternum

Superior view

Inferior view

(b) Right clavicle, superior and inferior views

(c) Right scapula, posterior aspect

(d) Right scapula, anterior aspect

FIGURE 5.21   Bones of the shoulder girdle.

manubrium of the sternum medially (at its sternal end) and to the scapula laterally, where it helps to form the shoulder joint. The clavicle acts as a brace to hold the arm away from the top of the thorax and helps prevent shoulder dislocation. When the clavicle is broken, the whole shoulder region caves in medially, which shows how important its bracing function is.

The **scapulae** (skap'u-le), or *shoulder blades,* are triangular and are commonly called "wings" because they flare when we move our arms posteriorly. Each scapula has a flattened body and two important processes—the **acromion** (ah-kro'me-on), which is the enlarged end of the spine of the scapula, and the beaklike **coracoid** (kor'ah-koid) **process.** The acromion connects with the clavicle laterally at the **acromioclavicular joint.** The coracoid process points over the top of the shoulder and anchors some of the muscles of the arm. Just medial to the coracoid process is the large **suprascapular notch,** which serves as a nerve passageway. The scapula is not directly attached to the axial skeleton; it is loosely held in place by trunk muscles. The scapula has three borders—superior, medial (vertebral), and lateral (axillary). It also has three angles—superior, inferior, and lateral. The **glenoid cavity,** a shallow socket that receives the head of the arm bone, is in the lateral angle.

The shoulder girdle is very light and allows the upper limb to have exceptionally free movement. This is due to the following factors:

1. Each shoulder girdle attaches to the axial skeleton at only one point—the *sternoclavicular joint.*

2. The loose attachment of the scapula allows it to slide back and forth against the thorax as muscles act.

3. The glenoid cavity is shallow, and the shoulder joint is poorly reinforced by ligaments.

However, this exceptional flexibility also has a drawback; the shoulder girdle is very easily dislocated.

Bones of the Upper Limbs

Thirty separate bones form the skeletal framework of each upper limb (Figures 5.22 and 5.23). They form the foundations of the arm, forearm, and hand.

Arm

The arm is formed by a single bone, the **humerus** (hu'mer-us), which is a typical long bone (see Figure 5.22a and b). At its proximal end is a rounded head that fits into the shallow glenoid cavity of the scapula. Immediately inferior to the head is a slight constriction called the **anatomical neck.** Anterolateral to the head are two bony projections separated by the **intertubercular sulcus**—the **greater** and **lesser tubercles,** which are sites of muscle attachment. Just distal to the tubercles is the **surgical neck,** so named because it is the most frequently fractured part of the humerus. In the midpoint of the shaft is a roughened area called the **deltoid tuberosity,** where the large, fleshy deltoid muscle of the shoulder attaches. Nearby, the **radial groove** runs obliquely down the posterior aspect of the shaft. This groove marks the course of the radial nerve, an important nerve of the upper limb. At the distal end of the humerus is the medial **trochlea** (trok'le-ah), which looks somewhat like a spool, and the lateral ball-like **capitulum** (kah-pit'u-lum). Both of these processes articulate with bones of the forearm. Above the trochlea anteriorly is a depression, the **coronoid fossa;** on the posterior surface is the **olecranon** (o-lek'rah-non) **fossa.** These two depressions, which are flanked by **medial** and **lateral epicondyles,** allow the corresponding processes of the ulna to move freely when the elbow is bent and extended.

Forearm

Two bones, the radius and the ulna, form the skeleton of the forearm (see Figure 5.22c). When the body is in the anatomical position, the **radius** is the lateral bone; that is, it is on the thumb side of the forearm. When the hand is rotated so that the palm faces backward, the distal end of the radius crosses over and ends up medial to the ulna. Both proximally and distally the radius and ulna articulate at small **radioulnar joints,** and the two bones are connected along their entire length by the flexible **interosseous membrane.** Both the ulna and the radius have a **styloid process** at their distal end.

The disc-shaped head of the radius also forms a joint with the capitulum of the humerus. Just below the head is the **radial tuberosity,** where the tendon of the biceps muscle attaches.

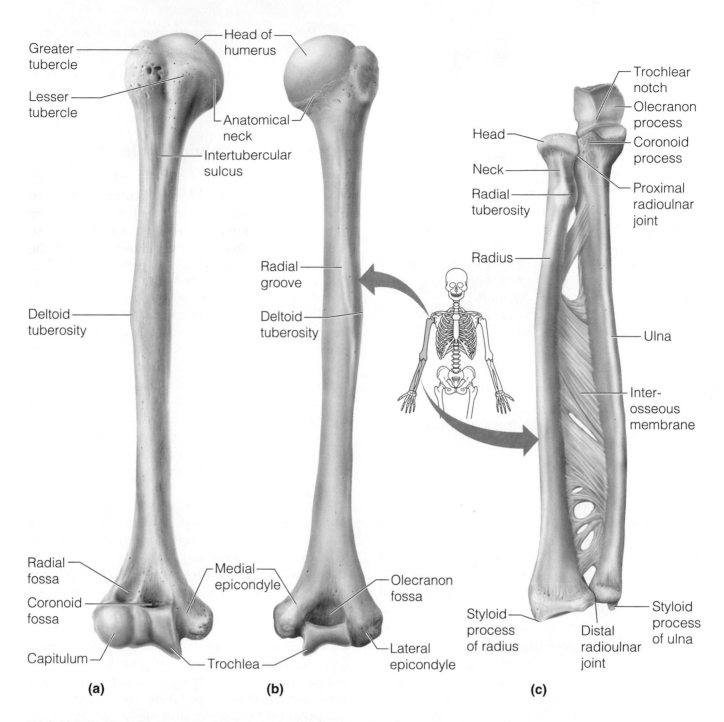

FIGURE 5.22 **Bones of the right arm and forearm. (a)** Humerus, anterior view. **(b)** Humerus, posterior view. **(c)** Anterior view of the bones of the forearm: the radius and the ulna.

When the upper limb is in the anatomical position, the **ulna** is the medial bone (on the little-finger side) of the forearm. On its proximal end are the anterior **coronoid process** and the posterior **olecranon process,** which are separated by the **trochlear notch.** Together these two processes grip the trochlea of the humerus in a pliers-like joint.

Hand

The skeleton of the hand consists of the carpals, the metacarpals, and the phalanges (Figure 5.23).

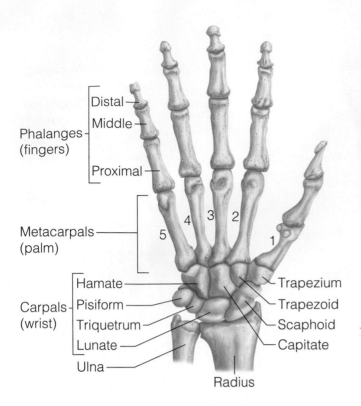

Phalanges (fingers)
- Distal
- Middle
- Proximal

Metacarpals (palm)

4 3 2
5   1

Carpals (wrist)
- Hamate
- Pisiform
- Triquetrum
- Lunate
- Ulna

- Trapezium
- Trapezoid
- Scaphoid
- Capitate

Radius

FIGURE 5.23 Bones of the right hand, anterior view.

The eight **carpal bones,** arranged in two irregular rows of four bones each, form the part of the hand called the **carpus** or, more commonly, the *wrist.* The carpals are bound together by ligaments that restrict movements between them. (In case you need to learn their names, the individual carpal bones are identified in Figure 5.23.)

The palm of the hand consists of the **metacarpals.** The **phalanges** (fah-lan'jēz) are the bones of the fingers. The metacarpals are numbered 1 to 5 from the thumb side of the hand toward the little finger. When the fist is clenched, the heads of the metacarpals become obvious as the "knuckles." Each hand contains 14 phalanges. There are three in each finger (proximal, middle, and distal), except in the thumb, which has only two (proximal and distal).

▶ *DID YOU GET IT?*

18. What is the single point of attachment of the shoulder girdle to the axial skeleton?

19. What bone forms the skeleton of the arm?

20. Where are the carpals found, and what type (long, short, irregular, or flat) of bone are they?

21. Which bones of the upper limb have a styloid process?

For answers, see Appendix D.

Bones of the Pelvic Girdle

The **pelvic girdle** is formed by two **coxal** (kok'sal) **bones,** or **ossa coxae,** commonly called **hip bones.** Together with the sacrum and the coccyx, the hip bones form the *bony pelvis* (Figure 5.24). Note that the terms *pelvic girdle* and *bony pelvis* have slightly different meanings (pelvic girdle = 2 coxal bones; bony pelvis = 2 coxal bones, sacrum, and coccyx).

The bones of the pelvic girdle are large and heavy, and they are attached securely to the axial skeleton. The sockets, which receive the thigh bones, are deep and heavily reinforced by ligaments that attach the limbs firmly to the girdle. Bearing weight is the most important function of this girdle, because the total weight of the upper body rests on the bony pelvis. The reproductive organs, urinary bladder, and part of the large intestine lie within and are protected by the bony pelvis.

Each hip bone is formed by the fusion of three bones: the *ilium, ischium,* and *pubis.* The **ilium** (il'e-um), which connects posteriorly with the sacrum at the **sacroiliac** (sak"ro-il'e-ac) **joint,** is a large, flaring bone that forms most of the hip bone. When you put your hands on your hips, they are resting over the *alae,* or winglike portions, of the ilia. The upper edge of an ala, the **iliac crest,** is an important anatomical landmark that is always kept in mind by those who give intramuscular injections. The iliac crest ends anteriorly in the **anterior superior iliac spine** and posteriorly in the **posterior superior iliac spine.** Small inferior spines are located below these.

The **ischium** (is'ke-um) is the "sit-down bone," so called because it forms the most inferior part of the coxal bone. The **ischial tuberosity** is a roughened area that receives body weight when you are sitting. The **ischial spine,** superior to the tuberosity, is another important anatomical landmark, particularly in the pregnant woman, because it narrows the outlet of the pelvis through which the baby must pass during the birth process. Another important structural feature of the ischium is

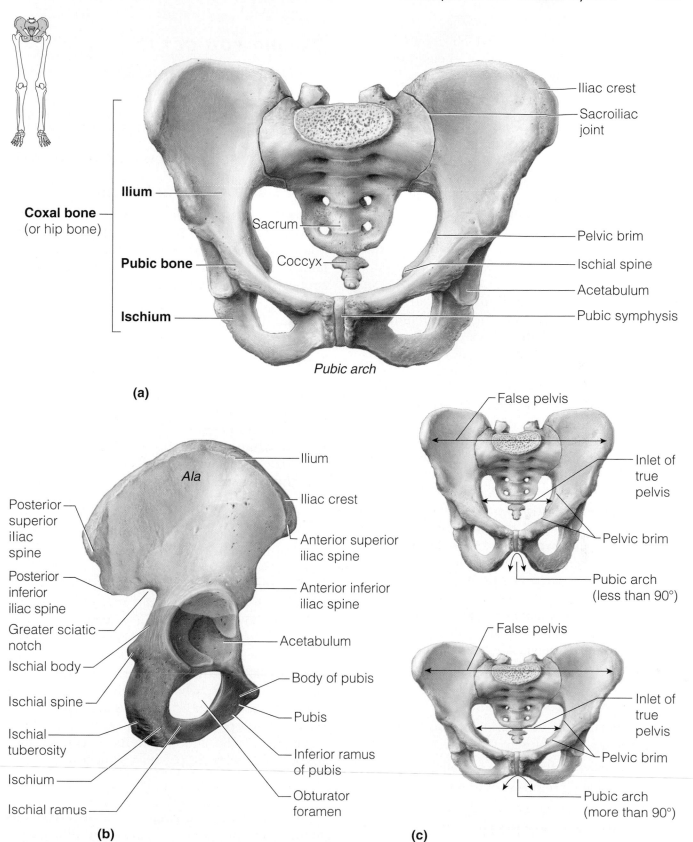

Coxal bone (or hip bone)

Ilium

Pubic bone

Ischium

Sacrum

Coccyx

Pubic arch

Iliac crest

Sacroiliac joint

Pelvic brim

Ischial spine

Acetabulum

Pubic symphysis

(a)

Posterior superior iliac spine

Posterior inferior iliac spine

Greater sciatic notch

Ischial body

Ischial spine

Ischial tuberosity

Ischium

Ischial ramus

Ala

Ilium

Iliac crest

Anterior superior iliac spine

Anterior inferior iliac spine

Acetabulum

Body of pubis

Pubis

Inferior ramus of pubis

Obturator foramen

(b)

False pelvis

Inlet of true pelvis

Pelvic brim

Pubic arch (less than 90°)

False pelvis

Inlet of true pelvis

Pelvic brim

Pubic arch (more than 90°)

(c)

FIGURE 5.24   The bony pelvis. (a) Articulated male pelvis. **(b)** Right coxal bone, showing the point of fusion of the ilium, ischium, and pubic bones. **(c)** Comparison of the pelves of the male (above) and female (below).

the **greater sciatic notch,** which allows blood vessels and the large sciatic nerve to pass from the pelvis posteriorly into the thigh. Injections in the buttock should always be given well away from this area.

The **pubis** (pu'bis), or **pubic bone,** is the most anterior part of a coxal bone. Fusion of the *rami* of the pubis anteriorly and the ischium posteriorly forms a bar of bone enclosing the **obturator** (ob'tu-ra"tor) **foramen,** an opening that allows blood vessels and nerves to pass into the anterior part of the thigh. The pubic bones of each hip bone fuse anteriorly to form a cartilaginous joint, the **pubic symphysis** (pu'bik sim'fĭ-sis).

The ilium, ischium, and pubis fuse at the deep socket called the **acetabulum** (as"ĕ-tab'u-lum), which means "vinegar cup." The acetabulum receives the head of the thigh bone.

The bony pelvis is divided into two regions. The **false pelvis** is superior to the true pelvis; it is the area medial to the flaring portions of the ilia. The **true pelvis** is surrounded by bone and lies inferior to the flaring parts of the ilia and the pelvic brim. The dimensions of the true pelvis of a woman are very important because they must be large enough to allow the infant's head (the largest part of the infant) to pass during childbirth. The dimensions of the cavity, particularly the **outlet** (the inferior opening of the pelvis measured between the ischial spines), and the **inlet** (superior opening between the right and left sides of the pelvic brim) are critical, and thus they are carefully measured by the obstetrician.

Of course, individual pelvic structures vary, but there are fairly consistent differences between a male and a female pelvis. Look at Figure 5.24c and notice the following characteristics that differ in the pelvis of the man and woman:

- The female inlet is larger and more circular.
- The female pelvis as a whole is shallower, and the bones are lighter and thinner.
- The female ilia flare more laterally.
- The female sacrum is shorter and less curved.
- The female ischial spines are shorter and farther apart; thus the outlet is larger.
- The female pubic arch is more rounded because the angle of the pubic arch is greater.

▶ *DID YOU GET IT?*

22. What three bones form the hipbone? What bones form the pelvic girdle?

23. In what three ways does the bony pelvis of a woman differ from that of a man?

For answers, see Appendix D.

Bones of the Lower Limbs

The lower limbs carry our total body weight when we are erect. Hence, it is not surprising that the bones forming the three segments of the lower limbs (thigh, leg, and foot) are much thicker and stronger than the comparable bones of the upper limb.

Thigh

The **femur** (fe'mur), or *thigh bone,* is the only bone in the thigh (Figure 5.25a and b). It is the heaviest, strongest bone in the body. Its proximal end has a ball-like head, a neck, and **greater** and **lesser trochanters** (separated anteriorly by the **intertrochanteric line** and posteriorly by the **intertrochanteric crest**). These markings and the **gluteal tuberosity,** located on the shaft, all serve as sites for muscle attachment. The head of the femur articulates with the acetabulum of the hip bone in a deep, secure socket. However, the neck of the femur is a common fracture site, especially in old age.

The femur slants medially as it runs downward to join with the leg bones; this brings the knees in line with the body's center of gravity. The medial course of the femur is more noticeable in women because the female pelvis is wider than that of the male. Distally on the femur are the **lateral** and **medial condyles,** which articulate with the tibia below. Posteriorly these condyles are separated by the deep **intercondylar fossa.** Anteriorly on the distal femur is the smooth **patellar surface,** which forms a joint with the patella, or kneecap.

Leg

Connected along their length by an **interosseous membrane,** two bones, the tibia and fibula, form the skeleton of the leg (see Figure 5.25c). The **tibia,** or *shinbone,* is larger and more medial. At the proximal end, the **medial** and **lateral condyles** (separated by the **intercondylar eminence**) articulate

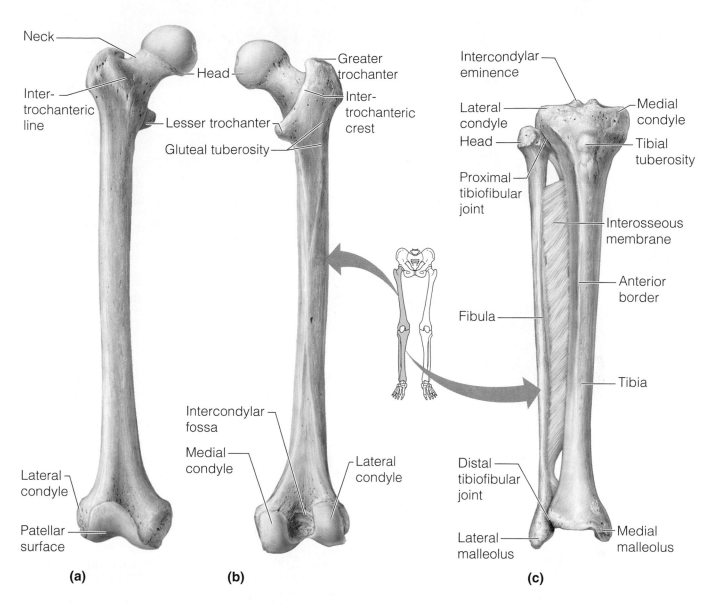

FIGURE 5.25 **Bones of the right thigh and leg. (a)** Femur (thigh bone), anterior view. **(b)** Femur, posterior view. **(c)** Tibia and fibula of the leg, anterior view.

with the distal end of the femur to form the knee joint. The patellar (kneecap) ligament attaches to the **tibial tuberosity,** a roughened area on the anterior tibial surface. Distally, a process called the **medial malleolus** (mal-le′o-lus) forms the inner bulge of the ankle. The anterior surface of the tibia is a sharp ridge, the **anterior border,** that is unprotected by muscles; thus, it is easily felt beneath the skin.

The **fibula,** which lies alongside the tibia and forms joints with it both proximally and distally, is thin and sticklike. The fibula has no part in forming

the knee joint. Its distal end, the **lateral malleolus,** forms the outer part of the ankle.

Foot

The foot, composed of the tarsals, metatarsals, and phalanges, has two important functions. It supports our body weight and serves as a lever that allows us to propel our bodies forward when we walk and run.

The **tarsus,** forming the posterior half of the foot, is composed of seven **tarsal bones** (Figure 5.26). Body weight is carried mostly by the two

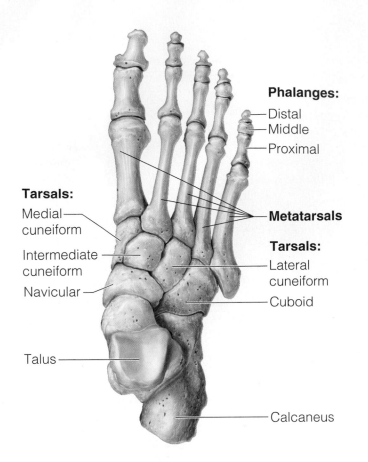

Phalanges:
- Distal
- Middle
- Proximal

Tarsals:
Medial cuneiform

Intermediate cuneiform

Navicular

Talus

Metatarsals

Tarsals:
Lateral cuneiform

Cuboid

Calcaneus

FIGURE 5.26   Bones of the right foot, superior view.

Medial longitudinal arch

Transverse arch

Lateral longitudinal arch

FIGURE 5.27   Arches of the foot.

largest tarsals, the **calcaneus** (kal-ka′ne-us), or heelbone, and the **talus** (ta′lus; "ankle"), which lies between the tibia and the calcaneus. Five **metatarsals** form the sole, and 14 **phalanges** form the toes. Like the fingers of the hand, each toe has three phalanges, except the great toe, which has two.

The bones in the foot are arranged to form three strong arches: two longitudinal (medial and lateral) and one transverse (Figure 5.27). *Ligaments,* which bind the foot bones together, and *tendons* of the foot muscles help to hold the bones firmly in the arched position but still allow a certain amount of give or springiness. Weak arches are referred to as "fallen arches" or "flat feet."

▶ *DID YOU GET IT?*

24. What two bones form the skeleton of the leg?

25. Bo's longitudinal and medial arches have suffered a collapse. What is the name of Bo's condition?

26. Which lower limb bone has an intertrochanteric line and crest and an intercondylar fossa?

For answers, see Appendix D.

Joints

With one exception (the hyoid bone of the neck), every bone in the body forms a joint with at least one other bone. **Joints,** also called **articulations,** have two functions: they hold the bones together securely but also give the rigid skeleton mobility.

The graceful movements of a ballet dancer and the rough-and-tumble grapplings of a football player illustrate the great variety of motion allowed by joints, the sites where two or more bones meet. With fewer joints, we would move like robots. Nevertheless, the bone-binding function of joints is just as important as their role in providing mobility. The immovable joints of the skull, for instance, form a snug enclosure for our vital brain.

Joints are classified in two ways—functionally and structurally. The functional classification focuses on the amount of movement the joint allows. On this basis, there are **synarthroses** (sin″ar-thro′sēz), or immovable joints; **amphiarthroses** (am″fe-ar-thro′sēz), or slightly movable joints; and **diarthroses** (di″ar-thro′sēz), or freely movable joints. Freely movable joints predominate in the limbs, where mobility is important. Immovable and slightly movable joints are restricted mainly to

A CLOSER LOOK

THEM BONES, THEM BONES GOIN' TO WALK AROUND — CLINICAL ADVANCES IN BONE REPAIR

Although bones have remarkable self-regenerative powers, some conditions are just too severe for bones to effect repair. Examples include extensive shattering (as in automobile accidents), poor circulation in old bones, and certain birth defects. Here we address healing problems that bones cannot handle themselves. Let's take a look at some techniques currently used to expedite bone repair.

Electrical stimulation of fracture sites dramatically increases the speed and completeness of healing in large or slowly healing fractures. For years it has been known that bone tissue is deposited in regions of negative electrical charge (its stressed regions) and absorbed in regions of positive charge, but we are still not sure how electricity promotes healing. One theory is that negative fields prevent parathyroid hormone from stimulating the bone-absorbing osteoclast cells at the fracture site, thus allowing bony tissue to accumulate. Another theory is that the fields induce production of growth chemicals that stimulate the osteoblasts.

Ultrasound, introduced as the basis of an imaging technique in Chapter 1, can speed the repair of fresh fractures. Daily exposure to pulsed low-power ultrasound waves reduces the healing time of broken arm and shin bones by 35 to 45 percent. It apparently stimulates cartilage cells to make callus.

The most troublesome injuries to bones are non-union fractures, in which the two parts of a split bone fail to join. Such fractures traditionally have been treated with grafts, in which sections of bone are taken from the hip and inserted into the gap. However, this requires several painful grafting sessions, and one-third of the grafts fail to heal. A

> ❝Much research has gone into developing bone substitutes.❞

potential improvement is the **free vascular fibular graft technique,** which uses pieces of the fibula to replace missing bone. One reason that traditional grafts often fail is that a blood supply cannot reach their interior. This new technique grafts normal blood vessels along with the bone sections, and subsequent remodeling leads to a good replica of the preinjury bone.

Although bone implants have proved effective in adults, they have been less satisfactory for children with growing bones. This problem has been partly resolved, at least for knee replacement candidates, with **self-extendible endoprostheses.** The

Telescopic/ extension portion

The self-extending leg implant. Lengthening occurs at the telescopic/extension portion.

telescopic sleeve of these devices (see the figure) undergoes continual automatic elongation of the limb enforced by knee bending. Tension in the surrounding tissue prevents the prosthesis from lengthening too much; tension increases after each elongation and then gradually decreases as the soft tissues grow.

Vascular endothelial growth factor (VEGF) is a protein that stimulates the growth of blood vessels. Researchers have been exploring its potential to create new arteries in people with heart disease, and more recently they began studying VEGF as a way to build new bone tissue. Experiments on mice with bone fractures show that VEGF stimulates the

A CLOSER LOOK Them Bones *(continued)*

formation of osteoblasts and proteins associated with bone growth.

Much research has gone into developing **bone substitutes** (crushed cadaver bone or synthetic materials) to fill the gaps in non-union defects. Crushed bone from human cadavers is mixed with water to form a paste that can be molded into the desired shape or packed into small, difficult-to-reach spaces. However, cadaver bone is a foreign tissue that the immune system may reject, and the body sometimes fails to replace it with new bone, as it must for healing to occur. Furthermore, there is a slight but real risk that the cadaver bone contains disease organisms.

ProOsteon, made from coral, avoids both problems. The coral is heat-treated to kill its living cells and convert its calcium carbonate to hydroxyapatite, the mineral in bone. The coral graft is then carved to the desired shape, sterilized by irradiation with gamma rays, coated with a natural substance that induces bone formation (bone morphogenic protein), and implanted. Osteoblasts and blood vessels migrate from the adjacent natural bone into the coral implant, gradually replacing it with living bone.

Research has also produced several types of ceramic bone substitutes. One is TCP, a biodegradable ceramic substance soft enough to be shaped but not very strong. TCP's biggest application has been to replace parts of nonweight-bearing bones, such as skull bones.

Norian SRS, a bone cement made of calcium phosphate, provides immediate structural support to fractured or osteoporotic sites. Mixed at the time of surgery, Norian SRS paste is injected into areas of damaged bone to create an internal "cast." The paste hardens in minutes and cures into a substance with greater compressive strength than spongy bone. Because its crystalline structure and chemistry are the same as those of natural bone, it is gradually remodeled and replaced by host bone. However, Norian SRS can be used only on the ends of long bones because it cannot resist the strong compressive and bending stresses occurring at the central shaft.

---

the axial skeleton, where firm attachments and protection of internal organs are priorities.

Structurally, there are *fibrous, cartilaginous,* and *synovial joints.* These classifications are based on whether fibrous tissue, cartilage, or a joint cavity separates the bony regions at the joint. As a general rule, fibrous joints are immovable, and synovial joints are freely movable. Although cartilaginous joints have both immovable and slightly movable examples, most are amphiarthrotic. Because the structural classification is more clear-cut, we will focus on that classification scheme here. The joint types are shown in Figure 5.28, described next, and summarized in Table 5.3.

Fibrous Joints

In **fibrous joints,** the bones are united by fibrous tissue. The best examples of this type of joint are the *sutures* of the skull (Figure 5.28a). In sutures, the irregular edges of the bones interlock and are bound tightly together by connective tissue fibers, allowing essentially no movement. In **syndesmoses** (sin-dez-mo′sēz), the connecting fibers are longer than those of sutures; thus the joint has more "give." The joint connecting the distal ends of the tibia and fibula is a syndesmosis (Figure 5.28b).

Cartilaginous Joints

In **cartilaginous joints,** the bone ends are connected by cartilage. Examples of this joint type that are slightly movable (amphiarthrotic) are the *pubic symphysis* of the pelvis (Figure 5.28e) and *intervertebral joints* of the spinal column (Figure 5.28d), where the articulating bone surfaces are connected by pads (discs) of fibrocartilage. The hyaline-cartilage epiphyseal plates of growing long bones and the cartilaginous joints between the first ribs and the sternum are immovable (synarthrotic) cartilaginous joints (Figure 5.28c).

Synovial Joints

Synovial joints are joints in which the articulating bone ends are separated by a joint cavity containing

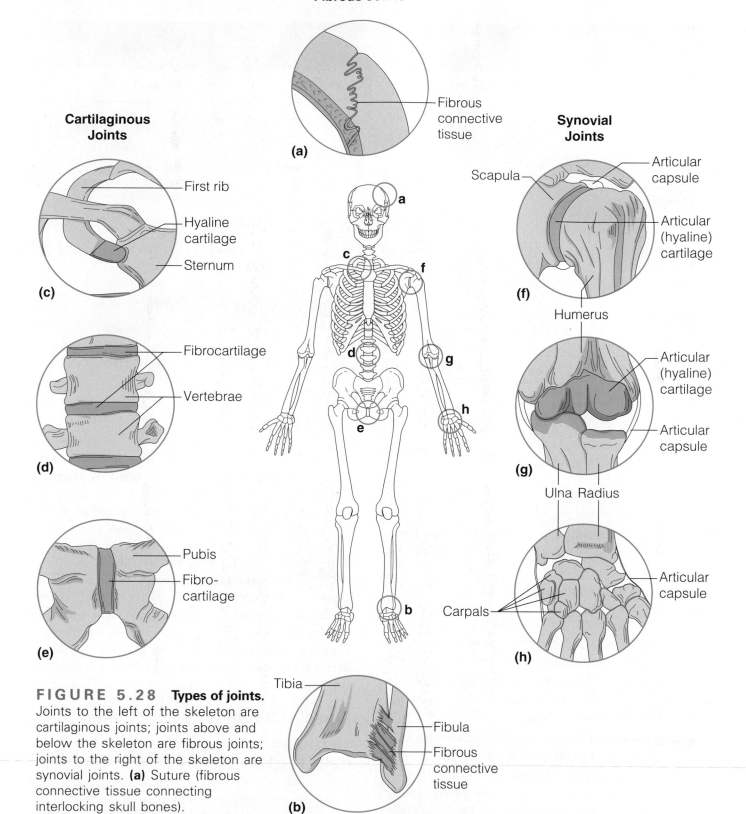

Fibrous Joints

Fibrous connective tissue

(a)

Cartilaginous Joints

First rib

Hyaline cartilage

Sternum

(c)

Fibrocartilage

Vertebrae

(d)

Pubis

Fibro-cartilage

(e)

a

c

d

e

f

g

h

b

Synovial Joints

Scapula

Articular capsule

Articular (hyaline) cartilage

Humerus

(f)

Articular (hyaline) cartilage

Articular capsule

Ulna Radius

(g)

Carpals

Articular capsule

(h)

Tibia

Fibula

Fibrous connective tissue

(b)

FIGURE 5.28   Types of joints.
Joints to the left of the skeleton are cartilaginous joints; joints above and below the skeleton are fibrous joints; joints to the right of the skeleton are synovial joints. **(a)** Suture (fibrous connective tissue connecting interlocking skull bones).
(b) Syndesmosis (fibrous connective tissue connecting the distal ends of the tibia and fibula). **(c)** Synchondrosis (joint between costal cartilage of rib 1 and the sternum). **(d)** Symphyses (intervertebral discs of fibrocartilage connecting adjacent vertebrae). **(e)** Symphysis (fibrocartilaginous pubic symphysis connecting the pubic bones anteriorly). **(f)** Synovial joint (multiaxial shoulder joint). **(g)** Synovial joint (uniaxial elbow joint). **(h)** Synovial joints (biaxial intercarpal joints of the hand).

TABLE 5.3	Summary of Joint Classes		
Structural class	**Structural characteristics**	**Types**	**Mobility**
Fibrous	Bone ends/parts united by collagenic fibers	Suture (short fibers)	Immobile (synarthrosis)
		Syndesmosis (longer fibers)	Slightly mobile (amphiarthrosis) and immobile
		Gomphosis (periodontal ligament)	Immobile
Cartilaginous	Bone ends/parts united by cartilage	Synchondrosis (hyaline cartilage)	Immobile
		Symphysis (fibrocartilage)	Slightly movable
Synovial	Bone ends/parts covered with articular cartilage and enclosed within an articular capsule lined with synovial membrane	Plane Condyloid Hinge Saddle Pivot Ball and socket	Freely movable (diarthrosis; movements depend on design of joint)

synovial fluid (see Figure 5.28f–h). They account for all joints of the limbs.

All synovial joints have four distinguishing features (Figure 5.29):

1. **Articular cartilage.** Articular (hyaline) cartilage covers the ends of the bones forming the joint.

2. **Fibrous articular capsule.** The joint surfaces are enclosed by a sleeve or capsule of fibrous connective tissue, and the capsule is lined with a smooth *synovial membrane* (the reason these joints are called synovial joints).

3. **Joint cavity.** The articular capsule encloses a cavity, called the joint cavity, which contains lubricating synovial fluid.

4. **Reinforcing ligaments.** The fibrous capsule is usually reinforced with ligaments.

Bursae and tendon sheaths are not strictly part of synovial joints, but they are often found closely associated with them (see Figure 5.29). Essentially bags of lubricant, they act like ball bearings to reduce friction between adjacent structures during joint activity. **Bursae** (ber′se; "purses") are flattened fibrous sacs lined with synovial membrane and containing a thin film of synovial fluid. They

are common where ligaments, muscles, skin, tendons, or bones rub together. A **tendon sheath,** also shown in Figure 5.29, is essentially an elongated bursa that wraps completely around a tendon subjected to friction, like a bun around a hot dog.

HOMEOSTATIC IMBALANCE

A **dislocation** happens when a bone is forced out of its normal position in the joint cavity. The process of returning the bone to its proper position, called **reduction,** should be done only by a physician. Attempts by an untrained person to "snap the bone back into its socket" are usually more harmful than helpful. ▲

Types of Synovial Joints Based on Shape

The shapes of the articulating bone surfaces determine what movements are allowed at a joint. Based on such shapes, our synovial joints can be classified as *plane, hinge, pivot, condyloid, saddle,* and *ball-and-socket joints* (Figure 5.30).

- In a **plane joint** (Figure 5.30a), the articular surfaces are essentially flat, and only short

How does this joint type differ structurally from cartilaginous and fibrous joints?

Acromion of scapula

Ligament

Bursa

Ligament

Tendon sheath

Tendon of biceps muscle

Joint cavity containing synovial fluid

Articular (hyaline) cartilage

Synovial membrane

Fibrous articular capsule

Humerus

FIGURE 5.29 **General structure of a synovial joint.**

slipping or gliding movements are allowed. The movements of plane joints are *nonaxial;* that is, gliding does not involve rotation around any axis. The intercarpal joints of the wrist are the best examples of plane joints.

- In a **hinge joint** (Figure 5.30b), the cylindrical end of one bone fits into a trough-shaped surface on another bone. Angular movement is allowed in just one plane, like a mechanical hinge. Examples are the elbow joint, ankle joint, and the joints between the phalanges of the fingers. Hinge joints are classified as *uniaxial* (u"ne-aks'e-al; "one axis"); they allow movement around one axis only, as indicated by the single magenta arrow in Figure 5.30b.

- In a **pivot joint** (Figure 5.30c), the rounded end of one bone fits into a sleeve or ring of bone (and possibly ligaments). Because the rotating bone can turn only around its long axis, pivot joints are also uniaxial joints (see the single arrow in Figure 5.30c). The proximal

radioulnar joint and the joint between the atlas and the dens of the axis are examples.

- In a **condyloid joint** (kon'dĭ-loid; "knuckle-like"), the egg-shaped articular surface of one bone fits into an oval concavity in another (Figure 5.30d). Both of these articular surfaces are oval. Condyloid joints allow the moving bone to travel (1) from side to side and (2) back and forth, but the bone cannot rotate around its long axis. Movement occurs around two axes, hence these joints are *biaxial* (*bi* = two), as in knuckle (metacarpophalangeal) joints.

- In **saddle joints,** each articular surface has both convex and concave areas, like a saddle (Figure 5.30e). These biaxial joints allow essentially the same movements as condyloid joints. The best examples of saddle joints are the carpometacarpal joints in the thumb, and the movements of these joints are clearly demonstrated by twiddling your thumbs.

- In a **ball-and-socket joint** (Figure 5.30f), the spherical head of one bone fits into a round socket in another. These *multiaxial* joints allow movement in all axes, including rotation

It has a joint cavity instead of cartilage or fibrous tissue separating the articulating bones.

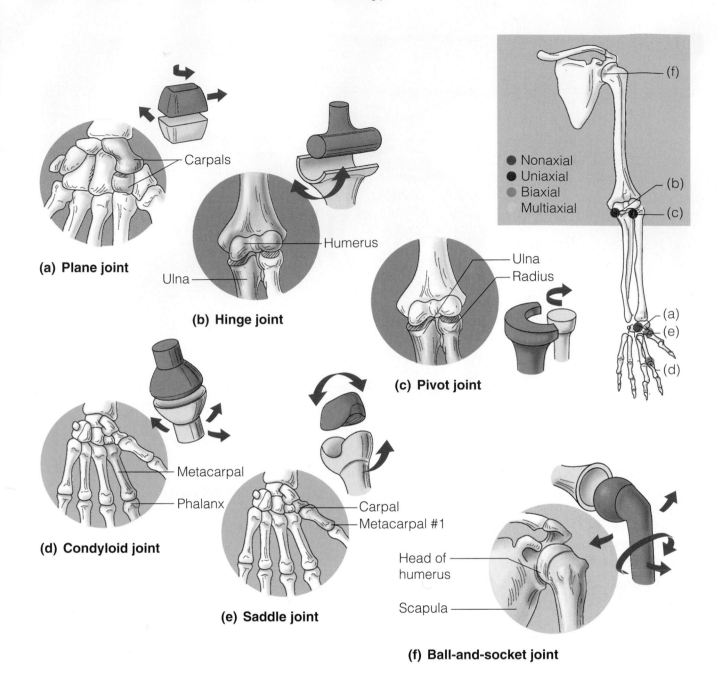

(a) Plane joint

(b) Hinge joint

Carpals

Humerus

Ulna

(c) Pivot joint

Ulna
Radius

● Nonaxial
● Uniaxial
● Biaxial
● Multiaxial

(f)
(b)
(c)
(a)
(e)
(d)

(d) Condyloid joint

Metacarpal

Phalanx

(e) Saddle joint

Carpal
Metacarpal #1

(f) Ball-and-socket joint

Head of humerus

Scapula

FIGURE 5.30 **Types of synovial joints. (a)** Plane joint (intercarpal and intertarsal joints). **(b)** Hinge joint (elbow and interpha-langeal joints). **(c)** Pivot joint (proximal joint between the radius and the ulna). **(d)** Condyloid joint (knuckles). **(e)** Saddle joint (carpometacarpal joint of the thumb). **(f)** Ball-and-socket joint (shoulder and hip joints).

(see the three arrows in Figure 5.30f), and are the most freely moving synovial joints. The shoulder and hip are examples.

Because they relate to muscle activity, the various types of movements that occur at synovial joints are discussed in detail in the next chapter.

HOMEOSTATIC IMBALANCE

Few of us pay attention to our joints unless something goes wrong with them. Joint pain and inflammation may be caused by many things. For example, falling on one's knee can cause a painful **bursitis,** called "water on the knee," due to inflammation of bursae or synovial membrane. Sprains and dislocations are other types of joint problems that result in swelling and pain. In a **sprain,** the ligaments or tendons reinforcing a joint are damaged by excessive stretching, or they are torn away from the bone. Both tendons and ligaments are cords of dense fibrous connective tissue with a poor blood supply; thus, sprains heal slowly and are extremely painful.

Few inflammatory joint disorders cause more pain and suffering than arthritis. The term **arthritis** (*arth* = joint; *itis* = inflammation) describes over 100 different inflammatory or degenerative diseases that damage the joints. In all its forms, arthritis is the most widespread, crippling disease in the United States. All forms of arthritis have the same initial symptoms: pain, stiffness, and swelling of the joint. Then, depending on the specific form, certain changes in the joint structure occur.

Acute forms of arthritis usually result from bacterial invasion and are treated with antibiotic drugs. The synovial membrane thickens and fluid production decreases, leading to increased friction and pain. Chronic forms of arthritis include osteoarthritis, rheumatoid arthritis, and gouty arthritis, which differ substantially in their later symptoms and consequences. We will focus on these forms here.

Osteoarthritis (OA), the most common form of arthritis, is a chronic degenerative condition that typically affects the aged. Eighty-five percent of people in the United States develop this condition. OA, also called "wear-and-tear arthritis," affects the articular cartilages. Over the years, the cartilage softens, frays, and eventually breaks down. As the disease progresses, the exposed bone thickens and extra bone tissue, called **bone spurs,** grows around the margins of the eroded cartilage and restricts joint movement. Patients complain of stiffness on arising that lessens with activity, and the affected joints may make a crunching noise **(crepitus)** when moved. The joints most commonly affected are those of the fingers, the cervical and lumbar joints of the spine, and the large, weight-bearing joints of the lower limbs (knees and hips).

The course of osteoarthritis is usually slow and irreversible, but it is rarely crippling. In most cases, its symptoms are controllable with a mild analgesic such as aspirin, moderate activity to maintain joint mobility, and rest when the joint becomes very painful. Some people with OA claim that rubbing capsaicin (a hot pepper extract) on the skin over painful joints provides relief. Others swear to the pain-reducing ability of glucosamine sulfate, a nutritional supplement.

FIGURE 5.31 **X-ray image of a hand deformed by rheumatoid arthritis.**

Rheumatoid (roo'mah-toid) **arthritis (RA)** is a chronic inflammatory disorder. Its onset is insidious and usually occurs between the ages of 40 and 50, but it may occur at any age. It affects three times as many women as men. Many joints, particularly those of the fingers, wrists, ankles, and feet, are affected at the same time and usually in a symmetrical manner. For example, if the right elbow is affected, most likely the left elbow will be affected also. The course of RA varies and is marked by remissions and flare-ups (*rheumat* = susceptible to change or flux).

RA is an autoimmune disease—a disorder in which the body's immune system attempts to destroy its own tissues. The initial trigger for this reaction is unknown, but some suspect that it results from certain bacterial or viral infections.

RA begins with inflammation of the synovial membranes. The membranes thicken and the joints swell as synovial fluid accumulates. Inflammatory cells (white blood cells and others) enter the joint cavity from the blood and release a deluge of inflamatory chemicals that destroy body tissues when released inappropriately as in RA. In time the inflamed synovial membrane thickens into a **pannus** ("rag"), an abnormal tissue that clings to and erodes articular cartilages. As the cartilage is destroyed, scar tissue forms and connects the bone ends. The scar tissue eventually ossifies, and the bone ends become firmly fused **(ankylosis)** and often deformed (see Figure 5.31). Not all cases of RA progress to the severely crippling ankylosis stage, but all cases involve restricted joint movement and extreme pain.

Current therapy for RA involves many different kinds of drugs. Some, like methotrexate, are immunosuppresants. Others, like etanercept (Embrel), neutralize the inflammatory chemicals in the joint space and (hopefully) prevent joint deformity. However, drug therapy often begins with aspirin, which in large doses is an effective anti-inflammatory agent. Exercise is recommended to maintain as much joint mobility as possible. Cold packs are used to relieve the swelling and pain, and heat helps to relieve morning stiffness. Replacement joints or bone removal are the last resort for severely crippled RA patients.

Gouty (gow'te) **arthritis,** or **gout,** is a disease in which uric acid (a normal waste product of nucleic acid metabolism) accumulates in the blood and may be deposited as needle-shaped crystals in the soft tissues of joints. This leads to an agonizingly painful attack that typically affects a single joint, often in the great toe. Gout is most common in men and rarely appears before the age of thirty. It tends to run in families, so genetic factors are definitely implicated.

Untreated gout can be very destructive; the bone ends fuse, and the joint becomes immobilized. Fortunately, several drugs (colchicine, ibuprofen, and others) are successful in preventing acute gout attacks. Patients are advised to lose weight if obese, to avoid foods such as liver, kidneys, and sardines, which are high in nucleic acids, and to avoid alcohol, which inhibits excretion of uric acid by the kidneys. ▲

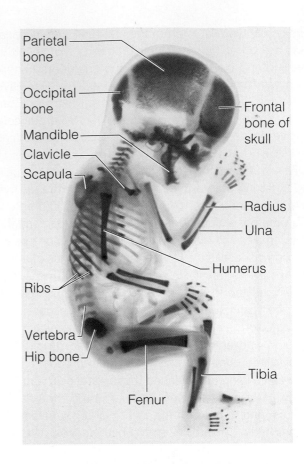

FIGURE 5.32 **Ossification centers in the skeleton of a 12-week-old fetus are indicated by the darker areas. Lighter regions are still fibrous or cartilaginous.**

▶ DID YOU GET IT?

27. What are the functions of joints?

28. What is the major difference between a fibrous joint and a cartilaginous joint?

29. Where is synovial membrane found, and what is its role?

30. What two joints of the body are ball-and-socket joints? What is the best example of a saddle joint?

For answers, see Appendix D.

Developmental Aspects of the Skeleton

As described earlier, the first "long bones" in the very young fetus are formed of hyaline cartilage, and the earliest "flat bones" of the skull are actually fibrous membranes. As the fetus develops and grows, both the flat and the long bone models are converted to bone (Figure 5.32). At birth, some fontanels still remain in the skull to allow for brain growth, but these areas are usually fully ossified by 2 years of age. By the end of adolescence, the epiphyseal plates of long bones that provide for longitudinal growth in childhood have become fully ossified, and long-bone growth ends.

The skeleton changes throughout life, but the changes in childhood are most dramatic. At birth, the baby's cranium is huge relative to its face (Figure 5.33a). The rapid growth of the cranium before and after birth is related to the growth of the brain. By 2 years, the skull is three-quarters of its adult size; and, by 8 to 9 years, the skull is almost of adult size and proportions. However,

Human newborn   Human adult

(a)

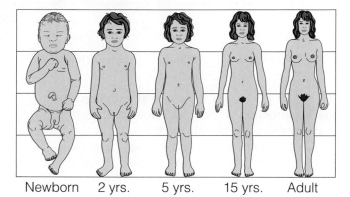

Newborn   2 yrs.   5 yrs.   15 yrs.   Adult

(b)

F I G U R E 5.33   Differences in the growth rates for some parts of the body compared to others determine body proportions. (a) Differential growth transforms the rounded, foreshortened skull of a newborn to the sloping skull characteristic of adults. **(b)** During growth of a human, the arms and legs grow faster than the head and trunk, as shown in this conceptualization of different-aged individuals all drawn at the same height.

between the ages of 6 and 11, the head appears to enlarge substantially as the face literally grows out from the skull. The jaws increase in size, and the cheekbones and nose become more prominent as respiratory passages expand and the permanent teeth develop.

The so-called primary curvatures of the vertebral column are present at birth and are convex posteriorly, so an infant's spine is arched, like that of a four-legged animal. The secondary curvatures are convex anteriorly and are associated with a child's later development. They result from reshaping of the intervertebral discs rather than from modifications of the bony vertebrae and produce the S-shaped spine typical of the adult.

Most cases of abnormal spinal curvatures, such as scoliosis and lordosis (see Figure 5.16), are congenital, but some can result from injuries. The abnormal curvatures are usually treated by surgery, braces, or casts when diagnosed. Generally speaking, young, healthy people have no skeletal problems, assuming that their diet is nutritious and they stay reasonably active.

During youth, growth of the skeleton not only increases overall body height and size but also changes body proportions (Figure 5.33b). At birth, the head and trunk are approximately 1½ times as long as the lower limbs. The lower limbs grow more rapidly than the trunk from this time on, and by the age of 10, the head and trunk are approximately the same height as the lower limbs and change little thereafter. During puberty, the female pelvis broadens in preparation for childbearing, and the entire male skeleton becomes more robust. Once adult height is reached, a healthy skeleton changes very little until late middle age. In old age, losses in bone mass become obvious.

It cannot be emphasized too strongly that bones have to be physically stressed to remain healthy. When we remain active physically and muscles and gravity pull on the skeleton, the bones respond by becoming stronger. By contrast, if we are totally inactive, they become thin and fragile. **Osteoporosis** is a bone-thinning disease that afflicts half of women over 65 and some 20 percent of men over the age of 70. Osteoporosis makes the bones so fragile that even a hug or a sneeze can cause bones to fracture (Figure 5.34). The bones of the spine and the neck of the femur are particularly susceptible. Vertebral collapse frequently results in a hunched-over posture (kyphosis) familiarly known as dowager's hump (Figure 5.35).

Estrogen helps to maintain the health and normal density of a woman's skeleton, and the estrogen deficiency that occurs after a woman goes through menopause ("change of life," when menstruation ceases) is strongly implicated as a cause of osteoporosis. Other factors that may contribute to osteoporosis are a diet poor in calcium and protein, lack of vitamin D, smoking, and insufficient weight-bearing exercise to stress the bones. Sadly, many older people feel that they are helping themselves by "saving their strength" and not doing anything too physical. Their reward for this is *pathologic fractures* (spontaneous breaks without

FIGURE 5.34 **Osteoporosis.** The architecture of osteoporotic bone, at top, is contrasted with that of normal bone, below.

Age 40   Age 60   Age 70

FIGURE 5.35 **Vertebral collapse due to osteoporosis.** Women with postmenopausal osteoporosis are at risk for fractures in the bones in their spine (vertebrae) as they age. Eventually these vertebrae tend to collapse, causing spinal curvature. Such curvature causes loss of height, a tilted rib cage, a dowager's hump, and a protruding abdomen.

apparent injury), which increase dramatically with age and are the single most common skeletal problem for this age group.

Advancing years also take their toll on joints. Weight-bearing joints in particular begin to degenerate, and *osteoarthritis* is common. Such degenerative, joint changes lead to the complaint often heard from the aging person: "My joints are getting so stiff...."

▶ *DID YOU GET IT?*

31. Which spinal curvatures are present at birth?

32. How does the shape of a newborn baby's spine differ from that of an adult?

33. Ninety-year-old Mrs. Pelky is groaning in pain. Her grandson has just picked her up and given her a bear hug. What do you think might just have happened to her spine, and what bone condition may she be suffering from?

34. Which two regions of the skeleton grow most rapidly during childhood?

For answers, see Appendix D.

SYSTEMS IN SYNC

HOMEOSTATIC RELATIONSHIPS BETWEEN THE
SKELETAL SYSTEM AND OTHER BODY SYSTEMS

Endocrine System

- Skeletal system provides some bony protection
- Hormones regulate uptake and release of calcium from bone; hormones promote long-bone growth and maturation

Lymphatic System/Immunity

- Skeletal system provides some protection to lymphatic organs; lymphocytes involved in immune response originate in bone marrow
- Lymphatic system drains leaked tissue fluids; immune cells protect against pathogens

Digestive System

- Skeletal system provides some bony protection to intestines, pelvic organs, and liver
- Digestive system provides nutrients needed for bone health and growth

Urinary System

- Skeletal system protects pelvic organs (bladder, etc.)
- Urinary system activates vitamin D; disposes of nitrogenous wastes

Muscular System

- Skeletal system provides levers plus calcium for muscle activity
- Muscle pull on bones increases bone strength and viability; helps determine bone shape

Nervous System

- Skeletal system protects brain and spinal cord; depot for calcium ions needed for neural function
- Nerves innervate bone and joint capsules, providing for pain and joint sense

Respiratory System

- Skeletal system (rib cage) protects lungs by enclosure
- Respiratory system provides oxygen; disposes of carbon dioxide

Cardiovascular System

- Bone marrow cavities provide site for blood cell formation; matrix stores calcium needed for cardiac muscle activity
- Cardiovascular system delivers nutrients and oxygen to bones; carries away wastes

Reproductive System

- Skeletal system protects some reproductive organs by enclosure
- Gonads produce hormones that influence form of skeleton and epiphyseal closure

Integumentary System

- Skeletal system provides support for body organs including the skin
- Skin provides vitamin D needed for proper calcium absorption and use

177

SUMMARY

Media study tools that provide additional review of key topics of Chapter 5 are referenced below.

> **IP** = *InterActive Physiology*
> **WEB** = The A&P Place

Bones: An Overview   (pp. 134–144)

1. Bones support and protect body organs; serve as levers for the muscles to pull on to cause movement at joints; store calcium, fats, and other substances for the body; and contain red marrow, the site of blood cell production.

2. Bones are classified into four groups—long, short, flat, and irregular—on the basis of their shape and the amount of compact or spongy bone they contain. Bone markings are important anatomical landmarks that reveal where muscles attach and where blood vessels and nerves pass.

3. A long bone is composed of a shaft (diaphysis) with two ends (epiphyses). The shaft is compact bone; its cavity contains yellow marrow. The epiphyses are covered with hyaline cartilage; they contain spongy bone (where red marrow is found).

   WEB Exercise: Chapter 5, Microscopic Structure of Compact Bone.

4. The organic parts of the matrix make bone flexible; calcium salts deposited in the matrix make bone hard.

5. Bones form on hyaline cartilage "models," or fibrous membranes. Eventually these initial supporting structures are replaced by bone tissue. Epiphyseal plates persist to provide for longitudinal growth of long bones during childhood and become inactive when adolescence ends.

6. Bones change in shape throughout life. This remodeling occurs in response to hormones (for example, PTH, which regulates blood calcium levels) and mechanical stresses acting on the skeleton.

7. A fracture is a break in a bone. Common types of fractures include simple, compound, compression, comminuted, and greenstick. Bone fractures must be reduced to heal properly.

   WEB Exercise: Chapter 5, Common Types of Fractures.

Axial Skeleton   (pp. 145–158)

1. The skull is formed by cranial and facial bones. Eight cranial bones protect the brain: frontal, occipital, ethmoid, and sphenoid bones, and the pairs of parietal and temporal bones. The 14 facial bones are all paired (maxillae, zygomatics, palatines, nasals, lacrimals, and inferior nasal conchae), except for the vomer and mandible. The hyoid bone, not really a skull bone, is supported in the neck by ligaments.

   WEB Exercise: Chapter 5, Facial Bones.

2. Skulls of newborns contain fontanels (membranous areas), which allow brain growth. The infant's facial bones are very small compared to the size of the cranium.

3. The vertebral column is formed from 24 vertebrae, the sacrum, and the coccyx. There are 7 cervical vertebrae, 12 thoracic vertebrae, and 5 lumbar vertebrae, which have common as well as unique features. The vertebrae are separated by fibrocartilage discs that allow the vertebral column to be flexible. The vertebral column is S-shaped to allow for upright posture. Primary spinal curvatures present at birth are the thoracic and sacral curvatures; secondary curvatures (cervical and lumbar) develop after birth.

   WEB Exercise: Chapter 5, Typical Vertebra.

4. The bony thorax is formed from the sternum and 12 pairs of ribs. All ribs attach posteriorly to thoracic vertebrae. Anteriorly, the first 7 pairs attach directly to the sternum (true ribs); the last 5 pairs attach indirectly or not at all (false ribs). The bony thorax encloses the lungs, heart, and other organs of the thoracic cavity.

Appendicular Skeleton   (pp. 158–166)

1. The shoulder girdle, composed of two bones—the scapula and the clavicle—attaches the upper limb to the axial skeleton. It is a light, poorly reinforced girdle that allows the upper limb a great deal of freedom. There are two shoulder girdles.

   WEB Exercise: Chapter 5, Articulations Case Study.

2. The bones of the upper limb include the humerus of the arm, the radius and ulna of the forearm, and the carpals, metacarpals, and phalanges of the hand.

3. The pelvic girdle is formed by the two coxal bones, or hip bones. Each hip bone is the result of fusion of the ilium, ischium, and pubis bones. The pelvic girdle is securely attached to the sacrum of the axial skeleton, and the socket for the thigh bone is deep and heavily reinforced. This girdle receives the weight of the upper body and transfers it to the lower limbs. The female pelvis is lighter and

broader than the male's; its inlet and outlet are larger, which reflects the childbearing function.

4. The bones of the lower limb include the femur of the thigh, the tibia and fibula of the leg, and the tarsals, metatarsals, and phalanges of the foot.

Joints   (pp. 166–174)

1. Joints hold bones together and allow movement of the skeleton.

2. Joints fall into three functional categories: synarthroses (immovable), amphiarthroses (slightly movable), and diarthroses (freely movable).

3. Joints also can be classified structurally as fibrous, cartilaginous, or synovial joints depending on the substance separating the articulating bones.

4. Most fibrous joints are synarthrotic, and most cartilaginous joints are amphiarthrotic. Fibrous and cartilaginous joints occur mainly in the axial skeleton.

5. Most joints of the body are synovial joints, which predominate in the limbs. In synovial joints, the articulating bone surfaces are covered with articular cartilage and enclosed within the joint cavity by a fibrous capsule lined with a synovial membrane. All synovial joints are diarthroses.

    WEB Exercise: Chapter 5, Types of Synovial Joints.

6. The most common joint problem is arthritis, or inflammation of the joints. Osteoarthritis, or degenerative arthritis, is a result of the "wear and tear" on joints over many years and is a common affliction of the aged. Rheumatoid arthritis occurs in both young and older adults; it is believed to be an autoimmune disease. Gouty arthritis, caused by the deposit of uric acid crystals in joints, typically affects a single joint.

Developmental Aspects of the Skeleton (pp. 174–176)

1. Fontanels, which allow brain growth and ease birth passage, are present in the skull at birth. Growth of the cranium after birth is related to brain growth; the increase in size of the facial skeleton follows tooth development and enlargement of the respiratory passageways.

2. The vertebral column is C-shaped at birth (thoracic and sacral curvatures are present); the secondary curvatures form when the baby begins to lift its head and walk.

3. Long bones continue to grow in length until late adolescence. By the age of 10, the head and trunk are approximately the same height as the lower limbs and change little thereafter.

4. Fractures are the most common bone problem in elderly people. Osteoporosis, a condition of bone wasting that results mainly from hormone deficit or inactivity, is also common in older individuals.

REVIEW QUESTIONS

Multiple Choice

More than one choice may apply.

1. Which of the following are correctly matched?
    a. Short bone—wrist
    b. Long bone—leg
    c. Irregular bone—sternum
    d. Flat bone—cranium

2. A passageway connecting neighboring osteocytes in an osteon is a
    a. central canal.   d. canaliculus.
    b. lamella.   e. perforating canal.
    c. lacuna.

3. Which of the following would you expect to be prominent in osteoclasts?
    a. Golgi apparatus   c. Microfilaments
    b. Lysosomes   d. Exocytosis

4. Bone pain behind the external acoustic meatus probably involves the
    a. maxilla.   d. temporal.
    b. ethmoid.   e. lacrimal.
    c. sphenoid.

5. Bones that articulate with the sphenoid include
    a. parietal.   d. zygomatic.
    b. vomer.   e. ethmoid.
    c. maxilla.

6. Which humeral process articulates with the radius?
    a. Trochlea   d. Capitulum
    b. Greater tubercle   e. Olecranon fossa
    c. Lesser tubercle

7. The parts of the thoracic vertebrae that articulate with the ribs are
    a. spinous process.
    b. transverse process.
    c. superior articular processes.
    d. body.
    e. pedicles.

8. Which of the following bones or bone parts articulate with the femur?

    a. Ischial tuberosity d. Fibula

    b. Pubis   e. Tibia

    c. Patella

9. Which bone of the arm corresponds to the femur of the leg?

    a. Ulna   d. Tibia

    b. Humerus   e. Fibula

    c. Radius

10. At what stage of life do the lower limbs attain the same height as the head and trunk?

    a. At birth

    b. By 10 years of age

    c. At puberty

    d. When the epiphyseal plates fuse

    e. Never

11. Match the types of joints to the descriptions that apply to them. (More than one description might apply.)

    a. Fibrous joints

    b. Cartilaginous joints

    c. Synovial joints

    ____ 1. Have no joint cavity

    ____ 2. Types are sutures and syndesmoses

    ____ 3. Dense connective tissue fills the space between the bones

    ____ 4. Almost all joints of the skull

    ____ 5. Types are synchondroses and symphyses

    ____ 6. All are diarthroses

    ____ 7. The most common type of joint in the body

    ____ 8. Nearly all are synarthrotic

    ____ 9. Shoulder, hip, knee, and elbow joints

12. Match the bone markings listed on the right with their function listed on the left.

    _____ 1. Attachment site for muscle or ligament   a. Trochanter
                                                             b. Condyle
    _____ 2. Forms a joint surface   c. Foramen
                                                             d. Process
    _____ 3. Passageway for vessels or nerves   e. Facet
                                                             f. Tuberosity

Short Answer Essay

13. Name three functions of the skeletal system.

14. What is yellow marrow? How do spongy and compact bone look different?

15. Why do bone injuries heal much more rapidly than injuries to cartilage?

16. Compare and contrast the role of PTH (hormone) and mechanical forces acting on the skeleton in bone remodeling.

17. Which fracture types are most common in older people? Why are greenstick fractures more common in children?

18. Name the eight bones of the cranium.

19. With one exception, all skull bones are joined by sutures. What is the exception?

20. What facial bone forms the chin? The cheekbone? The upper jaw? The bony eyebrow ridges?

21. Name two ways in which the fetal skull differs from the adult skull.

22. How many vertebrae are there in each of the three superior regions of the vertebral column?

23. Diagram the normal spinal curvatures and then the curvatures seen in scoliosis and lordosis.

24. What is the function of the intervertebral discs? What is a slipped disc?

25. Name the major components of the thorax.

26. Is a floating rib a true or a false rib? Why are floating ribs easily broken?

27. Name the bones of the shoulder girdle.

28. Name all the bones with which the ulna articulates.

29. What bones make up each hip bone (coxal bone)? Which of these is the largest? Which has tuberosities that we sit on? Which is the most anterior?

30. Name the bones of the lower limb from superior to inferior.

31. Compare the amount of movement possible in synarthrotic, amphiarthrotic, and diarthrotic joints. Relate these terms to the structural classification of joints; that is, to fibrous, cartilaginous, and synovial joints.

32. Describe the structure of a synovial joint.

33. Professor Rogers pointed to the foramen magnum of the skull and said, "The food passes through this hole when you swallow." Some students believed him, but others said that this was a big mistake. What do you think? Support your answer.

34. Yolanda is asked to review a bone slide that has been set up under a microscope. She sees concentric layers surrounding a central cavity or canal. Is this bone section taken from the diaphysis or the epiphyseal plate of the bone specimen?

35. List two factors that keep bones healthy. List two factors that can cause bones to become soft or to atrophy.

 CRITICAL THINKING AND CLINICAL APPLICATION QUESTIONS

36. A 75-year-old woman and her 9-year-old granddaughter were in a train crash in which both sustained trauma to the chest while seated next to each other. X-ray images showed that the grandmother had several fractured ribs, but her granddaughter had none. Explain these surprisingly (?) different findings.

37. The pediatrician at the clinic explains to parents of a newborn that their son suffers from cleft palate. She tells them that the normal palate fuses in an anterior-to-posterior pattern. The child's palatine processes have not fused. Have his palatine bones fused normally?

38. After having a severe cold accompanied by nasal congestion, Helen complained that she had a frontal headache and the right side of her face ached. What bony structures probably became infected by the bacteria or viruses causing the cold?

39. Bernice, a 75-year-old woman, stumbled slightly while walking, then felt a terrible pain in her left hip. At the hospital, X rays revealed that the hip was broken. Also, the compact and spongy bone throughout her spine were very thin. What was her probable condition?

40. At work, a box fell from a shelf onto Bertha's acromial region. In the emergency room, the physician felt that the head of her humerus had moved into the axilla. What had happened to Bertha?

41. An X-ray image of the arm of an accident victim reveals a faint line curving around and down the shaft. What kind of fracture might this indicate?

42. Bone X rays are sometimes used to determine whether a person has reached his or her final height. What are the clinicians checking out?

43. A patient complains of pain starting in the jaw and radiating down the neck. When he is questioned further, he states that when he is under stress he grinds his teeth. What joint is causing his pain?

44. Dr. Davis is palpating Jane's vertebral column to determine whether she is beginning to exhibit scoliosis. What part or region of her vertebrae was he feeling as he ran his fingers along her spine?

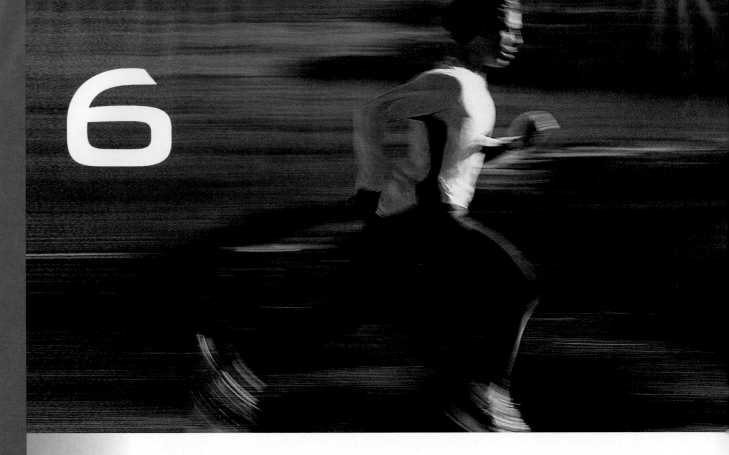

The Muscular System

YOUR GOALS

After completing this chapter, you will have a working knowledge of the functions of the muscular system and will have mastered the objectives listed below.

FUNCTION PREVIEW

- The muscular system provides for movement of the body and its parts, maintains posture, generates heat, and stabilizes joints.

OBJECTIVE CHECKLIST

Overview of Muscle Tissues (pp. 183–187)

➤ Describe similarities and differences in the structure and function of the three types of muscle tissue, and indicate where they are found in the body.

➤ Define *muscular system*.

➤ Define and explain the role of the following: *endomysium, perimysium, epimysium, tendon,* and *aponeurosis*.

Microscopic Anatomy of Skeletal Muscle (pp. 187–189)

➤ Describe the microscopic structure of skeletal muscle, and explain the role of actin- and myosin-containing myofilaments.

Skeletal Muscle Activity (pp. 189–198)

➤ Describe how an action potential is initiated in a muscle cell.

➤ Describe the events of muscle cell contraction.

➤ Define *graded response, tetanus, isotonic* and *isometric contractions,* and *muscle tone* as these terms apply to a skeletal muscle.

➤ Describe three ways in which ATP is regenerated during muscle activity.

➤ Define *oxygen deficit* and *muscle fatigue,* and list possible causes of muscle fatigue.

➤ Describe the effects of aerobic and resistance exercise on skeletal muscles and other body organs.

Muscle Movements, Types, and Names (pp. 198–206)

➤ Define *origin, insertion, prime mover, antagonist, synergist,* and *fixator* as they relate to muscles.

➤ Demonstrate or identify the different types of body movements.

➤ List some criteria used in naming muscles.

Gross Anatomy of Skeletal Muscles (pp. 206–219)

➤ Name and locate the major muscles of the human body (on a torso model, muscle chart,or diagram), and state the action of each.

Developmental Aspects of the Muscular System (p. 221)

➤ Explain the importance of a nerve supply and exercise in keeping muscles healthy.

➤ Describe the changes that occur in aging muscles.

Because flexing muscles look like mice scurrying beneath the skin, some scientist long ago dubbed them *muscles,* from the Latin word *mus* meaning "little mouse." Indeed, the rippling muscles of professional boxers or weight lifters are often the first thing that comes to mind when one hears the word *muscle.* But muscle is also the dominant tissue in the heart and in the walls of other hollow organs of the body. In all its forms, it makes up nearly half the body's mass.

The essential function of muscle is *contraction,* or *shortening*—a unique characteristic that sets it apart from any other body tissue. As a result of this ability, muscles are responsible for essentially all body movement and can be viewed as the "machines" of the body.

Overview of Muscle Tissues
Muscle Types

There are three types of muscle tissue—skeletal, cardiac, and smooth. As summarized in Table 6.1, these differ in their cell structure, body location,

and how they are stimulated to contract. But before we explore their differences, let's look at some of the ways they are the same.

First, skeletal and smooth muscle cells are elongated. For this reason, these types of muscle cells (but not cardiac muscle cells) are called **muscle fibers.** Second, the ability of muscle to shorten, or contract, depends on two types of *myofilaments,* the muscle cell equivalents of the microfilaments of the cytoskeleton studied in Chapter 3. A third similarity has to do with terminology. Whenever you see the prefixes *myo-* and *mys-* ("muscle") and *sarco-* ("flesh"), you will know that muscle is being referred to. For example, in muscle cells the cytoplasm is called *sarcoplasm* (sar'ko-plaz"um).

Skeletal Muscle

Skeletal muscle fibers are packaged into the organs called *skeletal muscles* that attach to the body's skeleton. As the skeletal muscles cover our bony "underpinnings," they help form the much smoother contours of the body. Skeletal muscle fibers are huge, cigar-shaped, multinucleate cells. They are the largest of the muscle fiber types—

TABLE 6.1   Comparison of Skeletal, Cardiac, and Smooth Muscles

Characteristic	Skeletal	Cardiac	Smooth
Body location	Attached to bones or, for some facial muscles, to skin	Walls of the heart	Mostly in walls of hollow visceral organs (other than the heart)
Cell shape and appearance	Single, very long, cylindrical, multinucleate cells with very obvious striations	Branching chains of cells; uninucleate, striations; intercalated discs	Single, fusiform, uninucleate; no striations
Connective tissue components	Epimysium, perimysium, and endomysium	Endomysium attached to the fibrous skeleton of the heart	Endomysium
	Endomysium Epimysium Perimysium Cells	Endomysium	Endomysium
Regulation of contraction	Voluntary; via nervous system controls	Involuntary; the heart has a pacemaker; also nervous system controls; hormones	Involuntary; nervous system controls; hormones, chemicals, stretch
Speed of contraction	Slow to fast	Slow	Very slow
Rhythmic contraction	No	Yes	Yes, in some

some ranging up to 30 cm (nearly 1 foot) in length. Indeed, the fibers of large, hardworking muscles, such as the antigravity muscles of the hip, are so big and coarse that they can be seen with the naked eye.

Skeletal muscle is also known as **striated muscle** (because its fibers have obvious stripes) and as **voluntary muscle** (because it is the only muscle type subject to conscious control). However, it is important to recognize that skeletal muscles are often activated by reflexes (without our "willed command") as well. When you think of skeletal muscle tissue, the key words to remember are *skeletal, striated,* and *voluntary.* Skeletal muscle tissue can contract rapidly and with great force, but it tires easily and must rest after short periods of activity.

Skeletal muscle fibers, like most cells, are soft and surprisingly fragile. Yet skeletal muscles can exert tremendous power—indeed, the force they generate in, say lifting a weight, is often much greater than that required to lift the weight. How so? The reason they are not ripped apart as they exert force is that thousands of their fibers are bundled together by connective tissue, which provides strength and support to the muscle as a whole (Figure 6.1). Each muscle fiber is enclosed in a delicate connective tissue sheath called an **endomysium** (en″do-mis′e-um). Several sheathed muscle fibers are then wrapped by a coarser fibrous membrane called a **perimysium** to form a bundle of fibers called a **fascicle** (fas′ĭ-kul). Many fascicles are bound together by an even tougher "overcoat" of connective tissue called an **epimysium,** which covers the entire muscle. The epimysia blend either into the strong, cordlike **tendons** or into sheetlike **aponeuroses** (ap″o-nu-ro′sēz), which attach muscles indirectly to bones, cartilages, or connective tissue coverings.

Besides simply acting to anchor muscles, tendons perform several other functions. The most important are providing durability and conserving space. Tendons are mostly tough collagenic fibers, so they can cross rough bony projections, which would tear the more delicate muscle tissues. Because of their relatively small size, more tendons than fleshy muscles can pass over a joint.

Many people think of muscles as always having an enlarged "belly" that tapers down to a tendon at each end. However, muscles vary considerably

What is the meaning of epi? Of mys? How do these word roots relate to the role and position of the epimysium?

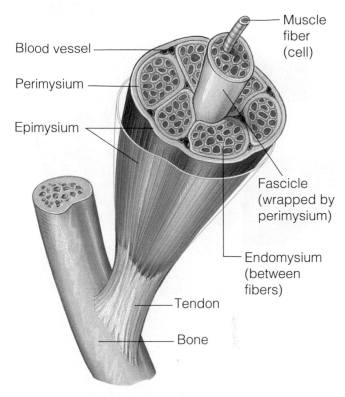

FIGURE 6.1 **Connective tissue wrappings of skeletal muscle.**

in the way their fibers are arranged. Many are spindle-shaped as just described, but in others, the fibers are arranged in a fan shape or a circle, as described on p. 205.

Smooth Muscle

Smooth muscle has no striations and is involuntary, which means that we cannot consciously control it. Found mainly in the walls of hollow visceral organs such as the stomach, urinary bladder, and respiratory passages, smooth muscle propels substances along a definite tract, or pathway, within the body. We can best describe smooth muscle using the terms *visceral, nonstriated,* and *involuntary.*

Epi = upon, over, beside and mys = muscle. The epimysium is a sheath upon or over a muscle.

Circular layer
of smooth muscle
(longitudinal view of cells)

Mucosa

Longitudinal layer
of smooth muscle
(cross-sectional view of cells)

Submucosa

(a)

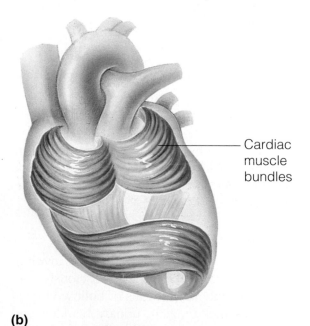

Cardiac
muscle
bundles

(b)

FIGURE 6.2 Arrangement of smooth and cardiac muscle cells. (a) Diagrammatic view of a cross section of the intestine. **(b)** Longitudinal view of the heart, showing the spiral arrangement of the cardiac muscle cells in its walls.

As described in Chapter 3, smooth muscle cells are spindle-shaped, have a single nucleus, and are surrounded by a scant endomysium (see also Table 6.1 on p. 184). They are arranged in layers and most often there are two such layers, one running circularly and the other longitudinally, as shown in Figure 6.2a. As the two layers alternately contract and relax, they change the size and shape of the organ. Moving food through the digestive tract and emptying the bowels and bladder are examples of "housekeeping" activities normally handled by smooth muscles. Smooth muscle contraction is slow and sustained. If skeletal muscle is like a speedy wind-up car that quickly runs down, then smooth muscle is like a steady, heavy-duty engine that lumbers along tirelessly.

Cardiac Muscle

Cardiac muscle is found in only one place in the body—the heart, where it forms the bulk of the heart walls. The heart serves as a pump, propelling blood into the blood vessels and to all tissues of the body. Cardiac muscle is like skeletal muscle in that it is striated and like smooth muscle in that it is involuntary and cannot be consciously controlled by most of us. Important key words to jog your memory for this muscle type are *cardiac, striated,* and *involuntary*.

The cardiac fibers are cushioned by small amounts of soft connective tissue (endomysium) and arranged in spiral or figure 8–shaped bundles, as shown in Figure 6.2b. When the heart contracts, its internal chambers become smaller, forcing the blood into the large arteries leaving the heart. Recall that cardiac muscle fibers are branching cells joined by special junctions called *intercalated discs* (see Figure 3.20 on p. 99). These two structural features and the spiral arrangement of the muscle bundles in the heart allow heart activity to be closely coordinated. Cardiac muscle usually contracts at a fairly steady rate set by the heart's "in-house" pacemaker, but the heart can also be stimulated by the nervous system to shift into "high gear" for short periods, as when you run to catch a bus.

As you can see, each of the three muscle types has a structure and function well suited for its job in the body. But because the term *muscular system* applies specifically to skeletal muscle, we will be concentrating on this muscle type in this chapter.

Muscle Functions

Producing movement is a common function of *all* muscle types, but skeletal muscle plays three other important roles in the body as well: it *maintains posture, stabilizes joints,* and *generates heat.* Let's take a look.

Producing Movement

Just about all movements of the human body are a result of muscle contraction. Mobility of the body as a whole reflects the activity of skeletal muscles, which are responsible for all locomotion (walking, swimming, and cross-country skiing, for instance) and manipulation. They enable us to respond quickly to changes in the external environment. For example, their speed and power enable us to jump out of the way of a runaway car and then follow its flight with our eyes. They also allow us to express our emotions with the silent language of smiles and frowns.

These are distinct from the smooth muscle of blood vessel walls and cardiac muscle of the heart, which work together to circulate blood and maintain blood pressure, and the smooth muscle of other hollow organs, which forces fluids (urine, bile) and other substances (food, a baby) through internal body channels.

Maintaining Posture

We are rarely aware of the workings of the skeletal muscles that maintain body posture. Yet, they function almost continuously, making one tiny adjustment after another so that we can maintain an erect or seated posture despite the never-ending downward pull of gravity.

Stabilizing Joints

As the skeletal muscles pull on bones to cause movements, they also stabilize the joints of the skeleton. Indeed, muscle tendons are extremely important in reinforcing and stabilizing joints that have poorly fitting articulating surfaces (the shoulder joint, for example).

Generating Heat

The fourth function of muscle, generation of body heat, is a by-product of muscle activity. As ATP is used to power muscle contraction, nearly three-quarters of its energy escapes as heat. This heat is vital in maintaining normal body temperature. Skeletal muscle accounts for at least 40 percent of

body mass, so it is the muscle type most responsible for heat generation.

 DID YOU GET IT?

1. How do cells of the three types of muscle tissues differ from one another anatomically?

2. Which muscle type has the most elaborate connective tissue wrappings?

3. What does *striated* mean relative to muscle cells?

4. How do the movements promoted by skeletal muscle differ from those promoted by smooth muscle?

For answers, see Appendix D.

Microscopic Anatomy of Skeletal Muscle

As mentioned above and illustrated in Figure 6.3a, skeletal muscle cells are multinucleate. Many oval nuclei can be seen just beneath the plasma membrane, which is called the **sarcolemma** (sar″ko-lem′ah; "muscle husk") in muscle cells. The nuclei are pushed aside by long ribbonlike organelles, the **myofibrils** (mi″o-fi′brilz), which nearly fill the cytoplasm. Alternating **light (I)** and **dark (A) bands** along the length of the perfectly aligned myofibrils give the muscle cell as a whole its striped appearance. (Think of the second letter of *light,* I, and the second letter of *dark,* A, to help you remember which band is which.) A closer look at the banding pattern reveals that the light I band has a midline interruption, a darker area called the *Z disc,* and the dark A band has a lighter central area called the *H zone* (Figure 6.3b). The *M line* in the center of the H zone contains tiny protein rods that hold adjacent thick filaments together.

So why are we bothering with all these terms—dark this and light that? Because the banding pattern reveals the working structure of the myofibrils. First, we find that the myofibrils are actually chains of tiny contractile units called **sarcomeres** (sar′ko-merz), which are aligned end-to-end like boxcars in a train along the length of the myofibrils. Second, it is the arrangement of even smaller structures (myofilaments) *within* sarcomeres that actually produces the banding pattern.

Let's examine how the arrangement of the myofilaments leads to the banding pattern. There are two types of threadlike protein **myofilaments**

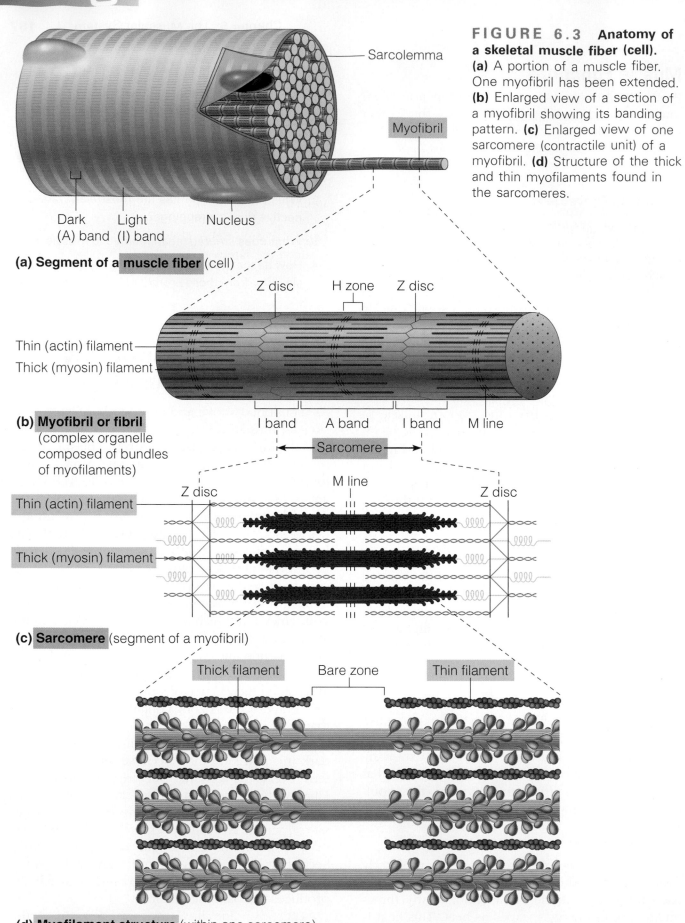

6

Sarcolemma

Myofibril

Dark (A) band   Light (I) band   Nucleus

(a) Segment of a muscle fiber (cell)

FIGURE 6.3   Anatomy of a skeletal muscle fiber (cell).
(a) A portion of a muscle fiber. One myofibril has been extended. **(b)** Enlarged view of a section of a myofibril showing its banding pattern. **(c)** Enlarged view of one sarcomere (contractile unit) of a myofibril. **(d)** Structure of the thick and thin myofilaments found in the sarcomeres.

Z disc   H zone   Z disc

Thin (actin) filament

Thick (myosin) filament

I band   A band   I band   M line

Sarcomere

(b) Myofibril or fibril
(complex organelle composed of bundles of myofilaments)

M line

Z disc   Z disc

Thin (actin) filament

Thick (myosin) filament

(c) Sarcomere (segment of a myofibril)

Thick filament   Bare zone   Thin filament

(d) Myofilament structure (within one sarcomere)

within each of our "boxcar" sarcomeres (Figure 6.3c). The larger **thick filaments,** also called *myosin filaments,* are made mostly of bundled molecules of the protein **myosin,** but they also contain ATPase enzymes, which split ATP to generate the power for muscle contraction. Notice that the thick filaments extend the entire length of the dark A band. Also, notice that the midparts of the thick filaments are smooth, but their ends are studded with small projections (Figure 6.3d). These projections, or myosin *heads,* are called **cross bridges** when they link the thick and thin filaments together during contraction. The **thin filaments** are composed of the contractile protein called **actin,** plus some regulatory proteins that play a role in allowing (or preventing) myosin head–binding to actin. The thin filaments, also called *actin filaments,* are anchored to the Z disc (a disclike membrane). Notice that the light I band includes parts of two adjacent sarcomeres and contains *only* the thin filaments. Although they overlap the ends of the thick filaments, the thin filaments do not extend into the middle of a relaxed sarcomere, and thus the central region (the H zone, which lacks actin filaments and looks a bit lighter) is sometimes called the *bare zone.* When contraction occurs and the actin-containing filaments slide toward each other into the center of the sarcomeres, these light zones disappear because the actin and myosin filaments are completely overlapped. For now, however, just recognize that it is the precise arrangement of the myofilaments in the myofibrils that produces the banding pattern, or striations, in skeletal muscle cells.

Not shown in Figure 6.3 is another very important muscle fiber organelle—the **sarcoplasmic reticulum (SR),** a specialized smooth endoplasmic reticulum. The interconnecting tubules and sacs of the SR surround each and every myofibril just as the sleeve of a loosely crocheted sweater surrounds your arm. The major role of this elaborate system is to store calcium and to release it on demand when the muscle fiber is stimulated to contract. As you will see, calcium provides the final "go" signal for contraction.

 DID YOU GET IT?

5. Specifically, what is responsible for the banding pattern in skeletal muscle cells?

For the answer, see Appendix D.

Skeletal Muscle Activity
Stimulation and Contraction of Single Skeletal Muscle Cells

Muscle cells have some special functional properties that enable them to perform their duties. The first of these is *excitability,* also termed *responsiveness* or *irritability,* which is the ability to receive and respond to a stimulus. The second, *contractility,* is the ability to shorten (forcibly) when adequately stimulated. *Extensibility* is the ability of muscle cells to be stretched, whereas *elasticity* is their ability to recoil and resume their resting length after being stretched.

The Nerve Stimulus and the Action Potential

To contract, skeletal muscle cells must be stimulated by nerve impulses. One motor neuron (nerve cell) may stimulate a few muscle cells or hundreds of them, depending on the particular muscle and the work it does. One neuron and all the skeletal muscle cells it stimulates are a **motor unit** (Figure 6.4). When a long, threadlike extension of the neuron, called the *nerve fiber* or **axon,** reaches the muscle, it branches into a number of **axon terminals,** each of which forms junctions with the sarcolemma of a different muscle cell (Figure 6.5). These junctions are called **neuromuscular** (literally, "nerve-muscle") **junctions.** Although the nerve endings and the muscle cells' membranes are very close, they never touch. The gap between them, the **synaptic cleft,** is filled with tissue (interstitial) fluid.

DID YOU GET IT?

6. What two structures are closely associated at a neuromuscular junction?

For the answer, see Appendix D.

Now that we have described the structure of the neuromuscular junction, we are ready to examine what happens there. When a nerve impulse reaches the axon terminals, a chemical referred to as a **neurotransmitter** is released. The specific neurotransmitter that stimulates skeletal muscle cells is **acetylcholine** (as"e-til-ko'lēn), or **ACh.** Acetylcholine diffuses across the synaptic cleft and attaches to receptors (membrane proteins) that are

(a)

(b)

FIGURE 6.4   Motor units. Each motor unit consists of a motor neuron and all the muscle fibers it activates. **(a)** Portions of two motor units are shown. The motor neurons reside in the spinal cord, and their axons extend to the muscle. Within the muscle, each axon divides into a number of axon terminals, distributed to muscle fibers scattered throughout the muscle. **(b)** Photo of a portion of a motor unit (80×).

part of the sarcolemma. If enough acetylcholine is released, the sarcolemma at that point becomes *temporarily* more permeable to sodium ions (Na^+), which rush into the muscle cell, and to potassium ions (K^+), which diffuse out of the cell. However, more Na^+ enters than K^+ leaves. This gives the cell interior an excess of positive ions, which reverses the electrical conditions of the sarcolemma and opens more channels that allow Na^+ entry only. This "upset" generates an electrical current called an **action potential.** Once begun, the action potential is unstoppable; it travels over the entire surface of the sarcolemma, conducting the electrical impulse from one end of the cell to the other. The result is contraction of the muscle cell.

It should be mentioned that while the action potential is occurring, acetylcholine, which began the process, is broken down to acetic acid and choline by enzymes (acetylcholinesterase, or AChE) present on the sarcolemma (see Figure 6.5c). For this reason, a single nerve impulse produces only one contraction. This prevents continued contraction of the muscle cell in the absence of additional nerve impulses. The muscle cell relaxes until stimulated by the next round of acetylcholine release.

This series of events is explained more fully on pp. 237–239 in the discussion of nerve physiology, but perhaps it would be helpful to compare this to some common event, such as lighting a

(a)

- Myelinated axon of motor neuron
- Action potential
- Axon terminal
- Sarcolemma of the muscle fiber
- Nucleus

(b)

- Axon terminal of a motor neuron
- Mitochondrion
- Synaptic cleft
- T tubule
- Invagination of the sarcolemma at neuromuscular junction
- Part of a myofibril
- Synaptic vesicle containing ACh
- Ca²⁺
- Synaptic cleft
- Action potential

(c)

- Axon terminal
- Fusing synaptic vesicle
- ACh molecules
- Acetic acid
- Choline
- AChE
- Binding of ACh to receptor opens Na⁺/K⁺ channel
- K⁺
- Na⁺

FIGURE 6.5 **The neuromuscular junction. (a)** Axon terminal of a motor neuron forming a neuromuscular junction with a muscle fiber. **(b)** The axon terminal contains vesicles filled with the neurotransmitter acetylcholine (ACh), which is released when the nerve impulse reaches the axon terminal. The sarcolemma is highly invaginated (folded) adjacent to the synaptic cleft, and acetylcholine receptors are present in these folds. **(c)** Acetylcholine diffuses across the synaptic cleft and attaches to ACh receptors on the sarcolemma, initiating changes in the electrical condition of the sarcolemma.

match under a small dry twig (Figure 6.6). The charring of the twig by the flame can be compared to the change in membrane permeability that allows sodium ions into the cell. When that part of the twig becomes hot enough (when enough sodium ions have entered the cell), the twig will suddenly burst into flame, and the flame will consume the twig (the action potential will be conducted along the entire length of the sarcolemma).

The events that return the cell to its resting state include (1) diffusion of potassium ions (K^+) out of the cell and (2) operation of the sodium-potassium pump, the active transport mechanism that moves the sodium and potassium ions back to their initial positions.

(a)

(b)

FIGURE 6.6 Comparison of the action potential to a flame consuming a dry twig. (a) The first event in igniting a dry twig is holding the match flame under one area of the twig. The second event is the twig's bursting into flame when it has been heated enough and spreading of the flame to burn the entire twig. **(b)** The first event in exciting a muscle cell is the rapid diffusion of sodium ions (Na^+) into the cell when the permeability of the sarcolemma changes. The second event is the spreading of the action potential along the sarcolemma when enough sodium ions have entered to upset the electrical conditions in the cell.

Mechanism of Muscle Contraction: The Sliding Filament Theory

What causes the filaments to slide? This question brings us back to the myosin heads that protrude all around the ends of the thick filaments. When muscle fibers are activated by the nervous system as just described, the myosin heads attach to binding sites on the thin filaments, and the sliding begins. Each cross bridge attaches and detaches several times during a contraction, generating tension that helps to pull the thin filaments toward the center of the sarcomere. As this event occurs simultaneously in sarcomeres throughout the muscle cell, the cell shortens (Figure 6.7).

This "walking" of the myosin cross bridges, or heads, along the thin filaments during muscle shortening is much like a centipede's gait. Some myosin heads ("legs") are always in contact with

(a)

(b)

FIGURE 6.7 Diagrammatic views of a sarcomere. (a) Relaxed; **(b)** fully contracted. Notice that in the contracted sarcomere, the light H zone in the center of the A band has disappeared, the Z discs are closer to the thick filaments, and the I bands have nearly disappeared. The A bands move closer together but do not change in length.

(a)

In a relaxed muscle cell, the regulatory proteins forming part of the actin myofilaments prevent myosin binding (see **a**). When an action potential sweeps along its sarcolemma and a muscle cell is excited, calcium ions (Ca^{2+}) are released from intracellular storage areas (the sacs of the sarcoplasmic reticulum).

(b)

The flood of calcium acts as the final trigger for contraction, because as calcium binds to the regulatory proteins on the actin filaments, they change both their shape and their position on the thin filaments. This action exposes myosin binding sites on the actin, to which the myosin heads can attach (see **b**), and the myosin heads immediately begin seeking out binding sites.

(c)

The free myosin heads are "cocked," much like a set mousetrap. The physical attachment of myosin to actin "springs the trap," causing the myosin heads to snap (pivot) toward the center of the sarcomere. Because actin and myosin are still firmly bound to each other when this happens, the thin filaments are slightly pulled toward the center of the sarcomere (see **c**). ATP provides the energy needed to release and recock each myosin head so that it is ready to take another "step" and attach to a binding site farther along the thin filament. When the action potential ends and calcium ions are reabsorbed into the SR storage areas, the regulatory proteins resume their original shape and position, and again block myosin binding to the thin filaments. Since myosin now has nothing to attach to, the muscle cell relaxes and settles back to its original length.

FIGURE 6.8 Schematic representation of contraction mechanism: The sliding filament theory.

actin ("the ground"), so that the thin filaments cannot slide backward as this cycle repeats again and again during contraction. Notice that the myofilaments themselves do not shorten during contraction; they simply slide past each other.

The attachment of the myosin cross bridges to actin requires calcium ions (Ca^{2+}). So where does the calcium come from? As indicated in Figure 6.5b, action potentials (black arrows) pass deep into the muscle cell along membranous tubules (T tubules) that fold inward from the sarcolemma. Inside the

cell, the action potentials stimulate the sarcoplasmic reticulum to release calcium ions into the cytoplasm. The calcium ions trigger the binding of myosin to actin initiating filament sliding. This sliding process and the precise role of calcium are depicted in Figure 6.8. When the action potential ends, calcium ions are immediately reabsorbed into the SR storage areas, and the muscle cell relaxes and settles back to its original length. This whole series of events takes a few thousandths of a second.

FIGURE 6.9 A whole muscle's response to different rates of stimulation. In **(a),** a single stimulus is delivered, and the muscle contracts and relaxes (a twitch contraction). In **(b),** stimuli are delivered more frequently, so the muscle does not have time to completely relax; contraction force increases because effects of the individual twitches are summed. In **(c),** more complete fusion of the twitches (unfused tetanus) occurs as stimuli are delivered at a still faster rate. In **(d),** fused tetanus, a smooth continuous contraction without any evidence of relaxation, results from a very rapid rate of stimulation. (Points at which stimuli are delivered are indicated by red arrows. Tension [measured in grams] on the vertical axis refers to the relative force of muscle contraction.)

▶ DID YOU GET IT?

7. What chemical—ATP or Ca^{2+}—triggers sliding of the muscle filaments?

8. What ions enter the muscle cell during action potential generation?

9. Which is a cross-bridge attachment more similar to: a precise rowing team or a person pulling a bucket on a rope out of a well?

For answers, see Appendix D.

Contraction of a Skeletal Muscle as a Whole

Graded Responses

In skeletal muscles, the "all-or-none" law of muscle physiology applies to the *muscle cell,* not to the whole muscle. It states that a muscle cell will contract to its fullest extent when it is stimulated adequately; it never partially contracts. However, the whole muscle reacts to stimuli with **graded responses,** or different degrees of shortening. In general, graded muscle contractions can be produced two ways: (1) by changing the *frequency* of muscle stimulation and (2) by changing the *number* of muscle cells being stimulated at one time. A muscle's response to each of these is briefly described next.

Muscle Response to Increasingly Rapid Stimulation
Although **muscle twitches** (single, brief, jerky contractions) sometimes result from certain nervous system problems, this is *not* the way our muscles normally operate. In most types of muscle activity, nerve impulses are delivered to the muscle at a very rapid rate—so rapid that the muscle does not get a chance to relax completely between stimuli. As a result, the effects of the successive contractions are "summed" (added) together, and the contractions of the muscle get stronger and smoother. When the muscle is stimulated so rapidly that no evidence of relaxation is seen and the contractions are completely smooth and sustained, the muscle is said to be in **fused,** or **complete, tetanus** (tet'ah-nus),* or in tetanic contraction.

---

*Tetanic contraction is normal and desirable and is quite different from the pathological condition of tetanus (commonly called *lockjaw*), which is caused by a toxin made by bacterium. Lockjaw causes muscles to go into uncontrollable spasms, finally causing respiratory arrest.

Until this point is reached, the muscle is said to be exhibiting **unfused,** or **incomplete, tetanus** (Figure 6.9).

Muscle Response to Stronger Stimuli Although tetanus also produces stronger muscle contractions, its primary role is to produce smooth and prolonged muscle contractions. How forcefully a muscle contracts depends to a large extent on how many of its cells are stimulated. When only a few cells are stimulated, the contraction of the muscle as a whole will be slight. In the strongest contractions, when all the motor units are active and all the muscle cells are being stimulated, the muscle contraction is as strong as it can get. Thus, muscle contractions can be slight or vigorous depending on what work has to be done. The same hand that gently soothes can also deliver a stinging slap!

Providing Energy for Muscle Contraction

As a muscle contracts, the bonds of ATP molecules are hydrolyzed to release the needed energy. Surprisingly, muscles store very limited supplies of ATP—only 4 to 6 seconds' worth, just enough to get you going. Because ATP is the *only* energy source that can be used directly to power muscle activity, ATP must be regenerated continuously if contraction is to continue.

Working muscles use three pathways for ATP regeneration:

1. **Direct phosphorylation of ADP by creatine phosphate** (Figure 6.10a). The unique high-energy molecule **creatine phosphate (CP)** is found in muscle fibers but not other cell types. As ATP is being depleted, interactions between CP and ADP result in transfers of a high-energy phosphate group from CP to ADP, thus regenerating more ATP in a fraction of a second. Although muscle cells store perhaps five times as much CP as ATP, the CP supplies are also soon exhausted (in less than 15 seconds).

2. **Aerobic respiration** (Figure 6.10b). At rest and during light to moderate exercise, some 95 percent of the ATP used for muscle activity comes from aerobic respiration. **Aerobic respiration** occurs in the mitochondria and involves a series of metabolic pathways that use oxygen. These pathways are collectively referred to as *oxidative phosphorylation.* During aerobic respiration, glucose is broken down completely to carbon dioxide and water, and some of the energy released as the bonds are broken is captured in the bonds of ATP molecules. Although aerobic respiration provides a rich ATP harvest (about 36 ATP per 1 glucose), it is fairly slow and requires continuous delivery of oxygen and nutrient fuels to the muscle to keep it going.

3. **Anaerobic glycolysis and lactic acid formation** (Figure 6.10c). The initial steps of glucose breakdown occur via a pathway called *glycolysis,* which does not use oxygen and hence is an *anaerobic* (literally "without oxygen") part of the metabolic pathway. During glycolysis, which occurs in the cytosol, glucose is broken down to pyruvic acid, and small amounts of energy are captured in ATP bonds (2 ATP per 1 glucose molecule). As long as enough oxygen is present, the pyruvic acid then enters the oxygen-requiring aerobic pathways that occur within the mitochondria to produce more ATP as described above. However, when muscle activity is intense, or oxygen and glucose delivery is temporarily inadequate to meet the needs of the working muscles, the sluggish aerobic mechanisms cannot keep up with the demands for ATP. Under these conditions, the pyruvic acid generated during glycolysis is converted to **lactic acid,** and the overall process is referred to as **anaerobic glycolysis.**

   Anaerobic glycolysis produces only about 5 percent as much ATP from each glucose molecule as aerobic respiration. However, it is some 2½ times faster, and it can provide most of the ATP needed for 30 to 60 seconds of strenuous muscle activity. The main shortcomings of anaerobic glycolysis are that it uses huge amounts of glucose for a small ATP harvest, and accumulating lactic acid promotes muscle fatigue and muscle soreness.

Muscle Fatigue and Oxygen Deficit

If we exercise our muscles strenuously for a long time, **muscle fatigue** occurs. A muscle is fatigued

Which of these methods of ATP generation is commonly used by the leg muscles of a long-distance cyclist?

(a) Direct phosphorylation of ADP by reaction with creatine phosphate (CP)

(b) Aerobic respiration (oxidative phosphorylation)

(c) Anaerobic glycolysis and lactic acid formation

(a)	(b)	(c)
Energy source: CP	Energy sources: glucose; pyruvic acid; free fatty acids from adipose tissue; amino acids from protein catabolism	Energy source: glucose
Oxygen use: None Products: 1 ATP per CP, creatine Duration of energy provision: 15 sec	Oxygen use: Required Products: 36 ATP per glucose, CO_2, H_2O Duration of energy provision: Hours	Oxygen use: None Products: 2 ATP per glucose, lactic acid Duration of energy provision: 30–60 sec

FIGURE 6.10   Methods of regenerating ATP during muscle activity. The fastest mechanism is **(a)** direct phosphorylation; the slowest is **(b)** aerobic respiration.

when it is unable to contract even though it is still being stimulated. Without rest, a working muscle begins to tire and contracts more weakly until it finally ceases reacting and stops contracting. Muscle fatigue is believed to result from the **oxygen deficit** that occurs during prolonged muscle activity: A person is not able to take in oxygen fast enough to keep the muscles supplied with all the oxygen they need when they are working vigorously. Obviously, then, the work that a muscle can do and how long it can work without becoming fatigued depend on how good its blood supply is. When

muscles lack oxygen, lactic acid begins to accumulate in the muscle via the anaerobic mechanism described above. In addition, the muscle's ATP supply starts to run low and ionic imbalance occurs. Together these factors cause the muscle to contract less and less effectively and finally to stop contracting altogether.

True muscle fatigue, in which the muscle quits entirely, rarely occurs in most of us because we feel fatigued long before it happens and we simply slow down or stop our activity. It *does* happen commonly in marathon runners. Many of them have literally collapsed when their muscles became fatigued and could no longer work.

Oxygen deficit, which always occurs to some extent during vigorous muscle activity, must be "paid back" whether fatigue occurs or not. During the recovery period after activity, the individual breathes rapidly and deeply. This continues until the muscles have received the amount of oxygen needed to get rid of the accumulated lactic acid and make ATP and creatine phosphate reserves.

Types of Muscle Contractions— Isotonic and Isometric

Until now, we have been discussing contraction in terms of shortening behavior, but muscles do not always shorten when they contract. (I can hear you saying, "What kind of double-talk is that?"—but pay attention.) The event that is common to all muscle contractions is that *tension* develops in the muscle as the actin and myosin myofilaments interact and the myosin cross bridges attempt to slide the thin actin-containing filaments past the thick myosin myofilaments.

Isotonic contractions (literally, "same tone" or tension) are familiar to most of us. In isotonic contractions, the myofilaments are successful in their sliding movements, the muscle shortens, and movement occurs. Bending the knee, rotating the arms, and smiling are all examples of isotonic contractions.

Contractions in which the muscles do not shorten are called **isometric contractions** (literally, "same measurement" or length). In isometric contractions, the myosin myofilaments are "spinning their wheels," and the tension in the muscle keeps increasing. They are trying to slide, but the muscle is pitted against some more or less immovable object. For example, muscles are contracting isometrically when you try to lift a 400-pound dresser alone. When you straighten a bent elbow, the triceps muscle is contracting isotonically. But when you push against a wall with bent elbows, the wall doesn't move, and the triceps muscles, which cannot shorten to straighten the elbows, are contracting isometrically.

Muscle Tone

One aspect of skeletal muscle activity cannot be consciously controlled. Even when a muscle is voluntarily relaxed, some of its fibers are contracting— first one group and then another. Their contraction is not visible, but, as a result of it, the muscle remains firm, healthy, and constantly ready for action. This state of continuous partial contractions is called **muscle tone.** Muscle tone is the result of different motor units, which are scattered through

(a)   **(b)**

FIGURE 6.11   **The effects of aerobic training versus strength training. (a)** A marathon runner. **(b)** A weight lifter.

the muscle, being stimulated by the nervous system in a systematic way.

HOMEOSTATIC IMBALANCE

If the nerve supply to a muscle is destroyed (as in an accident), the muscle is no longer stimulated in this manner, and it loses tone and becomes paralyzed. Soon after, it becomes **flaccid** (flak'sid), or soft and flabby, and begins to **atrophy** (waste away). ▲

Effect of Exercise on Muscles

The amount of work a muscle does is reflected in changes in the muscle itself. Muscle inactivity (due to a loss of nerve supply, immobilization, or whatever the cause) always leads to muscle weakness and wasting. Muscles are no exception to the saying "Use it or lose it!"

Conversely, regular exercise increases muscle size, strength, and endurance. However, not all types of exercise produce these effects—in fact, there are important differences in the benefits of exercise.

Aerobic, or **endurance,** types of exercise, such as participating in an aerobics class, jogging, or biking (Figure 6.11a), result in stronger, more flexible muscles with greater resistance to fatigue. These changes come about, at least partly, because

TABLE 6.2	The Five Golden Rules of Skeletal Muscle Activity
1.	With a few exceptions, all skeletal muscles cross at least one joint.
2.	Typically, the bulk of a skeletal muscle lies proximal to the joint crossed.
3.	All skeletal muscles have at least two attachments: the origin and the insertion.
4.	Skeletal muscles can only pull; they never push.
5.	During contraction, a skeletal muscle insertion moves toward the origin.

the blood supply to the muscles increases, and the individual muscle cells form more mitochondria and store more oxygen. However, aerobic exercise benefits much more than the skeletal muscles. It makes overall body metabolism more efficient, improves digestion (and elimination), enhances neuromuscular coordination, and makes the skeleton stronger. The heart enlarges (*hypertrophies*) so that more blood is pumped out with each beat, fat deposits are cleared from the blood vessel walls, and the lungs become more efficient in gas exchange. These benefits may be permanent or temporary, depending on how often and how vigorously one exercises.

Aerobic exercise does *not* cause the muscles to increase much in size, even though the exercise may go on for hours. The bulging muscles of a bodybuilder or professional weight lifter result mainly from **resistance, or isometric, exercises** (Figure 6.11b) in which the muscles are pitted against some immovable object (or nearly immovable). Resistance exercises require very little time and little or no special equipment. A few minutes every other day is usually sufficient. A wall can be pushed against, and buttock muscles can be strongly contracted even while standing in line at the grocery store. The key is forcing the muscles to contract with as much force as possible. The increased muscle size and strength that result are due mainly to enlargement of individual muscle cells (they make more contractile filaments)

rather than to an increase in their number. The amount of connective tissue that reinforces the muscle also increases.

Because endurance and resistance exercises produce different patterns of muscle response, it is important to know what your exercise goals are. Lifting weights will not improve your endurance for a marathon. By the same token, jogging will do little to improve your muscle definition for competing in the Mr. or Ms. Muscle contest, nor will it make you stronger for moving furniture. Obviously, the best exercise program for most people is one that includes both types of exercise.

▶ DID YOU GET IT?

10. What are the three energy sources for skeletal muscle contraction?

11. What is the immediate source of energy for muscle contraction?

12. Gary is trying with all his might to pull a tree stump out of the ground. It does not budge. Which type of contraction are his muscles undergoing?

13. What is meant by the term *oxygen deficit*?

14. To develop big, beautiful skeletal muscles, should your exercise focus be aerobic or resistance type exercise?

For answers, see Appendix D.

Muscle Movements, Types, and Names

This section is a bit of a hodge-podge. It includes some topics that don't really fit together, but they don't fit anywhere else any better. For example, there are five very basic understandings about gross muscle activity. I call these the *Five Golden Rules* of skeletal muscle activity because until you understand them, comprehending muscle movements and appreciating muscle interactions are nearly impossible. These golden rules are summarized for your quick review in Table 6.2.

Types of Body Movements

Every one of our 600-odd skeletal muscles is attached to bone, or to other connective tissue structures, at no fewer than two points. One of these points, the origin, is attached to the immovable or less movable bone (Figure 6.12). The **insertion** is attached to the movable bone, and when the muscle contracts, the insertion moves toward the origin. Some muscles have interchangeable origins and insertions. For example, the rectus femoris muscle of the anterior thigh crosses both the hip and knee joints. Its most common action is to extend the knee, in which case the proximal pelvic attachment is the origin. However, when the knee is bent (by other muscles), the rectus femoris can flex the hip, and then its distal attachment on the leg is considered the origin.

Generally speaking, body movement occurs when muscles contract across joints. The type of movement depends on the mobility of the joint and on where the muscle is located in relation to the joint. The most obvious examples of the action of muscles on bones are the movements that occur at the joints of the limbs. However, less freely movable bones are also tugged into motion by the muscles, such as the vertebrae's movements when the torso is bent to the side.

The most common types of body movements are described next and shown in Figure 6.13. Try to demonstrate each movement as you read the following descriptions:

- **Flexion.** Flexion is a movement, generally in the sagittal plane, that decreases the angle of the joint and brings two bones closer together (Figure 6.13a and b). Flexion is typical of hinge joints (bending the knee or elbow), but it is also common at ball-and-socket joints (for example, bending forward at the hip).

- **Extension.** Extension is the opposite of flexion, so it is a movement that increases the angle, or the distance, between two bones or parts of the body (straightening the knee or elbow). If extension is greater than 180° (as when you tip your head or your torso posteriorly so that your chin points toward the ceiling), it is hyperextension (Figure 6.13a and b).

- **Rotation.** Rotation is movement of a bone around its longitudinal axis (Figure 6.13c). Rotation is a common movement of ball-and-socket joints and describes the movement of the atlas around the dens of the axis (as in shaking your head "no").

- **Abduction.** Abduction is moving a limb away (generally on the frontal plane) from the midline, or median plane, of the body (Figure 6.13d).

The other movement that the biceps brachii muscle (shown in this illustration) can bring about is to move the torso toward the bar when you chin yourself. Would the forearm still be the insertion for that movement?

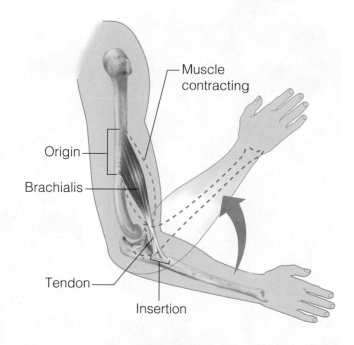

FIGURE 6.12 Muscle attachments (origin and insertion). When a skeletal muscle contracts, its insertion moves toward its origin.

The terminology also applies to the fanning movement of the fingers or toes when they are spread apart.

- **Adduction.** Adduction is the opposite of abduction, so it is the movement of a limb toward the body midline (Figure 6.13d).

- **Circumduction.** Circumduction is a combination of flexion, extension, abduction, and adduction commonly seen in ball-and-socket joints such as the shoulder. The proximal end of the limb is stationary, and its distal end moves in a circle. The limb as a whole outlines a cone (Figure 6.13d).

Special Movements

Certain movements do not fit into any of the previous categories and occur at only a few joints.

No, the insertion in this case would be its attachment to the humerus, and the attachment on the forearm (which is held steady during this movement) is the insertion.

(a) Flexion and extension of the shoulder and knee

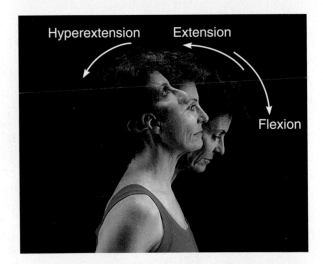

(b) Flexion, extension, and hyperextension

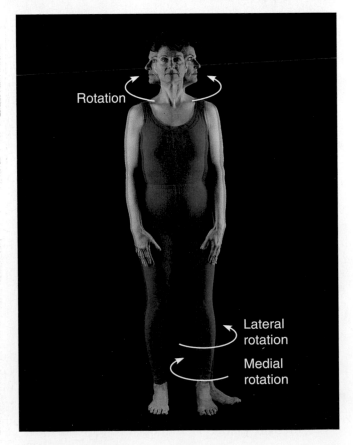

(c) Rotation

FIGURE 6.13 **Body movements.**

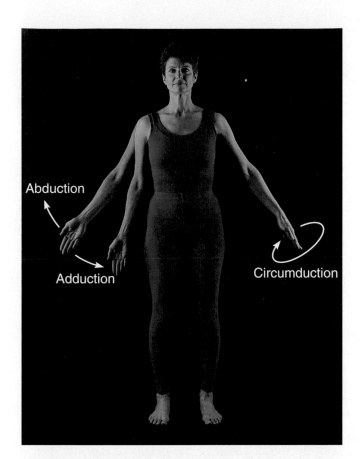

(d) Abduction, adduction, and circumduction

(e) Dorsiflexion and plantar flexion

(f) Inversion and eversion

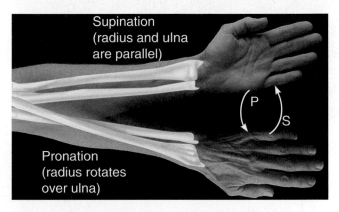

(g) Supination (S) and pronation (P)

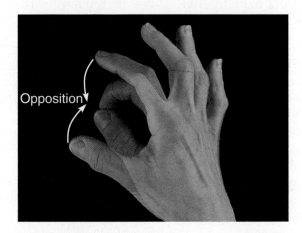

(h) Opposition

FIGURE 6.13   *(continued)*

Some of these special movements are shown in Figure 6.13.

- **Dorsiflexion and plantar flexion.** Up and down movements of the foot at the ankle are given special names. Lifting the foot so that its superior surface approaches the shin (standing on your heels) is called dorsiflexion, whereas depressing the foot (pointing the toes) is called plantar flexion (Figure 6.13e). Dorsiflexion of the foot corresponds to extension of the hand at the wrist, whereas plantar flexion of the foot corresponds to flexion of the hand.

- **Inversion and eversion.** Inversion and eversion are also special movements of the foot (Figure 6.13f). To invert the foot, turn the sole medially. To evert the foot, turn the sole laterally.

- **Supination and pronation.** The terms *supination* (soo″pĭ-na′shun; "turning backward") and *pronation* (pro-na′shun; "turning forward") refer to movements of the radius around the ulna (Figure 6.13g). Supination occurs when the forearm rotates laterally so that the palm faces anteriorly, and the radius and ulna are parallel. Pronation occurs when the forearm rotates medially so that the palm faces posteriorly. Pronation brings the radius across the ulna so that the two bones form an X. A helpful memory trick: If you lift a cup of soup up to your mouth *on your palm,* you are supinating ("soup"-inating).

- **Opposition.** In the palm of the hand, the saddle joint between metacarpal 1 and the carpals allows opposition of the thumb (Figure 6.13h). This is the action by which you move your thumb to touch the tips of the other fingers on the same hand. It is this unique action that makes the human hand such a fine tool for grasping and manipulating things.

Interactions of Skeletal Muscles in the Body

Muscles can't push—they can only pull as they contract—so most often body movements are the result of the activity of two or more muscles acting together or against each other. Muscles are arranged in such a way that whatever one muscle (or group of muscles) can do, other muscles can reverse. Because of this, muscles are able to bring about an immense variety of movements.

The muscle that has the major responsibility for causing a particular movement is called the **prime mover.** (This physiological term has been borrowed by the business world to label a person who gets things done.) Muscles that oppose or reverse a movement are **antagonists** (an-tag′o-nists). When a prime mover is active, its antagonist is stretched and relaxed. Antagonists can be prime movers in their own right. For example, the biceps of the arm (prime mover of elbow flexion) is antagonized by the triceps (a prime mover of elbow extension).

Synergists (sin′er-jists; *syn* = together, *erg* = work) help prime movers by producing the same movement or by reducing undesirable movements. When a muscle crosses two or more joints, its contraction will cause movement in all the joints crossed unless synergists are there to stabilize them. For example, the finger-flexor muscles cross both the wrist and the finger joints. You can make a fist without bending your wrist because synergist muscles stabilize the wrist joints and allow the prime mover to act on the finger joints.

Fixators are specialized synergists. They hold a bone still or stabilize the origin of a prime mover so all the tension can be used to move the insertion bone. The postural muscles that stabilize the vertebral column are fixators, as are the muscles that anchor the scapulae to the thorax.

In summary, although prime movers seem to get all the credit for causing certain movements, the actions of antagonistic and synergistic muscles are also important in effecting smooth, coordinated, and precise movements.

▶ *DID YOU GET IT?*

15. What action is being performed by a person who sticks out his thumb to hitch a ride?

16. What actions take place at the neck when you nod your head up and down as if saying "yes"?

For answers, see Appendix D.

Naming Skeletal Muscles

Like bones, muscles come in many shapes and sizes to suit their particular tasks in the body. Muscles are named on the basis of several criteria, each of which focuses on a particular structural or functional characteristic. Paying close attention to these

A CLOSER LOOK

ARE ATHLETES LOOKING GOOD AND DOING BETTER WITH ANABOLIC STEROIDS?

Everyone loves a winner, and top athletes are popular and make lots of money. It is not surprising that some will grasp at anything to increase their performance—including "juice" (anabolic steroids). These hormones, engineered by pharmaceutical companies, were introduced in the 1950s to treat victims of certain muscle-wasting diseases and anemia and to prevent muscle atrophy in patients immobilized after surgery. Testosterone, a natural anabolic steroid hormone made by the body, triggers the increase in muscle and bone mass and other physical changes that occur during puberty and convert boys into men. Convinced that huge doses of the anabolic steroids could enhance masculinizing effects in grown men, many athletes were using the steroids by the early 1960s, and the practice is still going strong today. In 2004, allegations of rampant steroid abuse by

Barry Bonds of the San Francisco Giants and by other baseball players surfaced. Investigations of this so-called Balco Scandal have stunned fans of major league baseball.

Steroid use today is not confined to athletes looking for an edge. Indeed, it is estimated that one out of every ten young men has tried steroids, and the practice is growing rapidly among young women.

The use of these drugs has been banned by most international athletic competitions, and users (and prescribing physicians or drug dealers) are naturally reluctant to talk about it. Nonetheless, there is little question that many professional body-builders and athletes competing in events that require great muscle strength (such as discus throwing and weight lifting) are heavy users. Sports figures such as football players have also admitted to using steroids to help them prepare for games. Advantages of anabolic steroids cited by athletes include increased muscle mass and strength, increased oxygen-carrying capacity of the blood (due to greater red blood cell volume), and an increase in aggressive behavior (the urge to "steamroller the other guy").

But do the drugs do all that is claimed for them? Research studies have reported increases in isometric strength and body weight in steroid users. Although these are results weight lifters dream about, there is hot dispute over whether the drugs

also enhance the fine muscle coordination and endurance needed by runners and others.

Do the claimed slight advantages conferred by steroid use outweigh the risks? Absolutely not! Physicians say that steroids cause bloated faces (a sign of steroid excess), shriveled testes, and infertility; damage the liver and promote liver cancer; and cause changes in blood-cholesterol levels (which may place long-term users at risk for coronary disease). Additionally, about one-third of anabolic

> **" About one-third of anabolic steroid users develop serious psychiatric problems. "**

steroid users develop serious psychiatric problems. Manic behavior in which the users undergo Jekyll–Hyde personality swings and become extremely violent (the so-called 'roid rage) is common; so, too, are depression and delusions.

A recent arrival on the scene, sold over the counter as a "nutritional performance enhancer," is androstenedione, which is converted to testosterone in the body. It is taken orally, and much of it is destroyed by the liver soon after ingestion, but the few milligrams that survive temporarily boost testosterone levels. Reports of its use by baseball great Mark McGwire before he retired and of "wannabe" athletes from the fifth grade up sweeping the supplement off the drugstore shelves are troubling. Androstenedione is not regulated by the U.S. Food and Drug Administration (FDA), and its long-term effects are unpredictable. Ongoing studies have found that boys and men who took the supplement developed elevated levels of the female hormone estrogen as well as testosterone (raising their risk of feminizing effects such as enlarged breasts), early puberty, and stunted bone growth leading to shorter than normal adult height.

The question of why athletes use these drugs is easy to answer. Some say they are willing to do almost anything to win, short of killing themselves. Are they unwittingly doing this as well?

cues can greatly simplify your task of learning muscle names and actions:

- **Direction of the muscle fibers.** Some muscles are named in reference to some imaginary line, usually the midline of the body or the long axis of a limb bone. When a muscle's name includes the term *rectus* (straight), its fibers run parallel to that imaginary line. For example, the rectus femoris is the straight muscle of the thigh, or femur. Similarly, the term *oblique* as part of a muscle's name tells you that the muscle fibers run obliquely (at a slant) to the imaginary line.

- **Relative size of the muscle.** Such terms as *maximus* (largest), *minimus* (smallest), and *longus* (long) are often used in the names of muscles—for example, the gluteus maximus is the largest muscle of the gluteus muscle group.

- **Location of the muscle.** Some muscles are named for the bone with which they are associated. For example, the temporalis and frontalis muscles overlie the temporal and frontal bones of the skull, respectively.

- **Number of origins.** When the term *biceps, triceps,* or *quadriceps* forms part of a muscle name, one can assume that the muscle has two, three, or four origins, respectively. For example, the biceps muscle of the arm has two heads, or origins, and the triceps muscle has three.

- **Location of the muscle's origin and insertion.** Occasionally, muscles are named for their attachment sites. For example, the sternocleidomastoid muscle has its origin on the sternum (*sterno*) and clavicle (*cleido*) and inserts on the *mastoid* process of the temporal bone.

- **Shape of the muscle.** Some muscles have a distinctive shape that helps to identify them. For example, the deltoid muscle is roughly triangular (*deltoid* means "triangular").

- **Action of the muscle.** When muscles are named for their actions, terms such as *flexor, extensor,* and *adductor* appear in their names. For example, the adductor muscles of the thigh all bring about its adduction, and the extensor muscles of the wrist all extend the wrist.

Arrangement of Fascicles

Skeletal muscles consist of fascicles, but fascicle arrangements vary, producing muscles with different structures and functional properties. The most common patterns of fascicle arrangement are described next.

The pattern is **circular** when the fascicles are arranged in concentric rings (Figure 6.14d). Circular muscles are typically found surrounding external body openings which they close by contracting. A general term for such muscles is *sphincters* ("squeezers"). Examples are the orbicularis muscles surrounding the eyes and mouth.

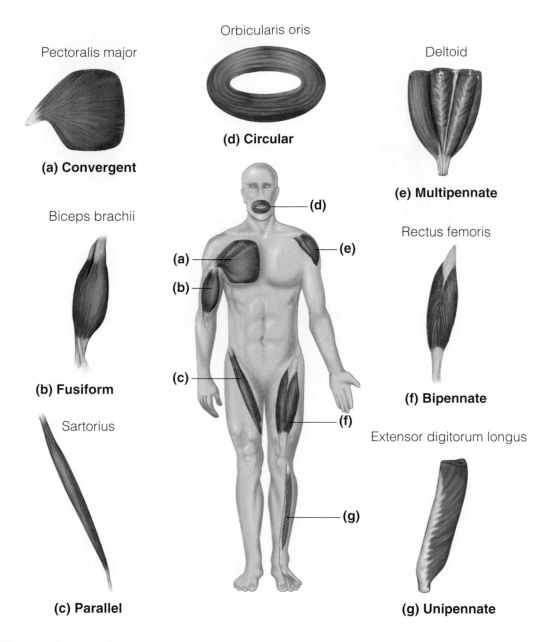

Pectoralis major

(a) Convergent

Orbicularis oris

(d) Circular

Deltoid

(e) Multipennate

Biceps brachii

(b) Fusiform

Rectus femoris

(f) Bipennate

Sartorius

(c) Parallel

Extensor digitorum longus

(g) Unipennate

FIGURE 6.14 Relationship of fascicle arrangement to muscle structure.

In a **convergent** muscle, the fascicles converge toward a single insertion tendon. Such a muscle is triangular or fan-shaped, such as the pectoralis major muscle of the anterior thorax (Figure 6.14a).

In a **parallel** arrangement, the length of the fascicles run parallel to the long axis of the muscle. These muscles are straplike (Figure 6.14c). A modification of the parallel arrangement, called **fusiform,** results in a spindle-shaped muscle with an expanded belly (midsection), such as the biceps brachii muscle of the arm (Figure 6.14b).

In a **pennate** (pen′āt; "feather") pattern, short fascicles attach obliquely to a central tendon. In the extensor digitorum muscle of the leg, the fascicles insert into only one side of the tendon and the muscle is *unipennate* (Figure 6.14g). If the fascicles insert into opposite sides of the tendon or from several different sides, the muscle is *bipennate* (Figure 6.14f) or *multipennate* (Figure 6.14e), respectively.

A muscle's fascicle arrangement determines its range of motion and power. The longer and the more nearly parallel the fascicles are to a muscle's

Frontalis

Orbicularis oculi

Zygomaticus

Buccinator

Orbicularis oris

Platysma

Cranial aponeurosis

Temporalis

Occipitalis

Masseter

Sternocleidomastoid

Trapezius

FIGURE 6.15 **Superficial muscles of the face and neck.**

long axis, the more the muscle can shorten, but such muscles are not usually very powerful. Muscle power depends more on the total number of muscle cells in the muscle. The stocky bipennate and multipennate muscles, which pack in the most fibers, shorten very little but are very powerful.

▶DID YOU GET IT?

17. Based on their names, deduce some characteristics of the following muscles: tibialis anterior, erector spinae, rectus abdominis.

18. What is the fascicle arrangement of the orbicularis oris muscle?

19. In what way are fixators and synergist muscles important?

For answers, see Appendix D.

Gross Anatomy of Skeletal Muscles

It is beyond the scope of this book to describe the hundreds of skeletal muscles of the human body. Only the most important muscles are described here. In addition, all the superficial muscles considered are summarized in Tables 6.3 and 6.4 and are illustrated in overall body views in Figures 6.21 and 6.22, which accompany the tables (pp. 216–219).

Head and Neck Muscles

The head muscles (Figure 6.15) are an interesting group. They have many specific functions but are usually grouped into two large categories—facial muscles and chewing muscles. Facial muscles are unique because they are inserted into soft tissues such as other muscles or skin. When they pull on the skin of the face, they permit us to smile faintly, grin widely, frown, pout, deliver a kiss, and so forth. The chewing muscles begin the breakdown of food for the body. All head and neck muscles described are paired except for the platysma, the orbicularis oris, the frontalis, and the occipitalis.

Facial Muscles

Frontalis   The frontalis, which covers the frontal bone, runs from the cranial aponeurosis to the skin of the eyebrows, where it inserts. This muscle allows you to raise your eyebrows, as in surprise, and to wrinkle your forehead. At the posterior end of the cranial aponeurosis is the small **occipitalis** muscle, which covers the posterior aspect of the skull and pulls the scalp posteriorly.*

Orbicularis Oculi   The orbicularis oculi (or-bik″u-la′ris ok′u-li) has fibers that run in circles around the eyes. It allows you to close your eyes, squint, blink, and wink.

Orbicularis Oris   The orbicularis oris is the circular muscle of the lips. Because it closes the mouth and protrudes the lips, it is often called the "kissing" muscle.

Buccinator   The fleshy buccinator (bu′sĭ-na″tor) muscle runs horizontally across the cheek and inserts into the orbicularis oris. It flattens the cheek (as in whistling or blowing a trumpet). It is also listed as a chewing muscle because it compresses the cheek to hold the food between the teeth during chewing.

Zygomaticus   The zygomaticus (zi″go-mat′i-kus) extends from the corner of the mouth to the cheekbone. It is often referred to as the "smiling" muscle because it raises the corners of the mouth upward.

Chewing Muscles

The buccinator muscle, which is a member of this group, is described with the facial muscles.

Masseter   As it runs from the zygomatic process of the temporal bone to the mandible, the masseter

---

*Although the current references on anatomic terminology refer to the frontalis and occipitalis as the *frontal* and *occipital bellies* of the *epicranius* ("over the cranium") muscle, we will continue to use the terms frontalis and occipitalis here.

(mă-se′ter) covers the angle of the lower jaw. This muscle closes the jaw by elevating the mandible.

Temporalis   The temporalis is a fan-shaped muscle overlying the temporal bone. It inserts into the mandible and acts as a synergist of the masseter in closing the jaw.

Neck Muscles

For the most part, the neck muscles, which move the head and shoulder girdle, are small and straplike. Only two neck muscles are considered here.

Platysma   The platysma is a single sheetlike muscle that covers the anterolateral neck (see Figure 6.15). It originates from the connective tissue covering of the chest muscles and inserts into the area around the mouth. Its action is to pull the corners of the mouth inferiorly, producing a downward sag of the mouth.

Sternocleidomastoid   The paired sternocleidomastoid (ster″no-kli″do-mas′toid) muscles are two-headed muscles, one found on each side of the neck. Of the two heads of each muscle, one arises from the sternum and the other arises from the clavicle. The heads fuse before inserting into the mastoid process of the temporal bone. When both sternocleidomastoid muscles contract together, they flex your neck. (It is this action of bowing the head that has led some people to call these muscles the "prayer" muscles.) If just one muscle contracts, the head is rotated toward the shoulder on the opposite side and tilts the head to its own side.

HOMEOSTATIC IMBALANCE

In some difficult births, one of the sternocleidomastoid muscles may be injured and develop spasms. A baby injured in this way has **torticollis** (tor″ti-kol′is), or wryneck. ▲

▶ *DID YOU GET IT?*

20. Which muscle raises your eyebrow?

21. Which two muscles are synergists in jaw closure?

For answers, see Appendix D.

Trunk Muscles

The trunk muscles include (1) those that move the vertebral column (most of which are posterior

FIGURE 6.16 Muscles of the anterior trunk, shoulder, and arm. (a) Muscles crossing the shoulder joint, causing movements of the arm. The platysma of the neck is removed. **(b)** Muscles of the abdominal wall. Portions of the superficial muscles of the right side of the abdomen are cut away to reveal the deeper muscles.

antigravity muscles); (2) anterior thorax muscles, which move the ribs, head, and arms; and (3) muscles of the abdominal wall, which help to move the vertebral column and, most important, form the muscular "natural girdle" of the abdominal body wall.

Anterior Muscles (Figure 6.16)

Pectoralis Major The pectoralis (pek″to-ra′lis) major is a large fan-shaped muscle covering the upper part of the chest. Its origin is from the sternum, shoulder girdle, and the first six ribs. It inserts on the proximal end of the humerus. This muscle forms the anterior wall of the axilla and acts to adduct and flex the arm.

Intercostal Muscles The intercostal muscles are deep muscles found between the ribs. (Although

they are not shown in Figure 6.16, which shows only superficial muscles, they are illustrated in Figure 6.21, p. 216.) The external intercostals are important in breathing because they help to raise the rib cage when you inhale. The internal intercostals, which lie deep to the external intercostals, depress the rib cage, which helps to move air out of the lungs when you exhale forcibly.

Muscles of the Abdominal Girdle The anterior abdominal muscles (rectus abdominis, external and internal obliques, and transversus abdominis) form a natural "girdle" that reinforces the body trunk. Taken together, they resemble the structure of plywood because the fibers of each muscle or muscle pair run in a different direction. Just as plywood is exceptionally strong for its thickness, the abdominal muscles form a muscular wall that is well suited

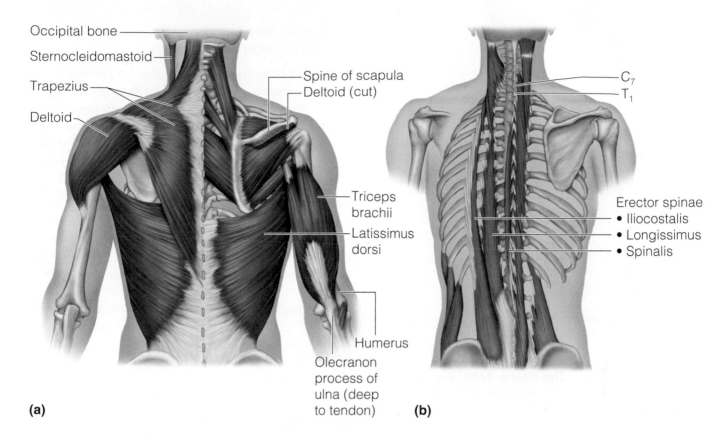

FIGURE 6.17   Muscles of the posterior neck, trunk, and arm.
(a) Superficial muscles. **(b)** The erector spinae muscles (longissimus, iliocostalis, and spinalis), deep muscles of the back.

for its job of containing and protecting the abdominal contents.

- **Rectus abdominis.** The paired straplike rectus abdominis muscles are the most superficial muscles of the abdomen. They run from the pubis to the rib cage, enclosed in an aponeurosis. Their main function is to flex the vertebral column. They also compress the abdominal contents during defecation and childbirth and are involved in forced breathing.

- **External oblique.** The external oblique muscles are paired superficial muscles that make up the lateral walls of the abdomen. Their fibers run downward and medially from the last eight ribs and insert into the ilium. Like the rectus abdominis, they flex the vertebral column, but they also rotate the trunk and bend it laterally.

- **Internal oblique.** The internal oblique muscles are paired muscles deep to the external obliques. Their fibers run at right angles to

those of the external obliques. They arise from the iliac crest and insert into the last three ribs. Their functions are the same as those of the external obliques.

- **Transversus abdominis.** The transversus abdominis is the deepest muscle of the abdominal wall and has fibers that run horizontally across the abdomen. It arises from the lower ribs and iliac crest and inserts into the pubis. This muscle compresses the abdominal contents.

Posterior Muscles   (Figure 6.17)

Trapezius   The trapezius (trah-pe′ze-us) muscles are the most superficial muscles of the posterior neck and upper trunk. When seen together, they form a diamond- or kite-shaped muscle mass. Their origin is very broad. Each muscle runs from the occipital bone of the skull down the vertebral column to the end of the thoracic vertebrae. They

FIGURE 6.18 **The fleshy deltoid muscle is a favored site for administering intramuscular injections.**

then flare laterally to insert on the scapular spine and clavicle. The trapezius muscles extend the head (thus they are antagonists of the sternocleidomastoids). They also can elevate, depress, adduct, and stabilize the scapula.

Latissimus Dorsi The latissimus (lah-tis′ĭ-mus) dorsi muscles are the two large, flat muscles that cover the lower back. They originate on the lower spine and ilium and then sweep superiorly to insert into the proximal end of the humerus. Each latissimus dorsi extends and adducts the humerus. These are very important muscles when the arm must be brought down in a power stroke, as when swimming or striking a blow.

Erector Spinae The erector spinae (e-rek′tor spi′ne) group is the prime mover of back extension. These paired muscles are deep muscles of the back; they are shown in Figure 6.17b. Each erector spinae is a composite muscle consisting of three muscle columns (longissimus, iliocostalis, and spinalis) that collectively span the entire length of the vertebral column. These muscles not only act as powerful back extensors ("erectors") but also provide resistance that helps control the action of bending over at the waist. Following injury to back

structures, these muscles go into spasms, a common source of lower back pain.

Quadratus Lumborum The fleshy quadratus lumborum (qwad-ra′tus lum-bor′um) muscles form part of the posterior abdominal wall. Acting separately, each muscle of the pair flexes the spine laterally. Acting together, they extend the lumbar spine. These muscles arise from the iliac crests and insert into the upper lumbar vertebrae (Figure 6.17b).

Deltoid The deltoids are fleshy, triangle-shaped muscles that form the rounded shape of your shoulders (see Figure 6.17a). Because they are so bulky, they are a favorite injection site (Figure 6.18) when relatively small amounts of medication (less than 5 ml) must be given intramuscularly (into muscle). The origin of each deltoid winds across the shoulder girdle from the spine of the scapula to the clavicle. It inserts into the proximal humerus. The deltoids are the prime movers of arm abduction.

▶ DID YOU GET IT?

22. Which muscle group is the prime mover of back extension?

23. What structural feature makes the abdominal musculature especially strong for its thickness?

24. Which muscle of the posterior trunk is the synergist of the pectoralis major muscle in arm adduction?

For answers, see Appendix D.

Muscles of the Upper Limb

The upper limb muscles fall into three groups. The first group includes muscles that arise from the shoulder girdle and cross the shoulder joint to insert into the humerus (see Figures 6.16 and 6.17a). These muscles, which move the arm, have already been considered—the pectoralis major, latissimus dorsi, and deltoid.

The second group causes movement at the elbow joint. These muscles enclose the humerus and insert on the forearm bones. Only the muscles of this second group will be described in this section.

The third group includes the muscles of the forearm, which insert on the hand bones and cause their movement. The muscles of this last group are thin and spindle-shaped, and there are many of them. We will not consider them here except to mention their general naming and function. As a rule, the forearm muscles have names that reflect their activities. For example, the flexor carpi and flexor digitorum muscles, found on the anterior aspect of the forearm, cause flexion of the wrist and fingers, respectively. The extensor carpi and extensor digitorum muscles, found on the lateral and posterior aspect of the forearm, extend the same structures. (Some of these muscles are described briefly in Table 6.4 and illustrated in Figure 6.22.)

Muscles of the Humerus That Act on the Forearm

All *anterior* arm muscles cause elbow flexion. In order of decreasing strength these are the brachialis, biceps brachii, and brachioradialis (Figures 6.16a and 6.21).

Biceps Brachii   The biceps brachii (bra′ke-i) is the most familiar muscle of the arm because it bulges when the elbow is flexed (see Figure 6.16a). It originates by two heads from the shoulder girdle and inserts into the radial tuberosity. This muscle is the powerful prime mover for flexion of the forearm and acts to supinate the forearm. The best way to remember its action is to think of opening a bottle of wine. The biceps supinates the forearm to turn the corkscrew *and* then flexes the elbow to pull the cork.

Brachialis   The brachialis lies deep to the biceps muscle and is as important as the biceps in elbow flexion. The brachialis lifts the ulna as the biceps lifts the radius.

Brachioradialis   The brachioradialis is a fairly weak muscle that arises on the humerus and inserts into the distal forearm (see Figure 6.21). Hence, it resides mainly in the forearm.

Triceps Brachii   The triceps brachii is the only muscle fleshing out the posterior humerus (see Figure 6.17a). Its three heads arise from the shoulder girdle and proximal humerus, and it inserts into the olecranon process of the ulna. Being the powerful prime mover of elbow extension, it is the antagonist of the biceps brachii. This muscle is often called the "boxer's" muscle because it can deliver a straight-arm knockout punch.

Muscles of the Lower Limb

Muscles that act on the lower limb cause movement at the hip, knee, and foot joints. They are among the largest, strongest muscles in the body and are specialized for walking and balancing the body. Because the pelvic girdle is composed of heavy, fused bones that allow little movement, no special group of muscles is necessary to stabilize it. This is very different from the shoulder girdle, which requires several fixator muscles.

Many muscles of the lower limb span two joints and can cause movement at both of them. Therefore, the terms *origin* and *insertion* are often interchangeable in referring to these muscles.

Muscles acting on the thigh are massive muscles that help hold the body upright against the pull of gravity and cause various movements at the hip joint. Muscles acting on the leg form the flesh of the thigh. (Recall that in common usage the term *leg* refers to the whole lower limb, but anatomically the term refers only to that part between the knee and the ankle.) The thigh muscles cross the knee and cause its flexion or extension. Because many of the thigh muscles also have attachments on the pelvic girdle, they can cause movement at the hip joint as well.

Muscles originating on the leg cause assorted movements of the ankle and foot. We will consider only three muscles of this group, but there are many others that act to extend and flex the ankle and toe joints.

Muscles Causing Movement at the Hip Joint   (Figure 6.19)

Gluteus Maximus   The gluteus maximus (gloo′te-us max′ĭ-mus) is a superficial muscle of the hip that forms most of the flesh of the buttock (Figure 6.19a). It is a powerful hip extensor that acts to bring the thigh in a straight line with the pelvis. Although it is not very important in walking, it is probably the most important muscle for extending the hip when power is needed, as when climbing stairs and when jumping. It originates from the sacrum and iliac bones and inserts on the gluteal tuberosity of the femur and into the large tendonous *iliotibial* tract.

Gluteus Medius   The gluteus medius runs from the ilium to the femur, beneath the gluteus maximus for most of its length. The gluteus medius is

(a)

- Gluteus medius
- Gluteus maximus
- Adductor magnus
- Iliotibial tract
- Biceps femoris
- Semitendinosus
- Semimembranosus
- Gastrocnemius

Hamstring group

(b)

- Posterior superior iliac spine
- Iliac crest
- Safe area in gluteus medius
- Gluteus maximus
- Sciatic nerve

FIGURE 6.19 Pelvic, hip, and thigh muscles of the right side of the body.
(a) Posterior view of hip and thigh muscles.
(b) Diagram showing deep structures of the gluteal region and the proper site for administering an injection into the gluteus medius muscle.

a hip abductor and is important in steadying the pelvis during walking. The gluteus medius is an important site for giving intramuscular injections, particularly when more than 5 ml is administered (see Figure 6.19b). Although it might appear that the large, fleshy gluteus maximus that forms the bulk of the buttock mass would be a better choice, notice that the medial part of each buttock overlies the large *sciatic nerve;* hence this area must be carefully avoided. This can be accomplished by *mentally* dividing the buttock into four equal quadrants (shown by the division lines on Figure 6.19b). The superolateral quadrant then overlies the gluteus medius muscle, which is usually a very safe site for an intramuscular injection.

Iliopsoas The iliopsoas (il″e-o-so′as; the *p* is silent) is a fused muscle composed of two muscles, the *iliacus* and the *psoas major* (Figure 6.19c). It runs from the iliac bone and lower vertebrae deep inside the pelvis to insert on the lesser trochanter of the femur. It is a prime mover of hip flexion. It also acts to keep the upper body from falling backward when we are standing erect.

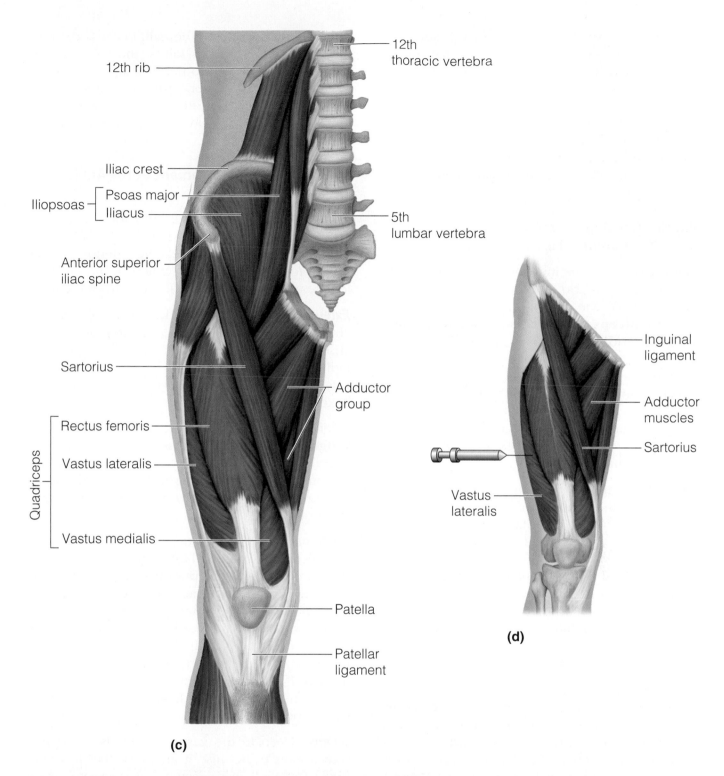

12th rib

12th thoracic vertebra

Iliac crest

Iliopsoas — Psoas major
            Iliacus

5th lumbar vertebra

Anterior superior iliac spine

Sartorius

Adductor group

Quadriceps — Rectus femoris

Vastus lateralis

Vastus medialis

Patella

Patellar ligament

(c)

Inguinal ligament

Adductor muscles

Sartorius

Vastus lateralis

(d)

FIGURE 6.19 *(continued)* **(c)** Anterior view of pelvic and thigh muscles. **(d)** Diagram showing the proper site for administration of an injection into the lateral thigh (vastus lateralis muscle).

Adductor Muscles The muscles of the adductor group form the muscle mass at the medial side of each thigh (Figure 6.19c). As their name indicates, they adduct, or press, the thighs together. However, because gravity does most of the work for them, they tend to become flabby very easily. Special exercises are usually needed to keep them toned. The adductors have their origin on the pelvis and insert on the proximal aspect of the femur.

Muscles Causing Movement at the Knee Joint   (Figure 6.19)

Hamstring Group The muscles forming the muscle mass of the posterior thigh are the hamstrings (Figure 6.19a). The group consists of three muscles, the **biceps femoris, semimembranosus,** and **semitendinosus,** which originate on the ischial tuberosity and run down the thigh to insert on both sides of the proximal tibia. They are prime movers of thigh extension and knee flexion. Their name comes from the fact that butchers use their tendons to hang hams (consisting of thigh and hip muscles) for smoking. These tendons can be felt at the back of the knee.

Sartorius Compared with other thigh muscles described here, the thin, straplike sartorius (sar-to're-us) muscle is not too important. However, it is the most superficial muscle of the thigh and so is rather hard to miss (Figure 6.19c). It runs obliquely across the thigh from the anterior iliac crest to the medial side of the tibia. It is a weak thigh flexor. The sartorius is commonly referred to as the "tailor's" muscle because it acts as a synergist to bring about the cross-legged position in which old-time tailors are often shown.

Quadriceps Group The quadriceps (kwod'rĭ-seps) group consists of four muscles—the **rectus femoris** and three **vastus muscles**—that flesh out the anterior thigh. (Only two vastus muscles are visible in Figure 6.19c. The third, the vastus intermedius, is obscured by the rectus femoris muscle, which lies over it.) The vastus muscles originate from the femur; the rectus femoris originates on the pelvis. All four muscles insert into the tibial tuberosity via the patellar ligament. The group as a whole acts to extend the knee powerfully, as when kicking a football. Because the rectus femoris crosses two joints, the hip and the knee, it can also help to flex the hip. The vastus lateralis and rectus femoris are sometimes used as intramuscular injection sites (Figure 6.19d), particularly in infants, who have poorly developed gluteus muscles.

Muscles Causing Movement at the Ankle and Foot   (Figure 6.20)

Tibialis Anterior The tibialis anterior is a superficial muscle on the anterior leg. It arises from the upper tibia and then parallels the anterior crest as it runs to the tarsal bones, where it inserts by a long tendon. It acts to dorsiflex and invert the foot.

Extensor Digitorum Longus Lateral to the tibialis anterior, the extensor digitorum longus muscle arises from the lateral tibial condyle and proximal radius and inserts into the phalanges of toes 2 to 5. It is a prime mover of toe extension and a dorsiflexor of the foot.

Fibularis Muscles The three fibularis muscles—**longus, brevis,** and **tertius**—are found on the lateral part of the leg. They arise from the fibula and insert into the metatarsal bones of the foot. The group as a whole plantar flexes and everts the foot.

Gastrocnemius The gastrocnemius (gas"trok-ne'me-us) muscle is a two-bellied muscle that forms the curved calf of the posterior leg. It arises by two heads, one from each side of the distal femur, and inserts through the large *calcaneal (Achilles) tendon* into the heel of the foot. It is a prime mover for plantar flexion of the foot; for this reason it is often called the "toe dancer's" muscle. If its insertion tendon is cut, walking is very difficult. The foot drags because the heel cannot be lifted.

Soleus Deep to the gastrocnemius is the fleshy soleus muscle. Because it arises on the tibia and fibula (rather than the femur), it does not affect knee movement, but like the gastrocnemius, it inserts into the calcaneal tendon and is a strong plantar flexor of the foot.

Remember that most of the superficial muscles previously described are shown in anterior

Fibularis longus

Fibularis brevis

Tibialis anterior

Extensor digitorum longus

Fibularis tertius

Tibia

Soleus

Gastrocnemius

Soleus

Calcaneal (Achilles) tendon

Medial malleolus

Lateral malleolus

(a)

(b)

FIGURE 6.20   Superficial muscles of the right leg. (a) Anterior view. **(b)** Posterior view.

and posterior views of the body as a whole in Figures 6.21 and 6.22 and are summarized in Tables 6.3 and 6.4. Take the time to review these muscles again before continuing with this chapter.

▶ *DID YOU GET IT?*

25. Which muscle is the antagonist of the biceps brachii when the biceps flexes the elbow?

26. Which muscle group is the antagonist of the hamstring muscles?

27. What are two good sites for intramuscular injections in adults?

28. Which two muscles insert into the calcaneal tendon? What movement do they effect?

For answers, see Appendix D.

Facial
- Frontalis
- Orbicularis oculi
- Zygomaticus
- Orbicularis oris

Facial
- Temporalis
- Masseter

Neck
- Platysma
- Sternocleidomastoid

Shoulder
- Trapezius
- Deltoid

Thorax
- Pectoralis minor
- Pectoralis major
- Serratus anterior
- Intercostals

Arm
- Triceps brachii
- Biceps brachii
- Brachialis

Abdomen
- Rectus abdominis
- External oblique
- Internal oblique
- Transversus abdominis

Forearm
- Brachioradialis
- Flexor carpi radialis

Pelvis/thigh
- Iliopsoas

Thigh
- Sartorius
- Adductor muscle
- Gracilis

Thigh (Quadriceps)
- Rectus femoris
- Vastus lateralis
- Vastus medialis

Leg
- Fibularis longus
- Extensor digitorum longus
- Tibialis anterior

Leg
- Gastrocnemius
- Soleus

FIGURE 6.21 Major superficial muscles of the anterior surface of the body.

TABLE 6.3   Superficial Anterior Muscles of the Body   (See Figure 6.21)

Name	Origin	Insertion	Primary action(s)
Head/Neck Muscles			
Frontalis	Cranial aponeurosis	Skin of eyebrows	Raises eyebrows
Orbicularis oculi	Frontal bone and maxilla	Tissue around eyes	Blinks and closes eyes
Orbicularis oris	Mandible and maxilla	Skin and muscle around mouth	Closes and protrudes lips
Temporalis	Temporal bone	Mandible	Closes jaw
Zygomaticus	Zygomatic bone	Skin and muscle at corner of lips	Raises corner of mouth
Masseter	Temporal bone	Mandible	Closes jaw
Buccinator	Maxilla and mandible near molars	Orbicularis oris	Compresses cheek as in whistling and sucking; holds food between teeth during chewing
Sternocleidomastoid	Sternum and clavicle	Temporal bone (mastoid process)	Flexes neck; rotates head
Platysma	Connective tissue covering of superior chest muscles	Tissue around mouth	Pulls corners of mouth inferiorly
Trunk Muscles			
Pectoralis major	Sternum, clavicle, and first to sixth ribs	Proximal humerus	Adducts and flexes humerus
Rectus abdominis	Pubis	Sternum and fifth to seventh ribs	Flexes vertebral column
External oblique	Lower eight ribs	Iliac crest	Flexes and rotates vertebral column
Arm/Shoulder Muscles			
Biceps brachii	Scapula of shoulder girdle	Proximal radius	Flexes elbow and supinates forearm
Brachialis	Distal humerus	Proximal ulna	Flexes elbow
Deltoid	See Table 6.4		Abducts arm
Hip/Thigh/Leg Muscles			
Iliopsoas	Ilium and lumbar vertebrae	Femur (lesser trochanter)	Flexes hip
Adductor muscles	Pelvis	Proximal femur	Adduct thigh
Sartorius	Ilium	Proximal tibia	Flexes thigh on hip
Quadriceps group (vastus medialis, intermedius, and lateralis; and the rectus femoris)	Vasti: Femur Rectus femoris: Pelvis	Tibial tuberosity via patellar ligament Tibial tuberosity via patellar ligament	All extend knee; rectus femoris also flexes hip on thigh
Tibialis anterior	Proximal tibia	First cuneiform (tarsal) and first metatarsal of foot	Dorsiflexes and inverts foot
Extensor digitorum longus	Proximal tibia and radius	Distal toes 2–5	Extends toes and dorsiflexes foot
Fibularis muscles	Fibula	Metatarsals of foot	Plantar flex and evert foot

Neck
• Occipitalis
• Sternocleidomastoid
• Trapezius

Shoulder/Back
• Deltoid
• Latissimus dorsi

Arm
• Triceps brachii
• Brachialis

Forearm
• Brachioradialis
• Extensor carpi radialis longus
• Flexor carpi ulnaris
• Extensor carpi ulnaris
• Extensor digitorum

Hip
• Gluteus medius
• Gluteus maximus

Iliotibial tract

Thigh
• Adductor muscle
• Hamstrings:
  Biceps femoris
  Semitendinosus
  Semimembranosus

Leg
• Gastrocnemius
• Soleus
• Fibularis longus

FIGURE 6.22 Major superficial muscles of the posterior surface of the body.

TABLE 6.4 — Superficial Posterior Muscles of the Body (Some Forearm Muscles Also Shown) (See Figure 6.22)

Name	Origin	Insertion	Primary action(s)
Neck/Trunk/Shoulder Muscles			
Trapezius	Occipital bone and all cervical and thoracic vertebrae	Scapular spine and clavicle	Extends neck and adducts scapula
Latissimus dorsi	Lower spine and iliac crest	Proximal humerus	Extends and adducts humerus
Erector spinae*	Iliac crests, ribs 3–12, and vertebrae	Ribs, thoracic and cervical vertebrae	Extends back
Quadratus lumborum	Iliac crest, lumbar fascia	Transverse processes of upper lumbar vertebrae	Flexes spine laterally; extends spine
Deltoid	Scapular spine and clavicle	Humerus (deltoid tuberosity)	Abducts humerus
Arm/Forearm Muscles			
Triceps brachii	Shoulder girdle and proximal humerus	Olecranon process of ulna	Extends elbow
Flexor carpi radialis	Distal humerus	Second and third metacarpals	Flexes wrist and abducts hand (see Figure 6.21)
Flexor carpi ulnaris	Distal humerus and posterior ulna	Carpals of wrist and fifth metacarpal	Flexes wrist and adducts hand
Flexor digitorum superficialis†	Distal humerus, ulna and radius	Middle phalanges of second to fifth fingers	Flexes wrist and fingers
Extensor carpi radialis	Humerus	Base of second and third metacarpals	Extends wrist and abducts hand
Extensor digitorum	Distal humerus	Distal phalanges of second to fifth fingers	Extends fingers and wrist
Hip/Thigh/Leg Muscles			
Gluteus maximus	Sacrum and ilium	Proximal femur (gluteal tuberosity)	Extends hip (when forceful extension is required)
Gluteus medius	Ilium	Proximal femur	Abducts thigh; steadies pelvis during walking
Hamstring muscles (semitendinosus, semimembranosus, biceps femoris)	Ischial tuberosity	Proximal tibia (head of fibula in the case of biceps femoris)	Flex knee and extend hip
Gastrocnemius	Distal femur	Calcaneus (heel via calcaneal tendon)	Plantar flexes foot and flexes knee
Soleus	Proximal tibia and fibula	Calcaneus	Plantar flexes foot

*Erector spinae and quadratus lumborum are deep muscles and not shown in Figure 6.22.
†Although its name indicates that it is a superficial muscle, the flexor digitorum superficialis lies deep to the flexor carpi radialis and is not visible in a superficial view.

focus on CAREERS

MASSAGE THERAPIST

To be effective, a massage therapist needs a thorough understanding of anatomy and physiology.

Many of us think of massage simply as something that feels good. Although this is certainly true, there's a lot of skill involved in massaging the body correctly.

Diana Syverud, part-owner of the Berkeley Massage and Self-Healing

Center in Berkeley, California, doesn't just make her clients feel good; she helps them recover from injuries and prevent further problems. Many of them suffer from pain due to overusing certain muscles. "Most often, I see people who spend hours at the computer," she explains. "This can lead to trouble with the flexor carpi ulnaris, and muscles in the neck and back. I also treat musicians who are sore from spending hours playing the violin and waitresses who have painful wrists from carrying heavy trays."

"When I was studying anatomy and physiology, sometimes I won-

dered why I had to learn all that information" she admits. "But today, I'm glad I did. I need to know where muscles are located in the body and where they attach. For instance, a muscle may contract and pinch the sciatic nerve, causing excruciating pain. I check to determine which muscle is contracted and use various massage techniques to release it. I also help clients who have no specific muscular problems stretch and strengthen their muscles, increasing their range of motion." She notes that "It's important to know the areas of the body where massage is contraindicated, such as in the area of the esophagus or hyoid bone."

"Anatomy and physiology classes are fascinating because you're really learning how your own body works," she comments. "This knowledge is valuable, for your clients' sake and for your own welfare."

Syverud's favorite aspect of her work is the one-on-one contact. "Typically I meet with a client for at least an hour at a time, often over a period of several months," she says. "Many initially come for a specific reason, then stay with me for years, long after we've resolved their original problem. We might meet weekly while they're in pain, then switch to monthly appointments to help prevent future problems." Some customers are referred to her by chiropractors, but most come on their own. If she feels their problems require more than massage, she refers them to appropriate healthcare practitioners such as chiropractors, psychiatrists, or internists.

Training for massage therapists varies widely. State requirements for

training vary from 200 to 500 hours or more. Some states require therapists to be licensed, whereas others do not, and accreditation procedures vary from state to state. Regardless of their length, all effective massage programs require an understanding of anatomy and physiology; Syverud estimates it made up more than one-third of her course work. Syverud is in private practice, but many

> **"Anatomy and physiology are fascinating—you're learning how your own body works."**

massage therapists work in spas, health clubs, or chiropractic offices. Often employers prefer to hire graduates of programs accredited by the American Massage Therapy Association (AMTA). For more information contact

AMTA
820 Davis Street, Suite 100
Evanston, IL 60201
(847) 864-0123
http://www.amtamassage.org

For additional information on this career, click the Focus on Careers link at www.anatomyandphysiology.com.

Developmental Aspects of the Muscular System

In the developing embryo, the muscular system is laid down in segments (much like the structural plan of an earthworm), and then each segment is invaded by nerves. The muscles of the thoracic and lumbar regions become very extensive because they must cover and move the bones of the limbs. The muscles and their control by the nervous system develop rather early in pregnancy. The expectant mother is often astonished by the first movements (called the *quickening*) of the fetus, which usually occur by the sixteenth week of pregnancy.

HOMEOSTATIC IMBALANCE

Very few congenital muscular problems occur. The exception to this is **muscular dystrophy**— a group of inherited muscle-destroying diseases that affect specific muscle groups. The muscles enlarge due to fat and connective tissue deposit, but the muscle fibers degenerate and atrophy.

The most common and serious form is **Duchenne's muscular dystrophy,** which is expressed almost exclusively in boys. This tragic disease is usually diagnosed between the ages of 2 and 7 years. Active, normal-appearing children become clumsy and fall frequently as their muscles weaken. The disease progresses from the extremities upward, finally affecting the head and chest muscles. Children with this disease rarely live beyond their early twenties and generally die of respiratory failure. Although the cause of muscular dystrophy has been pinned down—the diseased muscle fibers lack a protein (called dystrophin) that helps maintain the sarcolemma—a cure is still elusive. ▲

Initially after birth, a baby's movements are all gross reflex types of movements. Because the nervous system must mature before the baby can control muscles, we can trace the increasing efficiency of the nervous system by observing a baby's development of muscle control. This development proceeds in a cephalic/caudal direction, and gross muscular movements precede fine ones. Babies can raise their heads before they can sit up and can sit up before they can walk. Muscular control also proceeds in a proximal/distal direction; that is, babies can perform the gross movements like waving "bye-bye" and pulling objects to themselves before they can use the pincher grasp to pick up a pin. All through childhood, the nervous system's control of the skeletal muscles becomes more and more precise. By midadolescence, we have reached the peak level of development of this natural control and can simply accept it or bring it to a fine edge by athletic training.

Because of its rich blood supply, skeletal muscle is amazingly resistant to infection throughout life, and given good nutrition, relatively few problems afflict skeletal muscles. It should be repeated, however, that muscles, like bones, *will* atrophy, even with normal tone, if they are not used continually. A lifelong program of regular exercise keeps the whole body operating at its best possible level.

HOMEOSTATIC IMBALANCE

One rare disease that can affect muscles during adulthood is **myasthenia gravis** (mi"as-the'ne-ah gra'vis; *asthen* = weakness; *gravi* = heavy), a disease characterized by drooping of the upper eyelids, difficulty in swallowing and talking, and generalized muscle weakness and fatigability. The disease involves a shortage of acetylcholine receptors at neuromuscular junctions. The blood of many of these patients contains antibodies to acetylcholine receptors, which suggests that myasthenia gravis is an autoimmune disease. Although the receptors may initially be present in normal numbers, they appear to be destroyed as the disease progresses. Whatever the case, the muscle cells are not stimulated properly and get progressively weaker. Death usually occurs as a result of the inability of the respiratory muscles to function **(respiratory failure)**. ▲

As we age, the amount of connective tissue in the muscles increases, and the amount of muscle tissue decreases; thus the muscles become stringier, or more sinewy. Because the skeletal muscles represent so much of the body mass, body weight begins to decline in the older person as this natural loss in muscle mass occurs. Another result of the loss in muscle mass is a decrease in muscle strength; strength decreases by about 50 percent by the age of 80. Regular exercise can help offset the effects of aging on the muscular system, and frail older people who begin to "pump iron" (use leg and hand weights) can rebuild muscle mass and dramatically increase their strength.

▶ DID YOU GET IT?

29. What must happen before babies can control their muscles?

30. How does lifelong exercise affect our skeletal muscles and muscle mass in old age?

For answers, see Appendix D.

SYSTEMS IN SYNC

HOMEOSTATIC RELATIONSHIPS BETWEEN THE
MUSCULAR SYSTEM AND OTHER BODY SYSTEMS

Endocrine System
- Growth hormone and androgens influence skeletal muscle strength and mass

Lymphatic System/Immunity
- Physical exercise may enhance or depress immunity depending on its intensity
- Lymphatic vessels drain leaked tissue fluids; immune system protects muscles from disease

Digestive System
- Physical activity increases gastrointestinal mobility when at rest
- Digestive system provides nutrients needed for muscle health; liver metabolizes lactic acid

Urinary System
- Physical activity promotes normal voiding behavior; skeletal muscle forms the voluntary sphincter of the urethra
- Urinary system disposes of nitrogenous wastes

Muscular System

Nervous System
- Facial muscle activity allows emotions to be expressed
- Nervous system stimulates and regulates muscle activity

Respiratory System
- Muscular exercise increases respiratory capacity
- Respiratory system provides oxygen and disposes of carbon dioxide

Cardiovascular System
- Skeletal muscle activity increases efficiency of cardiovascular functioning; helps prevent atherosclerosis and causes cardiac hypertrophy
- Cardiovascular system delivers oxygen and nutrients to muscles; carries away wastes

Reproductive System
- Skeletal muscle helps support pelvic organs (e.g., uterus in females); assists erection of penis and clitoris
- Testicular androgen promotes increased skeletal muscle size

Integumentary System
- Muscular exercise enhances circulation to skin and improves skin health; exercise also increases body heat, which the skin helps dissipate
- Skin protects the muscles by external enclosure

Skeletal System
- Skeletal muscle activity maintains bone health and strength
- Bones provide levers for muscle activity

SUMMARY

Media study tools that provide additional review of key topics of Chapter 6 are referenced below.

> **IP** = *InterActive Physiology*
> **WEB** = The A&P Place

Overview of Muscle Tissues   (pp. 183–187)

1. Skeletal muscle forms the muscles attached to the skeleton, which move the limbs and other body parts. Its cells are long, striated and multinucleate, and they are subject to voluntary control. Connective tissue coverings (endomysium, perimysium, and epimysium) enclose and protect the muscle fibers and increase the strength of skeletal muscles. Skeletal muscles make up the muscular system.

   WEB Exercise: Chapter 6, Connective Tissue Wrappings of Skeletal Muscle.

2. Smooth muscle cells are uninucleate, spindle-shaped, and arranged in opposing layers in the walls of hollow organs. When they contract, substances (food, urine, a baby) are moved along internal pathways. Smooth muscle control is involuntary.

3. Cardiac muscle cells are striated, branching cells that fit closely together and are arranged in spiral bundles in the heart. Their contraction pumps blood through the blood vessels. Control is involuntary.

4. The sole function of muscle tissue is to contract or shorten. As it contracts, it causes movement, maintains posture, stabilizes joints, and generates heat.

Microscopic Anatomy of Skeletal Muscle (pp. 187–189)

1. The multinucleate cylindrical skeletal muscle fibers are packed with unique organelles called myofibrils. The banding pattern (striations) of the myofibrils and the cell as a whole reflects the regular arrangement of thin (actin-containing) and thick (myosin) filaments within the sarcomeres, the contractile units composing the myofibrils.

   WEB Exercise: Chapter 6, Microscopic Anatomy of a Skeletal Fiber.

   IP Muscular System Topic: Anatomy Review: Skeletal Muscle Tissue, pages 7–9.

2. Each myofibril is loosely enclosed by a specialized ER, called the sarcoplasmic reticulum (SR), which plays an important role in storing and releasing calcium ions. Calcium ions are the final trigger for muscle fiber contraction.

Skeletal Muscle Activity   (pp. 189–198)

1. All skeletal muscle cells are stimulated by motor neurons. When the neuron releases a neurotransmitter (acetylcholine), the permeability of the sarcolemma changes, allowing sodium ions to enter the muscle cell. This produces an electrical current (action potential), which flows across the entire sarcolemma, resulting in release of calcium ions from the SR.

   IP Muscular System Topic: The Neuromuscular Junction, pages 3–6.

2. Calcium binds to regulatory proteins on the thin filaments and exposes myosin binding sites, allowing the myosin heads on the thick filaments to attach. The attached heads pivot, sliding the thin filaments toward the center of the sarcomere, and contraction occurs. ATP provides the energy for the sliding process, which continues as long as ionic calcium is present.

   IP Muscular System Topic: Sliding Filament Theory, pages 3–28.

3. Although individual muscle cells contract completely when adequately stimulated, a muscle (an organ) responds to stimuli to different degrees, that is, it exhibits graded responses.

   WEB Exercise: Chapter 6, Graded Muscle Responses.

4. Most skeletal muscle contractions are tetanic (smooth and sustained) because rapid nerve impulses are reaching the muscle, and the muscle cannot relax completely between contractions. The strength of muscle contraction reflects the relative number of muscle cells contracting (more = stronger).

5. ATP, the immediate source of energy for muscle contraction, is stored in muscle fibers in small amounts that are quickly used up. ATP is regenerated via three routes. From the fastest to the slowest, these are via a coupled reaction of creatine phosphate with ADP, via anaerobic glycolysis and lactic acid formation, and via aerobic respiration. Only aerobic respiration requires oxygen.

   IP Muscular System Topic: Muscle Metabolism, pages 6–13.

6. If muscle activity is strenuous and prolonged, muscle fatigue occurs because of accumulation of lactic acid in the muscle and a decrease in its energy (ATP) supply. After exercise, the oxygen deficit is repaid by rapid, deep breathing.

7. Muscle contractions are isotonic (the muscle shortens, and movement occurs) or isometric (the muscle does not shorten, but its tension increases).

8. Muscle tone keeps muscles healthy and ready to re-act. It is a result of a staggered series of nerve impulses delivered to different cells within the muscle. If the nerve supply is destroyed, the muscle loses tone, becomes paralyzed, and atrophies.

9. Inactive muscles atrophy. Muscles challenged by resistance exercise to respond (almost) beyond their ability increase in size and strength. Muscles subjected to regular aerobic exercise become more efficient and stronger and can work longer without tiring. Aerobic exercise also benefits other body organ systems.

Muscle Movements, Types, and Names (pp. 198–206)

1. All muscles are attached to bones at two points. The origin is the immovable attachment; the insertion is the movable bony attachment. When contraction occurs, the insertion moves toward the origin.

2. Body movements include flexion, extension, abduction, adduction, circumduction, rotation, pronation, supination, inversion, eversion, dorsiflexion, plantar flexion, and opposition.

3. On the basis of their general functions in the body, muscles are classified as prime movers, antagonists, synergists, and fixators.

4. Muscles are named according to several criteria, including muscle size, shape, number and location of origins, associated bones, and action of the muscle.

5. Muscles have several fascicle arrangements that influence their force and degree of shortening.

   WEB Exercise: Chapter 6, Muscles of the Body; Posterior Surface Musculature.

Gross Anatomy of Skeletal Muscles (pp. 206–220)

1. Muscles of the head fall into two groups. The muscles of facial expression include the frontalis, orbicularis oris and oculi, and zygomaticus. The chewing muscles are the masseter, temporalis, and buccinator (which is also a muscle of facial expression).

2. Muscles of the trunk and neck move the head, shoulder girdle, and trunk and form the abdominal girdle. Anterior neck and trunk muscles include the sternocleidomastoid, pectoralis major, intercostals, rectus abdominis, external and internal obliques, and transversus abdominis. Posterior trunk and neck muscles include the trapezius, latissimus dorsi, and deltoid. Deep muscles of the back are the erector spinae muscles.

3. Muscles of the upper limb include muscles that cause movement at the shoulder joint, elbow, and hand. Muscles causing movement at the elbow include the brachialis, biceps brachii, brachioradialis, and triceps brachii.

4. Muscles of the lower extremity cause movement at the hip, knee, and foot. They include the iliopsoas, gluteus maximus and medius, adductors, quadriceps and hamstring groups, gastrocnemius, tibialis anterior, fibularis muscles, soleus, and extensor digitorum longus.

Developmental Aspects of the Muscular System   (p. 221)

1. Increasing muscular control reflects the myelination maturation of the nervous system. Muscle control is achieved in a cephalic/caudal and proximal/distal direction.

2. To remain healthy, muscles must be regularly exercised. Without exercise, they atrophy; with extremely vigorous exercise, they hypertrophy.

3. As we age, muscle mass decreases, and the muscles become more sinewy. Exercise helps to retain muscle mass and strength.

REVIEW QUESTIONS

Multiple Choice

More than one choice may apply.

1. If you compare electron micrographs of a relaxed skeletal muscle fiber and a fully contracted muscle fiber, which would you see only in the *relaxed* fiber?

   a. Z discs   d. A bands
   b. Triads   e. H zones
   c. I bands

2. After ACh attaches to its receptors at the neuromuscular junction, what is the next step?

   a. Sodium channels open.
   b. Calcium binds to regulatory proteins on the thin filaments.
   c. Cross bridges attach.
   d. ATP is hydrolyzed.

3. Your ability to lift that heavy couch would be increased by which type of exercise?

   a. Aerobic   c. Resistance
   b. Endurance   d. Swimming

4. Someone who sticks out a thumb to hitch a ride is _____ the thumb.
   a. extending   c. adducting
   b. abducting   d. opposing

5. Which are ways in which muscle names have been derived?
   a. Attachments
   b. Size
   c. Function
   d. Location

6. Which of the following muscles attach to the hip bones?
   a. Rectus abdominis
   b. Rectus femoris
   c. Vastus medialis
   d. Longissimus group of erector spinae

7. Which of these thigh muscles causes movement at the hip joint?
   a. Rectus femoris
   b. Biceps femoris
   c. Vastus lateralis
   d. Semitendinosus

8. Which of the following insert on the arm?
   a. Biceps brachii
   b. Triceps brachii
   c. Trapezius
   d. Latissimus dorsi

Short Answer Essay

9. What is the major function of muscle?

10. Compare skeletal, smooth, and cardiac muscles as to their microscopic anatomy, location and arrangement in body organs, and function in the body.

11. What two types of muscle tissue are striated?

12. Why are the connective tissue wrappings of skeletal muscles important? Name these connective tissue coverings, beginning with the finest and ending with the most coarse.

13. What is the function of tendons?

14. Define *neuromuscular junction, motor unit, tetanus, graded response, aerobic respiration, anaerobic glycolysis, muscle fatigue,* and *neurotransmitter.*

15. Describe the events that occur from the time a motor neuron releases acetylcholine at the neuromuscular junction until muscle cell contraction occurs.

16. How do isotonic and isometric contractions differ?

17. Muscle tone keeps muscles healthy. What is muscle tone, and what causes it? What happens to a muscle that loses its tone?

18. A skeletal muscle is attached to bones at two points. Name each of these attachment points, and indicate which is movable and which is immovable.

19. List the 12 body movements studied in this chapter and demonstrate each.

20. How is a prime mover different from a synergist muscle? How can a prime mover also be considered an antagonist?

21. If you were alternately contracting and relaxing your masseter muscle, what would you be doing? Name three other muscles of the face, and give the location and function of each.

22. The sternocleidomastoid muscles help to flex the neck. What are their antagonists?

23. Name two muscles that reverse the movement of the deltoid muscle.

24. Name the prime mover of elbow flexion. Name its antagonist.

25. Other than acting to flex the spine and compress the abdominal contents, the abdominal muscles are extremely important in protecting and containing the abdominal viscera. What is it about the arrangement of these muscles that makes them so well suited for their job?

26. The hamstring and quadriceps muscle groups are antagonists of each other, and each group is a prime mover in its own right. What action does each muscle group perform?

27. What two-bellied muscle makes up the calf region of the leg? What is its function?

28. What happens to muscles when they are exercised regularly? Exercised vigorously as in weight lifting? Not used?

29. What is the effect of aging on skeletal muscles?

30. Should a triathlete engage in aerobic or resistance training? Explain.

CRITICAL THINKING AND CLINICAL APPLICATION QUESTIONS

31. Name three muscles or muscle groups used as sites for intramuscular injections. Which is most often used in babies?

32. Mr. Ahmadi was advised by his physician to lose weight and start jogging. He began to jog daily. On the sixth day, he was forced to jump out of the way of a speeding car. He heard a snapping sound that was immediately followed by pain in his right lower calf. A gap was visible between his swollen calf and his heel, and he was unable to plantar flex that foot. What do you think happened?

33. While painting her house, Sally fell off the ladder and fractured her right clavicle. Treatment prescribed by the emergency room physician included using a sling for her right arm to immobilize the clavicle and speed its healing. What muscles are temporarily "put out of business" by the sling?

34. When Eric returned from jogging, he was breathing heavily and sweating profusely, and he complained that his legs ached and felt weak. His wife poured him a sport drink and urged him to take it easy until he could "catch his breath." On the basis of what you have learned about muscle energy metabolism, respond to the following questions:

    a. Why is Eric breathing heavily?

    b. What ATP-harvesting pathway have his working muscles been using that leads to such a breathing pattern?

    c. What metabolic product(s) might account for his sore muscles and his feeling of muscle weakness?

35. Chemical A binds and blocks acetylcholine receptors of muscle cells. Chemical B floods the cytoplasm of muscle cells with calcium ions. Which chemical would make the best muscle relaxant and why?

36. Mr. Posibo has had colon surgery. Now he is experiencing weakness of the muscles on his right side only, the side in which the incision was made through the abdominal musculature. Consequently, the abdominal muscles on his left side contract more strongly, throwing his torso into a lateral flexion. Mr. Posibo needs physical therapy. What abnormal spinal curvature will result if he doesn't get it, and why?

37. When a person dies, rigor mortis sets in as ATP synthesis ceases. Explain why the lack of ATP in muscle cells would cause the muscles to become rigid rather than limp soon after death.

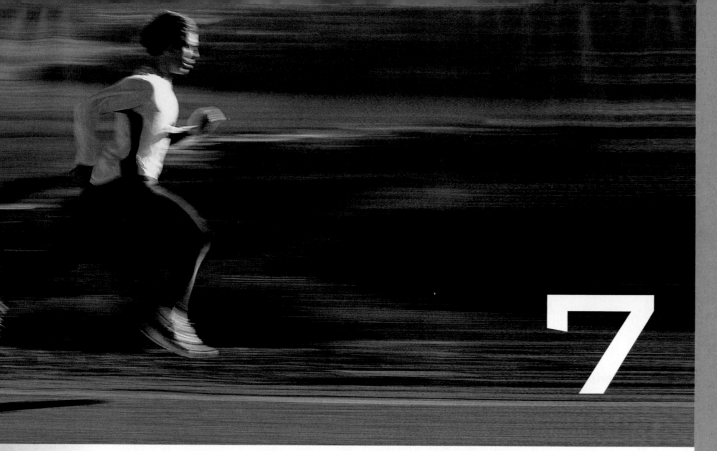

The Nervous System

YOUR GOALS

After completing this chapter, you will have working knowledge of the functions of the nervous system and will have mastered the objectives listed below.

FUNCTION PREVIEW

- The nervous system maintains body homeostasis with electrical signals; provides for sensation, higher mental functioning, and emotional response; and activates muscles and glands.

OBJECTIVE CHECKLIST

Organization of the Nervous System   (pp. 229–230)

➤ List the general functions of the nervous system.

➤ Explain the structural and functional classifications of the nervous system.

➤ Define *central nervous system* and *peripheral nervous system,* and list the major parts of each.

Nervous Tissue: Structure and Function   (pp. 230–242)

➤ State the function of neurons and neuroglia.

➤ Describe the general structure of a neuron, and name its important anatomical regions.

➤ Describe the composition of gray matter and white matter.

➤ List the two major functional properties of neurons.

➤ Classify neurons according to structure and function.

➤ List the types of general sensory receptors, and describe their functions.

➤ Describe the events that lead to the generation of a nerve impulse and its conduction from one neuron to another.

➤ Define *reflex arc*, and list its elements.

Central Nervous System (pp. 242–258)

➤ dentify and indicate the functions of the major regions of the cerebral hemispheres, diencephalon, brain stem, and cerebellum on a human brain model or diagram.

➤ Name the three meningeal layers, and state their functions.

➤ Discuss the formation and function of cerebrospinal fluid and the blood-brain barrier.

➤ Compare the signs of a CVA with those of Alzheimer's disease; of a contusion with those of a concussion.

➤ Define *EEG*, and explain how it evaluates neural functioning.

➤ List two important functions of the spinal cord.

➤ Describe spinal cord structure.

Peripheral Nervous System (pp. 258–270)

➤ Describe the general structure of a nerve.

➤ Identify the cranial nerves by number and by name, and list the major functions of each.

➤ Describe the origin and fiber composition of (1) ventral and dorsal roots, (2) the spinal nerve proper, and (3) ventral and dorsal rami.

➤ Discuss the distribution of the dorsal and ventral rami of spinal nerves.

➤ Name the four major nerve plexuses, give the major nerves of each, and describe their distribution.

➤ Identify the site of origin, and explain the function of the sympathetic and parasympathetic divisions of the autonomic nervous system.

➤ Contrast the effect of the parasympathetic and sympathetic divisions on the following organs: heart, lungs, digestive system, blood vessels.

Developmental Aspects of the Nervous System (pp. 272–275)

➤ List several factors that may have harmful effects on brain development.

➤ Briefly describe the cause, signs, and consequences of the following congenital disorders: spina bifida, anencephaly, and cerebral palsy.

➤ Explain the decline in brain size and weight that occurs with age.

➤ Define *senility*, and list some possible causes.

You are driving down the freeway, and a horn blares on your right. You swerve to your left. Charlie leaves a note on the kitchen table: "See you later—have the stuff ready at 6." You know that the "stuff" is chili with taco chips. You are dozing, and your infant son makes a soft cry. Instantly, you awaken. What do all these events have in common? They are all everyday examples of the functioning of your nervous system, which has your body cells humming with activity nearly all the time.

The **nervous system** is the master controlling and communicating system of the body. Every thought, action, and emotion reflects its activity. Its signaling device, or means of communicating with body cells, is electrical impulses, which are rapid and specific and cause almost immediate responses.

To carry out its normal role, the nervous system has three overlapping functions (Figure 7.1): (1) Much like a sentry, it uses its millions of sensory receptors to *monitor changes* occurring both inside and outside the body. These changes are called *stimuli,* and the gathered information is called **sensory input.** (2) It *processes and interprets* the sensory input and decides what should be done at each moment—a process called **integration.** (3) It then *effects a response* by activating muscles or glands (effectors) via **motor output.** An example will illustrate how these functions work together. When you are driving and see a red light just ahead (sensory input), your nervous system integrates this information (red light means "stop") and sends motor output to the muscles of your right leg and foot, and your foot goes for the brake pedal (the response).

The nervous system does not work alone to regulate and maintain body homeostasis; the endocrine system is a second important regulating system. Whereas the nervous system controls with rapid electrical nerve impulses, the endocrine system organs produce hormones that are released into the blood. Thus, the endocrine system typically brings about its effects in a more leisurely way.

Organization of the Nervous System

We have only one nervous system, but, because of its complexity, it is difficult to consider all its parts at the same time. So, to simplify its study, we divide it in terms of its structures (structural classification) or in terms of its activities (functional classification). Each of these classification schemes is described briefly below, and their relationships are illustrated in Figure 7.2. It is not necessary to memorize this whole scheme now, but as you are reading the descriptions, try to get a "feel" for the major parts and how they fit together. This will make your learning task easier as you make your way through this chapter. Later you will meet all these terms and concepts again and in more detail.

Structural Classification

The structural classification, which includes all nervous system organs, has two subdivisions—the central nervous system and the peripheral nervous system (see Figure 7.2).

The **central nervous system (CNS)** consists of the brain and spinal cord, which occupy the dorsal body cavity and act as the integrating and command centers of the nervous system. They

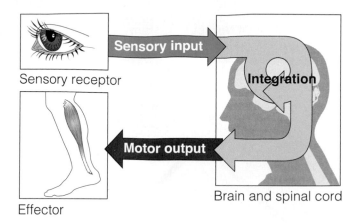

FIGURE 7.1 **The nervous system's functions.**

interpret incoming sensory information and issue instructions based on past experience and current conditions.

The **peripheral** (pĕ-rif′er-al) **nervous system (PNS),** the part of the nervous system outside the CNS, consists mainly of the nerves that extend from the brain and spinal cord. *Spinal nerves* carry impulses to and from the spinal cord. *Cranial* (kra′ne-al) *nerves* carry impulses to and from the brain. These nerves serve as communication lines. They link all parts of the body by carrying impulses from the sensory receptors to the CNS and from the CNS to the appropriate glands or muscles.

The organs making up the CNS and PNS are discussed at length later in this chapter.

Functional Classification

The functional classification scheme is concerned only with PNS structures. It divides them into two principal subdivisions (see Figure 7.2).

The **sensory,** or **afferent** (af′er-ent), **division** consists of nerves (composed of nerve fibers) that convey impulses *to* the central nervous system from sensory receptors located in various parts of the body. Sensory fibers delivering impulses from the skin, skeletal muscles, and joints are called *somatic (soma* = body) *sensory* (afferent) *fibers,* whereas those transmitting impulses from the visceral organs are called *visceral sensory fibers,* or *visceral afferents.* The sensory division keeps the CNS constantly informed of events going on both inside and outside the body.

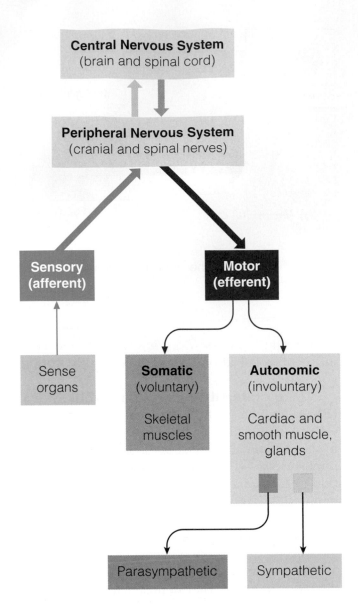

FIGURE 7.2 **Organization of the nervous system.** Organizational flowchart showing that the central nervous system receives input via sensory fibers and issues commands via motor fibers. The sensory and motor fibers together form the nerves that constitute the peripheral nervous system.

The **motor,** or **efferent** (ef'er-rent), **division** carries impulses *from* the CNS to effector organs, the muscles and glands. These impulses activate muscles and glands; that is, they *effect* (bring about) a motor response.

The motor division in turn has two subdivisions (see Figure 7.2):

1. The **somatic** (so-mat'ik) **nervous system** allows us to consciously, or voluntarily, control

our skeletal muscles. Hence, this subdivision is often referred to as the **voluntary nervous system.** However, not all skeletal muscle activity controlled by this motor division is voluntary. Skeletal muscle reflexes, like the stretch reflex for example, are initiated involuntarily by these same fibers.

2. The **autonomic** (aw"to-nom'ik) **nervous system (ANS)** regulates events that are automatic, or involuntary, such as the activity of smooth and cardiac muscles and glands. This subdivision, commonly called the **involuntary nervous system,** itself has two parts, the *sympathetic* and *parasympathetic,* which typically bring about opposite effects. What one stimulates, the other inhibits. These will be described later.

Although it is simpler to study the nervous system in terms of its subdivisions, you should recognize that these subdivisions are made for the sake of convenience only. Remember that the nervous system acts as a coordinated unit, both structurally and functionally.

▶ *DID YOU GET IT?*

1. Name the structures that make up the CNS and those that make up the PNS.

For the answer, see Appendix D.

Nervous Tissue: Structure and Function

Even though it is complex, nervous tissue is made up of just two principal types of cells—*supporting cells* and *neurons.*

Supporting Cells

Supporting cells in the CNS are "lumped together" as **neuroglia** (nu-rog'le-ah), literally, "nerve glue." Neuroglia includes many types of cells that generally support, insulate, and protect the delicate neurons (Figure 7.3). In addition, each of the different types of neuroglia, also simply called either **glia** (gle'ah) or *glial cells,* has special functions. The CNS glia include the following:

● **Astrocytes:** abundant star-shaped cells that account for nearly half of the neural tissue. Their numerous projections have swollen ends

Capillary
Neuron

(a) Astrocyte

(b) Microglial cell

Fluid-filled cavity

(c) Ependymal cells / Brain or spinal cord tissue

Myelin sheath

Process of
oligodendrocyte

Nerve fibers

(d) Oligodendrocyte

Cell body
of neuron
Satellite cells

Schwann cells
(forming myelin sheath)

Nerve fiber

(e) Sensory neuron with Schwann cells and satellite cells

FIGURE 7.3   Supporting (glial) cells of nervous tissues.
Astrocytes **(a)** form a living barrier between neurons and capillaries in
the CNS. Microglia **(b)** are phagocytes, whereas ependymal cells
(c) line the fluid-filled cavities of the CNS. The oligodendrocytes
(d) form myelin sheaths around nerve fibers in the CNS. **(e)** The
relationship of Schwann cells (myelinating cells) and satellite cells
to a neuron in the peripheral nervous system.

that cling to neurons, bracing them and anchoring them to their nutrient supply lines, the blood capillaries (Figure 7.3a). Astrocytes form a living barrier between capillaries and neurons and play a role in making exchanges between the two. In this way, they help protect the neurons from harmful substances that might be in the blood. Astrocytes also help control the chemical environment in the brain by "mopping up" leaked potassium ions and recapturing released neurotransmitters.

- **Microglia** (mi-krog′le-ah): spiderlike phagocytes that dispose of debris, including dead brain cells and bacteria (Figure 7.3b).

- **Ependymal** (ĕ-pen′dĭ-mal) **cells:** these glial cells line the central cavities of the brain and the spinal cord (Figure 7.3c). The beating of their cilia helps to circulate the cerebrospinal fluid that fills those cavities and forms a protective cushion around the CNS.

- **Oligodendrocytes** (ol″ĭ-go-den′dro-sītz): glia that wrap their flat extensions tightly around the nerve fibers, producing fatty insulating coverings called *myelin sheaths* (Figure 7.3d).

Although they somewhat resemble neurons structurally (both cell types have cell extensions), glia are not able to transmit nerve impulses, a function that is highly developed in neurons. Another important difference is that glia never lose their ability to divide, whereas most neurons do. Consequently, most brain tumors are *gliomas,* or tumors formed by glial cells (neuroglia).

Supporting cells in the PNS come in two major varieties—Schwann cells and satellite cells (Figure 7.3e). **Schwann cells** form the myelin sheaths around nerve fibers that are found in the PNS. **Satellite cells** act as protective, cushioning cells.

DID YOU GET IT?

2. Which glial cells are most abundant in the body? Which produce the insulating material called myelin?

3. Why is a brain tumor more likely to be formed from glial cells than from neurons?

For answers, see Appendix D.

Neurons

Anatomy

Neurons, also called **nerve cells,** are highly specialized to transmit messages (nerve impulses) from one part of the body to another. Although neurons differ structurally from one another, they have many common features (Figure 7.4). All have a cell body, which contains the nucleus and is the metabolic center of the cell, and one or more slender processes extending from the cell body.

Cell Body The **cell body** is the metabolic center of the neuron. Its transparent nucleus contains a conspicuous nucleolus. The cytoplasm surrounding the nucleus contains the usual organelles except for centrioles (which confirms the amitotic nature of most neurons). The rough ER, called **Nissl** (nis′l) **substance,** and **neurofibrils** (intermediate filaments that are important in maintaining cell shape) are particularly abundant in the cell body.

Processes The armlike **processes,** or **fibers,** vary in length from microscopic to 3 to 4 feet. The longest ones in humans reach from the lumbar region of the spine to the great toe. Neuron processes that convey incoming messages (electrical signals) *toward* the cell body are **dendrites** (den′drīt), whereas those that generate nerve impulses and typically conduct them *away* from the cell body are **axons** (ak′sonz). Neurons may have hundreds of the branching dendrites (*dendr* = tree), depending on the neuron type, but each neuron has only one axon, which arises from a conelike region of the cell body called the **axon hillock.**

An occasional axon gives off a *collateral branch* along its length, but all axons branch profusely at their terminal end, forming hundreds to thousands of **axon terminals.** These terminals contain hundreds of tiny vesicles, or membranous sacs, that contain chemicals called **neurotransmitters.** As we said, axons transmit nerve impulses away from the cell body. When these impulses reach the axon terminals, they stimulate the release of neurotransmitters into the extracellular space.

Each axon terminal is separated from the next neuron by a tiny gap called the **synaptic** (sĭ-nap′tik) **cleft.** Such a functional junction is called a **synapse** (*syn* = to clasp or join). Although they are close, neurons never actually touch other neurons. We will learn more about synapses and the events that occur there a bit later.

Myelin Sheaths Most long nerve fibers are covered with a whitish, fatty material called **myelin** (mi′ĕ-lin), which has a waxy appearance. Myelin protects and insulates the fibers and increases the transmission rate of nerve impulses. Axons outside the CNS are myelinated by Schwann cells, as just noted. These cells wrap themselves around the axon in a jelly-roll fashion (Figure 7.5). Initially, the membrane coil is loose, but the Schwann cell cytoplasm is gradually squeezed from between the membrane layers. When the wrapping process is done, a tight coil of wrapped membranes, the **myelin sheath,** encloses the axon. Most of the Schwann cell cytoplasm ends up just beneath the outermost part of its plasma membrane. This part of the Schwann cell, external to the myelin sheath, is called the **neurilemma** (nu″rĭ-lem′mah, "neuron husk"). Because the myelin sheath is formed by many individual Schwann cells, it has gaps, or

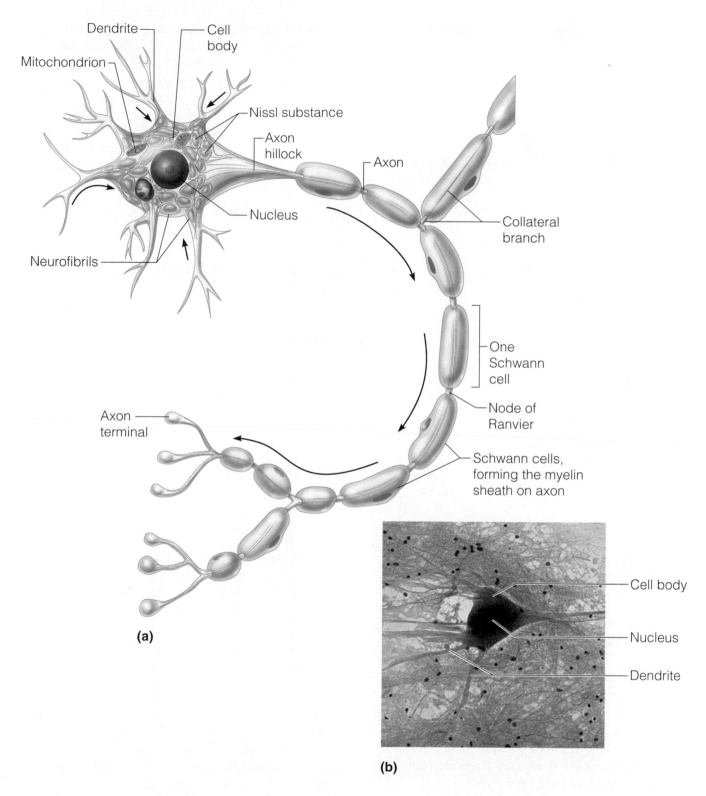

(a)

(b)

F I G U R E   7 . 4   Structure of a typical motor neuron.
(a) Diagrammatic view. **(b)** Photomicrograph (200×).

Schwann cell cytoplasm

Axon

Schwann cell plasma membrane

Schwann cell nucleus

(a)

(b)

Neurilemma

Myelin sheath

(c)

FIGURE 7.5 **Relationship of Schwann cells to axons in the peripheral nervous system.** **(a–c)** As illustrated (top to bottom), a Schwann cell envelops part of an axon in a trough and then rotates around the axon. Most of the Schwann cell cytoplasm comes to lie just beneath the exposed part of its plasma membrane. The tight coil of plasma membrane material surrounding the axon is the myelin sheath. The Schwann cell cytoplasm and exposed membrane are referred to as the *neurilemma.*

indentations, called **nodes of Ranvier** (rahn-vēr), at regular intervals (see Figure 7.4).

Myelinated fibers are also found in the central nervous system. However, there it is oligodendro-

Because the sheath is produced by several Schwann cells that arrange themselves end to end along the nerve fiber, each Schwann cell forming only one tiny segment of the sheath.

cytes that form CNS myelin sheaths (see Figure 7.3d). In contrast to Schwann cells, each of which deposits myelin around a small segment of one nerve fiber, the oligodendrocytes with their many flat extensions can coil around as many as 60 different fibers at the same time. Although the myelin sheaths formed by oligodendrocytes and those formed by Schwann cells are similar, the CNS sheaths lack a neurilemma. Because the neurilemma remains intact (for the most part) when a peripheral nerve fiber is damaged, it plays an important role in fiber regeneration, an ability that is largely lacking in the central nervous system.

HOMEOSTATIC IMBALANCE

The importance of the myelin insulation to nerve transmission is best illustrated by observing what happens when it is not there. In people with **multiple sclerosis (MS),** the myelin sheaths around the fibers are gradually destroyed, converted to hardened sheaths called *scleroses.* As this happens, the electrical current is short-circuited. The affected person may have visual and speech disturbances, lose the ability to control his or her muscles, and become increasingly disabled. Multiple sclerosis is an autoimmune disease in which a protein component of the sheath is attacked. As yet there is no cure, but injections of interferon (a hormonelike substance released by some immune cells) appear to hold the symptoms at bay and provide some relief. ▲

Terminology Clusters of neuron cell bodies and collections of nerve fibers are named differently when they are in the CNS than when they are part of the PNS. For the most part, cell bodies are found in the CNS in clusters called **nuclei.** This well-protected location within the bony skull or vertebral column is essential to the well-being of the nervous system—remember that neurons do not routinely undergo cell division after birth. The cell body carries out most of the metabolic functions of a neuron, so if it is damaged, the cell dies and is not replaced. Small collections of cell bodies called **ganglia** (gang'le-ah; *ganglion,* singular) are found in a few sites outside the CNS in the PNS.

Bundles of nerve fibers (neuron processes) running through the CNS are called **tracts,** whereas in the PNS they are called **nerves.** The terms *white matter* and *gray matter* refer respectively to myelinated versus unmyelinated regions

FIGURE 7.6 **Neurons classified by function.** Sensory (afferent) neurons conduct impulses from sensory receptors (in the skin, viscera, muscles) to the central nervous system; most cell bodies are in ganglia in the PNS. Motor (efferent) neurons transmit impulses from the CNS (brain or spinal cord) to effectors in the body periphery. Interneurons (association neurons) complete the communication pathway between sensory and motor neurons; their cell bodies reside in the CNS.

of the CNS. As a general rule, the **white matter** consists of dense collections of myelinated fibers (tracts), and **gray matter** contains mostly unmyelinated fibers and cell bodies.

Classification

Neurons may be classified either according to how they function or according to their structure.

Functional Classification Functional classification groups neurons according to the direction the nerve impulse is traveling relative to the CNS. On this basis, there are sensory, motor, and association neurons (interneurons) (Figure 7.6). Neurons carrying impulses from sensory receptors (in the internal organs or the skin) to the CNS are **sensory, or afferent, neurons.** (*Afferent* literally means "to go toward.") The cell bodies of sensory neurons are always found in a ganglion outside the CNS. Sensory neurons keep us informed about what is happening both inside and outside the body.

The dendrite endings of the sensory neurons are usually associated with specialized **receptors** that are activated by specific changes occurring nearby. The very complex receptors of the special sense organs (vision, hearing, equilibrium, taste, and smell) are covered separately in Chapter 8. The simpler types of sensory receptors seen in the skin (**cutaneous sense organs**) and in the muscles and tendons (**proprioceptors** [pro″pre-o-sep′torz]) are shown in Figure 4.4 and Figure 7.7. The pain receptors (actually bare nerve endings) are the least specialized of the cutaneous receptors. They are also the most numerous, because pain warns us that some type of body damage is occurring or is about to occur. However, strong stimulation of any of the cutaneous receptors (for example, by searing heat, extreme cold, or excessive pressure) is also interpreted as pain.

The proprioceptors detect the amount of stretch, or tension, in skeletal muscles, their tendons, and

FIGURE 7.7 **Types of sensory receptors. (a)** Naked nerve endings (pain and temperature receptors). **(b)** Meissner's corpuscle (touch receptor). **(c)** Pacinian corpuscle (deep pressure receptor). **(d)** Golgi tendon organ (proprioceptor). **(e)** Muscle spindle (proprioceptor).

joints. They send this information to the brain so that the proper adjustments can be made to maintain balance and normal posture. *Propria* comes from the Latin word meaning "one's own," and the proprioceptors constantly advise our brain of our own movements.

Neurons carrying impulses from the CNS to the viscera and/or muscles and glands are **motor,** or **efferent, neurons** (see Figure 7.6). The cell bodies of motor neurons are always located in the CNS.

The third category of neurons is known as the **interneurons,** or **association neurons.** They connect the motor and sensory neurons in neural pathways. Like the motor neurons, their cell bodies are always located in the CNS.

Structural Classification Structural classification is based on the number of processes extending from the cell body (Figure 7.8). If there are several, the neuron is a **multipolar neuron.** Because all motor and association neurons are multipolar, this is the most common structural type. Neurons with two processes—an axon and a dendrite—are called **bipolar neurons.** Bipolar neurons are rare in adults, found only in some special sense organs (eye, nose), where they act in sensory processing as receptor cells. **Unipolar neurons** have a single process emerging from the cell body. However, it is very short and divides almost immediately into proximal (central) and distal (peripheral) processes. Unipolar neurons are unique in that only the small branches at the end of the peripheral process are dendrites. The remainder of the peripheral process and the central process function as axons; thus, in this case, the axon conducts nerve impulses both toward *and* away from the cell body. Sensory neurons found in PNS ganglia are unipolar.

(a) Multipolar neuron

(b) Bipolar neuron

(c) Unipolar neuron

FIGURE 7.8   Classification of neurons on the basis of structure. (a) Multipolar. **(b)** Bipolar. **(c)** Unipolar.

 DID YOU GET IT?

4. How does a tract differ from a nerve?

5. How does a ganglion differ from a nucleus?

6. Which part of a neuron conducts impulses toward the cell body? Which part releases neurotransmitters?

7. Your professor tells you that one neuron transmits a nerve impulse at the rate of 1 meter per second and that another neuron conducts at the rate of 40 meters per second. Which neuron has the myelinated axon?

For answers, see Appendix D.

Physiology

Nerve Impulses   Neurons have two major functional properties: *irritability,* the ability to respond to a stimulus and convert it into a nerve impulse, and *conductivity,* the ability to transmit the impulse to other neurons, muscles, or glands. We will consider these functional abilities next.

Electrical Conditions of a Resting Neuron's Membrane   The plasma membrane of a resting, or inactive, neuron is **polarized,** which means that there are fewer positive ions sitting on the inner face of the neuron's plasma membrane than there are on its outer face (Figure 7.9). The major positive ions inside the cell are potassium (K^+), whereas the major positive ions outside the cell are sodium (Na^+). As long as the inside remains more negative than the outside, the neuron will stay inactive.

Action Potential Initiation and Generation   Many different types of stimuli excite neurons to become active and generate an impulse. For example, light excites the eye receptors, sound excites some of the ear receptors, and pressure excites some cutaneous receptors of the skin. However, *most* neurons in the body are excited by neurotransmitters released by other neurons, as will be described shortly. Regardless of what the stimulus is, the result is always the same—the permeability properties of the cell's plasma membrane change for a very brief period. *Normally,* sodium ions cannot diffuse through the plasma membrane to any great extent, but when the neuron is adequately stimulated, the "gates" of sodium channels in the membrane open. Because sodium is in much higher concentration outside the cell, it will then

[Na+]

[K+]

(a) **Resting membrane electrical conditions.** The external face of the membrane is slightly positive; its internal face is slightly negative. The chief extracellular ion is sodium (Na+), whereas the chief intracellular ion is potassium (K+). The membrane is relatively impermeable to both ions.

Na+

(b) **Stimulus initiates local depolarization.** A stimulus changes the permeability of a "patch" of the membrane, and sodium ions diffuse rapidly into the cell. This changes the polarity of the membrane (the inside becomes more positive; the outside becomes more negative) at that site.

Na+

(c) **Depolarization and generation of an action potential.** If the stimulus is strong enough, depolarization causes membrane polarity to be completely reversed and an action potential is initiated.

(d) **Propagation of the action potential.** Depolarization of the first membrane patch causes permeability changes in the adjacent membrane, and the events described in (b) are repeated. Thus, the action potential propagates rapidly along the entire length of the membrane.

K+

(e) **Repolarization.** Potassium ions diffuse out of the cell as the membrane permeability changes again, restoring the negative charge on the inside of the membrane and the positive charge on the outside surface. Repolarization occurs in the same direction as depolarization.

Cell exterior

Na+–K+ pump

Plasma membrane

Cell interior

(f) **Initial ionic conditions restored.** The ionic conditions of the resting state are restored later by the activity of the sodium-potassium pump. Three sodium ions are ejected for every two potassium ions carried back into the cell.

FIGURE 7.9 The nerve impulse.

diffuse quickly into the neuron. (Remember the laws of diffusion?) This inward rush of sodium ions changes the polarity of the neuron's membrane at that site, an event called **depolarization.** Locally, the inside is now more positive, and the outside is less positive, a situation called a **graded potential.** However, if the stimulus is strong enough and the sodium influx is great enough, the *local depolarization* (graded potential) activates the neuron to initiate and transmit a long-distance signal called an **action potential,** also called a **nerve impulse** in neurons. The nerve impulse is an *all-or-none response,* like firing a gun. It is either propagated (conducted) over the entire axon, or it doesn't happen at all. The nerve impulse never goes partway along an axon's length, nor does it die out with distance as do graded potentials.

Almost immediately after the sodium ions rush into the neuron, the membrane permeability changes again, becoming impermeable to sodium ions but permeable to potassium ions. So potassium ions are allowed to diffuse out of the neuron into the tissue fluid, and they do so very rapidly. This outflow of positive ions from the cell restores the electrical conditions at the membrane to the polarized, or resting, state, an event called **repolarization.** *Until repolarization occurs, a neuron cannot conduct another impulse.* After repolarization occurs, the initial concentrations of the sodium and potassium ions inside and outside the neuron are restored by activation of the sodium-potassium pump. This pump uses ATP (cellular energy) to pump excess sodium ions out of the cell and to bring potassium ions back into it. Once begun, these sequential events spread along the entire neuronal membrane.

The events just described explain propagation of a nerve impulse along unmyelinated fibers. Fibers that have myelin sheaths conduct impulses much faster because the nerve impulse literally jumps, or leaps, from node to node along the length of the fiber. This occurs because no electrical current can flow across the axon membrane where there is fatty myelin insulation. This faster type of electrical impulse propagation is called *saltatory* (sal'tah-to"re) *conduction* (*saltare* = to dance or leap).

HOMEOSTATIC IMBALANCE

A number of factors can impair the conduction of impulses. For example, sedatives and anesthetics block nerve impulses by altering membrane permeability to ions, mainly sodium ions. As we have seen, no sodium entry = no action potential.

Cold and continuous pressure hinder impulse conduction because they interrupt blood circulation (and hence the delivery of oxygen and nutrients) to the neurons. For example, your fingers get numb when you hold an ice cube for more than a few seconds. Likewise, when you sit on your foot, it "goes to sleep." When you warm the fingers or remove the pressure from your foot, the impulses begin to be transmitted once again, leading to an unpleasant prickly feeling. ▲

Transmission of the Signal at Synapses   So far we have explained only the irritability aspect of neuronal functioning. What about conductivity—how does the electrical impulse traveling along one neuron get across the synapse to the next neuron (or effector cell) to influence its activity? The answer is that the *impulse* doesn't! When the action potential reaches an axon terminal, the tiny vesicles containing the neurotransmitter chemical fuse with the axonal membrane, causing porelike openings to form and releasing the neurotransmitter. The neurotransmitter molecules diffuse across the synapse* and bind to receptors on the membrane of the next neuron (Figure 7.10). If enough neurotransmitter is released, the whole series of events described above (sodium entry, depolarization, etc.) will occur, leading to generation of a nerve impulse in the neuron beyond the synapse. The electrical changes prompted by neurotransmitter binding are very brief because the neurotransmitter is quickly removed from the synapse, either by reuptake into the axonal terminal or by enzymatic breakdown. This limits the effect of each nerve impulse to a period shorter than the blink of an eye.

Notice that the transmission of an impulse is an *electrochemical event.* Transmission down the length of the neuron's membrane is basically *electrical,* but the next neuron is stimulated by a neurotransmitter, which is a *chemical.* Because each neuron both receives signals from and sends signals to scores of other neurons, it carries on "conversations" with many different neurons at the same time.

---

*Although most neurons communicate via the *chemical* type of synapse described above, there are some examples of *electrical* synapses in which the neurons are physically joined by gap junctions and electrical currents actually flow from one neuron to the next.

Synapse

Transmitting neuron

② Vesicle fuses with plasma membrane

③ Neurotransmitter is released into synaptic cleft

④ Neurotransmitter binds to receptor on receiving neuron's membrane

Neurotransmitter molecules

Synaptic cleft

Ion channels

Receiving neuron

Neurotransmitter broken down and released

Neurotransmitter

Receptor

Na⁺

⑤ Ion channel opens

Na⁺

⑥ Ion channel closes

FIGURE 7.10 How neurons communicate at chemical synapses. The events occurring at the synapse are numbered in order.

Reflexes Although there are many types of communication between neurons, much of what the body *must* do every day is programmed as reflexes. **Reflexes** are *rapid, predictable, and involuntary responses* to stimuli. They are much like one-way streets—once a reflex begins, it always goes in the same direction. Reflexes occur over neural pathways called **reflex arcs** and involve both CNS and PNS structures.

The types of reflexes that occur in the body are classed as either somatic or autonomic reflexes. **Somatic reflexes** include all reflexes that stimulate the skeletal muscles. When you quickly pull your hand away from a hot object, a somatic reflex is working. **Autonomic reflexes** regulate the activity of smooth muscles, the heart, and glands. Secretion of saliva (salivary reflex) and changes in the size of the eye pupils (pupillary reflex) are two such reflexes. Autonomic reflexes regulate such body functions as digestion, elimination, blood pressure, and sweating.

All reflex arcs have a minimum of five elements (Figure 7.11a): a *sensory receptor* (which reacts to a stimulus), an *effector organ* (the muscle or gland eventually stimulated), and *sensory* and *motor neurons* to connect the two. The synapse between the sensory and motor neurons represents the central element—the CNS *integration center*.

The simple *patellar* (pah-tel′ar), or *knee-jerk, reflex,* shown in Figure 7.11b and d, is an example of a two-neuron reflex arc, the simplest type in humans. The patellar reflex (in which the quadriceps muscle attached to the hit tendon is stretched) is familiar to most of us. It is usually tested during a physical exam to determine the general health of the motor portion of the nervous system. Most reflexes are much more complex than the two-neuron reflex, involving synapses between one or more interneurons in the CNS (integration center). A three-neuron reflex arc, the *flexor,* or *withdrawal, reflex,* in which the limb is withdrawn from a painful stimulus, is diagrammed in Figure 7.11c. The three-neuron reflex arc consists of five elements—receptor, sensory neuron, interneuron, motor neuron, and effector. Because there is always a delay at synapses (it takes time for the neurotransmitter to diffuse through the synaptic cleft), the more synapses there are in a reflex pathway, the longer the reflex takes to happen.

Many spinal reflexes involve only spinal cord neurons and occur without brain involvement. As

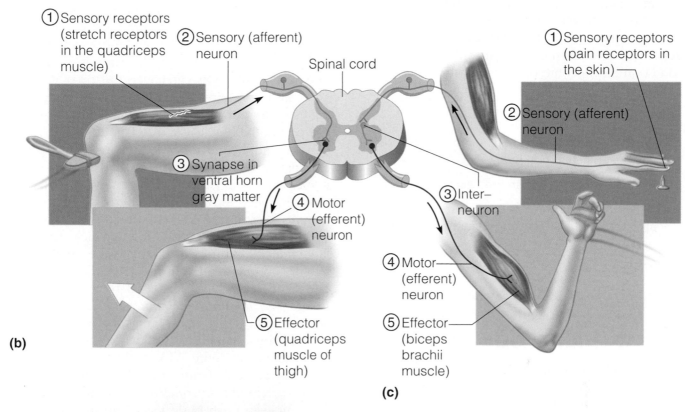

(a)

Stimulus at distal end of neuron

Skin

① **Receptor**

② **Sensory neuron**

④ **Motor neuron**

③ **Integration center**

Spinal cord (in cross section)

Interneuron

⑤ **Effector**

(b)

① Sensory receptors (stretch receptors in the quadriceps muscle)

② Sensory (afferent) neuron

Spinal cord

③ Synapse in ventral horn gray matter

④ Motor (efferent) neuron

⑤ Effector (quadriceps muscle of thigh)

① Sensory receptors (pain receptors in the skin)

② Sensory (afferent) neuron

③ Inter– neuron

④ Motor (efferent) neuron

⑤ Effector (biceps brachii muscle)

(c)

(d)

FIGURE 7.11 Simple reflex arcs. (a) The five basic elements of all reflex arcs. **(b)** A two-neuron reflex arc (example, patellar reflex). **(c)** A three-neuron reflex arc (example, the flexor reflex). **(d)** Photo of a physician testing the patellar (knee-jerk) reflex.

long as the spinal cord is functional, spinal reflexes, such as the flexor reflex, will work. By contrast, some reflexes require that the brain become involved because many different types of information have to be evaluated to arrive at the "right" response. The response of the pupils of the eyes to light is a reflex of this type.

As noted earlier, reflex testing is an important tool in evaluating the condition of the nervous system. Whenever reflexes are exaggerated, distorted, or absent, nervous system disorders are indicated. Reflex changes often occur before the pathological condition has become obvious in other ways.

 DID YOU GET IT?

8. What is the difference between a graded potential and an action potential?

9. How is a stimulus transmitted across a synapse?

10. Which portion(s) of a neuron is(are) likely to be associated with a sensory receptor or a sensory organ?

11. What is a reflex?

For answers, see Appendix D.

Central Nervous System

During embryonic development, the CNS first appears as a simple tube, the **neural tube,** which extends down the dorsal median plane of the developing embryo's body. By the fourth week, the anterior end of the neural tube begins to expand, and brain formation begins. The rest of the neural tube posterior to the forming brain becomes the spinal cord. The central canal of the neural tube, which is continuous between the brain and spinal cord, becomes enlarged in four regions of the brain to form chambers called **ventricles** (see Figure 7.18a and b, p. 250).

Functional Anatomy of the Brain

The adult brain's unimpressive appearance gives few hints of its remarkable abilities. It is about two good fistfuls of pinkish gray tissue, wrinkled like a walnut and with the texture of cold oatmeal. It weighs a little over three pounds. Because the brain is the largest and most complex mass of nervous tissue in the body, it is commonly discussed in terms of its four major regions—*cerebral hemi-*

spheres, diencephalon (di″en-sef′ah-lon), *brain stem,* and *cerebellum* (Figure 7.12).

Cerebral Hemispheres

The paired **cerebral** (ser′e-bral) **hemispheres,** collectively called the **cerebrum,** are the most superior part of the brain and together are a good deal larger than the other three brain regions combined. In fact, as the cerebral hemispheres develop and grow, they enclose and obscure most of the brain stem, so many brain stem structures cannot normally be seen unless a sagittal section is made. Picture how a mushroom cap covers the top of its stalk, and you have a fairly good idea of how the cerebral hemispheres cover the diencephalon and the superior part of the brain stem (see Figure 7.12).

The entire surface of the cerebral hemispheres exhibits elevated ridges of tissue called **gyri** (ji′re; *gyrus,* singular; "twisters"), separated by shallow grooves called **sulci** (sul′ki; *sulcus,* singular; "furrows"). Less numerous are the deeper grooves called **fissures** (Figure 7.13a), which separate large regions of the brain. Many of the fissures and gyri are important anatomical landmarks. The cerebral hemispheres are separated by a single deep fissure, the *longitudinal fissure.* Other fissures or sulci divide each cerebral hemisphere into a number of **lobes,** named for the cranial bones that lie over them (see Figure 7.13a and b).

Each cerebral hemisphere has three basic regions: a superficial *cortex* of gray matter, which looks gray in fresh brain tissue; an internal *white matter*; and the *basal nuclei,* islands of gray matter situated deep within the white matter. We consider these regions next.

Cerebral Cortex Speech, memory, logical and emotional response, as well as consciousness, interpretation of sensation, and voluntary movement, are all functions of neurons of the **cerebral cortex,** and many of the functional areas of the cerebral hemispheres have been identified (Figure 7.13c). The **primary somatic sensory area** is located in the **parietal lobe** posterior to the **central sulcus.** Impulses traveling from the body's sensory receptors (except for the special senses) are localized and interpreted in this area of the brain. The primary somatic sensory area allows you to recognize pain, coldness, or a light touch. As illustrated in Figure 7.14, the body is represented in an upside-down manner in the sensory area. This spatial map is called the **sensory homunculus**

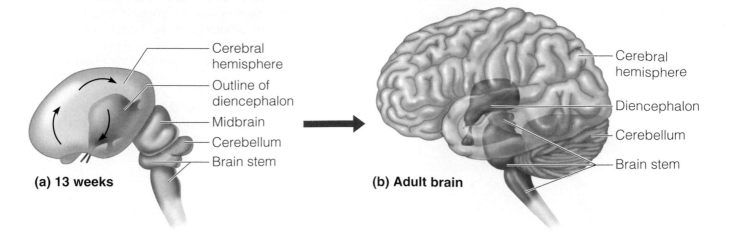

FIGURE 7.12   Development and regions of the human brain.
The brain can be considered in terms of four main parts: cerebral hemispheres, diencephalon, brain stem, and cerebellum. **(a)** In the developing brain, the cerebral hemispheres, initially smooth, are forced to grow posteriorly and laterally over the other brain regions by the bones of the skull. **(b)** In the adult brain, the cerebral hemispheres, now highly convoluted, enclose the diencephalon and the superior part of the brain stem. The left cerebral hemisphere is drawn so that it looks transparent, to reveal the location of the deeply situated diencephalon and superior part of the brain stem.

(ho-mung′ku-lus; "little man"). Body regions with the most sensory receptors—the lips and fingertips—send impulses to neurons that make up a large part of the sensory area. Furthermore, the sensory pathways are crossed pathways—meaning that the left side of the primary somatic sensory area receives impulses from the right side of the body, and vice versa.

Impulses from the special sense organs are interpreted in other cortical areas (see Figure 7.13b and c). For example, the visual area is located in the posterior part of the **occipital lobe,** the auditory area is in the **temporal lobe** bordering the *lateral sulcus,* and the olfactory area is found deep inside the temporal lobe.

The **primary motor area,** which allows us to consciously move our skeletal muscles, is anterior to the central sulcus in the **frontal lobe.** The axons of these motor neurons form the major voluntary motor tract—the **corticospinal** (kor″tǐ-ko-spi′nal), or **pyramidal, tract,** which descends to the cord. As in the primary somatic sensory cortex, the body is represented upside-down, and the pathways are crossed. Most of the neurons in the primary motor area control body areas having the finest motor control; that is, the face, mouth, and hands (see Figure 7.14). The body map on the motor cortex, as you might guess, is called the **motor homunculus.**

A specialized cortical area that is very involved in our ability to speak, **Broca's** (bro′kahz) **area** (see Figure 7.13c), is found at the base of the precentral gyrus (the gyrus anterior to the central sulcus). Damage to this area, which is located in only one cerebral hemisphere (usually the left), causes inability to say words properly. You know what you want to say, but you can't vocalize the words.

Areas involved in higher intellectual reasoning and socially acceptable behavior are believed to be in the anterior part of the frontal lobes. Complex memories appear to be stored in the temporal and frontal lobes. The **speech area** is located at the junction of the temporal, parietal, and occipital lobes. The speech area allows one to sound out words. This area (like Broca's area) is usually in only one cerebral hemisphere. The frontal lobes house areas involved with language comprehension (word meanings).

The cell bodies of neurons involved in the cerebral hemisphere functions named above are found only in the outermost **gray matter** of the cerebrum, the cerebral cortex (see Figure 7.13a). As noted earlier, the cortical region is highly ridged and convoluted, providing more room for the thousands of neurons found there.

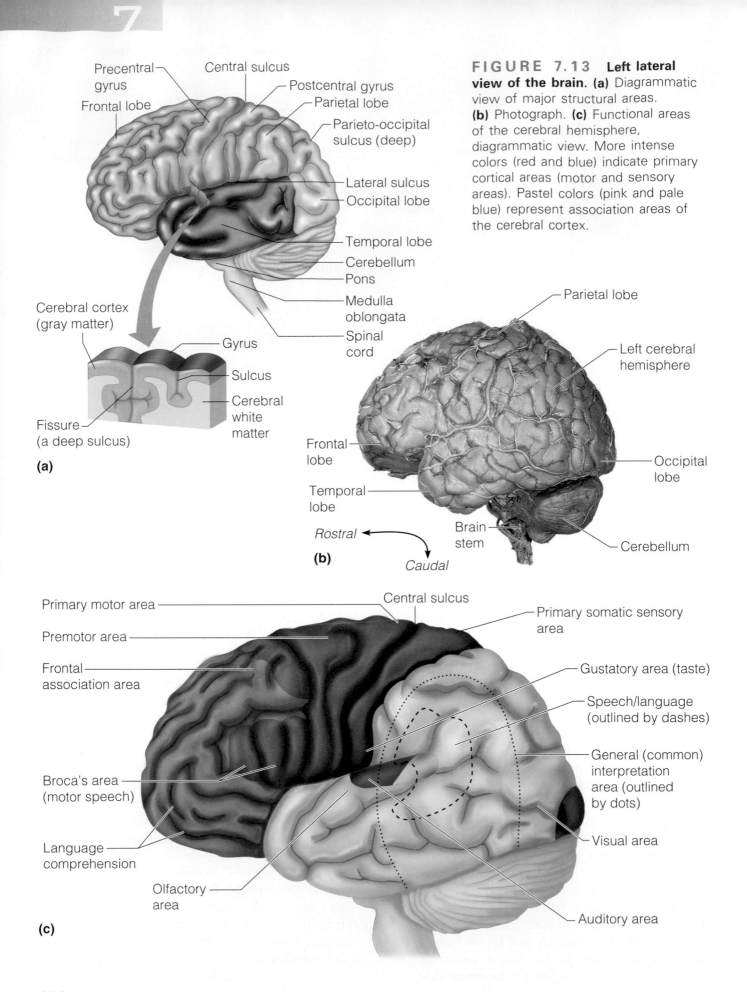

Precentral gyrus · **Central sulcus** · **Postcentral gyrus** · **Frontal lobe** · **Parietal lobe** · **Parieto-occipital sulcus (deep)** · **Lateral sulcus** · **Occipital lobe** · **Temporal lobe** · **Cerebellum** · **Pons** · **Medulla oblongata** · **Spinal cord**

Cerebral cortex (gray matter) · Gyrus · Sulcus · Cerebral white matter · Fissure (a deep sulcus)

(a)

FIGURE 7.13 Left lateral view of the brain. **(a)** Diagrammatic view of major structural areas. **(b)** Photograph. **(c)** Functional areas of the cerebral hemisphere, diagrammatic view. More intense colors (red and blue) indicate primary cortical areas (motor and sensory areas). Pastel colors (pink and pale blue) represent association areas of the cerebral cortex.

Parietal lobe · Left cerebral hemisphere · Occipital lobe · Frontal lobe · Temporal lobe · Brain stem · Cerebellum

Rostral ← *Caudal*

(b)

Primary motor area · Premotor area · Frontal association area · Broca's area (motor speech) · Language comprehension · Olfactory area · Central sulcus · Primary somatic sensory area · Gustatory area (taste) · Speech/language (outlined by dashes) · General (common) interpretation area (outlined by dots) · Visual area · Auditory area

(c)

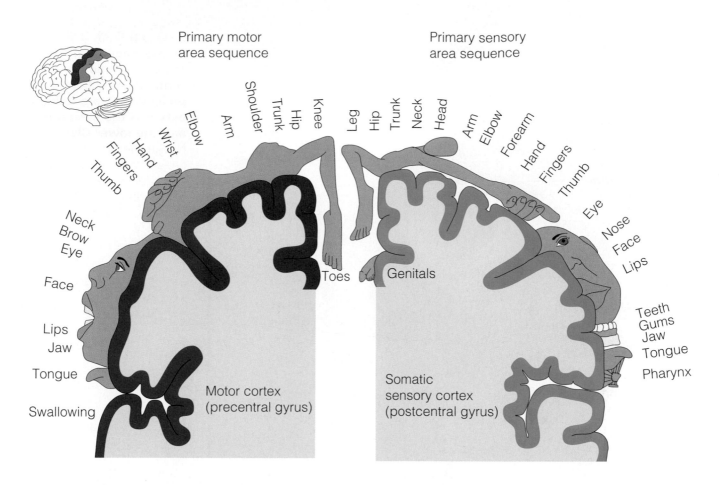

Primary motor
area sequence

Primary sensory
area sequence

Thumb
Fingers
Hand
Wrist
Elbow
Arm
Shoulder
Trunk
Hip
Knee
Leg
Hip
Trunk
Neck
Head
Arm
Elbow
Forearm
Hand
Fingers
Thumb
Eye
Nose
Face
Lips

Neck
Brow
Eye

Face

Lips
Jaw

Tongue

Swallowing

Toes   Genitals

Teeth
Gums
Jaw
Tongue

Pharynx

Motor cortex
(precentral gyrus)

Somatic
sensory cortex
(postcentral gyrus)

FIGURE 7.14   Sensory and motor areas of the cerebral cortex.
The relative amount of cortical tissue devoted to each function is
indicated by the amount of the gyrus occupied by the body area diagrams
(homunculi). The primary motor cortex is shown on the right, the somatic
sensory cortex is on the left.

Cerebral White Matter   Most of the remaining cerebral hemisphere tissue—the deeper **cerebral white matter** (see Figure 7.13a and Figure 7.15)—is composed of fiber tracts carrying impulses to, from, or within the cortex. One very large fiber tract, the **corpus callosum** (kah-lo′sum), connects the cerebral hemispheres (Figures 7.15 and 7.16). Such fiber tracts are called *commisures.* The corpus callosum arches above the structures of the brain stem and allows the cerebral hemispheres to communicate with one another. This is important because, as already noted, some of the cortical functional areas are in only one hemisphere. *Association fiber tracts* connect areas within a hemisphere, and *projection fiber tracts* connect the cerebrum with lower CNS centers.

Basal Nuclei   Although most of the gray matter is in the cerebral cortex, there are several "islands" of gray matter, called the **basal nuclei,** or **basal ganglia,*** buried deep within the white matter of the cerebral hemispheres (see Figure 7.15). The basal nuclei help regulate voluntary motor activities by modifying instructions (particularly in relation to starting or stopping movement) sent to the skeletal muscles by the primary motor cortex.

HOMEOSTATIC IMBALANCE

Individuals who have problems with their basal nuclei are often unable to walk normally or carry out other voluntary movements in the usual normal way. **Huntington's disease** (or **Huntington's chorea**)

---

*The term *basal ganglia* is a historical misnomer. Ganglia are peripheral nervous system structures, but the basal ganglia are collections of nerve cell bodies *in the CNS.* Hence, *basal nuclei* is a more accurate term.

Superior

Corpus callosum (commissural fibers)

Basal nuclei (basal ganglia)

Internal capsule

Projection fibers

Longitudinal fissure

Gray matter

White matter

Lateral ventricle

Fornix

Third ventricle

Thalamus

Pons

Medulla oblongata

FIGURE 7.15
Frontal section of the brain showing commissural fibers and projection fibers running between the cerebrum and the lower CNS. Notice the tight band of projection fibers, called the *internal capsule*, that passes between the thalamus and the basal nuclei.

and **Parkinson's disease,** two examples of such syndromes, are discussed in the "A Closer Look" box on pages 253–254. ▲

 DID YOU GET IT?

12. What are the three major regions of the cerebrum?

13. What is the composition of white matter of the brain?

For answers, see Appendix D.

Diencephalon

The **diencephalon,** or **interbrain,** sits atop the brain stem and is enclosed by the cerebral hemispheres (see Figure 7.12). The major structures of the diencephalon are the *thalamus, hypothalamus,* and *epithalamus* (see Figure 7.16). The **thalamus,** which encloses the shallow *third ventricle* of the brain, is a relay station for sensory impulses passing upward to the sensory cortex. As impulses surge through the thalamus, we have a crude recognition of whether the sensation we are about to have is pleasant or unpleasant. It is the neurons of the sensory cortex that actually localize and interpret the sensation.

The **hypothalamus** (literally, "under the thalamus") makes up the floor of the diencephalon. It is an important autonomic nervous system center because it plays a role in the regulation of body temperature, water balance, and metabolism. The hypothalamus is also the center for many drives and emotions, and as such it is an important part of the so-called **limbic system,** or "emotional-visceral brain." For example, thirst, appetite, sex, pain, and pleasure centers are in the hypothalamus. Additionally, the hypothalamus regulates the pituitary gland (an endocrine organ) and produces two hormones of its own. The **pituitary gland** hangs from the anterior floor of the hypothalamus by a slender stalk. (Its function is discussed in Chapter 9.) The **mammillary bodies,** reflex centers

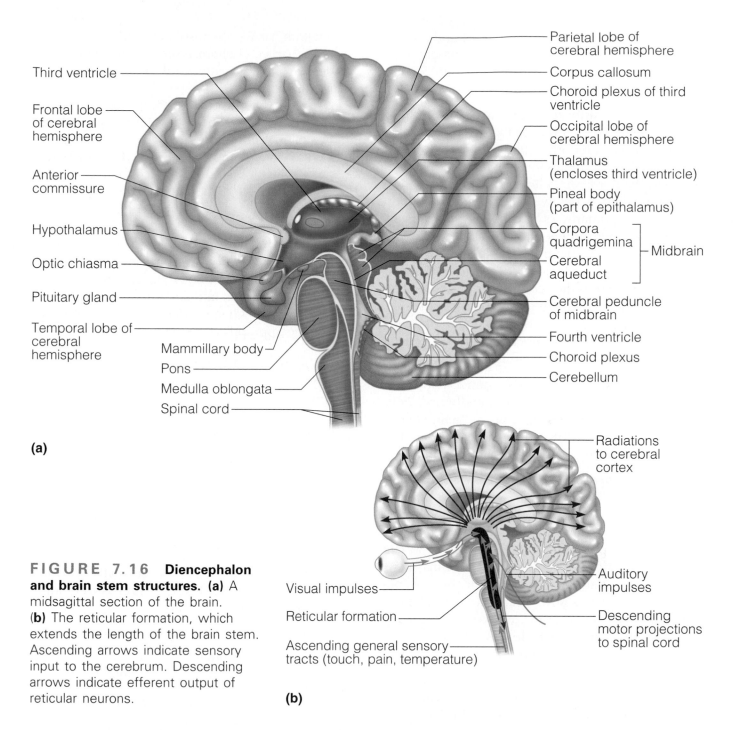

Third ventricle

Frontal lobe of cerebral hemisphere

Anterior commissure

Hypothalamus

Optic chiasma

Pituitary gland

Temporal lobe of cerebral hemisphere

Mammillary body

Pons

Medulla oblongata

Spinal cord

Parietal lobe of cerebral hemisphere

Corpus callosum

Choroid plexus of third ventricle

Occipital lobe of cerebral hemisphere

Thalamus (encloses third ventricle)

Pineal body (part of epithalamus)

Corpora quadrigemina ⎤
Cerebral aqueduct ⎦ Midbrain

Cerebral peduncle of midbrain

Fourth ventricle

Choroid plexus

Cerebellum

(a)

FIGURE 7.16   Diencephalon and brain stem structures. (a) A midsagittal section of the brain. **(b)** The reticular formation, which extends the length of the brain stem. Ascending arrows indicate sensory input to the cerebrum. Descending arrows indicate efferent output of reticular neurons.

Radiations to cerebral cortex

Visual impulses

Reticular formation

Ascending general sensory tracts (touch, pain, temperature)

Auditory impulses

Descending motor projections to spinal cord

(b)

involved in olfaction (the sense of smell), bulge from the floor of the hypothalamus posterior to the pituitary gland.

The **epithalamus** (ep″ĭ-thal′ah-mus) forms the roof of the third ventricle. Important parts of the epithalamus are the **pineal body** (part of the endocrine system) and the **choroid** (ko′roid) **plexus** of the third ventricle. The choroid plexuses, knots of capillaries within each ventricle, form the cerebrospinal fluid.

Brain Stem

The **brain stem** is about the size of a thumb in diameter and approximately 3 inches (approximately 7.5 cm) long. Its structures are the *midbrain, pons,* and *medulla oblongata.* In addition to providing a pathway for ascending and descending tracts, the brain stem has many small gray matter areas. These nuclei produce the rigidly programmed autonomic behaviors necessary for survival. In addition, some are associated with the cranial nerves and control vital activities such as breathing and blood pressure. Identify the brain stem areas in Figure 7.16 as you read their descriptions that follow.

Midbrain The **midbrain** is a relatively small part of the brain stem. It extends from the mammillary bodies to the pons inferiorly. The **cerebral aqueduct** is a tiny canal that travels through the midbrain and connects the third ventricle of the diencephalon to the fourth ventricle below. Anteriorly, the midbrain is composed primarily of two bulging fiber tracts, the **cerebral peduncles** (literally, "little feet of the cerebrum"), which convey ascending and descending impulses. Dorsally located are four rounded protrusions called the **corpora quadrigemina** (kor'por-ah kwah"drĭ-jem'ĭ-nah) because they reminded some anatomist of two pairs of twins (*gemini*). These bulging nuclei are reflex centers involved with vision and hearing.

Pons The **pons** (ponz) is the rounded structure that protrudes just below the midbrain. *Pons* means "bridge," and this area of the brain stem is mostly fiber tracts. However, it does have important nuclei involved in the control of breathing.

Medulla Oblongata The **medulla oblongata** (mĕ-dul'ah ob"long-gă'tah) is the most inferior part of the brain stem. It merges into the spinal cord below without any obvious change in structure. Like the pons, the medulla is an important fiber tract area. The medulla also contains many nuclei that regulate vital visceral activities. It contains centers that control heart rate, blood pressure, breathing, swallowing, and vomiting, among others. The **fourth ventricle** lies posterior to the pons and medulla and anterior to the cerebellum.

Reticular Formation Extending the entire length of the brain stem is a diffuse mass of gray matter, the **reticular formation.** The neurons of the reticular formation are involved in motor control of the visceral organs. A special group of reticular formation neurons, the **reticular activating system (RAS),** plays a role in consciousness and the awake/sleep cycles (Figure 7.16b). Damage to this area can result in permanent unconsciousness (coma).

Cerebellum

The large, cauliflower-like **cerebellum** (ser"e-bel'um) projects dorsally from under the occipital lobe of the cerebrum. Like the cerebrum, the cerebellum has two hemispheres and a convoluted surface. The cerebellum also has an outer cortex made up of gray matter and an inner region of white matter.

The cerebellum provides the precise timing for skeletal muscle activity and controls our balance and equilibrium. Because of its activity, body movements are smooth and coordinated. It plays its role less well when it is sedated by alcohol. Fibers reach the cerebellum from the equilibrium apparatus of the inner ear, the eye, the proprioceptors of the skeletal muscles and tendons, and many other areas. The cerebellum can be compared to an automatic pilot, continuously comparing the brain's "intentions" with actual body performance by monitoring body position and amount of tension in various body parts. When needed, it sends messages to initiate the appropriate corrective measures.

HOMEOSTATIC IMBALANCE

If the cerebellum is damaged (for example, by a blow to the head, a tumor, or a stroke), movements become clumsy and disorganized—a condition called **ataxia.** Victims cannot keep their balance and may appear to be drunk because of the loss of muscle coordination. They are no longer able to touch their finger to their nose with eyes closed—a feat that normal individuals accomplish easily. ▲

▶ *DID YOU GET IT?*

14. Which brain region controls such vital activities as breathing and blood pressure—cerebrum, brain stem, or cerebellum?

15. What is the function of the cerebellum?

16. In what major brain region are the thalamus, hypothalamus, and pineal body found?

For answers, see Appendix D.

Protection of the Central Nervous System

Nervous tissue is very soft and delicate, and the irreplaceable neurons are injured by even the slightest pressure. Nature has tried to protect the brain and spinal cord by enclosing them within bone (the skull and vertebral column), membranes (the meninges), and a watery cushion (cerebrospinal fluid). Protection from harmful substances in the blood is provided by the so-called blood-brain

What would be the consequence of blocked arachnoid villi?

(a)

FIGURE 7.17
Meninges of the brain.
(a) Three-dimensional frontal section showing the meninges—the dura mater, arachnoid mater, and pia mater—that surround and protect the brain. The relationship of the dura mater to the falx cerebri and the superior sagittal (dural) sinus is also shown. **(b)** Posterior view of the brain in place surrounded by the dura mater.

(b)

barrier. We have already considered the bony enclosures (Chapter 5), so we will focus on the other protective devices here.

Meninges

The three connective tissue membranes covering and protecting the CNS structures are **meninges**

(mĕ-nin′jēz) (Figure 7.17). The outermost layer, the leathery **dura mater** (du′rah ma′ter), meaning "tough or hard mother," is a double-layered membrane where it surrounds the brain. One of its layers is attached to the inner surface of the skull, forming the periosteum (*periosteal layer*). The other, called the *meningeal layer*, forms the outermost covering of the brain and continues as the dura mater of the spinal cord. The dural layers are fused together except in three areas where they separate to enclose *dural venous sinuses* that collect venous blood.

(a) Anterior view

Lateral ventricle

Third ventricle

Cerebral aqueduct

Fourth ventricle

Central canal of spinal cord

(b) Left lateral view

Lateral ventricles

Third ventricle

Cerebral aqueduct

Fourth ventricle

Central canal of spinal cord

Superior sagittal sinus

Choroid plexus

Cerebrum covered with pia mater

Corpus callosum

Third ventricle

Pituitary gland

Cerebral aqueduct

Fourth ventricle

(c)

Arachnoid villus

Subarachnoid space

Arachnoid

Meningeal dura mater

Periosteal dura mater

Tentorium cerebelli

Cerebellum

Choroid plexus

Central canal of spinal cord

FIGURE 7.18 Ventricles and location of the cerebrospinal fluid. **(a)** and **(b)** Three-dimensional views of the ventricles of the brain. **(c)** Circulatory pathway of the cerebrospinal fluid (indicated by arrows) within the central nervous system and the subarachnoid space. (The relative position of the right lateral ventricle is indicated by the pale blue area deep to the corpus callosum.)

In several places, the inner dural membrane extends inward to form a fold that attaches the brain to the cranial cavity. One of these folds, the **falx** (falks) **cerebri,** is shown in Figure 7.17a. Another such fold, the **tentorium cerebelli** separating the cerebellum from the cerebrum, is shown in Figures 7.17b and 7.18c.

The middle meningeal layer is the weblike **arachnoid** (ah-rak′noid) **mater** (see Fig. 7.17). *Arachnida* means "spider," and some think the arachnoid membrane looks like a cobweb. Its threadlike extensions span the **subarachnoid space** to attach it to the innermost membrane, the **pia** (pi′ah) **mater** ("gentle mother"). The delicate pia mater clings tightly to the surface of the brain and spinal cord, following every fold.

The subarachnoid space is filled with cerebrospinal fluid. Specialized projections of the arachnoid membrane, **arachnoid villi** (vih′li), protrude through the dura mater. The cerebrospinal fluid is absorbed into the venous blood in the dural sinuses through the arachnoid villi.

HOMEOSTATIC IMBALANCE

Meningitis, an inflammation of the meninges, is a serious threat to the brain because bacterial or viral meningitis may spread into the nervous tissue of the CNS. This condition of brain inflammation is called **encephalitis** (en-sef-ah-li′tis). Meningitis is usually diagnosed by taking a sample of cerebrospinal fluid from the subarachnoid space. ▲

Cerebrospinal Fluid

Cerebrospinal (ser″e-bro-spi′nal) **fluid (CSF)** is a watery "broth" similar in its makeup to blood plasma, from which it forms. However, it contains less protein and more vitamin C, and its ion composition is different.

CSF is continually formed from blood by the choroid plexuses. Choroid plexuses are clusters of capillaries hanging from the "roof" in each of the brain's ventricles. The CSF in and around the brain and cord forms a watery cushion that protects the fragile nervous tissue from blows and other trauma.

Inside the brain, CSF is continually moving (see Figure 7.18c). It circulates from the two lateral ventricles (in the cerebral hemispheres) into the third ventricle (in the diencephalon), and then through the cerebral aqueduct of the midbrain into the fourth ventricle dorsal to the pons and medulla oblongata. Some of the fluid reaching the fourth ventricle simply continues down into the spinal

FIGURE 7.19   Hydrocephalus in a newborn.

cord, but most of it circulates into the subarachnoid space through three openings in the walls of the fourth ventricle. The CSF returns to the blood in the dural venous sinuses through the arachnoid villi. Ordinarily, CSF forms and drains at a constant rate so that its normal pressure and volume (150 ml—about half a cup) are maintained. Any significant changes in CSF composition (or the appearance of blood cells in it) may be a sign of meningitis or certain other brain pathologies (such as tumors and multiple sclerosis). The CSF sample for testing is obtained by a procedure called a *lumbar (spinal) tap.* Because the withdrawal of fluid for testing decreases CSF fluid pressure, the patient must remain in a horizontal position (lying down) for 6 to 12 hours after the procedure to prevent an agonizingly painful "spinal headache."

HOMEOSTATIC IMBALANCE

If something obstructs its drainage (for example, a tumor), CSF begins to accumulate and exert pressure on the brain. This condition is **hydrocephalus** (hi-dro-sef′ah-lus), literally, "water on the brain." Hydrocephalus in a newborn baby causes the head to enlarge as the brain increases in size (Figure 7.19). This is possible in an infant because the skull bones have not yet fused. However, in an adult this condition is likely to result in brain damage because the skull is hard, and the accumulating fluid crushes soft nervous tissue. Today hydrocephalus is treated surgically by inserting a shunt (a plastic tube) to drain the excess fluid into a vein in the neck or into the abdomen. ▲

The Blood-Brain Barrier

No other body organ is so absolutely dependent on a constant internal environment as is the brain. Other body tissues can withstand the rather small fluctuations in the concentrations of hormones, ions, and nutrients that continually occur, particularly after eating or exercising. If the brain were exposed to such chemical changes, uncontrolled neural activity might result—remember that certain ions (sodium and potassium) are involved in initiating nerve impulses, and some amino acids serve as neurotransmitters. Consequently, neurons are kept separated from bloodborne substances by the so-called **blood-brain barrier,** composed of the *least* permeable capillaries in the whole body. These capillaries are almost seamlessly bound together by tight junctions all around. Of water-soluble substances, only water, glucose, and essential amino acids pass easily through the walls of these capillaries. Metabolic wastes, such as urea, toxins, proteins, and most drugs are prevented from entering the brain tissue. Nonessential amino acids and potassium ions not only are prevented from entering the brain, but also are actively pumped from the brain into the blood across capillary walls. Although the bulbous "feet" of the astrocytes that cling to the capillaries may contribute to the barrier, the relative impermeability of the brain capillaries is most responsible for providing this protection.

The blood-brain barrier is virtually useless against fats, respiratory gases, and other fat-soluble molecules that diffuse easily through all plasma membranes. This explains why blood-borne alcohol, nicotine, and anesthetics can affect the brain.

▶ DID YOU GET IT?

17. What name is given to the cerebrospinal fluid–filled cavities within the brain?

18. What name is given to the barrier that protects the brain from toxic chemicals?

19. Which meningeal layer provides the means for draining cerebrospinal fluid back into the blood—dura mater, arachnoid mater, or pia mater?

For answers, see Appendix D.

Brain Dysfunctions

◯ HOMEOSTATIC IMBALANCE

Brain dysfunctions are unbelievably varied. We mention some of them (the "terrible three" in the "A Closer Look" box on pages 253–254), and we will discuss developmental problems in the final section of this chapter. Here, we will focus on traumatic brain injuries and cerebrovascular accidents. Techniques used to diagnose many brain disorders are described in the "A Closer Look" box on pages 271–272.

Traumatic Brain Injuries

Head injuries are a leading cause of accidental death in the United States. Consider, for example, what happens when you forget to fasten your seat belt and then crash into the rear end of another car. Your head is moving and then is suddenly stopped as it hits the windshield. Brain damage is caused not only by injury at the site of the blow, but also by the effect of the ricocheting brain hitting the opposite end of the skull.

A **concussion** occurs when brain injury is slight. The victim may be dizzy, "see stars," or lose consciousness briefly, but no permanent brain damage occurs. A brain **contusion** is the result of marked tissue destruction. If the cerebral cortex is injured, the individual may remain conscious, but severe brain stem contusions always result in a coma lasting from hours to a lifetime because of injury to the reticular activating system.

After head blows, death may result from **intracranial hemorrhage** (bleeding from ruptured vessels) or **cerebral edema** (swelling of the brain due to inflammatory response to injury). Individuals who are initially alert and lucid following head trauma and then begin to deteriorate neurologically later are most likely hemorrhaging or suffering the consequences of edema, both of which compress vital brain tissue.

Cerebrovascular Accident

Commonly called *strokes*, **cerebrovascular** (ser"e-bro-vas'ku-lar) **accidents (CVAs)** are the third leading cause of death in the United States. CVAs occur when blood circulation to a brain area is blocked, as by a blood clot or a ruptured blood vessel, and vital brain tissue dies. After a CVA, it is often possible to determine

A CLOSER LOOK

ALZHEIMER'S, PARKINSON'S, AND HUNTINGTON'S— THE TERRIBLE THREE

What do former President Reagan and actor Michael J. Fox have in common? Not much, other than the fact that each was or is a victim of one of the terrible three CNS degenerative diseases.

Alzheimer's (altz'hi-merz) **disease (AD)** is a progressive degenerative disease of the brain that ultimately results in dementia (mental deterioration). Alzheimer's patients represent nearly half of all people in nursing homes. Between 5 and 15 percent of people over 65 develop this condition, and for up to half of those over 85 it is a major contributing cause in their deaths.

Its victims, which include President Reagan, exhibit memory loss (particularly for recent events), a short attention span and disorientation, and eventual language loss. Over a period of several years, formerly good-natured people may become irritable, moody, confused, and sometimes violent. Ultimately, hallucinations occur.

AD is associated with a shortage of acetylcholine (ACh) and with structural changes in the brain, particularly in areas involved with thought and memory. The gyri shrink, and the brain atrophies. Its precise cause is unknown, but some cases of AD appear to run in families.

Microscopic examinations of brain tissue reveal senile plaques (aggregations of *beta amyloid peptide*) littering the brain like shrapnel between the neurons. It has been frustratingly difficult for researchers to uncover how beta amyloid peptide acts as a neurotoxin, particularly because it is also present in healthy brain cells (but in lower amounts). Just what tips things off balance to favor production of more beta amyloid is not understood, but it is known that this tiny peptide does its damage by enhancing calcium entry into certain brain neurons.

> **" *Alzheimer's patients represent nearly half of all people in nursing homes.* "**

Another line of research has implicated a protein called *tau*, which appears to function like railroad ties to bind microtubule "tracks" together. In the brains of AD victims, tau abandons its microtubule stabilizing role and grabs onto other tau molecules, forming spaghetti-like neurofibrillary tangles within neuron cell bodies. These degenerative changes develop over a period of several years, during which time the family members watch the person they love "disappear." It is a long and painful process. It is hoped that the lines of investigation, particularly stem cell research, will eventually merge and point to a treatment, but at present drugs that ease symptoms by inhibiting ACh breakdown are most useful.

Parkinson's disease, an example of basal nuclei problems, typically strikes people in their fifties and sixties (Michael J. Fox is an exception). It results from a degeneration of the dopamine-releasing neurons of the substantia nigra. As those neurons deteriorate, the dopamine-deprived basal nuclei they target become overactive, causing the well-known symptoms of the disease. Afflicted individuals, including Michael J. Fox, have a persistent tremor at rest (exhibited by head nodding and a "pill-rolling" movement of the fingers), a forward-bent walking posture and shuffling gait, and a stiff facial expression. In addition, they have trouble initiating movement or getting their muscles going.

The cause of Parkinson's disease is still unknown. The drug L-dopa helps to alleviate some of the symptoms. However, L-dopa is not a cure, and as more and more neurons die off, it becomes ineffective. It also has undesirable side effects: severe nausea, dizziness, and in some, liver damage. A newer treatment drug is deprenyl. When given early on in the disease, deprenyl slows the neurological deterioration to some extent

A CLOSER LOOK Alzheimer's, Parkinson's, and Huntington's *(continued)*

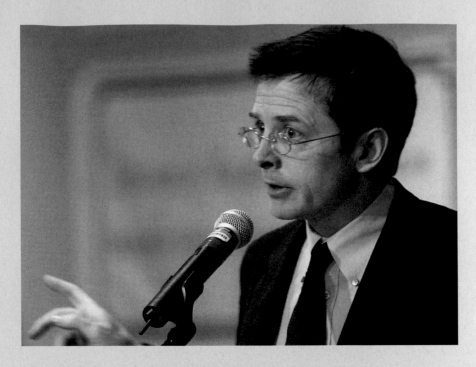

and delays the need to administer L-dopa for up to 18 months. Later in the disease, deprenyl can prolong the effectiveness of L-dopa.

Deep-brain (thalamic) stimulation via implanted electrodes has proved helpful in alleviating tremors but does little else. More promising for long-term results are the intrabrain transplants of embryonic substantia nigra tissue, genetically engineered adult nigral cells, or dopamine-producing cells from fetal pigs; all these have produced some regression of disease symptoms. However, the use of fetal tissue is controversial and

riddled with ethical and legal roadblocks.

Huntington's disease is a genetic disease that strikes during middle age and leads to massive degeneration of the basal nuclei and later of the cerebral cortex. Its initial symptoms in many are wild, jerky, and almost continuous flapping movements called *chorea* (Greek for "dance"). Although the movements appear to be voluntary, they are not. Late in the disease, marked mental deterioration occurs. Huntington's disease is progressive and usually fatal within 15 years of onset of symptoms.

The signs and symptoms of Huntington's disease are essentially the opposite of those of Parkinson's disease (overstimulation rather than inhibition of the motor drive), and Huntington's is usually treated with drugs that block, rather than enhance, dopamine's effects. As you can see, neurotransmitters, which are the "vocabulary" of neurons, can cause garbled neural language when things go wrong. As with Parkinson's disease, fetal tissue implants may provide promise for its treatment in the future.

the area of brain damage by observing the patient's symptoms. For example, if the patient has left-sided paralysis (a one-sided paralysis is called **hemiplegia**), the right motor cortex of the frontal lobe is most likely involved. **Aphasias** (ah-fa′ze-ahz) are a common result of damage to the left cerebral hemisphere, where the language areas are located. There are many types of

aphasias, but the most common are *motor aphasia*, which involves damage to Broca's area and a loss of ability to speak, and *sensory aphasia*, in which a person loses the ability to understand written or spoken language. Aphasias are maddening to the victims because, as a rule, their intellect is unimpaired. Brain lesions can also cause marked changes in a person's disposition (for example, a change from a sunny to a foul personality). In such cases, a tumor as well as a CVA might be suspected.

Fewer than a third of those surviving a CVA are alive three years later. Even so, the picture is not hopeless. Some patients recover at least part of their lost faculties because undamaged neurons spread into areas where neurons have died and take over some lost functions. Indeed, most of the recovery seen after brain injury is due to this phenomenon.

Not all strokes are "completed." Temporary brain ischemia, or restriction of blood flow, is called a **transient ischemic attack (TIA).** TIAs last from 5 to 50 minutes and are characterized by symptoms such as numbness, temporary paralysis, and impaired speech. Although these defects are not permanent, they do constitute "red flags" that warn of impending, more serious CVAs. ▲

▶ DID YOU GET IT?

20. If a person has suffered a bonk on the head with a baseball and then soon becomes comatose, has he suffered a concussion or a contusion?

For the answer, see Appendix D.

Spinal Cord

The cylindrical **spinal cord,** which is approximately 17 inches (42 cm) long, is a glistening white continuation of the brain stem. The spinal cord provides a two-way conduction pathway to and from the brain, and it is a major reflex center (spinal reflexes are completed at this level). Enclosed within the vertebral column, the spinal cord extends from the foramen magnum of the skull to the first or second lumbar vertebra, where it ends just below the ribs (Figure 7.20). Like the brain, the spinal cord is cushioned and protected by meninges. Meningeal coverings do not end at the second lumbar vertebra (L_2) but instead extend well beyond the end of the spinal cord in the vertebral canal. Because there is no possibility of damaging the cord beyond L_3, the meningeal sac inferior to that point provides a nearly ideal spot for removing CSF for testing.

In humans, 31 pairs of spinal nerves arise from the cord and exit from the vertebral column to serve the body area close by. The spinal cord is about the size of a thumb for most of its length, but it is obviously enlarged in the cervical and lumbar

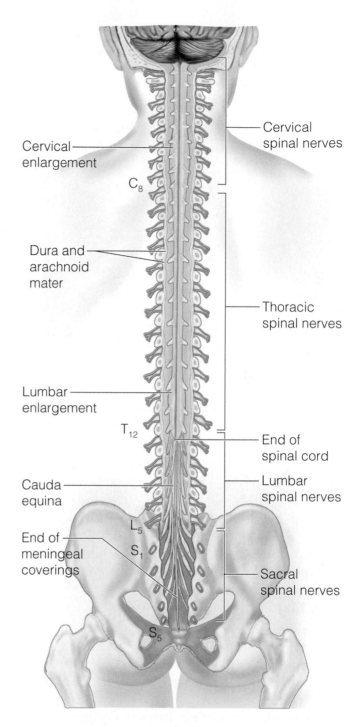

FIGURE 7.20 **Anatomy of the spinal cord, posterior view.**

Labels: Cervical enlargement — C_8 — Cervical spinal nerves — Dura and arachnoid mater — Thoracic spinal nerves — Lumbar enlargement — T_{12} — End of spinal cord — Cauda equina — L_5 — S_1 — Lumbar spinal nerves — End of meningeal coverings — S_5 — Sacral spinal nerves

regions where the nerves serving the upper and lower limbs arise and leave the cord. Because the vertebral column grows faster than the spinal cord, the spinal cord does not reach the end of the vertebral column, and the spinal nerves leaving its

FIGURE 7.21 Spinal cord with meninges (three-dimensional view).

inferior end must travel through the vertebral canal for some distance before exiting. This collection of spinal nerves at the inferior end of the vertebral canal is called the **cauda equina** (kaw'da e-kwi'nah) because it looks so much like a horse's tail (the literal translation of *cauda equina*).

Gray Matter of the Spinal Cord and Spinal Roots

The gray matter of the spinal cord looks like a butterfly or the letter H in cross section (Figure 7.21). The two posterior projections are the **dorsal,** or **posterior, horns;** the two anterior projections are the **ventral,** or **anterior, horns.** The gray matter surrounds the **central canal** of the cord, which contains CSF.

Neurons with specific functions can be located in the gray matter. The dorsal horns contain interneurons. The cell bodies of the sensory neurons, whose fibers enter the cord by the **dorsal root,** are found in an enlarged area called the **dorsal root ganglion.** If the dorsal root or its ganglion is damaged, sensation from the body area served will be lost. The ventral horns of the gray matter contain cell bodies of motor neurons of the somatic (volun-

tary) nervous system, which send their axons out the **ventral root** of the cord. The dorsal and ventral roots fuse to form the **spinal nerves.**

HOMEOSTATIC IMBALANCE

Damage to the ventral root results in a **flaccid paralysis** of the muscles served. In flaccid paralysis, nerve impulses do not reach the muscles affected; thus, no voluntary movement of those muscles is possible. The muscles begin to atrophy because they are no longer stimulated. ▲

White Matter of the Spinal Cord

White matter of the spinal cord is composed of myelinated fiber tracts—some running to higher centers, some traveling from the brain to the cord, and some conducting impulses from one side of the spinal cord to the other (Figure 7.22).

Because of the irregular shape of gray matter, the white matter on each side of the cord is divided into three regions—the **dorsal, lateral,** and **ventral columns.** Each of the columns contains a number of fiber tracts made up of axons with the same destination and function. Tracts conducting sensory impulses to the brain are *sensory,* or

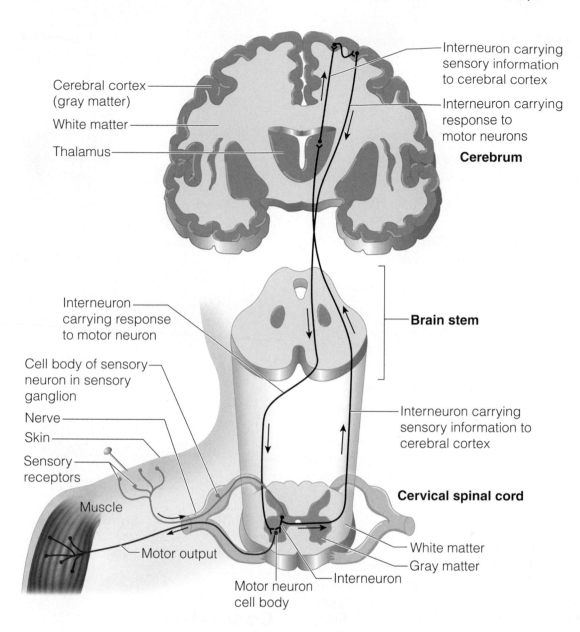

Cerebral cortex (gray matter)

White matter

Thalamus

Interneuron carrying sensory information to cerebral cortex

Interneuron carrying response to motor neurons

Cerebrum

Brain stem

Interneuron carrying response to motor neuron

Cell body of sensory neuron in sensory ganglion

Nerve

Skin

Sensory receptors

Muscle

Motor output

Interneuron carrying sensory information to cerebral cortex

Cervical spinal cord

White matter

Gray matter

Interneuron

Motor neuron cell body

FIGURE 7.22 **Schematic of ascending (sensory) and descending (motor) pathways between the brain and the spinal cord.**

afferent, tracts. Those carrying impulses from the brain to skeletal muscles are *motor,* or *efferent, tracts.* All tracts in the dorsal columns are ascending tracts that carry sensory input to the brain. The lateral and ventral tracts contain both ascending and descending (motor) tracts.

HOMEOSTATIC IMBALANCE

If the spinal cord is transected (cut crosswise) or crushed, **spastic paralysis** results. The affected muscles stay healthy because they are still stimulated by spinal reflex arcs, and movement of those muscles does occur. However, movements are involuntary and not controllable, and this can be as much of a problem as complete lack of mobility. In addition, because the spinal cord carries both sensory and motor impulses, a loss of feeling or sensory input occurs in the body areas below the point of cord destruction. Physicians often use a pin to see whether a person can feel pain after spinal cord injury—to find out whether regeneration is occurring. Pain is a hopeful sign in such cases. If the spinal cord injury occurs high in the cord, so that all four limbs are affected, the individual is a *quadriplegic* (kwod"rĭ-ple'jik). If only the legs are paralyzed, the individual is a *paraplegic* (par"ă-ple'jik). ▲

► **DID YOU GET IT?**

21. What is found in the gray matter of the spinal cord?

22. Which spinal cord pathways are sensory pathways—ascending or descending?

23. Why is the leash of nerve fibers at the end of the spinal cord called the cauda equina?

For answers, see Appendix D.

Peripheral Nervous System

The **peripheral nervous system (PNS)** consists of nerves and scattered groups of neuronal cell bodies (ganglia) found outside the CNS. One type of ganglion has already been considered—the dorsal root ganglion of the spinal cord. Others will be covered in the discussion of the autonomic nervous system. Here, we will concern ourselves only with nerves.

Structure of a Nerve

As noted earlier in this chapter, a **nerve** is a bundle of neuron fibers found outside the CNS. Within a nerve, neuron fibers, or processes, are wrapped in protective connective tissue coverings. Each fiber is surrounded by a delicate connective tissue sheath, an **endoneurium** (en"do-nu're-um). Groups of fibers are bound by a coarser connective tissue wrapping, the **perineurium** (per"ĭ-nu're-um), to form fiber bundles, or **fascicles.** Finally, all the fascicles are bound together by a tough fibrous sheath, the **epineurium,** to form the cordlike nerve (Figure 7.23).

Like neurons, nerves are classified according to the direction in which they transmit impulses. Nerves carrying both sensory and motor fibers are called **mixed nerves;** all spinal nerves are mixed nerves. Nerves that carry impulses toward the CNS only are called **sensory,** or **afferent, nerves,** whereas those that carry only motor fibers are **motor,** or **efferent, nerves.**

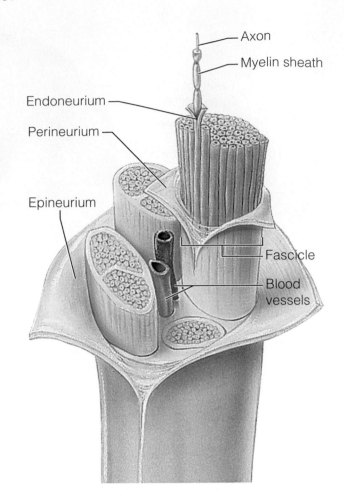

FIGURE 7.23 Structure of a nerve. Three-dimensional view of a portion of a nerve, showing its connective tissue wrappings.

Cranial Nerves

The 12 pairs of **cranial nerves** primarily serve the head and neck. Only one pair (the vagus nerves) extends to the thoracic and abdominal cavities.

The cranial nerves are numbered in order, and in most cases their names reveal the most important structures they control. The cranial nerves are described by name, number, course, and major function in Table 7.1. The last column of the table describes how cranial nerves are tested, which is an important part of any neurologic examination. You do not need to memorize these tests, but this information may help you understand cranial nerve function. As you read through the table, also look at Figure 7.24, which shows the location of the cranial nerves on the brain's anterior surface.

TABLE 7.1	The Cranial Nerves		
Name/number	**Origin/course**	**Function**	**Test**
I. Olfactory	Fibers arise from olfactory receptors in the nasal mucosa and synapse with the olfactory bulbs (which, in turn, send fibers to the olfactory cortex)	Purely sensory; carries impulses for the sense of smell	Subject is asked to sniff and identify aromatic substances, such as oil of cloves or vanilla
II. Optic	Fibers arise from the retina of the eye and form the optic nerve. The two optic nerves form the optic chiasma by partial crossover of fibers; the fibers continue to the optic cortex as the optic tracts	Purely sensory; carries impulses for vision	Vision and visual field are tested with an eye chart and by testing the point at which the subject first sees an object (finger) moving into the visual field; eye interior is viewed with an ophthalmoscope
III. Oculomotor	Fibers run from the midbrain to the eye	Supplies motor fibers to four of the six muscles (superior, inferior, and medial rectus, and inferior oblique) that direct the eyeball; to the eyelid; and to the internal eye muscles controlling lens shape and pupil size	Pupils are examined for size, shape, and size equality; pupillary reflex is tested with a penlight (pupils should constrict when illuminated); eye convergence is tested, as is the ability to follow moving objects
IV. Trochlear	Fibers run from the midbrain to the eye	Supplies motor fibers for one external eye muscle (superior oblique)	Tested in common with cranial nerve III for the ability to follow moving objects
V. Trigeminal	Fibers emerge from the pons and form three divisions that run to the face	Conducts sensory impulses from the skin of the face and mucosa of the nose and mouth; also contains motor fibers that activate the chewing muscles	Sensations of pain, touch, and temperature are tested with a safety pin and hot and cold objects; corneal reflex tested with a wisp of cotton; motor branch tested by asking the subject to open mouth against resistance and move jaw from side to side
VI. Abducens	Fibers leave the pons and run to the eye	Supplies motor fibers to the lateral rectus muscle, which rolls the eye laterally	Tested in common with cranial nerve III for the ability to move each eye laterally

TABLE 7.1   The Cranial Nerves (continued)

Name/number	Origin/course	Function	Test
VII. Facial	Fibers leave the pons and run to the face	Activates the muscles of facial expression and the lacrimal and salivary glands; carries sensory impulses from the taste buds of anterior tongue	Anterior two-thirds of tongue is tested for ability to taste sweet, salty, sour, and bitter substances; subject is asked to close eyes, smile, whistle, etc.; tearing is tested with ammonia fumes
VIII. Vestibulocochlear	Fibers run from the equilibrium and hearing receptors of the inner ear to the brain stem	Purely sensory; vestibular branch transmits impulses for the sense of balance, and cochlear branch transmits impulses for the sense of hearing	Hearing is checked by air and bone conduction, using a tuning fork
IX. Glossopharyngeal	Fibers emerge from the medulla and run to the throat	Supplies motor fibers to the pharynx (throat) that promote swallowing and saliva production; carries sensory impulses from taste buds of the posterior tongue and from pressure receptors of the carotid artery	Gag and swallowing reflexes are checked; subject is asked to speak and cough; posterior tongue may be tested for taste
X. Vagus	Fibers emerge from the medulla and descend into the thorax and abdominal cavity	Fibers carry sensory impulses from and motor impulses to the pharynx, larynx, and the abdominal and thoracic viscera; most motor fibers are parasympathetic fibers that promote digestive activity and help regulate heart activity	Tested in common with cranial nerve IX, because they both serve muscles of the throat
XI. Accessory	Fibers arise from the medulla and superior spinal cord and travel to muscles of the neck and back	Mostly motor fibers that activate the sternocleidomastoid and trapezius muscles	Sternocleidomastoid and trapezius muscles are checked for strength by asking the subject to rotate head and shrug shoulders against resistance
XII. Hypoglossal	Fibers run from the medulla to the tongue	Motor fibers control tongue movements; sensory fibers carry impulses from the tongue	Subject is asked to stick out tongue, and any position abnormalities are noted

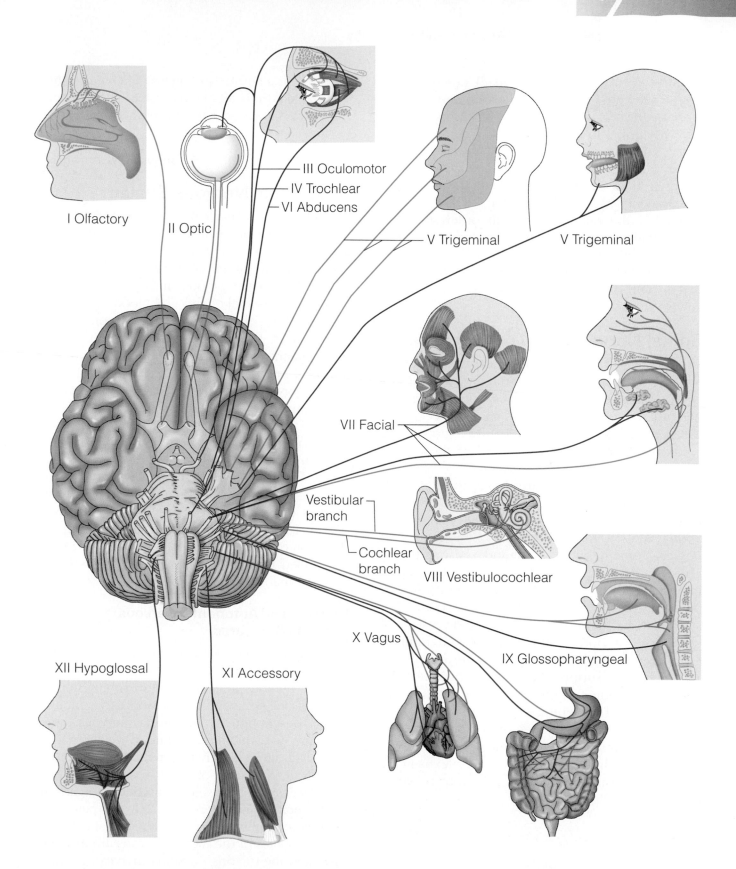

I Olfactory

II Optic

III Oculomotor
IV Trochlear
VI Abducens

V Trigeminal

V Trigeminal

VII Facial

Vestibular branch

Cochlear branch

VIII Vestibulocochlear

X Vagus

IX Glossopharyngeal

XII Hypoglossal

XI Accessory

FIGURE 7.24 **Distribution of cranial nerves.** Sensory nerves are shown in blue, motor nerves in red. Although cranial nerves III, IV, and VI have sensory fibers, these are not shown because the sensory fibers account for only minor parts of these nerves.

Most cranial nerves are mixed nerves; however, three pairs, the optic, olfactory, and vestibulocochlear (ves-tib"u-lo-kok'le-ar) nerves, are purely sensory in function. (The older name for the vestibulocochlear nerve is *acoustic nerve,* a name that reveals its role in hearing but not in equilibrium.) I give my students the following little saying as a memory jog to help them remember the cranial nerves in order; perhaps it will help you, too. The first letter of each word in the saying (and both letters of "ah") is the first letter of the cranial nerve to be remembered: "**O**h, **o**h, **o**h, **t**o **t**ouch **a**nd **f**eel **v**ery **g**ood **v**elvet, **ah.**"

Spinal Nerves and Nerve Plexuses

The 31 pairs of human **spinal nerves** are formed by the combination of the ventral and dorsal roots of the spinal cord. Although each of the cranial nerves issuing from the brain is named specifically, the spinal nerves are named for the region of the cord from which they arise. Figure 7.25 shows how the nerves are named in this scheme.

Almost immediately after being formed, each spinal nerve divides into **dorsal** and **ventral rami** (ra'mi), making each spinal nerve only about ½ inch long. The rami, like the spinal nerves, contain both motor and sensory fibers. Thus, damage to a spinal nerve or either of its rami results both in loss of sensation and flaccid paralysis of the area of the body served. The smaller dorsal rami serve the skin and muscles of the posterior body trunk. The ventral rami of spinal nerves T_1 through T_{12} form the *intercostal nerves,* which supply the muscles between the ribs and the skin and muscles of the anterior and lateral trunk. The ventral rami of all other spinal nerves form complex networks of nerves called **plexuses,** which serve the motor and sensory needs of the limbs. The four nerve plexuses are described in Table 7.2; three of the four plexuses are shown in Figure 7.26.

▶ *DID YOU GET IT?*

24. Where is the epineurium located?

25. Which cranial nerve pair is unique because it is the only one to serve structures outside the head and neck?

26. What is a nerve plexus?

27. Ron has a horrible pain in his right buttock, thigh, and leg. He is told he has sciatica. Which spinal nerve is involved, and what plexus does it belong to?

For answers, see Appendix D.

Autonomic Nervous System

The **autonomic nervous system (ANS)** is the motor subdivision of the PNS that controls body activities automatically. It is composed of a specialized group of neurons that regulate cardiac muscle (the heart), smooth muscles (found in the walls of the visceral organs and blood vessels), and glands. Although all body systems contribute to homeostasis, the relative stability of our internal environment depends largely on the workings of the ANS. At every moment, signals flood from the visceral organs into the CNS, and the autonomic nerves make adjustments as necessary to best support body activities. For example, blood flow may be shunted to more "needy" areas, heart and breathing rate may be speeded up or slowed down, blood pressure may be adjusted, and stomach secretions may be increased or decreased. Most of this fine-tuning occurs without our awareness or attention—few of us realize when our pupils dilate or our arteries constrict—hence the ANS is also called the **involuntary nervous system,** as noted at the beginning of this chapter.

Somatic and Autonomic Nervous Systems Compared

Our previous discussions of nerves in the efferent (motor) division of the PNS have focused on the somatic nervous system, the PNS subdivision that controls our skeletal muscles. So, before plunging into a description of autonomic nervous system anatomy, we will take the time to point out some important differences between the somatic and autonomic subdivisions of the PNS.

Besides differences in their effector organs and in the neurotransmitters released, the patterns of their motor pathways differ. In the somatic division, the cell bodies of the motor neurons are inside the CNS, and their axons (in spinal nerves) extend all the way to the skeletal muscles they serve. The autonomic nervous system, however, has a chain of *two* motor neurons. The first motor neuron of each pair is in the brain or spinal cord. Its axon, the **preganglionic axon** (literally, the "axon before

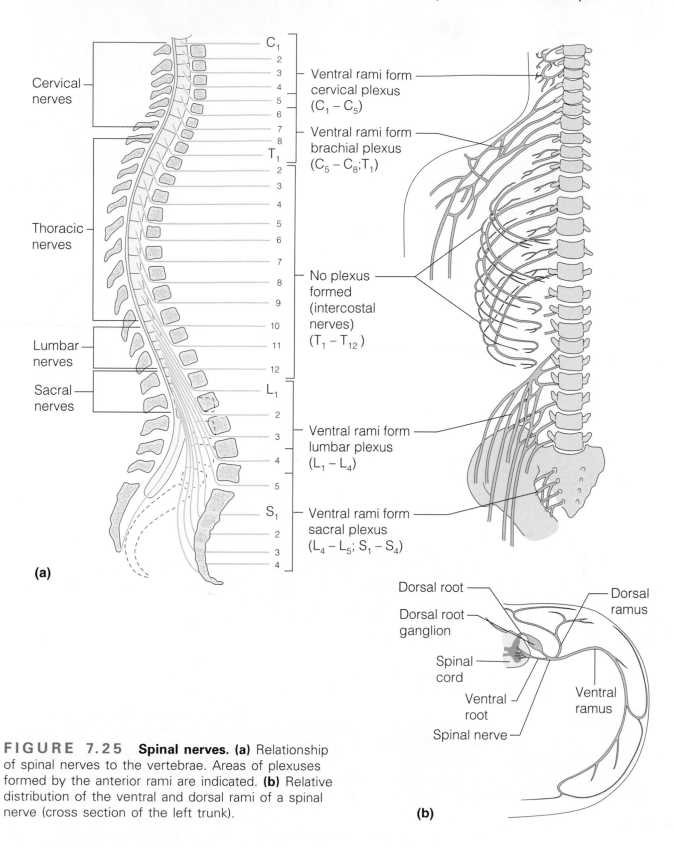

Cervical nerves

Thoracic nerves

Lumbar nerves

Sacral nerves

C_1
2
3
4
5
6
7
8
T_1
2
3
4
5
6
7
8
9
10
11
12
L_1
2
3
4
5
S_1
2
3
4

Ventral rami form cervical plexus ($C_1 – C_5$)

Ventral rami form brachial plexus ($C_5 – C_8; T_1$)

No plexus formed (intercostal nerves) ($T_1 – T_{12}$)

Ventral rami form lumbar plexus ($L_1 – L_4$)

Ventral rami form sacral plexus ($L_4 – L_5; S_1 – S_4$)

(a)

Dorsal root

Dorsal root ganglion

Spinal cord

Ventral root

Spinal nerve

Dorsal ramus

Ventral ramus

(b)

FIGURE 7.25 Spinal nerves. (a) Relationship of spinal nerves to the vertebrae. Areas of plexuses formed by the anterior rami are indicated. **(b)** Relative distribution of the ventral and dorsal rami of a spinal nerve (cross section of the left trunk).

		TABLE 7.2	Spinal Nerve Plexuses	
Plexus	**Origin (from ventral rami)**	**Important nerves**	**Body areas served**	**Result of damage to plexus or its nerves**
Cervical	C_1–C_5	Phrenic	Diaphragm; skin and muscles of shoulder and neck	Respiratory paralysis (and death if not treated promptly)
Brachial	C_5–C_8 and T_1	Axillary	Deltoid muscle and skin of shoulder; muscles and skin of superior thorax	Paralysis and atrophy of deltoid muscle
		Radial	Triceps and extensor muscles of the forearm; skin of posterior upper limb	Wristdrop—inability to extend hand at wrist
		Median	Flexor muscles and skin of forearm and some muscles of hand	Decreased ability to flex and abduct hand and flex and abduct thumb and index finger—therefore, inability to pick up small objects
		Musculocutaneous	Flexor muscles of arm; skin of lateral forearm	Decreased ability to flex forearm on arm
		Ulnar	Some flexor muscles of forearm; wrist and many hand muscles; skin of hand	Clawhand—inability to spread fingers apart
Lumbar	L_1–L_4	Femoral (including lateral and anterior cutaneous branches)	Lower abdomen, anterior and medial thigh muscles (hip flexors and knee extensors, and skin of anteromedial leg and thigh	Inability to extend leg and flex hip; loss of cutaneous sensation
		Obturator	Adductor muscles of medial thigh and small hip muscles; skin of medial thigh and hip joint	Inability to adduct thigh
Sacral	L_4–L_5 and S_1–S_4	Sciatic (largest nerve in body; splits to common fibular and tibial nerves just above knee)	Lower trunk and posterior surface of thigh (hip extensors and knee flexors)	Inability to extend hip and flex knee; sciatica
		• Common fibular (superficial and deep branches)	Lateral aspect of leg and foot	Footdrop—inability to dorsiflex foot
		• Tibial (including sural and plantar branches)	Posterior aspect of leg and foot	Inability to plantar flex and invert foot; shuffling gait
		Superior and inferior gluteal	Gluteus muscles of hip	Inability to extend hip (maximus) or abduct and medially rotate thigh (medius)

KEY:

Roots

C$_4$
C$_5$
C$_6$
C$_7$
C$_8$
T$_1$

Axillary nerve

Humerus

Radial nerve

Musculo-cutaneous nerve

Radius

Median nerve

Ulna

Ulnar nerve

Radial nerve (superficial branch)

(a) Brachial plexus

Femoral

Lateral femoral cutaneous

Obturator

Anterior femoral cutaneous

L$_1$
L$_2$

(b) Lumbar plexus

Superior gluteal

Inferior gluteal

Sciatic

Posterior femoral cutaneous

Common fibular

Tibial

Sural

Deep fibular

Superficial fibular

Plantar branches

(c) Sacral plexus

FIGURE 7.26 Distribution of the major peripheral nerves of the upper and lower limbs.

265

Transmission of nerve impulses along ANS pathways is generally much slower than along somatic fibers. Why?

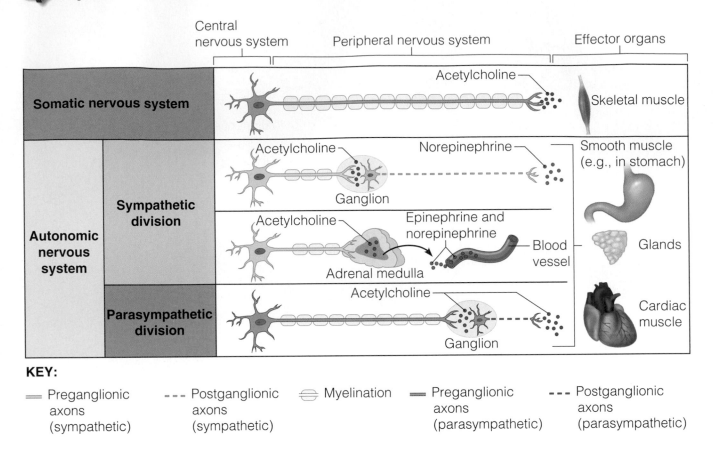

KEY:

— Preganglionic axons (sympathetic)   --- Postganglionic axons (sympathetic)   ⊖ Myelination   — Preganglionic axons (parasympathetic)   --- Postganglionic axons (parasympathetic)

FIGURE 7.27   Comparison of the somatic and autonomic nervous systems.

the ganglion"), leaves the CNS to synapse with the second motor neuron in a ganglion outside the CNS. The axon of this neuron, the **postganglionic axon,** then extends to the organ it serves. These differences are summarized in Figure 7.27.

The autonomic nervous system has two arms, the sympathetic and the parasympathetic (Figure 7.28). Both serve the same organs but cause essentially opposite effects, counterbalancing each other's activities to keep body systems running smoothly. The **sympathetic division** mobilizes the body during extreme situations (such as fear, exercise, or rage), whereas the **parasympathetic division** allows us to "unwind" and conserve en-

ergy. These differences are examined in more detail shortly, but first we will consider the structural characteristics of the two arms of the ANS.

Anatomy of the Parasympathetic Division

The preganglionic neurons of the parasympathetic division are located in brain nuclei of several cranial nerves—III, VII, IX, and X (the vagus being the most important of these) and in the S_2 through S_4 levels of the spinal cord (see Figure 7.28). For this reason, the parasympathetic division is also called the *craniosacral division.* The neurons of the cranial region send their axons out in cranial nerves to serve the head and neck organs. There they synapse with the ganglionic motor neuron in a **terminal ganglion.** From the terminal ganglion, the postganglionic axon extends a short distance to the organ it serves. In the sacral region, the

A *Postganglionic fibers of the ANS are unmyelinated fibers, which conduct much more slowly than the myelinated fibers that are typical of somatic nerve fibers.*

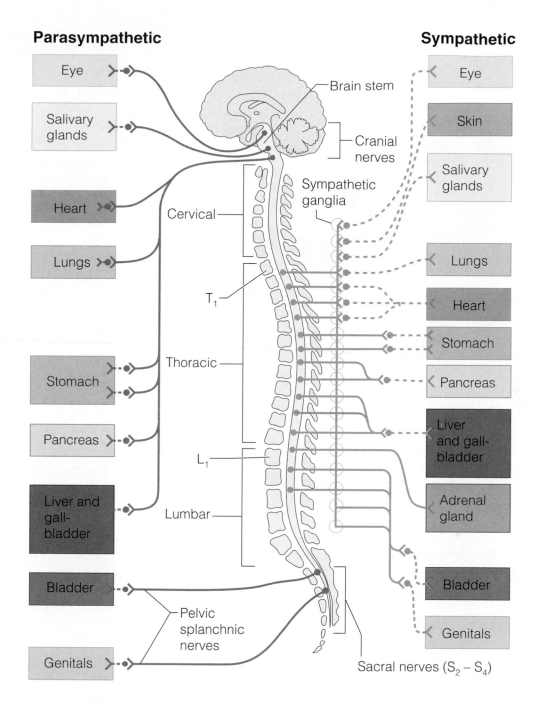

Parasympathetic

Eye

Salivary glands

Heart

Lungs

Stomach

Pancreas

Liver and gall-bladder

Bladder

Genitals

Brain stem

Cranial nerves

Cervical

T_1

Thoracic

L_1

Lumbar

Pelvic splanchnic nerves

Sympathetic ganglia

Sacral nerves (S_2 – S_4)

Sympathetic

Eye

Skin

Salivary glands

Lungs

Heart

Stomach

Pancreas

Liver and gall-bladder

Adrenal gland

Bladder

Genitals

FIGURE 7.28 **Anatomy of the autonomic nervous system.** Parasympathetic fibers are shown in purple, sympathetic fibers in green. Solid lines represent preganglionic fibers; dashed lines indicate postganglionic fibers.

preganglionic axons leave the spinal cord and form the *pelvic splanchnic* (splank′nik) *nerves,* also called the *pelvic nerves,* which travel to the pelvic cavity. In the pelvic cavity, the preganglionic axons synapse with the second motor neurons in terminal ganglia on, or close to, the organs they serve.

Anatomy of the Sympathetic Division

The sympathetic division is also called the *thoracolumbar* (tho″rah-ko-lum′bar) *division* because its preganglionic neurons are in the gray matter of the spinal cord from T_1 through L_2 (see Figure 7.28). The preganglionic axons leave the cord in

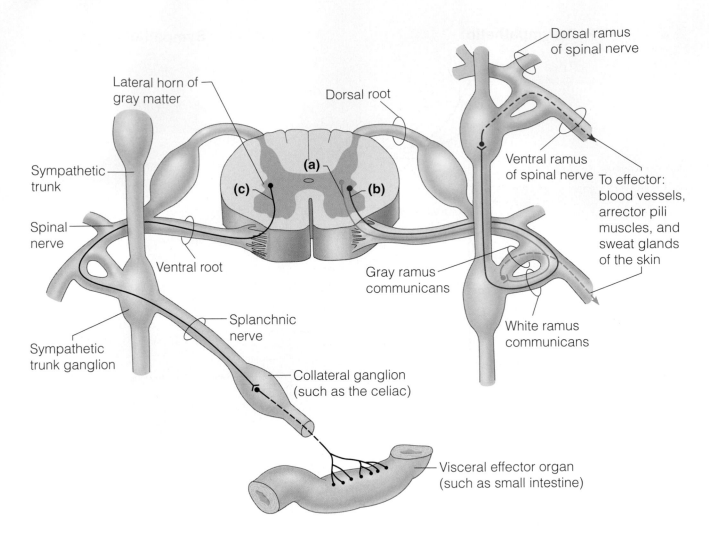

FIGURE 7.29 **Sympathetic pathways.** **(a)** Synapse in a sympathetic chain ganglion at the same level. **(b)** Synapse in a sympathetic chain ganglion at a different level. **(c)** Synapse in a collateral ganglion anterior to the vertebral column.

the ventral root, enter the spinal nerve, and then pass through a **ramus communicans,** or small communicating branch, to enter a **sympathetic chain ganglion** (Figure 7.29). The **sympathetic trunk,** or **chain,** lies alongside the vertebral column on each side. After it reaches the ganglion, the axon may synapse with the second (ganglionic) neuron in the sympathetic chain at the same or a different level (the postganglionic axon then reenters the spinal nerve to travel to the skin), or the axon may pass through the ganglion without synapsing and form part of the **splanchnic nerves.** The splanchnic nerves travel to the viscera to synapse with the ganglionic neuron, found in a **collateral ganglion** anterior to the vertebral column. The major collateral ganglia—the celiac and the superior and inferior mesenteric ganglia—supply the abdominal and pelvic organs. The postganglionic axon then leaves the collateral ganglion and travels to serve a nearby visceral organ.

Now that the anatomical details have been described, we are ready to examine ANS functions in a little more detail.

Autonomic Functioning

Body organs served by the autonomic nervous system receive fibers from both divisions. Exceptions are most blood vessels and most structures of the skin, some glands, and the adrenal medulla, all of

TABLE 7.3	Effects of the Sympathetic and Parasympathetic Divisions of the Autonomic Nervous System	
Target organ/system	**Parasympathetic effects**	**Sympathetic effects**
Digestive system	Increases smooth muscle mobility (peristalsis) and amount of secretion by digestive system glands; relaxes sphincters	Decreases activity of digestive system and constricts digestive system sphincters (for example, anal sphincter)
Liver	No effect	Causes glucose to be released to blood
Lungs	Constricts bronchioles	Dilates bronchioles
Urinary bladder/urethra	Relaxes sphincters (allows voiding)	Constricts sphincters (prevents voiding)
Kidneys	No effect	Decreases urine output
Heart	Decreases rate; slows and steadies	Increases rate and force of heartbeat
Blood vessels	No effect on most blood vessels	Constricts blood vessels in viscera and skin (dilates those in skeletal muscle and heart); increases blood pressure
Glands—salivary, lacrimal, gastric	Stimulates; increases production of saliva, tears, and gastric juice	Inhibits; result is dry mouth and dry eyes
Eye (iris)	Stimulates constrictor muscles; constricts pupils	Stimulates dilator muscles; dilates pupils
Eye (ciliary muscle)	Stimulates to increase bulging of lens for close vision	Inhibits; decreases bulging of lens; prepares for distant vision
Adrenal medulla	No effect	Stimulates medulla cells to secrete epinephrine and norepinephrine
Sweat glands of skin	No effect	Stimulates to produce perspiration
Arrector pili muscles attached to hair follicles	No effect	Stimulates; produces "goose bumps"
Penis	Causes erection due to vasodilation	Causes ejaculation (emission of semen)
Cellular metabolism	No effect	Increases metabolic rate; increases blood sugar levels; stimulates fat breakdown
Adipose tissue	No effect	Stimulates fat breakdown

which receive only sympathetic fibers (Table 7.3). When both divisions serve the same organ, they cause antagonistic effects, mainly because their postganglionic axons release different neurotransmitters (see Figure 7.27). The parasympathetic fibers, called *cholinergic* (ko"lin-er'jik) *fibers,* release acetylcholine. The sympathetic postganglionic fibers, called *adrenergic* (ad"ren-er'jik) *fibers,* release norepinephrine (nor"ep-ĭ-nef'rin). The preganglionic axons of *both* divisions release acetylcholine. To emphasize the *relative* roles of the two arms of the ANS, we will focus briefly on situations in which each division is "in control."

Sympathetic Division The **sympathetic division** is often referred to as the "fight-or-flight" system. Its activity is evident when we are excited or find ourselves in emergency or threatening situations, such as being frightened by street toughs late at night. A pounding heart; rapid, deep breathing; cold, sweaty skin; a prickly scalp; and dilated eye pupils are sure signs of sympathetic nervous system activity. Under such conditions, the sympathetic nervous system increases heart rate, blood pressure, and blood glucose levels; dilates the bronchioles of the lungs; and brings about many other effects that help the individual cope with the stressor. Other examples are dilation of blood vessels in skeletal muscles (so that one can run faster or fight better) and withdrawal of blood from the digestive organs (so that the bulk of the blood can be used to serve the heart, brain, and skeletal muscles).

The sympathetic nervous system is working at full speed not only when you are emotionally upset but also when you are physically stressed. For example, if you have just had surgery or run a marathon, your adrenal glands (activated by the sympathetic nervous system) will be pumping out epinephrine and norepinephrine (see Figure 7.27). The effects of sympathetic nervous system activation continue for several minutes until its hormones are destroyed by the liver. Thus, although sympathetic nerve impulses themselves may act only briefly, the hormonal effects they provoke linger. The widespread and prolonged effects of sympathetic activation help explain why we need time to "come down" after an extremely stressful situation.

The sympathetic division generates a head of steam that enables the body to cope rapidly and vigorously with situations that threaten homeostasis. Its function is to provide the best conditions for responding to some threat, whether the best response is to run, to see better, or to think more clearly.

HOMEOSTATIC IMBALANCE

Some illnesses or diseases are at least aggravated, if not caused, by excessive sympathetic nervous system stimulation. Certain individuals, called type A people, always work at breakneck speed and push themselves continually. These are people who are likely to have heart disease, high blood pressure, and ulcers, all of which may result from prolonged sympathetic nervous system activity or the rebound from it. ▲

Parasympathetic Division The **parasympathetic division** is most active when the body is at rest and not threatened in any way. This division, sometimes called the "resting-and-digesting" system, is chiefly concerned with promoting normal digestion, with elimination of feces and urine, and with conserving body energy, particularly by decreasing demands on the cardiovascular system. Its activity is best illustrated by a person who relaxes after a meal and reads the newspaper. Blood pressure and heart and respiratory rates are being regulated at low normal levels, the digestive tract is actively digesting food, and the skin is warm (indicating that there is no need to divert blood to skeletal muscles or vital organs). The eye pupils are constricted to protect the retinas from excessive damaging light, and the lenses of the eyes are "set" for close vision. We might also consider the parasympathetic division as the "housekeeping" system of the body.

An easy way to remember the most important roles of the two ANS divisions is to think of the parasympathetic division as the **D** (digestion, defecation, and diuresis [urination]) division and the sympathetic division as the **E** (exercise, excitement, emergency, and embarrassment) division. Remember, however, while it is easiest to think of the sympathetic and parasympathetic divisions as working in an all-or-none fashion, this is rarely the case. A dynamic balance exists between the two divisions, and both are continuously making fine adjustments. Also, although we have described the parasympathetic division as the "at-rest" system, most blood vessels are controlled only by the sympathetic fibers regardless of whether the body is "on alert" or relaxing.

A summary of the major effects of each division appears in Table 7.3.

▶ DID YOU GET IT?

28. Which regions or organs of the body are served by the autonomic nervous system? Which are served by the somatic nervous system?

29. How does the motor pathway of the autonomic nervous system differ from that of the somatic nervous system?

30. Which division of the autonomic nervous system is the "fight-or-flight" system?

For answers, see Appendix D.

A CLOSER LOOK

TRACKING DOWN CNS PROBLEMS

Anyone who has had a routine physical examination is familiar with the reflex tests done to assess neural function. The doctor taps your patellar tendon with a reflex hammer. Your thigh muscles contract, resulting in the knee-jerk response. This response shows that the spinal cord and upper brain centers are functioning normally. When reflex tests are abnormal or when brain cancer, intracranial hemorrhage, multiple sclerosis, or hydrocephalus are suspected, more sophisticated neurological tests may be ordered to try to localize and identify the problem.

An "oldie-but-goodie" procedure used to diagnose and localize many different types of brain lesions (such as epileptic lesions, tumors, and abscesses) is *electroencephalography* (e-lek"tro-en-sef-ah-lah'grah-fe). Normal brain function involves the continuous transmission of electrical impulses by neurons. A recording of their activity, called an **electroencephalogram,** or **EEG,** can be made by placing electrodes at various points on the scalp and connecting these to a recording device (see the figure). The patterns of electrical activity of the neurons are called *brain waves*. Because people differ genetically, and because everything we have ever experienced has left its imprint in our brain, each of us has a brain wave pattern that is as unique as our fingerprints. The four most commonly seen brain waves are illustrated and described in Figure b.

As might be expected, brain-wave patterns typical of the alert wide-awake state differ from those that occur during relaxation or deep sleep. Interference with the function of the cerebral cortex is suggested by brain waves that are too fast or too slow, and unconsciousness occurs at both extremes. Sleep and coma result in brain-wave patterns that are slower than normal, whereas fright, epileptic

> ❝ *Each of us has a brain wave pattern as unique as our fingerprints.* ❞

seizures, and some kinds of drug overdose cause abnormally fast brain waves. Because brain waves are seen even during coma, absence of brain waves (a flat EEG) is taken as evidence of clinical death.

The new imaging techniques described in Chapter 1 (pp. 8–9) have revolutionized the diagnosis of brain lesions. Together, **CT** and **MRI scans** allow most tumors, intracranial lesions, multiple sclerosis plaques, and areas of dead brain tissue (*infarcts*) to be identified quickly. **PET scans** can localize lesions that generate epileptic seizures and are also being used to diagnose Alzheimer's disease.

Take, for example, a patient arriving in emergency with a stroke. A race against time to save the affected area of the patient's brain begins. The first step is to determine whether the stroke is due to a clot or a bleed by imaging the brain, most often with CT. If the stroke is due to a clot, then the clot-busting drug tPA can be used, but only within the first hours. The drug tPA is usually given intravenously, but a longer time window can be obtained if tPA is applied directly to the clot using a catheter guided into position. To visualize the location of the catheter with respect to the clot, dye is injected to make arteries stand out in an X-ray image, a procedure called **cerebral angiography.**

Cerebral angiography is also used for patients who have had a warning stroke, or TIA. The carotid arteries of the neck feed most of the cerebral vessels and often become narrowed with age, which can lead to strokes. Cheaper and less invasive than angiography, ultrasound can be used to quickly examine the carotid arteries and even measure the flow of blood through them.

A CLOSER LOOK   Tracking Down CNS Problems *(continued)*

(a)

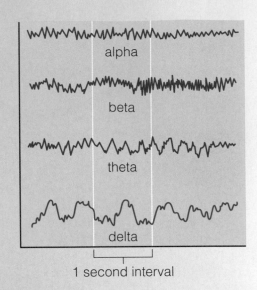

1 second interval

(b)

Electroencephalography and brain waves. (a) To obtain a recording of brain-wave activity (an EEG), electrodes are positioned on the patient's scalp and attached to a recording device called an electroencephalograph. **(b)** Typical EEGs. Alpha waves are typical of the awake, relaxed state; beta waves occur in the awake, alert state; theta waves are common in children but not in normal adults; and delta waves occur during deep sleep.

Developmental Aspects of the Nervous System

Because the nervous system forms during the first month of embryonic development, any maternal infection early in pregnancy can have extremely harmful effects on the fetal nervous system. For example, maternal measles *(rubella)* often causes deafness and other types of CNS damage. Also, because nervous tissue has the highest metabolic rate in the body, lack of oxygen for even a few minutes leads to death of neurons. (Because smoking decreases the amount of oxygen that can be carried in the blood, a smoking mother may be sentencing her infant to possible brain damage.) Radiation and various drugs (alcohol, opiates, cocaine, and others) can also be very damaging if administered during early fetal development.

HOMEOSTATIC IMBALANCE

In difficult deliveries, a temporary lack of oxygen may lead to **cerebral palsy** (pawl′ze), but this is only one of the suspected causes. Cerebral palsy is a neuromuscular disability in which the voluntary muscles are poorly controlled and spastic because of brain damage. About half of its victims have seizures, are mentally retarded, and/or have impaired hearing or vision. Cerebral palsy is the largest single cause of physical disabilities in children. A number of other congenital malformations, triggered by genetic or environmental factors, also plague the CNS. Most serious are hydrocephalus (see p. 251), **anencephaly**—a failure of the cerebrum to develop, resulting in a child who cannot hear, see, or process sensory inputs—and spina bifida. **Spina bifida** (spi′nah bi′fĭ-dah; "forked spine") results when the vertebrae form incompletely (typically in the lumbosacral region). There are several varieties.

In the least serious, a dimple, and perhaps a tuft of hair, appears over the site of malformation, but no neurological problems occur. In the most serious, meninges, nerve roots, and even parts of the spinal cord protrude from the spine, rendering the lower part of the spinal cord functionless. The child is unable to control the bowels or bladder, and the lower limbs are paralyzed. ▲

One of the last areas of the CNS to mature is the hypothalamus, which contains centers for regulating body temperature. For this reason, premature babies usually have problems in controlling their loss of body heat and must be carefully monitored. The nervous system grows and matures all through childhood, largely as a result of myelination that goes on during this period. A good indication of the degree of myelination of particular neural pathways is the level of neuromuscular control in that body area. As described in Chapter 6, neuromuscular coordination progresses in a superior to inferior (craniocaudal) direction and in a proximal to distal direction, and we know that myelination occurs in the same sequence.

The brain reaches its maximum weight in the young adult. Over the next 60 years or so, neurons are damaged and die; and brain weight and volume steadily decline. However, an unlimited number of neural pathways is always available and ready to be developed, allowing us to continue to learn throughout life.

As we grow older, the sympathetic nervous system gradually becomes less and less efficient, particularly in its ability to constrict blood vessels. When older people stand up quickly after sitting or lying down, they often become lightheaded or faint. The reason is that the sympathetic nervous system is not able to react quickly enough to counteract the pull of gravity by activating the vasoconstrictor fibers, and blood pools in the feet. This condition, **orthostatic hypotension,** is a type of low blood pressure resulting from changes in body position as described. Orthostatic hypotension can be prevented to some degree if the person changes position slowly. This gives the sympathetic nervous system a little more time to adjust and react.

The usual cause of nervous system deterioration is circulatory system problems. For example, **arteriosclerosis** (ar-ter″e-o-skle-ro′sis) and high blood pressure result in a decreasing supply of oxygen to the brain neurons. A gradual lack of oxygen due to the aging process finally leads to **senility,** characterized by forgetfulness, irritability, difficulty in concentrating and thinking clearly, and confusion. A sudden loss of blood and oxygen delivery to the brain results in a CVA, as described earlier (p. 252). However, many people continue to enjoy intellectual lives and to work at mentally demanding tasks through their entire life. In fact, fewer than 5 percent of people over the age of 65 demonstrate true senility.

Sadly, many cases of "reversible senility," caused by certain drugs, low blood pressure, constipation, poor nutrition, depression, dehydration, and hormone imbalances, go undiagnosed. The best way to maintain one's mental abilities in old age may be to seek regular medical checkups throughout life.

Although eventual shrinking of the brain is normal, it seems that some individuals (professional boxers and chronic alcoholics, for example) hasten the process long before aging plays its part. Whether a boxer wins the match or not, the likelihood of brain damage and atrophy increases with every blow. The expression "punch drunk" reflects the symptoms of slurred speech, tremors, abnormal gait, and dementia (mental illness) seen in many retired boxers.

Everyone recognizes that alcohol has a profound effect on the mind as well as the body. CT scans of chronic alcoholics reveal reduced brain size at a fairly early age. Like boxers, chronic alcoholics tend to exhibit signs of mental deterioration unrelated to the aging process.

▶ *DID YOU GET IT?*

31. Why must premature babies be placed in incubators until their hypothalamus matures?

32. What is orthostatic hypotension? Why do many older people suffer from this condition?

For answers, see Appendix D.

The human cerebral hemispheres—our "thinking caps"—are awesome in their complexity. No less amazing are the brain regions that oversee all our subconscious, autonomic body functions—the diencephalon and brain stem—particularly when you consider their relatively insignificant size. The spinal cord, which acts as a reflex center, and the peripheral nerves, which provide communication

SYSTEMS IN SYNC

HOMEOSTATIC RELATIONSHIPS BETWEEN THE
NERVOUS SYSTEM AND OTHER BODY SYSTEMS

Nervous System

Endocrine System
- Sympathetic division of the ANS activates the adrenal medulla; hypothalamus helps regulate the activity of the anterior pituitary gland and produces two hormones
- Hormones influence metabolism of neurons

Lymphatic System/Immunity
- Nerves innervate lymphoid organs; the brain plays a role in regulating immune function
- Lymphatic vessels carry away leaked tissue fluids from tissues surrounding nervous system structures; immune elements protect all body organs from pathogens (CNS has additional mechanisms)

Digestive System
- ANS (particularly the parasympathetic division) regulates digestive system activity
- Digestive system provides nutrients needed for health of neurons

Urinary System
- ANS regulates bladder emptying and renal blood pressure
- Kidneys help to dispose of metabolic wastes and maintain proper electrolyte composition and pH of blood for neural functioning

Muscular System
- Somatic division of nervous system activates skeletal muscles; maintains muscle health
- Skeletal muscles are the effectors of the somatic division

Respiratory System
- Nervous system regulates respiratory rhythm and depth
- Respiratory system provides life-sustaining oxygen; disposes of carbon dioxide

Cardiovascular System
- ANS helps regulate heart rate and blood pressure
- Cardiovascular system provides blood containing oxygen and nutrients to the nervous system; carries away wastes

Reproductive System
- ANS regulates sexual erection and ejaculation in males; erection of the clitoris in females
- Testosterone masculinizes the brain and underlies sex drive and aggressive behavior

Integumentary System
- Sympathetic division of the ANS regulates sweat glands and blood vessels of skin (therefore heat loss/retention)
- Skin serves as heat loss surface

Skeletal System
- Nerves innervate bones
- Bones serve as depot for calcium needed for neural function; protect CNS structures

links between the CNS and body periphery, are equally important to body homeostasis.

A good deal of new terminology has been introduced in this chapter and, as you will see, much of it will come up again in later chapters as we study the other organ systems of the body and examine how the nervous system helps to regulate their activity. The terms *are* essential, so try to learn them as you go along. Use the Glossary at the back of the book as often as you find it helpful.

SUMMARY

Media study tools that provide additional review of key topics of Chapter 7 are referenced below.

> **IP** = *InterActive Physiology*
> **WEB** = The A&P Place

Organization of the Nervous System (pp. 229–230)

1. Structural: All nervous system structures are classified as part of the CNS (brain and spinal cord) or PNS (nerves and ganglia).

2. Functional: Motor nerves of the PNS are classified on the basis of whether they stimulate skeletal muscle (somatic division) or smooth/cardiac muscle and glands (autonomic division).

Nervous Tissue: Structure and Function (pp. 230–242)

1. Supportive connective tissue cells

   a. Neuroglia support and protect neurons in the CNS. Specific glial cells are phagocytes; others myelinate neuron processes in the CNS or line cavities.

   b. Schwann cells myelinate neuron processes in the PNS.

   WEB Exercise: Chapter 7, Glial Cells and Their Functions.

2. Neurons

   a. Anatomy: All neurons have a cell body containing the nucleus and processes (fibers) of two types: (1) axons (one per cell) typically generate and conduct impulses away from the cell body and release a neurotransmitter, and (2) dendrites (one to many per cell) typically carry electrical currents toward the cell body. Most large fibers are myelinated; myelin increases the rate of nerve impulse transmission.

   IP Nervous System Topic; Anatomy Review, Synaptic Potentials and Neurotransmitters, pages 3–11.

   b. Classification

      (1) On the basis of function (direction of impulse transmission) there are sensory (afferent) and motor (efferent) neurons and association neurons (interneurons). Dendritic endings of sensory neurons are bare (pain receptors) or are associated with sensory receptors.

      (2) On the basis of structure, there are unipolar, bipolar, and multipolar neurons; the terminology reveals the number of processes extending from the cell body. Motor and association neurons are multipolar; most sensory neurons are unipolar. The exceptions are sensory neurons in certain special sense organs (ear, eye), which are bipolar.

   WEB Exercise: Chapter 7, Classification of Neurons.

   c. Physiology

      (1) A nerve impulse is an electrochemical event (initiated by various stimuli) that causes a change in neuron plasma membrane permeability, allowing sodium ions (Na^+) to enter the cell (depolarization). Once begun, the action potential, or nerve impulse, continues over the entire surface of the cell. Electrical conditions of the resting state are restored by the diffusion of potassium ions (K^+) out of the cell (repolarization). Ion concentrations of the resting state are restored by the sodium-potassium pump.

   IP Nervous System Topic: The Membrane Potential, pages 3–13.

      (2) A neuron influences other neurons or effector cells by releasing neurotransmitters, chemicals that diffuse across the synaptic cleft and attach to membrane receptors on the postsynaptic cell. The result is opening of specific ion channels and activation or inhibition, depending on the neurotransmitter released and the target cell.

      (3) A reflex is a rapid, predictable response to a stimulus. There are two types—autonomic

and somatic. The minimum number of components of a reflex arc is four: receptor, effector, and sensory and motor neurons (most, however, have one or more association neurons). Normal reflexes indicate normal nervous system function.

Central Nervous System (pp. 242–258)

1. The brain is located within the cranial cavity of the skull and consists of the cerebral hemispheres, diencephalon, brain stem structures, and cerebellum.

   WEB Exercise: Chapter 7, Parts of the Brain; The Human Brain: Sagittal Section.

   a. The two cerebral hemispheres form the largest part of the brain. Their surface, or cortex, is gray matter, and their interior is white matter. The cortex is convoluted and has gyri, sulci, and fissures. The cerebral hemispheres are involved in logical reasoning, moral conduct, emotional responses, sensory interpretation, and the initiation of voluntary muscle activity. Several functional areas of the cerebral lobes have been identified (see p. 244). The basal nuclei, regions of gray matter deep within the white matter of the cerebral hemispheres, modify voluntary motor activity. Parkinson's disease and Huntington's disease are disorders of the basal nuclei.

   b. The diencephalon is superior to the brain stem and is enclosed by the cerebral hemispheres. The major structures include the following:

      (1) The thalamus, which encloses the third ventricle, is the relay station for sensory impulses passing to the sensory cortex for interpretation.

      (2) The hypothalamus makes up the "floor" of the third ventricle and is the most important regulatory center of the autonomic nervous system (regulates water balance, metabolism, thirst, temperature, and the like).

      (3) The epithalamus includes the pineal body (an endocrine gland) and the choroid plexus of the third ventricle.

   c. The brain stem is the short region inferior to the hypothalamus that merges with the spinal cord.

      (1) The midbrain is most superior and is primarily fiber tracts.

      (2) The pons is inferior to the midbrain and has fiber tracts and nuclei involved in respiration.

      (3) The medulla oblongata is the most inferior part of the brain stem. In addition to fiber tracts, it contains autonomic nuclei involved in the regulation of vital life activities (breathing, heart rate, blood pressure, etc.).

   d. The cerebellum is a large, cauliflower-like part of the brain posterior to the fourth ventricle. It coordinates muscle activity and body balance.

2. Protection of the CNS

   a. Bones of the skull and vertebral column are the most external protective structures.

   b. Meninges are three connective tissue membranes—dura mater (tough outermost), arachnoid mater (middle weblike), and pia mater (innermost delicate). The meninges extend beyond the end of the spinal cord.

   WEB Exercise: Chapter 7, Meninges of the Brain.

   c. Cerebrospinal fluid (CSF) provides a watery cushion around the brain and cord. CSF is formed by the choroid plexuses of the brain. It is found in the subarachnoid space, ventricles, and central canal. CSF is continually formed and drained.

   d. The blood-brain barrier is composed of relatively impermeable capillaries.

3. Brain dysfunctions

   a. Head trauma may cause concussions (reversible damage) or contusions (nonreversible damage). When the brain stem is affected, unconsciousness (temporary or permanent) occurs. Trauma-induced brain injuries may be aggravated by intracranial hemorrhage or cerebral edema, both of which compress brain tissue.

   b. Cerebrovascular accidents (CVAs, or strokes) result when blood circulation to brain neurons is blocked and brain tissue dies. The result may be visual impairment, paralysis, and aphasias.

   c. Alzheimer's disease is a degenerative brain disease in which abnormal protein deposits and other structural changes appear. It results in slow, progressive loss of memory and motor control plus increasing dementia.

   d. Techniques used to diagnose brain dysfunctions include the EEG, simple reflex tests, pneumoencephalography, angiography, and CT, PET, and MRI scans.

4. The spinal cord is a reflex center and conduction pathway. Found within the vertebral canal, the cord extends from the foramen magnum to L_1 or L_2. The cord has a central bat-shaped area of gray matter surrounded by columns of white matter, which carry motor and sensory tracts from and to the brain.

   WEB Exercise: Chapter 7, Anatomy of the Spinal Cord.

Peripheral Nervous System (pp. 258–270)

1. A nerve is a bundle of neuron processes wrapped in connective tissue coverings (endoneurium, perineurium, and epineurium).

   WEB Exercise: Chapter 7, Structure of a Nerve.

2. Cranial nerves: 12 pairs of nerves that extend from the brain to serve the head and neck region. The exception is the vagus nerves, which extend into the thorax and abdomen.

   WEB Exercise: Chapter 7, Cranial Nerves; Descriptions of Cranial Nerves.

3. Spinal nerves: 31 pairs of nerves are formed by the union of the dorsal and ventral roots of the spinal cord on each side. The spinal nerve proper is very short and splits into dorsal and ventral rami. Dorsal rami serve the posterior body trunk; ventral rami (except T_1 through T_{12}) form plexuses (cervical, brachial, lumbar, sacral) that serve the limbs.

   WEB Exercise: Chapter 7, Distributions of Spinal Nerves.

4. Autonomic nervous system: Part of the PNS, composed of neurons that regulate the activity of smooth and cardiac muscle and glands. This system differs from the somatic nervous system in that there is a chain of two motor neurons from the CNS to the effector. Two subdivisions serve the same organs with different effects.

   a. The parasympathetic division is the "housekeeping" system and is in control most of the time. This division maintains homeostasis by seeing that normal digestion and elimination occur and that energy is conserved. The first motor neurons are in the brain or the sacral region of the cord. The second motor neurons are in the terminal ganglia close to the organ served. All parasympathetic axons secrete acetylcholine.

   b. The sympathetic division is the "fight-or-flight" subdivision, which prepares the body to cope with some threat. Its activation increases heart rate and blood pressure. The preganglionic neurons are in the gray matter of the cord. The parasympathetic neurons are in sympathetic chains or in collateral ganglia. Postganglionic axons secrete norepinephrine.

Developmental Aspects of the Nervous System (pp. 272–275)

1. Maternal and environmental factors may impair embryonic brain development. Oxygen deprivation destroys brain cells. Severe congenital brain diseases include cerebral palsy, anencephaly, hydrocephalus, and spina bifida.

2. Premature babies have trouble regulating body temperature because the hypothalamus is one of the last brain areas to mature prenatally.

3. Development of motor control indicates the progressive myelination and maturation of a child's nervous system. Brain growth ends in young adulthood. Neurons die throughout life and are not replaced; thus, brain mass declines with age.

4. Healthy aged people maintain nearly optimal intellectual function. Disease—particularly cardiovascular disease—is the major cause of declining mental function with age.

REVIEW QUESTIONS

Multiple Choice

More than one choice may apply.

1. An example of integration by the nervous system is
   a. the feel of a cold breeze.
   b. the shivering and goose bumps in response to cold.
   c. perceiving the sound of rain.
   d. the decision to go back for an umbrella.

2. Where might a gray matter nucleus be located?
   a. Alongside the vertebral column
   b. Within the brain
   c. Within the spinal cord
   d. In the sensory receptors

3. The innermost delicate meningeal layer is the
   a. dura mater.
   b. corpus callosum.
   c. arachnoid mater.
   d. pia mater.

4. Histological examination of a slice of neural tissue reveals a bundle of nerve fibers held together by cells whose multiple processes wrap around several fibers and form a myelin sheath. The specimen is likely to be
   a. a nucleus.   c. a nerve.
   b. a ganglion.   d. a tract.

5. The pineal gland is located in the
   a. hypothalamus.   c. epithalamus
   b. mesencephalon. d. corpus callosum

6. Choose the proper term to respond to the statements describing various brain areas.

   a. cerebellum
   b. corpora quadrigemina
   c. corpus callosum
   d. corpus striatum
   e. hypothalamus
   f. medulla
   g. midbrain
   h. pons
   i. thalamus

   ____ 1. Basal nuclei involved in fine control of motor activities

   ____ 2. Region where there is a gross crossover of fibers of descending pyramidal tracts

   ____ 3. Control of temperature, autonomic nervous system relfexes, hunger, and water balance

   ____ 4. Houses the substantia nigra and cerebral aqueduct

   ____ 5. Relay stations for visual and auditory stimuli input; found in midbrain

   ____ 6. Houses vital centers for control of the heart, respiration, and blood pressure

   ____ 7. Brain area through which all the sensory input is relayed to get to the cerebral cortex

   ____ 8. Brain area most concerned with equilibrium, body posture, and coordination of motor activity.

7. The spinal cord feature associated with the leash of nerves supplying the upper limbs is the

   a. brachial plexus.
   b. brachial enlargement.
   c. cervical enlargement.
   d. lateral gray horns.

8. Which contains only motor fibers?

   a. Dorsal root
   b. Dorsal ramus
   c. Ventral root
   d. Ventral ramus

9. Cranial nerves that have some function in vision include the

   a. trochlear.
   b. trigeminal.
   c. abducens.
   d. facial.

10. Motor functions of the extensor muscles of the arm, forearm, and fingers would be affected by damage to which one of these nerves?

   a. Radial
   b. Axillary
   c. Ulnar
   d. Median

11. Glial cells present in large numbers in areas of bacterial infection in the brain are most likely

   a. oligodendrocytes.
   b. astrocytes.
   c. ependymal cells.
   d. microglia.

12. Which of the following is true of the autonomic, but not the somatic, nervous system?

   a. Neurotransmitter is acetylcholine.
   b. Axons are myelinated.
   c. Effectors are muscle cells.
   d. Has motor neurons located in ganglia.

Short Answer Essay

13. What are the two great controlling systems of the body?

14. Explain both the structural and functional classifications of the nervous system. In your explanation, include the subdivisions of each.

15. What is the basis for the functional classification of neurons?

16. Two major cell groups make up the nervous system—neurons and connective tissue cells such as astrocytes and Schwann cells. Which are "nervous" cells? Why? What are the major functions of the other cell group?

17. Briefly explain how nerve impulses are initiated and transmitted, and why conduction at synapses is always one-way.

18. Name four types of cutaneous sensory receptors. Which of the cutaneous receptor types is most numerous? Why?

19. Name the minimum components of a reflex arc.

20. Make a rough drawing of the left cerebral hemisphere. On your drawing, locate at least five different functional areas, and then indicate their specific functions.

21. Other than serving as a conduction pathway, what is a major function of the pons? Why is the medulla the most vital part of the brain?

22. What is the function of the thalamus? The hypothalamus?

23. Discuss how the brain is protected by bone, membranes, fluid, and capillaries.

24. What is gray matter? White matter? How does the arrangement of gray and white matter differ in the cerebral hemispheres and the spinal cord?

25. What are two functions of the spinal cord?

26. How many pairs of cranial nerves are there? Which are purely sensory? Which activates the chewing muscles? Which helps regulate heart rate and activity of the digestive tract?

27. Except for the vagus nerves, what general area of the body do the cranial nerves serve?

28. How many pairs of spinal nerves are there? How do they arise?

29. What region of the body is served by the dorsal rami of the spinal nerves? the ventral rami?

30. Name the four major nerve plexuses formed by the ventral rami and the body region served by each.

31. How does the autonomic nervous system differ from the somatic nervous system?

32. What is the difference in function of the sympathetic and parasympathetic divisions of the autonomic nervous system **(a)** in general and **(b)** as specifically relates to the operation of the cardiovascular and digestive systems?

33. The sympathetic and parasympathetic fibers serve the same organs. How can their opposing effects be explained?

34. How does a Schwann cell help insulate a nerve fiber?

35. Compare CVAs and TIAs in terms of causes, symptoms, and consequences.

36. Define *senility*. Name possible causes of permanent and reversible senility.

CRITICAL THINKING AND CLINICAL APPLICATION QUESTIONS

37. Mrs. Jones has had a progressive decline in her mental capabilities in the past five or six years. At first, her family attributed her occasional memory lapses, confusion, and agitation to grief over her husband's death six years earlier. When examined, Mrs. Jones was aware of her cognitive problems and was shown to have an IQ score approximately 30 points lower than would be predicted by her work history. A CT scan showed diffuse cerebral atrophy. The physician prescribed a mild tranquilizer for Mrs. Jones and told her family that there was little else he could recommend. What is Mrs. Jones's problem?

38. Joseph, a man in his early 70s, was having problems chewing his food. He was asked to stick out his tongue. It deviated to the right, and its right side was quite wasted. What cranial nerve was impaired?

39. Jed, a couch potato, likes to eat a very large meal in the evening. After the meal, his wife asks him to help clean the dishes, but Jed explains that he is "too tired" and promptly goes to sleep. What seems to be his problem?

40. A semiconscious young woman is brought to the hospital by friends after falling from a roof. She did not lose consciousness immediately, and she was initially lucid. After a while, though, she became confused and then unresponsive. What is a likely explanation of her condition?

41. In John's checkup, one year after an accident severed his right accessory nerve, severe muscle atrophy was noted. What two prominent muscles have been affected?

42. Mrs. Tonegawa, a new mother, brings her infant to the clinic because he has suffered repeated seizures. When questioned, she states that her labor was unusually long and difficult. What condition do you suspect? Will the infant's condition worsen?

43. Three-year-old Samantha is sobbing that her right arm is "gone," and the examination shows her to have little muscle strength in that limb. Questioning the parents reveals that her father had been swinging her by the arms. What part of the PNS has been damaged?

44. Mr. Dingledine is an 82-year-old bedridden gentleman who has discovered a new interest in learning about his body. While being tended by the visiting nurse, he remarks that the supporting cells in nervous tissue (such as Schwann cells and oligodendrocytes) act like the rubber coating around household wiring. What does he mean by this analogy?

45. Jemal, an elderly man with a history of TIAs, complained to his daughter that he had a severe headache. Shortly thereafter, he lapsed into a coma. At the hospital, he was diagnosed as having a brain hemorrhage. Which part of the brain was damaged by the hemorrhage?

46. Why does exposure to toxins have more devastating neural effects during early pregnancy than in late pregnancy?

47. Clancy is the star of his hometown ice hockey team. During a game, he is walloped on his backside with a hockey stick so hard that he hits the ice. When he tries to get up he is unable to flex his left hip or extend his left knee, but he has no pain. Which nerve has been damaged?

48. Jerry got hit in the back of the neck with a baseball, and now he can't shrug one shoulder. What cranial nerve is involved?

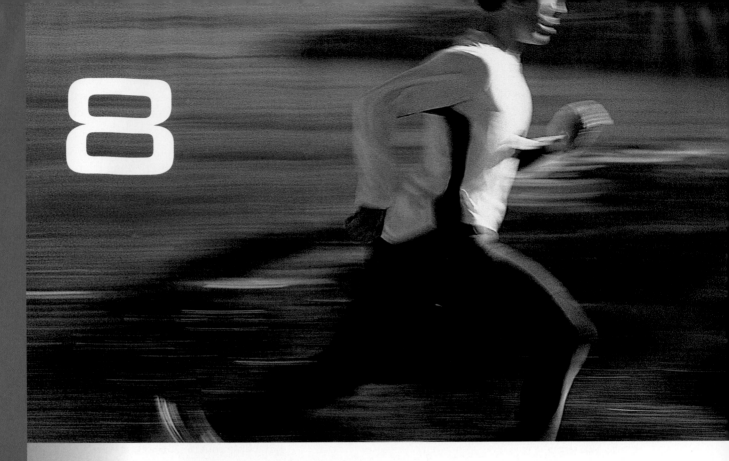

Special Senses

YOUR GOALS

After completing this chapter, you will have a working knowledge of the functions of special senses and will have mastered the objectives listed below.

FUNCTION PREVIEW

• The special senses respond to different types of energetic stimuli involved in vision, hearing, balance, smell, and taste.

OBJECTIVE CHECKLIST

PART I: THE EYE AND VISION   (pp. 281–294)

➤ When provided with a model or diagram, identify the accessory eye structures, and list the functions of each.

➤ Name the layers of the wall of the eye, and indicate the major function of each.

➤ Explain how the functions of rods and cones differ.

➤ Describe image formation on the retina.

➤ Trace the pathway of light through the eye to the retina.

➤ Discuss the importance of an ophthalmoscopic examination.

➤ Define the following terms: *accommodation, astigmatism, blind spot, cataract, emmetropia, glaucoma, hyperopia, myopia,* and *refraction.*

- Trace the visual pathway to the optic cortex.
- Discuss the importance of the pupillary and convergence reflexes.

PART II: THE EAR: HEARING AND BALANCE (pp. 294–300)

- Identify the structures of the external, middle, and internal ear, and list the functions of each.
- Describe how the equilibrium organs help maintain balance.
- Explain the function of the organ of Corti in hearing.
- Define *sensorineural* and *conductive deafness,* and list possible causes of each.
- Explain how one is able to localize the source of a sound.

PART III: CHEMICAL SENSES: TASTE AND SMELL (pp. 301–303)

- Describe the location, structure, and function of the olfactory and taste receptors.
- Name the four basic taste sensations and list factors that modify the sense of taste.

PART IV: DEVELOPMENTAL ASPECTS OF THE SPECIAL SENSES (pp. 303–305)

- Describe changes that occur with age in the special sense organs.

People are responsive creatures. Hold freshly baked bread before us, and our mouths water. A sudden clap of thunder makes us jump. These "irritants" (the bread and the thunderclap) and many others are the stimuli that continually greet us and are interpreted by our nervous system.

We are usually told that we have five senses that keep us in touch with what is going on in the external world: touch, taste, smell, sight, and hearing. Actually touch is a mixture of the general senses that we considered in Chapter 7—the temperature, pressure, and pain receptors of the skin and the proprioceptors of muscles and joints. The other four "traditional" senses—*smell, taste, sight,* and *hearing*—are called **special senses.** Receptors for a fifth special sense, *equilibrium,* are housed in the ear, along with the organ of hearing. In contrast to the small and widely distributed general receptors, the **special sense receptors** are either large, complex sensory organs (eyes and ears) or localized clusters of receptors (taste buds and olfactory epithelium).

This chapter focuses on the functional anatomy of each of the special sense organs individually, but keep in mind that sensory inputs are overlapping. What we finally experience—our "feel" of the world—is a blending of stimulus effects.

PART I: THE EYE AND VISION

How we see has captured the curiosity of many researchers. Vision is the sense that has been studied most. Of all the sensory receptors in the body, 70 percent are in the eyes. The optic tracts that carry information from the eyes to the brain are massive bundles, containing over a million nerve fibers. Vision is the sense that requires the most "learning," and the eye appears to delight in being fooled. The old expression "You see what you expect to see" is often very true.

Anatomy of the Eye
External and Accessory Structures

The adult eye is a sphere that measures about 1 inch (2.5 cm) in diameter. Only the anterior one-sixth of the eye's surface can normally be seen. The rest of it is enclosed and protected by a cushion of fat and the walls of the bony orbit. The **accessory structures** of the eye include the extrinsic eye muscles, eyelids, conjunctiva, and lacrimal apparatus.

Anteriorly the eyes are protected by the **eyelids,** which meet at the medial and lateral corners of the eye, the **medial** and **lateral commissure**

FIGURE 8.1 **Surface anatomy of the eye and accessory structures.**

(canthus), respectively (Figure 8.1). The space between the eyelids in an open eye is called the *palpebral fissure.* Projecting from the border of each eyelid are the **eyelashes.** Modified sebaceous glands associated with the eyelid edges are the **tarsal glands.** These glands produce an oily secretion that lubricates the eye (Figure 8.2a). *Ciliary glands,* modified sweat glands, lie between the eyelashes (*cilium* = eyelash).

A delicate membrane, the **conjunctiva** (kon-junk"ti'vah), lines the eyelids and covers part of the outer surface of the eyeball (Figures 8.1 and 8.2). It ends at the edge of the cornea by fusing with the corneal epithelium. The conjunctiva secretes mucus, which helps to lubricate the eyeball and keep it moist.

HOMEOSTATIC IMBALANCE

Inflammation of the conjunctiva, called **conjunctivitis,** results in reddened, irritated eyes. **Pinkeye,** its infectious form caused by bacteria or viruses, is highly contagious. ▲

The **lacrimal apparatus** (Figure 8.2b) consists of the lacrimal gland and a number of ducts that drain the lacrimal secretions into the nasal cavity. The **lacrimal glands** are located above the lateral end of each eye. They continually release a dilute salt solution *(tears)* onto the anterior surface of the eyeball through several small ducts. The tears flush across the eyeball into the **lacrimal canaliculi** medially, then into the **lacrimal sac,** and finally into

the **nasolacrimal duct,** which empties into the nasal cavity (see Figure 8.2b). Lacrimal secretion also contains antibodies and **lysozyme** (li'so-zīm), an enzyme that destroys bacteria. Thus, it cleanses and protects the eye surface as it moistens and lubricates it. When lacrimal secretion increases substantially, tears spill over the eyelids and fill the nasal cavities, causing congestion and the "sniffles." This happens when the eyes are irritated by foreign objects or chemicals and when we are emotionally upset. In the case of irritation, the enhanced tearing acts to wash away or dilute the irritating substance. The importance of "emotional tears" is poorly understood, but some suspect that crying is important in reducing stress. Anyone who has had a good cry would probably agree, but this has been difficult to prove scientifically.

HOMEOSTATIC IMBALANCE

Because the nasal cavity mucosa is continuous with that of the lacrimal duct system, a cold or nasal inflammation often causes the lacrimal mucosa to become inflamed and swell. This impairs the drainage of tears from the eye surface, causing "watery" eyes. ▲

Six **extrinsic,** or **external, eye muscles** are attached to the outer surface of each eye. These muscles produce gross eye movements and make it possible for the eyes to follow a moving object. The names, locations, actions, and cranial nerve serving each of the extrinsic muscles are given in Figure 8.3.

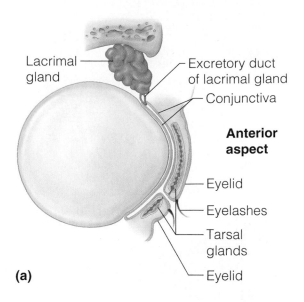

Anterior aspect

- Lacrimal gland
- Excretory duct of lacrimal gland
- Conjunctiva
- Eyelid
- Eyelashes
- Tarsal glands
- Eyelid

(a)

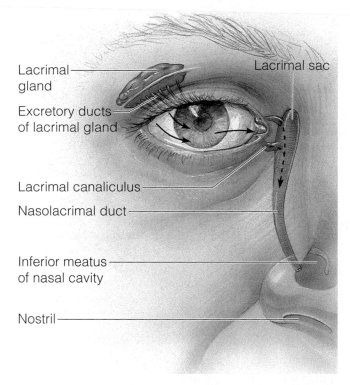

- Lacrimal gland
- Excretory ducts of lacrimal gland
- Lacrimal sac
- Lacrimal canaliculus
- Nasolacrimal duct
- Inferior meatus of nasal cavity
- Nostril

(b)

FIGURE 8.2 Accessory structures of the eye. (a) Sagittal section of the accessory structures associated with the anterior part of the eye. **(b)** Anterior view of the lacrimal apparatus.

Internal Structures: The Eyeball

The eye itself, commonly called the **eyeball,** is a hollow sphere (Figure 8.4). Its wall is composed of three *layers,* and its interior is filled with fluids called *humors* that help to maintain its shape. The lens, the main focusing apparatus of the eye, is supported upright within the eye cavity, dividing it into two chambers.

Layers Forming the Wall of the Eyeball

Now that we have covered the general anatomy of the eyeball, we are ready to get specific.

Fibrous Layer The outermost layer, called the **fibrous layer,** consists of the protective **sclera** (skle'rah) and the transparent **cornea** (kor'ne-ah). The sclera, thick, glistening white connective tissue, is seen anteriorly as the "white of the eye." The central anterior portion of the fibrous layer is crystal clear. This "window" is the cornea through which light enters the eye. The cornea is well supplied with nerve endings. Most are pain fibers, and when the cornea is touched, blinking and increased tearing occur. Even so, the cornea is the most exposed part of the eye, and it is very vulnerable to damage. Luckily, its ability to repair itself is extraordinary. Furthermore, the cornea is the only tissue in the body that can be transplanted from one person to another without the worry of rejection. Because it has no blood vessels, it is beyond the reach of the immune system.

Vascular Layer The middle layer of the eyeball, the **vascular layer,** has three distinguishable regions. Most posterior is the **choroid** (ko'roid), a blood-rich nutritive tunic that contains a dark pigment. The pigment prevents light from scattering inside the eye. Moving anteriorly, the choroid is modified to form two smooth muscle structures, the **ciliary** (sil'e-er-e) **body,** to which the lens is attached by a suspensory ligament called the **ciliary zonule,** and then the **iris.** The pigmented

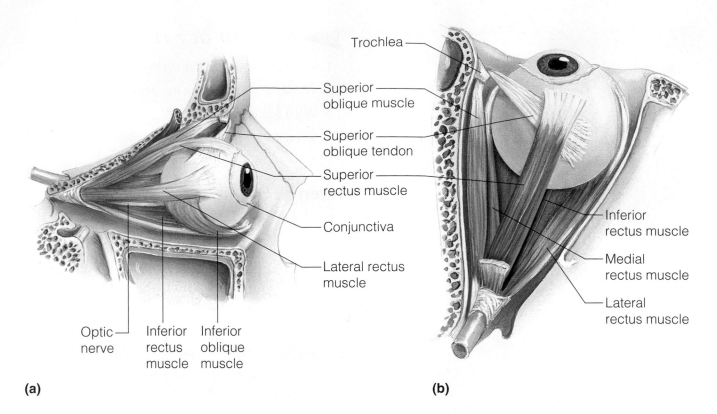

(a)

(b)

Name	Action	Controlling cranial nerve
Lateral rectus	Moves eye laterally	VI (abducens)
Medial rectus	Moves eye medially	III (oculomotor)
Superior rectus	Elevates eye and turns it medially	III (oculomotor)
Inferior rectus	Depresses eye and turns it medially	III (oculomotor)
Inferior oblique	Elevates eye and turns it laterally	III (oculomotor)
Superior oblique	Depresses eye and turns it laterally	IV (trochlear)

(c)

FIGURE 8.3
Extrinsic muscles of the eye. (a) Lateral view of the right eye. **(b)** Superior view of the right eye. The four rectus muscles originate from the anular ring, a ringlike tendon at the back of the eye socket. **(c)** Summary of cranial nerve supply and actions of the extrinsic eye muscles.

iris has a rounded opening, the **pupil,** through which light passes. Circularly and radially arranged smooth muscle fibers form the iris, which acts like the diaphragm of a camera. That is, it regulates the amount of light entering the eye so that one can see as clearly as possible in the available light. In close vision and bright light, the circular muscles contract, and the pupil constricts. In distant vision and dim light, the radial fibers contract to enlarge (dilate) the pupil, which allows more light to enter the eye.

Sensory Layer The innermost **sensory layer** of the eye is the delicate two-layered **retina** (ret'ĭ-

nah), which extends anteriorly only to the ciliary body. The outer **pigmented layer** of the retina is composed of pigmented cells that, like those of the choroid, absorb light and prevent light from scattering inside the eye. Additionally, these cells act as phagocytes to remove dead or damaged receptor cells and to store vitamin A needed for vision.

The transparent inner **neural layer** of the retina contains millions of receptor cells, the **rods** and **cones,** which are called **photoreceptors** because they respond to light (Figure 8.5). Electrical signals pass from the photoreceptors via a two-neuron chain—**bipolar cells** and then **ganglion cells**—

Which layer of the eye would be the first to be affected by deficient tear production?

Ciliary body

Ciliary zonule

Cornea

Iris

Pupil

Aqueous humor (in anterior segment)

Lens

Scleral venous sinus (canal of Schlemm)

Vitreous humor (in posterior segment)

Sclera

Choroid

Retina

Fovea centralis

Optic nerve

Central artery and vein of the retina

Optic disc (blind spot)

(a)

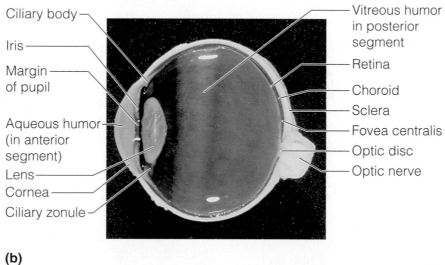

Ciliary body

Iris

Margin of pupil

Aqueous humor (in anterior segment)

Lens

Cornea

Ciliary zonule

Vitreous humor in posterior segment

Retina

Choroid

Sclera

Fovea centralis

Optic disc

Optic nerve

(b)

FIGURE 8.4 Internal anatomy of the eye (sagittal section).
(a) Diagrammatic view. **(b)** Photograph.

The outermost sclera (mostly its cornea), which is normally continuously washed by tears.

Pigmented layer of retina

Rod

Cone

Bipolar cells

Ganglion cells

Pathway of light

(a)

Pigmented layer of retina

Neural layer of retina

Central artery and vein of retina

Optic disc

Sclera

Optic nerve

Choroid

(b)

FIGURE 8.5 The three major types of neurons composing the retina. (a) Notice that light must pass through the thickness of the retina to excite the rods and cones. Electrical signals flow in the opposite direction: from the rods and cones to the bipolar cells and finally to the ganglion cells. The ganglion cells generate the nerve impulses that leave the eye via the optic nerve. **(b)** Schematic view of the posterior part of the eyeball illustrating how the axons of the ganglion cells form the optic nerve.

(composed of ganglion cell axons) leaves the eyeball; this site is called the **optic disc,** or **blind spot.** When light from an object is focused on the optic disc, the object disappears from our view and we cannot see it.

The rods and cones are not evenly distributed in the retina. The rods are most dense at the periphery, or edge, of the retina and decrease in number as the center of the retina is approached. The rods allow us to see in gray tones in dim light, and they provide for our peripheral vision.

HOMEOSTATIC IMBALANCE

Anything that interferes with rod function hinders our ability to see at night, a condition called **night blindness.** Night blindness dangerously impairs the ability to drive safely at night. Its most common cause is prolonged vitamin A deficiency, which eventually results in deterioration of much of the neural retina. As described in the "A Closer Look" box on pages 287–288, vitamin A is one of the building blocks of the pigments the photoreceptor cells need to respond to light. Vitamin A supplements will restore function if taken before degenerative changes occur. ▲

Cones are discriminatory receptors that allow us to see the details of our world in color under bright light conditions. They are densest in the center of the retina and decrease in number toward the retinal edge. Lateral to each blind spot is the **fovea centralis** (fo've-ah sen-tra'lis), a tiny pit that contains only cones (see Figure 8.4). Consequently, this is the area of greatest **visual acuity,** or point of sharpest vision, and anything we wish to view critically is focused on the fovea centralis.

There are three varieties of cones. Each type is most sensitive to particular wavelengths of visible light (Figure 8.6). One type responds most vigorously

before leaving the retina via the **optic nerve** as nerve impulses that are transmitted to the optic cortex. The result is vision.

The photoreceptor cells are distributed over the entire retina, except where the **optic nerve**

VISUAL PIGMENTS—THE ACTUAL PHOTORECEPTORS

Light

Light

Light

Process of bipolar cell

Rod cell body

Inner fibers

Synaptic endings

Rod cell body

Cone cell body

Nuclei

Outer fiber

Mitochondria

Inner segment

Discs containing visual pigments

Pigmented layer

Outer segment

Pigment cell nucleus

Melanin granules

The tiny photoreceptor cells of the retina have names that reflect their general shapes. As shown to the left, rods are slender, elongated neurons, whereas the fatter cones taper to pointed tips. In each type of photoreceptor, there is a region called an *outer segment*, attached to the cell body. The outer segment corresponds to a light-trapping dendrite, in which the discs containing the visual pigments are stacked like a row of pennies.

The behavior of the visual pigments is dramatic. When light strikes them, they lose their color, or are "bleached"; shortly afterward, they regenerate their pigment. Absorption of light and pigment bleaching cause electrical changes in the photoreceptor cells that ultimately cause nerve impulses to be transmitted to the brain for visual interpretation. Pigment regeneration ensures that one is not blinded and unable to see in bright sunlight.

A good deal is known about the structure and function of **rhodopsin,** the purple pigment found in rods (see figure below). It is formed from the union of a protein **(opsin)** and a modified vitamin A product **(retinal).** When combined in rhodopsin, retinal has a kinked shape that allows it to bind

> ## *Behavior of the visual pigments is dramatic.*

to opsin. But when light strikes rhodopsin, retinal straightens out and releases the protein. Once straightened out, the retinal continues its conversion until it is once again vitamin A.

Retinal (visual yellow)

Light absorption causes

Releases

Rhodopsin (visual purple)

Opsin

A CLOSER LOOK Visual Pigments—The Actual Photoreceptors *(continued)*

As these changes occur, the purple color of rhodopsin changes to the yellow of retinal and finally becomes colorless as the change to vitamin A occurs. Thus the term "bleaching of the pigment" accurately describes the color changes that occur when light hits the pigment. Rhodopsin is regenerated as vitamin A is again converted to the kinked form of retinal and recombined with opsin in an ATP-requiring process. The cone pigments, although similar to rhodopsin, differ in the specific kinds of proteins they contain.

FIGURE 8.6 **Sensitivities of the three cone types to the different wavelengths of visible light.**

to blue light, another to green light. The third cone variety responds to a range including both green and red wavelengths of light. However, this is the only cone population to respond to red light at all, so these are called the "red cones." Impulses received at the same time from more than one type of cone by the visual cortex are interpreted as *intermediate* colors. For example, simultaneous impulses from blue and red color receptors are seen as purple or violet tones. When all three cone types are being stimulated, we see white. If someone shines red light into one of your eyes and green into the other, you will see yellow, indicating that the "mixing" and interpretation of colors occurs in the brain, not in the retina.

HOMEOSTATIC IMBALANCE

Lack of all three cone types results in total **color blindness,** whereas lack of one cone type leads to partial color blindness. Most common is the lack of red or green receptors, which leads to two varieties of red-green color blindness. Red and green are seen as the same color—either red or green, depending on the cone type *present.* Many color-blind people are unaware of their condition because they have learned to rely on other cues—such as differences in intensities of the same color—to distinguish something green from something red, for example on traffic signals. Because the genes regulating color vision are on the X (female) sex chromosome, color blindness is a sex-linked condition. It occurs almost exclusively in males. ▲

Lens

Light entering the eye is focused on the retina by the lens, a flexible biconvex crystal-like structure. The lens is held upright in the eye by a suspensory ligament, the ciliary zonule, attached to the ciliary body (see Figure 8.4).

HOMEOSTATIC IMBALANCE

In youth, the lens is perfectly transparent and has the consistency of hardened jelly, but as we age it becomes increasingly hard and opaque.

Cataracts, which result from this process, cause vision to become hazy and distorted, and they eventually cause blindness in the affected eye (Figure 8.7). Other risk factors for forming cataracts include diabetes mellitus, frequent exposure to intense sunlight, and heavy smoking. Current treatment of cataracts is either surgical removal of the lens and replacement with a lens implant or special cataract glasses. ▲

The lens divides the eye into two segments, or chambers. The *anterior (aqueous) segment,* anterior to the lens, contains a clear watery fluid called **aqueous humor.** The *posterior (vitreous) segment,* posterior to the lens, is filled with a gel-like substance called either **vitreous** (vit′re-us) **humor** or the **vitreous body** (see Figure 8.4). Vitreous humor helps prevent the eyeball from collapsing inward by reinforcing it internally. Aqueous humor is similar to blood plasma and is continually secreted by a special area of the choroid. Like the vitreous humor, it helps maintain *intraocular* (in″trah-ok′u-lar) *pressure,* or the pressure inside the eye. It also provides nutrients for the lens and cornea, which lack a blood supply. Aqueous humor is reabsorbed into the venous blood through the **scleral venous sinus,** or **canal of Schlemm** (shlĕm), which is located at the junction of the sclera and cornea.

HOMEOSTATIC IMBALANCE

If drainage of aqueous humor is blocked, fluid backs up like a clogged sink. Pressure within the eye may increase to dangerous levels and compress the delicate retina and optic nerve. The resulting condition, **glaucoma** (glaw-ko′mah; "vision going gray"), eventually causes pain and possibly blindness unless detected early. Glaucoma is a common cause of blindness in the elderly. Unfortunately, many forms of glaucoma progress slowly and have almost no symptoms at first. Thus, it steals sight slowly and painlessly until the damage is done. Later signs include seeing halos around lights, headaches, and blurred vision. A simple instrument called a *tonometer* (to-nom′e-ter) is used to measure the intraocular pressure. This examination should be performed yearly in people over 40. Glaucoma is commonly treated with eyedrops that increase the rate of aqueous humor drainage. Laser or surgical enlargement of the drainage channel can also be used. ▲

The *ophthalmoscope* (of-thal′mo-skōp) is an instrument that illuminates the interior of the eyeball, allowing the retina, optic disc, and internal blood

FIGURE 8.7 **Photograph of a cataract.** The cataract appears as a milky structure that seems to fill the pupil.

vessels at the **fundus,** or posterior wall of the eye to be viewed and examined (Figure 8.8). Certain pathological conditions, such as diabetes, arteriosclerosis, and degeneration of the optic nerve and retina, can be detected by such an examination.

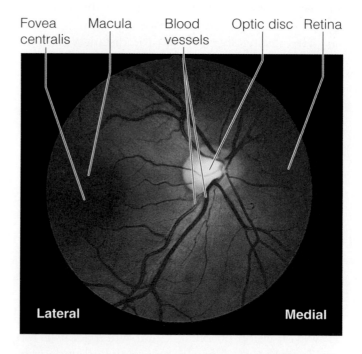

Fovea centralis   Macula   Blood vessels   Optic disc   Retina

Lateral   Medial

FIGURE 8.8 **The posterior wall (fundus) of the retina as seen with an ophthalmoscope.** Notice the optic disc, from which the blood vessels radiate.

► *DID YOU GET IT?*

5. What is the meaning of the term *blind spot* in relation to the eye?

6. What function does the choroid of the vascular layer have in common with the pigmented layer of the retina?

7. How do the rods and cones differ from each other?

For answers, see Appendix D.

Pathway of Light through the Eye and Light Refraction

When light passes from one substance to another substance that has a different density, its speed changes and its rays are bent, or **refracted.** Light rays are bent in the eye as they encounter the cornea, aqueous humor, lens, and vitreous humor.

The refractive, or bending, power of the cornea and humors is constant. However, that of the lens can be changed by changing its shape—that is, by making it more or less convex, so that light can be properly focused on the retina. The greater the lens convexity, or bulge, the more it bends the light. The flatter the lens, the less it bends the light.

The resting eye is "set" for distant vision. In general, light from a distant source (over 20 feet away) approaches the eye as parallel rays (Figure 8.9a), and the lens does not need to change shape to focus properly on the retina. However, light from a close object tends to scatter and to *diverge,* or spread out, and the lens must bulge more to make close vision possible (Figure 8.9b). To achieve this, the ciliary body contracts, allowing the lens to become more convex. This ability of the eye to focus specifically for close objects (those less than 20 feet away) is called **accommodation.** The image formed on the retina as a result of the light-bending activity of the lens is a *real image*—that is, it is reversed from left to right, upside down (inverted), and smaller than the object (Figure 8.10). The normal eye is able to accommodate properly. However, vision problems occur when a lens is too strong or too weak (overconverging and underconverging, respectively) or from structural problems of the eyeball (as described in the "A Closer Look" box on near- and farsightedness on pages 292–293).

 As you look at this figure, are your lenses relatively thick or relatively thin?

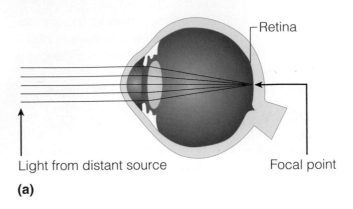

Retina

Light from distant source   Focal point

(a)

Light from near source   Focal point

Retina

(b)

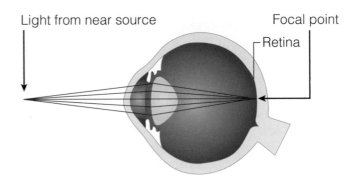

FIGURE 8.9   Relative convexity of the lens during focusing for distant and close vision. **(a)** Light rays from a distant object are nearly parallel as they reach the eye and can be focused without requiring changes in lens convexity. **(b)** Diverging light rays from close objects require that the lens bulge more to focus the image sharply on the retina.

Visual Fields and Visual Pathways to the Brain

Axons carrying impulses from the retina are bundled together at the posterior aspect of the eyeball and issue from the back of the eye as the optic

 You would be using your close vision, so your lenses would be bulged and thus relatively thick.

FIGURE 8.10 Real image (reversed left to right, and upside down) formed on the retina. Notice that the farther away the object, the smaller its image on the retina.

nerve. At the **optic chiasma** (ki-as′mah; *chiasm =* cross) the fibers from the medial side of each eye cross over to the opposite side of the brain. The fiber tracts that result are the **optic tracts.** Each optic tract contains fibers from the lateral side of the eye on the same side and the medial side of the opposite eye. The optic tract fibers synapse with neurons in the thalamus, whose axons form the **optic radiation,** which runs to the occipital lobe of the brain. There they synapse with the cortical cells, and visual interpretation, or seeing, occurs. The visual pathway from the eye to the brain is shown in Figure 8.11. As you can see, each side of the brain receives visual input from both eyes—from the lateral field of vision of the eye on its own side and from the medial field of the other eye. Also notice that each eye "sees" a slightly different view, but their *visual fields* overlap quite a bit. As a result of these two facts, humans have *binocular vision.* Binocular vision, literally "two-eyed vision," provides for depth perception, also called "three-dimensional" vision, as our visual cortex fuses the two slightly different images delivered by the two eyes.

HOMEOSTATIC IMBALANCE

Hemianopia (hem″e-ah-no′pe-ah) is the loss of the same side of the visual field of both eyes, which results from damage to the visual cortex on one side only (as occurs in some CVAs). Thus, the person would not be able to see things past the middle of his or her visual field on either the right or left side, depending on the site of the CVA. Such individuals should be carefully attended and warned of objects in the nonfunctional (nonseeing) side of the visual field. Their food and personal objects should always be placed on their functional side, or they might miss them. ▲

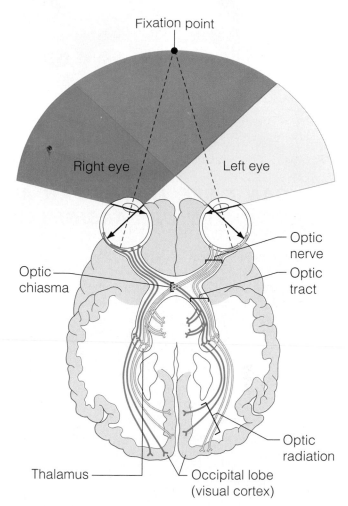

FIGURE 8.11 Visual fields of the eyes and visual pathway to the brain. Notice that the visual fields overlap considerably (area of binocular vision). Notice also the retinal sites at which a real image would be focused when both eyes are fixed on a close, pointlike object.

Eye Reflexes

Both the internal and the external (extrinsic) eye muscles are necessary for proper eye function. The internal muscles are controlled by the autonomic nervous system. As mentioned earlier, these muscles include those of the ciliary body, which alters lens curvature, and the radial and circular muscles of the iris, which control pupil size. As illustrated in Figure 8.3, the external muscles are the rectus and oblique muscles attached to the eyeball exterior. The external muscles control eye movements and make it possible to follow moving objects. They are also responsible for **convergence,** which is the reflexive

A CLOSER LOOK

IF I CAN'T SEE THINGS FAR AWAY, AM I NEARSIGHTED OR FARSIGHTED?

It seems that whenever people who wear glasses or contact lenses get together and discuss their vision, one of them says something like, "Nearby objects appear blurry to me, but I can't remember if that means I'm nearsighted or farsighted." Or, someone else may say, "My glasses allow me to see faraway objects more clearly, so does that mean I am farsighted?" Here we will explain the meaning of nearsightedness and farsightedness as we explore the basis of eye-focusing disorders.

The eye that focuses images correctly on the retina is said to have **emmetropia** (em" ĕ-tro'pe-ah), literally, "harmonious vision." Such an eye is shown in part (a) of the figure.

Nearsightedness is formally called **myopia** (mi"o'pe-ah; "short vision"). It occurs when the parallel light rays from distant objects fail to reach the retina and instead are focused in front of it; see part (b) in the figure. Therefore, *distant* objects appear blurry to myopic people. Nearby objects are in focus, however, because the lens "accommodates" (bulges) to focus the image properly on the retina. Myopia results from an eyeball that is too long, a lens that is too strong, or a cornea that is too curved.

Correction requires *concave* corrective lenses that diverge the light rays before they enter the eye, so that they converge farther back. To answer the first question posed above, *near*sighted people see *near* objects clearly and need corrective lenses to focus distant objects.

> **❝** *The eye that focuses images correctly on the retina is said to have emmetropia.* **❞**

Farsightedness is formally called **hyperopia** (hi"per-o'pe-ah; "far vision"). It occurs when the parallel light rays from distant objects are focused *behind* the retina—at least in the resting eye in which the lens is flat and the ciliary muscle is relaxed; see part (c) in the figure. Hyperopia usually results from an eyeball that is too short or a "lazy" lens. People with hyperopia can see distant objects

clearly because their ciliary muscles contract continuously to increase the light-bending power of the lens, which moves the focal point forward onto the retina. However, the diverging rays from *nearby* objects are focused so far behind the retina that even at full "bulge," the lens cannot focus the image on the retina. Therefore, nearby objects appear blurry. Furthermore, hyperopic individuals are subject to eyestrain as their endlessly contracting ciliary muscles tire from overwork. Correction of hyperopia requires *convex* corrective lenses that converge the light rays before they enter the eye. To answer the second question posed at the beginning of this essay, *far*sighted people can see *far*away objects clearly and require corrective lenses to focus on nearby objects. Unequal curvatures in different parts of the cornea or lens cause **astigmatism** (ah-stig'mah-tizm). In this condition, blurry images occur because points of light are focused not as points on the retina but as lines (*astigma* = not a point). Special cylindrically ground lenses or contacts are used to correct this problem. Eyes that are myopic or hyperopic *and* astigmatic require a more complex correction.

		Correction
(a) Emmetropic eye		None required
(b) Myopic eye (nearsighted)		Concave lens
(c) Hyperopic eye (farsighted)		Convex lens

Focal plane

movement of the eyes medially when we view close objects. When convergence occurs, both eyes are aimed toward the near object being viewed. The extrinsic muscles are controlled by somatic fibers of cranial nerves III, IV, and VI, as shown in Figure 8.3.

When the eyes are suddenly exposed to bright light, the pupils immediately constrict; this is the **photopupillary reflex.** This protective reflex prevents excessively bright light from damaging the delicate photoreceptors. The pupils also constrict reflexively when we view close objects; this

accommodation pupillary reflex provides for more acute vision.

Reading requires almost continuous work by both sets of muscles. The muscles of the ciliary body bring about the lens bulge, and the circular (or *constrictor*) muscles of the iris produce the accommodation pupillary reflex. In addition, the extrinsic muscles must converge the eyes as well as move them to follow the printed lines. This is why long periods of reading tire the eyes and often result in what is commonly called *eyestrain*. When you read for an extended time, it is helpful to look up from time to time and stare into the distance. This temporarily relaxes all the eye muscles.

►DID YOU GET IT?

8. What are the refractory media of the eye?

9. What name is given to the ability of the eye to focus on close objects?

10. What is the difference between the optic tract and the optic nerve?

11. In what way does the photopupillary reflex protect the eyes?

For answers, see Appendix D.

PART II: THE EAR: HEARING AND BALANCE

At first glance, the machinery for hearing and balance appears very crude. Fluids must be stirred to stimulate the receptors of the ear: sound vibrations move fluid to stimulate hearing receptors, whereas gross movements of the head disturb fluids surrounding the balance organs. Receptors that respond to such physical forces are called **mechanoreceptors** (mek"ah-no-re-sep'terz). Our hearing apparatus allows us to hear an extraordinary range of sound, and our highly sensitive equilibrium receptors keep our nervous system continually up to date on the position and movements of the head. Without this information, it would be difficult if not impossible to maintain our balance. Although these two sense organs are housed together in the ear, their receptors respond to different stimuli and are activated independently of one another.

Anatomy of the Ear

Anatomically, the ear is divided into three major areas: the external, or outer, ear; the middle ear; and the internal, or inner, ear (Figure 8.12). The external and middle ear structures are involved with hearing *only*. The internal ear functions in both equilibrium and hearing.

External (Outer) Ear

The **external,** or **outer, ear** is composed of the auricle and the external acoustic meatus. The **auricle** (aw'ri-kul), or **pinna** (pin'nah), is what most people call the "ear"—the shell-shaped structure surrounding the auditory canal opening. In many animals, the auricle collects and directs sound waves into the auditory canal, but in humans this function is largely lost.

The **external acoustic meatus** (or *auditory canal*) is a short, narrow chamber (about 1 inch long by ¼ inch wide) carved into the temporal bone of the skull. In its skin-lined walls are the **ceruminous** (sĕ-roo'mĭ-nus) **glands,** which secrete waxy yellow **cerumen** or **earwax,** which provides a sticky trap for foreign bodies and repels insects.

Sound waves entering the auditory canal eventually hit the **tympanic** (tim-pan'ik; *tympanum* = drum) **membrane,** or **eardrum,** and cause it to vibrate. The canal ends at the eardrum, which separates the external from the middle ear.

Middle Ear

The **middle ear,** or **tympanic cavity,** is a small, air-filled, mucosa-lined cavity within the temporal bone. It is flanked laterally by the eardrum and medially by a bony wall with two openings, the **oval window** and the inferior, membrane-covered **round window.** The **pharyngotympanic** (or **auditory**) **tube** runs obliquely downward to link the middle ear cavity with the throat, and the mucosae lining the two regions are continuous. Normally, the pharyngotympanic tube is flattened and closed, but swallowing or yawning can open it briefly to equalize the pressure in the middle ear cavity with the external, or atmospheric, pressure. This is an important function because the eardrum does not vibrate freely unless the pressure on both of its surfaces is the same. When the pressures are unequal, the eardrum bulges inward or outward, causing hearing difficulty (voices may sound far away) and sometimes earaches. The ear-popping sensation of the pressures equalizing is familiar to anyone who has flown in an airplane.

⚖ HOMEOSTATIC IMBALANCE

Inflammation of the middle ear, **otitis media** (o-ti'tis me'de-ah), is a fairly common result of a sore throat, especially in children, whose pharyngotympanic tubes run more horizontally. In otitis media, the eardrum bulges and often becomes inflamed. When large amounts of fluid or pus accumulate in the cavity, an emergency *myringotomy* (lancing of the eardrum) may be required to relieve the pressure. A tiny tube is implanted in the

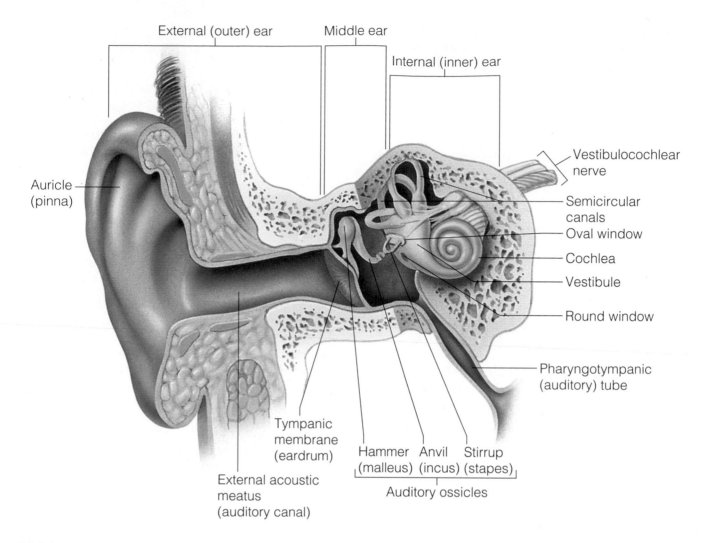

External (outer) ear   Middle ear

Internal (inner) ear

Vestibulocochlear nerve

Semicircular canals

Oval window

Cochlea

Vestibule

Round window

Pharyngotympanic (auditory) tube

Auricle (pinna)

Tympanic membrane (eardrum)

Hammer (malleus)   Anvil (incus)   Stirrup (stapes)

Auditory ossicles

External acoustic meatus (auditory canal)

FIGURE 8.12   Anatomy of the ear.

eardrum that allows pus to drain into the external ear canal. The tube usually falls out by itself within the year. ▲

The more horizontal course of the pharyngotympanic tube in infants also explains why it is never a good idea to "prop" a bottle or feed them when they are lying flat (a condition that favors the entry of the food into that tube).

The tympanic cavity is spanned by the three smallest bones in the body, the **ossicles** (os′sĭ-kulz), which transmit the vibratory motion of the eardrum to the fluids of the inner ear (see Figure 8.12). These bones, named for their shape, are the **hammer,** or **malleus** (mă′le-us), the **anvil,** or **incus** (in′kus), and the **stirrup,** or **stapes** (sta′pēz). When the eardrum moves, the hammer moves with it and transfers the vibration to the anvil. The anvil, in turn, passes the vibration on to

the stirrup, which presses on the oval window of the inner ear. The movement at the oval window sets the fluids of the inner ear into motion, eventually exciting the hearing receptors.

Internal (Inner) Ear

The **internal ear** is a maze of bony chambers called the **bony,** or **osseous, labyrinth** (lab′ĭ-rinth), located deep within the temporal bone behind the eye socket. The three subdivisions of the bony labyrinth are the spiraling, pea-sized **cochlea** (kok′le-ah, "snail"), the **vestibule** (ves′ti-būl), and the **semicircular canals.** The vestibule is situated between the semicircular canals and the cochlea. The views of the bony labyrinth typically seen in textbooks, including this one, are somewhat misleading because we are really talking about a cavity. The view seen in Figure 8.12 can be compared to a *cast* of the bony labyrinth; that is, a labyrinth that was filled with plaster of paris and then had the bony walls removed after the plaster hardened. The shape of the plaster then reveals the shape of the *cavity* that worms through the temporal bone.

The bony labyrinth is filled with a plasmalike fluid called **perilymph** (per′ĭ-limf). Suspended in the perilymph is a **membranous labyrinth,** a system of membrane sacs that more or less follows the shape of the bony labyrinth. The membranous labyrinth itself contains a thicker fluid called **endolymph** (en′do-limf).

 DID YOU GET IT?

12. Which region(s) of the ear (external, middle, or internal) serve hearing only?

13. Which structures of the ear transmit sound vibrations from the eardrum to the oval window?

For answers, see Appendix D.

Mechanisms of Equilibrium

The equilibrium sense is not easy to describe because it does not "see," "hear," or "feel." What it *does* is respond (frequently without our awareness) to various head movements. The equilibrium receptors of the inner ear, collectively called the **vestibular apparatus,** can be divided into two functional arms—one arm responsible for monitoring *static equilibrium,* and the other involved with *dynamic equilibrium.*

Static Equilibrium

Within the membrane sacs of the vestibule are receptors called **maculae** (mak′u-le; "spots") that are essential to our sense of **static equilibrium** (Figure 8.13). The maculae report on changes in the position of the head in space with respect to the pull of gravity when the body is not moving (*static* = at rest). Because they provide information on which way is up or down, they help us keep our head erect. The maculae are extremely important to divers swimming in the dark depths (where most other orienting cues are absent), enabling them to tell which way is up (to the surface).

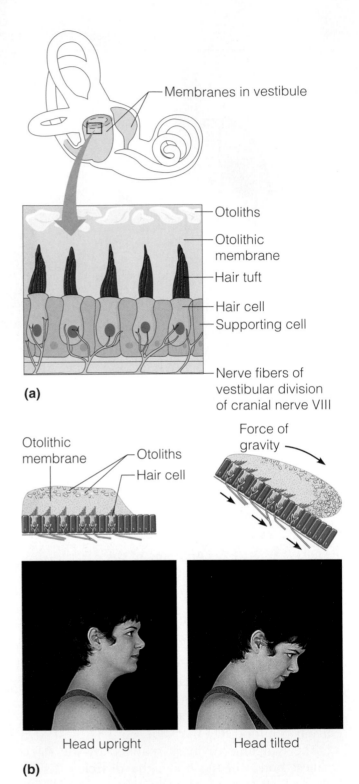

(a)

(b)

FIGURE 8.13 **Structure and function of maculae (static equilibrium receptors).** **(a)** Diagrammatic view of part of a macula. **(b)** When the head is tipped, the maculae are stimulated by movement of the otoliths in the gelatinous otolithic membrane in the direction of gravitational pull, which creates a pull on the hair cells.

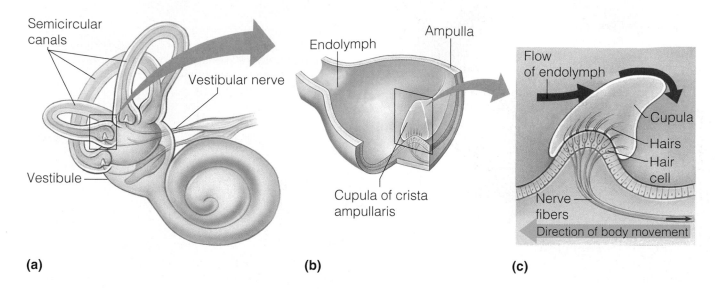

(a)   (b)   (c)

FIGURE 8.14 **Structure and function of the crista ampullaris (dynamic equilibrium receptor region). (a)** Arranged in the three spatial planes, the semicircular ducts in the semicircular canals each have a swelling called an ampulla at their base. **(b)** Each ampulla contains a crista ampullaris, a receptor that is essentially a cluster of hair cells with hairs projecting into a gelatinous cap called the cupula. **(c)** When head position changes in an angular direction, inertia causes the endolymph in the semicircular ducts to lag behind, and as the cupula moves it drags across the endolymph bending the hair cells in the opposite direction. The bending results in increased impulse transmission in the sensory neurons. This mechanism adjusts quickly if the angular motion (or rotation) continues at a constant speed.

Each macula is a patch of receptor (hair) cells with their "hairs" embedded in the **otolithic hair membrane,** a jellylike mass studded with **otoliths** (o'to-lithz), tiny stones made of calcium salts. As the head moves, the otoliths roll in response to changes in the pull of gravity. This movement creates a pull on the gel, which in turn slides like a greased plate over the hair cells, bending their hairs. This event activates the hair cells, which send impulses along the **vestibular nerve** (a division of cranial nerve VIII) to the cerebellum of the brain, informing it of the position of the head in space.

Dynamic Equilibrium

The **dynamic equilibrium** receptors, found in the semicircular canals, respond to angular or rotatory movements of the head rather than to straight-line movements. When you twirl on the dance floor or suffer through a rough boat ride, these receptors

are working overtime. The semicircular canals (each about ½ inch, or 1.3 cm, around) are oriented in the three planes of space. Thus, regardless of which plane one moves in, there will be receptors to detect the movement.

Within the *ampulla,* a swollen region at the base of each membranous semicircular canal, is a receptor region called a **crista ampullaris** (kris'tah am"pu-lar'is), or simply *crista*, which consists of a tuft of hair cells covered with a gelatinous cap called the **cupula** (ku'pu-lah) (Figure 8.14). When your head moves in an arclike or angular direction, the endolymph in the canal lags behind. Then, as the cupula drags against the stationary endolymph, the cupula bends—like a swinging door—with the body's motion. This stimulates the hair cells, and impulses are transmitted up the **vestibular nerve** to the cerebellum. Bending the cupula in the opposite direction reduces impulse generation. When you are moving at a constant rate, the receptors gradually stop sending impulses,

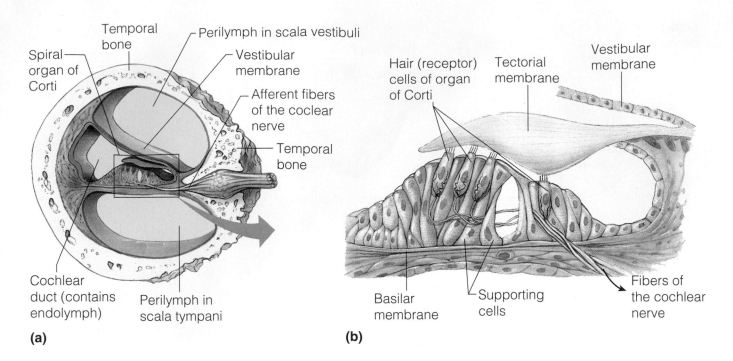

FIGURE 8.15 **Anatomy of the cochlea. (a)** A cross-sectional view of one turn of the cochlea, showing the position of the spiral organ of Corti in the cochlear duct. The cavities of the bony labyrinth contain perilymph. The cochlear duct contains endolymph. **(b)** Detailed structure of the organ of Corti. The receptor cells (hair cells) rest on the basilar membrane.

and you no longer have the sensation of motion until your speed or direction of movement changes.

Although the receptors of the semicircular canals and vestibule are responsible for dynamic and static equilibrium, respectively, they usually act together. Besides these equilibrium senses, sight and the proprioceptors of the muscles and tendons are also important in providing information used to control balance to the cerebellum.

▶ *DID YOU GET IT?*

14. What sense do the vestibule and semicircular canals serve?

15. Benji is enjoying a boat ride until a storm suddenly descends on the bay. Soon he is nauseated and can barely stand up. Which equilibrium receptors—static or dynamic—are operating furiously during such a rough voyage?

16. What are otoliths, and what is their role in equilibrium?

For answers, see Appendix D.

Mechanism of Hearing

Within the **cochlear duct,** the endolymph-containing membranous labyrinth of the cochlea is the **spiral organ of Corti** (kor′te), which contains the hearing receptors, or **hair cells** (Figure 8.15a). The chambers (scalae) above and below the cochlear duct contain perilymph. Sound waves that reach the cochlea through vibrations of the eardrum, ossicles, and oval window set the cochlear fluids into motion (Figure 8.16). As the sound waves are transmitted by the ossicles from the eardrum to the oval window, their force (amplitude) is increased by the lever activity of the ossicles. In this way, nearly the total force exerted on the much larger eardrum reaches the tiny oval window, which in turn sets the fluids of the inner ear into motion, and these pressure waves set up vibrations in the **basilar membrane.** The receptor cells, positioned on the basilar membrane in the spiral organ of Corti, are stimulated when their "hairs" are bent or tweaked by the movement of the gel-like **tectorial** (tek-to′re-al) **membrane**

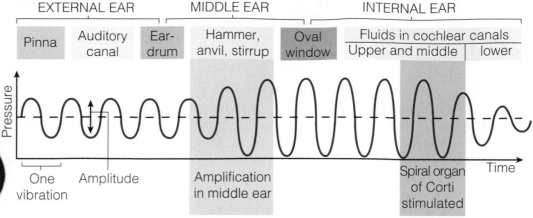

EXTERNAL EAR | MIDDLE EAR | INTERNAL EAR

| Pinna | Auditory canal | Ear-drum | Hammer, anvil, stirrup | Oval window | Fluids in cochlear canals |
| | | | | | Upper and middle | lower |

Pressure

One vibration   Amplitude   Amplification in middle ear   Spiral organ of Corti stimulated   Time

(a)

FIGURE 8.16 **Route of sound waves through the ear and activation of the cochlear hair cells. (a)** To excite the hair cells in the organ of Corti in the inner ear, sound wave vibrations must pass through air, membranes, bone, and fluid. **(b)** The cochlea is drawn as though it were uncoiled to make the events of sound transmission occurring there easier to follow. Sound waves of low frequency that are below the level of hearing travel entirely around the cochlear duct without exciting hair cells. But sounds of higher frequency result in pressure waves that penetrate through the cochlear duct and basilar membrane to reach the scala tympani. This causes the basilar membrane to vibrate maximally in certain areas in response to certain frequencies of sound, stimulating particular hair cells and sensory neurons. The differential stimulation of hair cells is perceived in the brain as sound of a certain pitch. **(c)** The length of the fibers spanning the basilar membrane tune specific regions to vibrate at specific frequencies. The higher notes—20,000 Hertz (Hz)— are detected by shorter hair cells along the base of the basilar membrane.

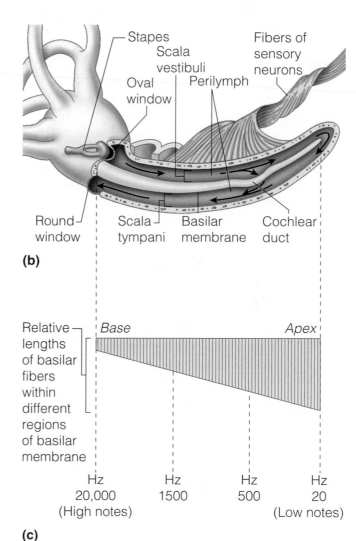

Stapes
Scala vestibuli
Oval window
Perilymph
Fibers of sensory neurons

Round window | Scala tympani | Basilar membrane | Cochlear duct

(b)

Relative lengths of basilar fibers within different regions of basilar membrane

Base   *Apex*

| Hz 20,000 (High notes) | Hz 1500 | Hz 500 | Hz 20 (Low notes) |

(c)

that lies over them (Figure 8.15b). The length of the fibers spanning the basilar membrane "tunes" specific regions to vibrate at specific frequencies. In general, high-pitched sounds disturb the shorter fibers of the basilar membrane and stimulate receptor cells close to the oval window, whereas low-pitched sounds affect longer fibers and activate specific hair cells further along the cochlea (see Figure 8.16). Once stimulated, the hair cells transmit impulses along the **cochlear nerve** (a division of cranial nerve VIII—the vestibulo-cochlear nerve) to the auditory cortex in the temporal lobe, where interpretation of the sound, or hearing, occurs. Because sound usually reaches the two ears at different times, we could say that we hear "in stereo." Functionally, this helps us to determine where sounds are coming from in our environment.

When the same sounds, or tones, keep reaching the ears, the auditory receptors tend to *adapt*, or stop responding, to those sounds, and we are no longer aware of them. This is why the drone of a continuously running motor does not demand our attention after the first few seconds. However, hearing is the last sense to leave our awareness when we fall asleep or receive anesthesia (or die) and is the first to return as we awaken.

Hearing and Equilibrium Deficits

HOMEOSTATIC IMBALANCE

Children with ear problems or hearing deficits often pull on their ears or fail to respond when spoken to. Under such conditions, tuning fork or audiometry testing is done to try to diagnose the problem. **Deafness** is defined as *hearing loss of any degree*—from a slight loss to a total inability to hear sound. Generally speaking, there are two kinds of deafness, conduction and sensorineural. Temporary or permanent **conduction deafness** results when something interferes with the conduction of sound vibrations to the fluids of the inner ear. Something as simple as a buildup of earwax may be the cause. Other causes of conduction deafness include fusion of the ossicles (a problem called **otosclerosis** [o"to-sklĕ-ro'sis]), a ruptured eardrum, and *otitis media.*

Sensorineural deafness occurs when there is degeneration or damage to the receptor cells in the spiral organ of Corti, to the cochlear nerve, or to neurons of the auditory cortex. This often results from extended listening to excessively loud sounds. Thus, whereas conduction deafness results from mechanical factors, sensorineural deafness is a problem of nervous system structures.

A person who has a hearing loss due to conduction deafness will still be able to hear by bone conduction, even though his or her ability to hear air-conducted sounds (the normal conduction route) is decreased or lost. In contrast, individuals with sensorineural deafness cannot hear better by *either* conduction route. Hearing aids, which use skull bones to conduct sound vibrations to the inner ear, are generally very successful in helping people with conduction deafness to hear. They are less helpful for sensorineural deafness.

Equilibrium problems are usually obvious. Nausea, dizziness, and problems in maintaining balance are common symptoms, particularly when impulses from the vestibular apparatus "disagree" with what we see (visual input). There also may be strange (jerky or rolling) eye movements.

A serious pathology of the inner ear is **Ménière's** (mān"e-airz') **syndrome.** The exact cause of this condition is not fully known, but suspected causes are arteriosclerosis, degeneration of cranial nerve VIII, and increased pressure of the inner ear fluids. In Ménière's syndrome, progressive deafness occurs. Affected individuals become nauseated and often have howling or ringing sounds in their ears and **vertigo** (a sensation of spinning) that is so severe that they cannot stand up without extreme discomfort. Anti–motion sickness drugs are often prescribed to decrease the discomfort. ▲

▶ *DID YOU GET IT?*

17. From the air outside the body, through what substances do sound waves travel to excite the receptor cells of the cochlea?

18. Which nerve transmits impulses from the spiral organ of Corti to the brain?

19. Do high-pitched sounds peak close to or far from the oval window?

20. How do sensorineural and conductive deafness differ from each other?

For answers, see Appendix D.

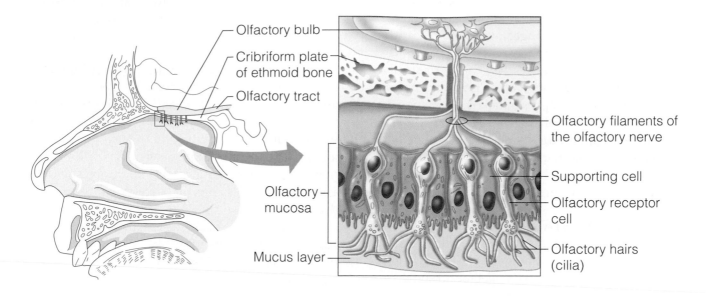

FIGURE 8.17   **Location and cellular makeup of the olfactory epithelium.**

PART III: CHEMICAL SENSES: TASTE AND SMELL

The receptors for taste and olfaction are classified as **chemoreceptors** (ke″mo-re-sep′terz) because they respond to chemicals in solution. Five types of taste receptors have been identified, but the olfactory receptors (for smell) are believed to be sensitive to a much wider range of chemicals. The receptors for smell and taste complement each other and respond to many of the same stimuli.

Olfactory Receptors and the Sense of Smell

Even though our sense of smell is far less acute than that of many other animals, the human nose is still no slouch in picking up small differences in odors. Some people capitalize on this ability by becoming tea and coffee blenders, perfumers, or wine tasters.

The thousands of **olfactory receptors,** receptors for the sense of smell, occupy a postage

 It brings more odor-containing air into contact with the olfactory receptors in the superior part of the nasal cavity.

stamp–sized area in the roof of each nasal cavity (Figure 8.17). Air entering the nasal cavities must make a hairpin turn to enter the respiratory passageway below, so sniffing, which causes more air to flow superiorly across the olfactory receptors, intensifies the sense of smell.

The **olfactory receptor cells** are neurons equipped with **olfactory hairs,** long cilia that protrude from the nasal epithelium and are continuously bathed by a layer of mucus secreted by underlying glands. When the olfactory receptors located on the cilia are stimulated by chemicals dissolved in the mucus, they transmit impulses along the **olfactory filaments,** which are bundled axons of olfactory neurons that collectively make up the **olfactory nerve** (cranial nerve I). The olfactory nerve conducts the impulses to the olfactory cortex of the brain. There the odor is interpreted, and an "odor snapshot" is made. The olfactory pathways are closely tied into the limbic system (emotional-visceral part of the brain). Thus, olfactory impressions are long-lasting and very much a part of our memories and emotions. For example, the smell of chocolate chip cookies may remind you of your grandmother, and the smell of a special pipe tobacco may make you think of your father. There are hospital smells, school smells, baby smells, travel smells. The list can be continued almost without end. Our reactions to odors are rarely neutral. We tend to either like or dislike certain odors, and we change, avoid, or add odors according to our preferences.

The olfactory receptors are exquisitely sensitive—just a few molecules can activate them. Like the auditory receptors, the olfactory neurons tend to adapt rather quickly when they are exposed to an unchanging stimulus, in this case, an odor. This is why a woman stops smelling her own perfume after a while but will quickly pick up the scent of another perfume on someone else.

HOMEOSTATIC IMBALANCE

While it is possible to have either taste or smell deficits, most people seeking medical help for loss of chemical senses have olfactory disorders, or **anosmias** (ah-noz′me-uz). Most anosmias result from head injuries, the aftereffects of nasal cavity inflammation (due to a cold, an allergy, or smoking), or aging. Some brain disorders can destroy the sense of smell or mimic it. For example, **olfactory auras** (olfactory hallucinations) are experienced by some epileptics just before they go into seizures. ▲

Taste Buds and the Sense of Taste

The word *taste* comes from the Latin word *taxare,* which means "to touch, estimate, or judge." When we taste things, we are, in fact, testing or judging our environment in an intimate way, and the sense of taste is considered by many to be the most pleasurable of our special senses.

The **taste buds,** or specific receptors for the sense of taste, are widely scattered in the oral cavity. Of the 10,000 or so taste buds that we have, most are on the tongue. A few are scattered on the soft palate and inner surface of the cheeks.

The dorsal tongue surface is covered with small peglike projections, or **papillae** (pah-pil′e). The taste buds are found on the sides of the large round **circumvallate** (ser″kum-val′at) **papillae** and on the tops of the more numerous **fungiform** (fun′jĭ-form) **papillae** (Figure 8.18). The specific cells that respond to chemicals dissolved in the saliva are epithelial cells called **gustatory cells.** Their long microvilli—the **gustatory hairs**—

protrude through the **taste pore,** and when they are stimulated, they depolarize and impulses are transmitted to the brain. Three cranial nerves—VII, IX, and X—carry taste impulses from the various taste buds to the gustatory cortex. The **facial nerve** (VII) serves the anterior part of the tongue. The other two cranial nerves—the **glossopharyngeal** and **vagus**—serve the other taste bud–containing areas. Because of their location, taste bud cells are subjected to huge amounts of friction and are routinely burned by hot foods. Luckily, they are among the most dynamic cells in the body, and they are replaced every seven to ten days by **basal cells** (stem cells) found in the deeper regions of the taste buds.

There are five basic taste sensations, each corresponding to stimulation of one of the five major types of taste buds. The *sweet receptors* respond to substances such as sugars, saccharine, some amino acids, and some lead salts (such as those found in lead paint). *Sour receptors* respond to hydrogen ions (H^+), or the acidity of the solution; *bitter receptors* to alkaloids; and *salty receptors* to metal ions in solution. *Umami* (u-mah′me; "delicious"), a taste discovered by the Japanese, is elicited by the amino acid glutamate, which appears to be responsible for the "beef taste" of steak and the flavor of monosodium glutamate, a food additive.

Historically, the tip of the tongue was believed to be most sensitive to sweet and salty substances, its sides to sour, the back of the tongue to bitter, and the pharynx to umami. Actually there are only slight differences in the locations of the taste receptors in different regions of the tongue, and most taste buds respond to two, three, four, or even all five taste modalities.

Taste likes and dislikes have homeostatic value. A liking for sugar and salt will satisfy the body's need for carbohydrates and minerals (as well as some amino acids). Many sour, naturally acidic foods (such as oranges, lemons, and tomatoes) are rich sources of vitamin C, an essential vitamin. Umami guides the intake of proteins, and because many natural poisons and spoiled foods are bitter, our dislike for bitterness is protective.

Taste is affected by many factors, and what is commonly referred to as our sense of taste depends heavily on stimulation of our olfactory receptors by aromas. Think of how bland food is when your nasal passages are congested by a cold. Without the sense of smell, our morning coffee would simply

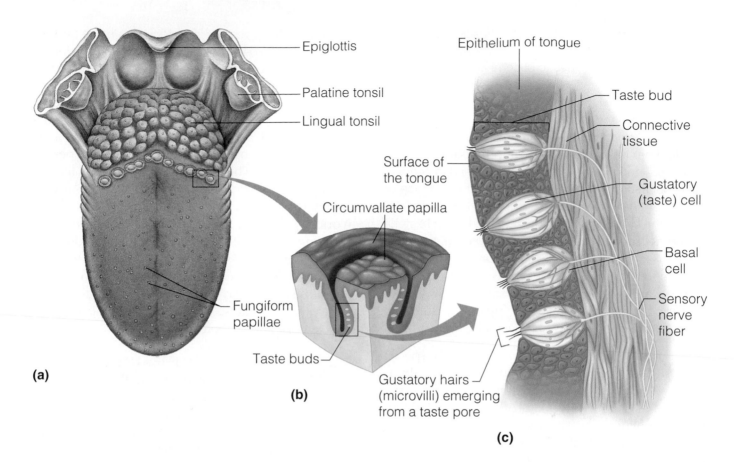

FIGURE 8.18 **Location and structure of taste buds. (a)** Taste buds on the tongue are associated with papillae, projections of the tongue mucosa. **(b)** A sectioned circumvallate papilla shows the position of the taste buds in its lateral walls. **(c)** An enlarged view of four taste buds.

taste bitter. In addition, the temperature and texture of food can enhance or spoil its taste for us. For example, some people will not eat foods that have a pasty texture (avocados) or that are gritty (pears), and almost everyone considers a cold greasy hamburger unfit to eat. "Hot" foods such as chili peppers actually excite pain receptors in the mouth.

DID YOU GET IT?

21. What name is used to describe both taste and smell receptors? Why?

22. Where, relative to specific structures, are most taste buds located?

23. Why does it help to sniff substances you are smelling?

For answers, see Appendix D.

PART IV:
DEVELOPMENTAL ASPECTS OF THE SPECIAL SENSES

The special sense organs, essentially part of the nervous system, are formed very early in embryonic development. For example, the eyes, which are literally outgrowths of the brain, are developing by the fourth week. All of the special senses are functional, to a greater or lesser degree, at birth.

HOMEOSTATIC IMBALANCE

Congenital eye problems are relatively uncommon, but some examples can be given. **Strabismus** (strah-biz′mus), which is commonly called "crossed eyes," results from unequal pulls by the external eye muscles that prevent the baby from coordinating movement of the two eyes. First, exercises are used to strengthen the weaker eye muscles, and/or the stronger eye may be covered with an eye patch to force the weaker muscles to become stronger. If these measures are not successful, surgery is always used to correct the condition because, if it is allowed to persist, the brain may stop recognizing signals from the deviating eye, causing that eye to become functionally blind.

Maternal infections, particularly *rubella* (measles), that occur during early pregnancy may lead to congenital blindness or cataracts. If the mother has a type of sexually transmitted disease called *gonorrhea* (gon"o-re'ah), the baby's eyes will be infected by the bacteria during delivery. In the resulting *conjunctivitis*, specifically called **ophthalmia neonatorum** (of-thal'me-ah ne"o-na-to'rum), the baby's eyelids become red and swollen, and pus is produced. All states legally require that all newborn babies' eyes be routinely treated with silver nitrate or antibiotics shortly after birth. ▲

Generally speaking, vision is the only special sense that is not fully functional when the baby is born, and many years of "learning" are needed before the eyes are fully mature. The eyeballs continue to enlarge until the age of 8 or 9, but the lens grows throughout life. At birth, the eyeballs are foreshortened, and all babies are hyperopic (farsighted). As the eyes grow, this condition usually corrects itself. The newborn infant sees only in gray tones, eye movements are uncoordinated, and often only one eye at a time is used. Because the lacrimal glands are not fully developed until about two weeks after birth, the baby is tearless for this period, even though he or she may cry lustily.

By 5 months, the infant is able to focus on articles within easy reach and to follow moving objects, but visual acuity is still poor. For example, an object that someone with mature vision can see clearly 200 feet away has to be a mere 20 feet away before an infant can see it clearly. (Such vision is said to be 20/200.) By the time the child is 5 years old, color vision is well developed, visual acuity has improved to about 20/30, and depth perception is present, providing a readiness to begin reading. By school age, the earlier hyperopia has usually been replaced by emmetropia. This condition continues until about age 40, when **presbyopia** (pres"be-o'pe-ah) begins to set in. Presbyopia (literally, "old vision") results from decreasing lens elasticity that accompanies aging. This condition makes it difficult to focus for close vision; it is basically farsightedness. The person who holds the newspaper at

arm's length to read it provides the most familiar example of this developmental change in vision.

As aging occurs, the lacrimal glands become less active, and the eyes tend to become dry and more vulnerable to bacterial infection and irritation. The lens loses its crystal clarity and becomes discolored. As a result, it begins to scatter light, causing a glare that is distressing when the person drives at night. The dilator muscles of the iris become less efficient; thus, the pupils are always somewhat constricted. These last two conditions work together to decrease the amount of light reaching the retina, and visual acuity is dramatically lower by one's seventies. In addition to these changes, older people are susceptible to certain conditions that may result in blindness, such as glaucoma, cataracts, macular degeneration, arteriosclerosis, and diabetes.

HOMEOSTATIC IMBALANCE

Congenital abnormalities of the ears are fairly common. Examples include partly or completely missing pinnas and closed or absent external acoustic meatuses. Maternal infections can have a devastating effect on ear development, and maternal rubella during the early weeks of pregnancy results in sensorineural deafness. ▲

A newborn infant can hear after his or her first cry, but early responses to sound are mostly reflexive—for example, crying and clenching the eyelids in response to a loud noise. By the age of 3 or 4 months, the infant is able to localize sounds and will turn to the voices of family members. The toddler listens critically as he or she begins to imitate sounds, and good language skills are very closely tied to an ability to hear well.

Except for ear inflammations *(otitis)* resulting from bacterial infections or allergies, few problems affect the ears during childhood and adult life. By the sixties, however, a gradual deterioration and atrophy of the spiral organ of Corti begins and leads to a loss in the ability to hear high tones and speech sounds. This condition, **presbycusis** (pres"bĭ-ku'sis), is a type of sensorineural deafness. In some cases, the ear ossicles fuse **(otosclerosis),** which compounds the hearing problem by interfering with sound conduction to the inner ear. Because many elderly people refuse to accept their hearing loss and resist using hearing aids, they begin to rely more and more on their vision for clues as to what is going on around them and may be accused of ignoring people. Although presbycusis was once considered a disability of old age, it is becoming much more common in younger people as our world grows noisier day by day. The damage caused by excessively loud sounds is progressive and cumulative. Music played and heard at deafening levels is definitely a contributing factor to the deterioration of the hearing receptors.

The chemical senses, taste and smell, are sharp at birth, and infants relish some food that adults consider bland or tasteless. Some researchers claim the sense of smell is just as important as the sense of touch in guiding a newborn baby to its mother's breast. However, very young children seem indifferent to odors and can play happily with their own feces. As they get older, their emotional responses to specific odors increase.

There appear to be few problems with the chemical senses throughout childhood and young adulthood. Beginning in the midforties, our ability to taste and smell diminishes, which reflects the gradual decrease in the number of these receptor cells. Almost half of people over the age of 80 cannot smell at all, and their sense of taste is poor. This may explain their inattention to formerly disagreeable odors, and why older adults often prefer highly seasoned (although not necessarily spicy) foods or lose their appetite entirely.

▶DID YOU GET IT?

24. Fifty-year-old Mrs. Bates is complaining that she can't read without holding the newspaper out at arm's length. What name is given to her problem?

25. Which of the special senses is least mature at birth?

26. What is presbycusis?

For answers, see Appendix D.

SUMMARY

Media study tools that provide additional review of key topics of Chapter 8 are referenced below.

    IP = *InterActive Physiology*
    WEB = The A&P Place

PART I: THE EYE AND VISION   (pp. 281–294)

1. External/accessory structures of the eye:

   a. Extrinsic eye muscles aim the eyes for following moving objects and for convergence.

   b. The lacrimal apparatus includes a series of ducts and the lacrimal glands that produce a saline solution, which washes and lubricates the eyeball.

   c. Eyelids protect the eyes. Associated with the eyelashes are the ciliary glands (modified sweat glands) and the tarsal glands (which produce an oily secretion that helps keep the eye lubricated).

   d. The conjunctiva is a mucous membrane that covers the anterior eyeball and lines the eyelids. It produces a lubricating mucus.

2. Three layers form the eyeball.

   a. The sclera forms most of the outer, tough, protective fibrous layer. The anterior portion is the cornea, which is transparent to allow light to enter the eye.

   b. The vascular layer, or middle coat, provides nutrition to the internal eye structures. Its posterior portion, the choroid, is pigmented and prevents light's scattering in the eye. Anterior modifications include two smooth muscle structures: the ciliary body and the iris (which controls the size of the pupil).

   c. The sensory layer consists of the two-layered retina—a pigmented epithelium and the innermost (neural) coat, which contains the photoreceptors. Rods are dim light receptors. Cones are receptors that provide for color vision and high visual acuity. The fovea centralis, on which acute focusing occurs, contains only cones.

   WEB Exercise: Chapter 8, Internal Structures of the Eye.

3. The blind spot (optic disc) is the point where the optic nerve leaves the back of the eyeball.

4. The lens is the major light-bending (refractory) structure of the eye. Its convexity is increased by the ciliary body for close focus. Anterior to the lens is the aqueous humor; posterior to the lens is the vitreous humor. Both humors reinforce the eye internally. The aqueous humor also provides nutrients to the avascular lens and cornea.

5. Errors of refraction include myopia, hyperopia, and astigmatism. All are correctable with specially ground lenses.

   WEB Exercise: Chapter 8, Optics of the Eye; Special Senses Case Study.

6. The pathway of light through the eye is cornea → aqueous humor → (through pupil) → aqueous humor → lens → vitreous humor → retina.

7. Overlap of the visual fields and inputs from both eyes to each optic cortex provide for depth perception.

8. The pathway of nerve impulses from the retina of the eye is optic nerve → optic chiasma → optic tract → thalamus → optic radiation → visual cortex in occipital lobe of brain.

9. Eye reflexes include the photopupillary, accommodation pupillary, and convergence.

PART II: THE EAR: HEARING AND BALANCE   (pp. 294–300)

1. The ear is divided into three major areas.

   a. External ear structures are the pinna, external acoustic meatus, and tympanic membrane. Sound entering the external acoustic meatus sets the eardrum into vibration. These structures are involved with sound transmission only.

   b. Middle ear structures are the ossicles and pharyngotympanic tube within the tympanic cavity. Auditory ossicles transmit the vibratory motion from the eardrum to the oval window. The pharyngotympanic tube allows pressure to be equalized on both sides of the eardrum. These structures are involved with sound transmission only.

   c. The internal ear, or bony labyrinth, consists of bony chambers (cochlea, vestibule, and semicircular canals) in the temporal bone. The bony labyrinth contains perilymph and membranous sacs filled with endolymph. Within the membranous sacs of the vestibule and semicircular canals are equilibrium receptors. Hearing receptors are found within the membranes of the cochlea.

   WEB Exercise: Chapter 8, Internal Structures of the Ear.

2. Receptors of the semicircular canals (cristae ampullaris) are dynamic equilibrium receptors, which respond to angular or rotational body movements. Receptors of the vestibule (maculae) are static equilibrium receptors, which respond to the pull of gravity and report on head position. Visual and proprioceptor input are also necessary for normal balance.

3. Symptoms of equilibrium apparatus problems include involuntary rolling of the eyes, nausea, vertigo, and an inability to stand erect.

4. Hair cells of the spiral organ of Corti (the receptor for hearing within the cochlea) are stimulated by sound vibrations transmitted through air, membranes, bone, and fluids.

5. Deafness is any degree of hearing loss. Conduction deafness results when the transmission of sound vibrations through the external and middle ears is hindered. Sensorineural deafness occurs when there is damage to the nervous system structures involved in hearing.

PART III: CHEMICAL SENSES: SMELL AND TASTE   (pp. 301–303)

1. Chemical substances must be dissolved in aqueous solution to excite the receptors for smell and taste.

2. The olfactory (smell) receptors are located in the superior aspect of each nasal cavity. Sniffing helps to bring more air (containing odors) over the olfactory mucosa.

3. Olfactory pathways are closely linked to the limbic system; odors stimulate the recall of memories and arouse emotional responses.

4. Gustatory (taste) cells are located in the taste buds, primarily on the tongue. The five major taste sensations are sweet, salt, sour, bitter, and umami.

5. Taste and appreciation of foods is influenced by the sense of smell and the temperature and texture of foods.

PART IV: DEVELOPMENTAL ASPECTS OF THE SPECIAL SENSES   (pp. 303–305)

1. Special sense organs are formed early in embryonic development. Maternal infections during the first five or six weeks of pregnancy may cause visual abnormalities as well as sensorineural deafness in the developing child. An important congenital eye problem is strabismus. The most important congenital ear problem is lack of the external acoustic meatus.

2. Vision requires the most learning. The infant has poor visual acuity (is farsighted) and lacks color vision and depth perception at birth. The eye continues to grow and mature until the eighth or ninth year of life.

3. Problems of aging associated with vision include presbyopia, glaucoma, cataracts, and arteriosclerosis of the eye's blood vessels.

4. The newborn infant can hear sounds, but initial responses are reflexive. By the toddler stage, the child is listening critically and beginning to imitate sounds as language development begins.

5. Sensorineural deafness (presbycusis) is a normal consequence of aging.

6. Taste and smell are most acute at birth and decrease in sensitivity after the age of 40 as the number of olfactory and gustatory receptors decreases.

REVIEW QUESTIONS

Multiple Choice

More than one choice may apply.

1. Gustatory cells are
   a. bipolar neurons.
   b. multipolar neurons.
   c. unipolar neurons.
   d. epithelial cells.

2. Alkaloids excite gustatory hairs mostly at the
   a. tip of the tongue.
   b. back of the tongue.
   c. circumvallate papillae.
   d. fungiform papillae.

3. Cranial nerves that are part of the gustatory pathway include
   a. trigeminal.   c. hypoglossal.
   b. facial.   d. glossopharyngeal.

4. Which cranial nerve controls contraction of the circular smooth muscle of the iris?
   a. Trigeminal   c. Oculomotor
   b. Facial   d. Abducens

5. The cornea is nourished by
   a. corneal blood vessels.
   b. aqueous humor.
   c. vitreous humor.
   d. scleral blood vessels.

6. In focusing for far vision
   a. the lens is at its thinnest.
   b. the ciliary muscles contract.
   c. the light rays are nearly parallel.
   d. suspensory fibers of the ciliary zonule are slack.

7. Convergence
   a. requires contraction of the medial rectus muscles of both eyes.
   b. is needed for near vision.
   c. involves transmission of impulses along the abducens nerves.
   d. can promote eyestrain.

8. Which of the following are paired *incorrectly*?
   a. Cochlear duct—cupula
   b. Vestibule—macula
   c. Ampulla—otoliths
   d. Semicircular duct—ampulla

9. Movement of the _____ membrane triggers bending of hairs of the hair cells in the organ of Corti.
   a. tympanic   c. basilar
   b. tectorial   d. vestibular

10. Sounds entering the external acoustic meatus are eventually converted to nerve impulses via a chain of events including
    a. vibration of the eardrum.
    b. vibratory motion of the ossicles against the round window.
    c. stimulation of hair cells in the organ of Corti.
    d. resonance of the cupula.

Short Answer Essay

11. Name three accessory eye structures that help to lubricate the eyeball, and name the secretion of each.

12. Why do you often have to blow your nose after crying?

13. Diagram and label the internal structures of the eye, and give the major function of each structure.

14. Name the extrinsic eye muscles that allow you to direct your eyes.

15. Locate and describe the functions of the two humors of the eye.

16. What is the blind spot, and why is it called this?

17. What name is given to the structure that controls light entry into the eye?

18. What is the fovea centralis, and why is it important?

19. Trace the pathway of light from the time it hits the cornea until it excites the rods and cones.

20. Trace the pathway of nerve impulses from the photoreceptors in the retina to the visual cortex of the brain.

21. Define *hyperopia, myopia,* and *emmetropia*.

22. Why do most people develop presbyopia as they age? Which of the conditions in question 21 does it most resemble?

23. There are only three types of cones. How can you explain the fact that we see many more colors?

24. Why are ophthalmoscopic examinations important?

25. Many students struggling through mountains of reading assignments are told that they need glasses for eyestrain. Why is it more of a strain on the extrinsic and intrinsic muscles to look at close objects than at far objects?

26. Name the structures of the outer, middle, and inner ears and give the general function of each structure and each group of structures.

27. Sound waves hitting the eardrum set it into motion. Trace the pathway of vibrations from the eardrum to the spiral organ of Corti, where the hair cells are stimulated.

28. Give two causes of *conductive* deafness.

29. Normal balance depends on information transmitted from a number of sensory receptor types. Name at least three of these receptors.

30. What name is given to the taste receptors?

31. Name the five primary taste sensations.

32. Where are the olfactory receptors located, and why is that site poorly suited for their job?

33. Describe the effects or results of aging on the special sense organs.

34. Which special sense requires the most learning?

CRITICAL THINKING AND CLINICAL APPLICATION QUESTIONS

35. An engineering student has been working in a disco to earn money to pay for his education. After about eight months, he notices that he is having problems hearing high-pitched tones. What is the cause-and-effect relationship here?

36. Nine children attending the same day-care center developed red, inflamed eyes and eyelids. What is the most likely cause and name of this condition?

37. Dr. Nakvarati used an instrument to press on Mr. Cruz's eye during his annual physical examination on his sixtieth birthday. The eye deformed very little, indicating the intraocular pressure was too high. What was Mr. Cruz's probable condition?

38. Lionel suffered a ruptured artery in his middle cranial fossa, and a pool of blood compressed his left optic tract, destroying its axons. What part of the visual field was blinded?

39. Sylvia Marcus, age 70, recently underwent surgery for otosclerosis. The operation was a failure and did not improve her condition. What was the purpose of the surgery, and exactly what was it trying to accomplish?

40. Janie is referred to the eye clinic by her teacher, who suspects a need for glasses. Examination demonstrates that Janie is myopic. Will she need concave or convex lenses? Explain.

41. Julie and her father loved to find the constellations in the sky on starry nights. One evening, Julie came running into the house and whispered excitedly to her mother. "Mom, I've got power! When I look hard at a star it disappears!" What was happening?

42. While visiting at her father's office on the 25th floor of the Harris Building, five-year-old Katie wandered away into the hall. Fascinated by the buttons in the elevator, she entered, pressed 1, and the high-speed elevator plummeted to the first floor. Later she told her father that she felt like she "kept on going" when the elevator stopped. Explain her sensation.

43. Mrs. Miniver has an immune disorder that causes dry mouth, and she complains to her doctor that she's lost her sense of taste. How might her symptoms be explained?

The Endocrine System

YOUR GOALS

After completing this chapter, you will have a working knowledge of the functions of the endocrine system and will have mastered the objectives listed below.

FUNCTION PREVIEW

- The endocrine system maintains homeostasis by releasing chemicals called *hormones,* and it controls prolonged or continuous processes such as growth and development, reproduction, and metabolism.

OBJECTIVE CHECKLIST

The Endocrine System and Hormone Function—An Overview (pp. 310–313)

➤ Define *hormone* and *target organ.*

➤ Describe how hormones bring about their effects in the body.

➤ Explain how various endocrine glands are stimulated to release their hormonal products.

➤ Define *negative feedback,* and describe its role in regulating blood levels of the various hormones.

The Major Endocrine Organs (pp. 313–332)

➤ Describe the difference between endocrine and exocrine glands.

➤ On an appropriate diagram, identify the major endocrine glands and tissues.

➤ List hormones produced by the endocrine glands, and discuss their general functions.

➤ Discuss ways in which hormones promote body homeostasis by giving examples of hormonal actions.

➤ Describe the functional relationship between the hypothalamus and the pituitary gland.

➤ Describe major pathological consequences of hypersecretion and hyposecretion of the hormones considered in this chapter.

Other Hormone-Producing Tissues and Organs (p. 332)

➤ Indicate the endocrine role of the kidneys, the stomach and intestine, the heart, and the placenta.

Developmental Aspects of the Endocrine System (pp. 332, 335)

➤ Describe the effect of aging on the endocrine system and body homeostasis.

You don't have to watch *CSI* to experience action-packed drama. Your body cells have dynamic adventures on microscopic levels all the time. For instance, when insulin molecules, carried passively along in the blood, leave the blood and bind tightly to protein receptors of nearby cells, the response is dramatic: bloodborne glucose molecules begin to disappear into the cells, and cellular activity accelerates. Such is the power of the second great controlling system of the body, the **endocrine system.** Along with the nervous system, it coordinates and directs the activity of the body's cells. However, the speed of control in these two great regulating systems is very different. The nervous system is "built for speed." It uses nerve impulses to prod the muscles and glands into immediate action so that rapid adjustments can be made in response to changes occurring both inside and outside the body. By contrast, the more slowly acting endocrine system uses chemical messengers called *hormones,* which are released into the blood to be transported leisurely throughout the body.

Although hormones have widespread effects, the major processes they control are reproduction; growth and development; mobilizing body defenses against stressors; maintaining electrolyte, water, and nutrient balance of the blood; and regulating cellular metabolism and energy balance. As you can see, the endocrine system regulates processes that go on for relatively long periods and, in some cases, continuously. The scientific study of hormones and endocrine organs is called **endocrinology.**

The Endocrine System and Hormone Function— An Overview

Compared to other organs of the body, the organs of the endocrine system are small and unimpressive. Indeed, to collect 1 kg (about 2.2 pounds) of hormone-producing tissue, you would need to collect *all* the endocrine tissue from eight or nine adults! The endocrine system also lacks the structural or anatomical continuity typical of most organ systems. Instead, bits and pieces of endocrine tissue are tucked away in widely separated regions of the body (see Figure 9.3, p. 314). However, functionally the endocrine organs are very impressive, and when their role in maintaining body homeostasis is considered, they are true giants.

The Chemistry of Hormones

The key to the incredible power of the endocrine glands is the hormones they produce and secrete. **Hormones** may be defined as chemical substances that are secreted by endocrine cells into the extracellular fluids and regulate the metabolic activity of other cells in the body. Although many different hormones are produced, nearly all of them can be classified chemically as either **amino acid–based molecules** (including proteins, peptides, and amines) or **steroids.** Steroid hormones (made from cholesterol) include the sex hormones made by the gonads (ovaries and testes) and the hormones produced by the adrenal cortex. All others are nonsteroidal amino acid derivatives. If we also consider the local hormones called **prostaglandins** (pros"tah-glan'dinz), described later in the chapter (see Table 9.2, p. 333), we must add a third chemical class, because the prostaglandins are made from highly active lipids released from nearly all cell membranes.

Mechanisms of Hormone Action

Although the bloodborne hormones circulate to all the organs of the body, a given hormone affects only certain tissue cells or organs, referred to as its **target cells** or **target organs.** For a target cell to respond to a hormone, specific protein receptors must be present on its plasma membrane or in its interior to which *that* hormone can attach. Only when this binding occurs can the hormone influence the workings of a cell.

The term *hormone* comes from a Greek word meaning "to arouse." In fact, the body's hormones do just that. They "arouse," or bring about their effects on, the body's cells primarily by *altering* cellular activity—that is, by increasing or decreasing the rate of a normal, or usual, metabolic process rather than by stimulating a new one. The precise changes that follow hormone binding depend on the specific hormone and the target cell type, but typically one or more of the following occurs:

1. Changes in plasma membrane permeability or electrical state
2. Synthesis of proteins or certain regulatory molecules (such as enzymes) in the cell
3. Activation or inactivation of enzymes
4. Stimulation of mitosis
5. Promotion of secretory activity

Direct Gene Activation

Despite the huge variety of hormones, there are really only two mechanisms by which hormones trigger changes in cells. Steroidal hormones (and, strangely, thyroid hormone) use the mechanism shown in Figure 9.1a. Being lipid-soluble molecules, the steroid hormones can (1) diffuse through the plasma membranes of their target cells. Once inside, the steroid hormone (2) enters the nucleus and (3) binds to a specific receptor protein there. The hormone-receptor complex then (4) binds to specific sites on the cell's DNA, (5) activating certain genes to transcribe messen-

ger RNA (mRNA). The mRNA then (6) is translated in the cytoplasm, resulting in the synthesis of new proteins.

Second-Messenger System

Water-soluble, nonsteroidal hormones—protein and peptide hormones—are unable to enter the target cells. Instead they bind to receptors situated on the target cell's plasma membrane and utilize a **second-messenger system.** In these cases (Figure 9.1b), (1) the hormone binds to the membrane receptor and (2) the activated receptor sets off a series of reactions (a cascade) that activates an enzyme. In turn, (3) the enzyme, catalyzes reactions that produce second-messenger molecules (in this case, *cyclic AMP,* also known as *cAMP* or cyclic adenine monophosphate) that (4) oversee additional intracellular changes that promote the typical response of the target cell to the hormone. As you might guess, there is a variety of possible second messengers (including *cyclic guanosine monophosphate (cGMP)* and *calcium ions*) and many possible target cell responses to the same hormone, depending on the tissue type stimulated.

Control of Hormone Release

Now that we've discussed *how* hormones work, the next question is, "What prompts the endocrine glands to release or not release their hormones?" Let's take a look.

Negative feedback mechanisms are the chief means of regulating blood levels of nearly all hormones (see Chapter 1, p. 13). In such systems, hormone secretion is triggered by some internal or external stimulus; then rising hormone levels inhibit further hormone release (even while promoting responses in their target organs). As a result, blood levels of many hormones vary only within a very narrow range.

Endocrine Gland Stimuli

The stimuli that activate the endocrine organs fall into three major categories—hormonal, humoral, and neural (Figure 9.2).

Hormonal Stimuli   The most common stimulus is a *hormonal stimulus,* in which endocrine organs are prodded into action by other hormones. For example, hypothalamic hormones stimulate the anterior

What determines whether a hormone will influence a given body cell?

(a) Steroid hormone action

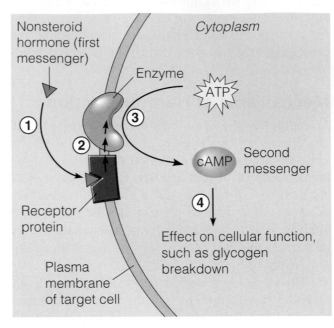

(b) Nonsteroid hormone action

FIGURE 9.1   Mechanisms of hormone action. (a) Direct gene activation: the steroid hormone mechanism. **(b)** A second messenger system: the nonsteroid (amino acid–based) hormone mechanism.

pituitary gland to secrete its hormones, and many anterior pituitary hormones stimulate other endocrine organs to release their hormones into the blood (Figure 9.2a). As the hormones produced by the final target glands increase in the blood, they "feed back" to inhibit the release of anterior pituitary hormones and thus their own release. Hormone release promoted by this mechanism tends to be rhythmic, with hormone blood levels rising and falling again and again.

Humoral Stimuli   Changing blood levels of certain ions and nutrients may also stimulate hormone release. Such stimuli are referred to as *humoral* (hyoo-mor'al) *stimuli* to distinguish them from hormonal stimuli, which are also bloodborne chemicals. The term *humoral* refers to the ancient use of the word *humor* to indicate the various

body fluids (blood, bile, and others). For example, the release of parathyroid hormone (PTH) by cells of the parathyroid glands is prompted by decreasing blood calcium levels. Because PTH acts by several routes to reverse that decline, blood Ca^{2+} levels soon rise, ending the stimulus for PTH release (Figure 9.2b). Other hormones released in response to humoral stimuli include calcitonin, released by the thyroid gland, and insulin, produced by the pancreas.

Neural Stimuli   In isolated cases, nerve fibers stimulate hormone release, and the target cells are said to respond to *neural stimuli*. The classic example is sympathetic nervous system stimulation of the adrenal medulla to release norepinephrine and epinephrine during periods of stress (Figure 9.2c). Although these three mechanisms typify most systems that control hormone release, they by no means explain all of them, and some endocrine organs respond to many different stimuli.

A *A hormone can influence a body cell only if that cell has receptors for that hormone on its plasma membrane or internally.*

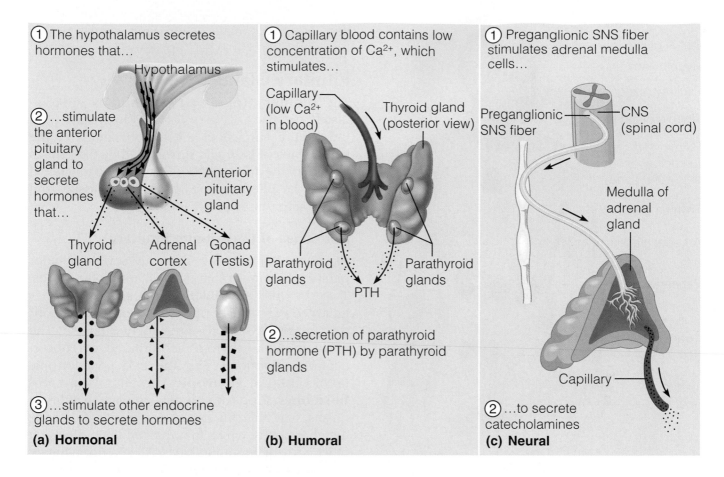

① The hypothalamus secretes hormones that...

Hypothalamus

② ...stimulate the anterior pituitary gland to secrete hormones that...

Anterior pituitary gland

Thyroid gland

Adrenal cortex

Gonad (Testis)

③ ...stimulate other endocrine glands to secrete hormones

(a) Hormonal

① Capillary blood contains low concentration of Ca^{2+}, which stimulates...

Capillary (low Ca^{2+} in blood)

Thyroid gland (posterior view)

Parathyroid glands

Parathyroid glands

PTH

② ...secretion of parathyroid hormone (PTH) by parathyroid glands

(b) Humoral

① Preganglionic SNS fiber stimulates adrenal medulla cells...

Preganglionic SNS fiber

CNS (spinal cord)

Medulla of adrenal gland

Capillary

② ...to secrete catecholamines

(c) Neural

FIGURE 9.2 **Endocrine gland stimuli. (a)** Hormonal stimulus. In this example, hormones released by the hypothalamus stimulate the anterior pituitary to release hormones that stimulate other endocrine organs to secrete hormones. **(b)** Humoral stimulus. Low blood calcium levels trigger parathyroid hormone (PTH) release from the parathyroid glands. PTH causes blood calcium levels to rise by stimulating release of Ca^{2+} from bone. Consequently, the stimulus for PTH secretion ends. **(c)** Neural stimulus. The stimulation of adrenal medullary cells by sympathetic nervous system (SNS) fibers triggers the release of catecholamines (epinephrine and norepinephrine) to the blood.

▶ *DID YOU GET IT?*

1. Walking barefoot, you step on a piece of broken glass and immediately pull your foot back. Why is it important that the signal triggering this motion come from the nervous system and not from the endocrine system?

2. What is a *hormone*? What does *target organ* mean?

3. Why is cAMP called a second messenger?

4. What are three ways in which endocrine glands are stimulated to secrete their hormones?

For answers, see Appendix D.

The Major Endocrine Organs

The major endocrine organs of the body include the **pituitary, thyroid, parathyroid, adrenal, pineal,** and **thymus glands,** the **pancreas,** and the gonads (**ovaries** and **testes**) (Figure 9.3). The **hypothalamus,** which is part of the nervous system, is also recognized as a major endocrine organ because it produces several hormones. Although the function of some hormone-producing glands (the anterior pituitary, thyroid, adrenals,

Pineal gland

Hypothalamus

Pituitary gland

Thyroid gland

Parathyroid glands
(on dorsal aspect
of thyroid gland)

Thymus gland

Adrenal glands

Pancreas

Ovary
(female)

Testis
(male)

FIGURE 9.3 **Location of the major endocrine organs of the body.** (The parathyroid glands, which appear to be on the anterior surface of the thyroid gland in this illustration, are actually located on its posterior aspect in most cases.)

and parathyroids) is purely endocrine, the function of others (pancreas and gonads) is mixed—both endocrine and exocrine. Both types of glands are formed from epithelial tissue, but the endocrine glands are **ductless glands** that produce hormones that they release into the blood or lymph. (As you might expect, the endocrine glands have a very rich blood supply.) Conversely, the exocrine glands release their products at the body's surface or into body cavities through ducts. The formation of and differences and similarities between these two types of glands have already been discussed in Chapter 3. Here we will direct our attention to the endocrine glands only.

Besides the more detailed descriptions of the endocrine organs provided next, a summary of

their hormones' main actions and regulatory factors appears in Table 9.1 (pp. 330–331).

Pituitary Gland

The **pituitary** (pĭ-tu′ĭ-tār″e) **gland** is approximately the size of a pea. It hangs by a stalk from the inferior surface of the hypothalamus of the brain, where it is snugly surrounded by the "Turk's saddle" of the sphenoid bone. It has two functional lobes—the anterior pituitary (glandular tissue) and the posterior pituitary (nervous tissue).

Hormones of the Anterior Pituitary

As shown in Figure 9.4, there are several anterior pituitary hormones that affect many body organs. Two of the six anterior pituitary hormones indicated—growth hormone and prolactin—exert their major effects on nonendocrine targets. The remaining four—thyrotropic hormone, adrenocorticotropic hormone, and the two gonadotropic hormones—are all **tropic** (tro′pik = turn on) **hormones.** Tropic hormones stimulate their target organs, which are also endocrine glands, to secrete their hormones, which in turn exert their effects on other body organs and tissues. All anterior pituitary hormones (1) are proteins (or peptides), (2) act through second-messenger systems, and (3) are regulated by hormonal stimuli and, in most cases, negative feedback.

Growth hormone (GH) is a general metabolic hormone. However, its major effects are directed to the growth of skeletal muscles and long bones of the body, and thus it plays an important role in determining final body size. GH is a protein-sparing and anabolic hormone that causes amino acids to be built into proteins and stimulates most target cells to grow in size and divide. At the same time, it causes fats to be broken down and used for energy while it spares glucose, helping to maintain blood sugar homeostasis.

HOMEOSTATIC IMBALANCE

If untreated, both deficits and excesses of GH may result in structural abnormalities. Hyposecretion of GH during childhood leads to **pituitary dwarfism** (Figure 9.5). Body proportions are fairly normal, but the person as a whole is a living miniature (with a maximum adult height of 4 feet). Hypersecretion during childhood results in **gigantism.** The individual becomes extremely tall; 8 to 9 feet is common. Again,

What effect would elevated levels of thyroid hormone in the blood have on TSH secretion?

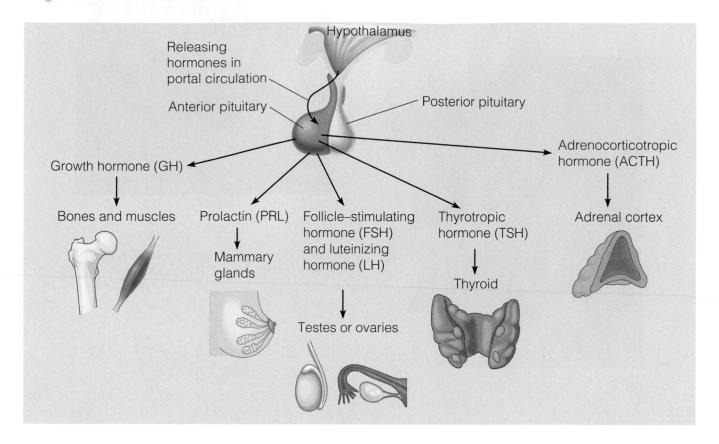

FIGURE 9.4 Hormones of the anterior pituitary and their major target organs. Secretion of anterior pituitary hormones is stimulated by releasing hormones secreted by hypothalamic neurons. The releasing hormones are secreted into a capillary network that connects via portal veins to a second capillary bed in the anterior lobe of the pituitary gland.

body proportions are fairly normal. If hypersecretion occurs after long-bone growth has ended, **acromegaly** (ak″ro-meg′ah-le) results. The facial bones, particularly the lower jaw and the bony ridges underlying the eyebrows, enlarge tremendously, as do the feet and hands. Thickening of soft tissues leads to coarse or malformed facial features. Most cases of hypersecretion by endocrine organs (the pituitary and the other endocrine organs) result from tumors of the affected gland. The tumor cells act in much the same way as the normal glandular cells do; that is, they produce the hormones normally made by that gland. The use of

pharmacological doses of GH to reverse some of the effects of aging is highlighted in the "A Closer Look" box on pp. 317–318. ▲

Prolactin (PRL) is a protein hormone structurally similar to growth hormone. Its only known target in humans is the breast (*pro* = for; *lact* = milk). After childbirth, it stimulates and maintains milk production by the mother's breasts. Its function in men is not known.

Adrenocorticotropic (ad-re″no-kor″tĭ-ko-tro′pik) **hormone (ACTH)** regulates the endocrine activity of the cortex portion of the adrenal gland. **Thyroid-stimulating hormone (TSH),** also called **thyrotropic hormone (TH),**

A *It would inhibit TSH secretion by the anterior pituitary.*

(a)

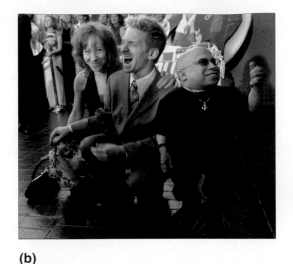

(b)

FIGURE 9.5 **Disorders of pituitary growth hormone. (a)** Prolonged overproduction of human growth hormone during development, which usually is due to a benign tumor within the pituitary gland, causes gigantism, while normal production of GH during childhood results in an adult of normal height. **(b)** Underproduction of GH during development causes dwarfism.

influences the growth and activity of the thyroid gland.

The **gonadotropic** (gon″ă-do-trop′ik) **hormones** regulate the hormonal activity of the **gonads** (ovaries and testes). In women, the gonadotropin **follicle-stimulating hormone (FSH)** stimulates follicle development in the ovaries. As the follicles mature, they produce estrogen, and eggs are readied for ovulation. In men, FSH stimulates sperm development by the testes. **Luteinizing** (lu′te-in-īz″ing) **hormone (LH)** triggers ovulation of an egg from the ovary and causes the ruptured follicle to produce progesterone and some estrogen. In men, LH stimulates testosterone production by the interstitial cells of the testes.

 HOMEOSTATIC IMBALANCE

Hyposecretion of FSH or LH leads to **sterility** in both males and females. In general, hypersecretion does not appear to cause any problems. However, some drugs used to promote fertility stimulate the release of the gonadotropic hormones, and multiple births (indicating multiple ovulations at the same time rather than the usual single ovulation each month) are fairly common after their use. ▲

Pituitary-Hypothalamus Relationship

Despite its insignificant size, the anterior pituitary gland controls the activity of so many other endocrine glands that it has often been called the "master endocrine gland." Its removal or destruction has a dramatic effect on the body. The adrenal and thyroid glands and the gonads atrophy, and results of hyposecretion by those glands quickly become obvious. However, the anterior pituitary is not as all-powerful in its control as it might appear because the release of each of its hormones is controlled by **releasing** and **inhibiting hormones** produced by the hypothalamus. The hypothalamus liberates these regulatory hormones into the blood of the portal circulation, which connects the blood supply of the hypothalamus with that of the anterior pituitary. (In a *portal circulation,* two capillary beds are connected by vein(s); in this case, the capillaries of the hypothalamus are drained by veins that empty into the capillaries of the anterior pituitary.)

POTENTIAL USES FOR GROWTH HORMONE

Growth hormone (GH) has been used for pharmaceutical purposes (that is, as a drug) since its discovery in the 1950s. Originally obtained from the pituitary glands of cadavers, it is now biosynthesized and administered by injection. Although GH is widely used in clinical trials, its use as a prescription drug is restricted until its helpful and harmful effects—many of which are very intriguing—can be fully documented.

GH is administered legally to children who do not produce it naturally to allow these children to grow to near-normal heights. Unfortunately, some physicians succumb to parental pressures to prescribe GH to children who *do* produce it but are extremely short.

When GH is administered to *adults* with a growth-hormone deficiency, body fat decreases and lean body mass, bone density, and muscle mass increase. It also appears to increase the performance and muscle mass of the heart, decreases blood cholesterol, boosts the immune system, and perhaps improves one's psychological outlook. Such effects (particularly those involving increased muscle mass and decreased body fat) have led to abuse of GH by bodybuilders and athletes, which is one reason why this substance remains restricted.

Because GH may also reverse some effects of aging, anti-aging clinics using GH injections to delay aging have sprung up. Many people naturally stop producing GH after age 60, and this may explain why their ratio of lean-to-fat mass declines and their skin thins. GH already is the drug treatment of choice for many aging Hollywood stars who dread the loss of their youth and vitality. Administration of GH to older patients reverses these declines. However, clinical studies reveal that the administered

> ❝ *Media claims that GH is a 'youth potion' have proven to be dangerously misleading.* ❞

GH does not increase strength or exercise tolerance in older patients, and a careful study of very sick patients in intensive care units (where GH is routinely given to restore nitrogen balance) found that high doses of GH are associated with increased mortality. For these reasons, earlier media claims that GH is a "youth potion" have proven to be dangerously misleading, and GH should not be administered to the very old or the critically ill.

GH may help AIDS patients. Because of improved antibiotics, fewer AIDS patients are dying from opportunistic infections. The other side of this picture is that more die from the weight loss called "wasting." It has been shown that injections of GH can actually reverse wasting during AIDS, leading to a gain of lean muscle and weight gain. In 1996, the U.S. Food and Drug Administration approved the use of GH to treat such wasting.

GH is not a wonder drug, even in cases where it is clearly beneficial.

Can growth hormone help older patients?

The hypothalamus also makes two additional hormones, oxytocin and antidiuretic hormone, which are transported along the axons of the hypothalamic **neurosecretory cells** to the posterior pituitary for storage (Figure 9.6). They are later released into the blood in response to nerve impulses from the hypothalamus.

Hormones of the Posterior Pituitary

The posterior pituitary is not an endocrine gland in the strict sense because it *does not make* the peptide hormones it releases. Instead, as mentioned above, it simply acts as a storage area for hormones made by hypothalamic neurons.

Oxytocin (ok″se-to′sin) is released in significant amounts only during childbirth and in nursing women. It stimulates powerful contractions of the uterine muscle during labor, during sexual relations, and during breastfeeding. It also causes milk ejection (the *let-down reflex*) in a nursing woman. Both natural and synthetic oxytocic drugs (Pitocin and others) are used to induce labor or to hasten labor that is progressing normally but at a slow pace. Less frequently, oxytocics are used to stop postpartum bleeding (by causing constriction of the ruptured blood vessels at the placental site) and to stimulate the milk ejection reflex.

The second hormone released by the posterior pituitary is **antidiuretic** (an″ti-di″u-ret′ik) **hormone (ADH)**. *Diuresis* is urine production. Thus, an antidiuretic is a chemical that inhibits or prevents urine production. ADH causes the kidneys to reabsorb more water from the forming urine; as a result, urine volume decreases and blood volume increases. In larger amounts, ADH also increases blood pressure by causing constriction of the arterioles (small

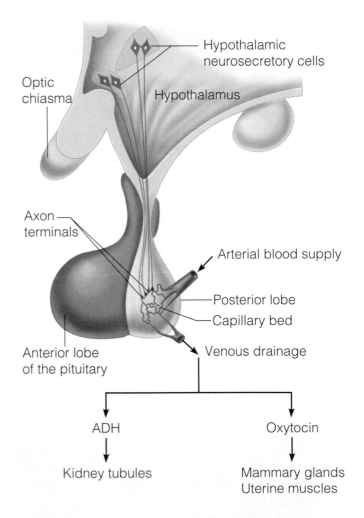

FIGURE 9.6   Hormones released by the posterior lobe of the pituitary and the target organs of such hormones. Neurosecretory cells in the hypothalamus synthesize oxytocin and antidiuretic hormone (ADH) and transport them down their axons to the posterior pituitary. There, the hormones are stored until their release is triggered by nerve impulses from the hypothalamus.

arteries). For this reason, it is sometimes referred to as **vasopressin** (vas″o-pres′in).

Drinking alcoholic beverages inhibits ADH secretion and results in output of large amounts of urine. The dry mouth and intense thirst experienced "the morning after" reflect this dehydrating effect of alcohol. Certain drugs, classed together as *diuretics,* antagonize the effects of ADH, causing water to be flushed from the body. These drugs are used to manage the edema (water retention in tissues) typical of congestive heart failure.

 HOMEOSTATIC IMBALANCE

Hyposecretion of ADH leads to a condition of excessive urine output called **diabetes insipidus** (di″ah-be′tez in-sip′ĭ-dus). People with this problem are continually thirsty and drink huge amounts of water. ▲

▶ *DID YOU GET IT?*

5. Both the anterior pituitary and the posterior pituitary release hormones, but the posterior pituitary is not an endocrine gland. What is it?

6. What are two important differences between endocrine and exocrine glands?

7. What are tropic hormones?

8. Barry is excreting huge amounts of urine. He has an endocrine system problem, but it is not diabetes mellitus, which has a similar sign. What is his possible problem?

For answers, see Appendix D.

Thyroid Gland

The **thyroid gland** is a hormone-producing gland that is familiar to most people primarily because many obese individuals blame their overweight condition on their "glands" (meaning the thyroid). Actually, the effect of thyroid hormones on body weight is not as great as many believe it to be.

The thyroid gland is located at the base of the throat, just inferior to the Adam's apple, where it is easily palpated during a physical examination. It is a fairly large gland consisting of two lobes joined by a central mass, or *isthmus* (Figure 9.7). The thyroid gland makes two hormones, one called *thyroid hormone,* the other called *calcitonin.* Internally, the thyroid gland is composed of hollow structures called **follicles,** which store a sticky colloidal

material (Figure 9.7b). Thyroid hormone is derived from this colloid.

Thyroid hormone, often referred to as the body's major metabolic hormone, is actually two active iodine-containing hormones, **thyroxine** (thi-rok′sin), or **T₄,** and **triiodothyronine** (tri″i″o-do-thi′ro-nēn), or **T₃.** Thyroxine is the major hormone secreted by the thyroid follicles. Most triiodothyronine is formed at the target tissues by conversion of thyroxine to triiodothyronine. These two hormones are very much alike. Each is constructed from two tyrosine amino acids linked together, but thyroxine has four bound iodine atoms, whereas triiodothyronine has three (thus, T_4 and T_3, respectively).

Thyroid hormone controls the rate at which glucose is "burned," or oxidized, and converted to body heat and chemical energy. Because all body cells depend on a continuous supply of chemical energy to power their activities, every cell in the body is a target. Thyroid hormone is also important for normal tissue growth and development, especially in the reproductive and nervous systems.

 HOMEOSTATIC IMBALANCE

Without iodine, functional hormones cannot be made. The source of iodine is our diet, and the foods richest in iodine are seafoods. Years ago many people who lived in the Midwest, in areas with iodine-deficient soil that were far from the seashore (and a supply of fresh seafood), developed **goiters** (goy′terz). That region of the country came to be known as the "goiter belt." A goiter is an enlargement of the thyroid gland (Figure 9.8) that results when the diet is deficient in iodine. TSH keeps "calling" for thyroxine, and the thyroid gland enlarges, but without iodine the thyroid makes only the peptide part of the molecule, which is nonfunctional and thus fails to provide negative feedback to inhibit TSH release. Simple goiter is uncommon in the United States today because most of our salt is iodized, but it is still a problem in some other areas of the world.

Hyposecretion of thyroxine may indicate problems other than iodine deficiency, such as lack of stimulation by TSH. If it occurs in early childhood, the result is **cretinism** (kre′tin-izm). Cretinism results in dwarfism in which adult body proportions remain childlike. Together the head and trunk are about 1½ times the length of the legs rather than approximately the same length, as in normal adults. Untreated cretins are mentally retarded. Their hair is scanty, and their skin is dry. If discovered

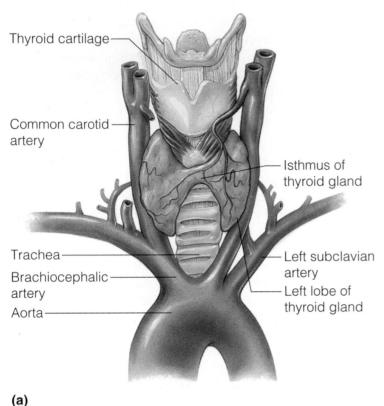

Thyroid gland

Thyroid cartilage

Common carotid artery

Isthmus of thyroid gland

Trachea

Brachiocephalic artery

Aorta

Left subclavian artery

Left lobe of thyroid gland

(a)

FIGURE 9.7 **Anatomy of the thyroid gland. (a)** Location of the thyroid gland, anterior view. **(b)** Photomicrograph of the thyroid gland (250×).

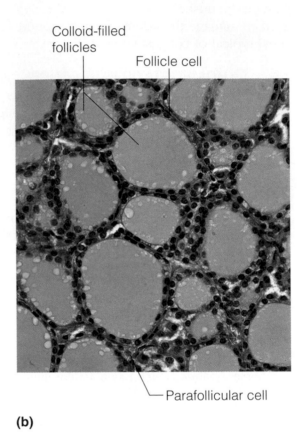

Colloid-filled follicles

Follicle cell

Parafollicular cell

(b)

early, hormone replacement will prevent mental retardation and other signs and symptoms of the deficiency. Hypothyroidism occurring in adults results in **myxedema** (mik"se-de'mah), which is characterized by both physical and mental sluggishness (however, mental retardation does not occur). Other signs are puffiness of the face, fatigue, poor muscle tone, low body temperature (the person is always cold), obesity, and dry skin. Oral thyroxine is prescribed to treat this condition.

Hyperthyroidism generally results from a tumor of the thyroid gland. Extreme overproduction of thyroxine results in a high basal metabolic rate, intolerance of heat, rapid heartbeat, weight loss, nervous and agitated behavior, and a general inability to relax. **Graves' disease** is one form of hyperthyroidism. In addition to the symptoms of hyperthyroidism given earlier, the thyroid gland enlarges and the eyes may bulge, or protrude anteriorly (a condition called **exophthalmos** (ek"sof-thal'mos) (Figure 9.9). Hyperthyroidism may be treated surgically by removal of part of the thyroid (and/or a tumor if present) or chemically by administering thyroid-blocking drugs or radioactive iodine, which destroy some of the thyroid cells. ▲

The second important hormone product of the thyroid gland, **calcitonin,** decreases blood calcium levels by causing calcium to be deposited in the bones. It acts antagonistically to parathyroid hormone, the hormone produced by the parathyroid glands. Whereas thyroxine is made and stored in follicles before it is released to the blood, calcitonin is made by the so-called **parafollicular cells** found in the connective tissue *between* the follicles (Figure 9.7b). It is released directly to the blood in

FIGURE 9.8 **Goiter.** An enlarged thyroid (goiter) of a boy from Bangladesh.

FIGURE 9.9 **The exophthalmos of Graves' disease.**

response to increasing levels of blood calcium. Few effects of hypo- or hypersecretion of calcitonin are known, and calcitonin production is meager or ceases entirely in adults. This may help to explain (at least in part) the progressive decalcification of bones that accompanies aging.

Parathyroid Glands

The **parathyroid glands** are tiny masses of glandular tissue most often found on the posterior surface of the thyroid gland (see Figure 9.3). Typically, there are two parathyroid glands on each thyroid lobe; that is, a total of four parathyroids; but as many as eight have been reported, and some may be in other regions of the neck or even in the thorax. The parathyroids secrete **parathyroid hormone (PTH),** or **parathormone** (par"ah-thor'mōn), which is the most important regulator of calcium ion (Ca^{2+}) homeostasis of the blood. When blood calcium levels drop below a certain level, the parathyroids release PTH, which stimulates bone destruction cells (osteoclasts) to break down bone matrix and release calcium into the blood. Thus, PTH is a *hypercalcemic* hormone (that is, it acts to increase blood levels of calcium), whereas calcitonin is a *hypocalcemic* hormone. The negative feedback interaction between these two hormones as they control blood calcium level during youth is illustrated in Figure 9.10. Although the skeleton is the major PTH target, PTH also stimulates the kidneys and intestine to absorb more calcium (from urinary filtrate and foodstuffs, respectively).

HOMEOSTATIC IMBALANCE

If blood calcium levels fall too low, neurons become extremely irritable and overactive. They deliver impulses to the muscles at such a rapid rate that the muscles go into uncontrollable spasms **(tetany),** which may be fatal. Before surgeons knew the importance of the tiny parathyroid glands on the backside of the thyroid, they would remove a hyperthyroid patient's gland entirely. Many times this resulted in death. Once it was revealed that the parathyroids are functionally very different from the thyroid gland, surgeons began to leave at least some parathyroid-containing tissue (if at all possible) to take care of blood calcium homeostasis.

Severe hyperparathyroidism causes massive bone destruction—an X-ray examination of the bones shows large punched-out holes in the bony matrix. The bones become very fragile, and spontaneous fractures begin to occur. ▲

DID YOU GET IT?

9. How are the thyroid and parathyroid glands linked anatomically?

10. What hormone increases blood calcium levels, and which endocrine gland produces this hormone?

11. What hormone reduces blood calcium levels, and which endocrine gland produces this hormone?

12. Why is iodine important for proper thyroid gland function?

For answers, see Appendix D.

What effect would removal of the parathyroid glands have on blood calcium levels?

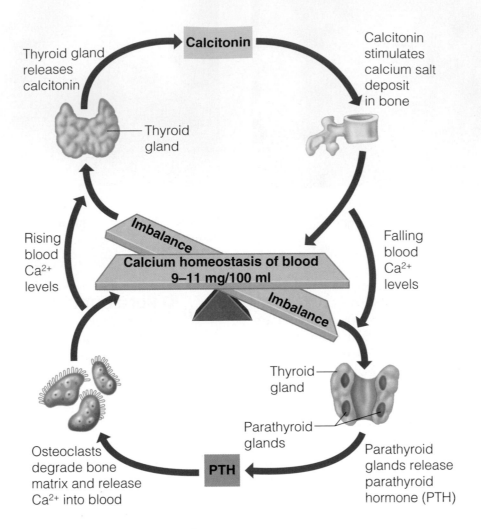

FIGURE 9.10 Hormonal controls of ionic calcium levels in the blood. PTH and calcitonin operate in negative feedback control systems that influence each other.

Adrenal Glands

As illustrated in Figure 9.3, the two bean-shaped **adrenal glands** curve over the top of the kidneys. Although the adrenal gland looks like a single organ, it is structurally and functionally two endocrine organs in one. Much like the pituitary gland, it has glandular (cortex) and neural tissue (medulla) parts. The central medulla region is enclosed by the adrenal cortex, which contains three separate layers of cells (Figure 9.11).

Hormones of the Adrenal Cortex

The **adrenal cortex** produces three major groups of steroid hormones, which are collectively called **corticosteroids** (kor″ti-ko-ster′oidz)—mineralocorticoids, glucocorticoids, and sex hormones.

The **mineralocorticoids,** mainly **aldosterone** (al″dos-ter′ōn), are produced by the outermost adrenal cortex cell layer. As their name suggests, the mineralocorticoids are important in regulating the mineral (or salt) content of the blood,

Blood calcium levels would drop because the bones would no longer be exposed to the bone-digesting stimulus of PTH.

FIGURE 9.11 **Microscopic structure of the adrenal gland.**
Diagram of the three regions of the adrenal cortex and part of the adrenal medulla (200×).

particularly the concentrations of sodium and potassium ions. Their target is the kidney tubules that selectively reabsorb the minerals or allow them to be flushed out of the body in urine. When blood levels of aldosterone rise, the kidney tubule cells reclaim increasing amounts of sodium ions and secrete more potassium ions into the urine. When sodium is reabsorbed, water follows. Thus, the mineralocorticoids help regulate both water and electrolyte balance in body fluids. As shown in Figure 9.12, the release of aldosterone is stimulated by humoral factors, such as fewer sodium ions or more potassium ions in the blood (and by ACTH to a lesser degree). **Renin,** an enzyme produced by the kidneys when blood pressure drops, also causes the release of aldosterone by triggering a series of reactions that form **angiotensin II,** a potent stimulator of aldosterone release. A hormone released by the heart, **atrial natriuretic** (na″tre-u-ret′ik) **peptide (ANP),** prevents aldosterone release, its

goal being to *reduce* blood volume and blood pressure.

The middle cortical layer mainly produces **glucocorticoids,** which include **cortisone** and **cortisol.** Glucocorticoids promote normal cell metabolism and help the body to resist *long-term stressors,* primarily by increasing blood glucose levels. When blood levels of glucocorticoids are high, fats and even proteins are broken down by body cells and converted to glucose, which is released to the blood. For this reason, glucocorticoids are said to be *hyperglycemic hormones.* Glucocorticoids also seem to control the more unpleasant effects of inflammation by decreasing edema, and they reduce pain by inhibiting some pain-causing molecules called *prostaglandins* (see Table 9.2, p. 333). Because of their anti-inflammatory properties, glucocorticoids are often prescribed as drugs to suppress inflammation for patients with rheumatoid arthritis. Glucocorticoids are released

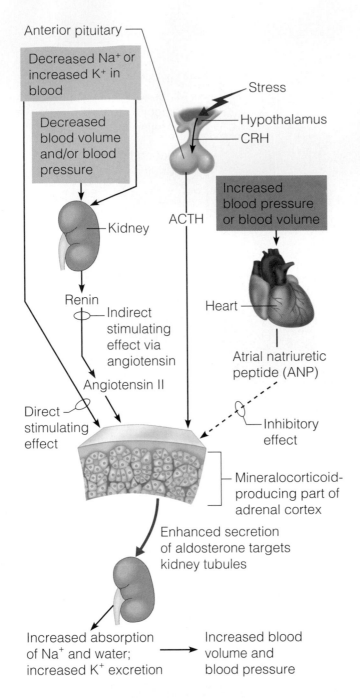

Although the bulk of the sex hormones produced by the innermost cortex layer are **androgens** (male sex hormones), some **estrogens** (female sex hormones) are also formed.

HOMEOSTATIC IMBALANCE

A generalized hyposecretion of all the adrenal cortex hormones leads to **Addison's disease,** characterized by a peculiar bronze tone of the skin. Because aldosterone levels are low, sodium and water are lost from the body, which leads to problems with electrolyte and water balance. This, in turn, causes the muscles to become weak, and shock is a possibility. Other signs and symptoms of Addison's disease result from deficient levels of glucocorticoids, such as hypoglycemia, a lessened ability to cope with stress (burnout), and suppression of the immune system (and thereby increased susceptibility to infection). A complete lack of glucocorticoids is incompatible with life.

Hypersecretion problems may result from an ACTH–releasing tumor, and the resulting condition depends on the cortical area involved. Hyperactivity of the outermost cortical area results in **hyperaldosteronism** (hi"per-al"dos-ter'on-izm). Excessive water and sodium are retained, leading to high blood pressure and edema, and potassium is lost to such an extent that the activity of the heart and nervous system may be disrupted. When the tumor is in the middle cortical area or the client has been receiving pharmacological doses (amounts higher than those released in the body) of glucocorticoids to counteract inflammatory disease, **Cushing's syndrome** occurs. Excessive glucocorticoids result in a swollen "moon face" and the appearance of a "buffalo hump" of fat on the upper back. Other common and undesirable effects include high blood pressure, hyperglycemia (steroid diabetes), weakening of the bones (as protein is withdrawn to be converted to glucose), and severe depression of the immune system.

Hypersecretion of the sex hormones leads to **masculinization**, regardless of sex. In adult males these effects may be masked, but in females the results are often dramatic. A beard develops, and a masculine pattern of body hair distribution occurs, among other effects. ▲

FIGURE 9.12 Major mechanisms controlling aldosterone release from the adrenal cortex. Solid arrows indicate factors that stimulate aldosterone release; dashed arrow indicates an inhibitory factor.

from the adrenal cortex in response to rising blood levels of ACTH.

In both men and women, both male and female **sex hormones** are produced by the adrenal cortex throughout life in relatively small amounts.

Hormones of the Adrenal Medulla

The **adrenal medulla,** like the posterior pituitary, develops from a knot of nervous tissue. When the medulla is stimulated by sympathetic nervous system

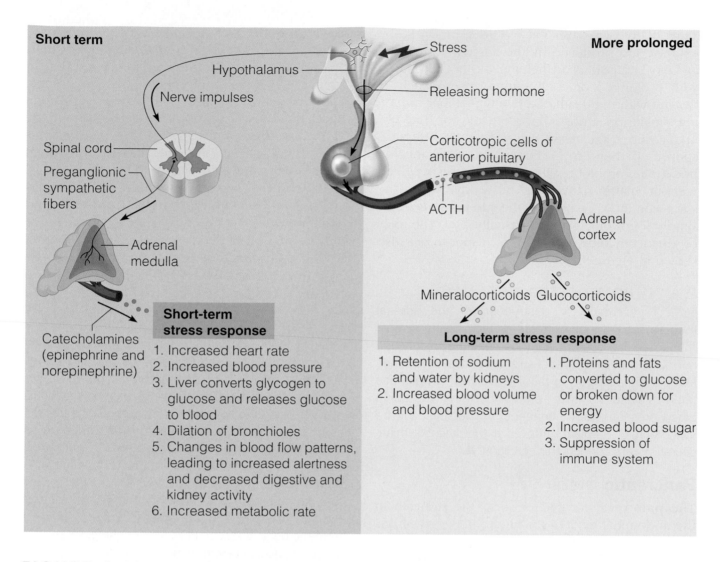

Short term

Stress

Hypothalamus

Nerve impulses

Releasing hormone

Spinal cord

Corticotropic cells of anterior pituitary

Preganglionic sympathetic fibers

More prolonged

ACTH

Adrenal medulla

Adrenal cortex

Catecholamines (epinephrine and norepinephrine)

Mineralocorticoids   Glucocorticoids

Short-term stress response

1. Increased heart rate
2. Increased blood pressure
3. Liver converts glycogen to glucose and releases glucose to blood
4. Dilation of bronchioles
5. Changes in blood flow patterns, leading to increased alertness and decreased digestive and kidney activity
6. Increased metabolic rate

Long-term stress response

1. Retention of sodium and water by kidneys
2. Increased blood volume and blood pressure

1. Proteins and fats converted to glucose or broken down for energy
2. Increased blood sugar
3. Suppression of immune system

FIGURE 9.13   Roles of the hypothalamus, adrenal medulla, and adrenal cortex in the stress response. (Note that ACTH is only a weak stimulator of mineralocorticoid release under normal conditions.)

neurons, its cells release two similar hormones, **epinephrine** (ep″ĭ-nef′rin), also called **adrenaline,** and **norepinephrine (noradrenaline),** into the bloodstream. Collectively, these hormones are referred to as **catecholamines** (kat″ĕ-kol-ah′menz). Because some sympathetic neurons also release norepinephrine as a neurotransmitter, the adrenal medulla is often thought of as a "misplaced sympathetic nervous system ganglion."

When you are (or feel) threatened physically or emotionally, your sympathetic nervous system brings about the "fight-or-flight" response to help you cope with the stressful situation. One of the organs it stimulates is the adrenal medulla, which literally pumps its hormones into the blood-

stream to enhance and prolong the effects of the neurotransmitters of the sympathetic nervous system. Basically, the catecholamines increase heart rate, blood pressure, and blood glucose levels and dilate the small passageways of the lungs. These events result in more oxygen and glucose in the blood and a faster circulation of blood to the body organs (most importantly, to the brain, muscles, and heart). Thus, the body is better able to deal with a short-term stressor, whether the job at hand is to fight, begin the inflammatory process, or alert you so you think more clearly (Figure 9.13).

The catecholamines of the adrenal medulla prepare the body to cope with a brief or short-term stressful situation and cause the so-called *alarm stage* of the stress response. Glucocorticoids, by contrast, are produced by the adrenal cortex and are more important in helping the body to cope with prolonged or continuing stressors, such as dealing with the death of a family member or having a major operation. Glucocorticoids operate primarily during the *resistance stage* of the stress response. If they are successful in protecting the body, the problem will eventually be resolved without lasting damage to the body. When the stress continues on and on, the adrenal cortex may simply "burn out," which is usually fatal. The roles of glucocorticoids in the stress response are also shown in Figure 9.13.

HOMEOSTATIC IMBALANCE

Damage or destruction of the adrenal medulla has no major effects as long as the sympathetic nervous system neurons continue to function normally. However, hypersecretion of catecholamines leads to symptoms typical of excessive sympathetic nervous system activity—a rapidly beating heart, high blood pressure, and a tendency to perspire and be very irritable. Surgical removal of the catecholamine-secreting cells corrects this condition. ▲

Pancreatic Islets

The **pancreas,** located close to the stomach in the abdominal cavity (see Figure 9.3), is a mixed gland. Probably the best-hidden endocrine glands in the body are the **pancreatic islets,** also called the **islets of Langerhans** (lahng′er-hanz). These little masses of hormone-producing tissue are scattered among the enzyme-producing acinar tissue of the pancreas. The exocrine (enzyme-producing) part of the pancreas, which acts as part of the digestive system, will be discussed later; only the pancreatic islets will be considered here.

Although there are more than a million islets, separated by exocrine cells, each of these tiny clumps of cells busily manufactures its hormones and works like an organ within an organ. Two important hormones produced by the islet cells are **insulin** and **glucagon** (gloo′kah-gon). The islets also produce small amounts of other hormones, but those will not be discussed here.

Islet cells act as fuel sensors, secreting insulin and glucagon appropriately during fed and fasting states. High levels of glucose in the blood stimulate the release of insulin from the **beta** (ba′tah) **cells** (Figure 9.14) of the islets. Insulin acts on just

about all body cells and increases their ability to transport glucose across their plasma membranes. Once inside the cells, glucose is oxidized for energy or converted to glycogen or fat for storage. These activities are also speeded up by insulin. Because insulin sweeps the glucose out of the blood, its effect is said to be *hypoglycemic.* As blood glucose levels fall, the stimulus for insulin release ends—another classic case of negative feedback control. Many hormones have hyperglycemic effects (glucagon, glucocorticoids, and epinephrine, to name a few), but insulin is the only hormone that decreases blood glucose levels. Insulin is absolutely necessary for the use of glucose by the body cells. Without it, essentially no glucose can get into the cells to be used.

HOMEOSTATIC IMBALANCE

Without insulin, blood levels of glucose (which normally range from 80 to 120 mg/100 ml of blood) rise to dramatically high levels (for example, 600 mg/100 ml of blood). In such instances, glucose begins to spill into the urine because the kidney tubule cells cannot reabsorb it fast enough. As glucose flushes from the body, water follows, leading to dehydration. The clinical name for this condition is **diabetes mellitus** (me-li′tus), which literally means that something sweet (*mel* = honey) is passing through or siphoning (*diabetes* = Greek "siphon") from the body. Because cells cannot use glucose, fats and even proteins are broken down and used to meet the energy requirements of the body. As a result, body weight begins to decline. Loss of body proteins leads to a decreased ability to fight infections, so diabetics must be careful with their hygiene and in caring for even small cuts and bruises. When large amounts of fats (instead of sugars) are used for energy, the blood becomes very acidic (**acidosis** [as″ĭ-do′sis]) as ketones (intermediate products of fat breakdown) appear in the blood. On the basis of cause, this condition of acidosis (as″i-do′sis) is referred to as **ketosis.** Unless corrected, coma and death result. The three cardinal signs of diabetes mellitus are (1) **polyuria** (pol″e-u′re-ah)—excessive urination to flush out the glucose and ketones; (2) **polydipsia** (pol″e-dip′se-ah)—excessive thirst resulting from water loss; and (3) **polyphagia** (pol″e-fa′je-ah)—hunger due to inability to use sugars and the loss of fat and proteins from the body.

Those with mild cases of diabetes mellitus (most cases of type 2, or adult-onset, diabetes) produce insulin, but for some reason their insulin receptors are unable to

FIGURE 9.14   Pancreatic tissue.
(a) Location of pancreas relative to the stomach and small intestine. **(b)** Photomicrograph of pancreas with exocrine and endocrine (islets) areas clearly visible (110×). **(c)** Diagrammatic view of a pancreatic islet. Beta cells produce insulin, which aids cells in taking up glucose from the blood. Alpha cells produce glucagon, which stimulates liver cells to release glucose to the blood.

respond to it, a situation called **insulin resistance.** Type 2 diabetics are treated with special diets or oral hypoglycemic medications that prod the sluggish islets into action and increase the sensitivity of the target tissues to insulin and of beta cells to the stimulating effects of glucose. To regulate blood glucose levels in the more severe type 1 (juvenile, or brittle) diabetic, insulin is infused continuously by an insulin pump worn externally, or a regimen of carefully planned insulin injections is administered throughout the day. ▲

Glucagon acts as an antagonist of insulin; that is, it helps to regulate blood glucose levels but in a way opposite that of insulin (Figure 9.15). Its release by the **alpha** (al'fah) **cells** (see Figure 9.14c) of the islets is stimulated by low blood levels of glucose. Its action is basically hyperglycemic. Its primary target organ is the liver, which it stimulates to break down stored glycogen to glucose and to release the glucose into the blood. No important disorders resulting from hypo- or hyper-secretion of glucagon are known.

▶ DID YOU GET IT?

13. What hormone stimulates the kidneys to reabsorb more sodium?

14. Mrs. Bellamy's husband has suffered a heart attack and is hospitalized. Would you expect her blood glucose levels to be elevated, normal, or lower than normal? Why?

15. Which group of hormones produced by the adrenal cortex has some of the same effects as the ovaries and the testes?

16. Insulin and glucagon are both pancreatic hormones. Which stimulates cellular uptake of glucose?

For answers, see Appendix D.

Q *What happens to the liver's ability to synthesize and store glycogen when glucagon blood levels rise?*

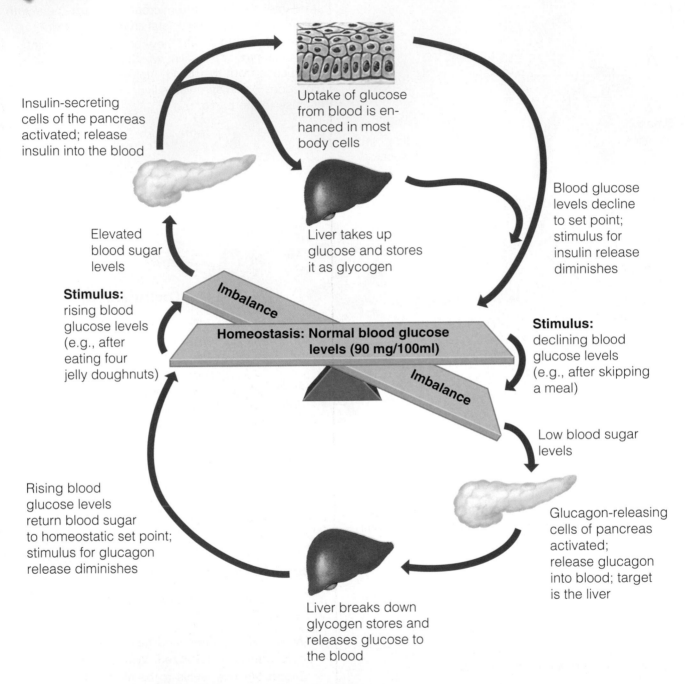

Uptake of glucose from blood is enhanced in most body cells

Insulin-secreting cells of the pancreas activated; release insulin into the blood

Blood glucose levels decline to set point; stimulus for insulin release diminishes

Elevated blood sugar levels

Liver takes up glucose and stores it as glycogen

Imbalance

Stimulus: rising blood glucose levels (e.g., after eating four jelly doughnuts)

Homeostasis: Normal blood glucose levels (90 mg/100ml)

Imbalance

Stimulus: declining blood glucose levels (e.g., after skipping a meal)

Low blood sugar levels

Rising blood glucose levels return blood sugar to homeostatic set point; stimulus for glucagon release diminishes

Glucagon-releasing cells of pancreas activated; release glucagon into blood; target is the liver

Liver breaks down glycogen stores and releases glucose to the blood

FIGURE 9.15 **Regulation of blood glucose levels by a negative feedback mechanism involving pancreatic hormones.**

A *Glucagon inhibits those activities in the liver, so the liver's ability to perform them decreases as glucagon levels rise.*

Pineal Gland

The **pineal** (pin'e-al) **gland,** also called the **pineal body,** is a small, cone-shaped gland that hangs from the roof of the third ventricle of the brain (see Figure 9.3). The endocrine function of this tiny gland is still somewhat of a mystery. Although many chemical substances have been identified in the pineal gland, only the hormone **melatonin** (mel″ah-to'nin) appears to be secreted in substantial amounts. The levels of melatonin rise and fall during the course of the day and night. Peak levels occur at night and make us drowsy; the lowest levels occur during daylight around noon. Melatonin is believed to be a "sleep trigger" that plays an important role in establishing the body's day-night cycle. In some animals, melatonin also helps regulate mating behavior and rhythms. In humans, it is believed to coordinate the hormones of fertility and to inhibit the reproductive system (especially the ovaries of females) so that sexual maturation is prevented from occurring before adult body size has been reached.

Thymus Gland

The **thymus gland** is located in the upper thorax, posterior to the sternum. Large in infants and children, it decreases in size throughout adulthood. By old age, it is composed mostly of fibrous connective tissue and fat. The thymus produces a hormone called **thymosin** (thi'mo-sin) and others that appear to be essential for normal development of a special group of white blood cells (*T lymphocytes,* or *T cells*) and the immune response. The role of the thymus (and its hormones) in immunity is described in Chapter 12.

Gonads

The female and male gonads (see Figure 9.3) produce sex hormones that are identical to those produced by adrenal cortex cells. The major differences are the source and relative amounts produced.

Hormones of the Ovaries

The female *gonads* (go'nadz), or **ovaries**, are paired, almond-sized organs located in the pelvic cavity. Besides producing female sex cells (ova, or eggs), ovaries produce two groups of steroid hormones, **estrogens** and **progesterone.**

Alone, the estrogens are responsible for the development of sex characteristics in women (primarily growth and maturation of the reproductive organs) and the appearance of secondary sex characteristics (hair in the pubic and axillary regions) at puberty. Acting with progesterone, estrogens promote breast development and cyclic changes in the uterine lining (the **menstrual cycle**).

Progesterone (pro-jes'tĕ-rōn), as already noted, acts with estrogen to bring about the menstrual cycle. During pregnancy, it quiets the muscles of the uterus so that an implanted embryo will not be aborted and helps prepare breast tissue for lactation.

Ovaries are stimulated to release their estrogens and progesterone in a cyclic way by the anterior pituitary gonadotropic hormones. More detail on this feedback cycle and on the structure, function, and controls of the ovaries is given in Chapter 16, but it should be obvious that hyposecretion of the ovarian hormones severely hampers the ability of a woman to conceive and bear children.

Hormones of the Testes

The paired oval **testes** of the male are suspended in a sac, the *scrotum,* outside the pelvic cavity. In addition to male sex cells, or *sperm,* the testes also produce male sex hormones, or **androgens,** of which **testosterone** (tes-tos'tĕ-rōn) is the most important. At puberty, testosterone promotes the growth and maturation of the reproductive system organs to prepare the young man for reproduction. It also causes the male's secondary sex characteristics (growth of facial hair, development of heavy bones and muscles, and lowering of the voice) to appear and stimulates the male sex drive.

In adults, testosterone is necessary for continuous production of sperm. In cases of hyposecretion, the man becomes sterile; such cases are usually treated by testosterone injections. The release of gonadal hormones is controlled by anterior pituitary gonadotropins, as described earlier. Testosterone production is specifically stimulated by LH. Chapter 16, which deals with the reproductive system, contains more information on the structure and exocrine function of the testes.

Table 9.1 summarizes the major endocrine glands and some of their hormones.

TABLE 9.1	Major Endocrine Glands and Some of Their Hormones

Gland	Hormone	Chemical class	Representative actions	Regulated by
Pineal body	Melatonin	Amine	Involved in biological rhythms (daily and seasonal)	Light/dark cycles
Hypothalamus	Hormones released by the posterior pituitary; releasing and inhibiting hormones that regulate the anterior pituitary (see below)			
Pituitary gland				
• Posterior lobe (releases hormones made by the hypothalamus)	Oxytocin	Peptide	Stimulates contraction of uterus and the milk "let-down" reflex	Nervous system (hypothalamus) in response to uterine stretching and/or suckling of a baby
	Antidiuretic hormone (ADH)	Peptide	Promotes retention of water by kidneys	Hypothalamus in response to water/salt imbalance
• Anterior lobe	Growth hormone (GH)	Protein	Stimulates growth (especially of bones and muscles) and metabolism	Hypothalamic releasing and inhibiting hormones
	Prolactin (PRL)	Protein	Stimulates milk production	Hypothalamic hormones
	Follicle-stimulating hormone (FSH)	Protein	Stimulates production of ova and sperm	Hypothalamic hormones
	Luteinizing hormone (LH)	Protein	Stimulates ovaries and testes	Hypothalamic hormones
	Thyroid-stimulating hormone (TSH)	Protein	Stimulates thyroid gland	Thyroxine in blood; hypothalamic hormones
	Adrenocorticotropic hormone (ACTH)	Protein	Stimulates adrenal cortex to secrete glucocorticoids	Glucocorticoids; hypothalamic hormones
Thyroid gland	Thyroxine (T_4) and triiodothyronine (T_3)	Amine	Stimulates metabolism	TSH

TABLE 9.1	*(continued)*

Gland		Hormone	Chemical class	Representative actions	Regulated by
Thyroid gland		Calcitonin	Peptide	Reduces blood calcium level	Calcium level in blood
Parathyroid glands		Parathyroid hormone (PTH)	Peptide	Raises blood calcium level	Calcium level in blood
Thymus gland		Thymosin	Peptide	"Programs" T lymphocytes	Not known
Adrenal glands					
• Adrenal medulla		Epinephrine and norepinephrine	Amines	Raise blood glucose level; increase rate of metabolism; constrict certain blood vessels	Nervous system (sympathetic division)
• Adrenal cortex		Glucocorticoids	Steroids	Increase blood glucose	ACTH
		Mineralocorticoids	Steroids	Promote reabsorption of Na^+ and excretion of K^+ in kidneys	Changes in blood volume or blood pressure; K^+ (potassium) or Na^+ levels in blood
Pancreas		Insulin	Protein	Reduces blood glucose	Glucose level in blood
		Glucagon	Protein	Raises blood glucose	Glucose level in blood
Gonads					
• Testes		Androgens	Steroids	Support sperm formation; development and maintenance of male secondary sex characteristics	FSH and LH
• Ovaries		Estrogens	Steroids	Stimulate uterine lining growth; development and maintenance of female secondary sex characteristics	FSH and LH
		Progesterone	Steroids	Promotes growth of uterine living	FSH and LH

▶ **DID YOU GET IT?**

17. What hormone is called the sleep hormone, and which endocrine organ produces it?

18. How do thymosin and other thymus hormones help to protect the body?

19. Which gonadal hormone causes a young girl's body to develop feminine characteristics at puberty—estrogen or progesterone?

For answers, see Appendix D.

Other Hormone-Producing Tissues and Organs

Besides the major endocrine organs, pockets of hormone-producing cells are found in fatty tissue and in the walls of the small intestine, stomach, kidneys, and heart—organs whose chief functions have little to do with hormone production. Because most of these hormones are described in later chapters, their chief characteristics are only summarized in Table 9.2. Only the placental hormones are considered further here.

Placenta

The **placenta** (plah-sen'tah) is a remarkable organ formed temporarily in the uterus of pregnant women. In addition to its roles as the respiratory, excretory, and nutrition-delivery systems for the fetus, it also produces several protein and steroid hormones that help to maintain the pregnancy and pave the way for delivery of the baby.

During very early pregnancy, a hormone called **human chorionic** (ko"re-on'ik) **gonadotropin (hCG)** is produced by the developing embryo and then by the fetal part of the placenta. Similar to LH (luteinizing hormone), hCG stimulates the ovaries to *continue* producing estrogen and progesterone so that the lining of the uterus is not sloughed off in menses. (The home pregnancy tests sold over the counter test for the presence of hCG in the woman's urine.) In the third month, the placenta assumes the job of producing estrogen and progesterone, and the ovaries become inactive for the rest of the pregnancy. The high estrogen and progesterone blood levels maintain the lining of the uterus (thus, the pregnancy) and prepare the breasts for producing milk. **Human placental lactogen (hPL)** works cooperatively with estrogen and progesterone in preparing the breasts for lactation. **Relaxin**, another placental hormone, causes the mother's pelvic ligaments and the pubic symphysis to relax and become more flexible, which eases birth passage.

Developmental Aspects of the Endocrine System

The embryonic development of the endocrine glands varies. The pituitary gland is derived from epithelium of the oral cavity and a neural tissue projection of the hypothalamus. The pineal body is entirely neural tissue. Most strictly epithelial glands develop as little saclike outpocketings of the mucosa of the digestive tract. These are the thyroid, thymus, and pancreas. Formation of the gonads and the adrenal and parathyroid glands is much more complex and is not considered here.

Barring outright malfunctions of the endocrine glands, most endocrine organs seem to operate smoothly until old age. In late middle age, the efficiency of the ovaries begins to decline, causing **menopause** (commonly called "the change of life"). During this period, a woman's reproductive organs begin to atrophy, and the ability to bear children ends. Problems associated with estrogen deficiency begin to occur, such as arteriosclerosis, osteoporosis, decreased skin elasticity, and changes in the operation of the sympathetic nervous system that result in "hot flashes." In addition, fatigue, nervousness, and mood changes such as depression are common. No such dramatic changes seem to happen in men. In fact, many men remain fertile throughout their life span, indicating that testosterone is still being produced in adequate amounts.

The efficiency of the endocrine system as a whole gradually declines in old age. Striking changes in aging women are due to decreasing levels of female hormones, and there is no question that growth hormone output by the anterior pituitary declines, which partially explains muscle atrophy in old age. Elderly persons are less able to resist stress and infection. This decreased resistance may result from overproduction or underproduction of the defensive hormones, because both

TABLE 9.2	Hormones Produced by Organs Other Than the Major Endocrine Organs			
Hormone	**Chemical composition**	**Source**	**Stimulus for secretion**	**Target organ/Effects**
Prostaglandins (PGs); several groups indicated by letters A–I (PGA–PGI)	Derived from fatty acid molecules	Plasma membranes of virtually all body cells	Various (local irritation, hormones, etc.)	Have many targets, but act locally at site of release. Examples of effects include: increase blood pressure by acting as vasoconstrictors; cause constriction of respiratory passageways; stimulate muscle of the uterus, promoting labor; enhance blood clotting; promote inflammation and pain; increase output of digestive secretions by stomach; cause fever.
Gastrin	Peptide	Stomach	Food	*Stomach:* stimulates glands to release hydrochloric acid (HCl).
Intestinal gastrin	Peptide	Duodenum of small intestine	Food, especially fats	*Stomach:* inhibits HCl secretion and gastrointestinal tract mobility.
Secretin	Peptide	Duodenum	Food	*Pancreas:* stimulates release of bicarbonate-rich juice. *Liver:* increases release of bile. *Stomach:* reduces secretions.
Cholecystokinin (CCK)	Peptide	Duodenum	Food	*Pancreas:* stimulates release of enzyme-rich juice. *Gallbladder:* stimulates expulsion of stored bile. *Duodenal papilla:* causes sphincter to relax, allowing bile and pancreatic juice to enter duodenum.
Erythropoietin	Glycoprotein	Kidney	Hypoxia	*Bone marrow:* stimulates production of red blood cells.
Active vitamin D_3	Steroid	Kidney (activates provitamin D made by epidermal cells)	PTH	*Intestine:* stimulates active transport of dietary calcium across intestinal cell membranes.
Atrial natriuretic peptide (ANP)	Peptide	Heart	Stretching of atria of heart	*Kidney:* inhibits sodium ion reabsorption and renin release. *Adrenal cortex:* inhibits secretion of aldosterone, thereby decreasing blood volume and blood pressure.
Leptin	Peptide	Adipose tissue	Fatty foods	*Brain:* suppresses appetite and increases energy expenditure.
Resistin	Peptide	Adipose tissue	Unknown	*Fat, muscle, liver:* antagonizes insulin's action on liver cells.

SYSTEMS IN SYNC

HOMEOSTATIC RELATIONSHIPS BETWEEN THE
ENDOCRINE SYSTEM AND OTHER BODY SYSTEMS

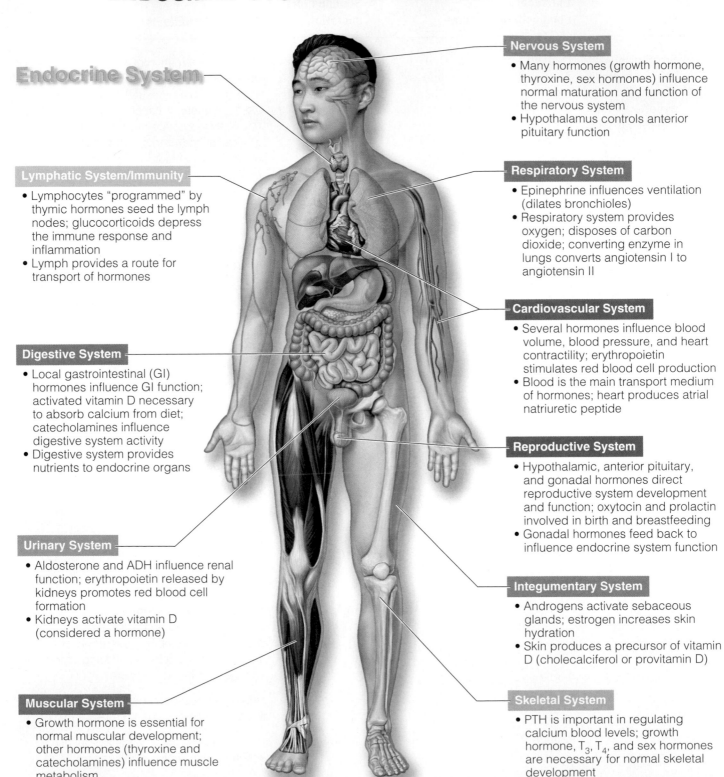

Endocrine System

Nervous System
- Many hormones (growth hormone, thyroxine, sex hormones) influence normal maturation and function of the nervous system
- Hypothalamus controls anterior pituitary function

Lymphatic System/Immunity
- Lymphocytes "programmed" by thymic hormones seed the lymph nodes; glucocorticoids depress the immune response and inflammation
- Lymph provides a route for transport of hormones

Respiratory System
- Epinephrine influences ventilation (dilates bronchioles)
- Respiratory system provides oxygen; disposes of carbon dioxide; converting enzyme in lungs converts angiotensin I to angiotensin II

Cardiovascular System
- Several hormones influence blood volume, blood pressure, and heart contractility; erythropoietin stimulates red blood cell production
- Blood is the main transport medium of hormones; heart produces atrial natriuretic peptide

Digestive System
- Local gastrointestinal (GI) hormones influence GI function; activated vitamin D necessary to absorb calcium from diet; catecholamines influence digestive system activity
- Digestive system provides nutrients to endocrine organs

Reproductive System
- Hypothalamic, anterior pituitary, and gonadal hormones direct reproductive system development and function; oxytocin and prolactin involved in birth and breastfeeding
- Gonadal hormones feed back to influence endocrine system function

Urinary System
- Aldosterone and ADH influence renal function; erythropoietin released by kidneys promotes red blood cell formation
- Kidneys activate vitamin D (considered a hormone)

Integumentary System
- Androgens activate sebaceous glands; estrogen increases skin hydration
- Skin produces a precursor of vitamin D (cholecalciferol or provitamin D)

Muscular System
- Growth hormone is essential for normal muscular development; other hormones (thyroxine and catecholamines) influence muscle metabolism
- Muscular system mechanically protects some endocrine glands; muscular activity promotes catecholamine release

Skeletal System
- PTH is important in regulating calcium blood levels; growth hormone, T_3, T_4, and sex hormones are necessary for normal skeletal development
- The skeleton protects some endocrine organs, especially those in brain, chest, and pelvis

"derail" the stress defense equilibrium and alter general body metabolism. Additionally, exposure to many pesticides, industrial chemicals, dioxin, and other soil and water pollutants diminishes endocrine function, which may explain the higher cancer rates among older adults in certain areas of the country. Older people are often mildly hypothyroid, and all older people have some decline in insulin production, and type 2 diabetes is most common in this age group.

▶ DID YOU GET IT?

20. Which two digestive system organs are important sources of hormones associated with digestion?

21. What temporary organ produces the same hormones as the ovaries?

22. Failure of which endocrine organ(s) leads to menopause in women?

For answers, see Appendix D.

SUMMARY

Media study tools that provide additional review of key topics of Chapter 9 are referenced below.

IP = *InterActive Physiology*
WEB = The A&P Place

The Endocrine System and Hormone Function—An Overview   (pp. 310–313)

1. The endocrine system is a major controlling system of the body. Through hormones, it stimulates such long-term processes as growth and development, metabolism, reproduction, and body defense.

2. Endocrine organs are small and widely separated in the body. Some are part of mixed glands (both endocrine and exocrine in function). Others are purely hormone producing.

3. Nearly all hormones are amino acid–based or steroids.

4. Endocrine organs are activated to release their hormones into the blood by hormonal, humoral, or neural stimuli. Negative feedback is important in regulating hormone levels in the blood.

5. Bloodborne hormones alter the metabolic activities of their target organs. The ability of a target organ to respond to a hormone depends on the presence of receptors in or on its cells to which the hormone binds or attaches.

6. Amino acid–based hormones act through second messengers. Steroid hormones directly influence the target cell's DNA.

IP Endocrine System; Topic: Endocrine System Review, pp. 1–5.

IP Endocrine System; Topic: Biochemistry, Secretion and Transport of Hormones, pp. 1–3.

IP Endocrine System; Topic: The Actions of Hormones on Target Cells, pp. 1–3.

WEB Exercise: Chapter 9, Hormones and Their Target Cells.

The Major Endocrine Organs   (pp. 313–332)

1. Pituitary gland

   a. The pituitary gland hangs from the hypothalamus of the brain by a stalk and is enclosed by bone. It consists of a glandular (anterior) portion and a neural (posterior) portion.

   b. Except for growth hormone and prolactin, hormones of the anterior pituitary are all tropic hormones.

      (1) Growth hormone (GH): An anabolic and protein-conserving hormone that promotes total body growth. Its most important effect is on skeletal muscles and bones. Untreated hyposecretion during childhood results in pituitary dwarfism; hypersecretion produces gigantism (in childhood) and acromegaly (in adulthood).

      (2) Prolactin (PRL): Stimulates production of breast milk.

      (3) Adrenocorticotropic hormone (ACTH): Stimulates the adrenal cortex to release its hormones.

      (4) Thyroid-stimulating hormone (TSH): Stimulates the thyroid gland to release thyroid hormone.

      (5) Gonadotropic hormones

         (a) Follicle-stimulating hormone (FSH): Beginning at puberty, stimulates follicle development and estrogen production by the female ovaries; promotes sperm production in the male.

         (b) Luteinizing hormone (LH): Beginning at puberty, stimulates ovulation, causes the ruptured ovarian follicle to produce progesterone; stimulates the male's testes to produce testosterone.

c.   Releasing and inhibiting hormones made by the hypothalamus regulate release of hormones made by the anterior pituitary. The hypothalamus also makes two hormones that are transported to the posterior pituitary for storage and later release.

IP Endocrine System; Topic: Hypothalamic-Pituitary Axis, pp. 1–3.

d.   The posterior pituitary stores and releases hypothalamic hormones on command.

(1) Oxytocin: Stimulates powerful uterine contractions and causes milk ejection in the nursing woman.

(2) Antidiuretic hormone (ADH): Causes kidney tubule cells to reabsorb and conserve body water and increases blood pressure by constricting blood vessels. Hyposecretion leads to diabetes insipidus.

WEB Exercise: Chapter 9, Endocrine Case Study.

2. Thyroid gland

a.   The thyroid gland is located in the anterior throat.

b.   Thyroid hormone (thyroxine [T_4] and triiodothyronine [T_3]) is released from the thyroid follicles when blood levels of TSH rise. Thyroid hormone is the body's metabolic hormone. It increases the rate at which cells oxidize glucose and is necessary for normal growth and development. Lack of iodine leads to goiter. Hyposecretion of thyroxine results in cretinism in children and myxedema in adults. Hypersecretion results from Graves' disease or other forms of hyperthyroidism.

IP Endocrine System; Topic: Hormone Imbalances, p. 3.

WEB Exercise: Chapter 9, At the Clinic: Endocrine System.

c.   Calcitonin is released by parafollicular cells surrounding the thyroid follicles in response to high blood levels of calcium. It causes calcium to be deposited in bones.

3. Parathyroid glands

a.   The parathyroid glands are four small glands located on the posterior aspect of the thyroid gland.

b.   Low blood levels of calcium stimulate the parathyroid glands to release parathyroid hormone (PTH). It causes bone calcium to be liberated into the blood. Hyposecretion of PTH results in tetany; hypersecretion leads to extreme bone wasting and fractures.

WEB Exercise: Chapter 9, Ionic Calcium Levels in the Blood.

4. Adrenal glands

a.   The adrenal glands are paired glands perched on the kidneys. Each gland has two functional endocrine portions, the cortex and the medulla.

b.   Adrenal cortex hormones include:

(1) Mineralocorticoids, primarily aldosterone, regulate sodium ion (Na^+) and potassium ion (K^+) reabsorption by the kidneys. Their release is stimulated primarily by low Na^+ and/or high K^+ levels in blood.

(2) Glucocorticoids enable the body to resist long-term stress by increasing blood glucose levels and depressing the inflammatory response.

(3) Sex hormones (mainly androgens) are produced in small amounts throughout life.

c.   Generalized hypoactivity of the adrenal cortex results in Addison's disease. Hypersecretion can result in hyperaldosteronism, Cushing's disease, and/or masculinization.

d.   The adrenal medulla produces catecholamines (epinephrine and norepinephrine) in response to sympathetic nervous system stimulation. Its catecholamines enhance and prolong the effects of the "fight-or-flight" (sympathetic nervous system) response to short-term stress. Hypersecretion leads to symptoms typical of sympathetic nervous system overactivity.

IP Endocrine System; Topic: Hormone Imbalances, pp. 4–5.

5. Pancreatic islets

a.   Located in the abdomen close to the stomach, the pancreas is both an exocrine and endocrine gland. The endocrine portion (islets) releases insulin and glucagon to blood.

b.   Insulin is released when blood levels of glucose are high. It increases the rate of glucose uptake and metabolism by body cells. Hyposecretion of insulin results in diabetes mellitus, which severely disturbs body metabolism. Cardinal signs are polyuria, polydipsia, and polyphagia.

c.   Glucagon, released when blood levels of glucose are low, stimulates the liver to release glucose to blood, thus increasing blood glucose levels.

IP Endocrine System; Topic: Hormone Imbalances, p. 2.

WEB Exercise: Chapter 9, Regulation of Blood Sugar Levels by Insulin and Glycogen.

6. The pineal gland, located posterior to the third ventricle of the brain, releases melatonin, which affects sleep as well as biological rhythms and reproductive behavior in other animals.

7. The thymus gland, located in the upper thorax, functions during youth but atrophies in old age. Its hormone, thymosin, promotes maturation of T lymphocytes, important in body defense.

8. Gonads

   a. The ovaries of the female release:

      (1) Estrogens: Release of estrogens by ovarian follicles begins at puberty under the influence of FSH. Estrogens stimulate maturation of the female reproductive organs and female secondary sex characteristics. With progesterone, they cause the menstrual cycle.

      (2) Progesterone: Progesterone is released from the ovary in response to high blood levels of LH. It works with estrogens in establishing the menstrual cycle.

   b. The testes of the male begin to produce testosterone at puberty in response to LH stimulation. Testosterone promotes maturation of the male reproductive organs, male secondary sex characteristics, and production of sperm by the testes.

   c. Hyposecretion of gonadal hormones results in sterility in both females and males.

Other Hormone-Producing Tissues and Organs (p. 332)

1. The placenta is a temporary organ formed in the uterus of pregnant women. Its primary endocrine role is to produce estrogen and progesterone, which maintain pregnancy and ready breasts for lactation.

2. Several organs that are generally nonendocrine in overall function, such as the stomach, small intestine, kidneys, and heart, have cells that secrete hormones.

3. Certain cancer cells secrete hormones.

Developmental Aspects of the Endocrine System (pp. 332, 335)

1. In the absence of disease, efficiency of the endocrine system remains high until old age.

2. Decreasing function of female ovaries at menopause leads to such symptoms as osteoporosis, increased chance of heart disease, and possible mood changes.

3. Efficiency of all endocrine glands gradually decreases with aging, which leads to a generalized increase in incidence of diabetes mellitus, immune system depression, lower metabolic rate, and, in some areas, cancer rates.

REVIEW QUESTIONS

Multiple Choice

More than one choice may apply.

1. The major endocrine organs of the body
   a. tend to be very large organs.
   b. are closely connected with each other.
   c. all contribute to the same function (digestion).
   d. tend to lie near the midline of the body.

2. Which is generally true of hormones?
   a. Exocrine glands produce them.
   b. They travel throughout the body in the blood.
   c. They affect only nonhormone-producing organs.
   d. All steroid hormones produce very similar physiological effects in the body.

3. Which of the following hormones is (are) secreted by neurons?
   a. Oxytocin   c. ADH
   b. Insulin   d. Cortisol

4. ANP, the hormone secreted by the heart, has exactly the opposite function to this hormone secreted by the outermost zone of the adrenal cortex.
   a. Epinephrine   c. Aldosterone
   b. Cortisol   d. Testosterone

5. Hormones that act directly or indirectly to elevate blood glucose include which of the following?
   a. GH   c. insulin
   b. Cortisol   d. ACTH

6. Hypertension may result from hypersecretion of
   a. thyroxine.   c. aldosterone.
   b. cortisol.   d. ADH.

7. Hormones that regulate mineral (salt) levels include
   a. calcitonin.   c. atrial natriuretic peptide.
   b. aldosterone.   d. glucagon.

8. Which of the following is given as a drug to reduce inflammation?
   a. Epinephrine   c. Aldosterone
   b. Cortisol   d. ADH

9. The element needed for thyroid gland function is
    a. potassium.   c. calcium.
    b. iodine.   d. manganese.

Short Answer Essay

10. Explain how the nervous and endocrine systems differ in **(a)** the rate of their control, **(b)** the way in which they communicate with body cells, and **(c)** the types of body processes they control.

11. Which endocrine organs are actually mixed (endocrine and exocrine) glands? Which are purely endocrine?

12. Describe the chemical nature of hormones.

13. Provide one example for each way endocrine glands are stimulated to release their hormones.

14. Define *negative feedback,* and explain how it regulates blood levels of the various hormones.

15. Explain why not all organs are target organs for all hormones.

16. Describe the body location of each of the following endocrine organs: anterior pituitary, pineal gland, thymus, pancreas, ovaries, testes. Then, for each organ, name its hormones and their effect(s) on body processes. Finally, for each hormone, list the important results of its hypersecretion or hyposecretion.

17. Name two endocrine-producing glands (or regions) that are important in the stress response, and explain *why* they are important.

18. The anterior pituitary is often referred to as the master endocrine gland, but it too has a "master." What controls the release of hormones by the anterior pituitary?

19. What is the most common cause of hypersecretion by endocrine organs?

20. Name three hormone antagonists of insulin and one of PTH.

21. Two hormones are closely involved in the regulation of the fluid and electrolyte balance of the body. Name them, and explain their effects on their common target organ.

22. What causes a simple goiter?

23. In general, the endocrine system becomes less efficient as we age. List some examples of problems that elderly individuals have as a result of decreasing hormone production.

CRITICAL THINKING AND CLINICAL APPLICATION QUESTIONS

24. A woman with excessive body hair and a deep voice shows the outward symptoms of which hormonal dysfunction?

25. The parents of 14-year-old Megan are concerned about her height because she is only 4 feet tall and they are both close to 6 feet tall. After tests by their doctor, certain hormones are prescribed for the girl. What is the probable diagnosis? What hormones are prescribed, and why might the girl expect to reach normal height?

26. Paula, a 28-year-old, has been in the first stage of labor for 15 hours. Her uterine contractions are weak, and her labor is not progressing normally. Paula and her doctor desire a vaginal delivery, so the physician orders that Pitocin (a synthetic oxytocin) be infused. What is the effect of this hormone?

27. Mr. Holdt brings his wife to the clinic, concerned about her nervousness, heart palpitations, and excessive sweating. Tests show hyperglycemia and hypertension. What hormones are probably being hypersecreted? What is the cause? What physical factors allow you to rule out thyroid problems?

28. What are the possible harmful effects of using anabolic steroids to increase muscle mass and strength?

29. Bertha Wise, age 40, comes to the clinic, troubled by swelling in her face and unusual fat deposition on her back and abdomen. She reports that she bruises easily. Blood tests show elevated glucose levels. What is your diagnosis, and what glands might be causing the problem?

30. Maryanne, a street person, is pregnant. She has had no prenatal care, and her diet consists of what she is able to salvage from trash cans. What could you surmise about the PTH levels in her blood?

31. Richard Neis had symptoms of excessive secretion of PTH (high blood calcium levels), and his physicians were certain he had a parathyroid gland tumor. Yet when surgery was performed on his neck, the surgeon could not find the parathyroid glands at all. Where should the surgeon look next to find the tumorous parathyroid gland?

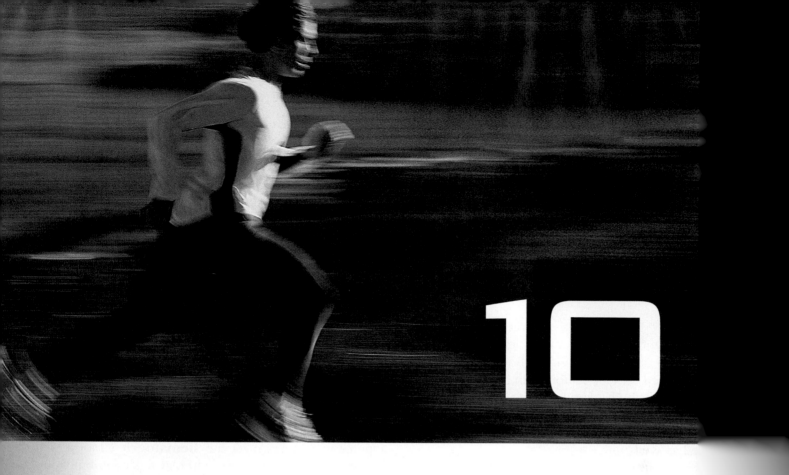

Blood

YOUR GOALS

After completing this chapter, you will have a working knowledge of the functions of blood and will have mastered the objectives listed below.

FUNCTION PREVIEW

• Blood serves as a vehicle for distributing body heat and for transporting nutrients, respiratory gases, and other substances throughout the body.

OBJECTIVE CHECKLIST

Composition and Functions of Blood (pp. 340–349)

➤ Describe the composition and volume of whole blood.

➤ Describe the composition of plasma, and discuss its importance in the body.

➤ List the cell types making up the formed elements, and describe the major functions of each type.

➤ Define *anemia, polycythemia, leukopenia,* and *leukocytosis,* and list possible causes for each condition.

➤ Explain the role of the hemocytoblast.

Hemostasis (pp. 349–351)

➤ Describe the blood-clotting process.

➤ Name some factors that may inhibit or enhance the blood-clotting process.

Blood Groups and Transfusions (pp. 351–354)

➤ Describe the ABO and Rh blood groups.

➤ Explain the basis for a transfusion reaction.

Developmental Aspects of Blood (pp. 354, 356)

➤ Explain the basis of physiologic jaundice seen in some newborn babies.

➤ Indicate blood disorders that increase in frequency in the aged.

Blood is the "river of life" that surges within us. It transports everything that must be carried from one place to another within the body—nutrients, wastes (headed for elimination from the body), and body heat—through blood vessels. Long before modern medicine, blood was viewed as magical, because when it drained from the body, life departed as well.

In this chapter, we consider the composition and function of this life-sustaining fluid. The means by which it is propelled throughout the body is discussed in Chapter 11.

Composition and Functions of Blood

Components

Blood is unique: It is the only *fluid* tissue in the body. Although blood appears to be a thick, homogeneous liquid, the microscope reveals that it has both solid and liquid components. Essentially, blood is a complex connective tissue in which living blood cells, the **formed elements,** are suspended in a nonliving fluid matrix called **plasma** (plaz'muh). The collagen and elastin fibers typical of other connective tissues are absent from blood, but dissolved proteins become visible as fibrin strands during blood clotting.

If a sample of blood is spun in a centrifuge, the formed elements, being heavier, are packed down by centrifugal force and the plasma rises to the top (Figure 10.1). Most of the reddish mass at the bottom of the tube is *erythrocytes* (eh-rith'ro-sīts; *erythro* = red), or red blood cells, the formed elements that function in oxygen transport. Although it is barely visible in Figure 10.1, there is a thin, whitish layer called the **buffy coat** at the junction between the erythrocytes and the plasma. This layer contains the remaining formed elements, *leukocytes* (lu'ko-sīts *leuko* = white), the white blood cells that act in various ways to protect the body, and *platelets,* cell fragments that help stop bleeding. Erythrocytes normally account for about 45 percent of the total volume of a blood sample, a percentage known as the **hematocrit** ("blood fraction"). White blood cells and platelets contribute less than 1 percent, and plasma makes up most of the remaining 55 percent of whole blood.

Physical Characteristics and Volume

Blood is a sticky opaque fluid with a characteristic metallic taste. As children, we discover its saltiness the first time we stick a cut finger into our mouth. Depending on the amount of oxygen it is carrying, the color of blood varies from scarlet (oxygen-rich) to a dull red (oxygen-poor). Blood is heavier than water and about five times thicker, or more viscous, largely because of its formed elements. Blood is slightly alkaline, with a pH between 7.35 and 7.45. Its temperature (38°C, or 100.4°F) is always slightly higher than body temperature.

Blood accounts for approximately 8 percent of body weight, and its volume in healthy men is 5 to 6 liters, or about 6 quarts.

Plasma

Plasma, which is approximately 90 percent water, is the liquid part of the blood. Over 100 different substances are dissolved in this straw-colored fluid. Examples of dissolved substances include nutrients, salts (electrolytes), respiratory gases, hormones, plasma proteins, and various wastes and products of cell metabolism.

How would a decrease in the amount of plasma proteins affect plasma volume?

Plasma 55%	
Constituent	**Major Functions**
Water	Solvent for carrying other substances; absorbs heat
Salts (electrolytes) Sodium Potassium Calcium Magnesium Chloride Bicarbonate	Osmotic balance, pH buffering, regulation of membrane permeability
Plasma proteins Albumin	Osmotic balance, pH buffering
Fibrinogen	Clotting of blood
Globulins	Defense (antibodies) and lipid transport
Substances transported by blood Nutrients (glucose, fatty acids, amino acids, vitamins)	
Waste products of metabolism (urea, uric acid)	
Respiratory gases (O_2 and CO_2) Hormones	

Formed elements (cells) 45%		
Cell Type	**Number (per mm³ of blood)**	**Functions**
Erythrocytes (red blood cells)	4 – 6 million	Transport oxygen and help transport carbon dioxide
Leukocytes (white blood cells)	4000 – 11,000	Defense and immunity
Basophil Lymphocyte Eosinophil Neutrophil Monocyte		
Platelets	250,000 – 500,000	Blood clotting

FIGURE 10.1 **The composition of blood.**

Plasma proteins create the osmotic pressure that helps to maintain plasma volume and draws leaked fluid back into the circulation. Hence, a decrease in the amount of plasma proteins would result in a reduced plasma volume.

Lymphocyte   Platelets

Erythrocytes   Neutrophils

FIGURE 10.2 Photomicrograph of a blood smear. Most of the cells in this view are erythrocytes (red blood cells). Two kinds of leukocytes (white blood cells) are also present: lymphocytes and neutrophils. Also note the platelets.

Plasma proteins are the most abundant solutes in plasma. Except for antibodies and protein-based hormones, most plasma proteins are made by the liver. The plasma proteins serve a variety of functions. For instance, **albumin** (al-bu'min) acts as a carrier to shuttle certain molecules through the circulation, is an important blood buffer, and contributes to the osmotic pressure of blood, which acts to keep water in the bloodstream. Clotting proteins help stem blood loss when a blood vessel is injured, and antibodies help protect the body from pathogens. Plasma proteins are *not* taken up by cells to be used as food fuels or metabolic nutrients, as are other solutes such as glucose, fatty acids, and oxygen.

The composition of plasma varies continuously as cells remove or add substances to the blood. Assuming a healthy diet, however, the composition of plasma is kept relatively constant by various homeostatic mechanisms of the body. For example, when blood proteins drop to undesirable

levels, the liver is stimulated to make more proteins, and when the blood starts to become too acid *(acidosis)* or too basic *(alkalosis),* both the respiratory system and the kidneys are called into action to restore it to its normal, slightly alkaline pH range of 7.35 to 7.45. Various body organs make dozens of adjustments day in and day out to maintain the many plasma solutes at life-sustaining levels. Besides transporting various substances around the body, plasma helps to distribute body heat, a by-product of cellular metabolism, evenly throughout the body.

▶ DID YOU GET IT?

1. Which body organ plays the main role in producing blood proteins?

2. What are the three major categories of formed elements?

3. What determines whether blood is bright red (scarlet) or dull red?

For answers, see Appendix D.

Formed Elements

If you observe a stained smear of human blood under a light microscope, you will see disc-shaped red blood cells, a variety of gaudily stained spherical white blood cells, and some scattered platelets that look like debris (Figure 10.2). However, erythrocytes vastly outnumber the other types of formed elements. Table 10.2 on p. 346 provides a summary of the important characteristics of the various formed elements.

Erythrocytes

Erythrocytes, or **red blood cells (RBCs),** function primarily to ferry oxygen in blood to all cells of the body. They are superb examples of the "fit" between cell structure and function. RBCs differ from other blood cells because they are *anucleate* (a-nu'kle-at); that is, they lack a nucleus. They also contain very few organelles. In fact, mature RBCs circulating in the blood are literally "bags" of hemoglobin molecules. **Hemoglobin** (he"mo-glo'bin) **(Hb),** an iron-bearing protein, transports the bulk of the oxygen that is carried in the blood. (It also binds with a small amount of carbon dioxide.) Moreover, because erythrocytes lack mitochondria and make ATP by anaerobic mechanisms, they do not use up any of the oxygen they are transporting, making them very efficient oxygen transporters indeed.

Erythrocytes are small, flexible cells shaped like biconcave discs—flattened discs with depressed centers on both sides (Figure 10.2). Because of their thinner centers, they look like miniature doughnuts when viewed with a microscope. Their small size and peculiar shape provide a large surface area relative to their volume, making them ideally suited for gas exchange.

RBCs outnumber white blood cells by about 1000 to 1 and are the major factor contributing to blood viscosity. Although the numbers of RBCs in the circulation do vary, there are normally about 5 million cells per cubic millimeter of blood. (A cubic millimeter [mm^3] is a very tiny drop of blood, almost not enough to be seen.) When the number of RBC/mm^3 increases, blood viscosity increases. Similarly, as the number of RBCs decreases, blood thins and flows more rapidly. However, let's not get carried away talking about RBC *numbers.* Although their numbers are important, it is the amount of hemoglobin in the bloodstream at any time that really determines how well the erythrocytes are performing their role of oxygen transport.

The more hemoglobin molecules the RBCs contain, the more oxygen they will be able to carry. Perhaps the most accurate way of measuring the oxygen-carrying capacity of the blood is to determine how much hemoglobin it contains. A single red blood cell contains about 250 million hemoglobin molecules, each capable of binding 4 molecules of oxygen, so each of these tiny cells can carry about 1 billion molecules of oxygen! This information is astounding but not very practical. Much more important clinically is the fact that normal blood contains 12–18 grams (g) of hemoglobin per 100 milliliters (ml) blood. The hemoglobin content is slightly higher in men (13–18 g/ml) than in women (12–16 g/ml).

⚖ HOMEOSTATIC IMBALANCE

A decrease in the oxygen-carrying ability of the blood, whatever the reason, is **anemia** (ah-ne′me-ah; "lacking blood"). Anemia may be the result of (1) a lower-than-normal *number* of RBCs or (2) abnormal or deficient *hemoglobin content* in the RBCs. Several types of anemia are classified and described briefly in Table 10.1, but one of these, *sickle cell anemia,* deserves a little more attention because people with this

(a) Normal hemoglobin

(b) Sickle cell hemoglobin

FIGURE 10.3   Comparison of (a) normal erythrocyte to a (b) sickled erythrocyte (6700×).

genetic disorder are frequently seen in hospital emergency rooms.

In **sickle cell anemia (SCA),** the abnormal hemoglobin formed becomes spiky and sharp (Figure 10.3b) when the RBCs unload oxygen molecules or when the oxygen content of the blood is lower than normal, as during vigorous exercise, anxiety, or other stressful situations. The stiff, deformed (crescent-shaped) erythrocytes rupture easily and dam up in small blood vessels. These events interfere with oxygen delivery (leaving victims gasping for air) and cause extreme pain. It is amazing that this havoc results from a change in just *one* of the amino acids in two of the four polypeptide chains of the hemoglobin molecule!

TABLE 10.1	Types of Anemia	
Direct cause	**Resulting from**	**Leading to**
Decrease in RBC number	Sudden hemorrhage	Hemorrhagic anemia
	Lysis of RBCs as a result of bacterial infections	Hemolytic (he"mo-lit'ik) anemia
	Lack of vitamin B_{12} (usually due to lack of intrinsic factor required for absorption of the vitamin; intrinsic factor is formed by stomach mucosa cells)	Pernicious (per-nish'us) anemia
	Depression/destruction of bone marrow by cancer, radiation, or certain medications	Aplastic anemia
Inadequate hemoglobin content in RBCs	Lack of iron in diet or slow/prolonged bleeding (such as heavy menstrual flow or bleeding ulcer), which depletes iron reserves needed to make hemoglobin; RBCs are small and pale because they lack hemoglobin	Iron deficiency anemia
Abnormal hemoglobin in RBCs	Genetic defect leads to abnormal hemoglobin, which becomes sharp and sickle-shaped under conditions of increased oxygen use by body; occurs mainly in people of African descent	Sickle cell anemia

Sickle cell anemia occurs chiefly in black people who live in the malaria belt of Africa and among their descendants. Apparently, the same gene that causes sickling makes red blood cells infected by the malaria-causing parasite stick to the capillary walls and then lose potassium, an essential nutrient for survival of the parasite. Hence, the malaria-causing parasite is prevented from multiplying within the red blood cells, and individuals with the sickle cell gene have a better chance of surviving where malaria is prevalent. Only those carrying two copies of the defective gene have sickle cell anemia. Those carrying just one sickling gene have **sickle cell trait (SCT);** they generally do not display the symptoms but can pass on the sickling gene to their offspring.

An excessive or abnormal increase in the number of erythrocytes is **polycythemia** pol"e-si-the'me-ah). Polycythemia may result from bone marrow cancer (*polycythemia vera*). It may also be a normal physiologic (homeostatic) response to living at high altitudes, where the air is thinner and less oxygen is available (*secondary polycythemia*). The major problem that results from excessive numbers of RBCs is increased blood viscosity, which causes it to flow sluggishly in the body and impairs circulation. ▲

Leukocytes

Although **leukocytes,** or **white blood cells (WBCs),** are far less numerous than red blood cells, they are crucial to body defense against disease. On average, there are 4000 to 11,000 WBC/mm^3, and they account for less than 1 percent of total blood volume. White blood cells are the only complete cells in blood; that is, they contain nuclei and the usual organelles.

Leukocytes form a protective, movable army that helps defend the body against damage by bacteria, viruses, parasites, and tumor cells. As such, they have some very special characteristics. Red blood cells are confined to the bloodstream and carry out their functions in the blood. White blood cells, by contrast, are able to slip into and out of the blood vessels—a process called **diapedesis** (di"ah-peh-de'sis; "leaping across"). The circulatory system is simply their means of transportation to areas of the body where their services are needed for inflammatory or immune responses (as described in Chapter 12).

In addition, WBCs can locate areas of tissue damage and infection in the body by responding to certain chemicals that diffuse from the damaged cells. This capability is called **positive chemotaxis** (ke"mo-tax'is). Once they have "caught the scent," the WBCs move through the tissue spaces by **ameboid** (ah-me'boid) **motion** (they form flowing cytoplasmic extensions that help move them along). By following the diffusion gradient, they pinpoint areas of tissue damage and rally round in large numbers to destroy microorganisms and dispose of dead cells.

Whenever WBCs mobilize for action, the body speeds up their production, and as many as twice the normal number of WBCs may appear in the blood within a few hours. A total WBC count above 11,000 cells/mm^3 is referred to as **leukocytosis** (lu"ko-si-to'sis). Leukocytosis generally indicates that a bacterial or viral infection is stewing in the body. The opposite condition, **leukopenia** (lu"ko-pe'ne-ah), is an abnormally low WBC count. It is commonly caused by certain drugs, such as corticosteroids and anticancer agents.

HOMEOSTATIC IMBALANCE

Leukocytosis is a normal and desirable response to infectious threats to the body. By contrast, the excessive production of abnormal WBCs that occurs in infectious mononucleosis and leukemia is distinctly pathological. In **leukemia** (lu-ke'me-ah), literally "white blood," the bone marrow becomes cancerous, and huge numbers of WBCs are turned out rapidly. Although this might not appear to present a problem, the "newborn" WBCs are immature and incapable of carrying out their normal protective functions. Consequently, the body becomes the easy prey of disease-causing bacteria and viruses. Additionally, because other blood cell lines are crowded out, severe anemia and bleeding problems result. ▲

WBCs are classified into two major groups—granulocytes and agranulocytes—depending on whether or not they contain visible granules in their cytoplasm. Specific characteristics of the leukocytes are listed in Table 10.2. Microscopic views can be seen in Figure 10.1.

Granulocytes (gran'u-lo-sītz") are granule-containing WBCs. They have lobed nuclei, which typically consist of several rounded nuclear areas connected by thin strands of nuclear material. The granules in their cytoplasm stain specifically with Wright's stain. The granulocytes include the neutrophils (nu'tro-filz), eosinophils (e"o-sin'o-filz), and basophils (ba'so-filz).

1. **Neutrophils** are the most numerous of the WBCs. They have a multilobed nucleus and very fine granules that respond to both acidic and basic stains. Consequently, the cytoplasm as a whole stains pink. Neutrophils are avid phagocytes at sites of acute infection, and are particularly partial to bacteria and fungi.

2. **Eosinophils** have a blue-red nucleus that resembles an old-fashioned telephone receiver and sport coarse, lysosome-like, brick-red cytoplasmic granules. Their number increases rapidly during allergies and infections by parasitic worms (flatworms, tapeworms, etc.) ingested in food (raw fish) or entering via the skin.

3. **Basophils,** the rarest of the WBCs, contain large histamine-containing granules that stain dark blue. **Histamine** is an inflammatory chemical that makes blood vessels leaky and attracts other WBCs to the inflammatory site.

The second group of WBCs, **agranulocytes,** lack *visible* cytoplasmic granules. Their nuclei are closer to the norm—that is, they are spherical, oval, or kidney-shaped. The agranulocytes include lymphocytes (lim'fo-sīts) and monocytes (mon'o-sīts).

1. **Lymphocytes** have a large dark purple nucleus that occupies most of the cell volume. Only slightly larger than RBCs, lymphocytes tend to take up residence in lymphatic tissues, where they play an important role in the immune response. They are the second most numerous leukocytes in the blood.

2. **Monocytes** are the largest of the WBCs. Except for their more abundant cytoplasm and distinctive U- or kidney-shaped nucleus, they resemble large lymphocytes. When they migrate into the tissues, they change into macrophages with huge appetites. Macrophages are very important in fighting chronic infections, such as tuberculosis.

Students are often asked to list the WBCs in order of relative abundance in the blood—from most to least. The following phrase may help you with this task: **N**ever **l**et **m**onkeys **e**at **b**ananas (neutrophils, lymphocytes, monocytes, eosinophils, basophils).

TABLE 10.2	Characteristics of Formed Elements of the Blood		
Cell type	**Occurrence in blood (per mm³)**	**Cell anatomy***	**Function**
ERYTHROCYTES (red blood cells)	4–6 million	Salmon-colored biconcave disks; anucleate; literally, sacs of hemoglobin; most organelles have been ejected	Transport oxygen bound to hemoglobin molecules; also transport small amount of carbon dioxide
LEUKOCYTES (white blood cells)	4000–11,000		
Granulocytes			
• Neutrophils	3000–7000 (40–70% of WBCs)	Cytoplasm stains pale pink and contains fine granules, which are difficult to see; deep purple nucleus consists of three to seven lobes connected by thin strands of nucleoplasm	Active phagocytes; number increases rapidly during short-term or acute infections
• Eosinophils	100–400 (1–4% of WBCs)	Red coarse cytoplasmic granules; figure-8 or bilobed nucleus stains blue-red	Kill parasitic worms by deluging them with digestive enzymes; increase during allergy attacks; might phagocytize antigen-antibody complexes and inactivate some inflammatory chemicals
• Basophils	20–50 (0–1% of WBCs)	Cytoplasm has a few large blue-purple granules; U- or S-shaped nucleus with constrictions, stains dark blue	Release histamine (vasodilator chemical), at sites of inflammation; contain heparin, an anticoagulant
Agranulocytes			
• Lymphocytes	1500–3000 (20–45% of WBCs)	Cytoplasm pale blue and appears as thin rim around nucleus; spherical (or slightly indented) dark purple-blue nucleus	Part of immune system; one group (B lymphocytes) produces antibodies; other group (T lymphocytes) involved in graft rejection, fighting tumors and viruses, via direct cell attack
• Monocytes	100–700 (4–8% of WBCs)	Abundant gray-blue cytoplasm; dark blue-purple nucleus often kidney-shaped	Active phagocytes that become macrophages in the tissues; long-term "clean-up team"; increase in number during chronic infections such as tuberculosis
PLATELETS	150,000–500,000	Essentially irregularly shaped cell fragments; stain deep purple	Needed for normal blood clotting; initiate clotting cascade by clinging to torn area; help to control blood loss from broken blood vessels

*Appearance when stained with Wright's stain.

Platelets

Platelets are not cells in the strict sense. They are fragments of bizarre multinucleate cells called **megakaryocytes** (meg″ah-kar′e-o-sītz), which pinch off thousands of anucleate platelet "pieces" that quickly seal themselves off from the surrounding fluids. The platelets appear as darkly staining, irregularly shaped bodies scattered among the other blood cells. The normal platelet count in blood is about 300,000/mm³. As indicated in Table 10.2, platelets are needed for the clotting process that occurs in plasma when blood vessels are ruptured or broken. (This process is explained on pp. 349–350.)

DID YOU GET IT?

4. What is the role of hemoglobin in the red blood cell?

5. Which white blood cells are most important in body immunity?

6. If you had a severe infection, would you expect your WBC count to be closest to 5000, 10,000, or 15,000/mm³?

7. Little Lisa is pale and listless. What disorder of erythrocytes might she be suffering from?

For answers, see Appendix D.

Hematopoiesis (Blood Cell Formation)

Blood cell formation, or **hematopoiesis** (hem″ah-to-poi-e′sis), occurs in red bone marrow, or *myeloid* tissue. In adults, this tissue is found chiefly in the flat bones of the skull and pelvis, the ribs, sternum, and proximal epiphyses of the humerus and femur. Each type of blood cell is produced in different numbers in response to changing body needs and different stimuli. After they mature, they are discharged into the blood vessels surrounding the area. On average, the red marrow turns out, each and every day, an ounce of new blood containing 100 billion new cells.

All the formed elements arise from a common type of *stem cell,* the **hemocytoblast** (he″mo-si′to-blast; "blood cell former"), which resides in the red bone marrow. Their development differs, however, and once a cell is committed to a specific blood pathway, it cannot change. As indicated in the flowchart in Figure 10.4, the hemocytoblast forms two types of descendants—the *lymphoid stem cell,*

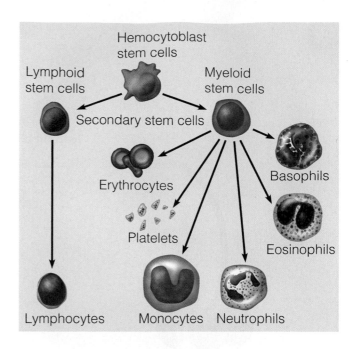

FIGURE 10.4 The development of blood cells. All blood cells differentiate from hemocytoblast stem cells in red bone marrow. The population of stem cells renews itself by mitosis. Some of these daughter cells become lymphoid stem cells, which then develop into two classes of lymphocytes that function in the immune response. All other blood cells differentiate from myeloid stem cells.

which produces lymphocytes, and the *myeloid stem cell,* which can produce all other classes of formed elements.

Formation of Red Blood Cells

Because they are anucleate, RBCs are unable to synthesize proteins, grow, or divide. As they age, RBCs become more rigid and begin to fragment, or fall apart, in 100 to 120 days. Their remains are eliminated by phagocytes in the spleen, liver, and other body tissues. Lost cells are replaced more or less continuously by the division of hemocytoblasts in the red bone marrow. The developing RBCs divide many times and then begin synthesizing huge amounts of hemoglobin. Suddenly, when enough hemoglobin has been accumulated, the nucleus and most organelles are ejected and the cell collapses inward. The result is the young RBC, called a *reticulocyte* (rĕ-tik′u-lo-sīt) because it still contains some rough endoplasmic reticulum (ER). The reticulocytes enter the bloodstream to begin their task of transporting oxygen. Within

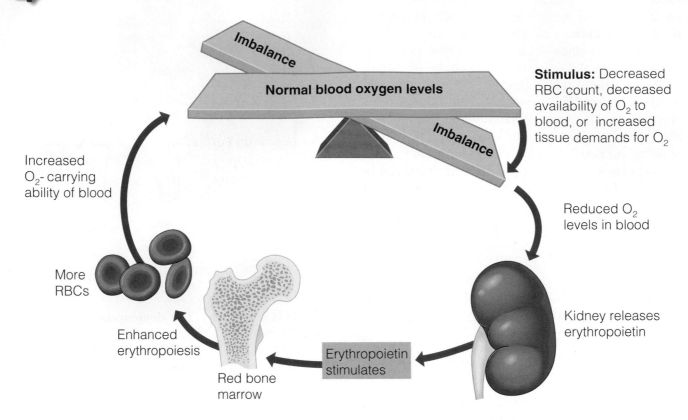

Imbalance

Normal blood oxygen levels

Imbalance

Stimulus: Decreased RBC count, decreased availability of O_2 to blood, or increased tissue demands for O_2

Reduced O_2 levels in blood

Increased O_2- carrying ability of blood

More RBCs

Kidney releases erythropoietin

Enhanced erythropoiesis

Erythropoietin stimulates

Red bone marrow

FIGURE 10.5 **Mechanism for regulating the rate of RBC production.** When oxygen levels in the blood become inadequate to support normal cellular activity, whatever the cause, the kidneys release more erythropoietin. The increased levels of erythropoietin stimulate RBC production in bone marrow.

2 days of release, they have ejected the remaining ER and have become fully functioning erythrocytes. The entire developmental process from hemocytoblast to mature RBC takes 3 to 5 days.

The rate of erythrocyte production is controlled by a hormone called **erythropoietin** (ĕ-rith″ro-poi-e′tin). Normally a small amount of erythropoietin circulates in the blood at all times, and red blood cells are formed at a fairly constant rate. Although the liver produces some, the kidneys play the major role in producing this hormone. When blood levels of oxygen begin to decline for any reason, the kidneys step up their release of erythropoietin (Figure 10.5). Erythropoietin targets the

bone marrow, prodding it into "high gear" to turn out more RBCs. As you might expect, an overabundance of erythrocytes, or an excessive amount of oxygen in the bloodstream, depresses erythropoietin release and red blood cell production. An important point to remember is that it is *not* the relative number of RBCs in the blood that controls RBC production. Control is based on their ability to transport enough oxygen to meet the body's demands.

Formation of White Blood Cells and Platelets

Like erythrocyte production, the formation of leukocytes and platelets is stimulated by hormones. These *colony stimulating factors (CSFs)* and *interleukins* not only prompt red bone marrow to turn out leukocytes, but also marshal up an army of

WBCs to ward off attacks by enhancing the ability of mature leukocytes to protect the body. Apparently, they are released in response to specific chemical signals in the environment, such as inflammatory chemicals and certain bacteria or their toxins. The hormone *thrombopoietin* accelerates the production of platelets, but little is known about how that process is regulated.

When bone marrow problems or disease conditions such as aplastic anemia or leukemia are suspected, a special needle is used to withdraw a small sample of red marrow from one of the flat bones (ilium or sternum) close to the body surface. This procedure provides cells for a microscopic examination called a *bone marrow biopsy*.

Hemostasis

Normally, blood flows smoothly past the intact lining (endothelium) of blood vessel walls. But if a blood vessel wall breaks, a series of reactions is set in motion to accomplish **hemostasis** (*hem* = blood; *stasis* = standing still), or stoppage of bleeding. This response, which is fast and localized, involves many substances normally present in plasma, as well as some that are released by platelets and injured tissue cells.

Hemostasis involves three major phases, which occur in rapid sequence: **vascular spasms, platelet plug formation,** and **coagulation,** or **blood clotting.** Blood loss at the site is permanently prevented when fibrous tissue grows into the clot and seals the hole in the blood vessel.

Basically, hemostasis occurs as follows (Figure 10.6):

1. **Vascular spasms occur.** The immediate response to blood vessel injury is vasoconstriction, which causes that blood vessel to go into spasms. The spasms narrow the blood vessel at that point, decreasing blood loss until clotting can occur. (Other factors causing vessel spasms include direct injury to the smooth muscle cells, stimulation of local pain receptors, and release of serotonin by anchored platelets.)

2. **Platelet plug forms.** Platelets are repelled by an intact endothelium, but when it is broken so that the underlying collagen fibers are exposed, the platelets become "sticky" and cling to the damaged site. Anchored platelets release chemicals that enhance the vascular spasms and

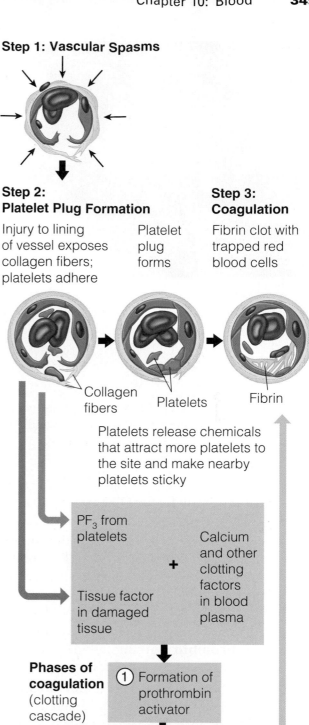

Step 1: Vascular Spasms

Step 2: Platelet Plug Formation

Injury to lining of vessel exposes collagen fibers; platelets adhere

Platelet plug forms

Step 3: Coagulation

Fibrin clot with trapped red blood cells

Collagen fibers   Platelets   Fibrin

Platelets release chemicals that attract more platelets to the site and make nearby platelets sticky

PF_3 from platelets

Tissue factor in damaged tissue

+

Calcium and other clotting factors in blood plasma

Phases of coagulation (clotting cascade)

① Formation of prothrombin activator

② Prothrombin → Thrombin

③ Fibrinogen (soluble) → Fibrin (insoluble)

FIGURE 10.6   Hemostasis. The multistep process, detailed in the text, begins when a blood vessel is damaged and connective tissue in the vessel wall is exposed to blood.

FIGURE 10.7   Fibrin clot. Scanning electron micrograph (artificially colored) of red blood cells trapped in a mesh of fibrin threads.

attract more platelets to the site. As more and more platelets pile up, a small mass called a *platelet plug,* or *white thrombus,* forms.

3. **Coagulation events occur.**

   a. At the same time, the injured tissues are releasing **tissue factor (TF),** a substance that plays an important role in clotting.

   b. **PF₃,** a phospholipid that coats the surfaces of the platelets, interacts with TF, vitamin K and other blood protein clotting factors, and calcium ions (Ca^{2+}) to form an activator that triggers the *clotting cascade.*

   c. This **prothrombin activator** converts **prothrombin** (pro-throm′bin), present in the plasma, to **thrombin,** an enzyme.

   d. Thrombin then joins soluble **fibrinogen** (fibrin′o-jen) proteins into long, hairlike molecules of insoluble **fibrin,** which forms a meshwork that traps the RBCs and forms the basis of the clot (Figure 10.7). Within the hour, the clot begins to retract, squeezing **serum** (plasma minus the clotting proteins) from the mass and pulling the ruptured edges of the blood vessel closer together.

Normally, blood clots within 3 to 6 minutes. As a rule, once the clotting cascade has started, the triggering factors are rapidly inactivated to prevent widespread clotting ("solid blood"). Eventually, the endothelium regenerates, and the clot is broken down. Once these events of the clotting cascade were understood, it became clear that placing a sterile gauze over a cut or applying pressure to a wound would speed up the clotting process. The gauze provides a rough surface to which the platelets can adhere, and the pressure fractures cells, increasing the release of tissue factor locally.

Disorders of Hemostasis

HOMEOSTATIC IMBALANCE

The two major disorders of hemostasis—undesirable clot formation and bleeding disorders—are at opposite poles.

Undesirable Clotting

Despite the body's safeguards against abnormal clotting, undesirable clots sometimes form in intact (unbroken) blood vessels, particularly in the legs. A clot that develops and persists in an unbroken blood vessel is called a **thrombus** (throm′bus). If the thrombus is large enough, it may prevent blood from flowing to the cells beyond the blockage. For example, if the blockage forms in the blood vessels serving the heart *(coronary thrombosis),* the consequences may be death of heart muscle and a fatal heart attack. If a thrombus breaks away from the vessel wall and floats freely in the bloodstream, it becomes an **embolus** (em′bo-lus; plural, *emboli*). An embolus is usually no problem unless or until it lodges in a blood vessel too narrow for it to pass through. For example, a *cerebral embolus* may cause a *stroke.*

Undesirable clotting may be caused by anything that roughens the endothelium of a blood vessel and encourages clinging of platelets, such as severe burns, physical blows, or an accumulation of fatty material. Slowly flowing blood, or blood pooling, is another risk factor, especially in immobilized patients. In this case, clotting factors are not washed away as usual and accumulate so that clot formation becomes possible. A number of anticoagulants, the most important of which are aspirin, heparin, and dicumarol, are used clinically for thrombus-prone patients.

Bleeding Disorders

The most common causes of abnormal bleeding are platelet deficiency (thrombocytopenia) and deficits of some of the clotting factors, such as might result from impaired liver function or certain genetic conditions.

Thrombocytopenia results from an insufficient number of circulating platelets. Even normal movements cause spontaneous bleeding from small blood vessels. This is evidenced by many small purplish blotches, called **petechiae** (pe-te′ke-e), on the skin. It can arise from any condition that suppresses the bone marrow, such as bone marrow cancer, radiation, or certain drugs.

When the liver is unable to synthesize its usual supply of clotting factors, abnormal and often severe bleeding episodes occur. If vitamin K (needed by the liver cells to produce the clotting factors) is deficient, the problem is easily corrected with vitamin K supplements. However, when liver function is severely impaired (as in hepatitis and cirrhosis), only whole blood transfusions are helpful. Transfusions of concentrated platelets provide temporary relief from bleeding.

The term **hemophilia** (he″mo-fil′e-ah) applies to several different hereditary bleeding disorders that result from a lack of any of the factors needed for clotting. Commonly called "bleeder's disease," the hemophilias have similar signs and symptoms that begin early in life. Even minor tissue trauma results in prolonged bleeding and can be life-threatening. Repeated bleeding into joints causes them to become disabled and painful. When a bleeding episode occurs, hemophiliacs are given a transfusion of fresh plasma or injections of the purified clotting factor they lack. Because hemophiliacs are absolutely dependent on one or the other of these therapies, some have become the victims of blood-transmitted viral diseases such as hepatitis and AIDS. (AIDS, acquired immunodeficiency syndrome, is a condition of depressed immunity and is described in Chapter 12.) These problems have been largely resolved because of the availability of genetically engineered clotting factors and hepatitis vaccines. ▲

▶ *DID YOU GET IT?*

8. What is the name of the stem cell that gives rise to all formed elements?

9. What property of RBCs dooms them to a limited life span of about 120 days?

10. How is the production of platelets different from that of all other formed elements?

11. What factors enhance the risk of thrombus formation in intact blood vessels?

For answers, see Appendix D.

Blood Groups and Transfusions

As we have seen, blood is vital for transporting substances through the body. When blood is lost, the blood vessels constrict and the bone marrow steps up blood cell formation in an attempt to keep the circulation going. However, the body can compensate for a loss of blood volume only up to a certain limit. Losses of 15 to 30 percent lead to pallor and weakness. Loss of over 30 percent causes severe shock, which can be fatal. Whole blood transfusions are routinely given to replace substantial blood loss and to treat severe anemia or thrombocytopenia. The usual blood bank procedure involves collecting blood from a donor and mixing it with an anticoagulant to prevent clotting. The treated blood can be stored (refrigerated at 4°C, or 39.2°F) for about 35 days until needed.

Human Blood Groups

Although whole blood transfusion can save lives, people have different blood groups, and transfusing incompatible or mismatched blood can be fatal. How so? The plasma membranes of RBCs, like those of all other body cells, bear genetically determined proteins (antigens), which identify each person as unique. An **antigen** (an′tǐ-jen) is a substance that the body recognizes as foreign; it stimulates the immune system to release antibodies or use other means to mount a defense against it. Most antigens are foreign proteins, such as those that are part of viruses or bacteria that have managed to invade the body. Although each of us tolerates our own cellular (self) antigens, one person's RBC proteins will be recognized as foreign if transfused into another person with different RBC antigens. The "recognizers" are **antibodies** present in the plasma that attach to RBCs bearing surface antigens different from those on the patient's (blood recipient's) RBCs. Binding of the antibodies causes the foreign RBCs to clump, a phenomenon called **agglutination*** (ah-gloo″tǐ-na′shun), which leads to the clogging of small blood vessels throughout the body. During the next few hours, the foreign RBCs are lysed (ruptured), and their hemoglobin is

---

*The RBC antigens that promote this clumping are sometimes called **agglutinogens** (ag″loo-tin′o-jenz), and the antibodies that bind them together are called **agglutinins** (ag″loo′tǐ-ninz).

PHLEBOTOMY TECHNICIAN

Phlebotomists must know where all the arteries and veins are located in the body.

"Phlebotomy is the most important procedure done for a medical laboratory," says Michael Coté, who supervises the phlebotomy staff at Palo

Alto Veterans Administration Hospital in California. "To make accurate diagnosis and effective treatment possible, it's vital to draw a good blood sample, place it correctly in a clean container, and process it accurately in the lab. Without a high-quality specimen, none of this can happen."

Phlebotomy is not exactly a household word. It derives from the Greek terms for "vein" and "to cut." A phlebotomy technician, or phlebotomist, is trained to collect and process blood samples that will be subjected to laboratory analysis.

Coté appreciates how important it is for phlebotomists to understand anatomy and physiology. "Anatomy

is a key requirement in phlebotomy training," he says, "because you have to learn where all the arteries and veins are located in the body. Some patients' veins are easy to find, but others have veins that are practically invisible. You need to know the right place to insert that needle. Although 90 percent of the blood we draw comes from the antecubital region inside the elbow, we may also draw blood from the cephalic vein in the forearm, or from veins in the hands."

Coté notes that knowledge of physiology is also important. "I have to be able to assess patients' overall health and physical condition, because this affects their ability to give an adequate blood sample and may demand that a different needle size be used to draw the blood sample. People who are dehydrated can be difficult because their blood pressure is lower and venous return is impaired. Patients with poor circulation are also harder to work with. The blood tends to stay in the body trunk rather than flowing freely into the extremities because they're cold, and it's difficult to get a good return from veins in the arms. Cancer patients often show increased sensitivity to pain, so we have to be very gentle and use the smallest needle possible." Patients with a history of drug abuse pose other challenges. "Frequent 'sticking' with needles causes scar tissue to form. You can tell people who have used intravenous drugs—their veins feel rock-hard and are much more difficult to penetrate with a needle."

Coté says that a good phlebotomist must also possess effective interpersonal skills: "People are apprehensive about being stuck with needles, so you have to be patient and be able to put them at ease. Above all, you have to be confident. If the phlebotomist is nervous, the patient will sense it and get nervous too."

To become certified, a phlebotomy technician must be a high

> ❝ *Anatomy is a key requirement in phlebotomy training.*❞

school graduate, complete a phlebotomy training program or acquire equivalent experience, and pass a certification exam offered by the American Society of Clinical Pathologists.

Accreditation procedures for phlebotomists vary from state to state. For more information, contact the American Society of Clinical Pathologists at

2100 W. Harrison Street
Chicago, IL 60612-3798
(312) 738-1336
http://www.ascp.org

For additional information on this career, click the Focus on Careers link at www.anatomyandphysiology.com.

TABLE 10.3	ABO Blood Groups

| Blood group | Frequency (% U.S. population) | | | | RBC antigens (agglutinogens) | Illustration | Plasma antibodies (agglutinins) | Blood that can be received |
	White	Black	Asian	Native American				
AB	4	4	5	<1	A B		None	A, B, AB, O Universal recipient
B	11	20	27	4	B		Anti-A	B, O
A	40	27	28	16	A		Anti-B	A, O
O	45	49	40	79	None		Anti-A Anti-B	O Universal donor

released into the bloodstream. Although the transfused blood is unable to deliver the increased oxygen-carrying capacity hoped for and some tissue areas may be deprived of blood, the most devastating consequence of severe transfusion reactions is that the freed hemoglobin molecules may block the kidney tubules, causing kidney failure and death. Transfusion reactions can also cause fever, chills, nausea, and vomiting, but in the absence of kidney shutdown these reactions are rarely fatal. Treatment is aimed at preventing kidney damage by infusing fluids to dilute and dissolve the hemoglobin and diuretics to flush it out of the body in urine.

There are over 30 common RBC antigens in humans, so each person's blood cells can be classified into several different blood groups. However, it is the antigens of the ABO and Rh blood groups that cause the most vigorous transfusion reactions. These two blood groups are described here.

As shown in Table 10.3, the **ABO blood groups** are based on which of two antigens, type A or type B, a person inherits. Absence of both antigens results in type O blood, presence of both antigens leads to type AB, and the presence of either A or B antigen yields type A or B blood, respectively. In the ABO blood group, antibodies form during infancy against the ABO antigens *not* present on your own RBCs. As shown in the table, a baby with neither the A nor the B antigen (group O) forms both anti-A and anti-B antibodies; those with type A antigens (group A) form anti-B antibodies, and so on.

The **Rh blood groups** are so named because one of the eight Rh antigens (agglutinogen D) was originally identified in **Rh**esus monkeys. Later the same antigen was discovered in human beings. Most Americans are Rh^+ (Rh positive), meaning that their RBCs carry the Rh antigen. Unlike the antibodies of the ABO system, anti-Rh antibodies are *not* automatically formed and present in the blood of Rh^- (Rh negative) individuals. However, if an Rh^- person receives mismatched blood (that is, Rh^+), shortly after the transfusion his or her immune system becomes sensitized and begins producing antibodies (anti-Rh^+ antibodies) against the foreign blood type. **Hemolysis** (rupture of RBCs) does not occur with the first transfusion because it takes time for the body to react and start making antibodies. However, the second time and every time thereafter, a typical transfusion reaction occurs in which the patient's antibodies attack and rupture the donor's Rh^+ RBCs.

An important Rh-related problem occurs in pregnant Rh⁻ women who are carrying Rh⁺ babies. The *first* such pregnancy usually results in the delivery of a healthy baby. But because the mother is sensitized by Rh⁺ antigens that have passed through the placenta into her bloodstream, she will form anti-Rh⁺ antibodies unless treated with RhoGAM shortly after giving birth. RhoGAM is an immune serum that prevents this sensitization and her subsequent immune response. If she is not treated and becomes pregnant again with an Rh⁺ baby, her antibodies will cross through the placenta and destroy the baby's RBCs, producing a condition known as *hemolytic disease of the newborn*. The baby is anemic and becomes hypoxic and cyanotic (the skin takes on a blue cast). Brain damage and even death may result unless fetal transfusions are done before birth to provide more RBCs for oxygen transport.

Blood Typing

The importance of determining the blood group of both the donor and the recipient *before* blood is transfused is glaringly obvious. The general procedure for determining ABO blood type is briefly outlined in Figure 10.8. Essentially, it involves testing the blood by mixing it with two different types of immune serum—anti-A and anti-B. Agglutination occurs when RBCs of a group A person are mixed with the anti-A serum but not when they are mixed with the anti-B serum. Likewise, RBCs of type B blood are clumped by anti-B serum but not by anti-A serum. Because it is critical that blood groups be compatible, cross matching is also done. *Cross matching* involves testing for agglutination of donor RBCs by the recipient's serum and of the recipient's RBCs by the donor serum. Typing for the Rh factors is done in the same manner as ABO blood typing.

▶ *DID YOU GET IT?*

12. What are the classes of human blood groups based on?

13. What is the probable result from infusion of mismatched blood?

14. Cary is bleeding profusely after being hit by a truck as he was pedaling his bike home. At the hospital, the nurse asked him whether he knew his blood type. He told her that he "had the same blood as most other people." What is his ABO blood type?

 Which blood types can be transfused into a person with type B blood?

Blood being tested   **Serum**

Type AB (contains antigens A and B); agglutinates with both sera

Agglutinated RBCs

Type B (contains antigen B); agglutinates with anti-B serum

Type A (contains antigen A); agglutinates with anti-A serum

Type O (contains no antigens); no agglutination occurs

FIGURE 10.8 **Blood typing of ABO blood groups.** When serum containing anti-A or anti-B antibodies is added to a blood sample diluted with saline, agglutination will occur between the antibody and the corresponding antigen (if present).

15. What is the difference between an antigen and an antibody?

For answers, see Appendix D.

Developmental Aspects of Blood

In the young embryo, the entire circulatory system develops early. Before birth, there are many sites of blood cell formation—the fetal liver and spleen, among others—but by the seventh month of development, the fetus's red marrow has become the

  Types B and O.

A CLOS ER LOOK

CONCOCTING BLOOD: ARTIFICIAL BLOOD SUBSTITUTES

The term *blood substitute* is somewhat misleading. Blood has many components and plays such a wide variety of roles—from fighting infection to transporting oxygen—that no single artificial substitute yet engineered can fulfill all those functions. However, substitute liquids are available that can transport oxygen from the lungs through the body and can "stretch" a limited blood supply while sidestepping transfusion reactions. An important benefit of these blood substitutes is that they do not transmit bloodborne disease factors.

Modified Hemoglobin

Let's pretend to be biomedical engineers for a moment. If you wanted a substance to transport oxygen in the blood, what would you use? Like many researchers, you'd probably start with hemoglobin, the blood's own oxygen carrier. You could obtain hemoglobin from human red blood cells too old for transfusion or from readily available cow blood. Unfortunately, hemoglobin by itself is unusable—it spontaneously splits in half in the plasma, and it is rapidly cleared by the kidneys (which can lead to renal shutdown). Chemically linking hemoglobin subunits together so that they don't come apart or tying hemoglobin molecules together into long chains reduces clearance by the kidneys. Some types of these hemoglobin chains can stay in the blood for as long as 24 hours.

Another problem with free human hemoglobin is that it binds oxygen much more tightly (has a higher affinity) than hemoglobin contained inside a red blood cell, only reluctantly giving up oxygen to needy tissues. Cow hemoglobin, by contrast, naturally binds oxygen less tightly. This solution has its own problems: the possible transmission of mad cow disease and the

> ❝ *It's unlikely that we will soon come up with one universal blood substitute.*❞

risk of immune reactions. Nevertheless, a cow-based product is licensed for use in South Africa, where the high prevalence of HIV has made collecting uninfected blood extremely difficult. It's also possible to modify the hemoglobin with chemicals that lower oxygen affinity. Hemoglobin's affinity for oxygen can also be lowered by genetically engineering its oxygen binding pocket. Each of these modified hemoglobins has undergone clinical trials with varying degrees of success.

A common problem in these trials is that the free hemoglobin provokes a generalized constriction of blood

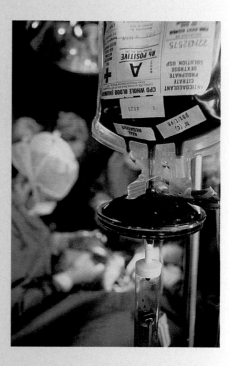

vessels and an increase in blood pressure when the hemoglobin compound is infused into the patient's blood.

To try to prevent that problem, researchers are making the hemoglobin physically bigger by tying on long chains of polyethylene glycol (PEG). Think of it as hemoglobin floating down a river in a big inner tube, bouncing off the banks. Such a molecule is currently undergoing clinical trials and appears not to have hypertensive effects.

And Now for Something Completely Different . . .

Some engineers have asked, "If hemoglobin has all of these problems, why use it? If you want a product with

A CLOSER LOOK Concocting Blood (continued)

long shelf life, no biological contamination, and available in industrial quantities, why not use industrial chemistry?" Enter perfluorinated hydrocarbon chains (PFCs). These compounds, chemically similar to Teflon used in nonstick cookware, can hold large amounts of dissolved oxygen, much more than plasma. In the 1960s, researchers were amazed to discover that they could fully immerse mice for up to 30 minutes in liquid PFCs. (Mice happily breathing liquid PFCs rather than air led researchers to try ventilating humans with PFCs. Premature newborns who would ordinarily be breathing amniotic fluid are obvious candidates, but liquid ventilation of adults with severe lung dysfunction is also currently in clinical trials.)

As artificial blood, PFCs have a serious shortcoming—they don't dissolve in plasma. Combining detergent and phospholipids with PFCs produces an emulsion of small droplets that can be suspended in the watery plasma. To load sufficient amounts of oxygen into PFCs, patients must breathe 70–100% oxygen by mask. Oxygen transported by PFCs is used more easily by the body tissues because the slippery particles are much smaller than erythrocytes and glide through the capillaries at a faster rate. PFCs are cleared from the circulation and stored in the spleen and liver until they are exhaled as vapor by the lungs over several days. Side effects include hypertension and flu-like symptoms. Currently, one

PFC is approved in the U.S. for use during cardiac catheterization.

Because each of these blood substitutes has both advantages and disadvantages, it's unlikely that we will soon come up with one universal blood substitute. Rather, it will be a matter of choosing the substitute that best fits the patient's clinical needs. Although the FDA has encouraged the development of artificial blood for over 30 years, no product, including those described above, has been approved in the U.S. for anything but experimental use in humans. Blood still remains a priceless commodity, and its beautiful complexity has yet to be replaced by modern medical technology.

---

chief site of hematopoiesis, and it remains so throughout life. Generally, embryonic blood cells are circulating in the newly formed blood vessels by day 28 of development. Fetal hemoglobin (HbF) differs from the hemoglobin formed after birth. It has a greater ability to pick up oxygen, a characteristic that is highly desirable because fetal blood is less oxygen rich than that of the mother. After birth, fetal blood cells are gradually replaced by RBCs that contain the more typical hemoglobin A (HbA). In situations in which the fetal RBCs are destroyed at such a rapid rate that the immature infant liver cannot rid the body of hemoglobin breakdown products in the bile fast enough, the infant becomes *jaundiced* (jawn'dist). This type of jaundice generally causes no major problems and is referred to as **physiologic jaundice,** to distinguish it from more serious disease conditions that result in jaundiced, or yellowed, tissues.

HOMEOSTATIC IMBALANCE

Various congenital diseases result from genetic factors (such as hemophilia and sickle cell anemia) and from interactions with maternal blood factors

(such as hemolytic disease of the newborn). Dietary factors can lead to abnormalities in blood cell formation as well as hemoglobin production. Iron deficiency anemia is especially common in women because of their monthly blood loss during menses. The young and the old are particularly at risk for leukemia. With increasing age, chronic types of leukemias, anemias, and diseases involving undesirable clot formation are more prevalent. However, these are usually secondary to disorders of the heart, blood vessels, or immune system. The elderly are particularly at risk for pernicious anemia because the stomach mucosa (which produces intrinsic factor) atrophies with age. ▲

▶ DID YOU GET IT?

16. How does fetal hemoglobin differ from that of the adult?

17. What blood-related disorders are particularly common in the elderly?

For answers, see Appendix D.

SUMMARY

Media study tools that provide additional review of key topics of Chapter 10 are referenced below.

IP = *InterActive Physiology*
WEB = The A&P Place

Composition and Functions of Blood (pp. 340–349)

1. Blood is composed of a nonliving fluid matrix (plasma) and formed elements. It is scarlet to dull red, depending on the amount of oxygen carried. Normal adult blood volume is 5 to 6 liters.

2. Dissolved in plasma (primarily water) are nutrients, gases, hormones, wastes, proteins, salts, and so on. Plasma composition changes as body cells remove or add substances to it, but homeostatic mechanisms act to keep it relatively constant. Plasma makes up 55 percent of whole blood.

3. Formed elements, the living blood cells that make up about 45 percent of whole blood, include the following:

   a. Erythrocytes, or RBCs—disc-shaped, anucleate cells that transport oxygen bound to their hemoglobin molecules. Their life span is 100 to 120 days.

   b. Leukocytes, or WBCs—ameboid cells involved in protection of the body.

   c. Platelets—cell fragments that act in blood clotting.

   WEB Exercise: Chapter 10, Formed Elements.

4. A decrease in oxygen-carrying ability of blood is anemia. Possible causes are decrease in number of functional RBCs or decrease in amount of hemoglobin they contain. Polycythemia is an excessive number of RBCs that may result from bone marrow cancer or a move to a location where less oxygen is available in the air (at high altitude, for example).

5. Leukocytes are nucleated cells, classed into two groups:

   a. Granulocytes include neutrophils, eosinophils, and basophils.

   b Agranulocytes include monocytes and lymphocytes.

6. When bacteria, viruses, or other foreign substances invade the body, WBCs increase in number (leukocytosis) and fight them in various ways.

7. An abnormal decrease in number of WBCs is leukopenia. An abnormal increase in WBCs is seen in infectious mononucleosis and leukemia (cancer of leukocytes).

8. All formed elements arise in red bone marrow from a common stem cell, the hemocytoblast. However, their developmental pathways differ. The stimulus for hematopoiesis is hormonal (erythropoietin in the case of RBCs).

Hemostasis (pp. 349–351)

1. Stoppage of blood loss from an injured blood vessel, or hemostasis, involves three steps: vascular spasms, platelet plug formation, and blood clot formation.

2. Hemostasis is started by a tear or interruption in the blood vessel lining. Vascular spasms and accumulation of platelets at the site temporarily stop or slow blood loss. Platelet PF_3 and tissue factor initiate the clotting cascade, leading to formation of fibrin threads. Fibrin traps RBCs as they flow past, forming the clot.

3. Normally, clots are digested when a vessel has been permanently repaired. An attached clot that forms or persists in an unbroken blood vessel is a thrombus; a clot traveling in the bloodstream is an embolus.

4. Abnormal bleeding may reflect a deficit of platelets (thrombocytopenia), genetic factors (hemophilia), or inability of the liver to make clotting factors.

Blood Groups and Transfusions (pp. 351–354)

1. Blood groups are classified on the basis of proteins (antigens) on RBC membranes. Complementary antibodies may (or may not) be present in blood. Antibodies act to agglutinate (clump) and lyse foreign RBCs.

2. The blood group most commonly typed for is ABO. Type O is most common; least common is AB. ABO antigens are accompanied by preformed antibodies in plasma, which act against RBCs that have "foreign" antigens.

3. Rh factor is found in most Americans. Rh^- people do not have preformed antibodies to Rh^+ RBCs but form them once exposed to Rh^+ blood.

Developmental Aspects of Blood (pp. 354, 356)

1. Congenital blood defects include various types of hemolytic anemias and hemophilia. Incompatibility between maternal and fetal blood can result in fetal cyanosis, resulting from destruction of fetal blood cells.

2. Fetal hemoglobin (HbF) binds more readily with oxygen than does HbA.

3. Physiologic jaundice in a newborn reflects immaturity of the infant's liver.

4. Excessive leukocytosis may be indicative of malignancy of blood-forming organs or leukemia. Leukemias are most common in the very young and very old.

5. Older adults are at risk for anemia, leukemia, and clotting disorders.

REVIEW QUESTIONS

Multiple Choice

More than one choice may apply.

1. Which would lead to increased erythropoiesis?
   a. Chronic bleeding ulcer
   b. Reduction in respiratory ventilation
   c. Decreased level of physical activity
   d. Reduced blood flow to the kidneys

2. Sickling of RBCs can be induced in a person with sickle cell anemia by
   a. blood loss.
   b. vigorous exercise.
   c. stress.
   d. fever.

3. A child is diagnosed with sickle cell anemia. This means that
   a. one parent had sickle cell anemia.
   b. one parent carried the sickle cell gene.
   c. both parents had sickle cell anemia.
   d. both parents carried the sickle cell gene.

4. Polycythemia vera will result in
   a. overproduction of WBCs.
   b. exceptionally high blood volume.
   c. abnormally high blood viscosity.
   d. abnormally low hematocrit.

5. Which of the following is not typical of leukocytes?
   a. Ameboid movement
   b. Phagocytic (some)
   c. Nucleated
   d. The most numerous cells in the bloodstream

6. The leukocyte that releases histamine and other inflammatory chemicals is the
   a. basophil.   c. eosinophil.
   b. monocyte.   d. neutrophil.

7. Which of the following formed elements are phagocytic?
   a. Erythrocytes   c. Monocytes
   b. Neutrophils   d. Lymphocytes

8. A condition resulting from thrombocytopenia is
   a. thrombus formation.
   b. embolus formation.
   c. petechiae.
   d. hemophilia.

9. Which of the following can cause problems in a transfusion reaction?
   a. Donor antibodies attacking recipient RBCs
   b. Clogging of small vessels by agglutinated clumps of RBCs
   c. Lysis of donated RBCs
   d. Blockage of kidney tubules

10. If an Rh^- mother becomes pregnant, when can hemolytic disease of the newborn *not possibly* occur in the child?
    a. If the child is Rh^-
    b. If the child is Rh^+
    c. If the father is Rh^+
    d. If the father is Rh^-

11. Plasma without the clotting proteins is called
    a. serum.   c. fibrin.
    b. whole blood.   d. tissue factor.

12. Albumin
    a. is a blood buffer.
    b. helps maintain blood's osmotic pressure.
    c. distributes body heat.
    d. transports certain molecules.

Short Answer Essay

13. What is the blood volume of an average-sized adult?

14. Name as many different categories of substances carried in plasma as you can.

15. Define *formed elements*. Which category is most numerous? Which makes up the buffy coat?

16. Define *anemia,* and give three possible causes.

17. Name the granular and agranular WBCs. Give the major function of each type in the body.

18. Name the formed elements that arise from myeloid stem cells. Name those arising from lymphoid stem cells.

19. What WBC type resides primarily in the tissues of the body?

20. Describe the process of hemostasis. Indicate what starts the process.

21. How can liver dysfunction cause bleeding disorders?

22. What are agglutinins?

23. Name the four ABO blood groups.

24. What is a transfusion reaction? Why does it happen?

25. Explain why an Rh$^-$ person does not have a transfusion reaction on the first exposure to Rh$^+$ blood. Why is there a transfusion reaction the second time he or she receives the Rh$^+$ blood?

26. If you had a high hematocrit, would you expect your hemoglobin determination to be high or low? Why?

CRITICAL THINKING AND CLINICAL APPLICATION QUESTIONS

27. A patient on renal dialysis has a low RBC count. What hormone, secreted by the kidney, can be assumed to be deficient?

28. A bone marrow biopsy of Mr. Bongalonga, a man on a long-term drug therapy, shows an abnormally high percentage of nonhematopoietic connective tissue. What condition does this indicate? If the symptoms are critical, what short-term and long-term treatments are indicated? Will infusion of whole blood or packed red cells be more likely?

29. A woman comes to the clinic complaining of fatigue, shortness of breath, and chills. Blood tests show anemia, and a bleeding ulcer is diagnosed. What type of anemia is this?

30. A patient is diagnosed with bone marrow cancer and has a hematocrit of 70 percent. What is this condition called?

31. A middle-aged college professor from Boston is in the Swiss Alps studying astronomy. He arrived two days ago and plans to stay the entire year. However, he notices that he is short of breath when he walks up steps and that he tires easily with any physical activity. His symptoms gradually disappear; after two months, he feels fine. Upon returning to the United States, he has a complete physical exam and is told that his erythrocyte count is higher than normal. (a) Attempt to explain this finding. (b) Will his RBC count remain at this higher-than-normal level? Why or why not?

32. Why is someone more likely to bleed to death when an artery is cleanly severed than when it is crushed and torn?

33. Explain how fetal hemoglobin, HbF, enhances oxygen transfer across the placenta from the mother to the fetus.

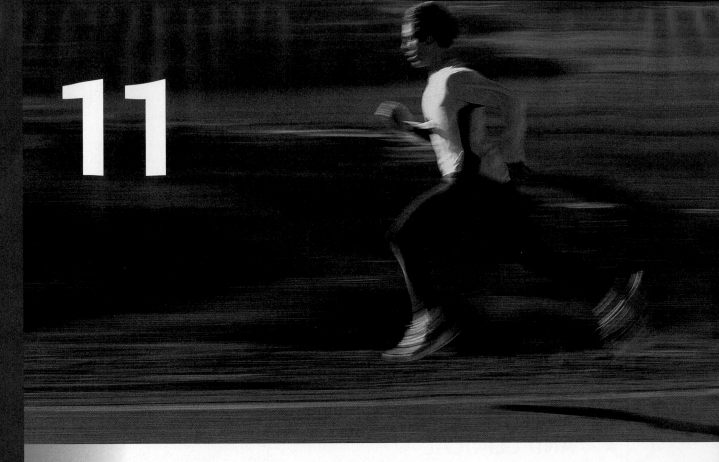

The Cardiovascular System

YOUR GOALS

After completing this chapter, you will have a working knowledge of the functions of the cardiovascular system and will have mastered the objectives listed below.

FUNCTION PREVIEW

- The heart pumps blood.
- Blood vessels provide the conduits within which blood circulates to all body tissues.

OBJECTIVE CHECKLIST

The Heart (pp. 362–374)

➤ Describe the location of the heart in the body, and identify its major anatomical areas on an appropriate model or diagram.

➤ Trace the pathway of blood through the heart.

➤ Compare the pulmonary and systemic circuits.

➤ Explain the operation of the heart valves.

➤ Name the functional blood supply of the heart.

➤ Name the elements of the intrinsic conduction system of the heart, and describe the pathway of impulses through this system.

- ➤ Define *systole, diastole, stroke volume,* and *cardiac cycle.*
- ➤ Define *heart sounds* and *murmur.*
- ➤ Explain what information can be gained from an electrocardiogram.
- ➤ Describe the effect of each of the following on heart rate: stimulation by the vagus nerve, exercise, epinephrine, and various ions.

Blood Vessels   (pp. 374–395)

- ➤ Compare and contrast the structure and function of arteries, veins, and capillaries.
- ➤ Identify the body's major arteries and veins, and name the body region supplied by each.
- ➤ Discuss the unique features of special circulations of the body: arterial circulation of the brain, hepatic portal circulation, and fetal circulation.
- ➤ Define *blood pressure* and *pulse,* and name several pulse points.
- ➤ List factors affecting and/or determining blood pressure.
- ➤ Define *hypertension* and *atherosclerosis,* and describe possible health consequences of these conditions.
- ➤ Describe the exchanges that occur across capillary walls.

Developmental Aspects of the Cardiovascular System (pp. 395, 397)

- ➤ Briefly describe the development of the cardiovascular system.
- ➤ Name the fetal vascular modifications, or "fetal shunts," and describe their function before birth.
- ➤ Explain how regular exercise and a diet low in fats and cholesterol may help maintain cardiovascular health.

When most people hear the term *cardiovascular system,* they immediately think of the heart. We have all felt our own heart "pound" from time to time, and we tend to get a bit nervous when this happens. The crucial importance of the heart has been recognized for ages. However, the **cardiovascular system** is much more than just the heart, and from a scientific and medical standpoint, it is important to understand *why* this system is so vital to life.

The almost continuous traffic into and out of a busy factory at rush hour occurs at a snail's pace compared to the endless activity going on within our bodies. Night and day, minute after minute, our trillions of cells take up nutrients and excrete wastes. Although the pace of these exchanges slows during sleep, they must go on continuously, because when they stop we die. Cells can make such exchanges only with the tissue fluid in their immediate vicinity. Thus, some means of changing

and "refreshing" these fluids is necessary to renew the nutrients and prevent pollution caused by the buildup of wastes. Like the bustling factory, the body must have a transportation system to carry its various "cargos" back and forth. Instead of roads, railway tracks, and airways, the body's delivery routes are its hollow blood vessels.

Most simply stated, the major function of the cardiovascular system is transportation. Using blood as the transport vehicle, the system carries oxygen, nutrients, cell wastes, hormones, and many other substances vital for body homeostasis to and from the cells. The force to move the blood around the body is provided by the beating heart and by blood pressure.

The cardiovascular system can be compared to a muscular pump equipped with one-way valves and a system of large and small plumbing tubes within which the blood travels. Blood (the substance

Midsternal line

2nd rib

Sternum

Diaphragm

(a)

Right lung

Heart

Anterior

(b)

Superior vena cava

Left lung

Aorta

Parietal pleura (cut)

Pulmonary trunk

Parietal pericardium (cut)

Apex of heart

Diaphragm

(c)

FIGURE 11.1 **Location of the heart within the thorax.** **(a)** Relationship of the heart to the sternum and ribs. **(b)** Cross-sectional view showing relative position of the heart in the thorax. **(c)** Relationship of the heart and great vessels to the lungs.

transported) is discussed in Chapter 10. Here we will consider the heart (the pump) and the blood vessels (the network of tubes).

The Heart

Anatomy of the Heart

Location and Size

The modest size and weight of the heart give few hints of its incredible strength. Approximately the size of a person's fist, the hollow, cone-shaped heart weighs less than a pound. Snugly enclosed within the inferior **mediastinum** (me″de-ah-sti′num), the medial cavity of the thorax, the heart is flanked on each side by the lungs (Figure 11.1). Its more pointed **apex** is directed toward the left hip and rests on the diaphragm, approximately at the level of the fifth intercostal space. (This is exactly where one would place a stethoscope to count the heart rate for an apical pulse.) Its broad posterosuperior aspect, or **base,** from which the great vessels of the body emerge, points toward the right shoulder and lies beneath the second rib.

Coverings and Wall

The heart is enclosed by a double-walled sac called the **pericardium** (per′i-kar″de-um). The loosely fitting superficial part of this sac is referred to as the **fibrous pericardium.** This fibrous layer

11

Q Which heart chamber has the thickest walls? What is the functional significance of this structural difference?

Brachiocephalic artery

Superior vena cava

Right pulmonary artery

Ascending aorta

Pulmonary trunk

Right pulmonary veins

Right atrium

Right coronary artery in coronary sulcus (right atrioventricular groove)

Anterior cardiac vein

Right ventricle

Marginal artery

Small cardiac vein

Inferior vena cava

Left common carotid artery

Left subclavian artery

Aortic arch

Ligamentum arteriosum

Left pulmonary artery

Left pulmonary veins

Left atrium

Auricle

Circumflex artery

Left coronary artery in coronary sulcus (left atrioventricular groove)

Left ventricle

Great cardiac vein

Anterior interventricular artery

Apex

(a) Anterior surface view.

FIGURE 11.2   Gross anatomy of the heart. *(Continued on page 364.)*

helps protect the heart and anchors it to surrounding structures, such as the diaphragm and sternum. Deep to the fibrous pericardium is the slippery, two-layer **serous pericardium.** Its **parietal layer** lines the interior of the fibrous pericardium. At the superior aspect of the heart, this parietal layer attaches to the large arteries leaving the heart and then makes a U-turn and continues inferiorly over the heart surface as the **visceral layer,** or **epicardium,** which is actually part of the heart wall (Figure 11.2b). A slippery lubricating fluid (serous fluid) is produced

by the serous pericardial membranes. This fluid allows the heart to beat easily in a relatively friction-less environment as the serous pericardial layers slide smoothly across each other.

HOMEOSTATIC IMBALANCE

Inflammation of the pericardium, **pericarditis** (per″ĭ-kar-di′tis), often results in a decrease in the serous fluid. This causes the pericardial layers to bind and stick to each other, forming painful *adhesions* that interfere with heart movements. ▲

The heart walls are composed of three layers: the outer *epicardium* (the visceral pericardium described above), the *myocardium,* and the innermost *endocardium* (Figure 11.2b). The **myocardium**

The left ventricle's walls are the thickest; that chamber pumps blood throughout the entire body and back to the heart; the right ventricle serves a short circuit through the lungs and back so it does not require as much muscle tissue.

(b) Heart wall and coverings.

Pericardium
Myocardium

Fibrous pericardium
Parietal layer of serous pericardium
Pericardial cavity
Epicardium (visceral layer of serous pericardium)
Myocardium
Endocardium
Heart wall
Heart chamber

Superior vena cava

Right pulmonary artery

Right atrium

Right pulmonary veins

Fossa ovalis

Right atrioventricular valve (tricuspid valve)

Right ventricle

Chordae tendineae

Inferior vena cava

Aorta

Left pulmonary artery

Left atrium

Left pulmonary veins

Pulmonary semilunar valve

Left atrioventricular valve (bicuspid valve)

Aortic semilunar valve

Left ventricle

Interventricular septum

Myocardium

Visceral pericardium

(c) Frontal section showing interior chambers and valves.

FIGURE 11.2 *(continued)* Gross anatomy of the heart.

(mi″o-kar′de-um) consists of thick bundles of cardiac muscle twisted and whorled into ringlike arrangements (see Figure 6.2b, p. 186). It is the layer that actually contracts. The myocardium is reinforced internally by a dense, fibrous connective tissue network called the "skeleton of the heart."

The **endocardium** (en″do-kar′de-um) is a thin, glistening sheet of endothelium that lines the heart chambers. It is continuous with the linings of the blood vessels leaving and entering the heart. Figure 11.2 shows two views of the heart—an external anterior view and a frontal section. As the anatomical areas of the heart are described in the next section, keep referring to Figure 11.2 to locate each of the heart structures or regions.

Chambers and Associated Great Vessels

The heart has four hollow chambers, or cavities—two **atria** (a'tre-ah; singular *atrium*) and two **ventricles** (ven'trĭ-kulz). Each of these chambers is lined with endocardium, which helps blood flow smoothly through the heart. The superior atria are primarily *receiving chambers*. As a rule, they are not important in the pumping activity of the heart. Blood flows into the atria under low pressure from the veins of the body and then continues on to fill the ventricles. The inferior, thick-walled ventricles are the *discharging chambers*, or actual pumps of the heart. When they contract, blood is propelled out of the heart and into the circulation. As illustrated in Figure 11.2a, the right ventricle forms most of the heart's anterior surface; the left ventricle forms its apex. The septum that divides the heart longitudinally is referred to as either the **interventricular septum** or the **interatrial septum,** depending on which chamber it separates.

Although it is a single organ, the heart functions as a double pump. The right side works as the pulmonary circuit pump. It receives relatively oxygen-poor blood from the veins of the body through the large **superior** and **inferior venae cavae** (ka've) and pumps it out through the **pulmonary trunk.** The pulmonary trunk splits into the right and left **pulmonary arteries,** which carry blood to the lungs, where oxygen is picked up and carbon dioxide is unloaded. Oxygen-rich blood drains from the lungs and is returned to the left side of the heart through the four **pulmonary veins.** The circulation just described, from the right side of the heart to the lungs and back to the left side of the heart, is called the **pulmonary circulation** (Figure 11.3). Its only function is to carry blood to the lungs for gas exchange and then return it to the heart.

Blood returned to the left side of the heart is pumped out of the heart into the **aorta** (a-or'tah), from which the systemic arteries branch to supply essentially all body tissues. Oxygen-poor blood circulates from the tissues back to the right atrium via the systemic veins, which finally empty their cargo into either the superior or inferior vena cava. This second circuit, from the left side of the heart

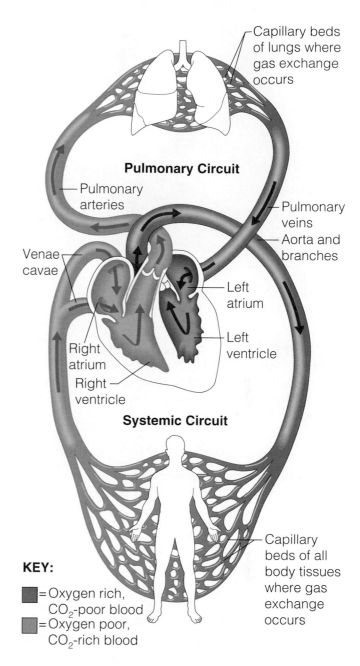

KEY:

■ = Oxygen rich, CO_2-poor blood
□ = Oxygen poor, CO_2-rich blood

FIGURE 11.3   The systemic and pulmonary circulations. The left side of the heart is the systemic pump; the right side is the pulmonary circuit pump. (Although there are two pulmonary arteries, one each to the right and left lung, for simplicity only one is shown.)

through the body tissues and back to the right side of the heart, is called the **systemic circulation** (see Figure 11.3). It supplies oxygen- and nutrient-rich blood to all body organs. Because the left ventricle is the systemic pump that pumps blood over a

Right ventricle

Muscular interventricular septum

Left ventricle

FIGURE 11.4 **Anatomical differences in right and left ventricles.** The left ventricle has a thicker wall, and its cavity is basically circular. The right ventricle cavity is crescent-shaped and wraps around the left ventricle.

much longer pathway through the body, its walls are substantially thicker than those of the right ventricle (Figure 11.4), and it is a much more powerful pump.

Valves

The heart is equipped with four valves, which allow blood to flow in only one direction through the heart chambers—from the atria through the ventricles and out the great arteries leaving the heart (see Figure 11.2a). The **atrioventricular** (a″tre-o-ven-trik′u-lar), or **AV, valves** are located between the atrial and ventricular chambers on each side. These valves prevent backflow into the atria when the ventricles contract. The left AV valve—the **bicuspid,** or **mitral** (mi′tral), **valve**—consists of two flaps, or cusps, of endocardium. The right AV valve, the **tricuspid valve,** has three flaps. Tiny white cords, the **chordae tendineae** (kor′de ten-din′e)—literally, "tendinous cords" (but I like to think of them as the "heart strings" of song)—anchor the flaps to the walls of the ventricles. When the heart is relaxed and blood is passively filling its chambers, the AV-valve flaps hang limply into the ventricles (Figure 11.5a). As the ventricles contract, they press on the blood in their chambers, and the

intraventricular pressure (pressure inside the ventricles) begins to rise. This forces the AV-valve flaps upward, closing the valves. At this point the chordae tendineae are working to anchor the flaps in a closed position. If the flaps were unanchored, they would blow upward into the atria like an umbrella being turned inside out by a gusty wind. In this manner, the AV valves prevent backflow into the atria when the ventricles are contracting.

The second set of valves, the **semilunar** (sem″e-lu′nar) **valves,** guards the bases of the two large arteries leaving the ventricular chambers. Thus, they are known as the **pulmonary** and **aortic semilunar valves** (see Figure 11.2c). Each semilunar valve has three leaflets that fit tightly together when the valves are closed. When the ventricles are contracting and forcing blood out of the heart, the leaflets are forced open and flattened against the walls of the arteries by the tremendous force of rushing blood (Figure 11.5b). Then, when the ventricles relax, the blood begins to flow backward toward the heart, and the leaflets fill with blood, closing the valves. This prevents arterial blood from reentering the heart.

Each set of valves operates at a different time. The AV valves are open during heart relaxation and closed when the ventricles are contracting. The semilunar valves are closed during heart relaxation and are forced open when the ventricles contract. As they open and close in response to pressure changes in the heart, the valves force blood to continually move forward in its journey through the heart.

HOMEOSTATIC IMBALANCE

Heart valves are basically simple devices, and the heart—like any mechanical pump—can function with "leaky" valves as long as the damage is not too great. However, severely deformed valves can seriously hamper cardiac function. For example, an *incompetent valve* forces the heart to pump and repump the same blood because the valve does not close properly and blood backflows. In *valvular stenosis,* the valve flaps become stiff, often because of repeated bacterial infection of the endocardium **(endocarditis).** This forces the heart to contract more vigorously than normal. In each case, the heart's workload increases, and ultimately the heart weakens and may fail. Under such conditions, the faulty valve is replaced with a synthetic valve, a cryopreserved human valve, or a chemically treated valve taken from a pig heart. ▲

Operation of the AV valves

Operation of the semilunar valves

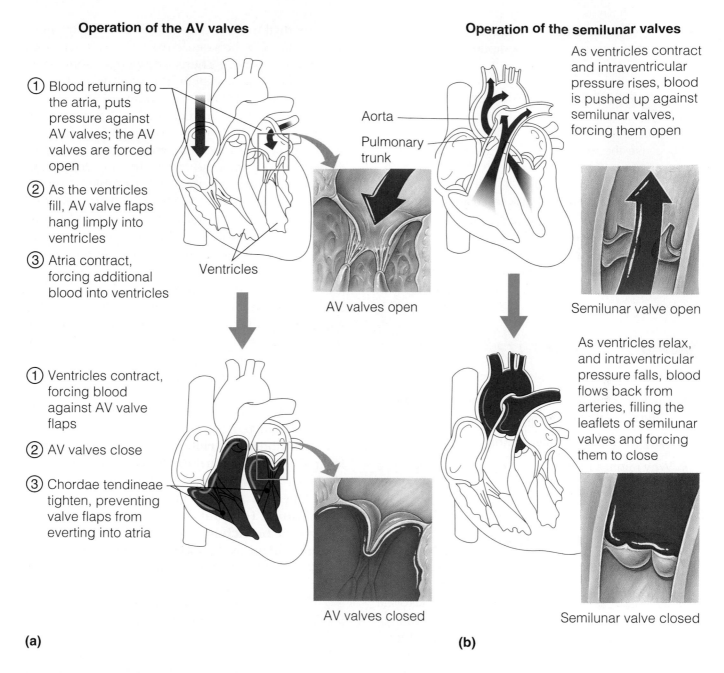

① Blood returning to the atria, puts pressure against AV valves; the AV valves are forced open

② As the ventricles fill, AV valve flaps hang limply into ventricles

③ Atria contract, forcing additional blood into ventricles

Ventricles

AV valves open

① Ventricles contract, forcing blood against AV valve flaps

② AV valves close

③ Chordae tendineae tighten, preventing valve flaps from everting into atria

AV valves closed

(a)

As ventricles contract and intraventricular pressure rises, blood is pushed up against semilunar valves, forcing them open

Aorta

Pulmonary trunk

Semilunar valve open

As ventricles relax, and intraventricular pressure falls, blood flows back from arteries, filling the leaflets of semilunar valves and forcing them to close

Semilunar valve closed

(b)

FIGURE 11.5   **Operation of the heart valves. (a)** Atrioventricular (AV) valves. **(b)** Semilunar valves.

Cardiac Circulation

Although the heart chambers are bathed with blood almost continuously, the blood contained in the heart does *not* nourish the myocardium. The blood supply that oxygenates and nourishes the heart is provided by the right and left coronary arteries. The **coronary arteries** branch from the base of the aorta and encircle the heart in the **coronary sulcus (atrioventricular groove)** at the junction of the atria and ventricles (see Figure 11.2a). The coronary arteries and their major branches (the **anterior interventricular** and **circumflex arteries** on the left, and the **posterior interventricular** and **marginal arteries** on the right) are compressed when the ventricles are contracting and fill when the heart is relaxed. The myocardium is drained by several **cardiac veins,** which empty into an enlarged vessel on the posterior of the heart called the **coronary sinus.** The coronary sinus, in turn, empties into the right atrium.

HOMEOSTATIC IMBALANCE

When the heart beats at a very rapid rate, the myocardium may receive an inadequate blood supply because the relaxation periods (when the blood is able to flow to the heart tissue) are shortened. Situations in which the myocardium is deprived of oxygen often result in crushing chest pain called **angina pectoris** (an-ji′nah pek′tor-is). This pain is a warning that should *never* be ignored, because if angina is prolonged the oxygen-deprived heart cells may die, forming an **infarct.** The resulting **myocardial infarction** (in-fark′shun) is commonly called a "heart attack" or "coronary." ▲

▶ DID YOU GET IT?

1. What is the location of the heart in the thorax?

2. How does the function of the systemic circulation differ from that of the pulmonary circulation?

3. Why are the heart valves important?

4. Why might a thrombus in a coronary artery cause sudden death?

For answers, see Appendix D.

Physiology of the Heart

As the heart beats, or contracts, the blood makes continuous round trips—into and out of the heart, through the rest of the body, and then back to the heart—only to be sent out again. The amount of work that a heart does is almost too incredible to believe. In one day it pushes the body's supply of 6 quarts or so of blood (6 liters [L]) through the blood vessels over 1000 times, meaning that it actually pumps about 6000 quarts of blood in a single day!

Intrinsic Conduction System of the Heart: Setting the Basic Rhythm

Unlike skeletal muscle cells, which must be stimulated by nerve impulses before they will contract, cardiac muscle cells can and do contract spontaneously and independently, even if all nervous connections are severed. Moreover, these spontaneous contractions occur in a regular and continuous way. Although cardiac muscle *can* beat independently, the muscle cells in different areas of the heart have different rhythms. The atrial cells beat about 60 times per minute, but the ventricular cells contract more slowly (20–40/min). Therefore, without some type of unifying control system, the heart would be an uncoordinated and inefficient pump.

Two systems act to regulate heart activity. One of these involves the nerves of the autonomic nervous system, which act like brakes and accelerators to decrease or increase the heart rate depending on which division is activated. This topic is considered later (see pp. 372–373). The second system is the **intrinsic conduction system,** or **nodal system,** that is built into the heart tissue (Figure 11.6) and sets its basic rhythm. The intrinsic conduction system is composed of a special tissue found nowhere else in the body; it is much like a cross between muscle and nervous tissue. This system causes heart muscle depolarization in only one direction—from the atria to the ventricles. In addition, it enforces a contraction rate of approximately 75 beats per minute on the heart; thus, the heart beats as a coordinated unit.

One of the most important parts of the intrinsic conduction system is a crescent-shaped node of tissue called the **sinoatrial** (si″no-a′tre-al) **(SA) node,** located in the right atrium. Other components include the **atrioventricular (AV) node** at the junction of the atria and ventricles, the **atrioventricular (AV) bundle (bundle of His)** and the right and left **bundle branches** located in the interventricular septum, and finally the **Purkinje** (pur-kin′je) **fibers,** which spread within the muscle of the ventricle walls.

The SA node is a tiny cell mass with a mammoth job. Because it has the highest rate of depolarization in the whole system, it starts each heartbeat and sets the pace for the whole heart. Consequently, the SA node is often called the **pacemaker.** From the SA node, the impulse spreads through the atria to the AV node, and then the atria contract. At the AV node, the impulse is delayed briefly to give the atria time to finish contracting. It then passes rapidly through the AV bundle, the bundle branches, and the Purkinje fibers, resulting in a "wringing" contraction of the ventricles that begins at the heart apex and moves toward the atria. This contraction effectively ejects blood superiorly into the large arteries leaving the heart. The "A Closer Look" box on p. 370 describes *electrocardiography,* the clinical procedure for mapping the electrical activity of the heart.

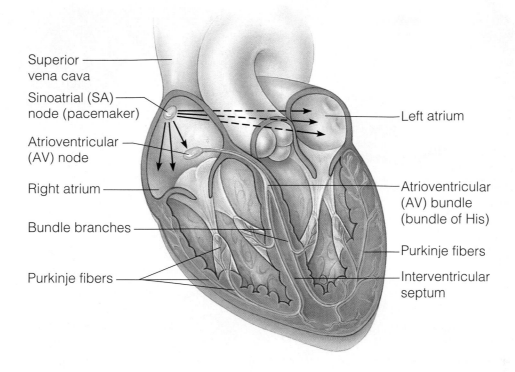

FIGURE 11.6   The intrinsic conduction system of the heart.
The depolarization wave initiated by the sinoatrial (SA) node passes successively through the atrial myocardium to the atrioventricular (AV) node, the AV bundle, the right and left bundle branches, and the Purkinje fibers in the ventricular walls.

HOMEOSTATIC IMBALANCE

Because the atria and ventricles are separated from one another by "insulating" connective tissue, which is part of the fibrous skeleton of the heart, depolarization waves can reach the ventricles only by traveling through the AV node. Thus, any damage to the AV node can partially or totally release the ventricles from the control of the SA node. When this occurs, the ventricles (thus the heart) begin to beat at their own rate, which is much slower, some or all of the time. This condition is called **heart block.**

There are other conditions that can interfere with the regular conduction of impulses across the heart—for example, damage to the SA node results in a slower heart rate. When this is a problem, artificial pacemakers are usually installed surgically. **Ischemia** (is-ke'me-ah), or lack of an adequate blood supply to the heart muscle, may lead to **fibrillation**—a rapid, uncoordinated shuddering of the heart muscle (it looks like a bag of worms). Fibrillation makes the heart totally useless as a pump and is a major cause of death from heart attacks in adults. ▲

Tachycardia (tak"e-kar'de-ah) is a rapid heart rate (over 100 beats per minute). **Bradycardia** (brad"e-kar'de-ah) is a heart rate that is substantially slower than normal (less than 60 beats per minute). Neither condition is pathological, but prolonged tachycardia may progress to fibrillation.

Cardiac Cycle and Heart Sounds

In a healthy heart, the atria contract simultaneously. Then, as they start to relax, contraction of the ventricles begins. **Systole** (sis'to-le) and **diastole** (di-as'to-le) mean heart *contraction* and *relaxation*, respectively. Because most of the pumping work is done by the ventricles, these terms always refer to the contraction and relaxation of the *ventricles* unless otherwise stated.

The term **cardiac cycle** refers to the events of one complete heartbeat, during which both atria and ventricles contract and then relax. The average heart beats approximately 75 times per minute, so the length of the cardiac cycle is normally about 0.8 second. We will consider the cardiac cycle in

A CLOSER LOOK

ELECTROCARDIOGRAPHY: (DON'T) BE STILL MY HEART

When impulses pass through the heart, electrical currents are generated that spread throughout the body. These impulses can be detected on the body surface and recorded with an *electrocardiograph*. The recording that is made, the **electrocardiogram (ECG),** traces the flow of current through the heart. The illustration shows a normal ECG tracing.

> ❝ *The typical ECG has three recognizable waves.* ❞

The typical ECG has three recognizable waves. The first wave, the **P wave,** is small and signals the depolarization of the atria immediately before they contract. The large **QRS complex,** which results from the depolarization of the ventricles, has a complicated shape. It precedes the contraction of the ventricles. The **T wave** results from currents flowing during the repolarization of the ventri-

An electrocardiogram tracing showing the three normally recognizable deflection waves—P, QRS, and T.

cles. (Atrial repolarization is generally hidden by the large QRS complex, which is being recorded at the same time.)

Abnormalities in the shape of the waves and changes in their timing send signals that something may be wrong with the intrinsic conduction system, or they may indicate a *myocardial infarct* (present or past). A myocardial infarct is an area of heart tissue in which the cardiac cells have died; it is generally a result of *ischemia.* During *fibrillation,* the normal pattern of the ECG is totally lost, and the heart ceases to act as a functioning pump.

Are the ventricular cardiac cells contracting isometrically or isotonically during the first part of phase 2?

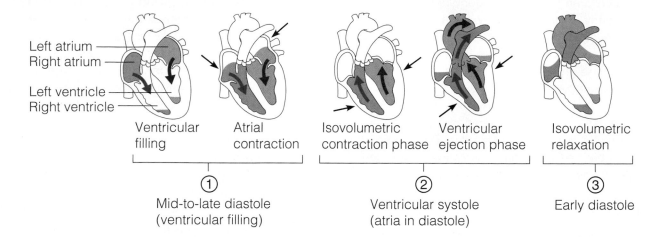

Left atrium
Right atrium
Left ventricle
Right ventricle

| Ventricular filling | Atrial contraction | Isovolumetric contraction phase | Ventricular ejection phase | Isovolumetric relaxation |

① Mid-to-late diastole (ventricular filling)

② Ventricular systole (atria in diastole)

③ Early diastole

FIGURE 11.7 **Summary of events occurring during the cardiac cycle.** Small black arrows indicate the regions of the heart that are contracting; thick red and blue arrows indicate direction of blood flow. During the *isovolumetric* (literally "same volume measurement") phases in periods 2 and 3, the ventricles are closed chambers and the volume of blood they contain is unchanging.

terms of events occurring during three periods—*mid-to-late diastole, ventricular systole,* and *early diastole* (Figure 11.7).

1. **Mid-to-late diastole.** Our discussion begins with the heart in complete relaxation. At this point, the pressure in the heart is low, and blood is flowing passively into and through the atria into the ventricles from the pulmonary and systemic circulations. The semilunar valves are closed, and the AV valves are open. Then the atria contract and force the blood remaining in their chambers into the ventricles.

2. **Ventricular systole.** Shortly after, ventricular contraction (systole) begins, and the pressure within the ventricles increases rapidly, closing the AV valves. When the intraventricular pressure (pressure in the ventricles) is higher than the pressure in the large arteries leaving the heart, the semilunar valves are forced open, and blood rushes through them out of the ventricles. During ventricular systole, the atria are relaxed, and their chambers are again filling with blood.

3. **Early diastole.** At the end of systole, the ventricles relax, the semilunar valves snap shut (preventing backflow), and for a moment the ventricles are completely closed chambers. During early diastole, the intraventricular pressure drops. When it drops below the pressure in the atria (which has been increasing as blood has been filling their chambers), the AV valves are forced open, and the ventricles again begin to refill rapidly with blood, completing the cycle.

When using a stethoscope, you can hear two distinct sounds during each cardiac cycle. These **heart sounds** are often described by the two syllables "lub" and "dup," and the sequence is lub-dup, pause, lub-dup, pause, and so on. The first heart sound (lub) is caused by the closing of the AV valves. The second heart sound (dup) occurs when the semilunar valves close at the end of systole. The first heart sound is longer and louder than the second heart sound, which tends to be short and sharp.

HOMEOSTATIC IMBALANCE
Abnormal or unusual heart sounds are called **murmurs.** Blood flows silently as long as the flow is smooth and uninterrupted. If it strikes obstructions, its flow becomes turbulent and generates

The cells contract isometrically until they have enough force to overcome the back pressure of the blood against the semilunar valves, at which point their contraction becomes isotonic.

sounds, such as heart murmurs, that can be heard with a stethoscope. Heart murmurs are fairly common in young children (and some elderly people) with perfectly healthy hearts, probably because their heart walls are relatively thin and vibrate with rushing blood. However, murmurs in patients who do not fall into either of these groups most often indicate valve problems. For example, if a valve does not close tightly (is *incompetent*), a swishing sound will be heard *after* that valve has (supposedly) closed, as the blood flows back through the partially open valve. Distinct sounds also can be heard when blood flows turbulently through *stenosed* (narrowed) valves. ▲

Cardiac Output

Cardiac output (CO) is the amount of blood pumped out by *each* side of the heart (actually each ventricle) in 1 minute. It is the product of the **heart rate (HR)** and the **stroke volume (SV).** Stroke volume is the volume of blood pumped out by a ventricle with each heartbeat. In general, stroke volume increases as the force of ventricular contraction increases. If we use the normal resting values for heart rate (75 beats per minute) and stroke volume (70 ml per beat), the average adult cardiac output can be easily figured:

CO = HR (75 beats/min) × SV (70 ml/beat)

CO = 5250 ml/min

The normal adult blood volume is about 6000 ml, so the entire blood supply passes through the body once each minute. Cardiac output varies with the demands of the body. It rises when the stroke volume is increased or the heart beats faster or both; it drops when either or both of these factors decrease. Let's take a look at how stroke volume and heart rate are regulated.

Regulation of Stroke Volume A healthy heart pumps out about 60 percent of the blood present in its ventricles. As noted above, this is approximately 70 ml (about 2 ounces) with each heartbeat. According to *Starling's law of the heart,* the critical factor controlling stroke volume is how much the cardiac muscle cells are stretched just before they contract. The more they are stretched, the stronger the contraction will be. The important factor stretching the heart muscle is *venous return,* the amount of blood entering the heart and distending its ventricles. If one side of the heart suddenly begins to pump more blood than the other, the increased venous return to the opposite ventricle will force it to pump out an equal amount, thus preventing backup of blood in the circulation.

Anything that increases the volume or speed of venous return also increases stroke volume and force of contraction (Figure 11.8). For example, a slow heartbeat allows more time for the ventricles to fill. Exercise speeds venous return because it results in increased heart rate and force. The enhanced squeezing action of active skeletal muscles on the veins returning blood to the heart, the so-called *muscular pump,* also plays a major role in increasing the venous return. In contrast, low venous return, such as might result from severe blood loss or an extremely rapid heart rate, decreases stroke volume, causing the heart to beat less forcefully.

Factors Modifying Basic Heart Rate In healthy people, stroke volume tends to be relatively constant. However, when blood volume drops suddenly or when the heart has been seriously weakened, stroke volume declines, and cardiac output is maintained by a faster heartbeat. Although heart contraction does not depend on the nervous system, its rate *can* be changed temporarily by the autonomic nerves. Indeed, the most important external influence on heart rate is the activity of the autonomic nervous system. Heart rate is also modified by various chemicals, hormones, and ions. Some of these factors are summarized in Figure 11.8.

Neural (ANS) Controls   During times of physical or emotional stress, the nerves of the *sympathetic division* of the autonomic nervous system more strongly stimulate the SA and AV nodes and the cardiac muscle itself. As a result, the heart beats more rapidly. This is a familiar phenomenon to anyone who has ever been frightened or has had to run to catch a bus. As fast as the heart pumps under ordinary conditions, it really speeds up when special demands are placed on it. Because a faster blood flow increases the rate at which fresh blood reaches body cells, more oxygen and glucose are made available to them during periods of stress. When demand declines, the heart adjusts. *Parasympathetic nerves,* primarily the vagus nerves, slow and steady the heart, giving it more time to rest during noncrisis times. In patients with *congestive heart failure,* a condition in which the heart is nearly "worn out" because of age, hypertensive heart disease, or another pathological process, the heart pumps weakly. For those patients, the drug

KEY:

← Increases, stimulates

← Reduces, inhibits

☐ Initial stimulus

☐ Physiological response

■ End result

FIGURE 11.8   **Influence of selected factors on cardiac output.**

digitalis is routinely prescribed. It enhances contractile force and stroke volume of the heart, resulting in greater cardiac output.

Various hormones and ions can have a dramatic effect on heart activity. *Epinephrine,* which mimics the effect of the sympathetic nerves, and *thyroxine* both increase heart rate. Electrolyte imbalances pose a real threat to the heart. For example, reduced levels of ionic calcium in the blood depress the heart, whereas excessive blood calcium causes such prolonged contractions that the heart may stop entirely. Either excess or lack of needed ions such as sodium and potassium also modifies heart activity. A deficit of potassium ions in the blood, for example, causes the heart to beat feebly, and abnormal heart rhythms appear.

Physical Factors   A number of physical factors, including age, gender, exercise, and body temperature, influence heart rate. Resting heart rate is fastest in the fetus (140–160 beats per minute) and then gradually decreases throughout life. The average heart rate is faster in females (72–80 beats per minute) than in males (64–72 beats per minute). Heat increases heart rate by boosting the metabolic rate of heart cells. This explains the rapid, pounding heartbeat you feel when you have a high fever and accounts in part for the effect of exercise on heart rate (remember, working muscles generate heat). Cold has the opposite effect; it directly decreases heart rate. As noted above, exercise acts through nervous system controls (sympathetic division) to increase heart rate (and also, through the action of the muscular pump, to increase stroke volume).

HOMEOSTATIC IMBALANCE

The pumping action of the healthy heart maintains a balance between cardiac output and venous return. But when the pumping efficiency of the heart is depressed so that circulation is inadequate to meet tissue needs, **congestive heart failure (CHF)** occurs. Congestive heart failure is usually a progressive condition that reflects weakening of the heart by *coronary atherosclerosis* (clogging of the coronary vessels with fatty buildup), persistent high blood pressure, or multiple myocardial infarctions (leading to repair with noncontracting scar tissue).

Because the heart is a double pump, each side can fail independently of the other. If the left heart fails, *pulmonary congestion* occurs. The right side of the heart continues to propel blood to the lungs, but the left side is unable to eject the returning blood into the systemic circulation. As blood vessels within the lungs become swollen with blood, the pressure within them increases, and fluid leaks from the circulation into the lung tissue, causing **pulmonary edema.** If untreated, the person suffocates.

If the right side of the heart fails, *peripheral congestion* occurs as blood backs up in the systemic circulation. Edema is most noticeable in the distal parts of the body: The feet, ankles, and fingers become swollen and puffy. Failure of one side of the heart puts a greater strain on the opposite side, and eventually the whole heart fails. ▲

▶ DID YOU GET IT?

5. What is the function of the intrinsic conduction system of the heart?

6. To which heart chambers do the terms *systole* and *diastole* usually apply?

7. What causes the lub-dup sounds heard with a stethoscope?

8. What does the term *cardiac output* mean?

9. What would you expect to happen to the heart rate of an individual with a fever? Why?

For answers, see Appendix D.

Blood Vessels

Blood circulates inside the blood vessels, which form a closed transport system, the so-called **vascular system.** The idea that blood circulates, or "makes rounds," through the body is only about 300 years old. The ancient Greeks believed that blood moved through the body like an ocean tide, first moving out from the heart and then ebbing back to it in the same vessels to get rid of its impurities in the lungs. It was not until the seventeenth century that William Harvey, an English physician, proved that blood did, in fact, move in circles.

Like a system of roads, the vascular system has its freeways, secondary roads, and alleys. As the heart beats, blood is propelled into the large **arteries** leaving the heart. It then moves into successively smaller and smaller arteries and then into the **arterioles** (ar-ter′e-ōlz), which feed the **capillary** (kap′ĭ-lar″e) **beds** in the tissues. Capillary beds are drained by **venules** (ven′ulz), which in turn empty into **veins** that finally empty into the great veins (venae cavae) entering the heart. Thus arteries, which carry blood away from the heart, and veins, which drain the tissues and return the blood to the heart, are simply conducting vessels—the freeways and secondary roads. Only the tiny hairlike capillaries, which extend and branch through the tissues and connect the smallest arteries (arterioles) to the smallest veins (venules), directly serve the needs of the body cells. The capillaries are the side streets or alleys that intimately intertwine among the body cells and provide access to individual "homes." It is only through their walls that exchanges between the tissue cells and the blood can occur.

Notice that this book routinely depicts arteries red and veins blue because, by convention, red indicates oxygen-rich blood, the normal status of blood in most of the body's arteries, and blue indicates relatively oxygen-depleted, carbon dioxide–rich blood, the normal status of blood in most of the veins. However, there are exceptions to this convention, and we will point them out as we encounter them.

Microscopic Anatomy of Blood Vessels

Tunics

Except for the microscopic capillaries, the walls of blood vessels have three coats, or tunics (Figure 11.9). The **tunica intima** (tu′nĭ-kah in-tim′ah), which lines the lumen, or interior, of the vessels, is a thin layer of endothelium (squamous epithelial cells) resting on a basement membrane. Its cells fit closely together and form a slick surface

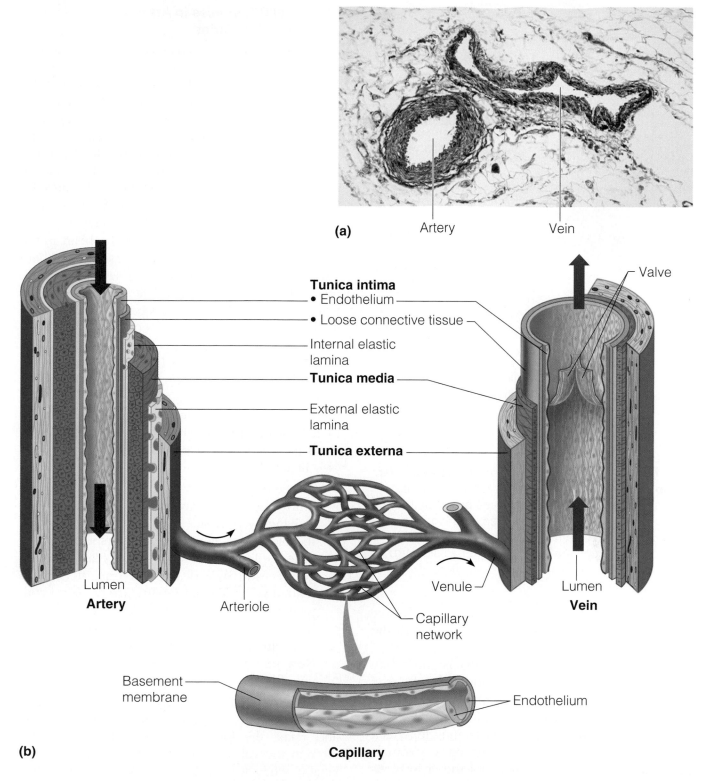

(a)   Artery   Vein

Tunica intima
• Endothelium
• Loose connective tissue
Internal elastic lamina
Tunica media
External elastic lamina
Tunica externa

Valve

Lumen
Artery   Arteriole   Venule   Lumen
Vein

Capillary network

Basement membrane   Endothelium

Capillary

(b)

FIGURE 11.9   Structure of blood vessels. (a) Light photomicrograph of a muscular artery and the corresponding vein in cross section (30×). **(b)** The walls of arteries and veins are composed of three tunics: the tunica intima (endothelium underlain by a basement membrane), tunica media (smooth muscle and elastic fibers), and tunica externa (largely collagen fibers). Capillaries—between arteries and veins in the circulatory pathway—are composed only of the tunica intima. Notice that the tunica media is thick in arteries and relatively thin in veins.

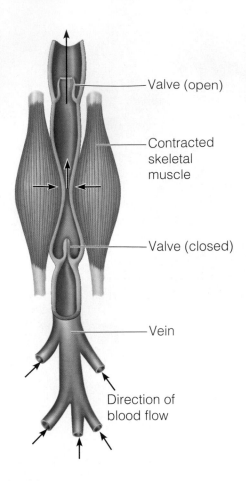

Valve (open)

Contracted skeletal muscle

Valve (closed)

Vein

Direction of blood flow

FIGURE 11.10 **Operation of the muscular pump.** When skeletal muscles contract and press against the flexible veins, the valves proximal to the area of contraction are forced open, and blood is squeezed toward the heart. The valves distal to the point of contraction are closed by the backflowing blood.

that decreases friction as blood flows through the vessel lumen.

The **tunica media** (me′de-ah) is the bulky middle coat. It is mostly smooth muscle and elastic fibers. Some of the larger arteries have *elastic laminae,* sheets of elastic tissue, in addition to the scattered elastic fibers. The smooth muscle, which is controlled by the sympathetic nervous system, is active in changing the diameter of the vessels. As the vessels constrict or dilate, blood pressure increases or decreases, respectively.

The **tunica externa** (eks′tern-ah) is the outermost tunic. This layer is composed largely of fibrous connective tissue, and its function is basically to support and protect the vessels.

Structural Differences in Arteries, Veins, and Capillaries

The walls of arteries are usually much thicker than those of veins. The arterial tunica media, in particular, tends to be much heavier. This structural difference is related to a difference in function of these two types of vessels. Arteries, which are closer to the pumping action of the heart, must be able to expand as blood is forced into them and then recoil passively as the blood flows off into the circulation during diastole. Their walls must be strong and stretchy enough to take these continuous changes in pressure (see Figure 11.19).

Veins, in contrast, are far from the heart in the circulatory pathway, and the pressure in them tends to be low all the time. Thus veins have thinner walls. However, because the blood pressure in veins is usually too low to force the blood back to the heart, and because blood returning to the heart often flows against gravity, veins are modified to ensure that the amount of blood returning to the heart *(venous return)* equals the amount being pumped out of the heart *(cardiac output)* at any time. The lumens of veins tend to be much larger than those of corresponding arteries, and the larger veins have **valves** that prevent backflow of blood (see Figure 11.9).

● To see the effect of venous valves, perform the following simple experiment: Allow one hand to hang by your side for a minute or two, until the blood vessels on its dorsal aspect become distended (swollen) with blood. Place two fingertips side by side against one of the distended veins. Then, pressing firmly, move your proximal finger along the vein toward your heart. Now release that finger. As you can see, the vein remains collapsed in spite of gravity. Now remove your distal finger, and watch the vein fill rapidly with blood.

Skeletal muscle activity also enhances venous return. As the muscles surrounding the veins contract and relax, the blood is squeezed, or "milked," through the veins toward the heart (Figure 11.10). Finally, when we inhale, the drop in pressure that occurs in the thorax causes the large veins near the heart to expand and fill. Thus, the "respiratory pump" also helps return blood to the heart (see Figure 11.8).

The transparent walls of the capillaries are only one cell layer thick—just the tunica intima. Because of this exceptional thinness, exchanges are easily made between the blood and the tissue cells.

The tiny capillaries tend to form interweaving networks called *capillary beds*. The flow of blood from an arteriole to a venule—that is, through a capillary bed—is called **microcirculation.** In most body regions, a capillary bed consists of two types of vessels: (1) a **vascular shunt,** a vessel that directly connects the arteriole and venule at opposite ends of the bed, and (2) true capillaries, the actual *exchange vessels* (Figure 11.11).

The *true capillaries* number 10 to 100 per capillary bed, depending on the organ or tissues served. They usually branch off the proximal end of the shunt and return to the distal end, but occasionally they spring from the **terminal arteriole** and empty directly into the **postcapillary venule.** A cuff of smooth muscle fibers, called a **precapillary sphincter,** surrounds the root of each true capillary and acts as a valve to regulate the flow of blood into the capillary. Blood flowing through a terminal arteriole may take one of two routes: through the true capillaries or through the shunt. When the precapillary sphincters are relaxed (open), blood flows through the true capillaries and takes part in exchanges with tissue cells. When the sphincters are contracted (closed), blood flows through the shunts and bypasses the tissue cells.

HOMEOSTATIC IMBALANCE

Varicose veins are common in people who stand for long periods of time (for example, dentists and hairdressers) and in obese (or pregnant) individuals. The common factors are the pooling of blood in the feet and legs and inefficient venous return resulting from inactivity or pressure on the veins. In any case, the overworked valves give way, and the veins become twisted and dilated. A serious complication of varicose veins is **thrombophlebitis** (throm"bo-fle-bi'tis), inflammation of a vein that results when a clot forms in a vessel with poor circulation. Because all venous blood must pass through the pulmonary circulation before traveling through the body tissues again, a common consequence of thrombophlebitis is clot detachment and **pulmonary embolism,** which is a life-threatening condition. ▲

▶ DID YOU GET IT?

10. Assume you are viewing a blood vessel under the microscope. It has a lopsided lumen, relatively thick externa, and a relatively thin media. Which kind of a blood vessel is this?

 Assume the capillary bed depicted here is in the biceps brachii muscle of your arm. What condition would the capillary bed be in (a or b) if you were doing push-ups at the gym?

(a) Sphincters open

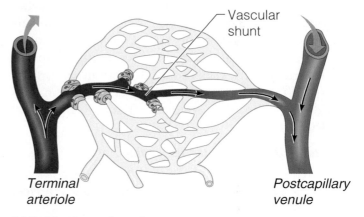

(b) Sphincters closed

FIGURE 11.11   Anatomy of a capillary bed. The vascular shunt bypasses the true capillaries when precapillary sphincters controlling blood entry into the true capillaries are constricted.

11. Arteries lack valves, but veins have them. How is this structural difference related to blood pressure?

12. How is the structure of capillaries related to their function in the body?

For answers, see Appendix D.

 a. The true capillaries would be flushed with blood to serve the working muscle cells.

Gross Anatomy of Blood Vessels
Major Arteries of the Systemic Circulation

The **aorta** is the largest artery of the body, and it is a truly splendid vessel. In adults, the aorta is about the size of a garden hose (with an internal diameter about equal to the diameter of your thumb) where it issues from the left ventricle of the heart. It decreases only slightly in diameter as it runs to its terminus. Different parts of the aorta are named for either their location or their shape. The aorta springs upward from the left ventricle of the heart as the **ascending aorta,** arches to the left as the **aortic arch,** and then plunges downward through the thorax, following the spine **(thoracic aorta)** finally to pass through the diaphragm into the abdominopelvic cavity, where it becomes the **abdominal aorta** (Figure 11.12).

The major branches of the aorta and the organs they serve are listed next in sequence from the heart. Figure 11.12 shows the course of the aorta and its major branches. As you locate the arteries on the figure, be aware of ways to make your learning easier. In many cases the name of the artery tells you the body region or organs served (renal artery, brachial artery, and coronary artery) or the bone followed (femoral artery and ulnar artery).

Arterial Branches of the Ascending Aorta

- The only branches of the ascending aorta are the **right (R.)** and **left (L.) coronary arteries,** which serve the heart.

Arterial Branches of the Aortic Arch

- The **brachiocephalic** (bra″ke-o-se-fal′ik) **trunk** (the first branch off the aortic arch) splits into the **R. common carotid** (kah-ro′tid) **artery** and **R. subclavian** (sub-kla′ve-an) **artery.** (See same-named vessels on left side of body for organs served.)
- The **L. common carotid artery** is the second branch off the aortic arch. It divides, forming the **L. internal carotid,** which serves the brain, and the **L. external carotid,** which serves the skin and muscles of the head and neck.
- The third branch of the aortic arch, the **L. subclavian artery,** gives off an important branch—the **vertebral artery,** which serves part of the brain. In the axilla, the subclavian artery becomes the **axillary artery** and then

continues into the arm as the **brachial artery,** which supplies the arm. At the elbow, the brachial artery splits to form the **radial** and **ulnar arteries,** which serve the forearm.

Arterial Branches of the Thoracic Aorta

- The *intercostal arteries* (ten pairs) supply the muscles of the thorax wall. Other branches of the thoracic aorta supply the lungs (*bronchial arteries*), the esophagus (*esophageal arteries*), and the diaphragm (*phrenic arteries*). These arteries are not illustrated in Figure 11.12.

Arterial Branches of the Abdominal Aorta

- The **celiac trunk** is the first branch of the abdominal aorta. It is a single vessel that has three branches: (1) the **L. gastric artery** supplies the stomach, (2) the **splenic artery** supplies the spleen, and (3) the **common hepatic artery** supplies the liver.
- The unpaired **superior mesenteric** (mes″en-ter′ik) **artery** supplies most of the small intestine and the first half of the large intestine, or colon.
- The **renal** (R. and L.) **arteries** serve the kidneys.
- The **gonadal** (R. and L.) **arteries** supply the gonads. They are called the *ovarian arteries* in females (serving the ovaries) and the *testicular arteries* in males (serving the testes).
- The *lumbar arteries* (not illustrated in Figure 11.12) are several pairs of arteries serving the heavy muscles of the abdomen and trunk walls.
- The **inferior mesenteric artery** is a small, unpaired artery supplying the second half of the large intestine.
- The **common iliac** (R. and L.) **arteries** are the final branches of the abdominal aorta. Each divides into an **internal iliac artery,** which supplies the pelvic organs (bladder, rectum, and so on), and an **external iliac artery,** which enters the thigh, where it becomes the **femoral artery.** The femoral artery and its branch, the **deep artery of the thigh,** serve the thigh. At the knee, the femoral artery becomes the **popliteal artery,** which then splits into the **anterior** and **posterior tibial arteries,** which supply the leg and foot. The anterior tibial artery terminates in the **dorsalis pedis artery,** which via the **arcuate artery** supplies the

Internal carotid artery
External carotid artery
Vertebral artery
Brachiocephalic trunk
Axillary artery
Ascending aorta
Brachial artery
Abdominal aorta
Superior mesenteric artery
Gonadal artery
Inferior mesenteric artery
Common iliac artery
External iliac artery
Internal iliac artery
Digital arteries
Femoral artery
Popliteal artery
Anterior tibial artery
Posterior tibial artery
Dorsalis pedis artery
Arcuate artery

Common carotid arteries
Subclavian artery
Aortic arch
Coronary artery
Thoracic aorta
Branches of celiac trunk:
• Left gastric artery
• Splenic artery
• Common hepatic artery
Renal artery
Radial artery
Ulnar artery
Deep palmar arch
Superficial palmar arch
Deep artery of the thigh

FIGURE 11.12 Major arteries of the systemic circulation, anterior view.

dorsum of the foot. (The dorsalis pedis is often palpated in patients with circulatory problems of the legs to determine whether the distal part of the leg has adequate circulation.)

Major Veins of the Systemic Circulation

Although arteries are generally located in deep, well-protected body areas, many veins are more superficial, and some are easily seen and palpated on the body surface. Most deep veins follow the course of the major arteries, and with a few exceptions, the naming of these veins is identical to that of their companion arteries. Major systemic arteries branch off the aorta, whereas the veins converge on the venae cavae, which enter the right atrium of the heart. Veins draining the head and arms empty into the **superior vena cava,** and those draining the lower body empty into the **inferior vena cava.** These veins are described next and shown in Figure 11.13. As before, locate the veins on the figure as you read their descriptions.

Veins Draining into the Superior Vena Cava Veins draining into the superior vena cava are named in a distal-to-proximal direction; that is, in the same direction the blood flows into the superior vena cava.

- The **radial** and **ulnar veins** are deep veins draining the forearm. They unite to form the deep **brachial vein,** which drains the arm and empties into the **axillary vein** in the axillary region.

- The **cephalic** (se-fal′ik) **vein** provides for the superficial drainage of the lateral aspect of the arm and empties into the axillary vein.

- The **basilic** (bah-sil′ik) **vein** is a superficial vein that drains the medial aspect of the arm and empties into the brachial vein proximally. The basilic and cephalic veins are joined at the anterior aspect of the elbow by the **median cubital vein.** (The median cubital vein is often chosen as the site for blood removal for the purpose of blood testing.)

- The **subclavian vein** receives venous blood from the arm through the axillary vein and from the skin and muscles of the head through the **external jugular vein.**

- The **vertebral vein** drains the posterior part of the head.

- The **internal jugular vein** drains the dural sinuses of the brain.

- The **brachiocephalic** (R. and L.) **veins** are large veins that receive venous drainage from the subclavian, vertebral, and internal jugular veins on their respective sides. The brachiocephalic veins join to form the superior vena cava, which enters the heart.

- The *azygos* (az′ĭ-gos) *vein* is a single vein that drains the thorax and enters the superior vena cava just before it joins the heart. (This vein is not illustrated in Figure 11.13.)

Veins Draining into the Inferior Vena Cava The inferior vena cava, which is much longer than the superior vena cava, returns blood to the heart from all body regions below the diaphragm. As before, we will trace the venous drainage in a distal-to-proximal direction.

- The **anterior** and **posterior tibial veins** and the **fibular vein** drain the leg (calf and foot). The posterior tibial vein becomes the **popliteal vein** at the knee and then the **femoral vein** in the thigh. The femoral vein becomes the **external iliac vein** as it enters the pelvis.

- The **great saphenous** (sah-fe′nus) **veins** are the longest veins in the body. They receive the superficial drainage of the leg. They begin at the **dorsal venous arch** in the foot and travel up the medial aspect of the leg to empty into the femoral vein in the thigh.

- Each **common iliac** (R. and L.) **vein** is formed by the union of the **external iliac vein** and the **internal iliac vein** (which drains the pelvis) on its own side. The common iliac veins join to form the inferior vena cava, which then ascends superiorly in the abdominal cavity.

- The **R. gonadal vein** drains the right ovary in females and the right testicle in males. (The **L. gonadal vein** empties into the left renal vein superiorly.) (The gonadal veins are not illustrated in Figure 11.13.)

- The **renal** (R. and L.) **veins** drain the kidneys.

- The **hepatic portal vein** is a single vein that drains the digestive tract organs and carries this blood through the liver before it enters the systemic circulation. (The hepatic portal circulation is discussed in the next section.)

- The **hepatic** (R. and L.) **veins** drain the liver.

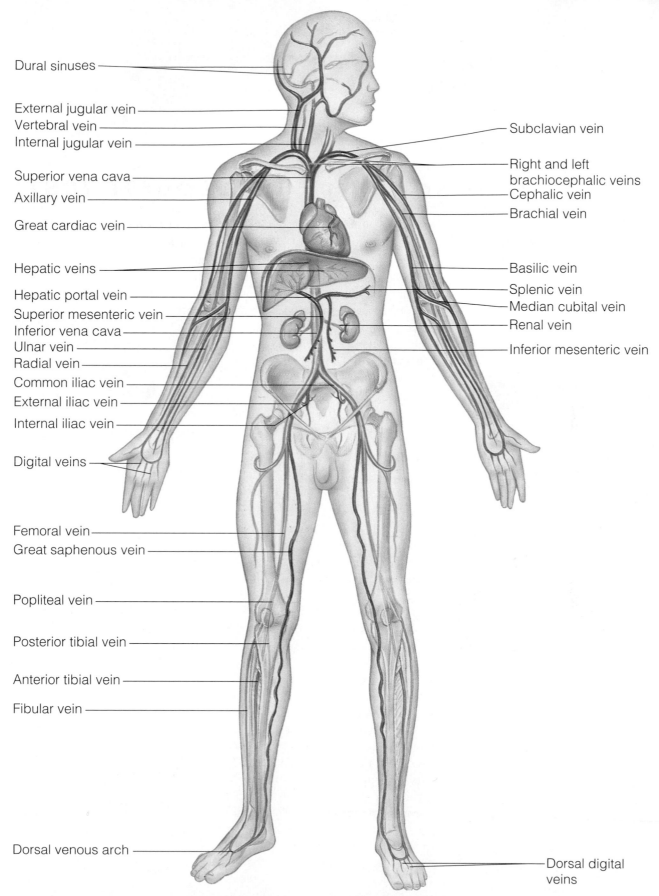

Dural sinuses

External jugular vein
Vertebral vein
Internal jugular vein

Superior vena cava

Axillary vein

Great cardiac vein

Hepatic veins

Hepatic portal vein
Superior mesenteric vein
Inferior vena cava
Ulnar vein
Radial vein
Common iliac vein
External iliac vein
Internal iliac vein

Digital veins

Femoral vein
Great saphenous vein

Popliteal vein

Posterior tibial vein

Anterior tibial vein

Fibular vein

Dorsal venous arch

Subclavian vein

Right and left
brachiocephalic veins
Cephalic vein
Brachial vein

Basilic vein
Splenic vein
Median cubital vein
Renal vein

Inferior mesenteric vein

Dorsal digital
veins

FIGURE 11.13 **Major veins of the systemic circulation, anterior view.** The vessels of the pulmonary circulation are not illustrated, accounting for the incomplete appearance of the circulation from the heart.

focus on CAREERS

CERTIFIED SURGICAL TECHNOLOGIST (CST)

Surgical technologists use their knowledge of anatomy to assist surgeons in the operating room.

Ask Nathan Williams what it takes to be a good surgical technologist, and he will list several key qualities. "Attention to detail is crucial," he says. "You have to be methodical,

orderly, and cool. There is a lot of stress in the operating room, and surgeons are under tremendous pressure. You have to remain calm and do your job well, so the surgeons can do theirs."

Surgical technologists (sometimes called surgical technicians) are allied health professionals who work under the supervision of a surgeon. They make sure that the operating room environment is safe, the equipment functions properly, and procedures are conducted safely. Surgical technologists combine their knowledge of anatomy, surgical procedures,

and surgical tools and technologies to facilitate a physician's performance in the operating room.

Says Williams, "My primary job is to maintain the sterility of the operating room environment. I start the day by setting up a sterile field—that is, I carefully open sealed surgical instruments and lay them out in an orderly fashion to prepare for each procedure. I try to anticipate everything the surgeon will need during that operation. Everything remains sterile until the end of the procedure, when I assist the patient onto a stretcher. After that, I sort out instruments for decontamination and remove my surgical gown and gloves. If this sterile environment is compromised, it can have devastating effects because the patient is contaminated. The most common result is a staph infection—an infection by *Staphylococcus* bacteria that can be life-threatening."

Another big part of Williams's job is anticipating the surgeon's next move. "I'm the surgeon's extra eyes and ears, and I have to be alert and stay a step ahead at all times. This is where my training in anatomy is crucial, because I have to be aware of which body tissues surgeons will encounter next. For instance, when they work in areas where there are lots of blood vessels, I always keep a clamp handy to stop bleeding. As another example, there are many types of forceps, some with smooth edges and some with teeth. During the initial incision, surgeons need forceps with teeth because they handle skin most effectively. But after surgeons pierce through the skin and enter the

body, I have to be sure to hand them only the smooth type, because forceps with teeth could puncture internal organs."

Surgical technologists must complete an accredited training program, usually 9 to 12 months long, and including at least 900 classroom and

> **"***I'm the surgeon's extra eyes and ears . . . This is where my training in anatomy is crucial.***"**

clinical hours. Then they must pass a national certifying exam to be certified for a six-year period. They can renew certification by earning continuing education credits or by retesting. Accreditation procedures vary from state to state.

For more information, contact the Association of Surgical Technologists:

7108-C South Alton Way
Englewood, CO 80112-2106
Telephone: (303) 694-9130
FAX: (303) 694-9169
http://www.ast.org

For additional information on this career, click the Focus on Careers link at www.anatomyandphysiology.com.

Frontal lobe
of cerebrum

Middle cerebral
artery

Anterior communicating
artery

Anterior cerebral
artery

Cerebral
arterial
circle

Posterior
communicating
artery

Posterior cerebral
artery

Basilar artery

Pons

Occipital lobe
of cerebrum

Vertebral
artery

Internal carotid
artery

Pituitary gland

Temporal lobe

Cerebellum

FIGURE 11.14   **Arterial supply of the brain.** (Cerebellum is shown only on the left side of the brain.)

Special Circulations

Arterial Supply of the Brain and the Circle of Willis

Because a lack of blood for even a few minutes causes the delicate brain cells to die, a continuous blood supply to the brain is crucial. The brain is supplied by two pairs of arteries, the internal carotid arteries and the vertebral arteries (Figure 11.14).

The **internal carotid arteries,** branches of the common carotid arteries, run through the neck and enter the skull through the temporal bone. Once inside the cranium, each divides into the **anterior** and **middle cerebral arteries,** which supply most of the cerebrum.

The paired **vertebral arteries** pass upward from the subclavian arteries at the base of the neck. Within the skull, the vertebral arteries join to form the single **basilar artery.** This artery serves the brain stem and cerebellum as it travels upward. At the base of the cerebrum, the basilar artery divides to form the **posterior cerebral arteries,** which supply the posterior part of the cerebrum.

The anterior and posterior blood supplies of the brain are united by small *communicating arterial branches.* The result is a complete circle of connecting blood vessels called either the **cerebral arterial circle** or the **circle of Willis,** which surrounds the base of the brain. The cerebral arterial circle protects the brain by providing more than one route for blood to reach brain tissue in case of a clot or impaired blood flow anywhere in the system.

Fetal Circulation

Because the lungs and digestive system are not yet functioning in a fetus, all nutrient, excretory, and gas exchanges occur through the placenta. Nutrients and oxygen move from the mother's blood into the fetal blood, and fetal wastes move in the opposite direction. As shown in Figure 11.15, the *umbilical cord* contains three blood vessels: one large **umbilical vein** and two smaller **umbilical arteries.** The umbilical vein

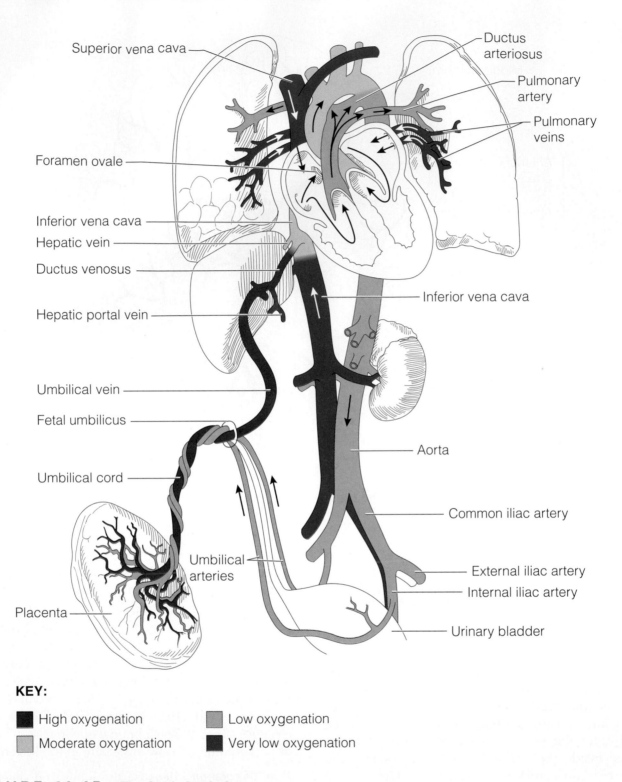

FIGURE 11.15 The fetal circulation.

carries blood rich in nutrients and oxygen to the fetus. The umbilical arteries carry carbon dioxide and debris-laden blood from the fetus to the placenta. As blood flows superiorly toward the heart of the fetus, most of it bypasses the immature liver

through the **ductus venosus** (duk'tus ve-no'sus) and enters the inferior vena cava, which carries the blood to the right atrium of the heart.

Because fetal lungs are nonfunctional and collapsed, two shunts see to it that they are

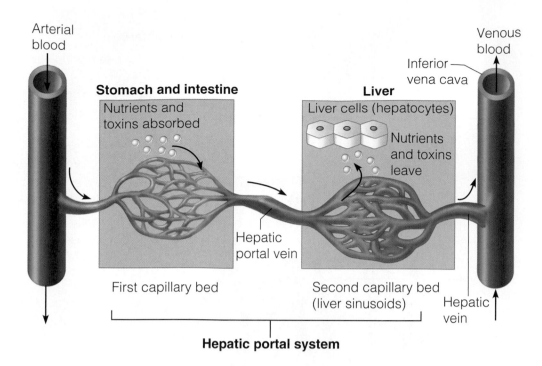

FIGURE 11.16   The basic scheme of the hepatic portal system and associated vessels. Note the presence of two capillary beds within the portal system. Nutrients and toxins picked up from capillaries in the stomach and intestine are transported to the liver cells for processing. From the liver sinusoids, the blood continues onward into the hepatic veins and inferior vena cava.

almost entirely bypassed. Some of the blood entering the right atrium is shunted directly into the left atrium through the **foramen ovale** (fo-ra'men o-val'e), a flaplike opening in the interatrial septum. Blood that does manage to enter the right ventricle is pumped out the pulmonary trunk, where it meets a second shunt, the **ductus arteriosus** (ar-ter"e-o'sus), a short vessel that connects the aorta and the pulmonary trunk. Because the collapsed lungs are a high-pressure area, blood tends to enter the systemic circulation through the ductus arteriosus. The aorta carries blood to the tissues of the fetal body and ultimately back to the placenta through the umbilical arteries.

At birth, or shortly after, the foramen ovale closes, and the ductus arteriosus collapses and is converted to the fibrous **ligamentum arteriosum** (lig"ah-men'tum ar-ter"e-o'sum) (see Figure 11.2a). As blood stops flowing through the umbilical vessels, they become obliterated, and the circulatory pattern converts to that of an adult.

Hepatic Portal Circulation The veins of the **hepatic portal circulation** drain the digestive organs, spleen, and pancreas and deliver this blood to the liver through the **hepatic portal vein** (Figure 11.17). When you have just eaten, the hepatic portal blood contains large amounts of nutrients. Because the liver is a key body organ involved in maintaining the proper glucose, fat, and protein concentrations in the blood, this system "takes a detour" to ensure that the liver processes these substances before they enter the systemic circulation. As blood flows slowly through the liver, some of the nutrients are removed to be stored or processed in various ways for later release to the blood. The liver is drained by the hepatic veins that enter the inferior vena cava. Like the portal circulation that links the hypothalamus of the brain and the anterior pituitary gland (see Chapter 9), the hepatic portal circulation is a unique and unusual circulation. Normally, arteries feed capillary beds, which in turn drain into veins. Here we see *veins* feeding the liver circulation (Figure 11.16).

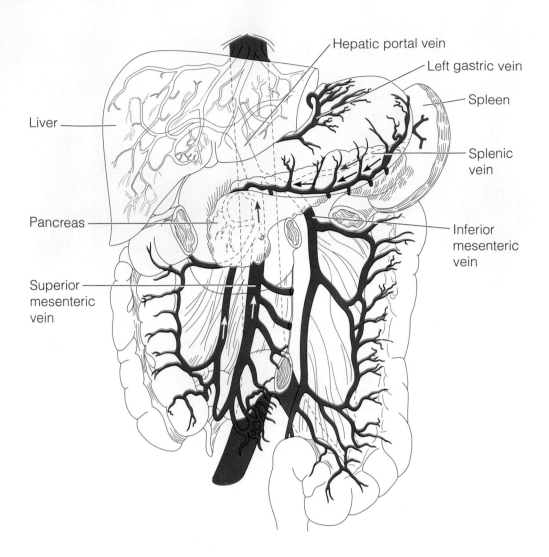

Liver

Pancreas

Superior mesenteric vein

Hepatic portal vein

Left gastric vein

Spleen

Splenic vein

Inferior mesenteric vein

FIGURE 11.17 **The hepatic portal circulation.**

The major vessels composing the hepatic portal circulation (Figure 11.17) include the inferior and superior mesenteric veins, the splenic vein, and the left gastric vein. The **inferior mesenteric vein,** draining the terminal part of the large intestine, drains into the **splenic vein,** which itself drains the spleen, pancreas, and the left side of the stomach. The splenic vein and **superior mesenteric vein** (which drains the small intestine and the first part of the colon) join to form the hepatic portal vein. The **L. gastric vein,** which drains the right side of the stomach, drains directly into the hepatic portal vein.

▶ *DID YOU GET IT?*

13. In what part of the body are the femoral, popliteal, and arcuate arteries found?

14. In what part of the body are the axillary, cephalic, and basilic veins located?

15. Which vessel—the hepatic portal vein, hepatic vein, or hepatic artery—has the highest content of nutrients after a meal?

16. In what two important ways is the pulmonary circulation different from the systemic circulation?

17. What is the ductus venosus, and what is its function?

For answers, see Appendix D.

Physiology of Circulation

A fairly good indication of the efficiency of a person's circulatory system can be obtained by taking arterial pulse and blood pressure measurements. These measurements, along with those of respiratory rate and body temperature, are referred to collectively as **vital signs** in clinical settings.

Arterial Pulse

The alternating expansion and recoil of an artery that occurs with each beat of the left ventricle creates a pressure wave—a **pulse**—that travels through the entire arterial system. Normally the pulse rate (pressure surges per minute) equals the heart rate (beats per minute). The pulse averages 70 to 76 beats per minute in a normal resting person. It is influenced by activity, postural changes, and emotions.

You can feel a pulse in any artery lying close to the body surface by compressing the artery against firm tissue; this provides an easy way of counting heart rate. Because it is so accessible, the point where the radial artery surfaces at the wrist (the radial pulse) is routinely used to take a pulse measurement, but there are several other clinically important arterial pulse points (Figure 11.18). Because these same points are compressed to stop blood flow into distal tissues during hemorrhage, they are also called **pressure points.** For example, if you seriously cut your hand, you can stop the bleeding somewhat by compressing the brachial artery.

●   Palpate each of the pulse points shown in Figure 11.18 by placing the tips of your first two or three fingers of one hand over the artery at the site indicated. Compress the artery firmly as you begin and then immediately ease up on your pressure slightly. In each case, notice the regularity and relative strength of the pulse.

Blood Pressure

Any system equipped with a pump that forces fluid through a network of closed tubes operates under pressure, and the closer the pump, the higher the pressure. **Blood pressure** is the pressure the blood exerts against the inner walls of the blood vessels, and it is the force that keeps blood circulating continuously even between heartbeats. Unless stated otherwise, the term *blood pressure* is understood to mean the pressure within the large systemic arteries near the heart.

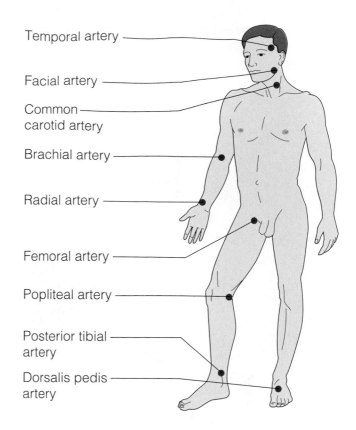

Temporal artery

Facial artery

Common carotid artery

Brachial artery

Radial artery

Femoral artery

Popliteal artery

Posterior tibial artery

Dorsalis pedis artery

FIGURE 11.18   Body sites where the pulse is most easily palpated. (The specific arteries indicated are discussed on p. 378.)

Blood Pressure Gradient   When the ventricles contract, they force blood into large, thick-walled elastic arteries close to the heart that expand as the blood is pushed into them. The high pressure in these arteries forces the blood to continuously move into areas where the pressure is lower. The pressure is highest in the large arteries and continues to drop throughout the systemic and pulmonary pathways, reaching either zero or negative pressure at the venae cavae (Figure 11.19). Recall that the blood flows into the smaller arteries, then arterioles, capillaries, venules, veins, and finally back to the large venae cavae entering the right atrium of the heart. It flows continuously along a pressure gradient (from high to low pressure) as it makes its circuit day in and day out. Notice that if venous return depended entirely on a high blood pressure throughout the system, blood would probably never be able to complete its circuit back to the heart. This is why the valves in the larger veins, the milking activity of the skeletal muscles, and pressure changes in the thorax are so important.

How does the pulsating blood pressure on the left side of the graph relate to the structure of the largest arteries?

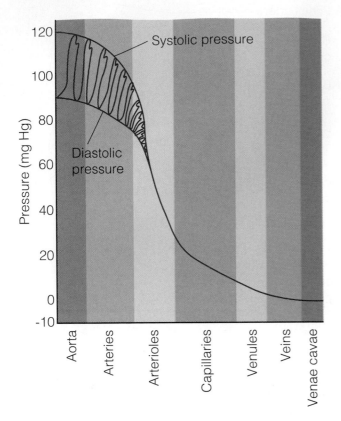

FIGURE 11.19   Blood pressure in various areas of the cardiovascular system.

The pressure differences between arteries and veins become very clear when these vessels are cut. If a vein is cut, the blood flows evenly from the wound; a lacerated artery produces rapid spurts of blood.

Continuous blood flow absolutely depends on the stretchiness of the larger arteries and their ability to recoil and keep exerting pressure on the blood as it flows off into the circulation. Think of a garden hose with relatively hard walls. When the water is turned on, the water spurts out under high pressure because the hose walls don't expand.

It reveals their elasticity. When the heart contracts and forces blood into the large arteries near the heart, they stretch to accommodate the greater blood volume (systolic pressured). Then, as the blood continues on in the circuit, their walls recoil, keeping pressure on the blood which keeps it moving (diastolic pressure).

However, when the water faucet is suddenly turned off, the flow of water stops just as abruptly. The reason is that the walls of the hose cannot recoil to keep pressure on the water; therefore, the pressure drops and the flow of water stops. The importance of the elasticity of the arteries is best appreciated when it is lost, as happens in *arteriosclerosis*. Arteriosclerosis, also called "hardening of the arteries," is discussed in the "A Closer Look" box on pp. 392–393.

Measuring Blood Pressure   Because the heart alternately contracts and relaxes, the off-and-on flow of blood into the arteries causes the blood pressure to rise and fall during each beat. Thus, two arterial blood pressure measurements are usually made: **systolic** (sis-to′lik) **pressure,** the pressure in the arteries at the peak of ventricular contraction, and **diastolic** (di″us-to′lik) **pressure,** the pressure when the ventricles are relaxing. Blood pressures are reported in millimeters of mercury (mm Hg), with the systolic pressure written first—120/80 (120 over 80) translates to a systolic pressure of 120 mm Hg and a diastolic pressure of 80 mm Hg. Most often, systemic arterial blood pressure is measured indirectly by the **auscultatory** (os-kul′tuh-tor-e) **method.** This procedure, as used to measure blood pressure in the brachial artery of the arm, is illustrated and described in Figure 11.20.

Effects of Various Factors on Blood Pressure   Arterial blood pressure (BP) is directly related to cardiac output (CO; the amount of blood pumped out of the left ventricle per minute) and peripheral resistance (PR). This relationship is expressed by the equation BP = CO × PR. We have already considered regulation of cardiac output, so we will concentrate on peripheral resistance here.

Peripheral resistance is the amount of friction the blood encounters as it flows through the blood vessels. Many factors increase peripheral resistance, but probably the most important is the constriction, or narrowing, of blood vessels, especially arterioles, as a result of either sympathetic nervous system activity or atherosclerosis. Increased blood volume or increased blood viscosity (thickness) also raises peripheral resistance. Any factor that increases either cardiac output or peripheral resistance causes an almost immediate reflex rise in blood pressure. Many factors can alter blood pressure—age, weight, time of day, exercise,

(a) The course of the brachial artery of the arm. Assume a blood pressure of 120/70 in a young, healthy person.

(b) The blood pressure cuff is wrapped snugly around the arm just above the elbow and inflated until the cuff pressure exceeds the systolic blood pressure. At this point, blood flow into the arm is stopped, and a brachial pulse cannot be felt or heard.

(c) The pressure in the cuff is gradually reduced while the examiner listens (auscultates) for sounds in the brachial artery with a stethoscope. The pressure read as the first soft tapping sounds are heard (the first point at which a small amount of blood is spurting through the constricted artery) is recorded as the systolic pressure.

(d) As the pressure is reduced still further, the sounds become louder and more distinct; when the artery is no longer constricted and blood flows freely, the sounds can no longer be heard. The pressure at which the sounds disappear is recorded as the diastolic pressure.

FIGURE 11.20   **Measuring blood pressure.**

body position, emotional state, and various drugs, to name a few. The influence of a few of these factors is discussed next.

1. **Neural factors: the autonomic nervous system.** The parasympathetic division of the autonomic nervous system has little or no effect on blood pressure, but the sympathetic division is important. The major action of the sympathetic nerves on the vascular system is to cause **vasoconstriction** (vas″o-kon-strik′shun), or narrowing of the blood vessels, which increases the blood pressure. The sympathetic center in the medulla of the brain is activated to cause vasoconstriction in many different circumstances (Figure 11.21). For example, when we stand up suddenly after lying down, the effect of gravity causes blood to pool in the vessels of the legs and feet, and blood pressure drops. This activates *pressoreceptors* (also called *baroreceptors*) in the large arteries of the neck and chest. They send off warning signals that result in reflexive vasoconstriction, increasing blood pressure back to homeostatic levels.

When blood volume suddenly decreases, as in hemorrhage, blood pressure drops, and the heart begins to beat more rapidly as it tries

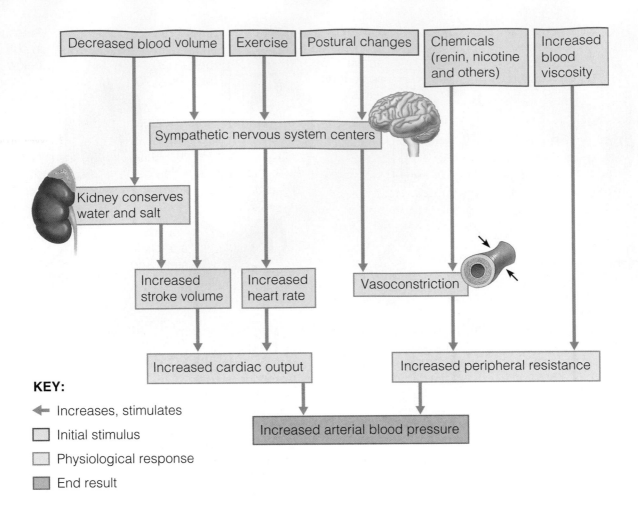

FIGURE 11.21   Summary of factors that increase arterial blood pressure.

to compensate. However, because blood loss reduces venous return, the heart also beats weakly and inefficiently. In such cases, the sympathetic nervous system causes vasoconstriction to increase the blood pressure so that (hopefully) venous return increases and circulation can continue.

The final example concerns sympathetic nervous system activity when we exercise vigorously or are frightened and have to make a hasty escape. Under these conditions, there is a generalized vasoconstriction *except* in the skeletal muscles. The vessels of the skeletal muscles dilate to increase the blood flow to the working muscles. (It should be noted that the sympathetic nerves *never* cause vasoconstriction of blood vessels of the heart or brain.)

2. **Renal factors: the kidneys.** The kidneys play a major role in regulating arterial blood pressure by altering blood volume. As blood pressure (and/or blood volume) increases beyond normal, the kidneys allow more water to leave the body in the urine. Because the source of this water is the bloodstream, blood volume decreases, which in turn decreases blood pressure. However, when arterial blood pressure falls, the kidneys retain body water, increasing blood volume, and blood pressure rises (see Figure 11.21).

In addition, when arterial blood pressure is low, certain kidney cells release the enzyme *renin* into the blood. Renin triggers a series of chemical reactions that result in the formation of *angiotensin II,* a potent vasoconstrictor chemical. Angiotensin also stimulates the adrenal cortex to release aldosterone, a hormone that enhances sodium ion reabsorption by the kidneys. As sodium moves into the blood, water follows. Thus, blood volume and blood pressure both rise.

3. **Temperature.** In general, cold has a *vasoconstricting* effect. This is why your exposed skin feels cold to the touch on a winter day and why cold compresses are recommended to prevent swelling of a bruised area. Heat has a *vasodilating effect,* and warm compresses are used to speed the circulation into an inflamed area.

4. **Chemicals.** The effects of chemical substances, many of which are drugs, on blood pressure are widespread and well known in many cases. Just a few examples will be given here. **Epinephrine** increases both heart rate and blood pressure. *Nicotine* increases blood pressure by causing vasoconstriction. Both *alcohol* and *histamine* cause vasodilation and decrease blood pressure. The reason a person who has "one too many" becomes flushed is that alcohol dilates the skin vessels.

5. **Diet.** Although medical opinions tend to change and are at odds from time to time, it is generally believed that a diet low in salt, saturated fats, and cholesterol helps to prevent *hypertension,* or high blood pressure.

Variations in Blood Pressure   In normal adults at rest, systolic blood pressure varies between 110 and 140 mm Hg, and diastolic pressure between 70 and 80 mm Hg—but blood pressure varies considerably from one person to another and cycles over a 24-hour period, peaking in the morning. What is normal for you may not be normal for your grandfather or your neighbor. Blood pressure varies with age, weight, race, mood, physical activity, and posture. Nearly all these variations can be explained in terms of the factors affecting blood pressure that have already been discussed.

Hypotension, or low blood pressure, is generally considered to be a systolic blood pressure below 100 mm Hg. In many cases, it simply reflects individual differences and is no cause for concern. In fact, low blood pressure is an expected result of physical conditioning and is often associated with long life and an old age free of illness.

HOMEOSTATIC IMBALANCE

Elderly people may experience temporary low blood pressure and dizziness when they rise suddenly from a reclining or sitting position—a condition called **orthostatic hypotension.** Because an aging sympathetic nervous system reacts more slowly to postural changes, blood pools briefly in the lower limbs, reducing blood pressure and, consequently, blood delivery to the brain. Making postural changes more slowly to give the nervous system time to make the necessary adjustments usually prevents this problem. ▲

Chronic hypotension (not explained by physical conditioning) may hint at poor nutrition and inadequate levels of blood proteins. Because blood viscosity is low, blood pressure is also lower than normal. Acute hypotension is one of the most important warnings of **circulatory shock,** a condition in which the blood vessels are inadequately filled and blood cannot circulate normally. The most common cause is blood loss.

A brief elevation in blood pressure is a normal response to fever, physical exertion, and emotional upset, such as anger and fear. Persistent **hypertension,** or **high blood pressure,** is pathological and is defined as a condition of sustained elevated arterial pressure of 140/90 or higher.

HOMEOSTATIC IMBALANCE

Chronic hypertension is a common and dangerous disease that warns of increased peripheral resistance. Although it progresses without symptoms for the first 10 to 20 years, it slowly and surely strains the heart and damages the arteries. For this reason, hypertension is often called the "silent killer." Because the heart is forced to pump against increased resistance, it must work harder, and in time, the myocardium enlarges. When finally strained beyond its capacity to respond, the heart weakens and its walls become flabby. Hypertension also ravages blood vessels, causing small tears in the endothelium that accelerate the progress of atherosclerosis.

Although hypertension and atherosclerosis are often linked, it is difficult to blame hypertension on any distinct anatomical pathology. In fact, about 90 percent of hypertensive people have **primary,** or **essential, hypertension,** which cannot be accounted for by any specific organic cause. However, factors such as diet, obesity, heredity, race, and stress appear to be

(continues on p. 394)

A CLOSER LOOK

ATHEROSCLEROSIS? GET OUT THE CARDIOVASCULAR DRĀNO!

When pipes get clogged, it is usually because something that shouldn't be there gets stuck in them—a greasy mass or a hair ball (see top photo). But when arteries are narrowed by **atherosclerosis,** the damming-up process occurs from the inside out: the walls of the vessels thicken and then protrude into the vessel lumen. Once this happens, it does not take much to close the vessel completely. A roaming blood clot or arterial spasms can do it.

Although all blood vessels are susceptible to atherosclerosis, for some unknown reason the aorta and the coronary arteries serving the heart are most often affected. The disease progresses through many stages before the arterial walls actually become hard and approach the stage of the rigid tube system described in the text, but some of the earlier stages are just as lethal.

Onset and Stages of Atherosclerosis

What triggers this scourge of blood vessels that indirectly causes half of the deaths in the Western world? According to the *response to injury hypothesis,* the initial event is damage to the tunica interna caused by bloodborne chemicals such as carbon monoxide (present in cigarette smoke or auto exhaust); by bacteria or viruses; or by physical factors such as a blow or persistent hypertension. Once a break has occurred, blood platelets cling to the injured site and initiate clotting to prevent blood loss. The injured endothelium sets off the alarm, summoning the immune system and the inflammatory process to repair the damage. If it is a one-time injury, when it's over, it's over. But most plaques grow slowly, through a series of injuries that heal, only to be

> ❝ *Arteries are narrowed by atherosclerosis.* ❞

ruptured again and again. As the plaque grows, the injured endothelial cells release chemotactic agents and chemicals that increase the permeability of the endothelium to fats and cholesterol, allowing them to take up residence just deep to the tunica intima. Monocytes attracted to the area migrate beneath the endothelium, where they become macrophages that gorge themselves on the fat. In particularly fatty plaques, these cells can become so engorged with oxidized fats that they are transformed into lipid-laden "foam cells" that lose their ability to act as scavengers. Soon they are joined by smooth muscle cells migrating from the media of the blood vessel wall. These cells deposit collagen and elastin fibers in the area and also take in fat, becoming foam cells.

Top A pipe clogged by accumulated deposits. **Bottom** Atherosclerotic plaques nearly close a human artery.

The result is the so-called **fatty streak stage** characterized by thickening of the tunica intima by greasy gray to yellow lesions called **fibrous** or **atherosclerotic plaques.** When these small, fatty mounds of muscle begin to protrude into the vessel wall (and ultimately the vessel lumen), the condition is called *atherosclerosis* (see bottom photo).

Arteriosclerosis is the end stage of the disease. As enlarging plaques hinder diffusion of nutrients from the blood to the deeper tissues of the artery wall, smooth muscle cells in the tunica media die and the elastic fibers deteriorate and are gradually replaced by nonelastic scar tissue. Then, calcium salts are deposited in the lesions forming **complicated plaques.** Collectively, these events cause the arterial wall to fray and ulcerate, conditions that encourage thrombus formation. The increased rigidity of the vessels leads to hypertension. Together, these events increase the risk of myocardial infarctions, strokes, and aneurysms.

However, the popular view that most heart attacks are the consequence of severe vessel narrowing and hardening is now being challenged, particularly since some 70 percent of heart attacks are caused by much smaller obstructions, too small to be seen on an arteriogram or to cause any symptoms in most cases. It now appears that the body's defense system betrays it. The inflammatory process that occurs in the still soft, unstable, cholesterol-rich plaques changes the biology of the vessel wall and makes the plaques susceptible to rupture, exploding off fragments that trigger massive clots that can cause lethal heart attacks. The victim appears perfectly healthy until he or she drops dead!

Treatment and Prevention

The *vulnerable plaque hypothesis* mentioned above has attracted many medical converts, but the question of what to do about it remains. Some medical centers test heart patients for elevated levels of cholesterol and C-reactive protein, a marker of inflammation. Electron beam CT scans may be able to identify people at risk by detecting calcium deposits in their coronary arteries. Antibiotics and anti-inflammatory drugs are being tested as preventative measures. Even the humble aspirin is gaining new respect, and more cardiologists recommend that people at high risk take one baby aspirin (81 mg) daily.

So what can help when the damage is done and the heart is at risk because of atherosclerotic coronary vessels? In the past, the only choice has been coronary artery bypass surgery, in which vessels removed from the legs or thoracic cavity are implanted in the heart to restore circulation. More recently, devices threaded through blood vessels to obstructed sites have become part of the ammunition of cardiovascular medicine. *Balloon angioplasty* uses a catheter with a balloon packed into its tip. When the catheter reaches the blockage, the balloon is inflated, and the fatty mass is compressed against the vessel wall. However, this procedure is useful to clear only very localized obstructions. A newer catheter device uses a laser beam to vaporize the arterial clogs. Although these intravascular devices are faster, cheaper, and less risky than bypass surgery, they carry with them the same major shortcoming: they do nothing to stop the underlying disease, and in time new blockages occur in 30 to 50 percent of cases.

When a blood clot is trapped by the diseased vessel walls, the answer may be a *clot-dissolving agent,* for example, *tissue plasminogen activator (t-PA),* a naturally occurring substance now being produced by genetic engineering techniques. Injecting t-PA directly into the heart restores blood flow quickly and puts an early end to many heart attacks in progress.

There is little doubt that lifestyle factors—emotional stress, smoking, obesity, high-fat and high-cholesterol diets, and lack of exercise—contribute to both atherosclerosis and hypertension. If these are the risk factors (and indeed they are), then why not just have patients at risk change their lifestyle? This is not as easy as it seems. Although taking antioxidants (E and C vitamins and beta carotene) and exercising more may "undo" some of the damage, old habits die hard, and North Americans like their burgers and butter. Can atherosclerosis be reversed to give the heart a longer and healthier life? If so, many more people with diseased arteries may be more willing to trade lifelong habits for a healthy old age!

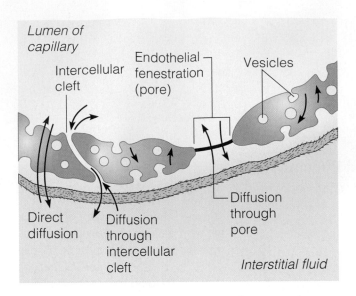

Lumen of
capillary

Intercellular   Endothelial   Vesicles
cleft   fenestration
(pore)

Direct   Diffusion   Diffusion
diffusion   through   through
    intercellular   pore
    cleft

Interstitial fluid

FIGURE 11.22   Capillary transport mechanisms. The four possible pathways or routes of transport across the wall of an endothelial cell of a capillary. (The endothelial cell is illustrated as if cut in cross section.)

involved. For instance, more women than men and more blacks than whites are hypertensive. Hypertension runs in families. The child of a hypertensive parent is twice as likely to develop high blood pressure as is a child of parents with normal blood pressure. High blood pressure is common in obese people because the total length of their blood vessels is relatively greater than that in thinner individuals. For each pound of fat, miles of additional blood vessels are required, making the heart work harder to pump blood over longer distances. ▲

Capillary Exchange of Gases and Nutrients

Capillaries form an intricate network among the body's cells such that no substance has to diffuse very far to enter or leave a cell. The substances exchanged first diffuse through an intervening space filled with **interstitial fluid (tissue fluid).**

Substances tend to move to and from body cells according to their concentration gradients. Thus, oxygen and nutrients leave the blood and move into the tissue cells, and carbon dioxide and other wastes exit the tissue cells and enter the blood. Basically, substances entering or leaving the blood may take one of four routes across the plasma membranes of the single layer of endothelial cells forming the capillary wall (Figure 11.22).

1. As with all cells, substances can diffuse directly through (cross) their plasma membranes if the substances are lipid-soluble (like the respiratory gases).

2. Certain lipid-insoluble substances may enter or leave the blood and/or pass through the plasma membranes of endothelial cells within vesicles, that is, by endocytosis or exocytosis.

Diffusion of substances via the other two routes depends on the specific structural (and permeability) characteristics of the capillary.

3. Limited passage of fluid and small solutes is allowed by **intercellular clefts** (gaps or areas of plasma membrane not joined by tight junctions). It is safe to say that, with the exception of brain capillaries—which are entirely secured together by tight junctions (the basis of the blood-brain barrier described in Chapter 7)—most of our capillaries have intercellular clefts.

4. Very free passage of small solutes and fluids is allowed by *fenestrated capillaries.* These unique capillaries are found where absorption is a priority (intestinal capillaries or capillaries serving endocrine glands) or where filtration occurs (the kidney). A fenestra is an oval pore (*fenestra* = window) or opening and is usually covered by a delicate membrane (see Figure 11.22). Even so, a fenestra is much more permeable than other regions of the plasma membrane.

Only substances unable to pass by one of these routes are prevented from leaving (or entering) the capillaries. These include protein molecules (in plasma or interstitial fluid) and blood cells.

Fluid Movements at Capillary Beds

Besides the exchanges made via vesicles and via passive diffusion through capillary endothelial cell plasma membranes, clefts, or fenestrations, there are active forces operating at capillary beds. Because of their intercellular clefts and fenestrations, some capillaries are leaky, and bulk fluid flows across their plasma membranes. Hence, blood pressure tends to force fluid (and solutes) out of the capillaries, and osmotic pressure tends to draw fluid into them because blood has a higher solute concentration (due to its plasma proteins) than does interstitial fluid. Whether fluid moves out of or into a capillary depends on the difference between the two pressures. As a rule, blood pressure is higher than osmotic pressure at the arterial end of the capillary bed, and lower than osmotic pressure at the venous end. Consequently, fluid moves out of the capillaries at the beginning of the bed and is reclaimed at the opposite (venule) end (Figure 11.23). However, not quite all of the fluid forced out of the blood is reclaimed at the venule end. Returning that lost fluid to the blood is the chore of the lymphatic system, discussed in Chapter 12.

▶ DID YOU GET IT?

18. Which artery is palpated at the wrist? At the groin? At the side of the neck?

19. How does blood pressure change throughout the systemic circulatory pathway?

20. What is the effect of hemorrhage on blood pressure? Why?

21. Would you expect fluid to be entering or leaving the capillaries at the venous end of a capillary bed?

For answers, see Appendix D.

Developmental Aspects of the Cardiovascular System

The heart begins as a simple tube in the embryo. It is beating and busily pumping blood by the fourth week of pregnancy. During the next three weeks, the heart continues to change and mature, finally becoming a four-chambered structure capable of acting as a double pump—all without missing a beat! During fetal life, the collapsed lungs and nonfunctional liver are mostly bypassed by the blood, through special vascular shunts. After the seventh week of development, few changes other than growth occur in the fetal circulation until birth. Shortly after birth, the bypass structures become blocked, and the special umbilical vessels stop functioning.

⚖ HOMEOSTATIC IMBALANCE

Congenital heart defects account for about half of infant deaths resulting from all congenital defects. Environmental interferences, such as maternal infection and ingested drugs during the first three months of pregnancy (when the embryonic heart is forming), seem to be the major causes of such

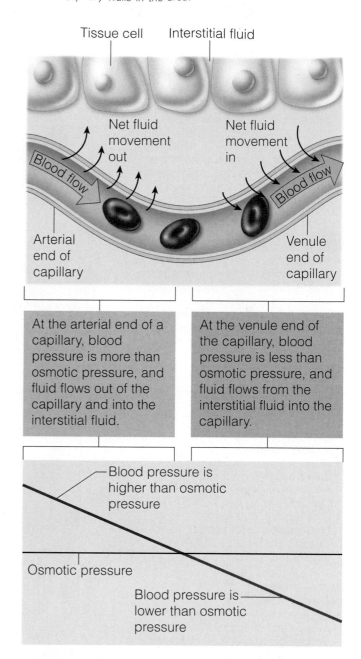

Assume there is a bacterial infection in the interstitial fluid. How would this affect fluid flows across the capillary walls in the area?

FIGURE 11.23   Flows of bulk fluid across capillary walls depend largely on the difference between the blood pressure and the osmotic pressure at different regions of the capillary bed.

It would increase it because the osmotic pressure of the interstitial fluid would rise as inflammatory molecules and debris accumulated in the area.

SYSTEMS IN SYNC

HOMEOSTATIC RELATIONSHIPS BETWEEN THE
CARDIOVASCULAR SYSTEM AND OTHER BODY SYSTEMS

Endocrine System

- The cardiovascular system delivers oxygen and nutrients; carries away wastes; blood serves as a transport vehicle for hormones
- Several hormones influence blood pressure (epinephrine, ANP, thyroxine, ADH); estrogen maintains vascular health in women

Lymphatic System/Immunity

- The cardiovascular system delivers oxygen and nutrients to lymphatic organs, which house immune cells; transports lymphocytes and antibodies; carries away wastes
- The lymphatic system picks up leaked fluid and plasma proteins and returns them to the cardiovascular system; its immune cells protect cardiovascular organs from specific pathogens

Digestive System

- The cardiovascular system delivers oxygen and nutrients; carries away wastes
- The digestive system provides nutrients to the blood including iron and B vitamins essential for RBC (and hemoglobin) formation

Urinary System

- The cardiovascular system delivers oxygen and nutrients; carries away wastes; blood pressure maintains kidney function
- The urinary system helps regulate blood volume and pressure by altering urine volume and releasing renin

Muscular System

- The cardiovascular system delivers oxygen and nutrients; carries away wastes
- Aerobic exercise enhances cardiovascular efficiency and helps prevent arteriosclerosis; the muscle "pump" aids venous return

Nervous System

- The cardiovascular system delivers oxygen and nutrients; removes wastes
- ANS regulates cardiac rate and force; sympathetic division maintains blood pressure and controls blood distribution according to need

Respiratory System

- The cardiovascular system delivers oxygen and nutrients; carries away wastes
- The respiratory system carries out gas exchange: loads oxygen and unloads carbon dioxide from the blood; respiratory "pump" aids venous return

Cardiovascular System

Reproductive System

- The cardiovascular system delivers oxygen and nutrients; carries away wastes
- Estrogen maintains vascular health in women

Integumentary System

- The cardiovascular system delivers oxygen and nutrients; carries away wastes
- The skin's blood vessels provide an important blood reservoir and a site for heat loss from body

Skeletal System

- The cardiovascular system delivers oxygen and nutrients and carries away wastes
- Bones are the site of hematopoiesis; protect cardiovascular organs by enclosure; provide a calcium depot

problems. Congenital heart defects may include a ductus arteriosus that does not close, septal openings, and other structural abnormalities of the heart. Such problems can usually be corrected surgically. ▲

In the absence of congenital heart problems, the heart usually functions smoothly throughout a long lifetime for most people. Homeostatic mechanisms are so effective that we rarely are aware of when the heart is working harder. The heart will hypertrophy and its cardiac output will increase substantially if we exercise regularly and aerobically (that is, vigorously enough to force it to beat at a higher-than-normal rate for extended periods of time). The heart becomes not only a more powerful pump but also a more efficient one: pulse rate and blood pressure decrease. An added benefit of aerobic exercise is that it clears fatty deposits from the blood vessel walls, helping to slow the progress of atherosclerosis. However, let's raise a caution flag here: The once-a-month or once-a-year tennis player or snow shoveler has not built up this type of heart endurance and strength. When such an individual pushes his or her heart too much, it may not be able to cope with the sudden demand. This is why many weekend athletes are myocardial infarction victims.

As we get older, more and more signs of cardiovascular system disturbances start to appear. In some, the venous valves weaken, and purple, snakelike varicose veins appear. Not everyone has varicose veins, but we all have progressive atherosclerosis. Some say the process begins at birth, and there's an old saying that goes, "You are only as old as your arteries," referring to this degenerative process. The gradual loss in elasticity in the blood vessels leads to hypertension and hypertensive heart disease. The insidious filling of the blood vessels with fatty, calcified deposits leads most commonly to **coronary artery disease.** Also, as described in Chapter 10, the roughening of the vessel walls encourages thrombus formation. At least 30 percent of the population in the United States has hypertension by the age of 50, and cardiovascular disease causes more than one-half of the deaths in people over age 65. Although the aging process itself contributes to changes in the walls of the blood vessels that can lead to strokes or myocardial infarctions, most researchers feel that diet, not aging, is the single most important contributing factor to cardiovascular diseases. There is some agreement that the risk is lowered if people eat less animal fat, cholesterol, and salt. Other recommendations include avoiding stress, eliminating cigarette smoking, and taking part in a regular, moderate exercise program.

SUMMARY

Media study tools that provide additional review of key topics of Chapter 11 are referenced below.

> **IP** = *InterActive Physiology*
> **WEB** = The A&P Place

The Heart   (pp. 362–374)

1. The heart, located in the thorax, is flanked laterally by the lungs and enclosed in a pericardium.

2. The bulk of the heart (myocardium) is composed of cardiac muscle. The heart has four hollow chambers—two atria (receiving chambers) and two ventricles (discharging chambers), each lined with endocardium. The heart is divided longitudinally by a septum.

   WEB Exercise: Chapter 11, External Anatomy of the Heart.

IP Cardiovascular System Topic: Anatomy Review: The Heart, pp. 3–5.

3. The heart functions as a double pump. The right heart is the pulmonary pump (right heart to lungs to left heart). The left heart is the systemic pump (left heart to body tissues to right heart).

4. Four valves prevent backflow of blood in the heart. The AV valves (mitral and tricuspid) prevent backflow into the atria when the ventricles are contracting. The semilunar valves prevent backflow into the ventricles when the heart is relaxing. The valves open and close in response to pressure changes in the heart.

   WEB Exercise: Chapter 11, Frontal Section of the Heart.

   IP Cardiovascular System Topic: Cardiac Cycle, p. 3.

5. The myocardium is nourished by the coronary circulation, which consists of the right and left coronary arteries and their branches, and is drained by the cardiac veins and the coronary sinus.

6. Cardiac muscle is able to initiate its own contraction in a regular way, but its rate is influenced by both intrinsic and extrinsic factors. The intrinsic conduction system increases the rate of heart contraction and ensures that the heart beats as a unit. The SA node is the heart's pacemaker.

   WEB Exercise: Chapter 11, Intrinsic Conduction System of the Heart.

   IP Cardiovascular System Topic: Intrinsic Conduction System, pp. 3–6.

7. The time and events occurring from one heartbeat to the next are the cardiac cycle.

8. As the heart beats, sounds resulting from the closing of the valves ("lub-dup") can be heard. Faulty valves reduce the efficiency of the heart as a pump and result in abnormal heart sounds (murmurs).

   IP Cardiovascular System Topic: Cardiac Cycle, pp. 4–10.

9. Cardiac output, the amount of blood pumped out by each ventricle in one minute, is the product of heart rate (HR) × stroke volume (SV). SV is the amount of blood ejected by a ventricle with each beat.

10. SV rises or falls with the volume of venous return. HR is influenced by the nerves of the autonomic nervous system, drugs (and other chemicals), and ion levels in the blood.

Blood Vessels (pp. 374–395)

1. Arteries, which transport blood from the heart, and veins, which carry blood back to the heart, are conducting vessels. Only capillaries play a role in actual exchanges with tissue cells.

2. Except for capillaries, blood vessels are composed of three tunics: The tunica intima forms a friction-reducing lining for the vessel. The tunica media is the bulky middle layer of muscle and elastic tissue. The tunica externa is the protective, outermost connective tissue layer. Capillary walls are formed of the tunica intima only.

   IP Cardiovascular System Topic: Anatomy Review: Blood Vessel Structure and Function, pp. 3–5.

3. Artery walls are thick and strong to withstand pressure fluctuations. They expand and recoil as the heart beats. Vein walls are thinner, their lumens are larger, and they are equipped with valves. These modifications reflect the low-pressure nature of veins.

IP Cardiovascular System Topic: Anatomy Review: Blood Vessel Structure and Function, pp. 25–27.

4. Capillary beds have two types of vessels—a vascular shunt and true capillaries the entrance to which are guarded by precapillary sphincters. Exchanges with tissue cells occur across the walls of the true capillaries. When the precapillary sphincters are closed, blood bypasses the local area via the vascular shunt.

   WEB Exercise: Chapter 11, Arterial Circulation.

5. Varicose veins, a structural defect due to incompetent valves, is a common vascular problem, especially in the obese and people who stand for long hours. It is a predisposing factor for thrombophlebitis.

   WEB Exercise: Chapter 11, Veins of the Systemic Circulation.

6. All the major arteries of the systemic circulation are branches of the aorta, which leaves the left ventricle. They branch into smaller arteries and then into the arterioles, which feed the capillary beds of the body tissues. For the names and locations of the systemic arteries, see pp. 378–379.

7. The major veins of the systemic circulation ultimately converge on one of the venae cavae. All veins above the diaphragm drain into the superior vena cava, and those below the diaphragm drain into the inferior vena cava. Both venae cavae enter the right atrium of the heart. See pp. 380–381 for the names and locations of the systemic veins.

8. The arterial circulation of the brain is formed by branches of paired vertebral and internal carotid arteries. The circle of Willis provides alternate routes for blood flow in case of a blockage in the brain's arterial supply.

9. The fetal circulation is a temporary circulation seen only in the fetus. It consists primarily of three special vessels: the single umbilical vein that carries nutrient- and oxygen-laden blood to the fetus from the placenta, and the two umbilical arteries that carry carbon dioxide and waste-laden blood from the fetus to the placenta. Shunts bypassing the lungs and liver are also present.

10. The hepatic portal circulation is formed by veins draining the digestive organs, which empty into the hepatic portal vein. The hepatic portal vein carries the nutrient-rich blood to the liver, where it is processed before the blood is allowed to enter the systemic circulation.

11. The pulse is the alternate expansion and recoil of a blood vessel wall (the pressure wave) that occurs as

the heart beats. It may be felt easily over any superficial artery; such sites are called pressure points.

12. Blood pressure is the pressure that blood exerts on the walls of the blood vessels. It is the force that causes blood to continue to flow in the blood vessels. It is high in the arteries, lower in the capillaries, and lowest in the veins. Blood is forced along a descending pressure gradient. Both systolic and diastolic pressures are recorded.

   IP Cardiovascular System Topic: Measuring Blood Pressure, pp. 3–12.

13. Arterial blood pressure is directly influenced by heart activity (increased heart rate leads to increased blood pressure) and by resistance to blood flow. The most important factors increasing the peripheral resistance are a decrease in the diameter or stretchiness of the arteries and arterioles and an increase in blood viscosity.

14. Many factors influence blood pressure, including the activity of the sympathetic nerves and kidneys, drugs, and diet.

15. Hypertension, which reflects an increase in peripheral resistance, strains the heart and damages blood vessels. In most cases, the precise cause is unknown.

16. Substances move to and from the blood and tissue cells through capillary walls. Some substances are transported in vesicles, but most move by diffusion—directly through the endothelial cell plasma membranes, through intercellular clefts, or through fenestrations. Fluid is forced from the bloodstream by blood pressure and drawn back into the blood by osmotic pressure.

Developmental Aspects of the Cardiovascular System (pp. 395, 397)

1. The heart begins as a tubelike structure that is beating and pumping blood by the fourth week of embryonic development.

2. Congenital heart defects account for half of all infant deaths resulting from congenital problems.

3. Arteriosclerosis is an expected consequence of aging. Gradual loss of elasticity in the arteries leads to hypertension and hypertensive heart disease, and clogging of the vessels with fatty substances leads to coronary artery disease and stroke. Cardiovascular disease is an important cause of death in individuals over age 65.

4. Modifications in diet (decreased fats, cholesterol, and salt), stopping smoking, and regular aerobic exercise may help to reverse the atherosclerotic process and prolong life.

REVIEW QUESTIONS
Multiple Choice

More than one choice may apply.

1. Freshly oxygenated blood is first received by the
   a. right ventricle.   c. right atrium.
   b. left ventricle.   d. left atrium.

2. Given an end-diastolic volume of 150 ml, an end-systolic volume of 50 ml, and a heart rate of 60 bpm, the cardiac output is
   a. 600 ml/min.   c. 1200 ml/min.
   b. 6 liters/min.   d. 3 liters/min.

3. Which of the following depolarizes next after the AV node?
   a. Atrial myocardium
   b. Ventricular myocardium
   c. Bundle branches
   d. AV bundle

4. During atrial systole,
   a. the atrial pressure exceeds ventricular pressure.
   b. 70 percent of ventricular filling occurs.
   c. the AV valves are open.
   d. valves prevent backflow into the great veins.

5. Atrial repolarization coincides in time with the
   a. P wave.   c. QRS wave.
   b. T wave.   d. P-Q interval.

6. Soon after the onset of ventricular systole, the
   a. AV valves close.
   b. semilunar valves open.
   c. first heart sound is heard.
   d. aortic pressure increases.

7. The base of the heart is its _____ surface.
   a. diaphragmatic   c. anterior
   b. posterior   d. inferior

8. In comparing a parallel artery and vein, you would find that
   a. the artery wall is thicker.
   b. the artery diameter is greater.
   c. the artery lumen is smaller.
   d. the artery endothelium is thicker.

9. Considering the vessels named pulmonary trunk and celiac trunk, the term *trunk* must refer to

   a. a vessel in the heart wall.

   b. a vein.

   c. a capillary.

   d. a large artery from which other arteries branch.

10. Which of these vessels is bilaterally symmetrical (i.e., one vessel of the pair occurs on each side of the body)?

    a. Internal carotid artery

    b. Brachiocephalic trunk

    c. Azygos vein

    d. Superior mesenteric vein

11. A stroke that occludes a posterior cerebral artery will most likely affect

    a. hearing.   c. smell.

    b. vision.   d. higher thought processes.

12. Vessels involved in the circulatory pathway to and from the brain are the

    a. brachiocephalic artery.

    b. subclavian artery.

    c. internal jugular vein.

    d. internal carotid artery.

13. Which layer of the artery wall thickens most in atherosclerosis?

    a. Tunica media   c. Tunica adventitia

    b. Tunica intima   d. Tunica externa

14. Which of the following are associated with aging?

    a. Increasing blood pressure

    b. Weakening of venous valves

    c. Arteriosclerosis

    d. Stenosis of the ductus arteriosus

15. An increase in BP would be caused by all of the following except

    a. increase in SV.

    b. increase in heart rate.

    c. increase in the length of ventricular diastole.

    d. constriction of the arterioles.

16. The most external part of the pericardium is the

    a. parietal layer of serous pericardium.

    b. fibrous pericardium.

    c. visceral layer of serous pericardium.

    d. pericardial cavity.

17. Which heart chamber forms most of the heart's inferior surface?

    a. Right atrium   c. Left atrium

    b. Right ventricle d. Left ventricle

18. How many cusps does the right atrioventricular valve have?

    a. Two

    b. Three

    c. Four

19. Which layer of the heart wall is the thickest?

    a. Endocardium   c. Epicardium

    b. Myocardium   d. Endothelium

Short Answer Essay

20. Draw a diagram of the heart showing the three layers composing its wall and its four chambers. Label each. Show where the AV and semilunar valves are. Show and label all blood vessels entering and leaving the heart chambers.

21. Trace one drop of blood from the time it enters the right atrium of the heart until it enters the left atrium. What is this circuit called?

22. What is the function of the fluid that fills the pericardial sac?

23. Define *systole, diastole, stroke volume,* and *cardiac cycle.*

24. How does the heart's ability to contract differ from that of other muscles of the body?

25. Name the elements of the intrinsic conduction system, *in order,* beginning with the pacemaker.

26. Name three different factors that increase heart rate.

27. Name and describe from the inside out the three tunics making up the walls of arteries and veins, and give the most important function of each layer.

28. Describe the structure of capillary walls.

29. Why are artery walls so much thicker than those of corresponding veins?

30. Name three factors that are important in promoting venous return.

31. Arteries are often described as vessels that carry oxygen-rich blood, and veins are said to carry oxygen-poor (carbon dioxide–rich) blood. Name two sets of exceptions to this rule that were discussed in this chapter.

32. Trace a drop of blood from the left ventricle of the heart to the wrist of the right hand and back to the heart. Now trace it to the dorsum of the right foot and back to the right heart.

33. What is the function of the hepatic portal circulation? In what way is a portal circulation a "strange" circulation?

34. In a fetus, the liver and lungs are almost entirely bypassed by blood. Why is this? Name the vessel that bypasses the liver. Name two lung bypasses. Three vessels travel in the umbilical cord; which of these carries oxygen- and nutrient-rich blood?

35. Define *pulse.*

36. Which artery is palpated at the front of the ear? At the back of the knee?

37. Define *systolic* pressure and *diastolic* pressure.

38. Two elements determine blood pressure—the cardiac output of the heart and the peripheral resistance, or friction, in the blood vessels. Name two factors that increase cardiac output. Name two factors that increase peripheral resistance.

39. In which position—sitting, lying down, or standing—is the blood pressure normally highest? Lowest?

40. What is different about the capillary exchanges seen in a capillary with fenestrations and intercellular clefts and the exchanges seen in a capillary lacking those modifications?

41. What are varicose veins? What factors seem to promote their formation?

42. Explain why blood flow in arteries is pulsatile and blood flow in veins is not.

43. What is the relationship between cross-sectional area of a blood vessel and velocity (speed) of blood flow in that vessel?

44. Which type of blood vessel is most important in regulating vascular resistance, and how does it achieve this?

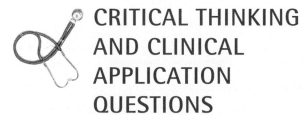

CRITICAL THINKING AND CLINICAL APPLICATION QUESTIONS

45. Define *hypertension* and *arteriosclerosis.* How are they often related? Why is hypertension called the "silent killer"? Name three changes in your lifestyle that might help prevent cardiovascular disease in your old age.

46. Mrs. Hamad, a middle-aged woman, is admitted to the coronary care unit with a diagnosis of left ventricular failure resulting from a myocardial infarction. Her chart indicates that she was awakened in the middle of the night by severe chest pain. Her skin is pale and cold, and moist sounds of pulmonary edema are heard over the lower regions of both lungs. Explain how failure of the left ventricle might cause these signs and symptoms.

47. Linda, a 14-year-old girl undergoing a physical examination before being admitted to summer camp, was found to have a loud heart murmur at the second intercostal space on the left side of the sternum. The murmur takes the form of a swishing sound with no high-pitched whistle. What, exactly, is producing the murmur?

48. Mrs. Johnson is brought to the emergency room after being involved in an auto accident. She is hemorrhaging and has a rapid, thready pulse, but her blood pressure is still within normal limits. Describe the compensatory mechanisms that are maintaining her blood pressure in the face of blood loss.

49. During a lethal heart attack, a blood clot lodges in the first part of the circumflex branch of the left coronary artery, blocking blood flow through this vessel. What parts of the heart will become ischemic and die?

50. Mr. Grimaldi was previously diagnosed as having a posterior pituitary tumor that causes hypersecretion of ADH. He comes to the clinic regularly to have his blood pressure checked. Would you expect his blood pressure to be chronically elevated or depressed? Why?

51. Explain why taking a vigorous swim right after eating is more likely to cause indigestion than cramping of your muscles.

52. The guards at the royal palace in London stand at attention while on duty. On a very hot day, it is not unusual for one (or more) to become lightheaded and faint. Explain this phenomenon.

12

The Lymphatic System and Body Defenses

YOUR GOALS

After completing this chapter, you will have a working knowledge of the functions of the lymphatic system and of body defenses and will have mastered the objectives listed below.

FUNCTION PREVIEW

- The lymphatic system returns leaked plasma to the blood vessels after cleansing it of bacteria and other foreign matter. It also provides sites for surveillance by immune system cells.

- The innate defenses hinder pathogen entry, prevent the spread of disease-causing microorganisms, and strengthen the immune response.

- The adaptive defenses protect against disease by destroying "foreign" cells and by inactivating toxins and other foreign chemicals with its antibodies.

O B J E C T I V E   C H E C K L I S T

PART I: THE LYMPHATIC SYSTEM   (pp. 403–408)

➤ Name the two major types of structures composing the lymphatic system.

➤ Describe the source of lymph, and explain its formation and transport.

➤ Describe the function(s) of lymphatic vessels, lymph nodes, tonsils, the thymus, Peyer's patches, and the spleen.

➤ Explain how the lymphatic system is functionally related to the cardiovascular and immune systems.

PART II: BODY DEFENSES (pp. 408–431)

➤ Describe the protective functions of skin and mucous membranes.

➤ Explain the importance of phagocytes and natural killer cells.

➤ Describe the inflammatory process.

➤ Name several antimicrobial substances produced by the body that act in innate body defense.

➤ Describe how fever helps protect the body.

➤ Define *antigen* and *hapten*, and name substances that act as complete antigens.

➤ Name the two arms of the adaptive defense system, and relate each to a specific lymphocyte type (B or T cell).

➤ Compare and contrast the development of B and T cells.

➤ State the roles of B cells, T cells, and plasma cells.

➤ Explain the importance of macrophages in immunity.

➤ List the five antibody classes, and describe their specific roles in immunity.

➤ Describe several ways in which antibodies act against antigens.

➤ Distinguish between active and passive immunity.

➤ Describe immunodeficiencies, allergies, and autoimmune diseases.

PART III: DEVELOPMENTAL ASPECTS OF THE LYMPHATIC SYSTEM AND BODY DEFENSES (pp. 431, 435)

➤ Describe the origin of the lymphatic vessels.

➤ Describe the effects of aging on immunity.

PART I: THE LYMPHATIC SYSTEM

They can't all be superstars! When we mentally tick off the names of the body's organ systems, the lymphatic (lim-fat'ik) system is probably not the first to come to mind. Yet without this quietly working system, our cardiovascular system would stop working, and our immune system would be hopelessly impaired. The **lymphatic system** actually consists of two semi-independent parts: (1) a meandering network of *lymphatic vessels* and (2) various *lymphoid tissues* and *organs* scattered throughout the body. The lymphatic vessels transport back to the blood fluids that have escaped from the blood vascular system. The lymphoid tissues and organs house phagocytic cells and lymphocytes, which play essential roles in body defense and resistance to disease.

Lymphatic Vessels

As blood circulates through the body, exchanges of nutrients, wastes, and gases occur between the blood and the interstitial fluid. As explained in Chapter 11, the hydrostatic and osmotic pressures operating at capillary beds force fluid out of the blood at the arterial ends of the beds ("upstream") and cause most of the expelled fluid to be reabsorbed at the venous ends ("downstream"). The fluid that remains behind in the tissue spaces, as much as 3 L daily, becomes part of the interstitial fluid. This leaked fluid, as well as any plasma proteins that escape from the blood, must be carried back to the blood if the vascular system is to have sufficient blood volume to operate properly. If it does not, fluid accumulates in the tissues, producing **edema.** Excessive edema impairs the ability of tissue cells to make exchanges with the interstitial fluid and ultimately the blood. The function of the

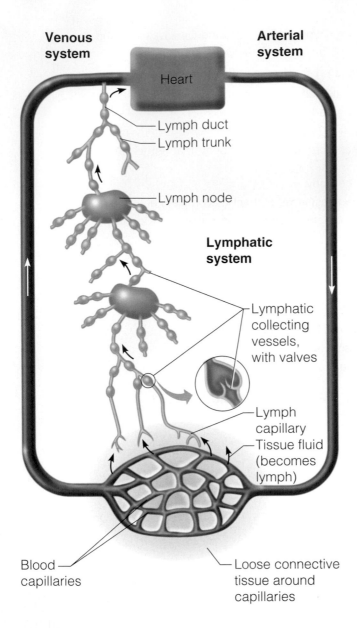

Venous system

Arterial system

Heart

Lymph duct

Lymph trunk

Lymph node

Lymphatic system

Lymphatic collecting vessels, with valves

Lymph capillary

Tissue fluid (becomes lymph)

Blood capillaries

Loose connective tissue around capillaries

FIGURE 12.1 **Relationship of lymphatic vessels to blood vessels.** Beginning at the bottom of this figure, we see that lymph, which begins as tissue fluid derived from blood capillaries, enters the lymph capillaries, travels through the lymphatic vessels and lymph nodes, and enters the bloodstream via the great veins at the root of the neck.

lymphatic vessels is to form an elaborate drainage system that picks up this excess tissue fluid, now called **lymph** (*lymph* = clear water), and returns it to the blood (Figure 12.1).

The lymphatic vessels, also called **lymphatics,** form a one-way system, and lymph flows only toward the heart. The microscopic, blind-ended

lymph capillaries weave between the tissue cells and blood capillaries in the loose connective tissues of the body (Figures 12.1 and 12.2a) and absorb the leaked fluid. Although similar to blood capillaries, lymphatic capillaries are so remarkably permeable that they were once thought to be open at one end like a straw. Not so—instead, what we find is that the edges of the endothelial cells forming their walls loosely overlap one another, forming flaplike *minivalves* (Figure 12.2b) that act as one-way swinging doors. The flaps, anchored by fine collagen fibers to surrounding structures, gape open when the fluid pressure is higher in the interstitial space, allowing fluid to enter the lymphatic capillary. However, when the pressure is higher inside the lymphatic vessels, the endothelial cell flaps are forced together, preventing the lymph from leaking back out and forcing it along the vessel. Proteins, and even larger particles such as cell debris, bacteria, and viruses, are normally prevented from entering blood capillaries, but they enter the lymphatic capillaries easily, particularly in inflamed areas. But there is a problem here—bacteria and viruses (and cancer cells) that enter the lymphatics can then use them to travel throughout the body. This dilemma is partly resolved by the fact that lymph takes "detours" through the lymph nodes, where it is cleansed of debris and "examined" by cells of the immune system, as explained in more detail shortly.

Lymph is transported from the lymph capillaries through successively larger lymphatic vessels, referred to as **lymphatic collecting vessels,** until it is finally returned to the venous system through one of the two large ducts in the thoracic region. The **right lymphatic duct** drains the lymph from the right arm and the right side of the head and thorax. The large **thoracic duct** receives lymph from the rest of the body, as shown in Figure 12.3. Both ducts empty the lymph into the subclavian vein on their own side of the body.

Like veins of the cardiovascular system, lymphatic vessels are thin-walled, and the larger ones have valves. The lymphatic system is a low-pressure, pumpless system. Lymph is transported by the same mechanisms that aid return of venous blood—the milking action of the skeletal muscles and the pressure changes in the thorax during breathing (that is, the muscular and respiratory "pumps"). In addition, smooth muscle in the walls of the larger lymphatics contracts

(a)   **(b)**

FIGURE 12.2   Distribution and special structural features of lymphatic capillaries. (a) Structural relationship between blood capillaries and lymph capillaries. Black arrows indicate direction of fluid movement. **(b)** Lymph capillaries begin as blind-ended tubes. The endothelial cells forming their walls overlap one another, forming flaplike minivalves.

rhythmically, actually helping to "pump" the lymph along.

 DID YOU GET IT?

1. What is the function of lymphatic vessels?

2. How do lymphatic capillaries and blood capillaries differ structurally from each other?

For answers, see Appendix D.

Lymph Nodes

The lymphoid tissues and organs are more closely related to the immune system than to the cardiovascular system. The **lymph nodes** in particular help protect the body by removing foreign material such as bacteria and tumor cells from the lymphatic stream and by producing lymphocytes that function in the immune response.

As lymph is transported toward the heart, it is filtered through the thousands of lymph nodes that cluster along the lymphatic vessels (see Figure 12.1). Particularly large clusters are found in the inguinal, axillary, and cervical regions of the body (see Figure 12.3). Within the lymph nodes are **macrophages** (mak'ro-fāj-ez), which engulf and destroy bacteria, viruses, and other foreign substances in the lymph before it is returned to the blood. Collections of **lymphocytes** (a type of white blood cell) are also strategically located in the lymph nodes and respond to foreign substances in the lymphatic stream. Although we are not usually aware of the protective nature of the lymph nodes, most of us have had "swollen glands" during an active infection. What are actually swollen in these cases are not glands of the endocrine system but rather nodes of the lymphatic system. (The term *swollen glands* is a historical misnomer.) This swelling of the lymph nodes is a result of the trapping function of the nodes.

Lymph nodes vary in shape and size, but most are kidney-shaped, less than 1 inch (approximately 2.5 centimeters [cm]) long, and "buried" in the

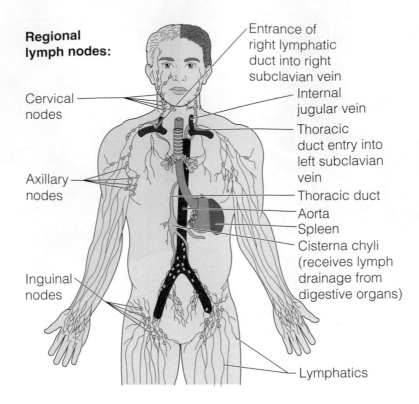

Regional lymph nodes:

Cervical nodes

Axillary nodes

Inguinal nodes

Entrance of right lymphatic duct into right subclavian vein

Internal jugular vein

Thoracic duct entry into left subclavian vein

Thoracic duct

Aorta

Spleen

Cisterna chyli (receives lymph drainage from digestive organs)

Lymphatics

FIGURE 12.3   Distribution of lymphatic vessels and lymph nodes. Shading shows the body area drained by the right lymphatic duct; the rest of the body is drained by the thoracic duct.

connective tissue that surrounds them. Each node is surrounded by a fibrous *capsule* from which strands called *trabeculae* (trah-bek'yu-le) extend inward to divide the node into a number of compartments (Figure 12.4). The internal framework is a network of soft reticular connective tissue that supports a continually changing population of lymphocytes. (As described in Chapter 10, lymphocytes arise from the red bone marrow but then migrate to the lymph nodes and other lymphoid organs, where they proliferate further.)

The outer part of the node, its **cortex,** contains collections of lymphocytes called **follicles,** many of which have dark-staining centers called **germinal centers.** These centers enlarge when specific lymphocytes (the *B cells*) are generating daughter cells called **plasma cells,** which release antibodies. The

rest of the cortical cells are lymphocytes "in transit," the so-called *T cells* that circulate continuously between the blood, lymph nodes, and lymphatic stream, performing their surveillance role. Phagocytic macrophages are located in the central **medulla** of the lymph node. (The precise roles of the cells of the lymph nodes in immunity are discussed shortly.)

Lymph enters the convex side of a lymph node through **afferent lymphatic vessels.** It then flows through a number of **sinuses** that cut through the lymph node and finally exits from the node at its indented region, the **hilum** (hi'lum), via **efferent lymphatic vessels.** Because there are fewer efferent vessels draining the node than afferent vessels feeding it, the flow of lymph through the node is very slow. This allows time for the lymphocytes and macrophages to perform their protective functions. Generally speaking, lymph passes through several nodes before its cleaning process is complete.

A *Edema in the areas that drain into the thoracic duct.*

What is the benefit of having fewer efferent than afferent lymphatic vessels?

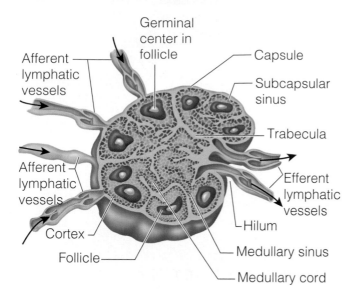

FIGURE 12.4   Structure of a lymph node.
Longitudinal section of a lymph node and associated lymphatics. Notice that several afferent lymphatics enter the node, whereas fewer efferent lymphatics exit at its hilum.

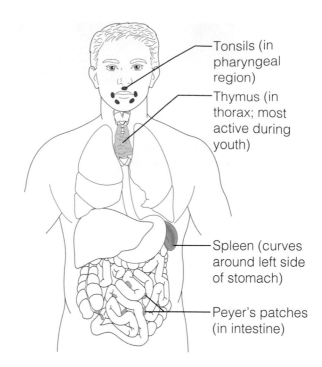

FIGURE 12.5   Lymphoid organs. Tonsils, thymus, spleen, and Peyer's patches.

HOMEOSTATIC IMBALANCE

Lymph nodes help rid the body of infectious agents and cancer cells, but sometimes they are overwhelmed by the very agents they are trying to destroy. For example, when large numbers of bacteria or viruses are trapped in the nodes, the nodes become inflamed and tender to the touch. The lymph nodes can also become secondary cancer sites, particularly in cancers that use lymphatic vessels to spread throughout the body. The fact that cancer-infiltrated lymph nodes are swollen but not painful helps to distinguish cancerous lymph nodes from those infected by microorganisms. ▲

Other Lymphoid Organs

Lymph nodes are just one of the many types of **lymphoid organs** in the body. Others are the spleen, thymus gland, tonsils, and Peyer's patches

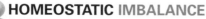

A *Because the outlet is smaller than the inlet to the lymph node, the lymph fluid stagnates (stops flowing) briefly in the lymph node, giving macrophages and lymphocytes time to monitor and process the lymph for pathogens.*

of the intestine (Figure 12.5), as well as bits of lymphoid tissue scattered in the epithelial and connective tissues. The common feature of all these organs is a predominance of reticular connective tissue and lymphocytes. Although all lymphoid organs have roles in protecting the body, only the lymph nodes filter lymph.

The **spleen** is a soft, blood-rich organ that filters blood. It is located in the left side of the abdominal cavity, just beneath the diaphragm, and curls around the anterior aspect of the stomach. Instead of filtering lymph, the spleen filters and cleanses blood of bacteria, viruses, and other debris. As with the other lymphoid organs, the spleen provides a site for lymphocyte proliferation and immune surveillance, but its most important function is to destroy worn-out red blood cells and return some of their breakdown products to the liver. For example, iron is used again for making hemoglobin, and the rest of the hemoglobin molecule is secreted in bile. Other functions of the spleen include storing platelets and acting as a blood reservoir (as does the liver). During hemorrhage, both the spleen and the liver contract and empty their contained blood into the circulation to help bring the blood volume back to normal levels. In the

The Immune System		
Innate (nonspecific) defense mechanisms		Adaptive (specific) defense mechanisms
First line of defense	Second line of defense	Third line of defense
• Skin • Mucous membranes • Secretions of skin and mucous membranes	• Phagocytic cells • Antimicrobial proteins • The inflammatory response	• Lymphocytes • Antibodies • Macrophages

FIGURE 12.6   An overview of the body's defenses.

fetus, the spleen is an important hematopoietic (blood cell–forming) site, but as a rule only lymphocytes are produced by the adult spleen.

The **thymus gland,** which functions at peak levels only during youth, is a lymphoid mass found low in the throat overlying the heart. As described in Chapter 9, the thymus produces hormones, *thymosin* and others, that function in the programming of certain lymphocytes so they can carry out their protective roles in the body.

The **tonsils** are small masses of lymphoid tissue that ring the pharynx (the throat), where they are found in the mucosa. Their job is to trap and remove any bacteria or other foreign pathogens entering the throat. They carry out this function so efficiently that sometimes they become congested with bacteria and become red, swollen, and sore, a condition called *tonsillitis.*

Peyer's patches, which resemble tonsils, are found in the wall of the small intestine. The macrophages of Peyer's patches are in an ideal position to capture and destroy bacteria (always present in tremendous numbers in the intestine), thereby preventing them from penetrating the intestinal wall. Peyer's patches and the tonsils are part of the collection of small lymphoid tissues referred to as **mucosa-associated lymphatic tissue (MALT).** Collectively, MALT acts as a sentinel to protect the upper respiratory and digestive tracts from the never-ending attacks of foreign matter entering those cavities.

Now that we have set the stage on which many of the body's defense mechanisms play their roles, we are ready to consider that topic in more detail.

DID YOU GET IT?

3. In which three regions of the body are the lymph nodes most dense?

4. What anatomical characteristic ensures that lymph flows through the lymph nodes slowly?

5. Which lymphoid organ gets rid of aged red blood cells?

6. What is MALT?

For answers, see Appendix D.

PART II: BODY DEFENSES

Every second of every day, an army of hostile bacteria, viruses, and fungi swarms on our skin and invades our inner passageways—yet we stay amazingly healthy most of the time. The body seems to have developed a single-minded approach toward such foes—if you're not with us, then you're against us!

The body's defenders against these tiny but mighty enemies are two systems, simply called the *innate* and the *adaptive defense systems* (Figure 12.6). Together they make up the **immune system.** The **innate defense system,** also called the **nonspecific defense system,** responds immediately to protect the body from all foreign substances, whatever they are. You could say that we come fully equipped with our innate defenses, which are provided by intact skin and mucous membranes, by the inflammatory response, and by a number of proteins produced by body cells. This system reduces the workload of the second protective arm, the adaptive defense system, by preventing entry and spread of microorganisms throughout the body.

The **adaptive,** or **specific, defense system** mounts the attack against *particular* foreign substances. Although certain body organs (lymphoid organs and blood vessels) are intimately involved with the immune response, the immune system is a *functional system* rather than an organ system in an anatomical sense. Its "structures" are a variety of molecules and trillions of immune cells that inhabit lymphoid tissues and organs and circulate in body fluids. The most important of the immune cells are *lymphocytes* and *macrophages.*

When our immune system is operating effectively, it protects us from most bacteria, viruses, transplanted organs or grafts, and even our own cells that have turned against us. The immune system does this both directly, by cell attack, and indirectly, by releasing mobilizing chemicals and protective antibody molecules. The resulting highly specific resistance to disease is called **immunity** (*immun* = free).

Unlike the innate defenses, which are always prepared to defend the body, the adaptive system must first "meet" or be primed by an initial exposure to a foreign substance (antigen) before it can protect the body against the invader. Nonetheless, what the adaptive system lacks in speed it makes up for in the precision of its counterattacks. Although we will consider them separately, keep in mind that innate and adaptive defenses always work hand-in-hand to protect the body.

Innate Body Defenses

Some innate resistance to disease is inherited. For instance, there are certain diseases that humans never get, such as some forms of tuberculosis that affect birds. Most often, however, the term *innate or nonspecific body defense* refers to the mechanical barriers that cover body surfaces and to the cells and chemicals that act on the initial battlefronts to protect the body from invading **pathogens** (harmful or disease-causing microorganisms). Table 12.1 (p. 414) provides a more detailed summary of the most important innate defenses.

Surface Membrane Barriers

The body's *first line of defense* against the invasion of disease-causing microorganisms is the *skin* and *mucous membranes.* As long as the skin is unbro-

ken, its keratinized epidermis is a strong physical barrier to most microorganisms that swarm on the skin. Intact mucous membranes provide similar mechanical barriers within the body. Recall that mucous membranes line all body cavities open to the exterior: the digestive, respiratory, urinary, and reproductive tracts. Besides serving as physical barriers, these membranes produce a variety of protective secretions:

1. The acidic pH of skin secretions (pH of 3–5) inhibits bacterial growth, and sebum contains chemicals that are toxic to bacteria. Vaginal secretions of adult females are also very acidic.

2. The stomach mucosa secretes hydrochloric acid and protein-digesting enzymes. Both kill pathogens.

3. Saliva and lacrimal fluid contain **lysozyme,** an enzyme that destroys bacteria.

4. Sticky mucus traps many microorganisms that enter digestive and respiratory passageways.

Some mucosae also have structural modifications that fend off potential invaders. Mucus-coated hairs inside the nasal cavity trap inhaled particles, and the respiratory tract mucosa is ciliated. The cilia sweep dust- and bacteria-laden mucus superiorly toward the mouth, preventing it from entering the lungs, where the warm, moist environment provides an ideal site for bacterial growth.

Although the surface barriers are quite effective, they *are* broken from time to time by small nicks and cuts resulting, for example, from brushing your teeth or shaving. When this happens and microorganisms do invade deeper tissues, the internal innate mechanisms come into play.

Internal Defenses: Cells and Chemicals

For its *second line of defense,* the body uses an enormous number of cells and chemicals to protect itself. These defenses rely on the destructive powers of *phagocytes* and *natural killer cells,* on the inflammatory response, and on a variety of chemical substances that kill pathogens and help repair tissue. Fever is also considered to be a nonspecific protective response.

Phagocytes

Pathogens that make it through the mechanical barriers are confronted by **phagocytes** (fa′go-sītz″;

(a)   (b)

FIGURE 12.7   Phagocytosis by a macrophage. (a) This scanning electron micrograph (2600×) in computer-generated color shows a macrophage pulling sausage-shaped *Escherichia coli* bacteria toward it with its long cytoplasmic extensions. Several bacteria on the macrophage's surface are being engulfed. **(b)** Events of phagocytosis.

phago = eat) in nearly every body organ. A phagocyte, such as a *macrophage* or *neutrophil,* engulfs a foreign particle much the way an amoeba ingests a food particle (Figure 12.7). Flowing cytoplasmic extensions bind to the particle and then pull it inside, enclosing it in a vacuole. The vacuole is then fused with the enzymatic contents of a *lysosome,* and its contents are broken down, or digested.

Natural Killer Cells

Natural killer (NK) cells, which "police" the body in blood and lymph, are a unique group of lymphocytes that can lyse and kill cancer cells and virus-infected body cells well before the adaptive arm of the immune system is enlisted in the fight. Unlike the lymphocytes of the adaptive system, which can recognize and react only against *specific* virus-infected or tumor cells, natural killer cells are far less

"picky." They can act spontaneously against *any* such target by recognizing certain sugars on the "intruder's" surface as well as their lack of certain "self" cell surface molecules. NK cells are not phagocytic. They attack the target cell's membrane and release a lytic chemical called *perforins.* Shortly thereafter, the target cell's membrane and nucleus disintegrate.

Inflammatory Response

The **inflammatory response** is a nonspecific response that is triggered whenever body tissues are injured (Figure 12.8). For example, it occurs in response to physical trauma, intense heat, and irritating chemicals, as well as to infection by viruses and bacteria. The four most common indicators (*cardinal signs*) of an acute inflammation are *redness, heat (inflamm = set on fire), swelling,*

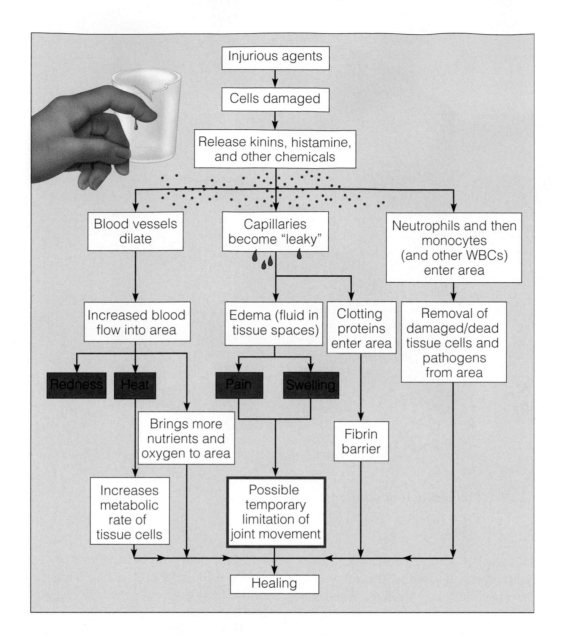

FIGURE 12.8 **Flowchart of inflammatory events.** The four most common indicators (cardinal signs) of acute inflammation are shown in red boxes. Limitation of joint movement (red outlined box) occurs in some cases and is considered to be the fifth cardinal sign of acute inflammation.

and *pain*. It is easy to understand why these signs and symptoms occur, once the events of the inflammatory response are understood.

The inflammatory process begins with a chemical "alarm." When cells are injured, they release inflammatory chemicals, including **histamine** and **kinins** (ki′ninz), that (1) cause blood vessels in the involved area to dilate and capillaries to become leaky, (2) activate pain receptors, and (3) attract

phagocytes and white blood cells to the area. (This latter phenomenon is called **chemotaxis** because the cells are following a chemical gradient.) Dilation of the blood vessels increases the blood flow to the area, accounting for the redness and heat observed. Increased permeability of the capillaries allows plasma to leak from the blood into the tissue spaces, causing local edema (swelling) that also activates pain receptors in the area. If the

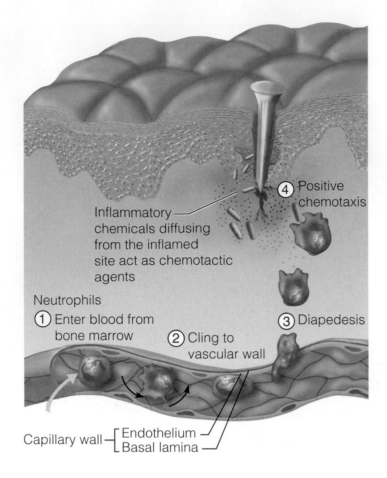

Inflammatory chemicals diffusing from the inflamed site act as chemotactic agents

④ Positive chemotaxis

Neutrophils
① Enter blood from bone marrow
② Cling to vascular wall
③ Diapedesis

Capillary wall — { Endothelium
Basal lamina }

FIGURE 12.9 **Phagocyte mobilization.**

swollen, painful area is a joint, its function (movement) may be impaired temporarily. This forces the injured part to rest, which aids healing. Some authorities consider limitation of joint movement to be an additional (fifth) cardinal sign of inflammation.

The inflammatory response (1) prevents the spread of damaging agents to nearby tissues, (2) disposes of cell debris and pathogens, and (3) sets the stage for repair. Let's look at how it accomplishes these tasks. Within an hour or so after the inflammatory process has begun, neutrophils are squeezing through the capillary walls, a process called **diapedesis** (Figure 12.9). Drawn to the area by inflammatory chemicals, the neutrophils begin the cleanup detail by engulfing damaged or dead tissue cells and/or pathogens. As the counterattack continues, monocytes begin to leave the blood and follow the neutrophils into the inflamed area. Monocytes are fairly poor phagocytes, but within 8 to 12 hours after entering the tissues they become macrophages with insatiable appetites. The macrophages continue to

wage the battle, replacing the short-lived neutrophils on the battlefield. Macrophages are the central actors in the final disposal of cell debris as the inflammation subsides.

Besides phagocytosis, other protective events are also occurring at the inflamed site. Clotting proteins, leaked into the area from the blood, are activated and begin to wall off the damaged area with fibrin to prevent the spread of pathogens or harmful agents to neighboring tissues. The fibrin mesh also forms a scaffolding for permanent repair. The local heat increases the metabolic rate of the tissue cells, speeding up their defensive actions and repair processes.

If the damaged area contains pathogens that have previously invaded the body, the *third line of defense* also comes into play—the adaptive response mediated by lymphocytes. Both protective antibodies and T cells (T lymphocytes) invade the area to act specifically and directly against the damaging agents. (We will speak more of this response shortly.)

Activated complement proteins attach to pathogen's membrane in step-by-step sequence, forming a membrane attack complex (a MAC attack).

MAC pores in the membrane cause cell lysis.

FIGURE 12.10   Activation of complement, resulting in lysis of a target cell.

HOMEOSTATIC IMBALANCE

In severely infected areas, the battle takes a considerable toll on both sides, and creamy, yellow pus may form in the wound. **Pus** is a mixture of dead or dying neutrophils, broken-down tissue cells, and living and dead pathogens. If the inflammatory mechanism fails to fully clear the area of debris, the sac of pus may become walled off, forming an *abscess*. Surgical drainage of abscesses is often necessary before healing can occur. ▲

Antimicrobial Proteins

A variety of **antimicrobial proteins** enhances the innate defenses either by attacking microorganisms directly or by hindering their ability to reproduce. The most important of these are *complement proteins* and *interferon*.

Complement The term **complement** refers to a group of at least 20 plasma proteins that circulate in the blood in an inactive state. However, when complement becomes attached, or *fixed*, to foreign cells such as bacteria, fungi, or mismatched red blood cells, it is activated and becomes a major factor in the fight against the foreign cells. This **complement fixation** occurs when complement

proteins bind to certain sugars or proteins (such as antibodies) on the foreign cell's surface. One result of complement fixation is the formation of **membrane attack complexes (MAC)** that produce lesions, complete with holes, in the foreign cell's surface (Figure 12.10). These lesions allow water to rush into the cell, causing it to burst. Activated complement also amplifies the inflammatory response. Some of the molecules released during the activation process are *vasodilators*, and some are *chemotaxis chemicals* that attract neutrophils and macrophages into the region. Still others cause the cell membranes of the foreign cells to become sticky so they are easier to phagocytize; this effect is called *opsonization*. Although the complement attack is often directed against specific microorganisms that have been "identified" by antibody binding, complement itself is a nonspecific defensive mechanism that "complements," or enhances, the effectiveness of *both* innate and adaptive defenses.

Interferon Viruses—essentially nucleic acids surrounded by a protein coat—lack the cellular machinery required to generate ATP or make proteins. They do their "dirty work" in the body by entering tissue cells and taking over the cellular

TABLE 12.1	Summary of Nonspecific Body Defenses

Category and associated elements	Protective mechanism
Surface Membrane Barriers—First Line of Defense	
Intact skin (epidermis)	Forms mechanical barrier that prevents entry of pathogens and other harmful substances into body.
• Acid mantle	Skin secretions make epidermal surface acidic, which inhibits bacterial growth; sebum also contains bacteria-killing chemicals.
• Keratin	Provides resistance against acids, alkalis, and bacterial enzymes.
Intact mucous membranes	Form mechanical barrier that prevents entry of pathogens.
• Mucus	Traps microorganisms in respiratory and digestive tracts.
• Nasal hairs	Filter and trap microorganisms in nasal passages.
• Cilia	Propel debris-laden mucus away from lower respiratory passages.
• Gastric juice	Contains concentrated hydrochloric acid and protein-digesting enzymes that destroy pathogens in stomach.
• Acid mantle of vagina	Inhibits growth of bacteria and fungi in female reproductive tract.
• Lacrimal secretion (tears); saliva	Continuously lubricate and cleanse eyes (tears) and oral cavity (saliva); contain lysozyme, an enzyme that destroys microorganisms.
Cellular and Chemical Defenses—Second Line of Defense	
Phagocytes	Engulf and destroy pathogens that breach surface membrane barriers; macrophages also contribute to immune response.
Natural killer cells	Promote cell lysis by direct cell attack against virus-infected or cancerous body cells; do not depend on specific antigen recognition.
Inflammatory response	Prevents spread of injurious agents to adjacent tissues, disposes of pathogens and dead tissue cells, and promotes tissue repair; releases chemical mediators that attract phagocytes (and immunocompetent cells) to the area.
Antimicrobial chemicals	
• Complement	Group of plasma proteins that lyses microorganisms, enhances phagocytosis by opsonization, and intensifies inflammatory response.
• Interferons	Proteins released by virus-infected cells that protect uninfected tissue cells from viral takeover; mobilize immune system.
• Urine	Normally acid pH inhibits bacterial growth; cleanses the lower urinary tract as it flushes from the body.
Fever	Systemic response triggered by pyrogens; high body temperature inhibits multiplication of bacteria and enhances body repair processes.

machinery needed to reproduce themselves. Although the virus-infected cells in an infected person can do little to save themselves, they help defend cells that have not yet been infected by secreting small proteins called **interferons** (in-ter-fer′onz). The interferon molecules diffuse to nearby cells and bind to their membrane receptors. This binding stimulates the synthesis of proteins that "interfere" with the ability of viruses to multiply within these still-healthy cells.

Fever

Fever, or abnormally high body temperature, is a systemic response to invading microorganisms. As described further in Chapter 14, body temperature is regulated by a part of the hypothalamus, commonly referred to as the body's "thermostat." Normally the thermostat is set at approximately 37°C (98.6°F), but it can be reset upward in response to **pyrogens** (*pyro* = fire), chemicals secreted by white blood cells and macrophages exposed to foreign cells or substances in the body.

Although high fevers are dangerous because excess heat "scrambles" enzymes and other body proteins, mild or moderate fever seems to benefit the body. Bacteria require large amounts of iron and zinc to multiply, but during a fever the liver and spleen gather up these nutrients, making them less available. Fever also increases the metabolic rate of tissue cells in general, speeding up repair processes.

▶ DID YOU GET IT?

7. How do the innate and adaptive defenses differ?

8. What are the four common indicators of inflammation?

9. How does complement cause lysis of a pathogenic microorganism?

10. Which type of infectious microorganism causes the body's level of interferons to rise?

For answers, see Appendix D.

Adaptive Body Defenses

Most of us would find it wonderfully convenient if we could walk into a single clothing store and buy a complete wardrobe—hat to shoes—that fit us "to a T" regardless of any special figure problems. We know that such a service would be next to impossible to

find—yet we take for granted our built-in *specific defense system,* which stalks and eliminates with nearly equal precision almost any type of pathogen that intrudes into the body.

The immune system's response to a threat, called the **immune response,** involves tremendously increased internal nonspecific defenses (inflammatory responses and others) and provides protection that is carefully targeted against *specific* antigens. Furthermore, the initial exposure to an antigen "primes" the body to react more vigorously to later meetings with the same antigen.

Sometimes referred to as the body's *third line of defense,* the specific defense system is a functional system that recognizes foreign molecules (antigens) and acts to inactivate or destroy them. Normally it protects us from a wide variety of pathogens, as well as from abnormal body cells. When it fails, malfunctions, or is disabled, some of the most devastating diseases—such as cancer, rheumatoid arthritis, and AIDS—may result.

Although *immunology,* the study of immunity, is a fairly new science, the ancient Greeks knew that once someone had suffered through a certain infectious disease, that person was unlikely to have the same disease again. The basis of this immunity was revealed in the late 1800s, when it was shown that animals surviving a serious bacterial infection have "factors" in their blood that protect them from future attacks by the same pathogen. (These factors are now known to be unique proteins called *antibodies.*) Furthermore, it was demonstrated that if antibody-containing serum from the surviving animals (immune serum) was injected into animals that had not been exposed to the pathogen, those animals would also be protected. These landmark experiments revealed three important aspects of the adaptive defense:

1. **It is antigen specific**—It recognizes and acts against *particular* pathogens or foreign substances.

2. **It is systemic**—Immunity is not restricted to the initial infection site.

3. **It has "memory"**—It recognizes and mounts even stronger attacks on previously encountered pathogens.

This was exciting news. But then, in the mid-1900s, it was discovered that injection of serum containing antibodies did not always protect a recipient from diseases the donor had survived. In such cases, however, injection of the donor's lymphocytes *did* provide immunity.

As the pieces began to fall into place, two separate but overlapping arms of the adaptive defense system were recognized. **Humoral** (hu'mor-al) **immunity,** also called **antibody-mediated immunity,** is provided by antibodies present in the body's "humors," or fluids. When lymphocytes themselves defend the body, the immunity is called either **cellular immunity** or **cell-mediated immunity** because the protective factor is living cells. The cellular arm also has cellular targets—virus-infected tissue cells, cancer cells, and cells of foreign grafts. The lymphocytes act against such targets either *directly,* by lysing the foreign cells, or *indirectly,* by releasing chemicals that enhance the inflammatory response or activate other immune cells. However, before we describe the humoral and cellular responses individually, we will consider the antigens that trigger the activity of the remarkable cells involved in these immune responses.

Antigens

An **antigen** (an'tĭ-jen) **(Ag)** is any substance capable of mobilizing our immune system and provoking an immune response. Most antigens are large, complex molecules that are not normally present in our bodies. Consequently, as far as our immune system is concerned, they are foreign intruders, or **nonself.** An almost limitless variety of substances can act as antigens, including virtually all foreign proteins, nucleic acids, many large carbohydrates, and some lipids. Of these, proteins are the strongest antigens. Pollen grains and microorganisms such as bacteria, fungi, and virus particles are *antigenic* because their surfaces bear such foreign molecules.

It is also important to remember that our own cells are richly studded with a variety of protein molecules (self-antigens). Somehow, as our immune system develops, it takes an inventory of all these proteins so that, thereafter, they are recognized as self. Although these **self-antigens** do not trigger an immune response in us, they *are* strongly antigenic to other people. This helps explain why our bodies reject cells of transplanted organs or foreign grafts unless special measures (drugs and others) are taken to cripple or stifle the immune response.

As a rule, small molecules are not antigenic, but when they link up with our own proteins, the immune system may recognize the combination as foreign and mount an attack that is harmful rather than protective. (Such reactions, called allergies, are described on pp. 429–430.) In such cases, the troublesome small molecule is called a **hapten** (*haptein* = to grasp), or **incomplete antigen.** Besides certain drugs, chemicals that act as haptens are found in poison ivy, animal dander, and even in some detergents, hair dyes, cosmetics, and other commonly used household and industrial products.

HOMEOSTATIC IMBALANCE

Perhaps the most dramatic and familiar example of a drug hapten's provoking an immune response involves the binding of penicillin to blood proteins, which causes a **penicillin reaction** in some people. In such cases, the immune system mounts such a vicious attack that the person's life is endangered. ▲

Cells of the Adaptive Defense System: An Overview

The crucial cells of the adaptive system are lymphocytes and macrophages. Lymphocytes exist in two major "flavors." The **B lymphocytes,** or **B cells,** produce antibodies and oversee humoral immunity, whereas the **T lymphocytes,** or **T cells,** are non–antibody-producing lymphocytes that constitute the cell-mediated arm of the adaptive defense system. Unlike the two types of lymphocytes, macrophages do not respond to specific antigens but instead play an essential role in helping the lymphocytes that do.

Lymphocytes

Like all blood cells, lymphocytes originate from hemocytoblasts in red bone marrow (Figure 12.11). The immature lymphocytes released from the marrow are essentially identical. Whether a given lymphocyte matures into a B cell or a T cell depends on where in the body it becomes **immunocompetent,** that is, capable of responding to a specific antigen by binding to it. T cells arise from lymphocytes that migrate to the **t**hymus (see Figure 12.11), where they undergo a maturation process of 2 to 3 days, directed by thymic hormones (*thymosin* and others). Within the thymus, the immature lymphocytes divide rapidly and their numbers increase enormously, but only those maturing T cells with the sharpest ability to identify *foreign* antigens survive. Lymphocytes

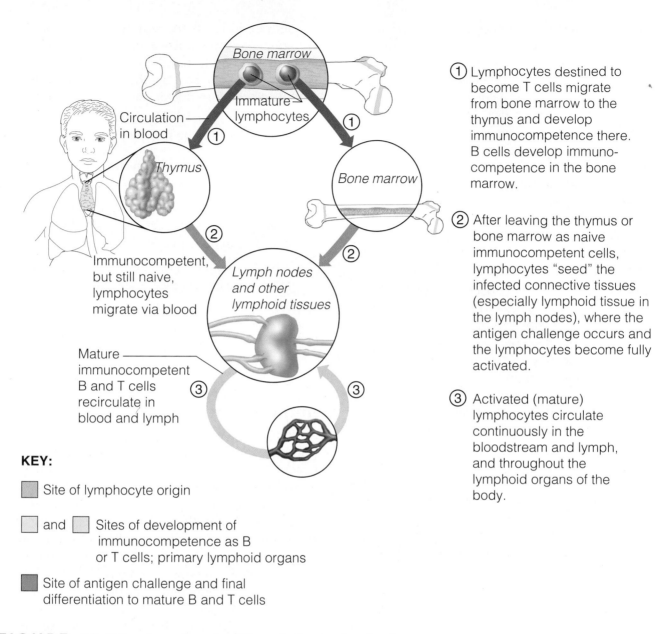

① Lymphocytes destined to become T cells migrate from bone marrow to the thymus and develop immunocompetence there. B cells develop immuno-competence in the bone marrow.

② After leaving the thymus or bone marrow as naive immunocompetent cells, lymphocytes "seed" the infected connective tissues (especially lymphoid tissue in the lymph nodes), where the antigen challenge occurs and the lymphocytes become fully activated.

③ Activated (mature) lymphocytes circulate continuously in the bloodstream and lymph, and throughout the lymphoid organs of the body.

KEY:

▨ Site of lymphocyte origin

▢ and ▢ Sites of development of immunocompetence as B or T cells; primary lymphoid organs

▨ Site of antigen challenge and final differentiation to mature B and T cells

FIGURE 12.11   **Lymphocyte differentiation and activation.**

capable of binding strongly with *self-antigens* (and of acting against body cells) are vigorously weeded out and destroyed. Thus, the development of **self-tolerance** for the body's own cells is an essential part of a lymphocyte's "education." This is true not only for T cells but also for B cells. **B** cells develop immunocompetence in **b**one marrow, but less is known about the factors that regulate B cell maturation.

Once a lymphocyte is immunocompetent, it will be able to react to one distinct antigen and one only, because *all* the antigen receptors on its

external surface are the same. For example, the receptors of one lymphocyte can recognize only a part of the hepatitis A virus, those of another lymphocyte can recognize only pneumococcus bacteria, and so forth.

Although all the details of the maturation process are still beyond our grasp, we know that lymphocytes become immunocompetent *before* meeting the antigens they may later attack. Thus, *it is our genes, not antigens, that determine what specific foreign substances our immune system will be able to recognize and resist.* Only some of the possible antigens our lymphocytes are programmed to resist will ever invade our bodies. Consequently, only some members of our army of immunocompetent cells will be mobilized during our lifetime. The others will be forever idle. As usual, our bodies have done their best to protect us.

After they become immunocompetent, both T cells and B cells migrate to the lymph nodes and spleen (and loose connective tissues), where their encounters with antigens will occur (see Figure 12.11). Then, when the lymphoctyes bind with recognized antigens, they complete their differentiation into fully mature T cells and B cells.

Macrophages

Macrophages, which also become widely distributed throughout the lymphoid organs and connective tissues, arise from *monocytes* formed in the bone marrow. As described earlier, a major role of macrophages (literally, "big eaters") in the innate defense system is to engulf foreign particles and rid them from the area. Their job doesn't stop there. They also present fragments of those antigens, like signal flags, on their own surfaces, where they can be recognized by immunocompetent T cells. Thus, they act as *antigen presenters* in the adaptive defense system. Macrophages also secrete **cytokines** proteins that are important in the immune response (see Table 12.3, pp. 426–427). Activated T cells, in turn, release chemicals that cause macrophages to become insatiable phagocytes, or *killer macrophages*. As you will see, interactions between lymphocytes and interactions between lymphocytes and macrophages underlie virtually all phases of the adaptive immune response.

Macrophages tend to remain fixed in the lymphoid organs (as if waiting for antigens to come to them), but lymphocytes, especially T cells, circulate continuously through the body (see Figure 12.11). This makes sense because circulating greatly increases a lymphocyte's chance of coming into contact with antigens collected by the lymph capillaries from the tissue spaces, as well as with huge numbers of macrophages and other lymphocytes.

To summarize, the adaptive immune system is a two-armed defensive system—a humoral arm and a cellular arm—that uses lymphocytes, macrophages, and specific molecules to identify and destroy all substances—both living and nonliving—that are in the body but are not recognized as being self. The immune system's ability to respond to such threats depends on the ability of its cells (1) to recognize foreign substances (antigens) in the body by binding to them and (2) to communicate with one another so that the system as a whole mounts a response specific to those antigens.

▶ *DID YOU GET IT?*

11. What is the difference between an antigen and a self-antigen?

12. What are the two types of lymphocytes involved in adaptive immune responses, and how do their functions in body protection differ?

13. Where does the "programming" phase leading to immunocompetence occur for T cells?

14. What is the essential role of macrophages in adaptive immunity?

For answers, see Appendix D.

Humoral (Antibody-Mediated) Immune Response

An immunocompetent but as yet immature B lymphocyte is stimulated to complete its development (into a fully mature B cell) when antigens bind to its surface receptors. This binding event *sensitizes,* or *activates,* the lymphocyte to "switch on" and undergo **clonal selection.** The lymphocyte begins to grow and then multiplies rapidly to form an army of cells all exactly like itself and bearing the same antigen-specific receptors (Figure 12.12). The resulting family of identical cells descended from the *same* ancestor cell is called a **clone,** and clone formation is the **primary humoral response** to that antigen. (As described later, T cells also influence B cell activation.)

Most of the B cell clone members, or descendants, become **plasma cells.** After an initial lag period, these antibody-producing "factories" swing into action, producing the same highly specific antibodies at an unbelievable rate of about 2000 antibody molecules per second. (The B cells themselves produce only very small amounts of antibodies.) However, this flurry of activity lasts only 4 or 5 days; then the plasma cells begin to die. Antibody levels in the blood during this primary response peak about 10 days after the response begins and then slowly decline (Figure 12.13).

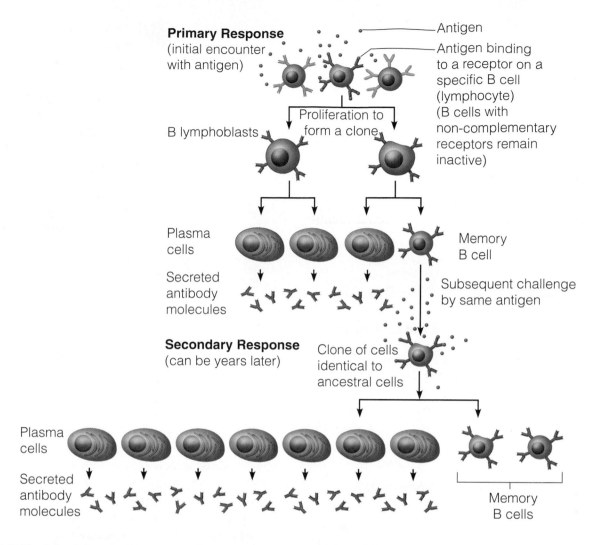

Primary Response
(initial encounter with antigen)

Antigen

Antigen binding to a receptor on a specific B cell (lymphocyte) (B cells with non-complementary receptors remain inactive)

Proliferation to form a clone

B lymphoblasts

Plasma cells

Memory B cell

Secreted antibody molecules

Subsequent challenge by same antigen

Secondary Response
(can be years later)

Clone of cells identical to ancestral cells

Plasma cells

Secreted antibody molecules

Memory B cells

FIGURE 12.12   Clonal selection of a B cell stimulated by antigen binding. The initial meeting stimulates the primary response in which the B cell proliferates rapidly, forming a clone of like cells (clonal expansion), most of which become antibody-producing plasma cells. Cells that do not differentiate into plasma cells become memory cells, which respond to subsequent exposures to the same antigen. Should such a meeting occur, the memory cells quickly produce more memory cells and larger numbers of effector plasma cells with the same antigen specificity. Responses generated by memory cells are called secondary responses.

B cell clone members that do not become plasma cells become long-lived **memory cells** capable of responding to the same antigen at later meetings with it. Memory cells are responsible for the **immunological memory** mentioned earlier. These later immune responses, called **secondary humoral responses,** are produced much faster, are more prolonged, and are more effective than the events of the primary response because all the preparations for this attack have already been made. Within hours after recognition of the "old-enemy" antigen, a new army of plasma cells is being generated, and antibodies flood into the bloodstream. Within 2 to 3 days, blood antibody levels peak (at much higher levels than seen in the primary response), and their levels remain high for weeks to months. How antibodies protect the body is described shortly.

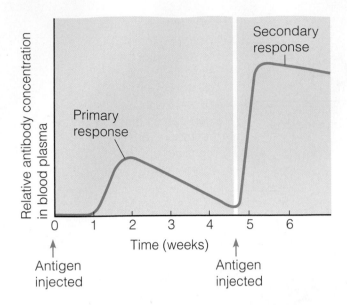

FIGURE 12.13 **Primary and secondary humoral responses to an antigen.** In the primary response, the level of antibodies in the blood gradually rises and then rapidly declines. The secondary response is both more rapid and more intense. Additionally, antibody levels remain high for a much longer time.

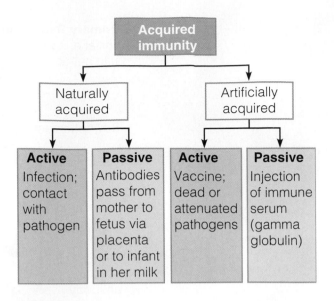

FIGURE 12.14 **Types of acquired immunity.** Orange boxes signify active types of immunity in which immunological memory is established. Gold boxes signify the short-lived passive types of immunity; no immunological memory is established.

Active and Passive Humoral Immunity

When your B cells encounter antigens and produce antibodies against them, you are exhibiting **active immunity** (Figure 12.14). Active immunity is (1) *naturally acquired* during bacterial and viral infections, during which we may develop the signs and symptoms of the disease and suffer a little (or a lot), and (2) *artificially acquired* when we receive **vaccines.** It makes little difference whether the antigen invades the body under its own power or is introduced in the form of a vaccine. The response of the immune system is pretty much the same. Indeed, once it was recognized that secondary responses are so much more vigorous, the race was on to develop vaccines to "prime" the immune response by providing a first meeting with the antigen. Most vaccines contain pathogens that are dead or *attenuated* (living, but extremely weakened).

We receive two benefits from vaccines: (1) they spare us most of the signs and symptoms (and discomfort) of the disease that would otherwise occur during the primary response and (2) the weakened antigens are still able to stimulate antibody production and promote immunological memory. So-called *booster shots,* which may intensify the immune response at later meetings with the same antigen, are also available. Vaccines have virtually wiped out smallpox and are currently available against microorganisms that cause pneumonia, polio, tetanus, diphtheria, whooping cough, measles, and many other diseases. In the United States, many potentially serious childhood diseases have been dramatically reduced by active immunization programs.

Passive immunity is quite different from active immunity, both in the antibody source and in the degree of protection it provides (see Figure 12.14). Instead of being made by your plasma cells, the antibodies are obtained from the serum of an immune human or animal donor. As a result, your B cells are *not* challenged by the antigen, immunological memory does *not* occur, and the temporary protection provided by the "borrowed antibodies" ends when they naturally degrade in the body.

Passive immunity is conferred *naturally* on a fetus when the mother's antibodies cross the placenta and enter the fetal circulation, and after birth during breastfeeding. For several months after birth, the baby is protected from all the antigens to which the mother has been exposed.

(a)

(b)

FIGURE 12.15   Basic antibody structure. (a) Computer-generated image. **(b)** Simplified diagrammatic structure. The basic structure (monomer) of each type of antibody is formed by four polypeptide chains (two light chains and two heavy chains) that are joined by disulfide bonds. Each chain has a variable (V) region (different in different antibodies) and a constant (C) region (essentially identical in different antibodies of the same class). The variable regions are the antigen-binding sites of the antibody.

Passive immunity is *artificially* conferred when one receives immune serum or gamma globulin. Gamma globulin is commonly administered after exposure to hepatitis. Other immune sera are used to treat poisonous snake bites (an *antivenom*), botulism, rabies, and tetanus (an *antitoxin*) because these diseases will kill a person before active immunity can be established. The donated antibodies provide immediate protection, but their effect is short-lived (2 to 3 weeks). Meanwhile, however, the body's own defenses take over.

In addition to their use to provide passive immunity, antibodies are prepared commercially for use in research, in clinical testing for diagnostic purposes, and in treating certain cancers. **Monoclonal antibodies** used for such purposes are produced by descendants of a single cell and are pure antibody preparations that exhibit specificity for one, and only one, antigen. Besides their use in delivering cancer-fighting drugs to cancerous tissue, monoclonal antibodies are being used for diagnosing pregnancy, hepatitis, and rabies. They are also used for early diagnosis and to track the extent of cancers hidden deep within the body.

Antibodies

Antibodies, also referred to as **immunoglobulins** (im″mu-no-glob′u-linz), or **Igs,** constitute the *gamma globulin* part of blood proteins. Antibodies are soluble proteins secreted by activated B cells or by their plasma-cell offspring in response to an antigen and they are capable of binding specifically with that antigen.

Antibodies are formed in response to a huge number of different antigens. Despite their variety, they all have a similar basic anatomy that allows them to be grouped into five Ig classes, each slightly different in structure and function.

Basic Antibody Structure   Regardless of its class, every antibody has a basic structure consisting of four amino acid (polypeptide) chains linked together by *disulfide* (sulfur-to-sulfur) *bonds* (Figure 12.15). Two of the four chains are identical and

TABLE 12.2		Immunoglobin Classes	
Class	**Generalized structure**	**Where found**	**Biological function**
IgD		Virtually always attached to B cell.	Believed to be cell surface receptor of immunocompetent B cell; important in activation of B cell.
IgM		Attached to B cell; free in plasma.	When bound to B cell membrane, serves as antigen receptor; first Ig class *released* to plasma by plasma cells during primary response; potent agglutinating agent; fixes complement.
IgG		Most abundant antibody in plasma; represents 75–85% of circulating antibodies.	Main antibody of both primary and secondary responses; crosses placenta and provides passive immunity to fetus; fixes complement.
IgA		Some (monomer) in plasma; dimer in secretions such as saliva, tears, intestinal juice, and milk.	Bathes and protects mucosal surfaces from attachment of pathogens
IgE		Secreted by plasma cells in skin, mucosae of gastrointestinal and respiratory tracts, and tonsils.	Binds to mast cells and basophils, and triggers release of histamine and other chemicals that mediate inflammation and certain allergic responses.

contain approximately 400 amino acids each; these are the *heavy chains.* The other two chains, the *light chains,* are also identical to each other but are only about half as long as the heavy chains. When the four chains are combined, the antibody molecule formed has two identical halves, each consisting of a heavy and a light chain, and the molecule as a whole is commonly described as being T- or Y-shaped.

When scientists began investigating antibody structure, they discovered something very peculiar. Each of the four chains forming an antibody had a **variable (V) region** at one end and a much larger **constant (C) region** at the other end. Antibodies responding to different antigens had different variable regions, but their constant regions were the same or nearly so. This made sense when it was discovered that the variable regions of the heavy and light chains in each arm combine their efforts to form an **antigen-binding site** (Figure 12.15) uniquely

shaped to "fit" its specific antigen. Hence, each antibody has two such antigen-binding regions.

The constant regions that form the "stem" of an antibody can be compared to the handle of a key. A key handle has a common function for all keys: it allows you to hold the key and place its tumbler-moving portion into the lock. Similarly, the constant regions of the antibody chains serve common functions in all antibodies: they determine the type of antibody formed (antibody class), as well as how the antibody class will carry out its immune roles in the body, and the cell types or chemicals with which the antibody can bind.

Antibody Classes There are five major immunoglobulin classes—IgM, IgA, IgD, IgG, and IgE. (Remember the woman's name MADGE to recall the five Ig types.) As illustrated in Table 12.2, IgD, IgG, and IgE antibodies have the same basic Y-shaped

Complement and agglutination aid phagocytosis, but they assist it in different ways. What is this difference?

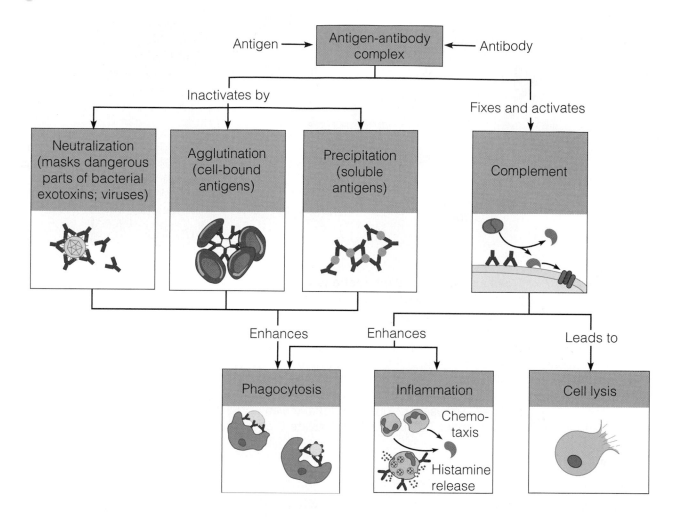

FIGURE 12.16 **Mechanisms of antibody action.**

structure described above and are referred to as *monomers*. IgA antibodies occur in both monomer and *dimer* (two linked monomers) forms. (Only the dimer form is shown in the table.) Compared to the other antibodies, IgM antibodies are huge. Because they are constructed of five linked monomers, IgM antibodies are called *pentamers* (*penta* = five).

The antibodies of each class have slightly different biological roles and locations in the body. For example, IgG is the most abundant antibody in blood plasma and is the only type that can cross the

placental barrier. Hence, the passive immunity that a mother transfers to her fetus is "with the compliments" of her IgG antibodies. Only IgM and IgG can fix complement. The IgA dimer, sometimes called *secretory IgA,* is found mainly in mucus and other secretions that bathe body surfaces. It plays a major role in preventing pathogens from gaining entry into the body. IgE antibodies are the "troublemaker" antibodies involved in allergies. These and other characteristics unique to each of the immunoglobulin classes are summarized in Table 12.2.

Antibody Function Antibodies inactivate antigens in a number of ways—by complement fixation, neutralization, agglutination, and precipitation (Figure 12.16). Of these, complement fixation

Complement fixation provides "knobs" for the phagocyte to attach to, whereas agglutination binds antigens (typically microorganisms) together into large masses that become nonmobile and easier to destroy.

FIGURE 12.17 **T cell activation and interactions with other cells of the immune response.** Macrophages are important as antigen presenters. After they have ingested an antigen, they display parts of it on their surface, where it can be recognized by a helper T cell that bears receptors for the same antigen. During the binding process, the T cell binds simultaneously to the antigen and to the macrophage (self) receptor, which leads to T cell activation and cloning (not illustrated). In addition, the macrophage releases cytokines, which enhance T cell activation. Activated helper T cells release cytokines, which stimulate proliferation and activity of other helper T Cells and help activate B cells and cytotoxic (killer) T cells.

and neutralization are most important to body protection.

Complement is the chief antibody ammunition used against cellular antigens, such as bacteria or mismatched red blood cells. As noted earlier, complement is fixed (activated) during innate defenses. It is also activated very efficiently when it binds to antibodies attached to cellular targets. This triggers events (described earlier) that result in lysis of the foreign cell and release of molecules that tremendously enhance the inflammatory process.

Neutralization occurs when antibodies bind to specific sites on bacterial *exotoxins* (toxic chemicals secreted by bacteria) or on viruses that can cause cell injury. In this way, they block the harmful effects of the exotoxin or virus.

Because antibodies have more than one antigen-binding site, they can bind to more than one antigen at a time; consequently, *antigen-antibody complexes* can be cross-linked into large lattices.

When the cross-linking involves cell-bound antigens, the process causes clumping of the foreign cells, a process called **agglutination.** This type of antigen-antibody reaction occurs when mismatched blood is transfused (the foreign red blood cells are clumped) and is the basis of tests used for blood typing. When the cross-linking process involves soluble antigenic molecules, the resulting antigen-antibody complexes are so large that they become insoluble and settle out of solution. This cross-linking reaction is more precisely called **precipitation.** There is little question that agglutinated bacteria and immobilized (precipitated) antigen molecules are much more easily captured and engulfed by the body's phagocytes than are freely moving antigens.

▶ *DID YOU GET IT?*

15. What is the importance of the variable region of antibodies?

16. Which class of antibody is found in saliva and tears?

17. Regarding the action of antibodies, what is neutralization?

18. The concentration of antibodies in John's lymphatic stream is increasing rapidly. Which cells would you expect to be increasing in number—B cells, plasma cells, or T cells?

For answers, see Appendix D.

Cellular (Cell-Mediated) Immune Response

Like B cells, immunocompetent T cells are activated to form a clone by binding with a "recognized" antigen (see Figure 12.19, p. 428). However, unlike B cells, T cells are not able to bind with *free* antigens. Instead, the antigens must be "presented" by a macrophage (or by other antigen–presenting cells), and a *double recognition* must occur. A macrophage engulfs an antigen, and processes it internally. Parts of the processed antigen are then displayed on the external surface of the macrophage in combination with one of the macrophage's own proteins (Figure 12.17).

Apparently, a T cell must recognize "nonself," the antigen fragment presented by the macrophage, and also "self" by coupling with a specific glycoprotein on the macrophage's surface at the same time. Antigen binding alone is not enough to sensitize T cells. They must be "spoon-fed" the antigens by macrophages, and something like a "double handshake" must occur. Although this idea seemed preposterous when it was first suggested, there is no longer any question that **antigen presentation** is essential for activation and clonal selection of the T cells. Without macrophage "presenters," the immune response is severely impaired. Cytokine chemicals (particularly interleukin 1) released by macrophages also play important roles in the immune response, as shown in Table 12.3.

The different classes of T cell clones, which provide for cell-mediated immunity, are a diverse lot and produce their deadly effects in a variety of ways (see Table 12.3). Some are **cytotoxic (killer) T cells,** cells that specialize in killing virus-infected, cancer, or foreign graft cells (Figure 12.18). One way a cytotoxic T cell accomplishes this is by binding tightly to a foreign cell and releasing toxic

FIGURE 12.18   A proposed mechanism by which cytotoxic T cells kill target cells.

chemicals called *perforins* and *granzymes* from its granules. The perforins enter the foreign cell's plasma membrane (delivering the so-called *lethal hit*). Shortly thereafter, pores appear in the target cell's membrane, allowing the granzymes (protein-digesting enzymes) to enter and kill the foreign cell. The cytotoxic T cell then detaches and seeks other foreign prey to attack.

Helper T cells are the T cells that act as the "directors" or "managers" of the immune system. Once activated, they circulate through the body, recruiting other cells to fight the invaders. For example, helper T cells interact directly with B cells (that have already attached to antigens), prodding the B cells into more rapid division (clone production) and then, like the "boss" of an assembly line, signaling for antibody formation to begin. The helper T cells also release a variety of cytokine chemicals (see Table 12.3) that act indirectly to

TABLE 12.3	Functions of Cells and Molecules Involved in Immunity
Element	**Function in the immune response**
Cells	
B cell	Lymphocyte that resides in the lymph nodes, spleen, or other lymphoid tissues, where it is induced to replicate by antigen-binding and helper T cell interactions; its progeny (clone members) form plasma cells and memory cells.
Plasma cell	Antibody-producing "machine"; produces huge numbers of the same antibody (immunoglobulin); represents further specialization of B cell clone descendants.
Helper T cell	A T cell that binds with a specific antigen presented by a macrophage; it stimulates the production of other immune cells (cytotoxic T cells and B cells) to help fight the invader; acts both directly and indirectly by releasing cytokines.
Cytotoxic T cell	Also called a killer T cell; activity enhanced by helper T cells; its specialty is killing virus-invaded body cells, as well as body cells that have become cancerous; involved in graft rejection.
Regulatory T cell	Slows or stops the activity of B and T cells once the infection (or attack by foreign cells) has been conquered. Thought to be important in preventing autoimmune diseases.
Memory cell	Descendant of an activated B cell or T cell; generated during the initial immune response (primary response); may exist in the body for years thereafter, enabling it to respond quickly and efficiently to subsequent infections or meetings with the same antigen.
Antigen-presenting cell	Any of several cell types (macrophage, dendritic cell, B cell) that engulfs and digests antigens that it encounters and presents parts of them on its plasma membrane for recognition by T cells bearing receptors for the same antigen; this function, *antigen presentation,* is essential for normal cell-mediated responses. Also releases chemicals (cytokines) that activate T cells.
Molecules	
Antibody (immunoglobulin)	Protein produced by a B cell or its plasma cell offspring and released into the body fluids (blood, lymph, saliva, mucus, etc.), where it attaches to antigens, causing neutralization, precipitation, or agglutination, which "marks" the antigens for destruction by phagocytes or complement.
Cytokines	Chemicals released by sensitized T cells, macrophages, and certain other cells: • Migration inhibiting factor (MIF)—"inhibits" macrophage migration and keeps them in the local area. • Interleukin 2—stimulates T cells and B cells to proliferate; activates NK cells. • Helper factors—enhance antibody formation by plasma cells. • Suppressor factors—suppress antibody formation or T cell–mediated immune responses (interleukin–10 transforming growth factor, and others). • Chemotactic factors—attract leukocytes (neutrophils, eosinophils, and basophils) into inflamed area.

TABLE 12.3 *(continued)*

Element	Function in the immune response
	• Gamma interferon—secreted by lymphocytes; helps make tissue cells resistant to viral infection; activates macrophages and NK cells; enhances maturation of cytotoxic T cells.
	• Perforin, granzymes—cell toxins released by cytotoxic T cells.
Tumor necrosis factor (TNF)	Like perforin, causes cell killing; attracts granulocytes; activates T cells and macrophages.
Complement	Group of bloodborne proteins activated after binding to antibody-covered antigens; when activated, complement causes lysis of the microorganism and enhances inflammatory response.
Antigen	Substance capable of provoking an immune response; typically a large complex molecule not normally present in the body.

rid the body of antigens by (1) stimulating cytotoxic T cells and B cells to grow and divide; (2) attracting other types of protective white blood cells, such as neutrophils, into the area; and (3) enhancing the ability of macrophages to engulf and destroy microorganisms. (Actually, the macrophages are pretty good phagocytes even in the absence of cytokines, but in the presence of cytokines they develop an insatiable appetite.) As the released cytokines summon more and more cells into the battle, the immune response gains momentum, and the antigens are overwhelmed by the sheer numbers of immune elements acting against them.

Another T cell population, the **regulatory T cells,** formerly called *suppressor T cells,* releases chemicals that suppress the activity of both T and B cells. Regulatory T cells are vital for winding down and finally stopping the immune response after an antigen has been successfully inactivated or destroyed. This helps prevent uncontrolled or unnecessary immune system activity.

Most of the T cells enlisted to fight in a particular immune response are dead within a few days. However, a few members of each clone are long-lived **memory cells** that remain behind to provide the immunological memory for each antigen encountered and enable the body to respond quickly to subsequent invasions.

A summary of the major elements of the immune response appears in Figure 12.19.

Organ Transplants and Rejection

For people suffering with end-stage heart or kidney disease, organ transplants are a desirable treatment option. However, organ transplants have had mixed success because the immune system is ever vigilant, and rejection is a real problem.

Essentially there are four major types of grafts:

1. **Autografts** are tissue grafts transplanted from one site to another in the *same person*.
2. **Isografts** are tissue grafts donated by a *genetically identical person,* the only example being an identical twin.
3. **Allografts** are tissue grafts taken from *a person other than an identical twin*.
4. **Xenografts** are tissue grafts harvested from a *different animal species*, such as transplanting a baboon heart into a human being.

Autografts and isografts are ideal donor organs or tissues and are just about always successful given an adequate blood supply and no infection. Although pig heart valves have been transplanted with success, xenografts of whole organs are virtually never successful. The graft type most used is an allograft taken from a recently deceased person.

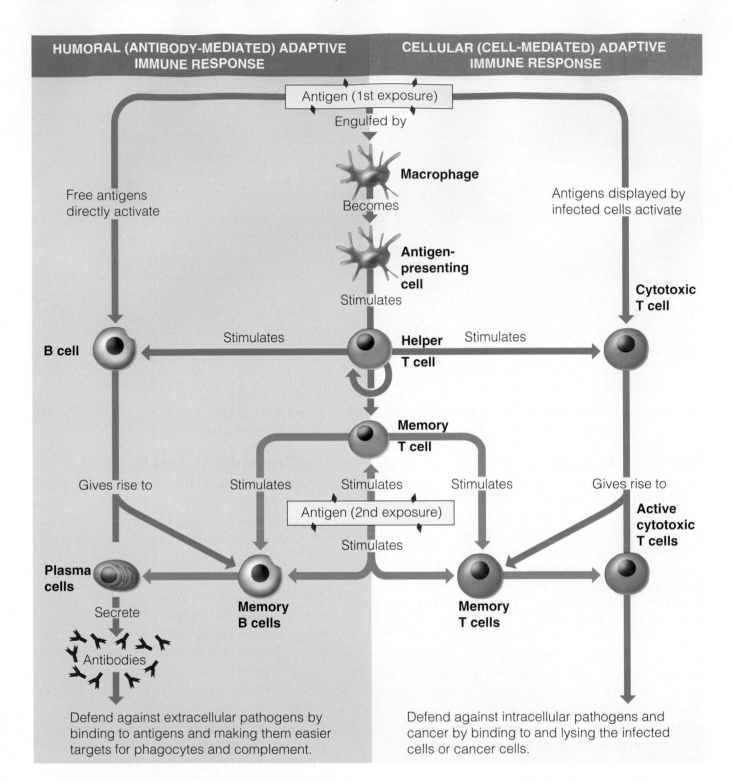

HUMORAL (ANTIBODY-MEDIATED) ADAPTIVE IMMUNE RESPONSE

CELLULAR (CELL-MEDIATED) ADAPTIVE IMMUNE RESPONSE

Antigen (1st exposure)

Engulfed by

Macrophage

Free antigens directly activate

Antigens displayed by infected cells activate

Becomes

Antigen-presenting cell

Stimulates

Cytotoxic T cell

B cell

Stimulates

Helper T cell

Stimulates

Memory T cell

Gives rise to

Stimulates

Stimulates

Stimulates

Gives rise to

Antigen (2nd exposure)

Active cytotoxic T cells

Stimulates

Plasma cells

Secrete

Memory B cells

Memory T cells

Antibodies

Defend against extracellular pathogens by binding to antigens and making them easier targets for phagocytes and complement.

Defend against intracellular pathogens and cancer by binding to and lysing the infected cells or cancer cells.

FIGURE 12.19 **A summary of the adaptive immune responses.** In this simple flowchart, green arrows track the primary response, and blue arrows track the secondary response.

Before an allograft is even attempted, the ABO and other blood group antigens of both the donor and recipient must be determined and must match. Then, the cell membrane antigens of their tissue cells are typed to determine how closely they match. At least a 75 percent match is needed to attempt a graft; as you might guess, good tissue matches between unrelated people are hard to find.

After surgery, to prevent rejection, the patient receives **immunosuppressive therapy,** including one or more of the following: corticosteroids to suppress inflammation, antiproliferative drugs, radiation (X-ray) therapy, and immunosuppressor drugs. Many of these drugs kill rapidly dividing cells (such as activated lymphocytes), and all of them have severe side effects. However, the major problem with immunosuppressive therapy is that while the immune system is suppressed, it cannot protect the body against other foreign agents. Explosive bacterial and viral infection is the most frequent cause of death in these patients.

▶ DID YOU GET IT?

19. T cells must take part in what is sometimes called the double handshake in order to be activated. What does this mean?

20. How is the lethal hit accomplished?

21. What is the role of regulatory T cells in the adaptive immune response?

22. Sheila is receiving a kidney transplant. The donor is her fraternal twin. What name is given to this type of graft?

For answers, see Appendix D.

Disorders of Immunity

 HOMEOSTATIC IMBALANCE

The most important disorders of the immune system are autoimmune diseases, allergies, and immunodeficiencies.

Autoimmune Diseases

Occasionally, the immune system loses its ability to distinguish friend from foe, that is, to tolerate self-antigens, while still recognizing and attacking foreign antigens. When this happens, the body produces antibodies (*auto-antibodies*) and sensitized T cells that attack and damage its own tissues. This puzzling phenomenon is called **autoimmune disease,** because it is one's own immune system that produces the disorder.

Some 5 percent of adults in North America—two-thirds of them women—are afflicted with autoimmune disease. Most common are the following:

- **Multiple sclerosis (MS),** which destroys the white matter (myelin sheaths) of the brain and spinal cord (see p. 234)

- **Myasthenia gravis,** which impairs communication between nerves and skeletal muscles (see p. 221)

- **Graves' disease,** in which the thyroid gland produces excessive amounts of thyroxine

- **Type 1 diabetes mellitus,** which destroys pancreatic beta cells, resulting in deficient production of insulin (see pp. 326–327)

- **Systemic lupus erythematosus (SLE),** a systemic disease that occurs mainly in young women and particularly affects the kidneys, heart, lungs, and skin

- **Glomerulonephritis,** a severe impairment of kidney function

- **Rheumatoid arthritis (RA),** which systematically destroys joints (see pp. 173–174)

Current therapies include treatments that depress certain aspects of the immune response.

How does the normal state of self-tolerance break down? It appears that one or more of the following may be triggers:

1. **Inefficient lymphocyte programming.** Instead of being silenced or eliminated, self-reactive B or T lymphocytes escape to the rest of the body. This is believed to occur in MS.

2. **Appearance in the circulation of self-proteins that were not previously exposed to the immune system.** Such "hidden" antigens are found in sperm cells, the eye lens, and certain proteins in the thyroid gland. In addition, "new self-antigens" may appear as a result of gene mutations that change the structure of self-proteins or as a result of alterations in self-proteins by hapten attachment or by bacterial or viral damage.

3. **Cross-reaction of antibodies produced against foreign antigens with self-antigens.** For instance, antibodies produced during an infection caused by streptococcus bacteria are known to

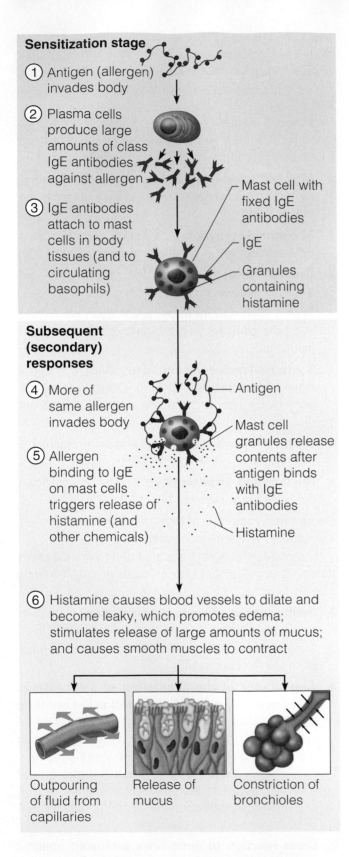

Sensitization stage

1. Antigen (allergen) invades body

2. Plasma cells produce large amounts of class IgE antibodies against allergen

3. IgE antibodies attach to mast cells in body tissues (and to circulating basophils)

Mast cell with fixed IgE antibodies

IgE

Granules containing histamine

Subsequent (secondary) responses

4. More of same allergen invades body

Antigen

5. Allergen binding to IgE on mast cells triggers release of histamine (and other chemicals)

Mast cell granules release contents after antigen binds with IgE antibodies

Histamine

6. Histamine causes blood vessels to dilate and become leaky, which promotes edema; stimulates release of large amounts of mucus; and causes smooth muscles to contract

Outpouring of fluid from capillaries

Release of mucus

Constriction of bronchioles

FIGURE 12.20 Mechanism of an immediate (acute) hypersensitivity response.

cross-react with heart antigens, causing damage to both the heart muscle and its valves, as well as to joints and kidneys. This age-old disease is called **rheumatic fever.** ▲

Allergies

At first, the immune response was thought to be purely protective. However, it was not long before its dangerous potentials were discovered. **Allergies,** or **hypersensitivities,** are abnormally vigorous immune responses in which the immune system causes tissue damage as it fights off a perceived "threat" that would otherwise be harmless to the body. The term *allergen* (*allo* = altered; *erg* = reaction) is used to distinguish this type of antigen from those producing essentially normal responses. People rarely die of allergies; they are just miserable with them.

Although there are several different types of allergies, the most common type is **immediate hypersensitivity** (Figure 12.20). This type of response, also called **acute hypersensitivity,** is triggered by the release of a flood of histamine when IgE antibodies bind to *mast cells*. Histamine causes small blood vessels in the area to become dilated and leaky and is largely to blame for the best-recognized symptoms of allergy: a runny nose, watery eyes, and itching, reddened skin (hives). When the allergen is inhaled, symptoms of asthma appear because smooth muscle in the walls of the bronchioles contracts, constricting the passages and restricting air flow. Over-the-counter (OTC) anti-allergy drugs contain *antihistamines* that counteract these effects. Most of these reactions begin within seconds after contact with the allergen and last about half an hour.

Fortunately, the bodywide, or systemic, acute allergic response known as **anaphylactic** (an"ah-fĭ-lak-tik) **shock** is fairly rare. Anaphylactic shock occurs when the allergen directly enters the blood and circulates rapidly through the body, as might happen with certain bee stings or spider bites. It may also follow an injection of a foreign substance (such as horse serum, penicillin, or other drugs that act as haptens) into susceptible individuals. The mechanism of anaphylactic shock is essentially the same as that of local responses, but when the entire body is involved, the outcome is life-threatening. For example, it is difficult to breathe when the smooth muscles of lung passages contract, and the sudden vasodilation (and fluid loss) that occurs may cause circulatory collapse and death within minutes. Epinephrine is the drug of choice to reverse these histamine-mediated effects.

Delayed hypersensitivities, mediated mainly by a special subgroup of helper T cells, cytotoxic T cells, and macrophages, take much longer to appear (1 to 3 days) than any of the acute reactions produced by antibodies. Instead of histamine, the chemicals mediating these reactions are cytokines released by the activated T cells. Hence, antihistamine drugs are *not* helpful against the delayed types of allergies. Corticosteroid drugs are used to provide relief.

The most familiar examples of delayed hypersensitivity reactions are those classed as **allergic contact dermatitis,** which follow skin contact with poison ivy, some heavy metals (lead, mercury, and others), and certain cosmetic and deodorant chemicals. These agents act as haptens; after diffusing through the skin and attaching to body proteins, they are perceived as foreign by the immune system. The *Mantoux* and *tine tests,* skin tests for detection of tuberculosis, depend on delayed hypersensitivity reactions. When the tubercle antigens are injected just under (or scratched into) the skin, a small, hard lesion forms if the person has been sensitized to the antigen.

Immunodeficiencies

The **immunodeficiencies** include both congenital and acquired conditions in which the production or function of immune cells or complement is abnormal. The most devastating congenital condition is **severe combined immunodeficiency disease (SCID),** in which there is a marked deficit of both B and T cells. Because T cells are absolutely required for normal operation of *both* arms of the adaptive response, afflicted children have essentially no protection against pathogens of any type. Minor infections easily shrugged off by most children are lethal to those with SCID. Bone marrow transplants and umbilical cord blood, which provide normal lymphocyte stem cells, have helped some SCID victims. Without such treatment, the only hope for survival is living behind protective barriers (in a plastic "bubble") that keep out all infectious agents.

Currently, the most important and most devastating of the acquired immunodeficiencies is **acquired immune deficiency syndrome (AIDS).** AIDS, which cripples the immune system by interfering with the activity of helper T cells, is highlighted in the "A Closer Look" box on pp. 432–433.

▶ *DID YOU GET IT?*

23. What is an allergy?

24. What causes the difficulty in breathing seen in anaphylactic shock?

25. What is the principal problem common to all immunodeficiency diseases?

26. What are two possible causes of autoimmune disease?

For answers, see Appendix D.

PART III: DEVELOPMENTAL ASPECTS OF THE LYMPHATIC SYSTEM AND BODY DEFENSES

The lymphatic vessels, which bud from the veins of the blood vascular system, and the main clusters of lymph nodes are obvious by the fifth week of development. Except for the thymus gland and the spleen, the lymphoid organs are poorly developed before birth. However, soon after birth, they become heavily populated with lymphocytes as the immune system begins to function.

Lymphatic system problems are relatively uncommon, but when they do occur they are painfully obvious. For example, when the lymphatic vessels are blocked (as in *elephantiasis,* a tropical disease in which the lymphatics become clogged with parasitic worms) or when lymphatics are removed (as in radical breast surgery), severe edema may result. However, lymphatic vessels removed surgically do grow back in time.

Stem cells of the immune system originate in the spleen and liver during the first month of embryonic development. Later, the bone marrow becomes the predominant source of stem cells (hemocytoblasts), and it persists in this role into adult life. In late fetal life and shortly after birth, the young lymphocytes develop self-tolerance and immunocompetence in their "programming organs" (thymus and bone marrow) and then populate the other lymphoid tissues. Upon meeting "their" antigens, the T and B cells complete their development to fully mature immune cells.

A CLOSER LOOK

AIDS: THE MODERN DAY PLAGUE

In October 1347, several ships made port in Sicily, and within days all the sailors they carried were dead of bubonic plague. By the end of the fourteenth century, approximately 25 percent of the population of Europe had been wiped out by this "black death." In January 1987, the U.S. Secretary of Health and Human Services warned that acquired immune deficiency syndrome, or AIDS, might be the plague of our time. These are strong words. Are they true?

Although AIDS was first identified in this country in 1981 among homosexual men and intravenous drug users of both sexes, it had begun afflicting the heterosexual population of Africa several years earlier. AIDS is characterized by severe weight loss, night sweats, swollen lymph nodes, and increasingly frequent infections, including a rare type of pneumonia called *pneumocystis pneumonia*, an eye infection called cytomegalovirus retinitis, and the bizarre malignancy *Kaposi's sarcoma*, a cancerlike condition of blood vessels evidenced by purple lesions of the skin. Some AIDS victims develop slurred speech and severe dementia. The course of untreated AIDS is grim and thus far inescapable, finally ending in complete debilitation and death from cancer or overwhelming infection.

> ❝ *The whole immune system is turned topsy-turvy.* ❞

AIDS is caused by a virus transmitted in blood, semen, and possibly vaginal secretions. Most commonly, the virus enters the body via blood transfusions or blood-contaminated needles and during intimate sexual contact in which the mucosa is torn or where open lesions caused by sexually transmitted diseases allow the virus access to the blood. It is *not* transmitted by casual contact, because the virus dries and dies when exposed to air.

The virus, named HIV (human immunodeficiency virus), specifically targets and destroys helper T cells, resulting in severe depression of cell-mediated immunity. Without helper T cells, the cytotoxic T cells and B cells cannot be activated or maintained, and the whole immune system is turned topsy-turvy. It is now clear that the virus multiplies steadily in the lymph nodes throughout most of the chronic asymptomatic period. Symptomatic AIDS appears when the lymph nodes can no longer contain the virus and the immune system collapses. The virus

A new HIV virus emerges from an infected human cell.

also invades the brain, which accounts for the dementia of some AIDS patients. Although there are exceptions, most AIDS victims have died within a few months to 8 years after diagnosis.

The years since 1981 have witnessed a global AIDS epidemic—worldwide, the number of people infected with the HIV virus jumped from 10 million in 1994 to more than 40 million people in 2005. Almost 90 percent of them live in the developing countries of Asia and southern Africa. During 2005, 5 million people were newly infected. In other words, about 1 of every 200 people on the planet now carries the virus. Furthermore, because there is a 6-month "window" during which antibodies may develop after exposure to HIV, there are probably 100 asymptomatic carriers of the virus for every newly diagnosed case. Moreover, the disease has a long incubation period (from a few months to 10 years) between exposure and the appearance of clinical symptoms. The Centers for Disease Control and Prevention (CDC) estimate that nearly 950,000 U.S. residents are HIV infected and that 25 percent of them do not realize it.

Not only has the number of identified cases jumped explosively in the at-risk populations, but the "face of AIDS" is changing. Victims have begun to include people who do not belong to the original high-risk group. Before reliable testing of donated blood was available, some people contracted the virus from blood transfusions. Hemophiliacs have been especially vulnerable because the blood factors they need are isolated from pooled blood donations. Although manufacturers began taking measures to kill the virus in 1984, by then an estimated 60 percent of the hemophiliacs in the United States were already infected. The virus can also be transmitted from an infected mother to her fetus. Although homosexual men still account for the bulk of cases transmitted by sexual contact, more and more heterosexuals are contracting this disease. Particularly disturbing is the near-epidemic increase in diagnosed cases among teenagers and young adults. AIDS is now the fifth leading killer of all Americans ages 25 to 44.

Large-city hospitals are seeing more AIDS patients daily, and statistics reporting the number of cases in inner-city ghettos, where intravenous drug use is the chief means of AIDS transmission, are alarming. Currently the drug-abusing community accounts for 25 percent of all AIDS cases. Furthermore, 75 percent of AIDS cases in newborns occur where drug abuse abounds.

Diagnostic tests to identify carriers of the AIDS virus are increasingly sophisticated. For example, a urine test provides a painless alternative to the standard HIV tests. However, no sure cure has yet been found. Over 100 drugs are now in the U.S. Food and Drug Administration pipeline, and more than 20 vaccines are undergoing clinical trials.

Now clinically available are several antiviral drugs (named like alphabet soups) that act by inhibiting the enzymes that the HIV virus needs to multiply in the body. The *reverse transcriptase inhibitors,* such as AZT, were early on the scene. AZT has been followed by others, including ddI, ddC, d4T, and 3TC. In late 1995 and early 1996, *protease inhibitors* (saquinavir, ritonavir, and others) were approved. Thus far, it appears that combination therapy using drugs from each class delivers a one-two punch to the HIV virus, at least for a while. Combination therapy postpones drug resistance (a problem with single drug therapy using AZT alone) and substantially reduces the amount of HIV virus in the blood while boosting the number of helper T cells. Sadly, the treatments are beginning to fail in about half of those treated, and even short breaks in treatment allow viral levels to soar. New hope comes from the integrase group of new drugs that block HIV's entry into DNA of the target helper cells and from new generations of AIDs vaccines.

Given the poor prognosis of AIDS, preventing infection is the way to go. Perhaps, as urged in the media, the best defense is to practice "safer sex" by using condoms and knowing one's sexual partner's history, but the only foolproof alternative is sexual abstinence.

SYSTEMS IN SYNC

HOMEOSTATIC RELATIONSHIPS BETWEEN THE
LYMPHATIC SYSTEM AND OTHER BODY SYSTEMS

Nervous System
- The lymphatic vessels pick up leaked plasma fluid and proteins in the peripheral nervous system structures; immune cells protect peripheral nervous system structures from specific pathogens
- The nervous system innervates larger lymphatic vessels; the brain helps regulate immune response

Endocrine System
- Lymphatic vessels pick up leaked fluids and proteins; lymph distributes hormones; immune cells protect endocrine organs from pathogens
- The thymus produces hormones that promote development of lymphatic organs and "program" T lymphocytes

Lymphatic System/Immunity

Respiratory System
- Lymphatic vessels pick up leaked fluid and proteins from respiratory organs; immune cells protect respiratory organs from specific pathogens; plasma cells in the respiratory mucosa secrete IgA to prevent pathogen invasion of deeper tissues
- The lungs provide oxygen needed by lymphoid/immune cells and eliminate carbon dioxide; the pharynx houses some lymphoid organs (tonsils); the respiratory "pump" aids lymph flow

Digestive System
- Lymphatic vessels pick up leaked fluids and proteins from digestive organs; lymph transports some products of fat digestion to the blood; lymphoid nodules in the wall of the intestine prevent invasion of pathogens
- The digestive system digests and absorbs nutrients needed by cells of lymphatic organs; gastric acidity inhibits pathogens' entry into blood

Muscular System
- Lymphatic vessels pick up leaked fluid and proteins from skeletal muscle; immune cells protect muscles from specific pathogens
- The skeletal muscle "pump" aids the flow of lymph; muscles protect superficial lymph nodes

Cardiovascular System
- Lymphatic vessels pick up leaked plasma and proteins; spleen destroys aged RBCs, stores iron, and removes debris from blood; immune cells protect cardiovascular organs from specific pathogens
- Blood is the source of lymph; lymphatics develop from veins; blood provides the route for circulation of immune elements

Urinary System
- Lymphatic vessels pick up leaked fluid and proteins from urinary organs; immune cells protect urinary organs from specific pathogens
- Urinary system eliminates wastes and maintains homeostatic water/acid-base/electrolyte balance of the blood for immune cell functioning; urine flushes some pathogens out of the body

Reproductive System
- Lymphatic vessels pick up leaked fluid and proteins from reproductive organs; immune cells protect the organs from specific pathogens
- Acidity of vaginal secretions prevents bacterial multiplication

Integumentary System
- Lymphatic vessels pick up leaked plasma fluid and proteins from the dermis; lymphocytes in lymph enhance the skin's protective role by defending against specific pathogens
- The skin's keratinized epithelium provides a mechanical barrier to pathogens; acid pH of skin secretions inhibits growth of bacteria on skin

Skeletal System
- Lymphatic vessels pick up leaked plasma fluid and proteins from the periostea; immune cells protect bones from specific pathogens
- The bones house hematopoietic tissue (red marrow) which produces the lymphocytes (and macrophages) that populate the lymphoid organs and provide body immunity

Although the ability of our adaptive immune system to recognize foreign substances is determined by our genes, the nervous system may help to control the activity of the immune response. The immune response is definitely impaired in individuals who are under severe stress—for example, in those mourning the death of a beloved family member or friend. Our immune system normally serves us well throughout our lifetime, until old age. But during the later years, its efficiency begins to wane. As a result, the body becomes less able to fight infections and destroy cells that have become cancerous. Additionally, we become more susceptible to both autoimmune and immunodeficiency diseases.

SUMMARY

Media study tools that provide additional review of key topics of Chapter 12 are referenced below.

> **IP** = *InterActive Physiology*
> **WEB** = The A&P Place

PART I: THE LYMPHATIC SYSTEM (pp. 403–408)

1. The lymphatic system consists of the lymphatic vessels, lymph nodes, and certain other lymphoid organs in the body.

    WEB Exercise: Chapter 12, Lymphatic Collecting Vessels and Regional Lymph Nodes.

2. Extremely porous blind-ended lymphatic capillaries pick up excess tissue fluid leaked from the blood capillaries. The fluid (lymph) flows into the larger lymphatics and finally into the blood vascular system through the right lymphatic duct and the left thoracic duct.

3. Lymph transport is aided by the muscular and respiratory pumps and by contraction of smooth muscle in the walls of the lymphatic vessels.

4. Lymph nodes are clustered along lymphatic vessels, and the lymphatic stream flows through them. Lymph nodes serve as multiplication sites for agranular WBCs (lymphocytes); phagocytic cells within them remove bacteria, viruses, and the like from the lymph stream before it is returned to the blood.

5. Other lymphoid organs include the tonsils (in the throat), which remove bacteria trying to enter the digestive or respiratory tracts; the thymus, a programming region for some lymphocytes of the body; Peyer's patches, which prevent bacteria in the intestine from penetrating deeper into the body; and the spleen, a RBC graveyard and blood reservoir.

PART II: BODY DEFENSES (pp. 408–431)

Innate Body Defenses (pp. 409–415)

1. Surface membranes (skin and mucous membranes) provide mechanical barriers to pathogens. Some produce secretions and/or have structural modifications that enhance their defensive effects; the skin's acidity, lysozyme, mucus, keratin, and ciliated cells are examples.

2. Phagocytes (macrophages and neutrophils) engulf and destroy pathogens that penetrate epithelial barriers. This process is enhanced when the pathogen's surface is altered by attachment of antibodies and/or complement.

3. Natural killer cells are nonimmune cells that act nonspecifically to lyse virus-infected and malignant cells.

4. The inflammatory response prevents spread of harmful agents, disposes of pathogens and dead tissue cells, and promotes healing. Protective leukocytes enter the area; fibrin walls off the area; and tissue repair occurs.

5. When complement (a group of plasma proteins) becomes fixed on the membrane of a foreign cell, lysis of the target cell occurs. Complement also enhances phagocytosis and the inflammatory and immune responses.

6. Interferon is a group of proteins synthesized by virus-infected cells and certain immune cells. It prevents viruses from multiplying in other body cells.

7. Fever enhances the fight against infectious microorganisms by increasing metabolism (which speeds up repair processes) and by causing the liver and spleen to store iron and zinc (which bacteria need for multiplication).

Adaptive Body Defenses (pp. 415–431)

1. The immune system recognizes something as foreign and acts to inactivate or remove it. Immune response is antigen-specific, is systemic, and has memory. The two arms of immune response are humoral immunity (mediated by antibodies) and cellular immunity (mediated by living cells, the lymphocytes).

2. Antigens

   a. Antigens are large, complex molecules (or parts of them) recognized as foreign by the body. Foreign proteins are the strongest antigens.

   b. Complete antigens provoke an immune response and bind with products of that response (antibodies or sensitized lymphocytes).

   c. Incomplete antigens, or haptens, are small molecules that are unable to cause an immune response by themselves but do so when they bind to body proteins and the complex is recognized as foreign.

3. Cells of the adaptive defense system: An overview

   a. Two main cell populations, lymphocytes and macrophages, are involved in adaptive defense.

   b. Lymphocytes arise from hemocytoblasts of bone marrow. T cells develop immunocompetence in the thymus and oversee cell-mediated immunity. B cells develop immunocompetence in bone marrow and provide humoral immunity. Immunocompetent lymphocytes seed lymphoid organs, where antigen challenge occurs, and circulate through blood, lymph, and lymphoid organs.

   c. Immunocompetence is signaled by the appearance of antigen-specific receptors on surfaces of lymphocytes.

   d. Macrophages arise from monocytes produced in bone marrow. They phagocytize pathogens and present parts of the antigens on their surfaces, for recognition by T cells.

4. Humoral (antibody-mediated) immune response

   a. Clonal selection of B cells occurs when antigens bind to their receptors, causing them to proliferate. Most clone members become plasma cells, which secrete antibodies. This is called the *primary immune response*.

   b. Other clone members become memory B cells, capable of mounting a rapid attack against the same antigen in subsequent meetings (*secondary immune responses*). These cells provide immunological "memory."

   c. Active humoral immunity is acquired during an infection or via vaccination and provides immunological memory. Passive immunity is conferred when a donor's antibodies are injected into the bloodstream or when the mother's antibodies cross the placenta. It does not provide immunological memory.

   d. Basic antibody structure

      (1) Antibodies are proteins produced by sensitized B cells or plasma cells in response to an antigen, and they are capable of binding with that antigen.

      (2) An antibody is composed of four polypeptide chains (two heavy and two light) that form a T- or Y-shaped molecule.

      (3) Each polypeptide chain has a variable and a constant region. Variable regions form antigen-binding sites, one on each arm of the T or Y. Constant regions determine antibody function and class.

      (4) Five classes of antibodies exist: IgA, IgG, IgM, IgD, IgE. They differ structurally and functionally.

      (5) Antibody functions include complement fixation, neutralization, precipitation, and agglutination.

      (6) Monoclonal antibodies are pure preparations of a single antibody type useful in diagnosing various infectious disorders and cancer and in treating certain cancers.

5. Cellular (cell-mediated) immune response

   a. T cells are sensitized by binding simultaneously to an antigen and a self-protein displayed on the surface of a macrophage or another type of antigen-presenting cell. Clonal selection occurs, and clone members differentiate into effector T cells or memory T cells.

   b. There are several different classes of T cells. Cytotoxic (killer) T cells directly attack and lyse infected and cancerous cells. Helper T cells interact directly with B cells bound to antigens. They also liberate cytokines, chemicals that enhance the killing activity of macrophages, attract other leukocytes, or act as helper factors that stimulate activity of B cells and cytotoxic T cells. A special subgroup of helper T cells, cytotoxic T cells, and macrophages promote a delayed allergic reaction. Regulatory T cells terminate the normal immune response by releasing suppressor chemicals.

6. Organ transplants include autografts, isografts, allografts, and xenografts. The most usual graft is an allograft. Blood group and tissue matching are done to ensure the best match possible, and organ transplant is followed by immunosuppressive therapy.

7. Disorders of immunity

    a. Autoimmune disease occurs when the body's self-tolerance breaks down, and antibodies and/or T cells attack the body's own tissues. Most forms of autoimmune disease result from inefficient lymphocyte programming in the fetus, changes in structure of self-antigens or appearance of formerly hidden self-antigens in blood, and cross-reactions with self-antigens and antibodies formed against foreign antigens.

    b. In allergy or hypersensitivity, the immune system overreacts to an otherwise harmless antigen, and tissue destruction occurs. Immediate (acute) hypersensitivity, as seen in hay fever, hives, and anaphylaxis, is due to IgE antibodies. Delayed hypersensitivity (for example, contact dermatitis) reflects activity of T cells, macrophages, and lymphokines.

    WEB Exercise: Chapter 12, Events in Allergic Reaction.

    c. Immunodeficiencies result from abnormalities in any immune element. Most serious is severe combined immunodeficiency disease (a congenital disease) and AIDS, an acquired immunodeficiency disease caused by a virus that attacks and cripples the helper T cells.

PART III: DEVELOPMENTAL ASPECTS OF THE LYMPHATIC SYSTEM AND BODY DEFENSES (pp. 431, 435)

1. Lymphatic vessels form by budding off veins. The thymus gland is the first lymphoid organ to appear in the embryo. Other lymphoid organs remain relatively undeveloped until after birth.

2. The immune response develops around the time of birth.

3. The ability of immunocompetent cells to recognize foreign antigens is genetically determined. Stress appears to interfere with normal immune response.

4. Efficiency of immune response wanes in old age, and infections, cancer, immunodeficiencies, and autoimmune diseases become more prevalent.

REVIEW QUESTIONS

Multiple Choice

More than one choice may apply.

1. Lymph capillaries
    a. are open-ended, like drinking straws.
    b. have continuous tight junctions, like the capillaries of the brain.
    c. contain endothelial cells separated by flaplike valves that can open wide.
    d. have special barriers that stop cancer cells from entering.

2. Which parts of the lymph node show increased activity when antibody production is high?
    a. Germinal centers   c. Medullary cords
    b. Outer follicle   d. Medullary sinuses

3. Which of the following connect to the lymph node at the hilum?
    a. Afferent lymphatic vessels
    b. Efferent lymphatic vessels
    c. Trabeculae
    d. Anchoring filaments

4. Which of the following are part of MALT?
    a. Tonsils
    b. Thymus
    c. Peyer's patches
    d. Any lymphoid tissue along the digestive tract

5. Developmentally, embryonic lymphatic vessels are most closely associated with the
    a. veins.   c. nerves.
    b. arteries.   d. thymus gland.

6. Which of the following are among the most common indicators of inflammation?
    a. Phagocytosis.   b. Leukocytosis.
    b. Edema.   d. Pain.

7. Chemical mediators of inflammation include
    a. interferon.   c. histamine.
    b. complement.   d. antibodies.

8. Against which of the following will interferon do some good?
    a. Infection of body cells by a virus
    b. Circulating free viruses
    c. Some types of cancer
    d. Bacterial infection

9. Which of these antibody classes is usually arranged as a pentamer?

a. IgG   c. IgA

b. IgM   d. IgD

10. Which parts of an antibody molecule are different for an IgG antibody than for an IgM antibody that attacks the same antigen?

a. Heavy chain constant region

b. Heavy chain variable region

c. Light chain constant region

d. Light chain variable region

11. Which of the following antibody capabilities causes a transfusion reaction with A or B erythrocyte antigens?

a. Neutralization   c. Complement fixation

b. Precipitation   d. Agglutination

12. Which of the following is/are examples of autoimmune disease?

a. Type 1 diabetes   c. Graves' disease

b. Multiple sclerosis   d. Rheumatoid arthritis

13. The main cellular target of the HIV virus that causes AIDS is

a. helper T cells.   c. macrophages.

b. cytotoxic T cells.   d. B cells.

Short Answer Essay

14. What is the most important function of the lymph nodes?

15. Compare and contrast blood, interstitial fluid, and lymph.

16. What is the special role of the tonsils? the spleen?

17. Besides acting as mechanical barriers, the skin and mucosae of the body contribute to body protection in other ways. Cite the common body locations and the importance of mucus, lysozyme, keratin, acid pH, and cilia.

18. What is complement? Besides bacterial lysis, what are some of the roles of complement?

19. Interferons are referred to as antiviral proteins. What stimulates their production, and how do they protect uninfected cells?

20. Define *immune response.*

21. What is the difference between a complete antigen and an incomplete antigen (hapten)?

22. Differentiate clearly between humoral and cellular immunity.

23. Although the immune system has two arms, it has been said, "No T cells, no immunity." How is this so?

24. Define *immunocompetence.* What indicates that a B cell or T cell has developed immunocompetence? Where does the "programming phase" occur in the case of B cells?

25. Binding of antigens to receptors of immunocompetent lymphocytes leads to clonal selection. Describe the process of clonal selection. What nonlymphocyte cell is a central actor in this process, and what is its function?

26. Name the cell types that would be present in a B cell clone, and give the function of each type.

27. Describe the specific roles of helper, cytotoxic, and regulatory T cells in cell-mediated immunity. Which is thought to be disabled in AIDS?

28. Compare and contrast a primary and a secondary immune response. Which is more rapid, and why?

29. Describe the structure of an antibody, and explain the importance of its variable and constant regions.

30. Name the five classes of immunoglobulins. Which is most likely to be found attached to a B cell membrane? Which is most abundant in plasma? Which is important in allergic responses? Which is the first Ig to be released during the primary response? Which can cross the placental barrier?

31. How do antibodies help to defend the body?

32. Distinguish between immediate types of allergy and delayed allergic reactions relative to cause and consequences.

33. What events can result in the loss of self-tolerance and autoimmune disease?

34. Would lack of memory B cells for a particular antigen impact the primary or secondary humoral response?

CRITICAL THINKING AND CLINICAL APPLICATION QUESTIONS

35. As an infant receives her first dose of oral polio vaccine, the nurse explains to her parents that the vaccine is a preparation of weakened virus. What type of immunity will the infant develop?

36. Some people with a deficit of IgA exhibit recurrent paranasal sinus and respiratory tract infections. Explain these symptoms.

37. Mr. James, an 80-year-old man, is grumbling about having to receive a flu shot every year. Flu viruses have a high mutation rate (undergo rapid genetic changes), which results in the appearance of new proteins on the flu virus's "coat." How does this help explain the need to get a flu shot each year?

38. Mrs. Morrow, a 59-year-old woman, has undergone a left radical mastectomy (removal of the left breast and left axillary lymph nodes and vessels). Her left arm is severely swollen and painful, and she is unable to raise it more than shoulder height. (a) Explain her signs and symptoms. (b) Can she expect relief from these symptoms in time? How so?

39. Lymphocytes continuously circulate through the body using blood and lymph as their transport vehicles. What is the importance of this recirculation behavior?

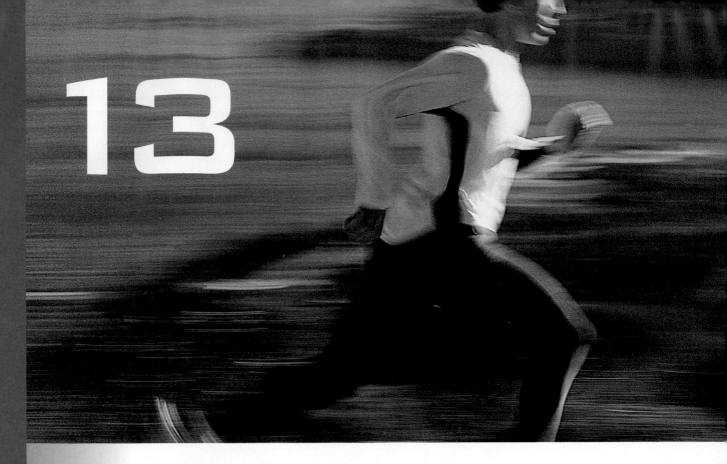

13

The Respiratory System

YOUR GOALS

After completing this chapter, you will have a working knowledge of the functions of the respiratory system and will have mastered the objectives listed below.

FUNCTION PREVIEW

- The respiratory system supplies oxygen to the blood while removing carbon dioxide.

OBJECTIVE CHECKLIST

Functional Anatomy of the Respiratory System   (pp. 441–448)

➤ Name the organs forming the respiratory passageway from the nasal cavity to the alveoli of the lungs (or identify them on a diagram or model), and describe the function of each.

➤ Describe several protective mechanisms of the respiratory system.

➤ Describe the structure and function of the lungs and the pleural coverings.

Respiratory Physiology   (pp. 448–460)

➤ Define *cellular respiration, external respiration, internal respiration, pulmonary ventilation, expiration,* and *inspiration.*

➤ Explain how the respiratory muscles cause volume changes that lead to air flow into and out of the lungs (breathing).

➤ Define the following respiratory volumes: *tidal volume, vital capacity, expiratory reserve volume, inspiratory reserve volume,* and *residual air.*

➤ Name several nonrespiratory air movements, and explain how they modify or differ from normal respiratory air movements.

➤ Describe the process of gas exchanges in the lungs and tissues.

➤ Describe how oxygen and carbon dioxide are transported in the blood.

➤ Name the brain areas involved in control of respiration.

➤ Name several physical factors that influence respiratory rate.

➤ Explain the relative importance of oxygen and carbon dioxide in modifying breathing rate and depth.

➤ Explain why it is not possible to stop breathing voluntarily.

➤ Define *apnea, dyspnea, hyperventilation, hypoventilation,* and *chronic obstructive pulmonary disease (COPD).*

Respiratory Disorders   (pp. 460–461)

➤ Describe symptoms and probable causes of COPD and lung cancer.

Developmental Aspects of the Respiratory System   (pp. 461, 464)

➤ Describe normal changes that occur in respiratory system functioning from infancy to old age.

The trillions of cells in the body require an abundant and continuous supply of oxygen to carry out their vital functions. We cannot "do without oxygen" for even a little while, as we can without food or water. Furthermore, as cells use oxygen, they give off carbon dioxide, a waste product the body must get rid of.

The *cardiovascular* and *respiratory systems* share responsibility for supplying the body with oxygen and disposing of carbon dioxide. The respiratory system organs oversee the gas exchanges that occur between the blood and the external environment. Using blood as the transporting fluid, the cardiovascular system organs transport respiratory gases between the lungs and the tissue cells. If either system fails, body cells begin to die from oxygen starvation and accumulation of carbon dioxide.

Functional Anatomy of the Respiratory System

The organs of the **respiratory system** include the nose, pharynx, larynx, trachea, bronchi and their smaller branches, and the lungs, which contain the *alveoli* (al-ve′o-li), or terminal air sacs. Because gas exchanges with the blood happen *only* in the alveoli, the other respiratory system structures are really just conducting passageways that allow air to reach the lungs. However, these passageways have another, very important job. They purify, humidify, and warm incoming air. Thus, the air finally reaching the lungs has many fewer irritants (such as dust or bacteria) than when it entered the system, and it is warm and damp. As the respiratory system organs are described in detail next, locate each on Figure 13.1.

The Nose

The **nose,** whether "pug" or "ski-jump" in shape, is the only externally visible part of the respiratory system. During breathing, air enters the nose by passing through the **nostrils,** or **nares.** The interior of the nose consists of the **nasal cavity,** divided by a midline **nasal septum.** The *olfactory receptors* for the sense of smell are located in the mucosa in the slitlike superior part of the nasal cavity, just beneath the ethmoid bone. The rest of the mucosa lining the nasal cavity, called the *respiratory mucosa,* rests on a rich network of thin-walled veins that warms the air as it flows past. (Because of the superficial location of these blood vessels, nosebleeds are common and often profuse.)

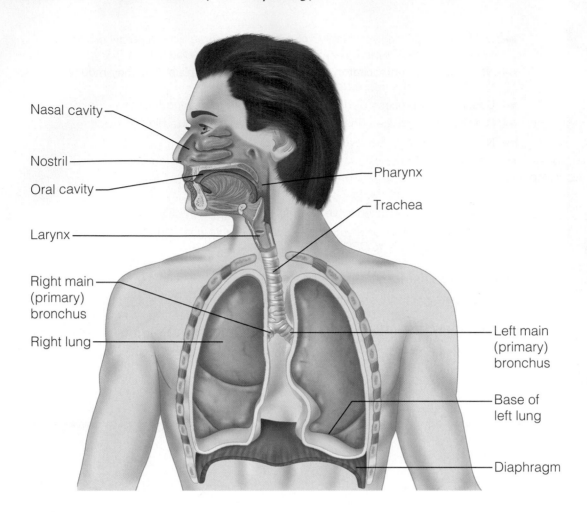

FIGURE 13.1   **The major respiratory organs shown in relation to surrounding structures.**

In addition, the sticky mucus produced by the mucosa's glands moistens the air and traps incoming bacteria and other foreign debris, and lysozyme enzymes in the mucus destroy bacteria chemically. The ciliated cells of the nasal mucosa create a gentle current that moves the sheet of contaminated mucus posteriorly toward the throat (pharynx), where it is swallowed and digested by stomach juices. We are usually unaware of this important ciliary action, but when the external temperature is extremely cold, these cilia become sluggish, allowing mucus to accumulate in the nasal cavity and to dribble outward through the nostrils. This helps explain why you might have a "runny" nose on a crisp, wintry day.

As shown in Figures 13.1 and 13.2, the lateral walls of the nasal cavity are uneven owing to three mucosa-covered projections, or lobes, called **conchae** (kong'ke), which greatly increase the surface area of the mucosa exposed to the air. The conchae also increase the air turbulence in the nasal cavity. As the air swirls through the twists and turns, inhaled particles are deflected onto the mucus-coated surfaces, where they are trapped and prevented from reaching the lungs.

The nasal cavity is separated from the oral cavity below by a partition, the **palate** (pal'et). Anteriorly, where the palate is supported by bone, is the **hard palate;** the unsupported posterior part is the **soft palate.**

HOMEOSTATIC IMBALANCE

The genetic defect **cleft palate** (failure of the bones forming the palate to fuse medially) results in breathing difficulty as well as problems with oral cavity functions such as chewing and speaking. ▲

The nasal cavity is surrounded by a ring of **paranasal sinuses** located in the frontal, sphenoid, ethmoid, and maxillary bones. (See Figure 5.10,

Posterior nasal aperture

Nasopharynx

Pharyngeal tonsil

Opening of pharyngotympanic tube

Uvula

Oropharynx

Palatine tonsil

Lingual tonsil

Laryngopharynx

Esophagus

Frontal sinus

Sphenoid sinus

Cribriform plate of ethmoid bone

Nasal cavity

Superior concha

Middle concha

Inferior concha

Nostrils (nares)

Hard palate

Soft palate

Tongue

Hyoid bone

Larynx

Epiglottis

Thyroid cartilage

Vocal fold

Cricoid cartilage

Trachea

FIGURE 13.2   Basic anatomy of the upper respiratory tract, sagittal section.

p. 147.) The sinuses lighten the skull, and they act as resonance chambers for speech. They also produce mucus, which drains into the nasal cavities. The suctioning effect created by nose blowing helps to drain the sinuses. The *nasolacrimal ducts,* which drain tears from the eyes, also empty into the nasal cavities.

HOMEOSTATIC IMBALANCE

Cold viruses and various allergens can cause **rhinitis** (ri-ni′tis), inflammation of the nasal mucosa. The excessive mucus produced results in nasal congestion and postnasal drip. Because the nasal mucosa is continuous throughout the respiratory tract and extends tentacle-like into the nasolacrimal (tear) ducts and paranasal sinuses, nasal cavity infections often spread to those regions as well. **Sinusitis,** or sinus inflammation, is difficult to treat and can cause marked changes in voice quality. When the passageways connecting the sinuses to the nasal cavity are blocked with mucus or infectious matter, the air in the sinus cavities is absorbed. The

result is a partial vacuum and a **sinus headache** localized over the inflamed area. ▲

Pharynx

The **pharynx** (far′inks) is a muscular passageway about 13 cm (5 inches) long that vaguely resembles a short length of red garden hose. Commonly called the *throat,* the pharynx serves as a common passageway for food and air (Figures 13.1 and 13.2). It is continuous with the nasal cavity anteriorly via the **posterior nasal aperture.**

Air enters the superior portion, the **nasopharynx** (na″zo-far′inks), from the nasal cavity and then descends through the **oropharynx** (o″ro-far′inks) and **laryngopharynx** (lah-ring″go-far′inks) to enter the larynx below. Food enters the mouth and then travels along with air through the oropharynx and laryngopharynx. But instead of entering the larynx, food is directed into the *esophagus* (ĕ-sof′ah-gus) posteriorly.

The *pharyngotympanic tubes,* which drain the middle ear, open into the nasopharynx. The mucosae of these two regions are continuous, so ear infections such as *otitis media* (o-ti'tis me'de-ah) may follow a sore throat or other types of pharyngeal infections.

Clusters of lymphatic tissue called *tonsils* are also found in the pharynx. The **pharyngeal** (far-rin'je-al) **tonsil,** often called *adenoid,* is located high in the nasopharynx. The **palatine tonsils** are in the oropharynx at the end of the soft palate, as are the **lingual tonsils,** which lie at the base of the tongue. The role of the tonsils in body protection is described in Chapter 12.

HOMEOSTATIC IMBALANCE

If the pharyngeal tonsil becomes inflamed and swollen (as during a bacterial infection), it obstructs the nasopharynx and forces the person to breathe through the mouth. In mouth breathing, air is not properly moistened, warmed, or filtered before reaching the lungs. Many children seem to have almost continuous **tonsillitis.** Years ago the belief was that the tonsils, though protective, were more trouble than they were worth in such cases, and they were routinely removed. Now, because of the widespread use of antibiotics, this is no longer necessary (or true). ▲

Larynx

The **larynx** (lar'inks), or *voice box,* routes air and food into the proper channels and plays a role in speech. Located inferior to the pharynx (see Figures 13.1 and 13.2), it is formed by eight rigid hyaline cartilages and a spoon-shaped flap of elastic cartilage, the epiglottis (ep"ĭ-glot'tis). The largest of the hyaline cartilages is the shield-shaped **thyroid cartilage,** which protrudes anteriorly and is commonly called the *Adam's apple.* Sometimes referred to as the "guardian of the airways," the **epiglottis** protects the superior opening of the larynx. When we are not swallowing, the epiglottis does not restrict the passage of air into the lower respiratory passages. When we swallow food or fluids, the situation changes dramatically; the larynx is pulled upward and the epiglottis tips, forming a lid over the opening of the larynx. This routes food into the esophagus, or food tube, posteriorly. If anything other than air enters the larynx, a *cough reflex* is triggered to expel the substance and prevent it from continuing into the lungs. Because this protective reflex does *not* work when we are unconscious, it is never a good idea to try to give fluids to an unconscious person when attempting to revive him or her.

- Palpate your larynx by placing your hand midway on the anterior surface of your neck. Swallow. Can you feel the larynx rising as you swallow?

Part of the mucous membrane of the larynx forms a pair of folds, called the **vocal folds,** or **true vocal cords,** which vibrate with expelled air. This ability of the vocal folds to vibrate allows us to speak. The slitlike passageway between the vocal folds is the **glottis.**

Trachea

Air entering the **trachea** (tra'ke-ah), or *windpipe,* from the larynx travels down its length (10–12 cm, or about 4 inches) to the level of the fifth thoracic vertebra, which is approximately midchest (see Figure 13.1).

The trachea is fairly rigid because its walls are reinforced with C-shaped rings of **hyaline cartilage.** These rings serve a double purpose. The open parts of the rings abut the *esophagus* and allow it to expand anteriorly when we swallow a large piece of food. The solid portions support the trachea walls and keep it *patent,* or open, in spite of the pressure changes that occur during breathing.

HOMEOSTATIC IMBALANCE

Because the trachea is the only way air can enter the lungs, tracheal obstruction is life-threatening. Many people have suffocated after choking on a piece of food that suddenly closed off the trachea (or the glottis of the larynx). The **Heimlich maneuver,** a procedure in which the air in a person's own lungs is used to "pop out," or expel, an obstructing piece of food, has saved many people from becoming victims of such "café coronaries." The Heimlich maneuver is simple to learn and easy to do. However, it is best learned by demonstration, because cracked ribs are a distinct possibility when it is done incorrectly. In some cases of obstructed breathing, an emergency *tracheostomy* (tra'ke-ost'o-me; surgical opening of the trachea) is done to provide an alternative route for air to reach the lungs. Individuals with tracheostomy tubes in place form huge amounts of mucus the first few days because of irritation to the trachea. Thus, they must be suctioned frequently during this time to prevent the mucus from pooling in their lungs. ▲

The trachea is lined with a ciliated mucosa (Figure 13.3). The cilia beat continuously and in a

In what direction is the power stroke of these cilia directed—superiorly toward the mouth or inferiorly toward the lungs?

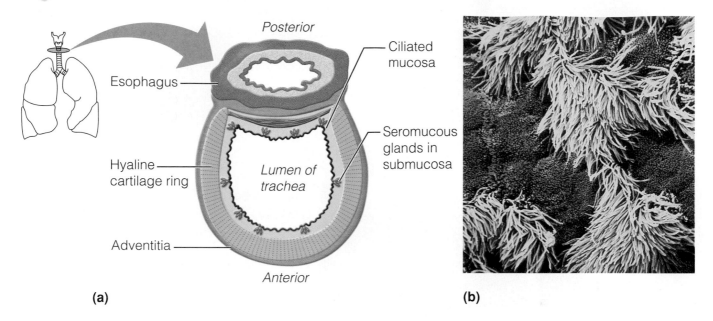

(a)   **(b)**

FIGURE 13.3 **Structural relationship of the trachea and esophagus.** **(a)** Cross-sectional view. **(b)** Cilia in the trachea. The cilia are the yellow, grasslike projections surrounded by the mucus-secreting goblet cells, which exhibit short microvilli (orange). (Scanning electron micrograph, 13,500×.)

direction opposite to that of the incoming air. They propel mucus, loaded with dust particles and other debris, away from the lungs to the throat, where it can be swallowed or spat out.

HOMEOSTATIC IMBALANCE

Smoking inhibits ciliary activity and ultimately destroys the cilia. Without these cilia, coughing is the only means of preventing mucus from accumulating in the lungs. Smokers with respiratory congestion should avoid medications that inhibit the cough reflex. ▲

▶ DID YOU GET IT?

1. Why is nose breathing preferable to mouth breathing?

2. What is the specific protective function of the cilia in the trachea?

For answers, see Appendix D.

  Superiorly toward the mouth to prevent unwanted substances from entering the lungs.

Main Bronchi

The right and left **main (primary) bronchi** (brong'ki) are formed by the division of the trachea. Each main bronchus runs obliquely before it plunges into the medial depression *(hilum)* of the lung on its own side (see Figures 13.1 and 13.4). The right main bronchus is wider, shorter, and straighter than the left. Consequently, it is the more common site for an inhaled foreign object to become lodged. By the time incoming air reaches the bronchi, it is warm, cleansed of most impurities, and well humidified. The smaller subdivisions of the main bronchi within the lungs are direct routes to the air sacs.

Lungs

The **lungs** are fairly large organs. They occupy the entire thoracic cavity except for the most central area, the **mediastinum** (me"de-as-ti'num), which houses the heart (in its inferior pericardial cavity region), the great blood vessels, bronchi, esophagus, and other organs (see Figure 13.4). The narrow superior portion of each lung, the **apex,** is just

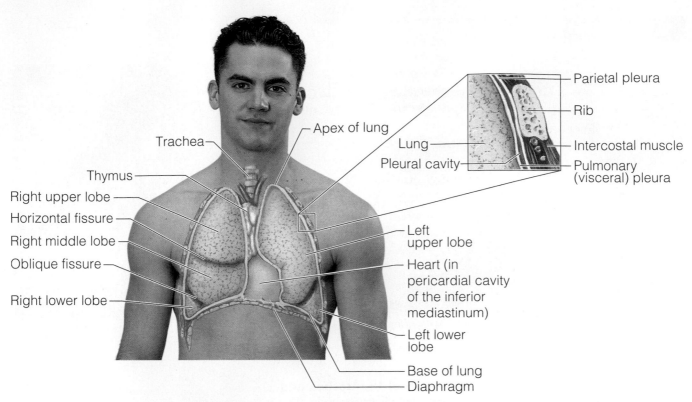

Parietal pleura

Rib

Lung

Intercostal muscle

Pleural cavity

Pulmonary (visceral) pleura

Apex of lung

Trachea

Thymus

Right upper lobe

Horizontal fissure

Right middle lobe

Oblique fissure

Right lower lobe

Left upper lobe

Heart (in pericardial cavity of the inferior mediastinum)

Left lower lobe

Base of lung

Diaphragm

(a) Anterior view of the thoracic cavity organs, showing the position of the lungs, which flank the heart laterally

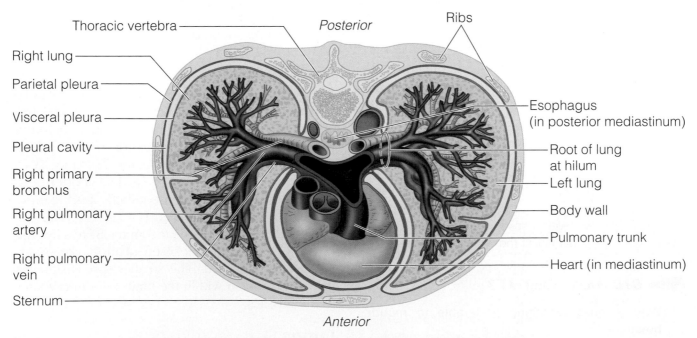

Thoracic vertebra

Posterior

Ribs

Right lung

Parietal pleura

Visceral pleura

Pleural cavity

Right primary bronchus

Right pulmonary artery

Right pulmonary vein

Sternum

Esophagus (in posterior mediastinum)

Root of lung at hilum

Left lung

Body wall

Pulmonary trunk

Heart (in mediastinum)

Anterior

(b) Transverse section through the thorax, showing the relationship of the major organs present in the thorax

FIGURE 13.4 **Anatomical relationships of organs in the thoracic cavity.**

deep to the clavicle. The broad lung area resting on the diaphragm is the **base.** Each lung is divided into lobes by fissures; the left lung has two lobes, and the right lung has three.

The surface of each lung is covered with a visceral serosa called the **pulmonary, or visceral, pleura** (ploor'ah), and the walls of the thoracic cavity are lined by the **parietal pleura.** The pleural membranes produce *pleural fluid,* a slippery serous secretion which allows the lungs to glide easily over the thorax wall during breathing movements and causes the two pleural layers to cling together. The pleurae can slide easily from side to side across one another, but they strongly resist being pulled apart. Consequently, the lungs are held tightly to the thorax wall, and the **pleural space** is more of a potential space than an actual one. As described shortly, this condition of tightly adhering pleural membranes is absolutely essential for normal breathing. Figure 13.4 shows the position of the pleura on the lungs and the thorax wall.

HOMEOSTATIC IMBALANCE

Pleurisy (ploo'rĭ-se), inflammation of the pleura, can be caused by decreased secretion of pleural fluid. The pleural surfaces become dry and rough, resulting in friction and stabbing pain with each breath. Conversely, the pleurae may produce excessive amounts of fluid, which exerts pressure on the lungs. This type of pleurisy hinders breathing movements, but it is much less painful than the dry rubbing type. ▲

After entering the lungs, the main bronchi subdivide into smaller and smaller branches (secondary and tertiary bronchi, and so on), finally ending in the smallest of the conducting passageways, the **bronchioles** (brong'ke-ōlz) (Figure 13.5). Because of this branching and rebranching of the respiratory passageways within the lungs, the network formed is often referred to as the *bronchial, or respiratory, tree.* All but the smallest branches have reinforcing cartilage in their walls.

The *terminal bronchioles* lead into *respiratory zone structures,* even smaller conduits that eventually terminate in **alveoli** (al-ve'o-li; *alveol* = small cavity), or air sacs. The **respiratory zone,** which includes the *respiratory bronchioles, alveolar ducts, alveolar sacs,* and alveoli, is the only site of gas exchange. All other respiratory passages are **conducting zone structures** that serve as conduits to and from the respiratory zone. There are millions of the clustered alveoli, which resemble bunches of grapes, and they make up the bulk of the lungs. Consequently, the lungs are mostly air spaces. The balance of the lung tissue, its *stroma,* is mainly elastic connective tissue that allows the lungs to recoil passively as we exhale. Thus, in spite of their relatively large size, the lungs weigh only about 2½ pounds, and they are soft and spongy.

The Respiratory Membrane

The walls of the alveoli are composed largely of a single, thin layer of squamous epithelial cells. The thinness of their walls is hard to imagine, but a sheet of tissue paper is much thicker. *Alveolar pores* connect neighboring air sacs and provide alternative routes for air to reach alveoli whose feeder bronchioles have been clogged by mucus or otherwise blocked. The external surfaces of the alveoli are covered with a "cobweb" of pulmonary capillaries. Together, the alveolar and capillary walls, their fused basement membranes, and occasional elastic fibers construct the **respiratory membrane (air-blood barrier),** which has gas (air) flowing past on one side and blood flowing past on the other (Figure 13.6). The gas exchanges occur by simple diffusion through the respiratory membrane—oxygen passing from the alveolar air into the capillary blood and carbon dioxide leaving the blood to enter the gas-filled alveoli. It has been estimated that the total gas exchange surface provided by the alveolar walls of a healthy man is 50 to 70 square meters, or approximately 40 times greater than the surface area of his skin.

The final line of defense for the respiratory system is in the alveoli. Remarkably efficient **alveolar macrophages,** sometimes called "dust cells," wander in and out of the alveoli picking up bacteria, carbon particles, and other debris. Also scattered amid the epithelial cells that form most of the alveolar walls are chunky cuboidal cells, which look very different from the squamous epithelial cells. The cuboidal cells produce a lipid (fat) molecule called *surfactant,* which coats the gas-exposed alveolar surfaces and is very important in lung function (as described on p. 461).

▶ *DID YOU GET IT?*

3. What is the order of the following parts of the human respiratory system from the site where air

(a) **Diagrammatic view of respiratory bronchioles, alveolar ducts, and alveoli**

(b) **Scanning electron micrograph (SEM) of human lung tissue, showing the final divisions of the respiratory tree** (475×)

FIGURE 13.5   **Respiratory zone structures.**

enters the nostrils to the site where air reaches the end passages of the lungs—bronchi, larynx, nasal cavity, alveoli, trachea, pharynx, bronchioles?

4. Which main bronchus is the most likely site for an inhaled object to become lodged? Why?

5. The lungs are mostly passageways and elastic tissue. What is the role of the passageways? Of the elastic tissue?

6. Name the four structures that make up the respiratory zone.

For answers, see Appendix D.

Respiratory Physiology

The major function of the respiratory system is to supply the body with oxygen and to dispose of carbon dioxide. To do this, at least four distinct events, collectively called **respiration,** must occur:

1. **Pulmonary ventilation.** Air must move into and out of the lungs so that the gases in the air sacs (alveoli) of the lungs are continuously refreshed. This process of pulmonary ventilation is commonly called **breathing.**

2. **External respiration.** Gas exchange (oxygen loading and carbon dioxide unloading) between

FIGURE 13.6 **Anatomy of the respiratory membrane (air-blood barrier).** The respiratory membrane is composed of squamous epithelial cells of the alveoli, the capillary endothelium, and the scant basement membranes between. Surfactant-secreting cells are also shown. Oxygen diffuses from the alveolar air into the pulmonary capillary blood; carbon dioxide diffuses from the pulmonary blood into the alveolus. Neighboring alveoli are connected by small pores.

the pulmonary blood and alveoli must take place. Remember that in **ex**ternal respiration, gas exchanges are being made between the blood and the body *exterior*.

3. **Respiratory gas transport.** Oxygen and carbon dioxide must be transported to and from the lungs and tissue cells of the body via the bloodstream.

4. **Internal respiration.** At systemic capillaries, gas exchanges must be made between the blood and tissue cells.* In **in**ternal respiration, gas exchanges are occurring between the blood and cells *inside* the body.

---

*The actual *use* of oxygen and production of carbon dioxide by tissue cells, that is, **cellular respiration,** is the cornerstone of all energy-producing chemical reactions in the body. Cellular respiration, which occurs in all body cells, is discussed in Chapter 14.

Although only the first two processes are the special responsibility of the respiratory system, all four processes are necessary for it to accomplish its goal of gas exchange. Thus, each process is described in turn next.

Mechanics of Breathing

Breathing, or pulmonary ventilation, is a completely mechanical process that depends on volume changes occurring in the thoracic cavity. Here is a rule to keep in mind about the mechanics of breathing: *Volume changes lead to pressure changes, which lead to the flow of gases to equalize the pressure.*

A gas, like a liquid, always conforms to the shape of its container. However, unlike a liquid, a gas *fills* its container. Therefore, in a large volume, the gas molecules will be far apart and the pressure (created by the gas molecules hitting each

Given that the lungs do not have any skeletal muscle, explain what causes them to inflate.

Changes in anterior-posterior and superior-inferior dimensions

Changes in lateral dimensions

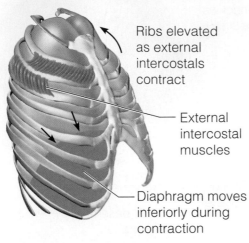

Ribs elevated as external intercostals contract

External intercostal muscles

Diaphragm moves inferiorly during contraction

(a) Inspiration: Air (gases) flows into the lungs

Ribs depressed as external intercostals relax

External intercostal muscles

Diaphragm moves superiorly as it relaxes

(b) Expiration: Air (gases) flows out of the lungs

Full inspiration

Expiration

FIGURE 13.7   Rib cage and diaphragm positions during breathing. (a) At the end of a normal inspiration: Chest is expanded laterally, rib cage is elevated, and diaphragm is depressed and flattened. Lungs are stretched to the larger thoracic volume, causing the intrapulmonary pressure to fall and air to flow into the lungs. **(b)** At the end of a normal expiration: Chest is depressed and the lateral dimension is reduced, rib cage is descended, and diaphragm is elevated and dome-shaped. Lungs recoil to smaller volume, intrapulmonary pressure rises, and air flows out of lung.

The enlargement of the thoracic cavity due to contraction of the diaphragm and intercostal muscles results in lower pressure in the lungs than outside the body. This difference in pressure leads to air flow into the lungs and to their expansion.

other and the walls of the container) will be low. If the volume is reduced, the gas molecules will be closer together, and the pressure will rise. Let's see how this relates to the two phases of breathing—**inspiration,** when air is flowing into the lungs, and **expiration,** when air is leaving the lungs.

Inspiration

When the inspiratory muscles, the **diaphragm** and **external intercostals,** contract, the size of the thoracic cavity increases. As the dome-shaped diaphragm contracts, it moves inferiorly and flattens out (is depressed). As a result, the superior-inferior dimension (height) of the thoracic cavity increases. Contraction of the external intercostals lifts the rib cage and thrusts the sternum forward, which increases the anteroposterior and lateral dimensions of the thorax (Figure 13.7a). The lungs adhere tightly to the thorax walls (because of the surface tension of the fluid between the pleural membranes), so they are stretched to the new, larger size of the thorax. As **intrapulmonary volume** (the volume within the lungs) increases, the gases within the lungs spread out to fill the larger space. The resulting decrease in the gas pressure in the lungs produces a partial vacuum (pressure less than atmospheric pressure), which sucks air into the lungs (Figure 13.8). Air continues to move into the lungs until the intrapulmonary pressure equals atmospheric pressure. This series of events is called *inspiration* (inhalation).

Expiration

Expiration (exhalation) in healthy people is largely a passive process that depends more on the natural elasticity of the lungs than on muscle contraction. As the inspiratory muscles relax and resume their initial resting length, the rib cage descends and the lungs recoil. Thus, both the thoracic and intrapulmonary volumes decrease (Figure 13.3b). As the intrapulmonary volume decreases, the gases inside the lungs are forced more closely together, and the intrapulmonary pressure rises to a point higher than atmospheric pressure (see Figure 13.8). This causes the gases to flow out to equalize the pressure inside and outside the lungs. Under normal circumstances, expiration is effortless, but if the respiratory passageways are narrowed by spasms of the bronchioles (as in *asthma*) or clogged with mucus or fluid (as in *chronic bronchitis* or *pneumonia*), expiration becomes an active process. In such cases of *forced expiration,* the internal intercostal muscles

(a)

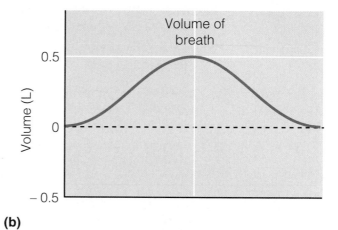

(b)

FIGURE 13.8 **Changes in intrapulmonary pressure and air flow during inspiration and expiration.**

are activated to help depress the rib cage, and the abdominal muscles contract and help to force air from the lungs by squeezing the abdominal organs upward against the diaphragm.

The normal pressure within the pleural space, the **intrapleural pressure,** is *always* negative, and this is the major factor preventing collapse of the lungs. If for any reason the intrapleural pressure becomes equal to the atmospheric pressure, the lungs immediately recoil completely and collapse.

HOMEOSTATIC IMBALANCE

During **atelectasis** (a"teh-lek'tuh-sis), or lung collapse, the lung is useless for ventilation. This phenomenon is seen when air enters the pleural space through a chest wound, but it may also result from a rupture of the visceral pleura, which allows air to enter the pleural space from the respiratory tract. The

TABLE 13.1	Nonrespiratory Air (Gas) Movements
Movement	**Mechanism and result**
Cough	Taking a deep breath, closing glottis, and forcing air superiorly from lungs against glottis. Then, the glottis opens suddenly and a blast of air rushes upward. Coughs act to clear the lower respiratory passageways.
Sneeze	Similar to a cough, except that expelled air is directed through nasal cavities instead of through oral cavity. The uvula (u'vu-lah), a tag of tissue hanging from the soft palate, becomes depressed and closes oral cavity off from pharynx, routing the air through nasal cavities. Sneezes clear upper respiratory passages.
Crying	Inspiration followed by release of air in a number of short expirations. Primarily an emotionally induced mechanism.
Laughing	Essentially same as crying in terms of the air movements produced. Also an emotionally induced response.
Hiccups	Sudden inspirations resulting from spasms of diaphragm; initiated by irritation of diaphragm or phrenic nerves, which serve diaphragm. The sound occurs when inspired air hits vocal folds of closed glottis.
Yawn	Very deep inspiration, taken with jaws wide open; ventilates all alveoli (this is not the case in normal quiet breathing).

presence of air in the intrapleural space, which disrupts the fluid bond between the pleurae, is referred to as **pneumothorax** (nu"mo-tho'rakz). Pneumothorax is reversed by drawing air out of the intrapleural space with chest tubes, which allows the lung to reinflate and resume its normal function. ▲

Nonrespiratory Air Movements

Many situations other than breathing move air into or out of the lungs and may modify the normal respiratory rhythm. Coughs and sneezes clear the air passages of debris or collected mucus. Laughing and crying reflect our emotions. For the most part, these **nonrespiratory air movements** are a result of reflex activity, but some may be produced voluntarily. Examples of the most common of these movements are given in Table 13.1.

Respiratory Volumes and Capacities

Many factors affect respiratory capacity—for example, a person's size, sex, age, and physical condition. Normal quiet breathing moves approximately 500 ml of air (about a pint) into and out of the lungs

with each breath (see Figure 13.8b). This respiratory volume is referred to as the **tidal volume (TV).**

As a rule, a person *can* inhale much more air than is taken in during a normal, or tidal, breath. The amount of air that can be taken in forcibly over the tidal volume is the **inspiratory reserve volume (IRV).** Normally, the inspiratory reserve volume is between 2100 and 3200 ml.

Similarly, after a normal expiration, more air can be exhaled. The amount of air that can be forcibly exhaled after a tidal expiration, the **expiratory reserve volume (ERV),** is approximately 1200 ml.

Even after the most strenuous expiration, about 1200 ml of air still remains in the lungs, and it cannot be voluntarily expelled. This is the **residual volume.** Residual volume air is important because it allows gas exchange to go on continuously even between breaths and helps to keep the alveoli open (inflated).

The total amount of exchangeable air is typically around 4800 ml in healthy young men, and this respiratory capacity is the **vital capacity (VC).** The vital capacity is the sum of the TV + IRV + ERV. The respiratory volumes are summarized in Figure 13.9.

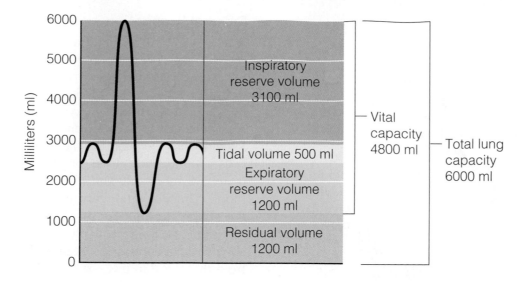

FIGURE 13.9 Idealized tracing of the various respiratory volumes of a healthy young adult male.

Obviously, much of the air that enters the respiratory tract remains in the conducting zone passageways and never reaches the alveoli. This is called the **dead space volume,** and during a normal tidal breath, it amounts to about 150 ml. The functional volume—air that actually reaches the respiratory zone and contributes to gas exchange—is about 350 ml.

Respiratory capacities are measured with a *spirometer* (spi-rom′ĕ-ter). As a person breathes, the volumes of air exhaled can be read on an indicator, which shows the changes in air volume inside the apparatus. Spirometer testing is useful for evaluating losses in respiratory functioning and in following the course of some respiratory diseases. In pneumonia, for example, inspiration is obstructed and the IRV and VC decrease. In emphysema, where expiration is hampered, the ERV is much lower than normal, and the residual volume is higher.

Respiratory Sounds

As air flows into and out of the respiratory tree, it produces two recognizable sounds that can be picked up with a stethoscope. **Bronchial sounds** are produced by air rushing through the large respiratory passageways (trachea and bronchi). **Vesicular** (vĕ-sik′u-lar) **breathing sounds** occur as air fills the alveoli. The vesicular sounds are soft and resemble a muffled breeze.

 HOMEOSTATIC IMBALANCE

Diseased respiratory tissue, mucus, or pus can produce abnormal sounds such as **crackle** (a bubbling sound) and **wheezing** (a whistling sound). ▲

▶ DID YOU GET IT?

7. What is the most basic function of respiration?

8. What causes air to flow out of the lungs during expiration?

9. Which is the largest respiratory volume—ERV, IRV, TV, or VC? Which is the smallest?

10. Dead space volume accounts for about 150 ml of tidal volume. How much of a tidal breath actually reaches the exchange chambers (alveoli)?

11. Jimmy broke a left rib during his fall from his bike. It punctured the chest wall. What happened to his left lung? Why?

For answers, see Appendix D.

External Respiration, Gas Transport, and Internal Respiration

As explained earlier, *external respiration* is the actual exchange of gases between the alveoli and the blood (pulmonary gas exchange), and *internal respiration* is the gas exchange process that occurs between the systemic capillaries and the tissue

Inspired air

$O_2 \, CO_2$

Alveolar spaces

Expired air

$O_2 \, CO_2$

$O_2 \, CO_2$

Alveolar epithelial cells

External respiration

Blood entering alveolar capillaries

CO_2

O_2

Alveolar capillaries of lung

Blood leaving alveolar capillaries

$O_2 \, CO_2$

$O_2 \, CO_2$

Heart

Blood leaving tissue capillaries

CO_2

Tissue capillaries

O_2

Blood entering tissue capillaries

$O_2 \, CO_2$

$O_2 \, CO_2$

Tissue cells

Internal respiration

$O_2 \, CO_2$

FIGURE 13.10 **Gas exchanges in the body occur according to the laws of diffusion.**

cells. It is important to remember that all gas exchanges are made according to the laws of diffusion; that is, movement occurs *toward* the area of lower concentration of the diffusing substance. The relative amounts of O_2 and CO_2 in the alveolar tissues, and in the arterial and venous blood, are illustrated in Figure 13.10.

External Respiration

During external respiration, dark red blood flowing through the pulmonary circuit is transformed into the scarlet river that is returned to the heart for distribution to the systemic circuit. Although this color change is due to oxygen pickup by hemoglobin in the lungs, carbon dioxide is being unloaded from the blood equally fast. Because body cells continually remove oxygen from blood, there is always more oxygen in the alveoli than in the blood. Thus, oxygen tends to move from the air of the alveoli through the respiratory membrane into the more oxygen-poor blood of the pulmonary capillaries. In contrast, as tissue cells remove oxygen from the blood in the systemic circulation, they release carbon dioxide into the blood. Because the concentration of carbon dioxide is much higher in the pulmonary capillaries than it is in the alveolar air, it will move from the blood into the alveoli and be flushed out of the lungs during expiration. Relatively speaking, blood draining from the lungs into the pulmonary veins is oxygen-rich and carbon dioxide–poor and is ready to be pumped to the systemic circulation.

Gas Transport in the Blood

Oxygen is transported in the blood in two ways. Most attaches to hemoglobin molecules inside the RBCs to form **oxyhemoglobin** (ok″se-he″mo-glo′bin)—HbO_2 in Figure 13.11a. A very small amount of oxygen is carried dissolved in the plasma.

Most carbon dioxide is transported in plasma as the **bicarbonate ion** (HCO_3^-), which plays a very important role in the blood buffer system. (The enzymatic conversion of carbon dioxide to bicarbonate ion actually occurs within the red blood cells, and then the newly formed bicarbonate ions diffuse into the plasma.) A smaller amount (between 20 and 30 percent of the transported CO_2) is carried inside the RBCs bound to hemoglobin. Carbon dioxide carried inside the RBCs binds to hemoglobin at a different site than oxygen does, and so it does not interfere in any way with oxygen transport. Before carbon dioxide can diffuse out of the blood into the alveoli, it must first be released from its bicarbonate ion form. For this to occur, bicarbonate ions must enter the red blood cells where they combine with hydrogen ions (H^+) to form carbonic acid (H_2CO_3). Carbonic acid

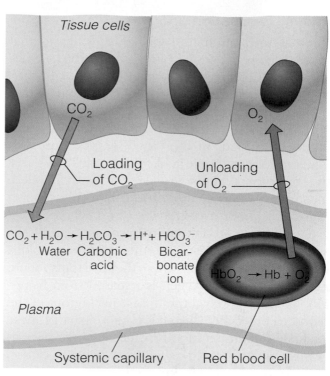

(a) External respiration in the lungs (pulmonary gas exchange): Oxygen is loaded and carbon dioxide is unloaded.

(b) Internal respiration in the body tissues (systemic capillary gas exchange): Oxygen is unloaded and carbon dioxide is loaded into the blood.

FIGURE 13.11 Diagrammatic representation of the major means of oxygen (O_2) and carbon dioxide (CO_2) loading and unloading in the body. Note that although the conversion of CO_2 to bicarbonate ion and the reverse reaction are shown occurring in the plasma in (b), most such conversions occur within the red blood cells. Additionally, though not illustrated, some CO_2 is carried within red blood cells bound to hemoglobin.

quickly splits to form water and carbon dioxide, and carbon dioxide then diffuses from the blood and enters the alveoli.

HOMEOSTATIC IMBALANCE

Impaired oxygen transport: Whatever the cause, inadequate oxygen delivery to body tissues is called **hypoxia** (hi-pok'se-ah). This condition is easy to recognize in fair-skinned people because their skin and mucosae take on a bluish cast (become **cyanotic**). In dark-skinned individuals, this color change can be observed only in the mucosae and nailbeds. Hypoxia may be the result of anemia, pulmonary disease, or impaired or blocked blood circulation.

Carbon monoxide poisoning represents a unique type of hypoxia. Carbon monoxide (CO) is an odorless, colorless gas that competes vigorously with oxygen for the same binding sites on hemoglobin. Moreover, because hemoglobin binds to CO more readily than to oxygen, carbon monoxide is a very successful competitor—so much so that it crowds out or displaces oxygen.

Carbon monoxide poisoning is the leading cause of death from fire. It is particularly dangerous because it kills its victims softly and quietly. It does not produce the characteristic signs of hypoxia—cyanosis and respiratory distress. Instead, the victim becomes confused and has a throbbing headache. In rare cases, the skin becomes cherry red (the color of the hemoglobin-CO complex), which is often interpreted as a healthy "blush." People with CO poisoning are given 100 percent oxygen until the carbon monoxide has been cleared from the body. ▲

Internal Respiration

Internal respiration, the exchange of gases that takes place between the blood and the tissue cells, is the opposite of what occurs in the lungs. This process, in which oxygen is unloaded and carbon dioxide is loaded into the blood, is shown in Figure 13.11b. Carbon dioxide diffusing out of tissue cells enters the blood. In the blood, it combines with water to form carbonic acid, which quickly releases the bicarbonate ions. As previously mentioned, most conversion of carbon dioxide to bicarbonate ions actually occurs *inside* the RBCs, where a special enzyme (carbonic anhydrase) is available to speed up this reaction. Then the bicarbonate ions diffuse out into plasma, where they are transported. At the same time, oxygen is released from hemoglobin, and the oxygen diffuses quickly out of the blood to enter the tissue cells. As a result of these exchanges, venous blood in the systemic circulation is much poorer in oxygen and richer in carbon dioxide than blood leaving the lungs.

Control of Respiration
Neural Regulation: Setting the Basic Rhythm

Although our tidelike breathing seems so beautifully simple, its control is fairly complex. We will cover only the most basic aspects of the respiratory controls. The activity of the respiratory muscles, the diaphragm and external intercostals, is regulated by nerve impulses transmitted to them from the brain by the **phrenic** and **intercostal nerves.**

Neural centers that control respiratory rhythm and depth are located mainly in the *medulla* and *pons* (Figure 13.12). The medulla, which sets the basic rhythm of breathing, contains a pacemaker, or **self-exciting inspiratory center.** When its neurons fire, a burst of impulses travels along the phrenic and intercostal nerves to excite the diaphragm and external intercostal muscles, respectively. The medulla also contains an expiratory center that inhibits the pacemaker in a rhythmic way. Impulses going back and forth between the medulla centers maintain a rate of 12–15 respirations/minute. This normal respiratory rate is referred to as **eupnea** (ūp-ne′ah). Pons centers appear to smooth out the basic rhythm of inspiration and expiration set by the medulla.

In addition, the bronchioles and alveoli have stretch receptors that respond to extreme overinflation (which might damage the lungs) by initiating protective reflexes. In the case of overinflation, the vagus nerves send impulses from the stretch receptors to the medulla; soon therafter, inspiration ends and expiration occurs.

During exercise, we breathe more vigorously and deeply because the brain centers send more impulses to the respiratory muscles. This respiratory pattern is called **hyperpnea** (hy-perp′ne-ah). However, the *rate* of breathing may not be significantly increased with exercising. After strenuous exercise, expiration becomes active, and the abdominal muscles and any other muscles capable of lifting the ribs are used to aid expiration.

⚖ HOMEOSTATIC IMBALANCE

If the medullary centers are completely suppressed (as with an overdose of sleeping pills, morphine, or alcohol), respiration stops completely, and death occurs. ▲

Non-neural Factors Influencing Respiratory Rate and Depth

Physical Factors Although the medulla's respiratory centers set the basic rhythm of breathing, there is no question that physical factors such as talking, coughing, and exercising can modify both the rate and depth of breathing. We have already examined some of these factors in the earlier discussion of nonrespiratory air movements. Increased body temperature causes an increase in the rate of breathing.

Volition (Conscious Control) We all have consciously controlled our breathing pattern at one time or another. During singing and swallowing, breath control is extremely important, and many of us have held our breath for short periods to swim underwater. However, voluntary control of breathing is limited, and the respiratory centers will simply ignore messages from the cortex (our wishes) when the oxygen supply in the blood is getting low or blood pH is falling. All you need do to prove this is to try to talk normally or to hold your breath after running at breakneck speed for a few minutes. It simply cannot be done. Many toddlers try to manipulate their parents by holding their breath "to death." Even though this threat causes many parents to become anxious, they need not worry because the involuntary controls take over and normal respiration begins again.

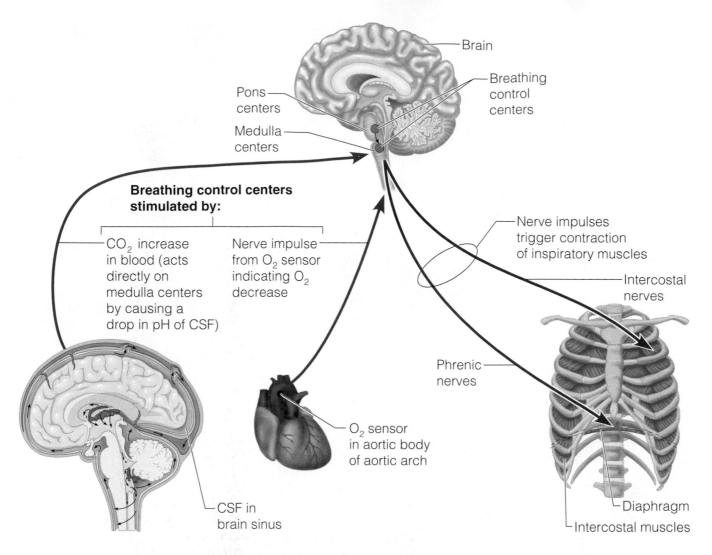

FIGURE 13.12   **Breathing control centers, sensory inputs, and effector nerves.**

Emotional Factors   Emotional factors also modify the rate and depth of breathing. Have you ever watched a horror movie with bated (held) breath or been so scared by what you saw that you were nearly panting? Have you ever touched something cold and clammy and gasped? All of these result from reflexes initiated by emotional stimuli acting through centers in the hypothalamus.

Chemical Factors   Although many factors can modify respiratory rate and depth, the most important factors are chemical—the levels of carbon dioxide and oxygen in the blood. Increased levels of carbon dioxide and decreased blood pH are the most important stimuli leading to an increase in the rate and depth of breathing. (Actually, an increase

in carbon dioxide levels and decreased blood pH are the same thing in this case, because carbon dioxide retention leads to increased levels of carbonic acid, which decrease the blood pH.) Changes in carbon dioxide concentrations in the blood seem to act directly on the medulla centers by influencing the pH of cerebrospinal fluid (CSF) (see Figure 13.12).

Conversely, changes in oxygen concentration in the blood are detected by peripheral chemoreceptor regions in the aorta (aortic body in the aortic arch) and in the fork of the common carotid artery (the carotid body). These, in turn, send impulses to the medulla when blood oxygen levels are dropping. Although every cell in the body must have oxygen to live, it is the body's need to rid itself

A CLOSER LOOK

LUNG CANCER: THE FACTS BEHIND THE SMOKE SCREEN

Lung cancer accounts for fully one-third of all cancer deaths in the United States, and its incidence is increasing daily. More than 174,000 new cases were expected in 2006, and over 162,000 people will die from the disease. It is the most prevalent type of malignancy in both sexes. Most types of lung cancer are tremendously aggressive and metastasize rapidly and widely. Because most cases cannot be diagnosed until they are advanced, it has a notoriously low survival rate: The overall five-year survival rate is just 15 percent, and the average person lives only nine months after diagnosis. (Only recently have new, whole-lung CT scans been shown to detect early-stage tumors well enough to make screening for this cancer worthwhile.)

For years, Americans were remarkably unaware of the link between lung cancer and cigarette smoking, despite the fact that over 90 percent of lung cancer patients are smokers. Professional athletes still promoted cigarettes in the 1950s, and cigarettes were advertised as a harmless way to keep one's weight down ("Reach for a cigarette rather than a sweet"). As late as the 1960s, smoking was considered socially desirable, even romantic, even though it gives smokers bad breath and yellow teeth, wrinkles their skin, and leaves an unpleasant residue on the clothes and hair of everyone

exposed to the smoke. Smoking even a single cigarette increases one's heart rate, constricts peripheral blood vessels throughout the body, disrupts the flow of air in the lungs, and affects one's brain and mood. Long-term smoking contributes to atherosclerosis and heart disease, strokes, cataracts, and early onset of osteoporosis. Furthermore, each year secondhand tobacco smoke causes 3,000 lung cancer deaths among nonsmokers in the United States, and it appears to be linked to

> ## 66 *Most types of lung cancer are tremendously aggressive.* "

heart disease. People who work in bars and restaurants are especially vulnerable.

Ordinarily, sticky mucus and the action of cilia do a fine job of protecting the lungs from chemical and biological irritants, but smoking overwhelms these cleansing devices and they eventually become nonfunctional. Continuous irritation prompts the production of more mucus, but smoking slows the movements of cilia that clear this mucus and depresses the activity of lung mac-

rophages. One result is a pooling of mucus in the lower respiratory tree and an increased frequency of pulmonary infections, including pneumonia and chronic obstructive pulmonary disease (COPD). However, it is the irritating effects of the "cocktail" of free radicals, highly addictive nicotine, and other carcinogens in tobacco smoke that ultimately lead to lung cancer. The worst of these is a chemical called nitrosamine, but the tars in tobacco also contain carcinogens that eventually cause the epithelial cells lining the bronchial tree to proliferate wildly and lose their normal structure.

The three most common types of lung cancer are (1) **squamous cell carcinoma** (25–30 percent of cases), which arises in the epithelium of the larger bronchi and tends to form masses that cavitate (hollow out) and bleed; (2) **adenocarcinoma** (40 percent), which originates in the peripheral areas of the lung as solitary nodules that develop from bronchial mucous glands and alveolar cells; and (3) **small cell carcinoma** (15 percent of cases, but rapidly increasing), which contains lymphocyte-like cells that originate in the main bronchi and grow aggressively in cords or small grapelike clusters within the mediastinum, a site from which metastasis is especially rapid.

The most effective treatment for lung cancer is complete removal of the diseased lung lobes in an attempt

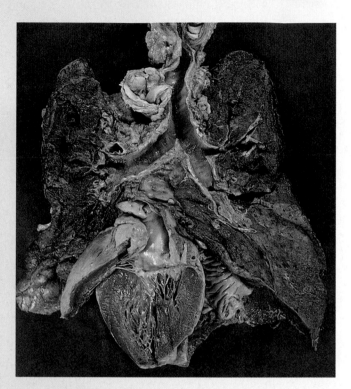

Photographs of healthy lungs of a nonsmoker (left) and cancerous lungs of a smoker (right).

to halt metastasis. However, removal is an option open to very few lung cancer patients because metastasis has usually occurred by the time of diagnosis, and most patients' chances of survival are too poor to justify the surgery. In most cases, radiation therapy and chemotherapy are the only options, but most lung cancers are resistant to these treatments. Only small cell carcinoma responds to chemotherapy, but frequently it returns quickly and spawns brain tumors.

The extreme addictiveness of nicotine in tobacco may explain why over 50 million Americans smoke cigarettes, even though smoking is

estimated to contribute to one-fifth of all deaths in the United States. Surprisingly, a recent survey showed that most smokers do not think they are at increased risk for lung cancer or heart disease. To the contrary, a 40-year lung cancer survey of British men indicates that death rates are three times higher during middle age (35–69 years) for long-term smokers than for nonsmokers. Half of all regular smokers were killed by their habit. Only 43 percent of those who smoked over 25 cigarettes per day lived to age 70, as compared to 79 percent of nonsmokers. Fortunately, fewer young people are taking up smoking in Great Britain and

the United States. Smoking among U.S. high school student peaked at 36 percent in 1997 but has declined to a current level of 22 percent.

The good news is that quitting helps: Whereas the incidence of lung cancer is 20 times greater in smokers versus nonsmokers, this ratio drops to 2:1 for former smokers who have not smoked in 15 years. Overall, 48.8 percent of U.S. adults who ever smoked have quit. Using such treatments as nicotine patches, nasal sprays, and inhalants has been shown to double the success rate of quitting smoking (from 10 to 20 percent). Quitting is a valuable goal; consider the alternative!

of carbon dioxide (not to take in oxygen) that is the *most* important stimulus for breathing in a healthy person. Decreases in oxygen levels become important stimuli only when the levels are dangerously low.

HOMEOSTATIC IMBALANCE

In people who retain carbon dioxide, such as people with emphysema, chronic bronchitis, or other chronic lung diseases, the brain no longer recognizes increased levels of carbon dioxide as important. In such cases, dropping oxygen levels become the respiratory stimulus. This is an interesting fact because it explains why such patients are always given low levels of oxygen. If they were given high levels, they would stop breathing because their respiratory stimulus (low oxygen levels) would be gone. ▲

Homeostatic mechanisms of the respiratory system, in healthy individuals, are obvious. As carbon dioxide or other sources of acids begin to accumulate in blood and blood pH starts to drop, you begin to breathe more deeply and more rapidly. Notice that this breathing pattern, called **hyperventilation,** is distinct from the hyperpnea of exercise. Hyperventilation blows off more carbon dioxide and decreases the amount of carbonic acid, which returns blood pH to the normal range. On the other hand, when blood starts to become slightly alkaline, or basic (for whatever reason), breathing slows and becomes more shallow. Slower breathing allows carbon dioxide to accumulate in the blood and brings blood pH back into normal range. Indeed, control of breathing during rest is aimed primarily at regulating the hydrogen ion concentration in the brain. *Hypoventilation* (extremely slow or shallow breathing) or *hyperventilation* can dramatically change the amount of carbonic acid in the blood. Carbonic acid increases dramatically during hypoventilation and decreases substantially during hyperventilation. In both situations, the buffering ability of the blood is likely to be overwhelmed; the result is *acidosis* or *alkalosis*.

HOMEOSTATIC IMBALANCE

Hyperventilation, often brought on by anxiety attacks, frequently leads to brief periods of **apnea** (ap'ne-ah), cessation of breathing, until the carbon dioxide builds up in the blood again. If breathing stops for an extended time, **cyanosis** (si"ah-no'sis) may occur as a result of insufficient oxygen in the blood. In addition, the hyperventilating person may get dizzy

and faint because the resulting alkalosis causes cerebral blood vessels to constrict. Such attacks can be prevented by having the hyperventilating individual breathe into a paper bag. Because exhaled air contains more carbon dioxide than atmospheric air, it upsets the normal diffusion gradient that causes carbon dioxide to be unloaded from the blood and leave the body. As a result, carbon dioxide (and thus carbonic acid) levels begin to rise in the blood, ending alkalosis. ▲

▶ DID YOU GET IT?

12. Which type of cellular transport moves respiratory gases between the blood and the body's cells?

13. What is the major form in which CO_2 is transported in the blood?

14. What is cyanosis?

15. Which brain area is most important in setting the basic respiratory rate and rhythm?

For answers, see Appendix D.

Respiratory Disorders

HOMEOSTATIC IMBALANCE

The respiratory system is particularly vulnerable to infections because it is open to airborne pathogens. We have already considered some of these inflammatory conditions, such as rhinitis and tonsillitis; now we will turn our attention to the most disabling respiratory disorders, the group of diseases collectively referred to as *chronic obstructive pulmonary disease (COPD)* and *lung cancer*. These disorders are "living proof" of cigarette smoking's devastating effects on the body. Long known to promote cardiovascular disease, cigarettes are perhaps even more effective at destroying the lungs. The photos in the "A Closer Look" box on pp. 458–459, which considers lung cancer, contrast healthy lungs with the blackened, cancer-ridden lungs of a smoker.

Chronic Obstructive Pulmonary Disease (COPD)

The **chronic obstructive pulmonary diseases,** exemplified by *chronic bronchitis* and *emphysema* (em"fĭ-se'mah), are a major cause of death and disability in the United States. These diseases have certain features in common: (1) Patients almost always have a history of smoking; (2) **dyspnea** (disp'ne-ah), difficult

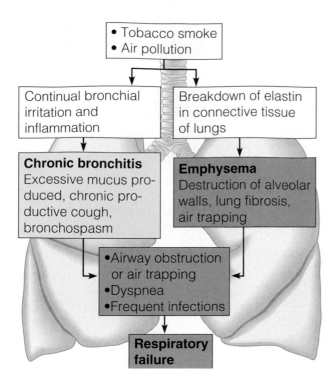

- Tobacco smoke
- Air pollution

Continual bronchial irritation and inflammation

Breakdown of elastin in connective tissue of lungs

Chronic bronchitis
Excessive mucus produced, chronic productive cough, bronchospasm

Emphysema
Destruction of alveolar walls, lung fibrosis, air trapping

- Airway obstruction or air trapping
- Dyspnea
- Frequent infections

Respiratory failure

FIGURE 13.13   **The pathogenesis of COPD.**

or labored breathing, often referred to as "air hunger," occurs and becomes progressively more severe; (3) coughing and frequent pulmonary infections are common; and (4) most COPD victims are hypoxic, retain carbon dioxide and have respiratory acidosis, and ultimately develop respiratory failure (Figure 13.13).

In **chronic bronchitis,** the mucosa of the lower respiratory passages becomes severely inflamed and produces excessive amounts of mucus. The pooled mucus impairs ventilation and gas exchange and dramatically increases the risk of lung infections, including pneumonias. Chronic bronchitis patients are sometimes called "blue bloaters" because hypoxia and carbon dioxide retention occur early in the disease and cyanosis is common.

In **emphysema,** the alveoli enlarge as the walls of adjacent chambers break through, and chronic inflammation promotes fibrosis of the lungs. As the lungs become less elastic, the airways collapse during expiration and obstruct outflow of air. As a result, these patients use an incredible amount of energy to exhale, and they are always exhausted. Because air is retained in the lungs, oxygen exchange is surprisingly efficient, and cyanosis does not usually appear until late in the disease. Consequently, emphysema sufferers are sometimes referred to as "pink puffers." However, overin-

flation of the lungs leads to a permanently expanded barrel chest. ▲

Developmental Aspects of the Respiratory System

In the fetus, the lungs are filled with fluid, and all respiratory exchanges are made by the placenta. At birth, the fluid-filled pathway is drained, and the respiratory passageways fill with air. The alveoli inflate and begin to function in gas exchange, but the lungs are not fully inflated for two weeks. The success of this change—that is, from nonfunctional to functional respiration—depends on the presence of **surfactant** (sur-fak′tant), a fatty molecule made by the cuboidal alveolar cells (see Figure 13.6). Surfactant lowers the surface tension of the film of water lining each alveolar sac so that the alveoli do not collapse between each breath. Surfactant is not usually present in large enough amounts to accomplish this function until late in pregnancy, that is, between 28 and 30 weeks.

HOMEOSTATIC IMBALANCE
Infants who are born prematurely (before week 28) or in whom surfactant production is inadequate for other reasons (as in many infants born to diabetic mothers) have **infant respiratory distress syndrome (IRDS).** These infants have dyspnea within a few hours after birth and use tremendous amounts of energy just to keep reinflating their alveoli, which collapse after each breath. Although IRDS still accounts for over 20,000 newborn deaths a year, many of these babies survive now because of the current use of equipment that supplies a positive pressure continuously and keeps the alveoli open and working in gas exchange until the maturing lungs produce adequate amounts of surfactant.

Important birth defects of the respiratory system include cleft palate and cystic fibrosis. **Cystic fibrosis (CF),** the most common lethal genetic disease in the United States, strikes in 1 out of every 2400 births, and every day two children die of it. CF causes oversecretion of a thick mucus that clogs the respiratory passages and puts the child at risk for fatal respiratory infections. It affects other secretory processes as well. Most important, it impairs food digestion by clogging ducts that deliver pancreatic enzymes and bile to the small intestine. Also, sweat glands produce an extremely salty

focus on CAREERS

LICENSED PRACTICAL NURSE (LPN)

Knowledge of anatomy and physiology helps licensed practical nurses care for their patients.

Originally, the term *practical nurse* was used to describe health workers who went into private homes to pro-

vide bedside nursing. Some licensed practical nurses (LPNs) still provide care in patients' homes, but others play important roles in hospitals, doctors' offices, and health care clinics.

Linda Davila, an LPN employed by Stein Hospice in Sandusky, Ohio, specializes in caring for the terminally ill. "Most of our patients, perhaps 60 percent, have cancer," she says. "Others have life-threatening kidney, lung, or cardiac conditions, or AIDS. Most hospice patients have been diagnosed as having six months or less to live, and they have chosen to forgo aggressive medical treatments. My job is to assist them in staying as comfortable and pain-free as possible

for the remaining days of their lives and to help maintain quality of life for them and their families."

Hospice care provides a multidisciplinary approach to help patients deal with a variety of physical and emotional issues. Davila's team includes social workers, spiritual advisers, registered nurses (RNs), and other LPNs. Explains Davila, "I provide personal care for our patients by helping them with bathing and grooming and monitoring their medications. I also work closely with their families and teach them how to care for the patient: how to empty catheters, bathe someone in bed, and change the sheets for someone who's bedridden."

Davila's clinical skills and anatomy/physiology training enable her to monitor a patient's condition closely and alert team members to any changes. "Hospice patients take many medications, including narcotics," she notes. The narcotics also slow down the digestive process and can make patients constipated. "I monitor patients for side effects and report any symptoms immediately to the RN on my team so we can adjust their medications."

In cancer patients, Davila can often gauge the extent of the disease and recognize when it spreads. "In class we learned that many types of cancer spread to the bone. Sometimes patients will complain of sudden pain in their ribs, which could indicate their cancer has progressed. With lung cancer patients, Davila monitors for shortness of breath, a bluish tinge in skin and fingernails, and mental confusion—signs of reduced oxygen, indicating that the cancer is

impairing lung function. She promptly alerts team members so appropriate treatment can begin.

LPN training follows a structured curriculum in state-approved schools. Applicants must hold a high school diploma or the equivalent and pass

> **❝** *Davila's anatomy and physiology training enable her to monitor patients closely.* **❞**

the school's entrance examination. Typical is a one-year program that includes anatomy and physiology as well as mathematics and other general educational requirements.

After graduating from training, an LPN must also pass a state licensing examination and earn continuing education credits to maintain licensure. Accreditation procedures vary from state to state. For more information about licensed practical nursing and testing requirements, contact:

National League for Nursing
61 Broadway, 33rd Floor
New York, New York 10006
(800) 669-1656

For additional information on this career, click the Focus on Careers link at www.anatomyandphysiology.com.

SYSTEMS IN SYNC

HOMEOSTATIC RELATIONSHIPS BETWEEN THE
RESPIRATORY SYSTEM AND OTHER BODY SYSTEMS

Endocrine System

- Respiratory system provides oxygen; disposes of carbon dioxide
- Epinephrine dilates the bronchioles; testosterone promotes laryngeal enlargement in pubertal males

Lymphatic System/Immunity

- Respiratory system provides oxygen; disposes of carbon dioxide; tonsils in pharynx house immune cells
- Lymphatic system helps to maintain blood volume required for respiratory gas transport; immune system protects respiratory organs from pathogens and cancer

Digestive System

- Respiratory system provides oxygen; disposes of carbon dioxide
- Digestive system provides nutrients needed by respiratory system

Urinary System

- Respiratory system provides oxygen; disposes of carbon dioxide
- Kidneys dispose of metabolic wastes of respiratory system organs (other than carbon dioxide)

Muscular System

- Respiratory system provides oxygen needed for muscle activity; disposes of carbon dioxide
- The diaphragm and intercostal muscles produce volume changes necessary for breathing; regular exercise increases respiratory efficiency

Nervous System

- Respiratory system provides oxygen needed for normal neural activity; disposes of carbon dioxide
- Medullary and pons centers regulate respiratory rate/depth; stretch receptors in lungs and chemoreceptors in large arteries provide feedback

Respiratory System

Cardiovascular System

- Respiratory system provides oxygen; disposes of carbon dioxide; carbon dioxide present in blood as HCO_3^- and H_2CO_3 contributes to blood buffering
- Blood transports respiratory gases

Reproductive System

- Respiratory system provides oxygen; disposes of carbon dioxide

Integumentary System

- Respiratory system provides oxygen; disposes of carbon dioxide
- Skin protects respiratory system organs by forming surface barriers

Skeletal System

- Respiratory system provides oxygen; disposes of carbon dioxide
- Bones enclose and protect lungs and bronchi

perspiration. At the heart of CF is a faulty gene that codes for the CFTR protein, which works as a chloride (Cl^-) channel to control the flow of Cl^- into and out of cells. In people with the mutated gene, CFTR gets "stuck" in the endoplasmic reticulum and is unable to reach the plasma membrane to perform its normal role. Consequently, less Cl^- is secreted and less water follows, resulting in the thick mucus typical of CF. Conventional therapy for CF is mucus-dissolving drugs, "clapping" the chest to loosen the thick mucus, and antibiotics to prevent infection. ▲

The respiratory rate is highest in newborn infants, about 40 to 80 respirations per minute. It continues to drop through life: in the infant it is around 30 per minute, at 5 years it is around 25 per minute, and in adults it is 12 to 18 per minute. However, the rate often increases again in old age. The lungs continue to mature throughout childhood, and more alveoli are formed until young adulthood. But in people who begin smoking during the early teens, the lungs never completely mature, and those additional alveoli are lost forever.

HOMEOSTATIC IMBALANCE

Sudden infant death syndrome (SIDS) claims many newborn infants. Apparently healthy infants stop breathing and die in their sleep, leaving their anguished parents to face charges of child abuse in some cases. Although some cases are believed to be a problem of neural control of respiration or viral infection, more than one-third of SIDS cases appear to result from a heart rhythm abnormality. Recent research indicates a genetic component is in involved. ▲

Except for sneezes or coughs (responses to irritants), and the occasional common cold that blocks the upper respiratory passageways with mucus, the respiratory system works so efficiently and smoothly that we are not even aware of it. Most problems that occur are a result of external factors—for example, obstruction of the trachea by a piece of food, or aspiration of food particles or vomitus (which leads to aspiration pneumonia). Some unfortunate individuals are plagued by **asthma,** caused by chronically inflamed, hypersensitive bronchial passages that respond to many irritants (such as dust mite and cockroach droppings, dog dander, and fungi) with dyspnea, coughing, and wheezing.

For many years, tuberculosis and pneumonia were the worst killers in the United States. Antibiotics have decreased their lethal threat to a large extent, but they are still dangerous diseases. Newly diagnosed, and frequently drug-resistant, tuberculosis cases in AIDS patients are increasing by leaps and bounds the world over, but *at present* the most damaging and disabling respiratory diseases are still those described above, COPD and lung cancer.

As we age, the chest wall becomes more rigid and the lungs begin to lose their elasticity, resulting in a slowly decreasing ability to ventilate the lungs. Vital capacity decreases by about one-third by the age of 70. In addition, blood oxygen levels decrease, and sensitivity to the stimulating effects of carbon dioxide decreases, particularly in a reclining or supine position. As a result, many old people tend to become hypoxic during sleep and exhibit **sleep apnea.**

Additionally, many of the respiratory system's protective mechanisms also become less efficient with age. Ciliary activity of the mucosa decreases, and the phagocytes in the lungs become sluggish. The net result is that the elderly population is more at risk for respiratory tract infections, particularly pneumonia and influenza.

▶ DID YOU GET IT?

16. Alvin, a smoker, sees his doctor because he has a persistent cough and is short of breath after very little exertion. He has a barrel chest and explains that it is difficult for him to exhale. What diagnosis will the doctor make?

17. What happens to the alveoli if surfactant is not produced in a new born baby? What name is given to this condition?

18. What are three factors currently thought to be possible causes of SIDS?

For answers, see Appendix D.

SUMMARY

Media study tools that provide additional review of key topics of Chapter 13 are referenced below.

IP = *InterActive Physiology*
WEB = The A&P Place

Functional Anatomy of the Respiratory System   (pp. 441–448)

1. The nasal cavity, the chamber within the nose, is divided medially by a nasal septum and separated from the oral cavity by the palate. The nasal cavity is lined with a mucosa, which warms, filters, and moistens incoming air. The mucosa also contains receptors for sense of smell. Paranasal sinuses and nasolacrimal ducts drain into the nasal cavity.

2. The pharynx (throat) is a mucosa-lined, muscular tube with three regions—nasopharynx, oropharynx, and laryngopharynx. The nasopharynx functions in respiration only; the others serve both respiratory and digestive functions. The pharynx contains tonsils, which act as part of the body's defense system.

3. The larynx (voice box) is a cartilaginous structure; most prominent is the thyroid cartilage (Adam's apple). The larynx connects the pharynx with the trachea below. The laryngeal opening (glottis) is hooded by the epiglottis, which prevents entry of food or drink into respiratory passages when swallowing. The larynx contains the vocal folds (true vocal cords), which produce sounds used in speech.

4. The trachea (windpipe) extends from the larynx to the main bronchi. The trachea is a smooth-muscle tube lined with a ciliated mucosa and reinforced with C-shaped cartilaginous rings, which keep the trachea patent.

5. Right and left main (primary) bronchi result from subdivision of the trachea. Each plunges into the hilum of the lung on its side.

6. The lungs are paired organs flanking the mediastinum in the thoracic cavity. The lungs are covered with pulmonary (visceral) pleura; the thorax wall is lined with parietal pleura. Pleural secretions decrease friction during breathing. The lungs are primarily elastic tissue and passageways of the respiratory tree. The smallest passageways end in clusters of alveoli.

7. The conducting zone includes all respiratory passages from the nasal cavity to the terminal bronchioles; they conduct air to and from the lungs. Respiratory bronchioles, alveolar ducts and sacs, and alveoli—which have thin walls through which all gas exchanges are made with pulmonary capillary blood—are respiratory zone structures.

WEB Exercise: Chapter 13, Anatomy of the Upper Respiratory Tract.

IP Respiratory System Topic: Anatomy Review: Respiratory Structures, pages 3–12.

Respiratory Physiology   (pp. 448–460)

1. Mechanics of breathing: Gas travels from high-pressure to low-pressure areas. Pressure outside the body is atmospheric pressure; pressure inside the lungs is intrapulmonary pressure; pressure in the intrapleural space is intrapleural pressure (which is always negative). Movement of air into and out of the lungs is called pulmonary ventilation, or breathing. When inspiratory muscles contract, intrapulmonary volume increases, its pressure decreases, and air rushes in (inspiration). When inspiratory muscles relax, the lungs recoil and air rushes out (expiration). Expansion of the lungs is helped by cohesion between pleurae and by the presence of surfactant in alveoli.

IP Respiratory System Topic: Pulmonary Ventilation, pages 3–10.

2. Nonrespiratory air movements: Nonrespiratory air movements are voluntary or reflex activities that move air into or out of the lungs. These include coughing, sneezing, laughing, crying, hiccuping, yawning.

3. Respiratory volumes and capacities: Air volumes exchanged during breathing are TV, IRV, ERV, and VC (see p. 453 for values). Residual volume is nonexchangeable respiratory volume and allows gas exchange to go on continually.

4. Respiratory sounds: Bronchial sounds are sounds of air passing through large respiratory passageways. Vesicular breathing sounds occur as air fills alveoli.

5. External respiration, gas transport, and internal respiration: Gases move according to the laws of diffusion. Oxygen moves from alveolar air into pulmonary blood. Most oxygen is transported bound to hemoglobin inside RBCs. Carbon dioxide moves from pulmonary blood into alveolar air. Most carbon dioxide is transported as bicarbonate ion in plasma. At body tissues, oxygen moves from blood to the tissues, whereas carbon dioxide moves from the tissues to blood.

WEB WEB Exercise: Chapter 13, Gas Transport.

IP IP Respiratory System Topic: Gas Transport, pages 3–12.

6. Control of respiration
   a. Nervous control: Neural centers for control of respiratory rhythm are in the medulla and pons. The medulla is the respiratory rate "pacemaker." Reflex arcs initiated by stretch

receptors in the lungs also play a role in respiration by notifying neural centers of excessive overinflation.

b. Physical factors: Increased body temperature, exercise, speech, singing, and nonrespiratory air movements modify both rate and depth of breathing.

c. Volition: To a degree, breathing may be consciously controlled if it does not interfere with homeostasis.

d. Emotional factors: Some emotional stimuli can modify breathing. Examples are fear, anger, and excitement.

e. Chemical factors: Changes in blood levels of carbon dioxide are the most important stimuli affecting respiratory rhythm and depth. Carbon dioxide acts directly on the medulla via its effect on reducing blood and CSF pH. Rising levels of carbon dioxide in blood result in faster, deeper breathing; falling levels lead to shallow, slow breathing. Hyperventilation may result in apnea and dizziness, due to alkalosis. Oxygen, monitored by peripheral chemoreceptors, is less important as a respiratory stimulus in normal, healthy people. It *is* the stimulus for people whose systems have become accustomed to high levels of carbon dioxide as a result of disease.

Respiratory Disorders   (pp. 460–461)

1. The major respiratory disorders are COPD (emphysema and chronic bronchitis) and lung cancer. A significant cause is cigarette smoking.

2. Emphysema is characterized by permanent enlargement and destruction of alveoli. The lungs lose their elasticity, and expiration becomes an active process.

3. Chronic bronchitis is characterized by excessive mucus production and its pooling in lower respiratory passageways, which severely impairs ventilation and gas exchange. Patients may become cyanotic as a result of chronic hypoxia.

4. Lung cancer is extremely aggressive and metastasizes rapidly. The three most common lung cancers are squamous cell carcinoma, adenocarcinoma, and small cell carcinoma.

Developmental Aspects of the Respiratory System   (pp. 461, 464)

1. Premature infants have problems keeping their lungs inflated because of lack of surfactant in their alveoli. (Surfactant is formed late in pregnancy.)

2. The most important birth defects of the respiratory system are cleft palate and cystic fibrosis.

3. The lungs continue to mature until young adulthood.

4. During youth and middle age, most respiratory system problems are a result of external factors, such as infections and substances that physically block respiratory passageways.

5. In old age, the thorax becomes more rigid and lungs become less elastic, leading to decreased vital capacity. Protective mechanisms of the respiratory system decrease in effectiveness in elderly persons, predisposing them to more respiratory tract infections.

REVIEW QUESTIONS

Multiple Choice

More than one choice may apply.

1. When you exhale, air flows through respiratory structures in which sequence?
   a. Alveolus, bronchiole, bronchus, larynx, trachea, pharynx, nasal cavity
   b. Alveolus, trachea, bronchus, bronchiole, larynx, pharynx, nasal cavity
   c. Alveolus, bronchus, bronchiole, trachea, larynx, pharynx, nasal cavity
   d. Alveolus, bronchiole, bronchus, trachea, larynx, pharynx, nasal cavity

2. When you inhale, the diaphragm
   a. relaxes and moves inferiorly.
   b. relaxes and moves superiorly.
   c. contracts and moves superiorly.
   d. contracts and moves inferiorly.

3. During inspiration, intrapulmonary pressure is
   a. greater than atmospheric pressure.
   b. less than atmospheric pressure.
   c. greater than intrapleural pressure.
   d. less than intrapleural pressure.

4. Lung collapse is prevented by
   a. high surface tension of alveolar fluid.
   b. adhesion of the pleural membranes.
   c. high pressure in the pleural cavities.
   d. high elasticity of lung tissue.

5. Disorders classified as COPDs include
   a. pneumonia.   c. bronchitis.
   b. emphysema.   d. sleep apnea.

6. Which of the following changes will accompany the loss of lung elasticity associated with aging?

    a. Increase in tidal volume

    b. Increase in inspiratory reserve volume

    c. Increase in residual volume

    d. Increase in vital capacity

7. Which of the following is not part of the conducting zone of the respiratory system?

    a. Pharynx   d. Secondary bronchioles

    b. Alveolar sac   e. Larynx

    c. Trachea

Short Answer Essay

8. Clearly explain the difference between external and internal respiration.

9. Trace the route of air from the nares to an alveolus.

10. Why is it important that the trachea be reinforced with cartilaginous rings? What is the advantage of the fact that the rings are incomplete posteriorly?

11. Where in the respiratory tract is the air filtered, warmed, and moistened?

12. The trachea has goblet cells that produce mucus. What is the specific protective function of the mucus?

13. In terms of general health, what is the importance of the fact that the pharyngotympanic tubes and the sinuses drain into the nasal cavities and nasopharynx?

14. What is it about the structure of the alveoli that makes them an ideal site for gas exchange?

15. What do TV, ERV, and VC mean?

16. Name several nonrespiratory air movements, and explain how each differs from normal breathing.

17. The contraction of the diaphragm and the external intercostal muscles begins inspiration. What happens, in terms of volume and pressure changes in the lungs, when these muscles contract?

18. What is the major way that oxygen is transported in the blood?

19. What determines in which direction carbon dioxide and oxygen will diffuse in the lungs? In the tissues?

20. Name the two major brain areas involved in the nervous control of breathing.

21. Name three physical factors that can modify respiratory rate or depth.

22. Name two chemical factors that modify respiratory rate and depth. Which is usually more important?

23. Define *hyperventilation*. If you hyperventilate, do you retain or expel more carbon dioxide? What effect does hyperventilation have on blood pH? On breathing rate?

24. Compare and contrast the signs and symptoms of emphysema and chronic bronchitis.

CRITICAL THINKING AND CLINICAL APPLICATION QUESTIONS

25. After putting her 1-year-old boy (who puts virtually everything in his mouth) down for a nap, a mother failed to find one of the larger beads she used to make the custom jewelry she produces for sale. Two days later, the boy developed a cough and became feverish. What is likely to have happened to the bead, and where (anatomically) would you expect it to be found?

26. Why doesn't Mom have to worry when 3-year-old Johnny threatens to "hold his breath till he dies"?

27. Mr. Rasputin bumped a bee's nest while making repairs on his roof. Not surprisingly, he was promptly stung several times. Because he knew he was allergic to bee stings, he rushed to the hospital. While waiting, he went into a state of shock and had extreme difficulty breathing. Examination showed his larynx to be edematous, and a tracheostomy was performed. Why is edema of the larynx likely to obstruct the airway? What is a tracheostomy, and what purpose does it serve?

28. As a result of a stroke, Mrs. Minnick's swallowing is uncoordinated. What detrimental effect might this have on her ability to breathe?

29. Aspirin is an acidic substance. Describe the pathway by which an aspirin overdose causes an increase in respiratory rate, and explain how this increase would be helpful to the victim.

30. Nine-year-old Jerry stumbled into the drug store gasping for breath. Blood was oozing from a small hole in his chest wall. When the paramedics arrived they said that Jerry had suffered a pneumothorax and atelectasis. Just what do both of these terms mean, and how do you explain his respiratory distress. How will it be treated?

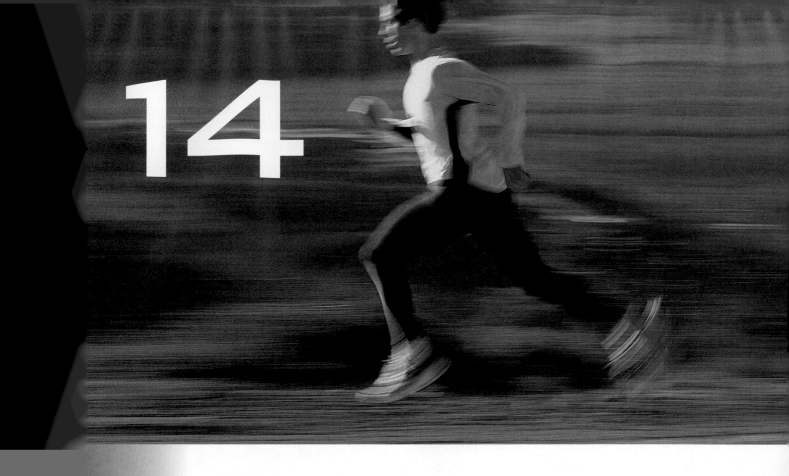

14

The Digestive System and Body Metabolism

YOUR GOALS

After completing this chapter, you will have a working knowledge of the functions of the digestive system and body metabolism and will have mastered the objectives listed below.

FUNCTION PREVIEW

- The digestive system breaks down ingested food into particles small enough to be absorbed into the blood.
- Metabolism produces cellular energy (ATP) and accounts for all constructive and degradative cellular activities.

OBJECTIVE CHECKLIST

PART I: ANATOMY AND PHYSIOLOGY OF THE DIGESTIVE SYSTEM

Anatomy of the Digestive System (pp. 469–481)

➤ Name the organs of the alimentary canal and accessory digestive organs, and identify each on an appropriate diagram or model.

➤ Identify the overall function of the digestive system as digestion and absorption of foodstuffs, and describe the general activities of each digestive system organ.

➤ Describe the composition and function(s) of saliva.

➤ Name the deciduous and permanent teeth, and describe the basic anatomy of a tooth.

➤ Explain how villi aid digestive processes in the small intestine.

Functions of the Digestive System (pp. 481–493)

➤ Describe the mechanisms of swallowing, vomiting, and defecation.

➤ Describe how foodstuffs in the digestive tract are mixed and moved along the tract.

➤ Describe the function of local hormones in the digestive process.

➤ List the major enzymes or enzyme groups produced by the digestive organs or accessory glands, and name the foodstuffs on which they act.

➤ Name the end products of protein, fat, and carbohydrate digestion.

➤ State the digestive function of bile.

PART II: NUTRITION AND METABOLISM

Nutrition (pp. 493–495)

➤ Define *nutrient* and *kilocalorie*.

➤ List the six major nutrient categories. Note important dietary sources and their main cellular uses.

Metabolism (pp. 495–506)

➤ Define *enzyme, metabolism, anabolism,* and *catabolism.*

➤ Describe the metabolic roles of the liver.

➤ Recognize the uses of carbohydrates, fats, and proteins in cell metabolism.

➤ Explain the importance of energy balance in the body, and indicate consequences of energy imbalance.

➤ List several factors that influence metabolic rate, and indicate each one's effect.

➤ Describe how body temperature is regulated.

PART III: DEVELOPMENTAL ASPECTS OF THE DIGESTIVE SYSTEM AND METABOLISM (pp. 506–507)

➤ Name important congenital disorders of the digestive system and significant inborn errors of metabolism.

➤ Describe the effect of aging on the digestive system.

Children are fascinated by the workings of the digestive system: They relish crunching a potato chip, delight in making "mustaches" with milk, and giggle when their stomach "growls." As adults, we know that a healthy digestive system is essential for good health because it converts food into the raw materials that build and fuel our body's cells. Specifically, the digestive system takes in food (*ingests* it), breaks it down physically and chemically into nutrient molecules (*digests* it), and *absorbs* the nutrients into the bloodstream. Then it rids the body of the indigestible remains (*defecates*).

PART I: ANATOMY AND PHYSIOLOGY OF THE DIGESTIVE SYSTEM

Anatomy of the Digestive System

The organs of the digestive system can be separated into two main groups: those forming the *alimentary* (al"ĕ-men'tar-e; *aliment* = nourish) *canal*

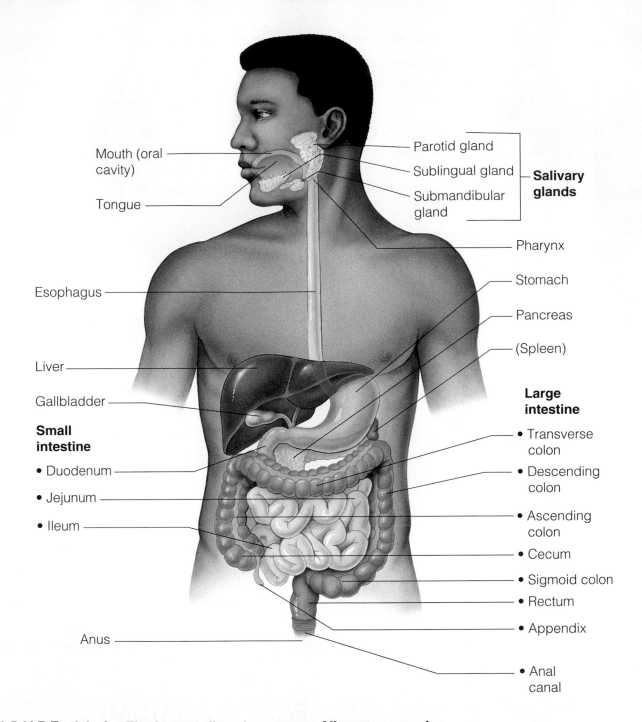

Mouth (oral cavity)

Tongue

Parotid gland

Sublingual gland

Submandibular gland

Salivary glands

Pharynx

Esophagus

Stomach

Pancreas

(Spleen)

Liver

Gallbladder

Large intestine

Small intestine

• Transverse colon

• Duodenum

• Descending colon

• Jejunum

• Ascending colon

• Ileum

• Cecum

• Sigmoid colon

• Rectum

• Appendix

Anus

• Anal canal

FIGURE 14.1 **The human digestive system: Alimentary canal and accessory organs.** (Liver and gallbladder are reflected superiorly and to the right side of the body.)

and the *accessory digestive organs* (Figure 14.1). The alimentary canal performs the whole menu of digestive functions (ingests, digests, absorbs, and defecates). The accessory organs (teeth, tongue, and several large digestive glands) assist the process of digestive breakdown in various ways.

Organs of the Alimentary Canal

The **alimentary canal,** also called the **gastrointestinal (GI) tract,** is a continuous, coiled, hollow muscular tube that winds through the ventral body cavity and is open at both ends. Its organs are the

What is the protective value of having several sets of tonsils at the oral entrance to the pharynx?

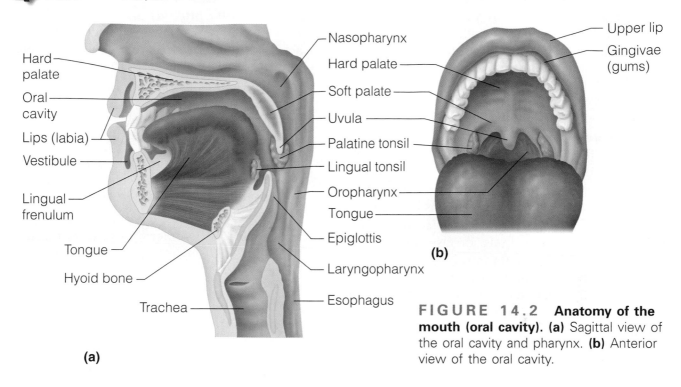

(a)

(b)

FIGURE 14.2 **Anatomy of the mouth (oral cavity).** **(a)** Sagittal view of the oral cavity and pharynx. **(b)** Anterior view of the oral cavity.

mouth, pharynx, esophagus, stomach, small intestine, and *large intestine.* The large intestine leads to the terminal opening, or *anus.* In a cadaver, the alimentary canal is approximately 9 m (about 30 feet) long, but in a living person, it is considerably shorter because of its relatively constant muscle tone. Food material within this tube is technically outside the body, because it has contact only with cells lining the tract and the tube is open to the external environment at both ends. This relationship becomes clearer if you think of your alimentary canal as an elongated doughnut. Then it's easy to see that if you stick your finger through a doughnut hole, your finger is not really *in* the doughnut. As each organ of the alimentary canal is described next, find it in Figure 14.1.

Mouth

Food enters the digestive tract through the **mouth,** or **oral cavity,** a mucous membrane–lined cavity

(Figure 14.2). The **lips (labia)** protect its anterior opening, the **cheeks** form its lateral walls, the **hard palate** forms its anterior roof, and the **soft palate** forms its posterior roof. The **uvula** (u'vu-lah) is a fleshy fingerlike projection of the soft palate, which extends inferiorly from the posterior edge of the soft palate. The space between the lips and cheeks externally and the teeth and gums internally is the **vestibule.** The area contained by the teeth is the **oral cavity proper.** The muscular **tongue** occupies the floor of the mouth. The tongue has several bony attachments—two of these are to the hyoid bone and the styloid processes of the skull. The **lingual frenulum** (ling'gwal fren'u-lum), a fold of mucous membrane, secures the tongue to the floor of the mouth and limits its posterior movements (see Figure 14.2a).

HOMEOSTATIC IMBALANCE

Children born with an extremely short lingual frenulum are often referred to as "tongue-tied" because the movement of the tongue is restricted, leading to distorted speech. This congenital condition can be corrected surgically by cutting the frenulum. ▲

The mouth is a favored site of body entry by bacteria, and the presence of the tonsils (lymphocyte- and macrophage-filled organs) is very effective in preventing many pathogens from getting further into the digestive tract.

At the posterior end of the oral cavity are paired masses of lymphatic tissue, the **palatine tonsils.** The **lingual tonsil** covers the base of the tongue just beyond. The tonsils, along with other lymphatic tissues, are part of the body's defense system. When the tonsils become inflamed and enlarge, they partially block the entrance into the throat (pharynx), making swallowing difficult and painful.

As food enters the mouth, it is mixed with saliva and **masticated** (chewed). The cheeks and closed lips hold the food between the teeth during chewing. The nimble tongue continuously mixes food with saliva during chewing and initiates swallowing. Thus, the breakdown of food begins before the food has even left the mouth. As noted in Chapter 8, *papillae* containing taste buds, or taste receptors, are found on the tongue surface. And so, besides its food-manipulating function, the tongue allows us to enjoy and appreciate the food as we eat it.

Pharynx

From the mouth, food passes posteriorly into the *oropharynx* and *laryngopharynx,* both of which are common passageways for food, fluids, and air. As explained in Chapter 13, the pharynx is subdivided into the *nasopharynx,* part of the respiratory passageway; the **oropharynx,** posterior to the oral cavity; and the **laryngopharynx,** which is continuous with the esophagus below.

The walls of the pharynx contain two skeletal muscle layers. The cells of the inner layer run longitudinally; those of the outer layer (the constrictor muscles) run around the wall in a circular fashion. Alternating contractions of these two muscle layers propel food through the pharynx into the esophagus below. This propelling mechanism, called *peristalsis* (per″i-stal′sis), is described later.

Esophagus

The **esophagus** (ĕ-sof′ah-gus), or *gullet,* runs from the pharynx through the diaphragm to the stomach. About 25 cm (10 inches) long, it is essentially a passageway that conducts food (by peristalsis) to the stomach.

The walls of the alimentary canal organs from the esophagus to the large intestine are made up of the same four basic tissue layers, or tunics (Figure 14.3):

1. The **mucosa** is the innermost layer, a moist membrane that lines the cavity, or **lumen,** of the organ. It consists primarily of a *surface epithelium,* plus a small amount of connective tissue *(lamina propria)* and a scanty *smooth muscle layer.* Beyond the esophagus, which has a friction-resisting stratified squamous epithelium, the epithelium is mostly simple columnar.

2. The **submucosa** is found just beneath the mucosa. It is a soft connective tissue layer containing blood vessels, nerve endings, lymph nodules, and lymphatic vessels.

3. The **muscularis externa** is a muscle layer typically made up of an inner *circular layer* and an outer *longitudinal layer* of smooth muscle cells.

4. The **serosa** is the outermost layer of the wall. It consists of a single layer of flat serous fluid-producing cells, the **visceral peritoneum** (per″i-to-ne′um). The visceral peritoneum is continuous with the slick, slippery **parietal peritoneum,** which lines the abdominopelvic cavity by way of a membrane extension, the **mesentery** (mes′en-ter″e). These relationships are illustrated in Figure 14.5 (p. 495).

HOMEOSTATIC IMBALANCE

When the peritoneum is infected, a condition called **peritonitis** (per″i-to-ni′tis), the peritoneal membranes tend to stick together around the infection site. This helps to seal off and localize many intraperitoneal infections (at least initially), providing time for macrophages in the lymphatic tissue to mount an attack. ▲

The alimentary canal wall contains two important *intrinsic nerve plexuses*—the **submucosal nerve plexus** and the **myenteric** (mi-en′ter-ik; "intestinal muscle") **nerve plexus.** These networks of nerve fibers are actually part of the autonomic nervous system. They help regulate the mobility and secretory activity of GI tract organs.

Stomach

The C-shaped **stomach** (Figure 14.4) is on the left side of the abdominal cavity, nearly hidden by the liver and diaphragm. Different regions of the stomach have been named. The *cardiac region* (named for its position near the heart) surrounds the **cardioesophageal** (kar″de-o-ĕ-sof″ah-je′al) **sphincter,** through which food enters the stomach from the esophagus. The *fundus* is the expanded

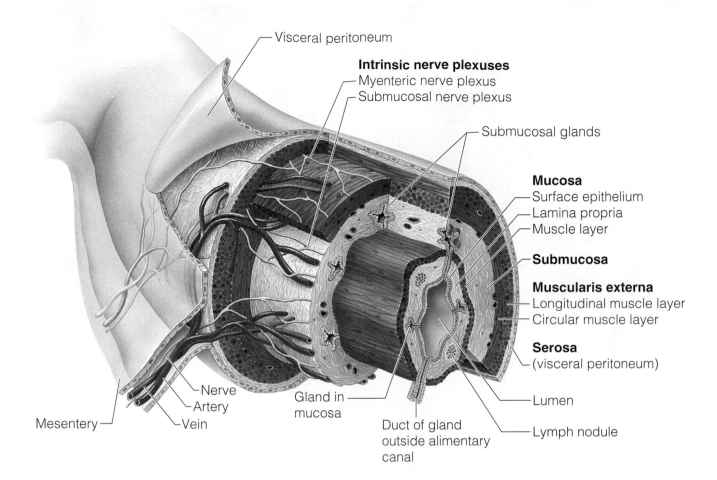

Visceral peritoneum

Intrinsic nerve plexuses
Myenteric nerve plexus
Submucosal nerve plexus

Submucosal glands

Mucosa
Surface epithelium
Lamina propria
Muscle layer

Submucosa

Muscularis externa
Longitudinal muscle layer
Circular muscle layer

Serosa
(visceral peritoneum)

Lumen

Lymph nodule

Nerve
Artery
Vein

Mesentery

Gland in
mucosa

Duct of gland
outside alimentary
canal

FIGURE 14.3   Basic structure of the alimentary canal wall.

part of the stomach lateral to the cardiac region. The *body* is the midportion, and as it narrows inferiorly, it becomes the *pyloric antrum,* and then the funnel-shaped *pylorus* (pi-lo′rus), the terminal part of the stomach. The pylorus is continuous with the small intestine through the **pyloric sphincter,** or **valve.** The stomach varies from 15 to 25 cm (6 to 10 inches) in length, but its diameter and volume depend on how much food it contains. When it is full, it can hold about 4 liters (1 gallon) of food. When it is empty, it collapses inward on itself, and its mucosa is thrown into large folds called **rugae** (roo′ge; *ruga* = wrinkle, fold). The convex lateral surface of the stomach is the **greater curvature;** its concave medial surface is the **lesser curvature.**

The **lesser omentum** (o-men′tum), a double layer of peritoneum, extends from the liver to the lesser curvature. The **greater omentum,** another extension of the peritoneum, drapes downward and covers the abdominal organs like a lacy apron

before attaching to the posterior body wall (Figure 14.5). The greater omentum is riddled with fat, which helps to insulate, cushion, and protect the abdominal organs, and has large collections of lymph nodules containing macrophages and defensive cells of the immune system.

The stomach acts as a temporary "storage tank" for food as well as a site for food breakdown. Besides the usual longitudinal and circular muscle layers, its wall contains a third obliquely arranged layer in the *muscularis externa* (see Figure 14.4a). This arrangement allows the stomach not only to move food along the tract, but also to churn, mix, and pummel the food, physically breaking it down to smaller fragments. In addition, chemical breakdown of proteins begins in the stomach. The mucosa of the stomach is a simple columnar epithelium composed entirely of mucous cells that produce a protective layer of bicarbonate-rich alkaline mucus that clings to the stomach mucosa and protects the

FIGURE 14.4 **Anatomy of the stomach.** Gross internal anatomy (frontal section). **(a)** Diagram. **(b)** Photo. **(c)** Enlarged view of gastric pits and glands (longitudinal section). **(d)** Schematic showing the sequence of events from ① the production of pepsinogen by the chief cells to ② its activation (to pepsin) by HCl secreted by the parietal cells.

A *Its third layer of smooth muscle, the oblique layer which allows it to knead or pummel the food.*

(a)

(b)

FIGURE 14.5   **Peritoneal attachments of the abdominal organs. (a)** Anterior view; the greater omentum is shown in its normal position, covering the abdominal viscera. **(b)** Sagittal view of the abdominopelvic cavity of a female.

stomach wall from being damaged by acid and digested by enzymes. This otherwise smooth lining is dotted with millions of deep *gastric pits,* which lead into *gastric glands* (Figure 14.4c) that secrete the solution called **gastric juice.** For example, some stomach cells produce **intrinsic factor,** a substance needed for the absorption of vitamin B_{12} from the small intestine. The **chief cells** produce protein-digesting enzymes, mostly **pepsinogens,** and the **parietal cells** produce corrosive hydrochloric acid, which makes the stomach contents acidic and activates the enzymes (Figure 14.4d). The *mucous neck cells* produce a thin acidic mucus that is quite different from that secreted by the mucous cells of the mucosa. It is not yet known what special role this mucus plays. Still other cells, the **enteroendocrine cells** (*entero* = gut), produce local hormones, such as *gastrin,* that are important to the digestive activities of the stomach (see Table 14.1 on p. 490).

Most digestive activity occurs in the pyloric region of the stomach. After food has been processed in the stomach, it resembles heavy cream and is called **chyme** (kīm). The chyme enters the small intestine through the pyloric sphincter.

▶ *DID YOU GET IT?*

1. What is the sequential order (mouth to anus) of the digestive organs making up the alimentary canal?

2. In which alimentary-canal organ does protein digestion begin?

3. The stomach epithelium secretes several substances, including alkaline mucus and intrinsic factor. What is the function of each of these two secretions?

For answers, see Appendix D.

Small Intestine

The **small intestine** is the body's major digestive organ. Within its twisted passageways, usable food is finally prepared for its journey into the cells of the body. The small intestine is a muscular tube extending from the pyloric sphincter to the **large intestine** (see Figure 14.1, p. 470). It is the longest section of the alimentary tube, with an average length of 2.5 to 7 m (8 to 20 feet) in a living person. Except for the initial part of the small intestine (the

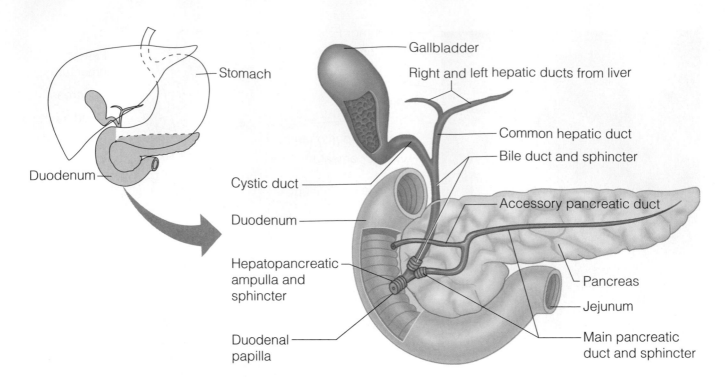

FIGURE 14.6 **The duodenum of the small intestine and related organs.**

duodenum), which mostly lies in a retroperitoneal position, the small intestine hangs in sausagelike coils in the abdominal cavity, suspended from the posterior abdominal wall by the fan-shaped mesentery (see Figure 14.5). The large intestine encircles and frames it in the abdominal cavity.

The small intestine has three subdivisions: the **duodenum** (du"o-de'num; "twelve finger widths long"), the **jejunum** (je-joo'num: "empty"), and the **ileum** (il'e-um; "twisted intestine"), which contribute 5 percent, nearly 40 percent, and almost 60 percent of the length of the small intestine, respectively (see Figure 14.1). The ileum meets the large intestine at the **ileocecal** (il"e-o-se'kal) **valve,** which joins the large and small intestines (see Figure 14.8, p. 478).

Chemical digestion of foods begins in earnest in the small intestine. The small intestine is able to process only a small amount of food at one time. The *pyloric sphincter* (literally, "gatekeeper") controls food movement into the small intestine from the stomach and prevents the small intestine from being overwhelmed. Though the **C**-shaped duodenum is the shortest subdivision of the small intestine, it has the most interesting features. Some enzymes are produced by the intestinal cells.

More important are enzymes that are produced by the pancreas and then ducted into the duodenum through the **pancreatic ducts,** where they complete the chemical breakdown of foods in the small intestine. *Bile* (formed by the liver) also enters the duodenum through the **bile duct** in the same area (Figure 14.6). The main pancreatic and bile ducts join at the duodenum to form the flasklike *hepatopancreatic ampulla* (he-pah"to-pan-kre-a'tik am-pu'lah), literally, the "liver-pancreatic enlargement." From there, the bile and pancreatic juice travel through the *duodenal papilla* and enter the duodenum together.

Nearly all food absorption occurs in the small intestine. The small intestine is well suited for its function. Its wall has three structures that increase the absorptive surface tremendously—microvilli, villi, and circular folds (Figure 14.7). **Microvilli** (mi"kro-vih'li) are tiny projections of the plasma membrane of the mucosa cells that give the cell surface a fuzzy appearance, sometimes referred to as the **brush border.** The plasma membranes bear enzymes *(brush border enzymes)* that complete the digestion of proteins and carbohydrates in the small intestine. **Villi** are fingerlike projections

Q *What is the functional value of the microvilli in the absorptive cells of the small intestine?*

(a) Small intestine

Blood vessels serving small intestine

Muscle layers

Large circular folds (plicae circulares)

Villi

Absorptive cells

Lacteal

Blood capillaries

Vein

Artery

Submucosa

(b) Villi

One villus

Microvilli

(c) Absorptive cells

FIGURE 14.7 Structural modifications of the small intestine. (a) Several circular folds (plicae circulares), seen on the inner surface of the small intestine. **(b)** Enlargement of one villus extension of the circular fold. **(c)** Enlargement of an absorptive cell to show microvilli (brush border).

of the mucosa that give it a velvety appearance and feel, much like the soft nap of a towel. Within each villus is a rich capillary bed and a modified lymphatic capillary called a **lacteal.** The digested foodstuffs are absorbed through the mucosal cells into both the capillaries and the lacteal, as discussed on p. 492. **Circular folds,** also called **plicae circulares** (pli'se ser-ku-la'res), are deep folds of both mucosa and submucosa layers. Unlike the rugae of the stomach, the circular folds do not disappear when food fills the small intestine. All these structural modifications, which increase the surface area, decrease in number toward the end of the small intestine. In contrast, local collections of lymphatic tissue (called **Peyer's patches**) found in the submucosa increase in number toward the end of the small

intestine. This reflects the fact that the remaining (undigested) food residue in the intestine contains huge numbers of bacteria, which must be prevented from entering the bloodstream if at all possible.

Large Intestine

The **large intestine** is much larger in diameter than the small intestine (thus its name, the *large* intestine) but shorter in length. About 1.5 m (5 feet) long, it extends from the ileocecal valve to the anus (Figure 14.8). Its major functions are to dry out the indigestible food residue by absorbing water and to eliminate these residues from the body as feces. It frames the small intestine on three sides and has the following subdivisions: **cecum** (se'kum), **appendix, colon, rectum,** and **anal canal.** The saclike cecum is the first part of the large intestine. Hanging from the cecum is the

A *They tremendously increase the surface area available for absorption of digested foodstuffs.*

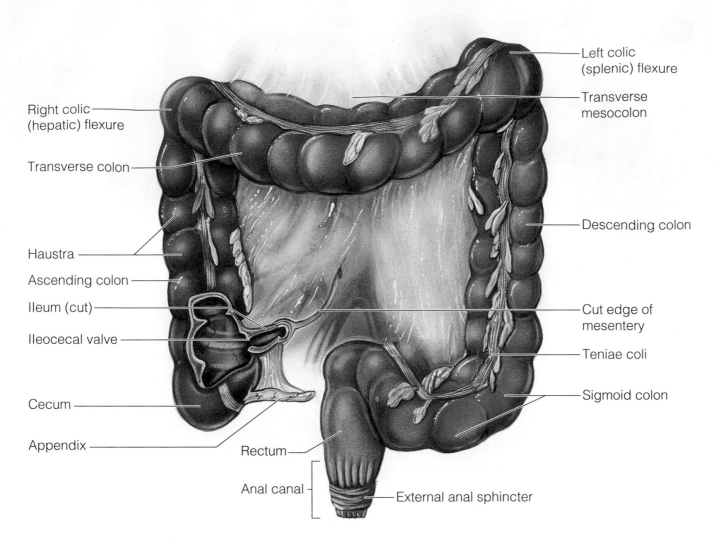

Right colic (hepatic) flexure

Transverse colon

Haustra

Ascending colon

Ileum (cut)

Ileocecal valve

Cecum

Appendix

Left colic (splenic) flexure

Transverse mesocolon

Descending colon

Cut edge of mesentery

Teniae coli

Sigmoid colon

Rectum

Anal canal

External anal sphincter

FIGURE 14.8 The large intestine. A section of the cecum is removed to show the ileocecal valve.

wormlike ("vermiform") appendix, a potential trouble spot. Because it is usually twisted, it is an ideal location for bacteria to accumulate and multiply. Inflammation of the appendix, **appendicitis,** is the usual result. The colon is divided into several distinct regions. The **ascending colon** travels up the right side of the abdominal cavity and makes a turn, the *right colic* (or *hepatic*) *flexure,* to travel across the abdominal cavity as the **transverse colon.** It then turns again at the *left colic* (or *splenic*) *flexure,* and continues down the left side as the **descending colon,** to enter the pelvis, where it becomes the S-shaped **sigmoid** (sig′moid) **colon.** The sigmoid colon, rectum, and anal canal lie in the pelvis. The anal canal ends at the **anus** (a′nus), which opens to the exterior. The anal canal has an external *voluntary sphincter* (the **external**

anal sphincter) composed of skeletal muscle and an internal *involuntary sphincter* (**internal involuntary sphincter**) formed by smooth muscle. These sphincters, which act rather like purse strings to open and close the anus, are ordinarily closed except during defecation, when feces are eliminated from the body.

Because most nutrients have been absorbed before the large intestine is reached, no villi are present in the large intestine, but there are tremendous numbers of *goblet cells* in its mucosa that produce alkaline (HCO_3^--rich) mucus. The mucus acts as a lubricant to ease the passage of feces to the end of the digestive tract.

In the large intestine, the longitudinal muscle layer of the muscularis externa is reduced to three bands of muscle called *teniae coli* (ten'ne-e ko'li; "ribbons of the colon"). Because these muscle bands usually display some degree of tone (are partially contracted), they cause the wall to pucker into small pocketlike sacs called **haustra** (haws'trah).

▶DID YOU GET IT?

4. Which muscular sphincter regulates the flow of chyme into the small intestine?

5. What are the two main functions of the large intestine?

6. What are villi, and why are they important?

For answers, see Appendix D.

Accessory Digestive Organs

Teeth

The role the teeth play in food processing needs little introduction. We **masticate,** or *chew,* by opening and closing our jaws and moving them from side to side while continuously using our tongue to move the food between our teeth. In the process, the teeth tear and grind the food, breaking it down into smaller fragments.

Ordinarily, by the age of 21, two sets of teeth have been formed (Figure 14.9). The first set is the **deciduous** (de-sid'u-us) **teeth,** also called **baby teeth** or **milk teeth.** The deciduous teeth begin to erupt around 6 months, and a baby has a full set (20 teeth) by the age of 2 years. The first teeth to appear are the lower central incisors, an event that is usually anxiously awaited by the child's parents.

As the second set of teeth, the deeper **permanent teeth,** enlarge and develop, the roots of the milk teeth are reabsorbed, and between the ages of 6 and 12 years they loosen and fall out. All of the permanent teeth but the third molars have erupted by the end of adolescence. The third molars, also called *wisdom teeth,* emerge later, between the ages of 17 and 25. Although there are 32 permanent teeth in a full set, the wisdom teeth often fail to erupt; sometimes they are completely absent.

HOMEOSTATIC IMBALANCE

When teeth remain embedded in the jawbone, they are said to be *impacted.* Impacted teeth exert pressure and cause a good deal of pain and must be removed surgically. Wisdom teeth are the most commonly impacted. ▲

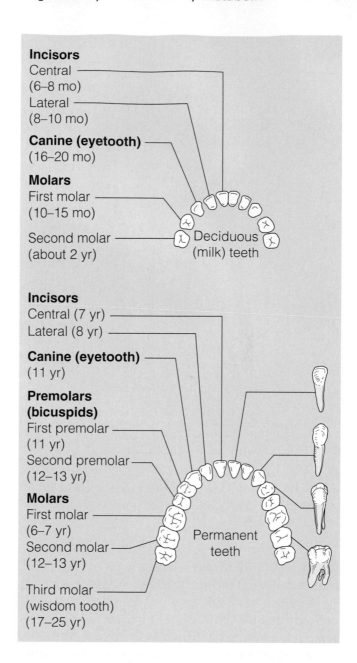

FIGURE 14.9   Human deciduous and permanent teeth. Approximate time of tooth eruption is shown in parentheses. The same number and arrangement of teeth exist in both upper and lower jaws, so only the lower jaw is shown in each case. The shapes of individual teeth are shown on the right.

The teeth are classified according to shape and function as incisors, canines, premolars, and molars (see Figure 14.9). The chisel-shaped **incisors** are adapted for cutting; the fanglike **canines** (eyeteeth) are for tearing or piercing. The **premolars**

Q *What substance forms the bulk of the tooth?*

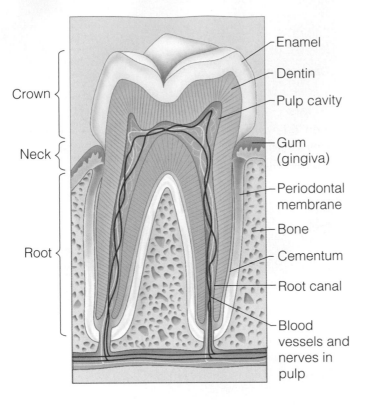

Enamel

Dentin

Pulp cavity

Crown

Neck

Root

Gum (gingiva)

Periodontal membrane

Bone

Cementum

Root canal

Blood vessels and nerves in pulp

FIGURE 14.10 **Longitudinal section of a molar.**

(bicuspids) and **molars** have broad crowns with rounded cusps (tips) and are best suited for grinding.

A tooth consists of two major regions, the **crown** and the **root,** as shown in Figure 14.10. The enamel-covered crown is the exposed part of the tooth above the **gingiva** (jin-ji′vah), or **gum. Enamel** is the hardest substance in the body and is fairly brittle because it is heavily mineralized with calcium salts. The portion of the tooth embedded in the jawbone is the root; the root and crown are connected by the tooth region called the **neck.** The outer surface of the root is covered by a substance called **cementum,** which attaches the tooth to the **periodontal** (per″e-o-don′tal) **membrane (ligament).** This ligament holds the tooth in place in the bony jaw. **Dentin,** a bonelike material, underlies the enamel and forms the bulk of the tooth. It surrounds a central **pulp cavity,**

which contains a number of structures (connective tissue, blood vessels, and nerve fibers) collectively called **pulp.** Pulp supplies nutrients to the tooth tissues and provides for tooth sensations. Where the pulp cavity extends into the root, it becomes the **root canal,** which provides a route for blood vessels, nerves, and other pulp structures to enter the pulp cavity of the tooth.

Salivary Glands

Three pairs of **salivary glands** empty their secretions into the mouth. The large **parotid** (pah-rot′id) **glands** lie anterior to the ears. **Mumps,** a common childhood disease, is an inflammation of the parotid glands. If you look at the location of the parotid glands in Figure 14.1, you can readily understand why people with mumps complain that it hurts to open their mouth or chew.

The **submandibular glands** and the small **sublingual** (sub-ling′gwal) **glands** empty their secretions into the floor of the mouth through tiny ducts. The product of the salivary glands, **saliva,** is a mixture of mucus and serous fluids. The mucus moistens and helps to bind food together into a mass called a **bolus** (bo′lus), which makes chewing and swallowing easier. The clear serous portion contains an enzyme, **salivary amylase** (am′ĭ-lās), in a bicarbonate-rich (alkaline) juice that begins the process of starch digestion in the mouth. Saliva also contains substances such as lysozyme and antibodies (IgA) that inhibit bacteria; therefore, it has a protective function as well. Last but not least, saliva dissolves food chemicals so they can be tasted.

Pancreas

The **pancreas** is a soft, pink, triangular gland that extends across the abdomen from the spleen to the duodenum (see Figures 14.1 and 14.6). Most of the pancreas lies posterior to the parietal peritoneum; hence its location is referred to as *retroperitoneal.*

Only the pancreas produces enzymes (described later) that break down all categories of digestible foods. The pancreatic enzymes are secreted into the duodenum in an alkaline fluid that neutralizes the acidic chyme coming in from the stomach. The pancreas also has an endocrine function; it produces the hormones insulin and glucagon, as explained in Chapter 9.

A *Dentin.*

Liver and Gallbladder

The **liver** is the largest gland in the body. Located under the diaphragm, more to the right side of the body, it overlies and almost completely covers the stomach (see Figures 14.1 and 14.5). The liver has four lobes and is suspended from the diaphragm and abdominal wall by a delicate mesentery cord, the **falciform** (fal'si-form) **ligament.**

There is no question that the liver is one of the body's most important organs. It has many metabolic and regulatory roles; however, its digestive function is to produce **bile.** Bile leaves the liver through the **common hepatic duct** and enters the duodenum through the *bile duct* (see Figure 14.6).

Bile is a yellow-to-green, watery solution containing bile salts, bile pigments (chiefly bilirubin, a breakdown product of hemoglobin), cholesterol, phospholipids, and a variety of electrolytes. Of these components, only the bile salts (derived from cholesterol) and phospholipids aid the digestive process. Bile does not contain enzymes, but its bile salts *emulsify* fats by physically breaking large fat globules into smaller ones, thus providing more surface area for the fat-digesting enzymes to work on.

The **gallbladder** is a small, thin-walled green sac that snuggles in a shallow fossa in the inferior surface of the liver (see Figures 14.1 and 14.6). When food digestion is not occurring, bile backs up the **cystic duct** and enters the gallbladder to be stored. While in the gallbladder, bile is concentrated by the removal of water. Later, when fatty food enters the duodenum, a hormonal stimulus prompts the gallbladder to contract and spurt out stored bile, making it available to the duodenum.

HOMEOSTATIC IMBALANCE

If bile is stored in the gallbladder for too long or too much water is removed, the cholesterol it contains may crystallize, forming **gallstones.** Because gallstones tend to be quite sharp, agonizing pain may occur when the gallbladder contracts (the typical *gallbladder attack*).

Blockage of the common hepatic or bile ducts (for example, by wedged gallstones) prevents bile from entering the small intestine, and it begins to accumulate and eventually backs up into the liver. This exerts pressure on the liver cells, and bile salts, and bile pigments begin to enter the bloodstream. As the bile pigments circulate through the body, the tissues become yellow, or **jaundiced.** Blockage of the ducts is just one cause of jaundice. More often it results from actual liver problems such as **hepatitis** (an inflammation of the liver) or **cirrhosis** (sir-ro'sis), a chronic inflammatory condition in which the liver is severely damaged and becomes hard and fibrous. Hepatitis is most often due to viral infection resulting from drinking contaminated water or transmitted in blood via transfusion or contaminated needles. Cirrhosis is almost guaranteed when one drinks alcoholic beverages in excess for many years, and it is a common consequence of severe hepatitis. ▲

▶ DID YOU GET IT?

7. Mary has a dry mouth—very little saliva is being secreted. Digestion of which type of food will be affected (decreased) by this situation?

8. What is the normal number of permanent teeth?

9. What is the digestive role of bile? What organ secretes bile?

10. Only one organ produces enzymes capable of digesting all groups of food. Which organ is this?

For answers, see Appendix D.

Functions of the Digestive System
Overview of Gastrointestinal Processes and Controls

The major functions of the digestive tract are usually summarized in two words—*digestion* and *absorption*. However, many of its specific activities (such as smooth muscle activity) and certain regulatory events are not really covered by either term. To describe digestive system processes a little more accurately, we really have to consider a few more functional terms. The essential activities of the GI tract include the following six processes, summarized in Figure 14.11.

1. **Ingestion.** Food must be placed into the mouth before it can be acted on. This is an active, voluntary process called ingestion.

2. **Propulsion.** If foods are to be processed by more than one digestive organ (and indeed they are), they must be propelled from one organ to the next. Swallowing is one example

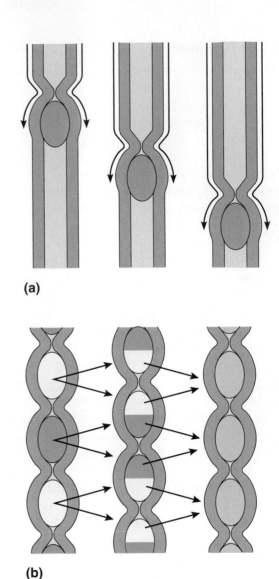

(a)

(b)

FIGURE 14.11 **Schematic summary of gastrointestinal tract activities.** Gastrointestinal tract activities include ingestion, mechanical digestion, chemical (enzymatic) digestion, propulsion, absorption, and defecation. Sites of chemical digestion are also sites that produce enzymes or that receive enzymes or other secretions made by accessory organs. The entire GI tract mucosa secretes mucus, which protects and lubricates.

FIGURE 14.12 **Peristaltic and segmental movements of the digestive tract. (a)** In peristalsis, adjacent or neighboring segments of the intestine (or other alimentary canal organs) alternately contract and relax, thereby moving food distally along the tract. **(b)** In segmentation, single segments of the intestine alternately contract and relax. Because active segments are separated by inactive ones, the food is moved forward and then backward. Thus the food is mixed rather than simply propelled along the tract.

of food movement that depends largely on the propulsive process called **peristalsis**. Peristalsis is involuntary and involves alternating waves of contraction and relaxation of the muscles in the organ wall (Figure 14.12a). The net effect is to squeeze the food along the tract. Although **segmentation** (Figure 14.12b) may

help to propel foodstuffs through the small intestine, it normally moves food only back and forth across the internal wall of the organ, serving to mix it with the digestive juices. Thus, segmentation is more an example of mechanical digestion than of propulsion.

3. **Food breakdown: mechanical digestion.**
Mixing of food in the mouth by the tongue, churning of food in the stomach, and segmentation in the small intestine are all examples of processes contributing to mechanical digestion. Mechanical digestion prepares food for further degradation by enzymes by physically fragmenting the foods into smaller particles.

4. **Food breakdown: chemical digestion.** The sequence of steps in which large food molecules are broken down to their building blocks by enzymes (protein molecules that act as catalysts) is called chemical digestion. Recall from Chapter 2 that these reactions are called *hydrolysis* reactions, because a water molecule is added to each bond to be broken. Water is also necessary as a dissolving medium and a softening agent for food digestion.

Because each of the major food groups has very different building blocks, it is worth taking a little time to review these chemical units, which we first introduced in Chapter 2. The building blocks, or units, of *carbohydrate* foods are *monosaccharides* (mon″o-sak′ah-rīdz), or simple sugars. We need to remember only three of these that are common in our diet—*glucose, fructose,* and *galactose.* Glucose is by far the most important, and when we talk about blood sugar levels, glucose is the "sugar" being referred to. Fructose is the most abundant sugar in fruits, and galactose is found in milk.

Essentially, the only carbohydrates that our digestive system digests, or breaks down to simple sugars, are *sucrose* (table sugar), *lactose* (milk sugar), *maltose* (malt sugar), and *starch.* Sucrose, maltose, and lactose are referred to as *disaccharides,* or double sugars, because each consists of two simple sugars linked together. Starch is a *polysaccharide* (literally, "many sugars") formed of hundreds of glucose units. Although we eat foods containing other polysaccharides, such as *cellulose,* we do not have enzymes capable of breaking them down. The indigestible polysaccharides do not provide us with any nutrients, but they help move the foodstuffs along the gastrointestinal tract by providing bulk, or *fiber,* in our diet.

Proteins are digested to their building blocks, which are *amino* (ah-me′no) acids. Intermediate products of protein digestion are polypeptides and peptides.

When lipids (fats) are digested, they yield two different types of building blocks—fatty acids and an alcohol called glycerol (glis′er-ol). The chemical breakdown of carbohydrates, proteins, and fats is summarized in Figure 14.13 and is described in more detail shortly.

5. **Absorption.** Transport of digested end products from the lumen of the GI tract to the blood or lymph is absorption. For absorption to occur, the digested foods must first enter the mucosal cells by active or passive transport processes. The small intestine is the major absorptive site.

6. **Defecation.** Defecation is the elimination of indigestible residues from the GI tract via the anus in the form of feces (fe′sēz).

Some of these processes are the job of a single organ. For example, only the mouth ingests, and only the large intestine defecates. But most digestive system activities occur bit by bit as food is moved along the tract. Thus, in one sense, the digestive tract can be viewed as a "disassembly line" in which food is carried from one stage of its processing to the next, and its nutrients are made available to the cells in the body en route.

A point that we have stressed throughout this book has been the body's drive to maintain a constant internal environment, particularly in terms of homeostasis of the blood, which comes into intimate contact with all body cells. The digestive system, however, creates an optimal environment for itself to function in the lumen (cavity) of the alimentary canal, an area that is actually *outside* the body. Conditions in that lumen are controlled so that digestive processes occur efficiently.

Digestive activity is mostly controlled by reflexes via the parasympathetic division of the autonomic nervous system. (Recall from Chapter 7 that this is the "resting-and-digesting" arm.) The sensors (mechanoreceptors, chemoreceptors) involved in these reflexes are located in the walls of the alimentary canal organs and respond to a number of stimuli, the most important being stretch of the organ by food in its lumen, pH of the contents, and presence of certain breakdown products of digestion. When these receptors are activated, they start reflexes that activate or inhibit (1) the glands that secrete digestive juices into the lumen or hormones into the blood, and (2) the smooth muscles of the muscularis that mix and propel the foods along the tract.

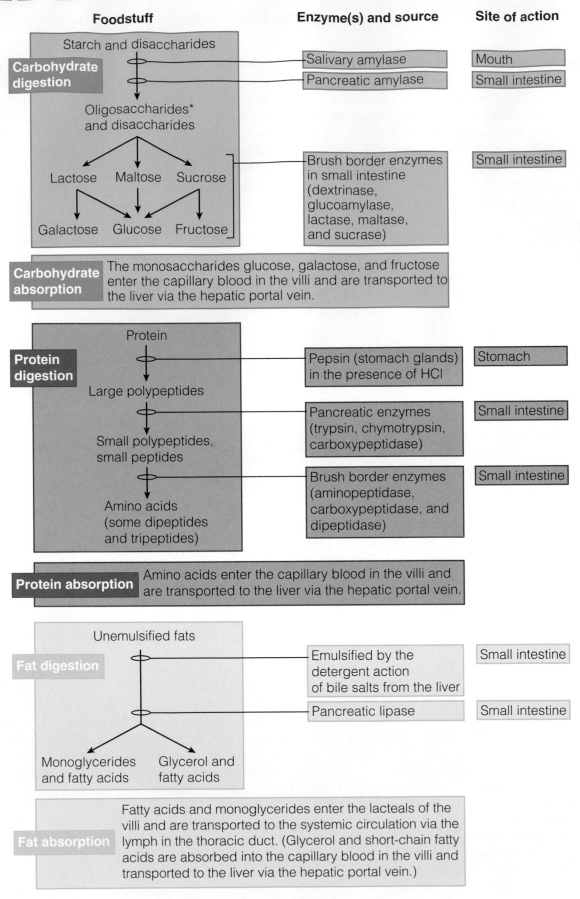

Foodstuff	Enzyme(s) and source	Site of action

Carbohydrate digestion

Starch and disaccharides → Oligosaccharides* and disaccharides

- Salivary amylase — Mouth
- Pancreatic amylase — Small intestine

Oligosaccharides* and disaccharides →

Lactose, Maltose, Sucrose → Galactose, Glucose, Fructose

- Brush border enzymes in small intestine (dextrinase, glucoamylase, lactase, maltase, and sucrase) — Small intestine

Carbohydrate absorption
The monosaccharides glucose, galactose, and fructose enter the capillary blood in the villi and are transported to the liver via the hepatic portal vein.

Protein digestion

Protein →

- Pepsin (stomach glands) in the presence of HCl — Stomach

Large polypeptides →

- Pancreatic enzymes (trypsin, chymotrypsin, carboxypeptidase) — Small intestine

Small polypeptides, small peptides →

- Brush border enzymes (aminopeptidase, carboxypeptidase, and dipeptidase) — Small intestine

Amino acids (some dipeptides and tripeptides)

Protein absorption
Amino acids enter the capillary blood in the villi and are transported to the liver via the hepatic portal vein.

Fat digestion

Unemulsified fats →

- Emulsified by the detergent action of bile salts from the liver — Small intestine
- Pancreatic lipase — Small intestine

Monoglycerides and fatty acids   Glycerol and fatty acids

Fat absorption
Fatty acids and monoglycerides enter the lacteals of the villi and are transported to the systemic circulation via the lymph in the thoracic duct. (Glycerol and short-chain fatty acids are absorbed into the capillary blood in the villi and transported to the liver via the hepatic portal vein.)

*Oligosaccharides consist of a few linked monosaccharides.

FIGURE 14.13 **Flow chart of chemical digestion and absorption of foodstuffs.**

Now that we have summarized some points that apply to the function of the digestive organs as a group, we are ready to look at their special capabilities.

Activities Occurring in the Mouth, Pharynx, and Esophagus
Food Ingestion and Breakdown

Once food has been placed in the mouth, both mechanical and chemical digestion begin. First the food is *physically* broken down into smaller particles by chewing. Then, as the food is mixed with saliva, salivary amylase begins the *chemical* digestion of starch, breaking it down into maltose (see Figure 14.13). The next time you eat a piece of bread, chew it for a few minutes before swallowing it. You will notice that it begins to taste sweet as the sugars are released.

Saliva is normally secreted continuously to keep the mouth moist; but, when food enters the mouth, much larger amounts of saliva pour out. However, the simple pressure of anything put in the mouth and chewed, such as rubber bands or sugarless gum, will also stimulate the release of saliva. Some emotional stimuli can also cause salivation. For example, the mere thought of a hot fudge sundae will make many a mouth water. All these reflexes, though initiated by different stimuli, are brought about by parasympathetic fibers in cranial nerves V and IX.

Essentially no food absorption occurs in the mouth. (However, some drugs, such as nitroglycerine, are absorbed easily through the oral mucosa.) The pharynx and esophagus have no digestive function; they simply provide passageways to carry food to the next processing site, the stomach.

Food Propulsion—Swallowing and Peristalsis

For food to be sent on its way from the mouth, it must first be swallowed. **Deglutition** (deg″loo-tish′un), or **swallowing,** is a complex process that involves the coordinated activity of several structures (tongue, soft palate, pharynx, and esophagus). It has two major phases. The first phase, the voluntary **buccal phase,** occurs in the mouth. Once the food has been chewed and well mixed with saliva, the bolus (food mass) is forced into the pharynx by the tongue. As food enters the pharynx, it passes out of our control and into the realm of reflex activity.

The second phase, the involuntary **pharyngeal-esophageal phase,** transports food through the pharynx and esophagus. The parasympathetic division of the autonomic nervous system (primarily the vagus nerves) controls this phase and promotes the mobility of the digestive organs from this point on. All routes that the food might take, except the desired route distal into the digestive tract, are blocked off. The tongue blocks off the mouth, and the soft palate closes off the nasal passages. The larynx rises so that its opening (into the respiratory passageways) is covered by the flaplike epiglottis. Food is moved through the pharynx and then into the esophagus below by wavelike peristaltic contractions of their muscular walls—first the longitudinal muscles contract, and then the circular muscles contract. The events of the swallowing process are illustrated in Figure 14.14.

If we try to talk while swallowing, our routing mechanisms may be "short-circuited," and food may enter the respiratory passages. This triggers still another protective reflex—coughing—during which air rushes upward from the lungs in an attempt to expel the food.

Once food reaches the distal end of the esophagus, it presses against the cardioesophageal sphincter, causing it to open, and the food enters the stomach. The movement of food through the pharynx and esophagus is so automatic that a person can swallow and food will reach the stomach even if he is standing on his head. Gravity plays no part in the transport of food once it has left the mouth, which explains why astronauts in the zero gravity of outer space can still swallow and get nourishment.

Activities of the Stomach
Food Breakdown

Secretion of **gastric juice** is regulated by both neural and hormonal factors. The sight, smell, and taste of food stimulate parasympathetic nervous system reflexes, which increase the secretion of gastric juice by the stomach glands. In addition, the presence of food and a rising pH in the stomach stimulate the stomach cells to release the hormone **gastrin.** Gastrin prods the stomach glands to produce still more of the protein-digesting enzymes (pepsinogens), mucus, and hydrochloric acid. Under normal conditions, 2 to 3 liters of gastric juice are produced every day.

Hydrochloric acid makes the stomach contents very acid. This is (somewhat) dangerous because both hydrochloric acid and the protein-digesting enzymes have the ability to digest the stomach itself, causing *ulcers* (see the "A Closer Look" box

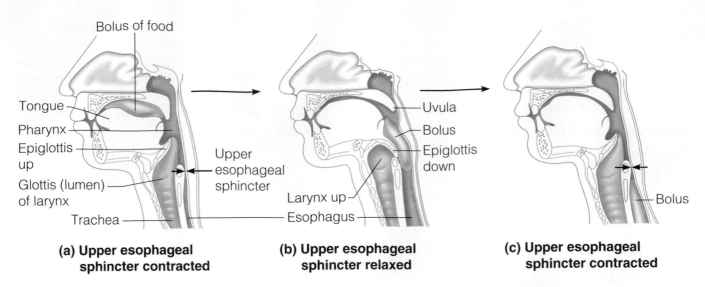

(a) Upper esophageal sphincter contracted

(b) Upper esophageal sphincter relaxed

(c) Upper esophageal sphincter contracted

(d) Cardioesophageal sphincter relaxed

FIGURE 14.14   Swallowing. (a) The tongue pushes the food bolus posteriorly and against the soft palate. **(b)** The soft palate rises to close off the nasal passages as the bolus enters the pharynx. The larynx rises so that the epiglottis covers its opening as peristalsis carries the food through the pharynx and into the esophagus. The upper esophageal sphincter relaxes to allow food entry. **(c)** The upper esophageal sphincter contracts again as the larynx and epiglottis return to their former positions and peristalsis moves the food bolus inferiorly to the stomach. **(d)** The cardioesophageal sphincter opens, and food enters the stomach.

on pp. 488–489). However, as long as enough mucus is made, the stomach is "safe" and will remain unharmed.

HOMEOSTATIC IMBALANCE

Occasionally, the cardioesophageal sphincter fails to close tightly and gastric juice backs up into the esophagus, which has little mucus protection. This results in a characteristic pain known as **heartburn,** which, if uncorrected, leads to inflammation of the esophagus (**esophagitis** [ě-sof′ah-ji′tis]) and perhaps even to ulceration of the esophagus. A common cause is a **hiatal hernia,** a structural abnormality in which the superior part of the stomach protrudes slightly above the diaphragm. Because the diaphragm no longer reinforces the cardioesophageal sphincter, which is a weak sphincter to begin with, gastric juice flows into the unprotected esophagus. Conservative treatment involves restricting food intake after the evening meal, taking antacids, and sleeping with the head elevated. ▲

The extremely acidic environment that hydrochloric acid provides *is* necessary, because it activates **pepsinogen** to **pepsin,** the active protein-digesting enzyme. *Rennin,* the second protein-digesting enzyme produced by the stomach, works primarily on milk protein and converts it to a substance that looks like sour milk. Many mothers mistakenly think that when their infants spit up a curdy substance after having their bottle that the milk has soured in their stomach. Rennin is produced in large amounts in infants, but it is not believed to be produced in adults.

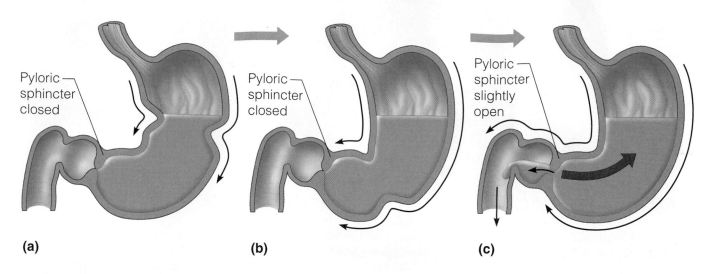

(a)   (b)   (c)

FIGURE 14.15 **Peristaltic waves act primarily in the inferior portion of the stomach to mix and move chyme through the pyloric valve. (a)** Peristaltic waves move toward the pylorus. **(b)** The most vigorous peristalsis and mixing action occurs close to the pylorus. **(c)** The pyloric end of the stomach acts as a pump that delivers small amounts of chyme into the duodenum while forcing most of the contained material backward into the stomach, where it undergoes further mixing.

Other than the beginning of protein digestion, little chemical digestion occurs in the stomach. Except for aspirin and alcohol (which seem somehow to have a "special pass"), virtually no absorption occurs through the stomach walls.

As food enters and fills the stomach, its wall begins to stretch (at the same time the gastric juices are being secreted, as just described). Then the three muscle layers of the stomach wall become active. They compress and pummel the food, breaking it apart physically, all the while continuously mixing the food with the enzyme-containing gastric juice so that the semifluid chyme is formed. The process looks something like the preparation of a cake mix, in which the floury mixture is repeatedly folded on itself and mixed with the liquid until it reaches uniform texture.

Food Propulsion

Once the food has been well mixed, a rippling peristalsis begins in the upper half of the stomach, and the contractions increase in force as the food approaches the pyloric valve. The pylorus of the stomach, which holds about 30 ml of chyme, acts like a meter that allows only liquids and very small particles to pass through the pyloric sphincter (Figure 14.15). Because the pyloric sphincter barely opens, each contraction of the stomach

muscle squirts 3 ml or less of chyme into the small intestine. The contraction also *closes* the valve, so the rest (about 27 ml) is propelled backward into the stomach for more mixing.

When the duodenum is filled with chyme and its wall is stretched, a nervous reflex, the *enterogastric* (en"ter-o-gas'trik) *reflex,* occurs. This reflex "puts the brakes on" gastric activity and slows the emptying of the stomach by inhibiting the vagus nerves and tightening the pyloric sphincter, thus allowing time for intestinal processing to catch up. Generally, it takes about 4 hours for the stomach to empty completely after the person eats a well-balanced meal and 6 hours or more if the meal has a high fat content.

HOMEOSTATIC IMBALANCE

Local irritation of the stomach, such as occurs with bacterial food poisoning, may activate the *emetic* (ē-met'ik) *center* in the brain (medulla). The emetic center, in turn, causes **vomiting (emesis).** Vomiting is essentially a reverse peristalsis occurring in the stomach (and perhaps the small intestine), accompanied by contraction of the abdominal muscles and the diaphragm, which increases the pressure on the abdominal organs. The emetic center may also be activated through other pathways; disturbance of the equilibrium apparatus of the inner ear during a boat ride on rough water is one example. ▲

A CLOSER LOOK

PEPTIC ULCERS: "SOMETHING IS EATING AT ME"

Archie, a 53-year-old factory worker, began to experience a burning pain in his upper abdomen an hour or two after each meal. At first, he blamed the poor quality of his home cooking, but he experienced the same symptoms after eating at the factory cafeteria or at restaurants. Archie always responded to stress by drinking and smoking heavily, and his abdominal pain became markedly worse during a hectic week when he worked 15 hours of overtime. After two months of increasingly severe pain, Archie consulted a physician and was told that he had a peptic ulcer.

Peptic ulcers affect one of every eight Americans. A peptic ulcer is a craterlike erosion in the mucosa of any part of the GI tract exposed to the hydrochloric acid and pepsin secretions of the stomach; see photo (a). A few peptic ulcers occur in the lower esophagus, following the reflux of stomach contents, but most (98 percent) occur in the pyloric part of the stomach (gastric ulcers) or the first part of the duodenum (duodenal ulcers). Duodenal ulcers are about three times more common than gastric ulcers. Peptic ulcers may appear at any age, but they develop most frequently between the ages of 50 and 70 years. After developing, they tend to recur—healing, then flaring up periodically—for the rest of one's life if not treated.

Gastric and duodenal ulcers may produce a gnawing or burning pain in the epigastric region of the abdomen. This pain often begins one to three

> ## "Peptic ulcers can produce serious complications."

hours after a meal (or awakens one at night) and is typically relieved by eating. Other symptoms include loss of appetite, bloating, nausea, and vomiting. Not all people with ulcers experience the above symptoms, however, and some exhibit no symptoms at all.

Traditionally, "common knowledge" held that stress causes ulcers, and the stereotypical ulcer patient was the overworked business executive. Recent studies have not been able to demonstrate a causal link between stress and ulcers. Nonetheless, a stressful lifestyle does seem to *aggravate* existing ulcers. Recent studies indicate that most ulcers (90 to 100 percent of duodenal ulcers and 80 to 90 percent of gastric ulcers) are actually caused by a strain of acid-resistant bacteria *(Helicobacter pylori)* that inhabit the stomachs of 40 percent of healthy people and 70 to 90 percent of those with ulcers; see photo (b).

The anatomy of a peptic ulcer is shown in photo (a) in this box. It typically is a round, sharply defined crater 1 to 4 cm in diameter in the mucosa. The base of the ulcer contains dead tissue cells, granulation tissue, and scar tissue. Eroded blood vessels may sometimes be seen there as well.

Peptic ulcers can produce serious complications. In about 20 percent of cases, eroded blood vessels bleed into the GI tract, causing vomiting of blood and blood in the feces. In such cases, anemia may result from a severe loss of blood. In 5 to 10 percent of patients, scarring within the stomach obstructs the pyloric opening, blocking digestion. About 5 percent of peptic ulcers *perforate,* leaking stomach or duodenal contents into the peritoneal cavity. This can cause either peritonitis or digestion and destruction of the nearby pancreas. A perforated ulcer is a life-threatening condition.

In spite of these potential complications, most peptic ulcers heal readily and respond well to treatment. The first steps in treatment are to avoid smoking, alcohol (especially wine), ibuprofen, and aspirin, all of which aggravate ulcers. Antacid drugs are often suggested to neutralize the stomach acids. In ulcers found to be colonized by the spiral-shaped *H. pylori* the goal is to kill the embedded bacteria. A simple 2-week regimen of antibiotics permanently

(a) A peptic ulcer lesion

Bacteria

Mucosa layer of stomach

(b) H. pylori bacteria

cures peptic ulcers in 95 percent of all such patients. Additional medication that suppresses acid production in the stomach can be combined with the antibiotic therapy to speed recovery.

The relatively few peptic ulcers not caused by *H. pylori* generally re-sult from long-term use of NSAIDs. They are treated with antihistamine drugs (such as Zantac) rather than antibiotics. These acid-suppressing drugs inhibit the stimulatory effect of histamine on the parietal cells of the stomach glands. The same treatment is used for *esophageal* peptic ulcers associated with gastroesophageal re-flux disease.

Recent animal trials using a newly developed vaccine against *H. pylori* have been successful. It is hoped that preventive vaccination, coupled with antibiotic cures, will eradicate peptic ulcers within the next 25 years.

Activities of the Small Intestine
Food Breakdown and Absorption

Food reaching the small intestine is only partially digested. Carbohydrate and protein digestion has begun, but virtually no fats have been digested up to this point. Here the process of chemical food digestion is accelerated as the food now takes a rather wild 3- to 6-hour journey through the loop-ing coils and twists of the small intestine. By the time the food reaches the end of the small intes-tine, digestion is complete and nearly all food ab-sorption has occurred.

As mentioned earlier, the microvilli of small intestine cells bear a few important enzymes, the so-called **brush border enzymes,** that break down double sugars into simple sugars and complete protein digestion (see Figure 14.13). *Intestinal juice* itself is relatively enzyme-poor, and protec-tive mucus is probably the most important intes-tinal gland secretion. However, foods entering the small intestine are literally deluged with enzyme-rich

TABLE 14.1	Hormones and Hormonelike Products That Act in Digestion		
Hormone	**Source**	**Stimulus for secretion**	**Action**
Gastrin	Stomach	Food in stomach (chemical stimulus); ACH released by nerve fibers	• Stimulates release of gastric juice • Stimulates stomach emptying
Intestinal gastrin	Duodenum	Acidic food in stomach	• Stimulates gastric secretion and emptying
Histamine	Stomach	Food in stomach	• Activates parietal cells to secrete hydrochloric acid.
Somatostatin	Stomach and duodenum	Food in stomach; stimulated by sympathetic nerve fibers	• Inhibits secretion of gastric juice and pancreatic juice • Inhibits emptying of stomach and gallbladder.
Secretin	Duodenum	Acidic chyme and partially digested foods in duodenum	• Increases output of pancreatic juice rich in bicarbonate ions • Increases bile output by liver • Inhibits gastric mobility and gastric gland secretion.
Cholecystokinin (CCK)	Duodenum	Fatty chyme and partially digested proteins in duodenum	• Increases output of enzyme-rich pancreatic juice • Stimulates gallbladder to expel stored bile • Relaxes sphincter of duodenal papilla to allow bile and pancreatic juice to enter the duodenum.
Gastric inhibitory peptide (GIP)	Duodenum	Fatty chyme in duodenum	• Inhibits secretion of gastric juice.

pancreatic juice ducted in from the pancreas, as well as bile from the liver.

Pancreatic juice contains enzymes that (1) along with brush border enzymes, complete the digestion of starch *(pancreatic amylase);* (2) carry out about half of protein digestion (via the action of *trypsin, chymotrypsin, carboxypeptidase,* and others); (3) are totally responsible for fat digestion, because the pancreas is essentially the only source of *lipases;* and (4) digest nucleic acids *(nucleases).*

In addition to enzymes, pancreatic juice contains a rich supply of bicarbonate, which makes it very basic (about pH 8). When pancreatic juice reaches the small intestine, it neutralizes the acidic chyme coming in from the stomach and provides the proper environment for activation and activity of intestinal and pancreatic digestive enzymes.

HOMEOSTATIC IMBALANCE

Pancreatitis (pan"kre-ah-ti'tis) is a rare but extremely serious inflammation of the pancreas that results from activation of pancreatic enzymes in the pancreatic duct. Because pancreatic enzymes break down all categories of biological molecules, they cause digestion of the pancreatic tissue and duct. This painful condition can lead to nutritional deficiencies, because pancreatic enzymes are essential for digestion in the small intestine. ▲

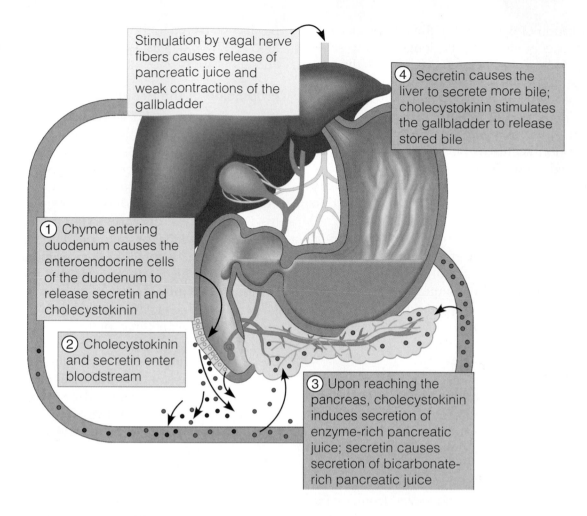

Stimulation by vagal nerve fibers causes release of pancreatic juice and weak contractions of the gallbladder

④ Secretin causes the liver to secrete more bile; cholecystokinin stimulates the gallbladder to release stored bile

① Chyme entering duodenum causes the enteroendocrine cells of the duodenum to release secretin and cholecystokinin

② Cholecystokinin and secretin enter bloodstream

③ Upon reaching the pancreas, cholecystokinin induces secretion of enzyme-rich pancreatic juice; secretin causes secretion of bicarbonate-rich pancreatic juice

FIGURE 14.16   Regulation of pancreatic juice secretion. Hormonal controls, exerted by secretin and cholecystokinin (steps 1–3), are the main regulatory factors. Neural control is mediated by the vagus nerves.

The release of pancreatic juice into the duodenum is stimulated by both the vagus nerves and local hormones. When chyme enters the small intestine, it stimulates the mucosa cells to produce several hormones (Table 14.1). Two of these hormones, **secretin** (se-kre′tin) and **cholecystokinin** (ko″le-sis″to-kin′in) **(CCK),** influence the release of pancreatic juice and bile.

The hormones enter the blood and circulate to their target organs, the pancreas, liver, and gallbladder. Both hormones work together to stimulate the pancreas to release its enzyme- and bicarbonate-rich product (Figure 14.16). In addition, secretin causes the liver to increase its output of bile, and cholecystokinin causes the gallbladder to contract and release stored bile into the bile duct so that bile and pancreatic juice enter the small intestine

together. As mentioned before, bile is not an enzyme. Instead, it acts like a detergent to emulsify, or mechanically break down, large fat globules into thousands of tiny ones, providing a much greater surface area for the pancreatic lipases to work on. Bile is also necessary for absorption of fats (and other fat-soluble vitamins [K, D, and A] that are absorbed along with them) from the intestinal tract.

HOMEOSTATIC IMBALANCE

If *either* bile or pancreatic juice is absent, essentially no fat digestion or absorption goes on, and fatty, bulky stools are the result. In such cases, blood-clotting problems also occur because the liver needs vitamin K to make prothrombin, one of the clotting factors. ▲

Absorption of water and of the end products of digestion occurs all along the length of the small intestine. Most substances are absorbed through the intestinal cell plasma membranes by the process of *active transport*. Then they enter the capillary beds in the villi to be transported in the blood to the liver via the hepatic portal vein. The exception seems to be lipids, or fats, which are absorbed passively by the process of *diffusion*. Lipid breakdown products enter both the capillary beds and the lacteals in the villi and are carried to the liver by both blood and lymphatic fluids.

At the end of the ileum, all that remains is some water, indigestible food materials (plant fibers such as cellulose), and large amounts of bacteria. This debris enters the large intestine through the ileocecal valve. The complete process of food digestion and absorption is summarized in Figure 14.13 (p. 484).

Food Propulsion

As mentioned previously, *peristalsis* is the major means of propelling food through the digestive tract. It involves waves of contraction that move along the length of the intestine, followed by waves of relaxation. The net effect is that the food is moved through the small intestine in much the same way that toothpaste is squeezed from a tube. Rhythmic segmental movements produce local constrictions of the intestine (see Figure 14.12b) that mix the chyme with the digestive juices, and help to propel food through the intestine.

Activities of the Large Intestine
Food Breakdown and Absorption

What is finally delivered to the large intestine contains few nutrients, but that residue still has 12 to 24 hours more to spend there. The colon itself produces no digestive enzymes. However, the "resident" bacteria that live in its lumen metabolize some of the remaining nutrients, releasing gases (methane and hydrogen sulfide) that contribute to the odor of feces. About 500 ml of gas (flatus) is produced each day, much more when certain carbohydrate-rich foods (such as beans) are eaten.

Bacteria residing in the large intestine also make some vitamins (vitamin K and some B vitamins). Absorption by the large intestine is limited to the absorption of these vitamins, some ions, and most of the remaining water. **Feces,** the more or less solid product delivered to the rectum, contain undigested food residues, mucus, millions of bacteria, and just enough water to allow their smooth passage.

Propulsion of the Residue and Defecation

When presented with food residue, the colon becomes motile, but its contractions are sluggish or short-lived. The movements most seen in the colon are **haustral contractions,** slow segmenting movements lasting about one minute that occur every 30 minutes or so. As a haustrum fills with food residue, the distension stimulates its muscle to contract, which propels the luminal contents into the next haustrum. These movements also mix the residue, which aids in water absorption.

Mass movements are long, slow-moving but powerful contractile waves that move over large areas of the colon three or four times daily and force the contents toward the rectum. Typically, they occur during or just after eating, when food begins to fill the stomach and small intestine. Bulk, or fiber, in the diet increases the strength of colon contractions and softens the stool, allowing the colon to act as a well-oiled machine.

HOMEOSTATIC IMBALANCE

When the diet lacks bulk, the colon narrows and its circular muscles contract more powerfully, which increases the pressure on its walls. This encourages formation of **diverticula** (di"ver-tik'u-lah), in which the mucosa protrudes through the colon walls, a condition called **diverticulosis. Diverticulitis,** a condition in which the diverticula become inflamed, can be life-threatening if ruptures occur. ▲

The rectum is generally empty, but when feces are forced into it by mass movements and its wall is stretched, the **defecation reflex** is initiated. The defecation reflex is a spinal (sacral region) reflex that causes the walls of the sigmoid colon and the rectum to contract and the anal sphincters to relax. As the feces are forced through the anal canal, messages reach the brain giving us time to make a decision as to whether the external voluntary sphincter should remain open or be constricted to stop passage of feces. If it is not convenient, defecation (or "moving the bowels") can be delayed temporarily. Within a few seconds, the reflex contractions end and the rectal walls relax. With the next mass movement, the defecation reflex is initiated again.

HOMEOSTATIC IMBALANCE

Watery stools, or **diarrhea** (di"ah-re'ah), result from any condition that rushes food residue through the large intestine before that organ has had sufficient time to absorb the water (as in irritation of the colon by bacteria). Because fluids and ions are lost from the body, prolonged diarrhea may result in dehydration and electrolyte imbalance which, if severe, can be fatal.

If food residue remains in the large intestine for extended periods, too much water is absorbed, and the stool becomes hard and difficult to pass. This condition, called **constipation,** may result from lack of fiber in the diet, poor bowel habits ("failing to heed the call"), and laxative abuse. ▲

▶ DID YOU GET IT?

11. How do mechanical and chemical digestion differ from each other?

12. What are the building blocks (and digestion products) of proteins?

13. What is the proper order of the following stages of food processing—defecation, absorption, digestion, ingestion?

14. Why is it necessary for the stomach contents to be so acidic?

15. What does it mean when we say that food "went down the wrong tube"?

For answers, see Appendix D.

PART II: NUTRITION AND METABOLISM

Although it seems at times that people can be divided into two camps—those who live to eat and those who eat to live—we all recognize the vital importance of food for life. It has been said that "you are what you eat," and this is true in that part of the food we eat is converted to our living flesh. In other words, a certain fraction of nutrients is used to build cellular molecules and structures and to replace worn-out parts. However, most foods are used as metabolic fuels. That is, they are oxidized and transformed into **ATP,** the chemical energy form needed by body cells to drive their many activities. The energy value of foods is measured in units called **kilocalories (kcal),** or Calories (with a capital C), the units conscientiously counted by dieters.

We have just considered how foods are digested and absorbed. But what happens to these foods once they enter the blood? Why do we need bread, meat, and fresh vegetables? Why does everything we eat seem to turn to fat? We will try to answer these questions in this section.

Nutrition

A **nutrient** is a substance in food that is used by the body to promote normal growth, maintenance, and repair. The nutrients divide neatly into six categories. The **major nutrients**—carbohydrates, lipids, and proteins—make up the bulk of what we eat. **Minor nutrients**—vitamins and minerals—while equally crucial for health, are required in minute amounts. Water, which accounts for about 60 percent of the volume of the food we eat, is also considered to be a major nutrient. However, because its importance as a solvent and in many other aspects of body functioning is described in Chapter 2, only the other five classes of nutrients will be considered here.

Most foods offer a combination of nutrients. For example, a bowl of cream of mushroom soup contains all of the major nutrients plus some vitamins and minerals. A diet consisting of foods selected from each of the five food groups (Table 14.2), that is, grains, fruits, vegetables, meats and fish, and milk products, normally guarantees adequate amounts of all of the needed nutrients.

More detailed are the several types of food guide pyramids that have been developed. The most recent version, issued by the U.S. Department of Agriculture in 2005—MyPyramid—is a significant departure from traditional food pyramids (Figure 14.17). MyPyramid separates the food categories vertically (rather than horizontally). Narrowing of each food group from bottom to top of the pyramid suggests moderation in selecting foods from each food group (more "picks" from food choices at the bottom of the food band, which contain less added sugar and solid fats). Also new to this food pyramid version is the emphasis on at least 30 minutes daily of physical activity, as represented by the stick person climbing the steps. Considered very important is the fact that you can personalize your diet by age, sex, and activity level by logging on to the Internet (www.mypyramid.gov), where information is available to help consumers make healthy choices and determine the size and number of servings recommended daily.

14

TABLE 14.2	Five Basic Food Groups and Some of Their Major Nutrients

Group	Example foods	Major nutrients supplied in significant amounts:	
		By all in group	By only some in group
Fruits	Apples, bananas, dates, oranges tomatoes	Carbohydrate Water	Vitamins: A, C, folic acid Minerals: iron, potassium Fiber
Vegetables	Broccoli, cabbage, green beans, lettuce, potatoes	Carbohydrate Water	Vitamins: A, C, E, K, and B vitamins except B_{12} Minerals: calcium, magnesium, iodine, manganese, phosphorus Fiber
Grain products (preferably whole grain; otherwise, enriched or fortified)	Breads, rolls, bagels; cereals, dry and cooked; pasta; rice, other grains; tortillas, pancakes, waffles; crackers; popcorn	Carbohydrate Protein Vitamins: thiamin (B_1), niacin	Water Fiber Minerals: iron, magnesium, selenium
Milk products	Milk, yogurt; cheese; ice cream, ice milk, frozen yogurt	Protein Fat Vitamins: riboflavin, B_{12} Minerals: calcium, phosphorus Water	Carbohydrate Vitamins: A, D
Meats and meat alternatives	Meat, fish, poultry; eggs; seeds; nuts, nut butters; soybeans, tofu; other legumes (peas and beans)	Protein Vitamins: niacin, B_6 Minerals: iron, zinc	Carbohydrate Fat Vitamins: B_{12}, thiamin (B_1) Water Fiber

Source: Christian, Janet, and Janet Greger. *Nutrition for Living,* 3rd ed. San Francisco, CA: Benjamin Cummings, 1991.

Dietary Sources of the Major Nutrients

Carbohydrates

Except for milk sugar (lactose) and small amounts of glycogen in meats, all the **carbohydrates**—sugars and starches—we ingest are derived from plants. Sugars come mainly from fruits, sugar cane, and milk. The polysaccharide starch is found in grains, legumes, and root vegetables. The polysaccharide cellulose, which is plentiful in most vegetables, is not digested by humans, but it provides roughage, or fiber, which increases the bulk of the stool and aids defecation.

Lipids

Although we also ingest cholesterol and phospholipids, most dietary **lipids** are triglycerides **(neutral fats).** We eat saturated fats in animal products such as meat and dairy foods and in a few plant products, such as coconut. Unsaturated fats are present in seeds, nuts, and most vegetable oils. Major sources of cholesterol are egg yolk, meats, and milk products.

Proteins

Animal products contain the highest-quality **proteins,** molecules that are basically amino acid polymers. Eggs, milk, fish, and most meat proteins are *complete proteins* that meet all of the body's amino acid requirements for tissue maintenance and growth. Legumes (beans and peas), nuts, and cereals are also protein-rich, but their proteins are nutritionally incomplete because they are low in one or more of the essential amino acids. The **essential amino acids** are the eight (ten in infants) amino acids that our body cannot make and that we must take in through the diet. As you can see, strict vegetarians must carefully plan their diets to obtain all the essential amino acids and prevent protein malnutrition. Cereal grains and legumes when ingested together provide all the needed amino acids, and some variety of this combination is found in the diets of all cultures (most obviously in the rice and beans seen on nearly every plate in a Mexican restaurant).

Vitamins

Vitamins are organic nutrients of various forms that the body requires in small amounts. Although vitamins are found in all major food groups, no one food contains all the required vitamins. Thus, a balanced diet is the best way to ensure a full vitamin complement, particularly because certain vitamins (A, C, and E) appear to have anticancer effects. Diets rich in broccoli, cabbage, and brussels sprouts (all good sources of vitamins A and C) appear to reduce cancer risk. However, controversy abounds concerning the ability of vitamins to work wonders.

Most vitamins function as **coenzymes** (or parts of coenzymes); that is, they act with an enzyme to accomplish a particular type of catalysis.

Minerals

The body also requires adequate supplies of seven **minerals** (that is, inorganic substances including calcium, phosphorus, potassium, sulfur, sodium, chloride, and magnesium) and trace amounts of about a dozen others.

Fats and sugars have practically no minerals, and cereals and grains are poor sources. The most mineral-rich foods are vegetables, legumes, milk, and some meats.

The main uses of the major nutrients in the body are discussed in the section on metabolism. Appendix C details some important roles of vitamins and minerals in the body.

Key:
- ▲ Grains
- ▲ Vegetables
- ▲ Fruits
- ▲ Oils
- ▲ Milk
- ▲ Meat and beans

MyPyramid.gov
STEPS TO A HEALTHIER YOU

FIGURE 14.17   USDA Food Guide Pyramid.

▶ DID YOU GET IT?

16. What is the major source of carbohydrates in our diet?

17. Why is it important to include cellulose in a healthy diet even though we cannot digest it?

18. Are oils saturated lipids or unsaturated lipids?

19. What is the most significant role that vitamins play in the body?

For answers, see Appendix D.

Metabolism

Metabolism (mĕ-tab′o-lizm; *metabol* = change) is a broad term referring to all chemical reactions that are necessary to maintain life. It involves **catabolism** (kah-tab′o-lizm), in which substances are broken down to simpler substances, and **anabolism** (ah-nab′o-lizm), in which larger molecules or structures are built from smaller ones. During catabolism, bond energy of foods is released and captured to make ATP, the energy-rich molecule used to energize all cellular activities, including catabolic reactions (Figure 14.18).

Not all foodstuffs are treated in the same way by body cells. For example, carbohydrates, particularly glucose, are usually broken down to make ATP. Fats are used to build cell membranes, make myelin sheaths, and insulate the body with a fatty cushion. They are also used as the body's main energy fuel for making ATP when there are

$C_6H_{12}O_6$ + 6 O_2 → 6 CO_2 + 6 H_2O + ATP

Glucose   Oxygen gas   Carbon dioxide   Water   Energy

FIGURE 14.18 **Summary equation for cellular respiration.**

inadequate carbohydrates in the diet. Proteins tend to be carefully conserved (even hoarded) by the body cells. This is easy to understand when you recognize that proteins are the major structural materials used for building cell structures.

Carbohydrate, Fat, and Protein Metabolism in Body Cells

Carbohydrate Metabolism

Just as an oil furnace uses oil (its fuel) to produce heat, the cells of the body use carbohydrates as their preferred fuel to produce cellular energy (ATP). **Glucose,** also known as **blood sugar,** is the major breakdown product of carbohydrate digestion. Glucose is also the major fuel used for making ATP in most body cells. The liver is an exception; it routinely uses fats as well, thus saving glucose for other body cells. Essentially, glucose is broken apart piece by piece, and some of the chemical energy released when its bonds are broken is captured and used to bind phosphate to ADP molecules to make ATP.

The overall reaction is summed up simply in Figure 14.18. Basically, the carbon atoms released leave the cells as carbon dioxide, and the hydrogen atoms removed (which contain energy-rich electrons) are eventually combined with oxygen to form water. These oxygen-using events are referred to collectively as **cellular respiration.** The events of the three main metabolic pathways that are involved in cellular respiration—*glycolysis,* the *Krebs cycle,* and the *electron transport chain*—are shown schematically in Figure 14.19.

Oxidation via the removal of hydrogen atoms (which are temporarily passed to vitamin-containing coenzymes) is a major role of glycolysis and the Krebs cycle. **Glycolysis** also energizes each glucose molecule so that it can be split into two pyruvic acid molecules and yield a small amount of ATP in the

process (Figure 14.19). The **Krebs cycle** produces virtually all the carbon dioxide and water that results during cell respiration. Like glycolysis, it yields a small amount of ATP by transferring high energy phosphate groups directly from phosphorylated substances to ADP. Free oxygen is not involved.

The **electron transport chain** is where the action is for ATP production. The hydrogen atoms removed during the first two metabolic phases are loaded with energy. These hydrogens are delivered by the coenzymes to the protein carriers of the electron transport chain, which form part of the mitochondrial cristae membranes (Figure 14.20). There the hydrogen atoms are split into hydrogen ions (H^+) and electrons (e^-). The electrons "fall down an energy hill" going from each carrier to a carrier of lower energy. They give off their "load" of energy in a series of steps in small enough amounts to enable the cell to attach phosphate to ADP and make ATP. Ultimately free oxygen is reduced (the electrons and hydrogen ions are united with molecular oxygen), forming water and a large amount of ATP. The beauty of this system is that, unlike the explosive reaction that usually happens when fuels are burned (O_2 is combined with hydrogen), relatively small amounts of energy are lost as heat (and light).

Because glucose is the major fuel for making ATP, homeostasis of blood glucose levels is critically important. If there are excessively high levels of glucose in the blood (**hyperglycemia** [hi″per-gli-se′me-ah]), some of the excess is stored in body cells (particularly liver and muscle cells) as glycogen. If blood glucose levels are still too high, excesses are converted to fat. There is no question that eating large amounts of empty-calorie foods such as candy and other sugary sweets causes a rapid deposit of fat in the body's adipose tissues. When blood glucose levels are too low (**hypoglycemia),** the liver breaks down stored

FIGURE 14.19   An overview of sites of ATP formation during cellular respiration. Glycolysis occurs outside the mitochondria in the cytosol. The Krebs cycle and the electron transport chain reactions occur within the mitochondria. ① During glycolysis, hydrogen atoms containing high-energy electrons are removed as each glucose molecule is broken down into two molecules of pyruvic acid. ② The pyruvic acid enters the mitochondrion, where Krebs cycle enzymes remove more hydrogen and decompose the pyruvic acid to carbon dioxide. During glycolysis and the Krebs cycle, small amounts of ATP are formed. ③ Chemical energy from glycolysis and the Krebs cycle, in the form of hydrogen atoms containing energy-rich electrons, is then transferred to the electron transport chain, which is built into the membrane of the cristae. The electron transport chain carries out oxidative phosphorylation, which produces most of the ATP generated by cellular respiration and finally unites the removed hydrogen with oxygen to form water.

glycogen and releases glucose to the blood for cellular use. These various fates of carbohydrates are shown in Figure 14.21a.

▶ DID YOU GET IT?

20. What name is given to the process in which glucose is combined with oxygen to yield CO_2, H_2O, and ATP?

21. What are the major end products of the Krebs cycle?

22. What are the major products of the electron transport chain?

For answers, see Appendix D.

Fat Metabolism

As described shortly, the liver handles most lipid, or fat, metabolism that goes on in the body. The liver cells use some fats to make ATP for their own use; use some to synthesize lipoproteins, thromboplastin (a clotting protein), and cholesterol; and then release the rest to the blood in the form of relatively small fat-breakdown products. Body cells remove the fat products and cholesterol from the blood and build them into their membranes or steroid hormones as needed. Fats are also used to form myelin sheaths of neurons (see Chapter 7) and fatty cushions around body organs. In addition, stored fats are the body's most concentrated

FIGURE 14.20   Electron transport chain versus one-step reduction of oxygen. (a) In cellular respiration, cascading electrons release energy in small steps and finally reduce O_2. The energy released is in quantities easily used to form ATP. (NADH is a niacin-containing coenzyme that delivers H^+ to the electron transport chain.) **(b)** When O_2 is reduced (combined with hydrogen) in one step, the result is an explosion.

source of energy. (Catabolism of 1 gram of fat yields twice as much energy as the breakdown of 1 gram of carbohydrate or protein.)

For fat products to be used for ATP synthesis, they must first be broken down to acetic acid (Figure 14.21d). Within the mitochondria, the acetic acid (like the pyruvic acid product of carbohydrates) is then completely oxidized, and carbon dioxide, water, and ATP are formed. When there is not enough glucose to fuel the needs of the cells for energy, larger amounts of fats are used to produce ATP. Under such conditions, fat oxidation is fast but incomplete, and some of the intermediate products, such as acetoacetic acid and acetone, begin to accumulate in the blood. These cause the blood to become acidic (a condition called **acidosis,** or **ketoacidosis**), and the breath takes on a fruity odor as acetone diffuses from the lungs. Ketoacidosis is a common consequence of "no-carbohydrate" diets, uncontrolled diabetes mellitus, and starvation in which the body is forced to rely almost totally on fats to fuel its energy needs. Although fats are an important energy source, cholesterol is *never* used

as a cellular fuel. Its importance lies in the functional molecules and in the structures it helps to form.

Excess fats are stored in fat depots such as the hips, abdomen, breasts, and subcutaneous tissues. Although the fat in subcutaneous tissue is important as insulation for the deeper body organs, excessive amounts restrict movement and place greater demands on the circulatory system. The metabolism and uses of fats are shown in Figure 14.21b.

Protein Metabolism

Proteins make up the bulk of cellular structures, and they are carefully conserved by body cells. Ingested proteins are broken down to amino acids. Once the liver has finished processing the blood draining the digestive tract and has taken its "fill" of amino acids, the remaining amino acids circulate to the body cells. The cells remove amino acids from the blood and use them to build proteins, both for their own use (enzymes, membranes, mitotic spindle proteins, muscle proteins) and for export (mucus, hormones, and others).

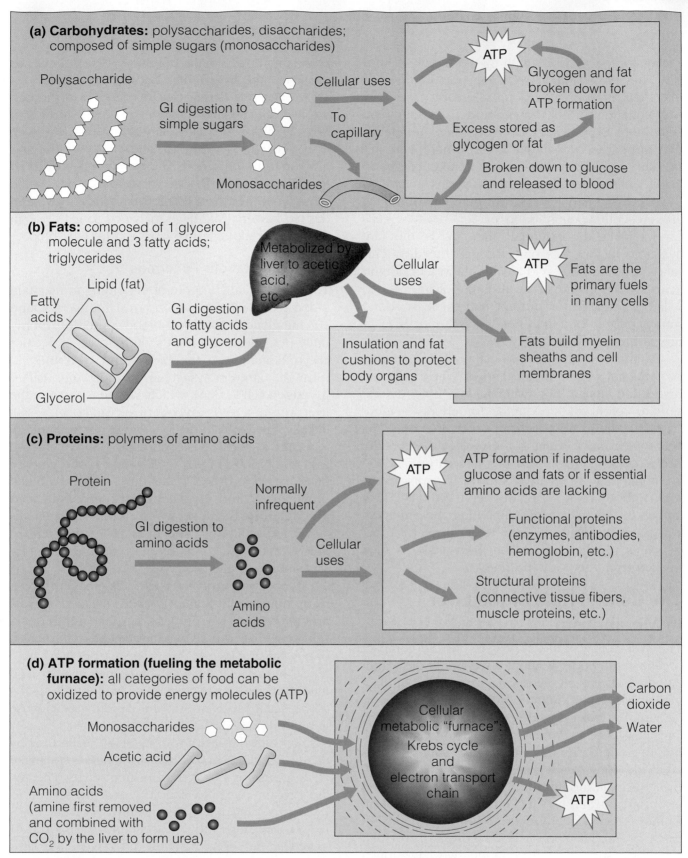

(a) Carbohydrates: polysaccharides, disaccharides; composed of simple sugars (monosaccharides)

Polysaccharide

GI digestion to simple sugars

Monosaccharides

To capillary

Cellular uses

ATP

Glycogen and fat broken down for ATP formation

Excess stored as glycogen or fat

Broken down to glucose and released to blood

(b) Fats: composed of 1 glycerol molecule and 3 fatty acids; triglycerides

Lipid (fat)

Fatty acids

Glycerol

GI digestion to fatty acids and glycerol

Metabolized by liver to acetic acid, etc.

Cellular uses

Insulation and fat cushions to protect body organs

ATP

Fats are the primary fuels in many cells

Fats build myelin sheaths and cell membranes

(c) Proteins: polymers of amino acids

Protein

GI digestion to amino acids

Amino acids

Normally infrequent

Cellular uses

ATP

ATP formation if inadequate glucose and fats or if essential amino acids are lacking

Functional proteins (enzymes, antibodies, hemoglobin, etc.)

Structural proteins (connective tissue fibers, muscle proteins, etc.)

(d) ATP formation (fueling the metabolic furnace): all categories of food can be oxidized to provide energy molecules (ATP)

Monosaccharides

Acetic acid

Amino acids (amine first removed and combined with CO_2 by the liver to form urea)

Cellular metabolic "furnace": Krebs cycle and electron transport chain

Carbon dioxide

Water

ATP

FIGURE 14.21   Metabolism by body cells. (a) Carbohydrate metabolism. **(b)** Fat metabolism. **(c)** Protein metabolism. **(d)** ATP formation.

Cells take few chances with their amino acid supply. They use ATP to actively transport amino acids into their interior even though in many cases they may contain more of those amino acids than there is in the blood flowing past them. Even though this may appear to be "cellular greed," there is an important reason for this active uptake of amino acids. Cells cannot build their proteins unless *all* the needed amino acids, which number around 20, are present. As mentioned earlier, because cells cannot make the essential amino acids, they are available to the cells only through the diet. This helps explain the avid accumulation of amino acids, which ensures that all amino acids needed will be available for present and (at least some) future protein-building needs of the cells (Figure 14.21c).

Amino acids are used to make ATP only when proteins are overabundant and/or when carbohydrates and fats are not available. When it is necessary to oxidize amino acids for energy (Figure 14.21d), their amine groups are removed as *ammonia,* and the rest of the molecule enters the Krebs cycle pathways in the mitochondria. The ammonia that is released during this process is toxic to body cells, especially nerve cells. The liver comes to the rescue by combining the ammonia with carbon dioxide to form **urea** (u-re′ah). Urea, which is not harmful to the body cells, is then flushed from the body in urine.

The Central Role of the Liver in Metabolism

The liver is one of the most versatile and complex organs in the body. Without it we would die within 24 hours. Its role in digestion (that is, the manufacture of bile) is important to the digestive process to be sure, but it is only one of the many functions of liver cells. The liver cells detoxify drugs and alcohol, degrade hormones, make many substances vital to the body as a whole (cholesterol, blood proteins such as albumin and clotting proteins, and lipoproteins), and play a central role in metabolism as they process nearly every class of nutrient. Because of the liver's key roles, nature has provided us with a surplus of liver tissue. We have much more than we need, and even if part of it is damaged or removed, it is one of the few body organs that can regenerate rapidly and easily.

As described in Chapter 11, a unique circulation, the *hepatic portal circulation,* brings nutrient-rich blood draining from the digestive viscera directly to the liver. The liver is the body's major metabolic organ, and this detour that nutrients take through the liver ensures that the liver's needs will be met first. As blood circulates slowly through the liver, liver cells remove amino acids, fatty acids, and glucose from the blood. These nutrients are stored for later use or processed in various ways. At the same time, the liver's phagocytic cells remove and destroy bacteria that have managed to get through the walls of the digestive tract and into the blood.

General Metabolic Functions

The liver is vitally important in helping to maintain blood glucose levels within normal range (around 100 mg glucose/100 ml of blood). After a carbohydrate-rich meal, thousands of glucose molecules are removed from the blood and combined to form the large polysaccharide molecules called **glycogen** (gli′ko-jen), which are then stored in the liver. This process is **glycogenesis** (gli″ko-jen′ĕ-sis), literally, "glycogen formation" (*genesis* = beginning).

Later, as body cells continue to remove glucose from the blood to meet their needs, blood glucose levels begin to drop. At this time, liver cells break down the stored glycogen, by a process called **glycogenolysis** (gli″ko-jen-ol′ĭ-sis), which means "glycogen splitting." The liver cells then release glucose bit by bit to the blood to maintain homeostasis of blood glucose levels.

If necessary, the liver can also make glucose from noncarbohydrate substances, such as fats and proteins. This process is **gluconeogenesis** (glu″ko-ne″o-jen′ĕ-sis), which means "formation of new sugar" (Figure 14.22). As described in Chapter 9, hormones such as thyroxine, insulin, and glucagon are vitally important in controlling the blood sugar levels and in the handling of glucose in all body cells.

Some of the fats and fatty acids picked up by the liver cells are oxidized for energy (to make ATP) for use by the liver cells themselves. The rest are broken down to simpler substances such as *acetic acid* and *acetoacetic acid* (two acetic acids linked together) and released into the blood, or stored as fat reserves in the liver. The liver also makes cholesterol and secretes cholesterol's breakdown products in bile.

All blood proteins made by the liver are built from the amino acids its cells pick up from the blood. The completed proteins are then released

Glycogenesis:
Glucose converted to glycogen and stored

Imbalance

Rising blood glucose level

Homeostatic blood sugar

Imbalance

Falling blood glucose level

Glycogenolysis:
Stored glycogen converted to glucose

Gluconeogenesis:
Amino acids and fats converted to glucose

FIGURE 14.22   Metabolic events occurring in the liver as blood glucose levels rise and fall. When the blood glucose level is rising, the liver removes glucose from the blood and stores it as glycogen (glycogenesis). When the blood glucose level falls, the liver breaks down stored glycogen (glycogenolysis) and makes new glucose from amino acids and fats (gluconeogenesis). The glucose is then released to the blood to restore homeostasis of blood sugar.

back into the blood to travel throughout the circulation. *Albumin,* the most abundant protein in blood, holds fluids in the bloodstream. When insufficient albumin is present in blood, fluid leaves the bloodstream and accumulates in the tissue spaces, causing edema. The role of the protective *clotting proteins* made by the liver was discussed in Chapter 10. Liver cells also synthesize nonessential amino acids and, as mentioned earlier, detoxify ammonia (produced when amino acids are oxidized for energy) by converting it to urea.

Nutrients not needed by the liver cells, as well as the products of liver metabolism, are released into the blood and drain from the liver in the hepatic vein to enter the systemic circulation, where they become available to other body cells.

Cholesterol Metabolism and Transport

Although it's a very important lipid in the diet, **cholesterol** is not used as an energy fuel. Instead, it serves as the structural basis of steroid hormones and vitamin D and is a major building block of plasma membranes. Because we hear so much about "cutting down our cholesterol intake" in the media, it is always surprising to learn that only about 15 percent of blood cholesterol comes from the diet. The other 85 percent or so is made by the liver. Cholesterol is lost from the body when it is broken down and secreted in bile salts, which eventually leave the body in feces.

Because of the important role they play in fat and cholesterol transport, the lipoproteins, one class of proteins made by the liver and known by the buzzwords *HDLs* and *LDLs*, deserve a bit more attention.

Fatty acids, fats, and cholesterol are insoluble in water, so they cannot circulate freely in the bloodstream. Instead they are transported bound to the small lipid-protein complexes called lipoproteins. Although the entire story is complex, the important thing to know is that the **low-density lipoproteins,** or **LDLs,** transport cholesterol and other lipids *to* body cells, where they are used in various ways. If large amounts of LDLs are circulating, the chance that fatty substances will be deposited on the arterial walls, initiating atherosclerosis, is high. Because of this possibility, the LDLs are unkindly tagged as "bad lipoproteins." By contrast, the lipoproteins that transport cholesterol *from* the tissue cells (or arteries) to the liver for disposal in bile are **high-density lipoproteins,** or **HDLs.** High HDL levels are considered "good" because the cholesterol is destined to be broken down and eliminated from the body. Obviously both LDLs and HDLs are "good and necessary"; it is just their relative ratio in the blood that determines whether or not potentially lethal cholesterol deposits are likely to be laid down in the artery walls. In general, aerobic exercise, a diet low in saturated fats and cholesterol, and abstaining from smoking and drinking coffee all appear to favor a desirable HDL/LDL ratio.

DID YOU GET IT?

23. What is gluconeogenesis?

24. If you had your choice, would you prefer to have high blood levels of HDLs or LDLs? Explain your answer.

For answers, see Appendix D.

Body Energy Balance

When any fuel is burned, it consumes oxygen and liberates heat. The "burning" of food fuels by body cells is no exception. As stated in Chapter 2, energy cannot be created or destroyed—it can only be converted from one form to another. If we apply this principle to cellular metabolism, it means that a dynamic balance exists between the body's energy intake and its energy output:

Energy intake = total energy output

(heat + work + energy storage)

Energy intake is the energy liberated during food oxidation—that is, during the reactions of glycolysis, the Krebs cycle, and the electron transport chain. **Energy output** includes the energy we immediately lose as heat (about 60 percent of the total), plus that used to do work (driven by ATP), plus energy that is stored in the form of fat or glycogen. Energy storage is important only during periods of growth and during net fat deposit.

Regulation of Food Intake

When energy intake and energy output are balanced, body weight remains stable. When they are not, weight is either gained or lost. Because body weight in most people is surprisingly stable, mechanisms that control food intake or heat production or both must exist.

But how is food intake controlled? That is a difficult question, and one that is still not fully answered. Researchers believe that several factors—such as rising or falling blood levels of nutrients (glucose and amino acids), hormones (insulin, glucagon, and leptin), or body temperature (rising temperature is inhibitory), and psychological factors—have an effect on eating behavior through feedback signals to the brain. Indeed, psychological factors are believed to be an important cause of obesity. However, even when psychological factors *are* the underlying cause of obesity, individuals do *not* continue to gain weight endlessly. It seems that their feeding controls still operate, but they act to maintain total body energy content at higher-than-normal levels.

Metabolic Rate and Body Heat Production

Basal Metabolic Rate When nutrients are broken down to produce cellular energy (ATP), they yield different amounts of energy. As mentioned earlier, the energy value of foods is measured in a unit called the *kilocalorie (kcal)*. In general, carbohydrates and proteins each yield 4 kcal/gram, and fats yield 9 kcal/gram when they are broken down for energy production. Most meals, and even many individual foods, are mixtures of carbohydrates, fats, and proteins. To determine the caloric value of a meal, we must know how many grams of each type of foodstuff it contains. For most of us, this is a difficult chore indeed, but approximations can easily be made with the help of a simple, calorie-values guide available in most drugstores.

TABLE 14.3	Factors Determining the Basal Metabolic Rate (BMR)	
Factor	**Variation**	**Effect on BMR**
Surface area	Large surface area in relation to body volume, as in thin, small individuals	Increased
	Small surface area in relation to body volume, as in large, heavy individuals	Decreased
Sex	Male	Increased
	Female	Decreased
Thyroxine production	Increased	Increased
	Decreased	Decreased
Age	Young, rapid growth	Increased
	Aging, elderly	Decreased
Strong emotions (anger or fear) and infections		Increased

The amount of energy used by the body is also measured in kilocalories. The **basal metabolic rate (BMR)** is the amount of heat produced by the body per unit of time when it is under basal conditions— that is, at rest. It reflects the energy supply a person's body needs just to perform essential life activities such as breathing, maintaining the heartbeat, and kidney function. An average 70-kg (154-pound) adult has a BMR of about 60 to 72 kcal/hour.

Many factors influence BMR, including surface area and gender. As shown in Table 14.3, small, thin males tend to have a higher BMR than large, obese females. Age is also important; children and adolescents require large amounts of energy for growth and have relatively high BMRs. In old age, the BMR decreases dramatically as the muscles begin to atrophy.

The amount of **thyroxine** produced by the thyroid gland is probably the most important factor in determining a person's BMR; hence, thyroxine has been dubbed the "metabolic hormone." The more thyroxine produced, the higher the oxygen consumption and ATP use, and the higher the metabolic rate. In the past, most BMR tests were done to determine whether sufficient thyroxine was being made. Today, thyroid activity is more easily assessed by blood tests.

HOMEOSTATIC IMBALANCE

Hyperthyroidism causes a host of effects due to the excessive metabolic rate it produces. The body catabolizes stored fats and tissue proteins, and despite increased hunger and food intake, the person often loses weight. Bones weaken and body muscles, including the heart, atrophy. In contrast, **hypothyroidism** results in slowed metabolism, obesity, and diminished thought processes. ▲

Total Metabolic Rate   When we are active, more glucose must be oxidized to provide energy for the additional activities. Digesting food and even modest physical activity increase the body's caloric requirements dramatically. These additional fuel requirements are above and beyond the energy required to maintain the body in the basal state. **Total metabolic rate (TMR)** refers to the total amount of kilocalories the body must consume to fuel all ongoing activities. Muscular work is the major body activity that increases the TMR. Even slight increases in skeletal muscle activity cause remarkable leaps in metabolic rate. When a well-trained athlete exercises vigorously for several minutes, the TMR may increase to 15 to 20 times normal, and it remains elevated for several hours afterward.

When the total number of kilocalories consumed is equal to the TMR, homeostasis is maintained, and our weight remains constant. However, if we eat more than we need to sustain our activities, excess kilocalories appear in the form of fat deposits. Conversely, if we are extremely active and do not properly feed the "metabolic furnace," we begin to break down fat reserves and even tissue proteins to satisfy our TMR. This principle is used in every good weight-loss diet. (The total kilocalories needed are calculated on the basis of body size and age. Then, 20 percent or more of the requirements are cut from the daily diet.) If the dieting person exercises regularly, weight drops off even more quickly because the TMR increases above the person's former rate.

Body Temperature Regulation

Although we have been emphasizing that foods are "burned" to produce ATP, remember that ATP is not the only product of cell catabolism. Most of the energy released as foods are oxidized escapes as heat. Less than 40 percent of available food energy is actually captured to form ATP. The heat released warms the tissues and, more important, the blood, which circulates to all body tissues, keeping them at homeostatic temperatures, which allows metabolism to occur efficiently.

Body temperature reflects the balance between heat production and heat loss. The body's thermostat is in the *hypothalamus* of the brain. Through autonomic nervous system pathways, the hypothalamus continuously regulates body temperature around a set point of 35.6° to 37.8°C (96° to 100°F) by initiating heat-loss or heat-promoting mechanisms (Figure 14.23).

Heat-Promoting Mechanisms When the environmental temperature is low, the body must produce more heat to maintain normal body temperature (37°C). And if, for whatever reason, the temperature of circulating blood falls, body heat must be conserved and more heat generated to restore normal body (blood) temperature. Short-term means of accomplishing this are **vasoconstriction** of blood vessels of the skin and **shivering.**

When the skin vasculature constricts, the skin is temporarily bypassed by the blood, and blood is rerouted to the deeper, more vital, body organs. When this happens, the temperature of the exposed skin drops to that of the external environment.

HOMEOSTATIC IMBALANCE

Restriction of blood delivery to the skin is no problem for brief periods of time. But if it is extended, the skin cells, chilled by internal ice crystals and deprived of oxygen and nutrients, begin to die. This condition, called **frostbite,** is extremely serious. ▲

When the *core* body temperature (the temperature of the deep organs) drops to the point beyond which simple constriction of skin capillaries can handle the situation, shivering begins. Shivering, involuntary shudderlike contractions of the voluntary muscles, is very effective in increasing the body temperature because skeletal muscle activity produces large amounts of heat.

HOMEOSTATIC IMBALANCE

Extremely low body temperature resulting from prolonged exposure to cold is **hypothermia.** In hypothermia, the individual's vital signs (respiratory rate, blood pressure, heart rate) decrease. The person becomes drowsy and oddly comfortable, even though previously he or she felt extremely cold. Uncorrected, the situation progresses to coma and finally death as metabolic processes grind to a stop. ▲

Heat-Loss Mechanisms Just as the body must be protected from becoming too cold, it must also be protected from excessively high temperatures. Most heat loss occurs through the skin via **radiation** or **evaporation.** When body temperature increases above what is desirable, the blood vessels serving the skin dilate and capillary beds in the skin become flushed with warm blood. As a result, heat radiates from the skin surface. However, if the external environment is as hot as or hotter than the body, heat cannot be lost by radiation, and the only means of getting rid of excess heat is by the evaporation of perspiration off the skin surface. This is an efficient means of body-heat loss as long as the air is dry. If it is humid, evaporation occurs at a much slower rate. In such cases, our heat-liberating mechanisms don't work well, and we feel miserable and irritable.

HOMEOSTATIC IMBALANCE

When normal heat loss processes become ineffective, the **hyperthermia,** or elevated body temperature, that results depresses the hypothalamus. As a result, a vicious positive feedback cycle occurs: Soaring body temperature increases the metabolic rate,

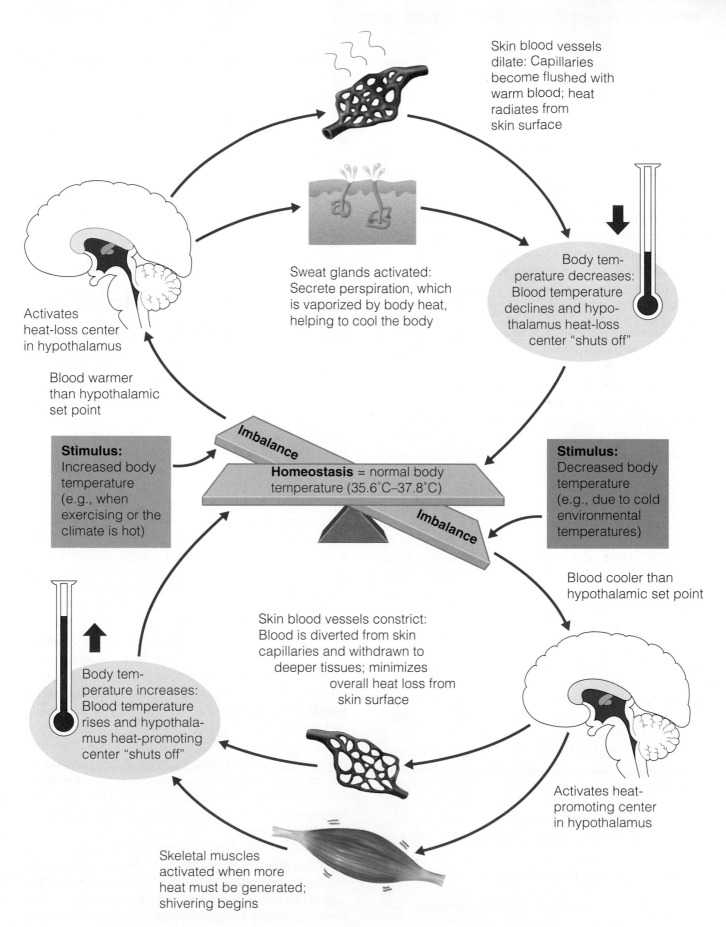

Skin blood vessels dilate: Capillaries become flushed with warm blood; heat radiates from skin surface

Sweat glands activated: Secrete perspiration, which is vaporized by body heat, helping to cool the body

Body temperature decreases: Blood temperature declines and hypothalamus heat-loss center "shuts off"

Activates heat-loss center in hypothalamus

Blood warmer than hypothalamic set point

Stimulus: Increased body temperature (e.g., when exercising or the climate is hot)

Imbalance

Homeostasis = normal body temperature (35.6°C–37.8°C)

Imbalance

Stimulus: Decreased body temperature (e.g., due to cold environmental temperatures)

Blood cooler than hypothalamic set point

Skin blood vessels constrict: Blood is diverted from skin capillaries and withdrawn to deeper tissues; minimizes overall heat loss from skin surface

Body temperature increases: Blood temperature rises and hypothalamus heat-promoting center "shuts off"

Activates heat-promoting center in hypothalamus

Skeletal muscles activated when more heat must be generated; shivering begins

FIGURE 14.23 **Mechanisms of body temperature regulation.**

which in turn increases heat production. The skin becomes hot and dry; and, as the temperature continues to spiral upward, permanent brain damage becomes a distinct possibility. This condition, called **heat stroke,** can be fatal unless rapid corrective measures are taken immediately (immersion in cool water and administration of fluids).

Heat exhaustion is the term used to describe the heat-associated collapse of an individual during or following vigorous physical activity. Heat exhaustion results from excessive loss of body fluids (dehydration) and is evidenced by low blood pressure, a rapid heartbeat, and cool, clammy skin. In contrast to heat stroke, heat-loss mechanisms still operate in heat exhaustion. ▲

Fever is controlled hyperthermia. Most often, it results from infection somewhere in the body, but it may be caused by other conditions (cancer, allergic reactions, and CNS injuries). Macrophages, white blood cells, and injured tissue cells release chemical substances called *pyrogens* (pi'ro-jenz) that act directly on the hypothalamus, causing its thermostat to be set to a higher temperature (*pyro* = fire). After thermostat resetting, heat-promoting mechanisms are initiated. Vasoconstriction causes the skin to become cool, and shivering begins to generate heat. This situation, called "the chills," is a sure sign that body temperature is rising. Body temperature is allowed to rise until it reaches the new setting. Then, it is maintained at the "fever setting" until natural body defense processes or antibiotics reverse the disease process. At that point, the thermostat is reset again to a lower (or normal) level, causing heat-loss mechanisms to swing into action—the individual begins to sweat, and the skin becomes flushed and warm. Physicians have long recognized that these signs signaled a turn for the better in their patients and said that the patient had "passed the crisis" because body temperature was falling.

As explained in Chapter 12, fever, by increasing the metabolic rate, helps speed the various healing processes, and it also appears to inhibit bacterial growth. The danger of fever is that if the body thermostat is set too high, body proteins may be denatured, and permanent brain damage may occur.

▶ DID YOU GET IT?

25. Which nutrient class provides the greatest number of kilocalories per gram of food?

26. Which of the following would you expect to yield a relatively high BMR: old age, large surface area relative to body volume, female sex, deficient thyroxine production?

27. What are two means of either maintaining or increasing body temperature?

28. How does vasodilation of skin blood vessels affect body temperature on a hot day?

For answers, see Appendix D.

PART III: DEVELOPMENTAL ASPECTS OF THE DIGESTIVE SYSTEM AND METABOLISM

The very young embryo is flat and pancake-shaped. However, it soon folds to form a cylindrical body, and its internal cavity becomes the cavity of the alimentary canal. By the fifth week of development, the alimentary canal is a continuous tube-like structure extending from the mouth to the anus. Shortly after, the digestive glands (salivary glands, liver, and pancreas) bud out from the mucosa of the alimentary tube. These glands retain their connections (ducts) and can easily empty their secretions into the alimentary canal to promote its digestive functions.

HOMEOSTATIC IMBALANCE

The digestive system is susceptible to many congenital defects that interfere with feeding. The most common is the **cleft palate/cleft lip defect.** Of the two, cleft palate is more serious because the child is unable to suck properly. Another relatively common congenital defect is a **tracheoesophageal fistula** (tra"ke-o-ĕ-sof'ah-je-al fis'tu-lah). In this condition, there is a connection between the esophagus and the trachea. In addition, the esophagus often (but not always) ends in a blind sac and does not connect to the stomach. The baby chokes, drools, and becomes cyanotic during feedings because food is entering the respiratory passageways. All three defects can be corrected surgically.

There are many types of inborn errors of metabolism (genetically based problems that interfere with metabolism), but perhaps the two most common are **cystic fibrosis (CF)** and **phenylketonuria** (fen"il-ke'to-nu"re-ah) **(PKU).** CF primarily affects the lungs, but it also significantly impairs the activity of the pancreas. In CF, huge amounts of mucus are produced, which block the passages of involved organs. Blockage of the pancreatic duct prevents pancreatic fluid from reaching the small intestine. As a result, fats and fat-soluble vitamins are not digested or absorbed, and bulky, fat-laden stools result. This condition is usually handled by administering pancreatic enzymes with meals.

PKU involves an inability of tissue cells to use phenylalanine (fen"il-al'ah-nin), an amino acid present in all protein foods. In such cases, brain damage and retardation occur unless a special diet low in phenylalanine is prescribed. ▲

The developing infant receives all its nutrients through the placenta, and at least at this period of life, obtaining and processing nutrients is no problem (assuming the mother is adequately nourished). Obtaining nutrition is the most important activity of the newborn baby, and several reflexes present at this time help in this activity. For example, the *rooting reflex* helps the infant find the nipple (mother's or bottle), and the *sucking reflex* helps him or her to hold on to the nipple and swallow. The stomach of a newborn infant is very small, so feeding must be frequent (every 3 to 4 hours). Peristalsis is rather inefficient at this time, and vomiting is not at all unusual.

Teething begins around age 6 months and continues until about the age of 2 years. During this interval, the infant progresses to more and more solid foods and usually is eating an adult diet by toddlerhood. Appetite decreases in the elementary school–aged child and then increases again during the rapid growth of adolescence. (Parents of adolescents usually bewail their high grocery bills!)

All through childhood and into adulthood, the digestive system operates with relatively few problems unless there are abnormal interferences such as contaminated food or extremely spicy or irritating foods (which may cause inflammation of the gastrointestinal tract, or **gastroenteritis** [gas"tro-en-ter-i'tis]). Inflammation of the appendix, **appendicitis,** is particularly common in teenagers for some unknown reason. Between middle age

and early old age, the metabolic rate decreases by 5 to 8 percent in every 10-year period. This is the time of life when the weight seems to creep up, and obesity often becomes a fact of life. To maintain desired weight, we must be aware of this gradual change and be prepared to reduce caloric intake. Two distinctly middle-age digestive problems are *ulcers* (see the "A Closer Look" box on pp. 488–489) and *gallbladder problems* (inflammation of the gallbladder or gallstones).

During old age, activity of the GI tract declines. Fewer digestive juices are produced, and peristalsis slows. Taste and smell become less acute, and periodontal disease often develops. Many elderly individuals live alone or on a reduced income. These factors, along with increasing physical disability, tend to make eating less appealing, and nutrition is inadequate in many of our elderly citizens. Diverticulosis and cancer of the gastrointestinal tract are fairly common problems. Cancer of the stomach and colon rarely have early signs and often progress to an inoperable stage (that is, spread to distant parts of the body as well) before the individual seeks medical attention. However, when detected early, both diseases are treatable, and it has been suggested that diets high in plant fiber and low in fat might help to decrease the incidence of colon cancer. Additionally, because most colorectal cancers derive from initially benign mucosal tumors called **polyps,** and because the incidence of polyp formation increases with age, a yearly colon examination should be a health priority in everyone over the age of 50.

▶ DID YOU GET IT?

29. How does cystic fibrosis affect digestion?

30. What dietary changes must be made to prevent brain damage in children with PKU?

31. What occurs when your total caloric intake exceeds your TMR?

For answers, see Appendix D.

A CLOSER LOOK

OBESITY: MAGICAL SOLUTION WANTED

How fat is too fat? What distinguishes an obese person from one that is merely overweight? The bathroom scale is an inaccurate guide, because body weight tells nothing of body composition. Dense bones and well-developed muscles may make a person technically overweight. Arnold Schwarzenegger, for example, has tipped the scales at a hefty 257 lb.

The most common view of obesity is that it is a condition of excessive triglyceride storage. Although we bewail our inability to rid ourselves of fat, the real problem is that we keep refilling the storehouses by consuming too many calories. A body fat content of 18 to 22 percent of body weight (males and females, respectively) is considered normal for adults. Anything over that is defined as obesity.

The official medical measure of obesity and body fatness is called the *body mass index (BMI)*, an index of a person's weight relative to height. To estimate BMI, multiply weight in pounds by 705 and then divide by your height in inches squared:

$$BMI = \frac{wt\ [lb] \times 705}{(height\ [inches])^2}$$

Overweight is defined by a BMI between 25 and 30; *obese* is a BMI greater than 30.

However it's defined, obesity is a perplexing and poorly understood disease. The term *disease* is appropriate because all forms of obesity involve some imbalance in food intake control mechanisms. Despite its well-known adverse effects on health (the obese have a higher incidence of arteriosclerosis, hypertension, coronary artery disease, and diabetes mellitus), it is the most common health problem in the United States. The United States is big and getting bigger, at least around the middle. Two out of three adults are obese. U.S. kids are getting fatter, too. Because they are opting for

> ❝ *Obesity is a perplexing and poorly understood disease.* ❞

home video games and nachos instead of touch football and apples, their general cardiovascular fitness is declining as well.

The social stigma and economic disadvantages of obesity are legendary. A fat person pays higher insurance premiums, is discriminated against in the job market, has fewer clothing choices, and endures frequent humiliation throughout life. With all its problems, it's a pretty fair bet that few people choose to be obese. So what causes obesity? Let's look at three of the more recent theories.

Overeating during Childhood

Some believe that overeating behaviors develop early in life (the "clean your plate" syndrome) and set the stage for adult obesity by increasing the number of fat cells formed during childhood. Then, during adulthood, increases in adipose tissue mass occur because more fat is deposited in the existing cells. Thus, the more cells there are, the more fat can be stored.

Greater Fuel Efficiency in Obese People

Obese people are more fuel efficient and more effective "fat storers." Although it is often assumed that obese people eat more than other people, this is not necessarily true—many actually eat less than those of normal weight.

When yo-yo dieters lose weight, their metabolic rate falls sharply. But when they subsequently gain weight, their metabolic rate increases like a furnace being stoked. Each successive weight loss occurs more slowly, but lost weight is regained three times as fast. Thus, it appears that people, like laboratory animals subjected to alternating "feasts and fasts," become increasingly food efficient. Furthermore, fats pack more wallop per calorie (are more fattening) than proteins or carbohydrates because very little energy is used in their processing. For example, when someone ingests 100 excess *carbohydrate* calories, 23 calories are used in metabolic processing and 77 are stored. However, if the excess calories come from fat, only 3 calories are "burned" and the rest (97) are stored.

These facts apply to everyone, but for obese people the picture is even bleaker. For example, fat cells of overweight people "sprout" more alpha receptors (the kind that favors fat accumulation), and their lipoprotein lipase enzyme, which unloads fat from the blood (usually to fat cells), is exceptionally efficient.

Genetic Predisposition

Morbid obesity is the fate of people inheriting two obesity genes. However, a true genetic predisposition for "fatness" appears to account for only about 5 percent of obese people in the United States. These people, given excess calories, will always deposit them as fat, as opposed to those who lay down more muscle with some of the excess calories.

False and Risky Cures

Rumors and poor choices for dealing with obesity abound. Some of the most unfortunate strategies used for coping with obesity are described below.

Water Pills

Diuretics prompt the kidneys to excrete more water. At best, these may cause a few pounds of weight loss for a few hours. They can also cause serious electrolyte imbalance and dehydration.

Diet Drugs

Some obese people use amphetamines (such as Dexedrine and Benzedrine ["speed"]) to reduce appetite and elevate the metabolic rate. These work, but only temporarily (until tolerance develops) and can cause a dangerous dependence. Diet aids that provide fiber to prevent absorption of nutrients can cause serious malnutrition.

Currently popular weight-loss drugs include phentermine, sibutramine, and orlistat. Phentermine is one-half of the former fen-phen (Redux) combination that caused heart valve problems, deaths, and litigation for its producer in the 1990s. Sibutramine (Meridia) has amphetamine-like effects and has recently come under fire because of suspected cardiovascular side effects. Orlistat (Xenical)

A CLOSER LOOK Obesity *(continued)*

interferes with pancreatic lipase so that part of the fat eaten is not digested or absorbed, which also interferes with the absorption of fat-soluble vitamins. Although it is effective as a weight-loss agent, its side effects, which include diarrhea and anal leakage, are unpleasant to say the least.

Some over-the-counter weight-loss supplements that are claimed to increase metabolism and burn calories at an accelerated rate have proved to be very dangerous. For example:

► Capsules containing usnic acid, a chemical found in some lichens, damages hepatocytes and has led to liver failure in a few cases.

► Ephedra-containing supplements are notorious—over 100 deaths and 16,000 cases of problems including strokes, seizures, and headaches have been reported.

When it comes to such supplements, the burden of proof is on the FDA to show that the product is unsafe. Hence, the true extent of ills caused by weight-loss supplements is not known.

Fad Diets

Diet products and books sell well, but do any of the currently popular diets work, and are they safe? At the present time there is a duel between those promoting low-carbohydrate (high-protein and -fat) diets such as the Atkins and South Beach diets, and those espousing the traditional low-fat (high–complex carbohydrates) diet. Clinical studies show that people on the low-carbohydrate diets lose weight more quickly at first but tend to plateau at 6 months. When dieting was continued for a year, people on the low-fat diets lost just as much weight as did those on the low-carbohydrate diets, and they experienced fewer episodes of diarrhea, constipation, headache, and muscle cramps. Although there was concern that the low-carbohydrate diets would promote undesirable plasma cholesterol and lipid values, for the most part this has not been the case.

Some over-the-counter liquid high-protein diets contain such poor-quality (incomplete) protein that they are actually dangerous. The worst are those that contain collagen protein instead of milk or soybean sources.

Surgery

Sometimes sheer desperation prompts surgical solutions, such as having the jaws wired shut or the stomach stapled, intestinal bypass surgery, the more radical biliopancreatic diversion (BPD), and liposuction. BPD "rearranges" the digestive tract: up to two-thirds of the stomach is removed; the small intestine is cut in half and one portion is sutured into the stomach opening. Because pancreatic juice and bile are diverted away from this "new intestine," fewer nutrients (and no fats) are digested and absorbed. Although the patients can eat anything they want without gaining weight, BPD is major surgery and carries all of its risks. Liposuction, the removal of adipose tissue by suction to reshape the body, does remove fat. Like BPD it carries all the risks of surgery, and unless the patient changes his or her eating habits, the remaining fat deposits elsewhere in the body overfill.

Unfortunately, there is no magical solution for obesity. The best way for most of us to lose weight is to take in fewer fat calories and increase physical activity. Fidgeting helps, and so does resistance exercise, which increases muscle mass (muscle consumes more energy at rest than does fat). Low activity levels actually stimulate eating, whereas physical exercise depresses food intake and increases metabolic rate not only during activity, but also for some time after. The only way to keep the weight off is to make dietary and exercise changes lifelong habits.

SYSTEMS IN SYNC

HOMEOSTATIC RELATIONSHIPS BETWEEN THE
DIGESTIVE SYSTEM *AND OTHER BODY SYSTEMS*

Endocrine System

- Liver removes hormones from blood, ending their activity; digestive system provides nutrients needed for energy fuel, growth, and repair; pancreas has hormone-producing cells
- Local hormones help regulate digestive function

Lymphatic System/Immunity

- Digestive system provides nutrients for normal functioning; HCl of stomach provides nonspecific protection against bacteria
- Lacteals drain fatty lymph from digestive tract organs and convey it to blood; Peyer's patches and lymphoid tissue in mesentery house macrophages and immune cells that protect digestive tract organs against infection

Digestive System

Urinary System

- Digestive system provides nutrients for energy fuel, growth, and repair; excretes some bilirubin produced by the liver
- Kidneys transform vitamin D to its active form, which is needed for calcium absorption

Muscular System

- Digestive system provides nutrients for energy fuel, growth, and repair; liver removes lactic acid, resulting from muscle activity, from the blood
- Skeletal muscle activity increases motility of GI tract

Nervous System

- Digestive system provides nutrients for normal neural functioning
- Neural controls of digestive function; in general, parasympathetic fibers accelerate and sympathetic fibers inhibit digestive activity; reflex and voluntary controls of defecation

Respiratory System

- Digestive system provides nutrients for energy metabolism, growth, and repair
- Respiratory system provides oxygen and carries away carbon dioxide produced by digestive system organs

Cardiovascular System

- Digestive system provides nutrients to heart and blood vessels; absorbs iron needed for hemoglobin synthesis; absorbs water necessary for normal blood volume
- Cardiovascular system transports nutrients absorbed by alimentary canal to all tissues of the body; distributes hormones of the digestive tract

Reproductive System

- Digestive system provides nutrients for energy fuel, growth, and repair and extra nutrition needed to support fetal growth

Integumentary System

- Digestive system provides nutrients for energy fuel, growth, and repair; supplies fats that provide insulation in the dermal and subcutaneous tissues
- The skin synthesizes vitamin D needed for calcium absorption from the intestine; protects by enclosure

Skeletal System

- Digestive system provides nutrients for energy fuel, growth, and repair; absorbs calcium needed for bone salts
- Skeletal system protects some digestive organs by bone; cavities store some nutrients (e.g., calcium, fats)

SUMMARY

Media study tools that provide additional review of key topics of Chapter 14 are referenced below.

IP = *InterActive Physiology*
WEB = The A&P Place

PART I: ANATOMY AND PHYSIOLOGY OF THE DIGESTIVE SYSTEM (pp. 469–493)

Anatomy of the Digestive System (pp. 469–481)

1. The digestive system consists of the alimentary canal (a hollow tube extending from mouth to anus) and several accessory digestive organs. The wall of the alimentary canal has four main tissue layers—mucosa, submucosa, muscularis externa, serosa. The serosa (visceral peritoneum) is continuous with the parietal peritoneum, which lines the abdominal cavity wall.

   WEB Exercise: Chapter 14, Digestive System; Basic Structure of the Alimentary Wall.

2. Organs of the alimentary canal:
   a. The mouth, or oral cavity, contains teeth and tongue and is bounded by lips, cheeks, and palate. Tonsils guard its posterior margin.
   b. The pharynx is a muscular tube that provides a passageway for food and air.
   c. The esophagus is a muscular tube that completes the passageway from the pharynx to the stomach.
   d. The stomach is a C-shaped organ located on the left side of the abdomen beneath the diaphragm. Food enters it through the cardioesophageal sphincter and leaves it to enter the small intestine through the pyloric sphincter. The stomach has a third oblique layer of muscle in its wall that allows it to perform mixing or churning movements. Gastric glands produce hydrochloric acid, pepsin, rennin, mucus, gastrin, and intrinsic factor. Mucus protects the stomach itself from being digested.
   e. The tubelike small intestine is suspended from the posterior body wall by the mesentery. Its subdivisions are the duodenum, jejunum, and ileum. Food digestion and absorption are completed here. Pancreatic juice and bile enter the duodenum through a sphincter at the distal end of the bile duct. Microvilli, villi, and circular folds increase the surface area of the small intestine for enhanced absorption.
   f. The large intestine frames the small intestine. Subdivisions are the cecum; appendix; ascending, transverse, and descending colon; sigmoid colon; rectum; and anal canal. The large intestine delivers undigested food residue (feces) to the body exterior.

   IP Digestive System Topic: Anatomy Review, pages 1–8.

   IP Digestive System Topic: Digestion and Absorption, page 1–8.

5. Salivary glands (three pairs—parotid, submandibular, and sublingual) secrete saliva into the oral cavity. Saliva contains mucus and serous fluids. The serous component contains salivary amylase.

6. Two sets of teeth are formed. The first set consists of 20 deciduous teeth that begin to appear at 6 months and are lost by 12 years of age. Permanent teeth (32) begin to replace deciduous teeth around 7 years. A typical tooth consists of crown covered with enamel and root covered with cementum. Most of the tooth is bonelike dentin. The pulp cavity contains blood vessels and nerves.

7. Several accessory organs duct substances into the alimentary tube.
   a. The pancreas is a soft gland lying in the mesentery between the stomach and small intestine. Pancreatic juice contains enzymes (which digest all categories of foods) in an alkaline fluid.
   b. The liver is a four-lobed organ overlying the stomach. Its digestive function is to produce bile, which it ducts into the small intestine.
   c. The gallbladder is a muscular sac that stores and concentrates bile. When fat digestion is not occurring, the continuously made bile backs up the cystic duct and enters the gallbladder.

Functions of the Digestive System (pp. 481–493)

1. Foods must be broken down to their building blocks to be absorbed. Building blocks of carbohydrates are simple sugars, or monosaccharides. Building blocks of proteins are amino acids. Building blocks of fats, or lipids, are fatty acids and glycerol.

   WEB Exercise: Chapter 14, Gastrointestinal Tract Activities.

2. Both mechanical (chewing) and chemical food breakdown begin in the mouth. Saliva contains mucus, which helps bind food together into a bolus, and salivary amylase, which begins the chemical breakdown of starch. Saliva is secreted in response to food in the mouth, mechanical pressure, and psychic stimuli. Essentially no food absorption occurs in the mouth.

3. Swallowing has two phases: The buccal phase is voluntary; the tongue pushes the bolus into the pharynx. The involuntary pharyngeal-esophageal phase involves the closing off of nasal and respiratory passages and the conduction of food to the stomach by peristalsis.

4. When food enters the stomach, gastric secretion is stimulated by vagus nerves and by gastrin (a local hormone). Hydrochloric acid activates the protein-digesting enzyme pepsin, and chemical digestion of proteins begins. Food is also mechanically broken down by the churning activity of stomach muscles. Movement of chyme into the small intestine is controlled by the enterogastric reflex.

   IP Digestive System Topic: Secretion, pages 4–8.

5. Chemical digestion of fats, proteins, and carbohydrates is completed in the small intestine by intestinal enzymes and, more importantly, pancreatic enzymes. Alkaline pancreatic juice neutralizes acid chyme and provides the proper environment for the operation of its enzymes. Both pancreatic juice (the only source of lipases) and bile (formed by the liver) are necessary for normal fat breakdown and absorption. Bile acts as a fat emulsifier. Secretin and cholecystokinin, hormones produced by the small intestine, stimulate release of bile and pancreatic juice. Segmental movements mix foods; peristaltic movements move foodstuffs along the small intestine. Most nutrient absorption occurs by active transport into the capillary blood of the villi. Fats are absorbed by diffusion into both capillary blood and lacteals in the villi.

6. The large intestine receives bacteria-laden indigestible food residue. Activities of the large intestine are absorption of water and salts and of vitamins made by resident bacteria. When feces are delivered to the rectum by peristalsis and mass peristalsis, the defecation reflex is initiated.

   IP Digestive System Topic: Digestion and Absorption, pages 3–7.

   IP Digestive System Topic: Motility, pages 3–7.

   IP Digestive System Topic: Secretion, pages 9–12.

PART II: NUTRITION AND METABOLISM (pp. 493–506)

Nutrition (pp. 493–495)

1. Most foods are used as fuels to form ATP; the exception is proteins.

2. A nutrient is a substance in food used to promote growth, maintenance, and repair of the body.

3. The major nutrients are carbohydrates, lipids, and proteins. Vitamins and minerals are required in minute amounts.

4. Dietary carbohydrates (sugars and starch) are included in fruits and vegetables (plant products).

5. Dietary lipids are found in meats, dairy products, and vegetable oils.

6. Eggs, milk, meats, poultry, and fish are rich sources of protein.

7. Vitamins, found mainly in fruits, vegetables, and milk, function mainly as coenzymes in the body.

8. Minerals, most plentiful in vegetables and legumes, are mainly important for enzyme activity. Iron is important to make hemoglobin, and calcium is important for building bone, blood clotting, and secretory activities.

Metabolism (pp. 495–506)

1. Metabolism includes all chemical breakdown (catabolic) and building (anabolic) reactions needed to maintain life.

2. Carbohydrates, the most important of which is glucose, are the body's major energy fuel. As glucose is oxidized, carbon dioxide, water, and ATP are formed. The sequential pathways of glucose catabolism are glycolysis, which occurs in the cytosol, and the Krebs cycle and electron transport chain (which function in the mitochondria). During hyperglycemia, glucose is stored as glycogen or converted to fat. In hypoglycemia, glycogenolysis, gluconeogenesis, and fat breakdown occur to restore normal blood glucose levels.

   WEB Exercise: Chapter 14, Overview of Cellular Respiration.

3. Fats insulate the body, protect organs, build some cell structures (membranes and myelin sheaths), and provide reserve energy. When carbohydrates are in limited supply, more fats are oxidized to produce ATP. Excessive fat breakdown causes blood to become acidic. Excess dietary fat is stored in subcutaneous tissue and other fat depots.

4. Proteins form the bulk of cell structure and most functional molecules. They are carefully conserved by body cells. Amino acids are actively taken up from blood by tissue cells; those that cannot be made by body cells are called *essential amino acids*. Amino acids are oxidized to form ATP mainly when other fuel sources are not available. Ammonia, released as amino acids are catabolized, is detoxified by liver cells that combine it with carbon dioxide to form urea.

5. The liver is the body's key metabolic organ. Its cells remove nutrients from hepatic portal blood. It performs glycogenesis, glycogenolysis, and gluconeogenesis to maintain homeostasis of blood glucose levels. Its cells make blood proteins and other substances and release them to blood. Fats are burned by liver cells to provide some of their energy (ATP); excesses are stored or released to blood in simpler forms that can be used by other tissue cells. Phagocytic cells remove bacteria from hepatic portal blood. Most cholesterol is made by the liver; cholesterol breakdown products are secreted in bile. Fats and cholesterol are transported in the blood by lipoproteins. LDLs transport cholesterol to body cells; HDLs carry cholesterol to the liver for degradation. Cholesterol is used to make functional molecules and for some structural purposes; it is not used for ATP synthesis.

6. A dynamic balance exists between energy intake and total energy output (heat + work + energy storage). Interference with this balance results in obesity or malnutrition leading to body wasting.

7. When the three major types of foods are oxidized for energy, they yield different amounts of energy. Carbohydrates and proteins yield 4 kcal/gram; fats yield 9 kcal/gram. Basal metabolic rate (BMR) is the total amount of energy used by the body when one is in a basal (resting) state. Age, sex, body surface area, and amount of thyroxine produced influence BMR.

8. Total metabolic rate (TMR) is number of calories used by the body to accomplish all ongoing daily activities. It increases dramatically as muscle activity increases. When TMR equals total caloric intake, weight remains constant.

9. As foods are catabolized to form ATP, more than 60 percent of energy released escapes as heat, warming the body. The hypothalamus initiates heat-loss processes (radiation of heat from skin and evaporation of sweat) or heat-promoting processes (vasoconstriction of skin blood vessels and shivering) as necessary to maintain body temperature within normal limits. Fever (hyperthermia) represents body temperature regulated at higher-than-normal levels.

PART III: DEVELOPMENTAL ASPECTS OF THE DIGESTIVE SYSTEM AND METABOLISM (pp. 506–507)

1. The alimentary tract forms as a hollow tube. Accessory glands form as outpocketings from this tube.

2. Common congenital defects include cleft palate, cleft lip, and tracheoesophageal fistula, all of which interfere with normal nutrition. Common inborn errors of metabolism are phenylketonuria (PKU) and cystic fibrosis (CF).

3. Various inflammatory conditions plague the digestive system throughout life. Appendicitis is common in adolescents, gastroenteritis and food poisoning can occur at any time (given the proper irritating factors), ulcers and gallbladder problems increase in middle age. Obesity and diabetes mellitus are bothersome during later middle age.

4. Efficiency of all digestive system processes decreases in the elderly. Gastrointestinal cancers, such as stomach and colon cancer, appear with increasing frequency in an aging population.

WEB Exercise: Chapter 14, Gastrointestinal Case Study.

REVIEW QUESTIONS

Multiple Choice

More than one choice may apply.

1. Which of the following terms are synonyms?
   a. Gastrointestinal tract   c. Digestive tract
   b. Digestive system   d. Alimentary canal

2. A digestive organ that is *not* part of the alimentary canal is the
   a. stomach.   d. large intestine.
   b. liver.   e. pharynx.
   c. small intestine.

3. The GI tube tissue layer responsible for the actions of segmentation and peristalsis is the
   a. serosa.   c. muscularis externa.
   b. mucosa.   d. submucosa.

4. Match the digestive organ listed in column B with the function listed in column A.

Column A	Column B
____ 1. produces bile	a. salivary glands
____ 2. absorbs water	b. esophagus
____ 3. churning occurs here	c. stomach
____ 4. muscular tube connecting the laryngeopharynx with the stomach	d. small intestine
	e. liver
____ 5. produces both endocrine and exocrine secretions	f. gallbladder
	g. pancreas
____ 6. secretes a substance that initiates carbohydrate digestion	h. large intestine
____ 7. stores bile	
____ 8. segmentation occurs here	

5. Where in the stomach do the strongest peristaltic waves occur?

   a. Body
   b. Cardiac region
   c. Fundus
   d. Pylorus

6. Which of these organs lies in the right hypochondriac region of the abdomen?

   a. Stomach
   b. Spleen
   c. Cecum
   d. Liver

7. Release of CCK leads to

   a. contraction of smooth muscle in the duodenal papilla.
   b. increased activity of liver cells.
   c. contraction of the gallbladder wall.
   d. release of enzymes by the pancreas.

8. The pH of chyme entering the duodenum is adjusted by

   a. bile.
   b. intestinal juice.
   c. enzyme secretions from the pancreas.
   d. bicarbonate-rich secretions from the pancreas.

9. A 3-year-old girl is rewarded with a hug because she is now completely toilet trained. Which muscle is one that she has learned to control?

   a. Levator ani
   b. Internal anal sphincter
   c. Internal and external obliques
   d. External anal sphincter

10. Hormones that act to decrease blood glucose level include

    a. insulin.
    b. glucagon.
    c. epinephrine.
    d. growth hormone.

11. Which events occur shortly after eating?

    a. Use of amino acids as a major source of energy
    b. Lipogenesis (and fat deposit)
    c. Breakdown of fat reserves
    d. Increased uptake of glucose by skeletal muscles and other body tissues

12. The material that forms the bulk of a tooth is

    a. cementum.
    b. dentin.
    c. enamel.
    d. pulp.

13. Complete this statement. In glycolysis _____ is oxidized and _____ is reduced.

    a. vitamin-containing coenzyme; glucose
    b. ATP; ADP
    c. glucose; oxygen
    d. glucose; vitamin-containing coenzyme

Short Answer Essay

14. Make a simple line drawing of the organs of the alimentary tube, and label each organ.

15. Add three labels to your drawing—salivary glands, liver, and pancreas—and use arrows to show where each of these organs empties its secretion into the alimentary tube.

16. Name the layers of the alimentary tube wall from the lumen outward.

17. What is the mesentery? The peritoneum?

18. Name the subdivisions of the small intestine in a proximal to distal direction. Do the same for the subdivisions of the large intestine.

19. What substance covers the tooth crown? What substance makes up the bulk of a tooth? What is pulp, and where is it?

20. Name the three pairs of salivary glands.

21. Assume you have been chewing a piece of bread for five or six minutes. How would you expect its taste to change during this time? Why?

22. Name two regions of the digestive tract where mechanical food breakdown occurs, and explain how it is accomplished in those regions.

23. How does the stomach protect itself from being digested?

24. Bile emulsifies fat. Define *emulsify*.

25. What is the function of gastrin?

26. Describe the two phases of swallowing.

27. How do segmental and peristaltic movements differ?

28. A cream cheese and jelly sandwich contains proteins, carbohydrates, and fats. Describe what happens to the sandwich when you eat it relative to events occurring in ingestion, digestion, absorption, and defecation.

29. What substances are absorbed in the large intestine?

30. What is the composition of feces?

31. Define *defecation reflex, constipation,* and *diarrhea.*

32. Define *metabolism, anabolism,* and *catabolism.*

33. Define *gluconeogenesis, glycogenolysis,* and *glycogenesis.*

34. Which food group is most important for building cell structures?

35. What is the harmful result when excessive amounts of fats are burned to produce ATP? Name two conditions that might lead to this result.

36. How many calories are produced when 1 gram of carbohydrate is oxidized? 1 gram of protein? 1 gram of fat? If you just ate 100 grams of food that was 20 percent protein, 30 percent carbohydrate, and 10 percent fat, how many kilocalories did you consume?

37. Some of the energy released as foods are oxidized is captured to make ATP. What happens to the rest of it?

38. Name two ways in which heat is lost from the body.

39. What is fever? What does it indicate?

40. Name three digestive system problems common to middle-aged adults. Name one common to teenagers. Name three common in elderly persons.

CRITICAL THINKING AND CLINICAL APPLICATION QUESTIONS

41. After chopping wood for about two hours on a hot but breezy afternoon, John stumbled into the house and then fainted. His T-shirt was wringing wet with perspiration, and his pulse was faint and rapid. Was he suffering from heat stroke or heat exhaustion? Explain your reasoning, and note what you should do to help John recover.

42. Harry is hospitalized with bacterial pneumonia. When you visit him, his teeth are chattering, his skin is cool and clammy to the touch, and he complains of feeling cold even though his room is quite warm. Explain his symptoms.

43. A young woman is put through an extensive battery of tests to determine the cause of her stomach pains. She is diagnosed with gastric ulcers. An antihistamine drug is prescribed, and she is sent home. What is the mechanism of her medication? What life-threatening problems can result from a poorly managed ulcer? Why did the clinic doctor warn the woman not to take aspirin?

44. Continuing from the previous question, the woman's ulcer got worse. She started complaining of back pain. The physician discovered that the back pain occurred because the pancreas was now damaged. Use logic to deduce how a perforating gastric ulcer could come to damage the pancreas.

45. Benny, a 6-year-old child who is allergic to milk, has extremely bowed legs. What condition do you suspect, and what is the connection to not drinking milk?

46. A new mother is worried about her week-old infant. The baby has begun to turn blue whenever she is fed and chokes during each feeding. What developmental abnormality do you suspect, and how will it be corrected?

47. An anorexic girl shows high levels of acetone in her blood. What is this condition called, and what has caused it?

48. Every year dozens of elderly people are found dead in their unheated apartments—victims of hypothermia. What is hypothermia, and how does it kill?

49. Mr. Harold has had nonstop diarrhea all day and is severely weakened. Why is his nurse concerned?

50. Ginny has been on antibiotics for an extended period. A visit to her physician reveals that she has a vitamin K deficiency. What is the cause-and-effect relationship here?

The Urinary System

YOUR GOALS

After completing this chapter, you will have a working knowledge of the functions of the urinary system and will have mastered the objectives listed below.

FUNCTION PREVIEW

* The urinary system rids the body of nitrogenous wastes while regulating water, electrolyte, and acid-base balance of the blood.

OBJECTIVE CHECKLIST

Kidneys (pp. 518–528)

▶ Describe the location of the kidneys in the body.

▶ Identify the following regions of a kidney (longitudinal section): hilum, cortex, medulla, medullary pyramids, calyces, pelvis, and renal columns.

▶ Recognize that the nephron is the structural and functional unit of the kidney, and describe its anatomy.

▶ Describe the process of urine formation, identifying the areas of the nephron that are responsible for filtration, reabsorption, and secretion.

▶ Describe the function of the kidneys in excretion of nitrogen-containing wastes.

▶ Define *polyuria, anuria, oliguria,* and *diuresis.*

▶ Describe the composition of normal urine.

▶ List abnormal urinary components.

Ureters, Urinary Bladder, and Urethra (pp. 528–531)

➤ Describe the general structure and function of the ureters, urinary bladder, and urethra.

➤ Compare the course and length of the male urethra to that of the female.

➤ Define *micturition*.

➤ Describe the difference in control of the external and internal urethral sphincters.

➤ Name three common urinary tract problems.

Fluid, Electrolyte, and Acid-Base Balance (pp. 531–537)

➤ Name and localize the three main fluid compartments of the body.

➤ Explain the role of antidiuretic hormone (ADH) in the regulation of water balance by the kidney.

➤ Explain the role of aldosterone in sodium and potassium balance of the blood.

➤ Compare and contrast the relative speed of buffers, the respiratory system, and the kidneys in maintaining the acid-base balance of the blood.

Developmental Aspects of the Urinary System (pp. 538, 540)

➤ Describe three common congenital problems of the urinary system.

➤ Describe the effect of aging on urinary system functioning.

The kidneys, which maintain the purity and constancy of our internal fluids, are perfect examples of homeostatic organs. Much like sanitation workers who keep a city's water supply drinkable and dispose of its waste, the kidneys are usually unappreciated until there is a malfunction and "internal garbage" piles up. Every day, the kidneys filter gallons of fluid from the bloodstream. They then process this filtrate, allowing wastes and excess ions to leave the body in urine while returning needed substances to the blood in just the right proportions. Although the lungs and the skin also play roles in excretion, the kidneys bear the major responsibility for eliminating nitrogenous (nitrogen-containing) wastes, toxins, and drugs from the body.

Disposing of wastes and excess ions is only one part of the work of the kidneys. As they perform these excretory functions, they also regulate the blood's volume and chemical makeup so that the proper balance between water and salts and between acids and bases is maintained. Frankly, this would be tricky work for a chemical engineer, but the kidneys do it efficiently most of the time.

The kidneys have other regulatory functions as well: By producing the enzyme *renin* (re'nin), they help regulate blood pressure, and their hormone *erythropoietin* stimulates red blood cell production in bone marrow (see Chapter 10). Kidney cells also convert vitamin D to its active form.

The kidneys alone perform the functions just described and manufacture urine in the process. The other organs of the **urinary system**—the paired ureters and the single urinary bladder and urethra (Figure 15.1)—provide temporary storage reservoirs for urine or serve as transportation channels to carry it from one body region to another.

Kidneys

Location and Structure

Although many believe that the **kidneys** are located in the lower back, this is *not* their location. Instead, these small, dark red organs with a kidney-bean shape lie against the dorsal body wall in a *retroperitoneal* position (beneath the parietal peritoneum) in the *superior* lumbar region. The kidneys extend from the T_{12} to the L_3 vertebra; thus they receive some protection from the lower part of the rib cage. Because it is crowded by the liver, the right kidney is positioned slightly lower than the left. An adult kidney is about 12 cm (5 inches)

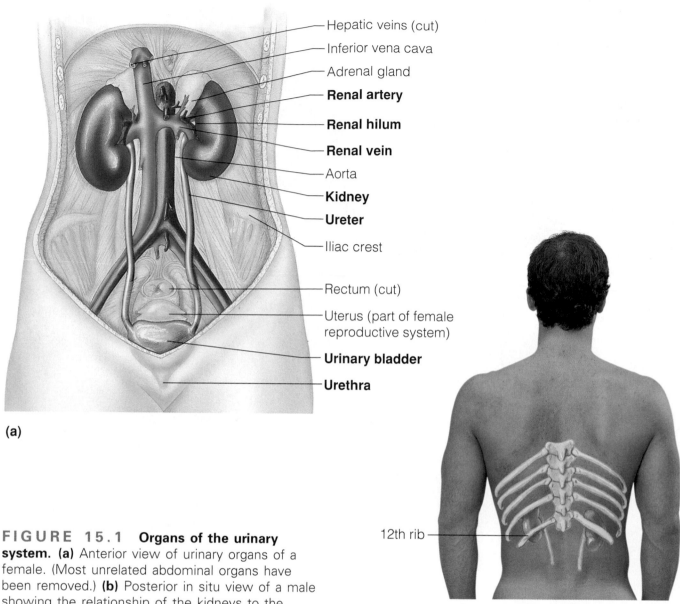

Hepatic veins (cut)

Inferior vena cava

Adrenal gland

Renal artery

Renal hilum

Renal vein

Aorta

Kidney

Ureter

Iliac crest

Rectum (cut)

Uterus (part of female reproductive system)

Urinary bladder

Urethra

(a)

12th rib

(b)

FIGURE 15.1 Organs of the urinary system. (a) Anterior view of urinary organs of a female. (Most unrelated abdominal organs have been removed.) **(b)** Posterior in situ view of a male showing the relationship of the kidneys to the 12th rib pair.

long, 6 cm (2.5 inches) wide, and 3 cm (1 inch) thick, about the size of a large bar of soap. It is convex laterally and has a medial indentation called the *renal hilum.* Several structures, including the ureters, the renal blood vessels, and nerves, enter or exit the kidney at the hilum (see Figures 15.1 and 15.2). Atop each kidney is an *adrenal gland,* which is part of the endocrine system and is a distinctly separate organ functionally.

A transparent *fibrous capsule* encloses each kidney and gives a fresh kidney a glistening appearance. A fatty mass, the *perirenal fat capsule,*

surrounds each kidney and acts to cushion it against blows. The *renal fascia,* the outermost capsule, anchors the kidney and helps hold it in place against the muscles of the trunk wall.

HOMEOSTATIC IMBALANCE

The fat surrounding the kidneys is extremely important in holding them in their normal body position. If the amount of fatty tissue dwindles (as with rapid weight loss), the kidneys may drop to a lower position, a condition called *ptosis* (to'sis; "a fall"). Ptosis creates problems if the ureters, which drain urine from

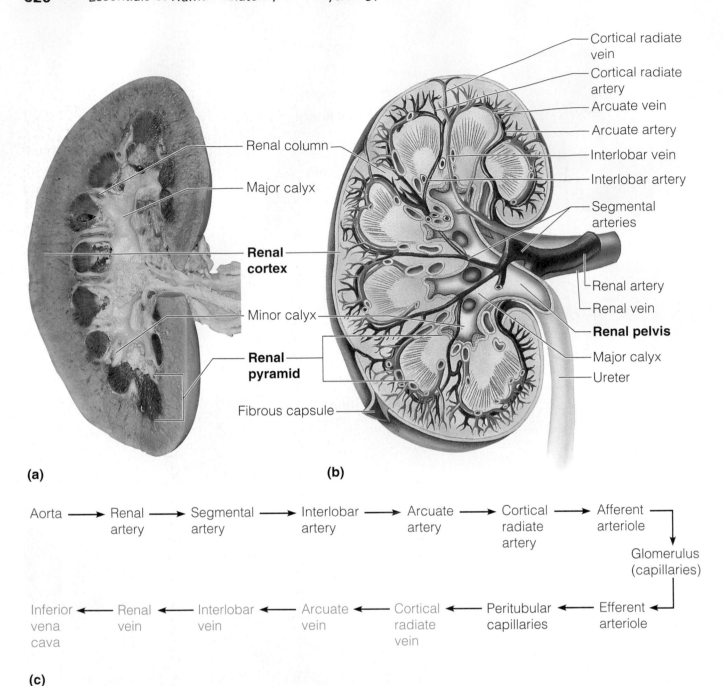

FIGURE 15.2 **Internal anatomy of the kidney. (a)** Photograph of a coronally sectioned kidney. **(b)** Diagrammatic view of a coronally sectioned kidney, illustrating major blood vessels. **(c)** Summary of the pathway of renal blood vessels.

the kidneys, become kinked. When this happens, urine that can no longer pass through the ureters backs up and exerts pressure on the kidney tissue. This condition, called **hydronephrosis** (hi"dro-nĕ-fro'sis), can severely damage the kidney. ▲

When a kidney is cut lengthwise, three distinct regions become apparent (see Figure 15.2). The outer region, which is light in color, is the **renal cortex.** (The word *cortex* comes from the Latin word meaning "bark.") Deep to the cortex is a darker reddish-brown area, the **renal medulla.** The medulla has many basically triangular regions with a striped appearance, the **renal,** or **medullary** (med′u-lar″e), **pyramids.** The broader *base* of each pyramid faces toward the cortex; its tip, the *apex,* points toward the inner region of the kidney. The pyramids are separated by extensions of cortex-like tissue, the **renal columns.**

Medial to the hilum is a flat, basinlike cavity, the **renal pelvis.** As Figure 15.2b shows, the pelvis is continuous with the ureter leaving the hilum. Extensions of the pelvis, **calyces** (kal′ĭ-sēz; singular *calyx*), form cup-shaped areas that enclose the tips of the pyramids. The calyces collect urine, which continuously drains from the tips of the pyramids into the renal pelvis. Urine then flows from the pelvis into the ureter, which transports it to the bladder for temporary storage.

Blood Supply

The kidneys continuously cleanse the blood and adjust its composition, so it is not surprising that they have a very rich blood supply (see Figure 15.2b and c). Approximately one-quarter of the total blood supply of the body passes through the kidneys each minute. The arterial supply of each kidney is the **renal artery.** As the renal artery approaches the hilum, it divides into **segmental arteries,** each of which gives off several branches called **interlobar arteries,** which travel through the renal columns to reach the cortex. At the cortex-medulla junction, interlobar arteries give off the **arcuate** (ar′ku-at) **arteries,** which curve over the medullary pyramids. Small **cortical radiate arteries** then branch off the arcuate arteries and run outward to supply the cortical tissue. Venous blood draining from the kidney flows through veins that trace the pathway of the arterial supply but in a reverse direction—**cortical radiate veins** to **arcuate veins** to **interlobar veins** to the **renal vein,** which emerges from the kidney hilum. (There are no segmental veins.)

▶ DID YOU GET IT?

1. The kidneys are retroperitoneal. What does that mean?

2. Mary lost lots of weight, and suddenly she was having problems with her urine flow. What would

you guess happened, and what caused the problem?

3. From the most superficial aspect of a kidney to its ureter, name its three major regions.

For answers, see Appendix D.

Nephrons and Urine Formation
Nephrons

Each kidney contains over a million tiny structures called **nephrons** (nef′ronz). Nephrons are the structural and functional units of the kidneys and, as such, are responsible for forming urine. Figure 15.3 shows the anatomy and relative positioning of nephrons in each kidney.

Each nephron consists of two main structures: a **glomerulus** (glo-mer′u-lus), which is a knot of capillaries, and a **renal tubule.** The closed end of the renal tubule is enlarged and cup-shaped and completely surrounds the glomerulus. This portion of the renal tubule is called the **glomerular** (*glom* = little ball), or **Bowman's, capsule.** The inner (visceral) layer of the capsule is made up of highly modified octopus-like cells called **podocytes** (pod′o-sītz). Podocytes have long branching processes called *foot processes* that intertwine with one another and cling to the glomerulus. Because openings, the so-called *filtration slits,* exist between their extensions, the podocytes form a porous, or "holey," membrane around the glomerulus (Figure 15.3c and d).

The rest of the tubule is about 3 cm (approximately 1.25 inches) long. As it extends from the glomerular capsule, it coils and twists before forming a hairpin loop and then again becomes coiled and twisted before entering a collecting tubule called the **collecting duct.** These different regions of the tubule have specific names (see Figure 15.3); in order from the glomerular capsule they are the **proximal convoluted tubule (PCT),** the **loop of Henle** (hen′le), and the **distal convoluted tubule (DCT).** The lumen surfaces (surface exposed to the filtrate) of the tubule cells in the proximal convoluted tubules are covered with dense microvilli, which increases their surface area tremendously. Microvilli also occur on the tubule cells in other parts of the tubule but in much reduced numbers.

FIGURE 15.3 **Structure of the nephron.**
(a) Wedge-shaped section of kidney tissue indicating the positioning of nephrons in the kidney. **(b)** Detailed anatomy of a nephron and its associated blood supply. Part of the distal convoluted tubule and afferent arteriole have been sectioned to reveal the location of the juxtaglomerular apparatus. **(c)** Diagrammatic view of the relationship of the visceral layer of the glomerular capsule to the glomerular capillaries. **(d)** Scanning electron micrograph of podocytes clinging to the glomerular capillaries.

Most nephrons are called **cortical nephrons** because they are located almost entirely within the cortex. In a few cases, the nephrons are called **juxtamedullary nephrons** because they are situated close to the cortex-medulla junction, and their loops of Henle dip deep into the medulla (see Figure 15.3a). The **collecting ducts,** each of which receives urine from many nephrons, run downward through the medullary pyramids, giving the pyramids a striped appearance. They deliver the final urine product into the calyces and renal pelvis.

Each and every nephron is associated with two capillary beds—the glomerulus (mentioned earlier) and the *peritubular* (per"ĭ-tu'bu-lar) *capillary bed*. The glomerulus is both fed and drained by *arterioles*. The **afferent arteriole,** which arises from a cortical radiate artery, is the "feeder vessel," and the **efferent arteriole** receives blood that has passed through the glomerulus. The glomerulus, specialized for filtration, is unlike any other capillary bed in the entire body. Because it is both fed *and* drained by arterioles, which are high-resistance vessels, and because the afferent arteriole has a larger diameter than the efferent, blood pressure in the glomerular capillaries is much higher than in other capillary beds. This extremely high pressure forces fluid and solutes (smaller than proteins) out of the blood into the glomerular capsule. Most of this filtrate (99 percent) is eventually reclaimed by the renal tubule cells and returned to the blood in the peritubular capillary beds.

The second capillary bed, the **peritubular capillaries,** arises from the efferent arteriole that drains the glomerulus. Unlike the high-pressure glomerulus, these capillaries are low-pressure, porous vessels that are adapted for absorption instead of filtration. They cling closely to the whole length of the renal tubule, where they are in an ideal position to receive solutes and water from the tubule cells as these substances are reabsorbed from the filtrate percolating through the tubule. The peritubular capillaries drain into interlobular veins leaving the cortex.

Urine Formation

Urine formation is a result of three processes— *glomerular filtration, tubular reabsorption,* and *tubular secretion*. Each of these processes is illustrated in Figure 15.4 and described in more detail next.

How would liver disease, in which the liver is unable to make many of the blood proteins, affect process a? (Reviewing Chapter 10 might help.)

KEY:

a **Glomerular Filtration:** Water and solutes smaller than proteins are forced through the capillary walls and pores of the glomerular capsule into the renal tubule.

b **Tubular Reabsorption:** Water, glucose, amino acids, and needed ions are transported out of the filtrate into the tubule cells and then enter the capillary blood.

c **Tubular Secretion:** H^+, K^+, creatinine, and drugs are removed from the peritubular blood and secreted by the tubule cells into the filtrate.

FIGURE 15.4 The kidney depicted schematically as a single large, uncoiled nephron. A kidney actually has millions of nephrons acting in parallel. The key indicates three processes by which the kidneys adjust the composition of plasma.

The amount of renal filtrate formed is a function of filtration (blood) pressure and blood osmotic pressure (exerted largely by blood proteins). In the situation described, more filtrate than normal will be formed because the blood pressure is opposed to a lesser extent by osmotic pressure of the blood.

Glomerular Filtration As just described, the glomerulus acts as a filter. **Glomerular filtration** is a nonselective, passive process in which fluid passes from the blood into the glomerular capsule part of the renal tubule. Once in the capsule, the fluid is called filtrate and it is essentially blood plasma without blood proteins. Both proteins and blood cells are normally too large to pass through the filtration membrane, and when either of these appear in the urine, it is a pretty fair bet that there is some problem with the glomerular filters. As long as the systemic blood pressure is normal, filtrate will be formed. If arterial blood pressure drops too low, glomerular pressure becomes inadequate to force substances out of the blood into the tubules, and filtrate formation stops.

HOMEOSTATIC IMBALANCE

An abnormally low urinary output is called **oliguria** (ol″i-gu′re-ah) if it is between 100 and 400 ml/day, and **anuria** (ah-nu′re-ah) if it is less than 100 ml/day. Low urinary output usually indicates that glomerular blood pressure is too low to cause filtration, but anuria may also result from transfusion reactions and acute inflammation or from crush injuries of the kidneys. ▲

Tubular Reabsorption Besides wastes and excess ions that must be removed from the blood, the filtrate contains many useful substances (including water, glucose, amino acids, and ions), which must be reclaimed from the filtrate and returned to the blood. **Tubular reabsorption** begins as soon as the filtrate enters the proximal convoluted tubule (Figure 15.5). The tubule cells are "transporters," taking up needed substances from the filtrate and then passing them out their posterior aspect into the extracellular space, from which they are absorbed into peritubular capillary blood. Some reabsorption is done passively (for example, water passes by osmosis), but reabsorption of most substances depends on active transport processes, which use membrane carriers and are very selective. There is an abundance of carriers for substances that need to be retained, and few or no carriers for substances of no use to the body. Needed substances (for example, glucose and amino acids) are usually entirely removed from the filtrate. **Nitrogenous waste products** are poorly reabsorbed, if at all. These include **urea** (u-re′ah), formed by the liver as an end product of protein breakdown when amino acids are used to produce energy; **uric acid** released when nucleic acids are metabolized; and **creatinine** (kre-at′ĭ-nin), associated with creatine (kre′ah-tin) metabolism in muscle tissue. Because tubule cells have few membrane carriers to reabsorb these substances, they tend to remain in the filtrate and are found in high concentrations in urine excreted from the body. Various ions are reabsorbed or allowed to go out in the urine, according to what is needed at a particular time to maintain the proper pH and electrolyte composition of the blood. Most reabsorption occurs in the proximal convoluted tubules, but the distal convoluted tubule and the collecting duct are also active.

Tubular Secretion **Tubular secretion** is essentially tubular reabsorption in reverse. Some substances, such as hydrogen and potassium ions and creatinine, also move from the blood of the peritubular capillaries through the tubule cells or from the tubule cells themselves into the filtrate to be eliminated in urine. This process seems to be important for getting rid of substances not already in the filtrate, such as certain drugs, excess potassium, or as an additional means for controlling blood pH (see Figure 15.5).

Characteristics of Urine

In 24 hours, the marvelously complex kidneys filter some 150 to 180 liters of blood plasma through their glomeruli into the tubules, which process the filtrate by taking substances out of it (reabsorption) and adding substances to it (secretion). In the same 24 hours, only about 1.0 to 1.8 liters of urine are produced. Obviously, urine and filtrate are quite different. Filtrate contains everything that blood plasma does (except proteins), but by the time it reaches the collecting ducts, the filtrate has lost most of its water and just about all of its nutrients and necessary ions. What remains, **urine,** contains nitrogenous wastes and unneeded substances. Assuming we are healthy, our kidneys can keep our blood composition fairly constant despite wide variations in diet and cell activity.

Freshly voided urine is generally clear and pale to deep yellow. The normal yellow color is due to *urochrome* (u′ro-krōm), a pigment that results from the body's destruction of hemoglobin. The more solutes are in the urine, the deeper yellow its color; on the other hand, dilute urine is a pale,

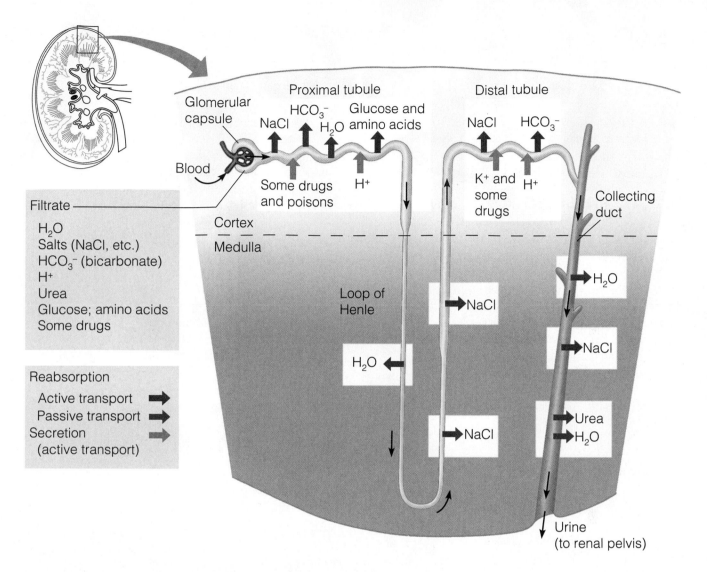

Filtrate

H₂O
Salts (NaCl, etc.)
HCO₃⁻ (bicarbonate)
H⁺
Urea
Glucose; amino acids
Some drugs

Reabsorption

Active transport
Passive transport
Secretion
(active transport)

FIGURE 15.5 **Sites of filtration, reabsorption, and secretion in a nephron.**

straw color. At times, urine may be a color other than yellow. This might be a result of eating certain foods (beets, for example) or the presence of bile or blood in the urine.

When formed, urine is sterile, and its odor is slightly aromatic. If it is allowed to stand, it takes on an ammonia odor caused by the action of bacteria on the urine solutes. Some drugs, vegetables (such as asparagus), and various diseases (such as diabetes mellitus) alter the usual odor of urine.

Urine pH is usually slightly acid (around 6), but changes in body metabolism and certain foods may cause it to be much more acidic or basic. For example, a diet with large amounts of protein (eggs and cheese) and whole-wheat products

causes urine to become quite acid; thus, such foods are called *acid-ash foods*. Conversely, a vegetarian diet is called an *alkaline-ash diet* because it makes urine quite alkaline as the kidneys excrete the excess bases. Bacterial infection of the urinary tract also may cause the urine to be alkaline.

Because urine is water plus solutes, urine weighs more, or is more dense, than distilled water. The term used to compare how *much* heavier urine is than distilled water is **specific gravity.** Whereas the specific gravity of pure water is 1.0, the specific gravity of urine usually ranges from 1.001 to 1.035 (dilute to concentrated urine, respectively). Urine is generally dilute (that is, it has a low specific gravity) when a person drinks excessive

A CLOSER LOOK

RENAL FAILURE AND THE ARTIFICIAL KIDNEY

How long has it been since you had a urinalysis? If you're like most of us, the answer is: too long. This simple, inexpensive, painless test can detect renal disease years before any symptoms appear, buying time for early treatment and preventing life-threatening complications.

Unfortunately, urinalysis is often omitted from routine medical check-ups. Unfortunate, because chronic renal disease is a major burden to the U.S. health care system. Some 10–20 million Americans—one out of every 15—have some degree of kidney dysfunction, and nearly 350,000 require dialysis or a kidney transplant just to stay alive.

Warning signs of kidney trouble may include high blood pressure, frequent urination, difficult or painful urination, puffy eyes, or swollen hands or feet. But all too often, there are few noticeable symptoms until advanced stages, when a significant percentage of kidney function has already been lost. Urinalysis is valuable because it can detect proteinuria, a sensitive early marker of kidney damage.

Where did this kidney crisis come from? In adults, chronic renal disease often develops in conjunction with other chronic health conditions. The leading cause is diabetes mellitus, which accounts for approximately 44 percent of new cases each year. Hypertension is a close second, accounting for about 28 percent of cases. Note that hypertension is both a cause and a symptom: High

A renal patient undergoing hemodialysis.

> *" In renal failure, filtrate formation decreases or stops."*

blood pressure impairs kidney function by damaging renal blood vessels and reducing circulation to the organs, even as hypertension-battered kidneys push blood pressure upward. Atherosclerosis compounds the problem by further impairing circulation.

Other possible causes of renal failure include the following:

▶ Repeated damaging infections of the kidneys

▶ Physical trauma to the kidneys (crush injury and others)

▶ Chemical poisoning of the tubule cells by heavy metals (mercury or lead) or organic solvents (dry-cleaning fluids, paint thinner)

▶ Prolonged pressure on skeletal muscles (causes release of myoglobin, a muscle pigment that can clog renal tubules)

In renal failure, filtrate formation decreases or stops completely. Because toxic wastes accumulate quickly in the blood when the kidney tubule cells are not working, *dialysis* (*dialys* = separate) is necessary to cleanse the blood while the kidneys are shut down. In *hemodialysis,* which uses an "artificial kidney" apparatus (see photo), the patient's blood is passed through a membrane tubing that is permeable only to selected substances, and the tubing is immersed in a bathing solution that differs slightly from normal "cleansed" plasma. As blood circulates through the tubing, substances such as nitrogenous wastes and potassium ions (K^+) present in the blood (but not in the bath) diffuse out of the blood through the tubing into the surrounding solution, and substances to be added to the blood (mainly buffers for hydrogen ions [H^+] and glucose for malnourished patients) move from the bathing solution into the blood. In this way, needed substances are retained in the blood or added to it, while wastes and ion excesses are removed. Hemodialysis is routinely done three times weekly, and each session takes four to eight hours. Serious problems occasionally encountered by hemodialysis patients are thrombosis, infection, and ischemia at the shunt site. Hemorrhage is an added risk, because the blood must be heparinized to prevent clotting during hemodialysis. (*Heparin* is an anticoagulant.)

When renal damage is nonreversible, as in chronic, slowly progressing renal failure, the kidneys become totally unable to process plasma or concentrate urine, and a kidney transplant is the only answer. Unless the new kidney comes from an identical twin, recipients must take immunosuppressive drugs for the rest of their lives to prevent rejection. Kidney transplants in the United States during 2001 numbered 15,311, almost 5000 of them from living donors. But this leaves 57,000 Americans still waiting for a kidney, more than for any other organ.

If this sounds bleak, consider that 40 years ago people who reached end-stage renal failure survived for only a few days. Today, they can live for years or even decades, and researchers are laboring to improve both life span and quality of life.

fluids, uses diuretics (drugs that increase urine output), or has chronic renal failure, a condition in which the kidney loses its ability to concentrate urine (see the "A Closer Look" box above). Conditions that produce urine with a high specific gravity include inadequate fluid intake, fever, and a kidney inflammation called *pyelonephritis* (pi″ĕ-lo-nĕ-fri′tis).

Solutes normally found in urine include sodium and potassium ions, urea, uric acid, creatinine, ammonia, bicarbonate ions, and various other ions, depending on blood composition. With certain diseases, urine composition can change dramatically, and the presence of abnormal substances in urine is often helpful in diagnosing the problem. This is why a routine urinalysis should always be part of any good physical examination.

Substances *not* normally found in urine are glucose, blood proteins, red blood cells, hemoglobin, white blood cells (pus), and bile. Names and possible causes of conditions in which abnormal urinary constituents and volumes might be present are given in Table 15.1.

 DID YOU GET IT?

4. What is the structural and functional unit of the kidney?

5. What are two functions of the renal tubule and one function of the peritubular capillaries?

6. How does a decrease in blood pressure affect glomerular pressure?

7. Is the specific gravity of urine higher or lower than that of water? Why?

For answers, see Appendix D.

15

TABLE 15.1	Abnormal Urinary Constituents	
Substance	**Name of condition**	**Possible causes**
Glucose	Glycosuria (gli"ko-su're-ah)	Nonpathological: Excessive intake of sugary foods Pathological: Diabetes mellitus
Proteins	Proteinuria (pro"te-ĭ-nu're-ah) (also called albuminuria)	Nonpathological: Physical exertion, pregnancy Pathological: Glomerulonephritis, hypertension
Pus (WBCs and bacteria)	Pyuria (pi-u're-ah)	Urinary tract infection
RBCs	Hematuria (he"mah-tu're-ah)	Bleeding in the urinary tract (due to trauma, kidney stones, infection)
Hemoglobin	Hemoglobinuria (he"mo-glo-bĭ-nu're-ah)	Various: Transfusion reaction, hemolytic anemia
Bile pigment	Bilirubinuria (bil"ĭ-roo-bĭ-nu're-ah)	Liver disease (hepatitis)

Ureters, Urinary Bladder, and Urethra

Ureters

The **ureters** (u-re'terz) are two slender tubes each 25 to 30 cm (10 to 12 inches) long and 6 mm (1/4 inch) in diameter. Each ureter runs behind the peritoneum from the renal hilum to the posterior aspect of the bladder, which it enters at a slight angle (see Figures 15.1 and 15.6). The superior end of each ureter is continuous with the pelvis of the kidney, and its mucosal lining is continuous with that lining the renal pelvis and the bladder below.

Essentially, the ureters are passageways that carry urine from the kidneys to the bladder. Although it might appear that urine could simply drain to the bladder below by gravity, the ureters *do* play an active role in urine transport. Smooth muscle layers in their walls contract to propel urine into the bladder by peristalsis. Once urine has entered the bladder, it is prevented from flowing back into the ureters by small valvelike folds of bladder mucosa that flap over the ureter openings.

HOMEOSTATIC IMBALANCE

When urine becomes extremely concentrated, solutes such as uric acid salts form crystals that precipitate in the renal pelvis. These crystals are called **renal calculi** ((kal'kyoo-li; *calculus* = little stone), or kidney stones. Excruciating pain that radiates to the flank occurs when the ureter walls close in on the sharp calculi as they are being eased through the ureter by peristalsis or when the calculi become wedged in a ureter. Frequent bacterial infections of the urinary tract, urinary retention, and alkaline urine all favor calculi formation. Surgery has been the treatment of choice, but a newer noninvasive procedure *(lithotripsy)* that uses ultrasound waves to shatter the calculi is becoming more popular. The pulverized, sandlike remnants of the calculi are painlessly eliminated in the urine. ▲

Urinary Bladder

The **urinary bladder** is a smooth, collapsible, muscular sac that stores urine temporarily. It is located retroperitoneally in the pelvis just posterior to the pubic symphysis. If the interior of the bladder is scanned, three openings are seen—the two ureter openings *(ureteral orifices)* and the single opening of the *urethra* (u-re'thrah) (the *internal urethral orifice)*, which drains the bladder (Figure 15.6). The smooth triangular region of the bladder base outlined by these three openings is called the **trigone** (tri'gon). The trigone is important clinically because infections tend to persist in this region. In males, the *prostate gland* (part of the male repro-

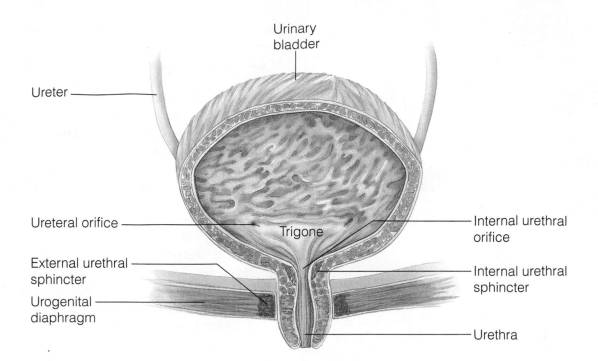

FIGURE 15.6 **Basic structure of the female urinary bladder and urethra.**

ductive system) surrounds the neck of the bladder where it empties into the urethra.

The bladder wall contains three layers of smooth muscle, collectively called the *detrusor muscle,* and its mucosa is a special type of epithelium, *transitional epithelium* (see p. 90). Both of these structural features make the bladder uniquely suited for its function of urine storage. When the bladder is empty, it is collapsed, 5 to 7.5 cm (2 to 3 inches) long at most, and its walls are thick and thrown into folds. As urine accumulates, the bladder expands and rises superiorly in the abdominal cavity (Figure 15.7). Its muscular wall stretches, and the transitional epithelial layer thins, increasing its volume and allowing the bladder to store more urine without substantially increasing its internal pressure. A moderately full bladder is about 12.5 cm (5 inches) long and holds about 500 ml (1 pint) of urine, but it is capable of holding more than twice that amount. When the bladder is really distended, or stretched by urine, it becomes firm and pear-shaped and may be felt just above the pubic symphysis. Urine is formed continuously by the kidneys, but it is usually stored in the bladder until its release is convenient.

Urethra

The **urethra** is a thin-walled tube that carries urine by peristalsis from the bladder to the outside of the body. At the bladder-urethra junction, a thickening of the smooth muscle forms the **internal urethral sphincter** (see Figure 15.6), an involuntary sphincter that keeps the urethra closed when urine is not being passed. A second sphincter, the **external urethral sphincter,** is fashioned by skeletal muscle as the urethra passes through the pelvic floor. This sphincter is voluntarily controlled.

The length and relative function of the urethra differ in the two sexes. In women, it is about 3 to 4 cm (1½ inches) long, and its external orifice, or opening, lies anteriorly to the vaginal opening (see also Figure 16.8a, p. 554). Its function is to conduct urine to the body exterior.

HOMEOSTATIC IMBALANCE

The female urinary orifice is close to the anal opening, and feces contain a good deal of bacteria, so improper toileting habits (wiping from back to front rather than from front to back) can carry bacteria into the urethra. Moreover, the mucosa of the urethra is continuous with that of the rest of the urinary tract organs,

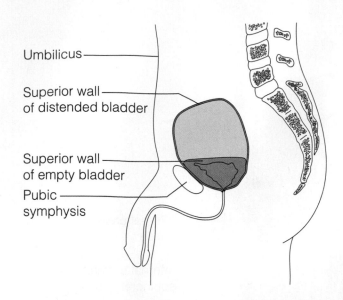

Umbilicus

Superior wall of distended bladder

Superior wall of empty bladder

Pubic symphysis

FIGURE 15.7 Position and shape of a distended and an empty urinary bladder in an adult man.

and an inflammation of the urethra, or **urethritis** (u″re-thri′tis), can easily ascend the tract to cause bladder inflammation *(cystitis)* or even kidney inflammation (**pyelonephritis,** or **pyelitis**). Symptoms of urinary tract infection include *dysuria* (painful urination), urinary *urgency* and *frequency,* fever, and sometimes cloudy or blood-tinged urine. When the kidneys are involved, back pain and a severe headache are common. ▲

In men, the urethra is approximately 20 cm (8 inches) long and has three named regions (see Figure 16.2, p. 547): the *prostatic, membranous,* and *spongy* (or *penile*) *urethrae.* The urethra opens at the tip of the penis after traveling down its length. The urethra of the male has a double function. It carries urine out of the body, and it provides the passageway through which sperm is ejected from the body. Thus, in males, the urethra is part of both the urinary and reproductive systems.

Micturition

Micturition (mik″tu-rish′un), or **voiding,** is the act of emptying the bladder. Two sphincters, or valves, the internal urethral sphincter (more superiorly located) and the external urethral sphincter (more inferiorly located) control the flow of urine from the bladder (see Figure 15.6). Ordinarily, the

bladder continues to collect urine until about 200 ml have accumulated. At about this point, stretching of the bladder wall activates stretch receptors. Impulses transmitted to the sacral region of the spinal cord and then back to the bladder via the *pelvic splanchnic nerves* cause the bladder to go into reflex contractions. As the contractions become stronger, stored urine is forced past the internal urethral sphincter (the smooth muscle, involuntary sphincter) into the upper part of the urethra. It is then that a person feels the urge to void. Because the lower external sphincter is skeletal muscle and is voluntarily controlled, we can choose to keep it closed and postpone bladder emptying temporarily. However, if it is convenient, the external sphincter can be relaxed so that urine is flushed from the body. When one chooses not to void, the reflex contractions of the bladder will stop within a minute or so, and urine will continue to accumulate in the bladder. After 200 to 300 ml more have been collected, the micturition reflex occurs again. Eventually, micturition occurs whether one wills it or not.

HOMEOSTATIC IMBALANCE

Incontinence (in-kon′tǐ-nens) occurs when we are unable to voluntarily control the external sphincter. Incontinence is normal in children 2 years old or younger, because they have not yet gained control over their voluntary sphincter. It may also occur in older children who sleep so soundly that they are not awakened by the stimulus. However, after the toddler years, incontinence is usually a result of emotional problems, pressure (as in pregnancy), or nervous system problems (stroke or spinal cord injury).

Urinary retention is essentially the opposite of incontinence. It is a condition in which the bladder is unable to expel its contained urine. There are various causes for urinary retention. It often occurs after surgery in which general anesthesia has been given, because it takes a little time for the smooth muscles to regain their activity. Another cause of urinary retention, occurring primarily in older men, is enlargement, or **hyperplasia,** of the prostate gland, which surrounds the neck of the bladder. As the prostate gland enlarges, it narrows the urethra, making it very difficult to void. When urinary retention is prolonged, a slender flexible drainage tube called a *catheter* (kath′ǐ-ter) must be inserted through the urethra to drain the urine and prevent bladder trauma from excessive stretching. ▲

15

DID YOU GET IT?

8. A kidney stone blocking a ureter would interfere with the flow of urine to which organ?

9. Why is the presence of transitional epithelium in the urinary bladder important?

10. Structurally and functionally, how does the male urethra differ from the female urethra?

11. What is a synonym for *micturition*?

For answers, see Appendix D.

Fluid, Electrolyte, and Acid-Base Balance

Blood composition depends on three major factors: diet, cellular metabolism, and urine output. In general, the kidneys have four major roles to play, which help keep the blood composition relatively constant. These are (1) excretion of nitrogen-containing wastes, maintaining (2) water and (3) electrolyte balance of the blood, and (4) ensuring proper blood pH. Excretion of nitrogenous wastes has already been considered; roles 2 through 4 are discussed briefly next.

Maintaining Water and Electrolyte Balance of Blood

Body Fluids and Fluid Compartments

If you are a healthy young adult, water probably accounts for half or more of your body weight—50 percent in women and about 60 percent in men. These differences reflect the fact that women have relatively less muscle and a larger amount of body fat (and of all body tissues, fat contains the least water). Babies, with little fat and low bone mass, are about 75 percent water, but total body water content declines through life and accounts for only about 45 percent of body weight in old age. The importance of water to the functioning of the body and its cells is described in Chapter 2. That information will not be repeated here except to say that water is the universal body solvent within which all solutes (including the very important electrolytes) are dissolved.

Water occupies three main locations within the body, referred to as *fluid compartments* (Figure 15.8). About two-thirds of body fluid, the so-called

Total body water volume = 40 L, 60% body weight

Extracellular fluid (ECF) volume =15 L, 20% body weight

Intracellular fluid volume = 25 L, 40% body weight	Interstitial fluid volume = 12 L, 80% of ECF	Plasma volume =3 L, 20% of ECF

FIGURE 15.8 The major fluid compartments of the body. Approximate values are noted for a 70-kg (154-pound) man.

intracellular fluid (ICF), is contained within the living cells. The remainder, called **extracellular fluid (ECF),** includes all body fluids located outside the cells. Although ECF most importantly includes blood plasma and interstitial (or tissue) fluid, it also accounts for cerebrospinal and serous fluids, the humors of the eye, lymph, and others.

Plasma circulates throughout the body and links the external and internal environments (Figure 15.9). Exchanges occur almost continuously in the lungs, gastrointestinal tract, and kidneys. Although these exchanges alter plasma composition and volume, adjustments in the other two fluid compartments follow quickly so that balance is restored as described below.

The Link between Water and Salt

Water certainly accounts for nearly the entire volume of body fluids, regardless of type, and all body fluids are similar, but there is more to *fluid balance* than just water. The types and amounts of solutes in body fluids, especially electrolytes such as sodium, potassium, and calcium ions, are also vitally important to overall body homeostasis, and water and electrolyte balance are tightly linked as the kidneys continuously process the blood. (Recall from Chapter 2 that electrolytes are charged

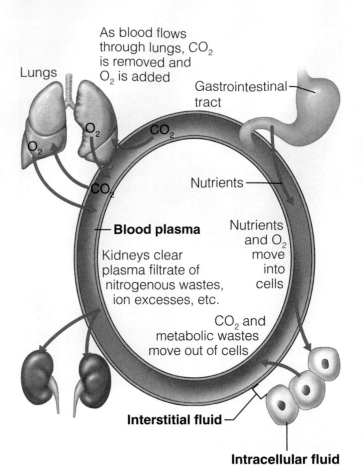

As blood flows through lungs, CO_2 is removed and O_2 is added

Lungs

Gastrointestinal tract

O_2

O_2

CO_2

CO_2

Nutrients

Blood plasma

Kidneys clear plasma filtrate of nitrogenous wastes, ion excesses, etc.

Nutrients and O_2 move into cells

CO_2 and metabolic wastes move out of cells

Interstitial fluid

Intracellular fluid

FIGURE 15.9 The continuous mixing of body fluids. Nutrients and wastes are exchanged between the intracellular fluid and the plasma through the interstitial fluid. Blood plasma transports nutrients and wastes between the cells and the external environment of the body.

particles [ions] that conduct an electrical current in an aqueous solution.) Very small changes in the solute **(electrolyte)** concentrations in the various fluid compartments, cause water to move from one compartment to another. This movement not only alters blood volume and blood pressure, but also can severely impair the activity of irritable cells like nerve and muscle cells. For example, a deficit of sodium ions (Na^+) in the ECF results in water loss from the bloodstream into the tissue spaces (edema) and muscular weakness.

Regulation of Water Intake and Output

If the body is to remain properly hydrated, we cannot lose more water than we take in. Most water intake is a result of fluids and foods we ingest in

our diet. However, a small amount (about 10 percent) is produced during cellular metabolism, as explained in Chapter 14 and indicated in Figure 15.10. The **thirst mechanism** is the driving force for water intake. An increase in plasma solute content of only 2 to 3 percent excites the hypothalamic *thirst center.* A dry mouth also occurs because the salivary glands obtain the water they require from the blood. When less fluid leaves the bloodstream, less saliva is produced, reinforcing the drive to drink. The same response is produced by a decline in blood volume (or pressure); however, this is the less potent stimulus.

There are several routes for water to leave the body. Some water vaporizes out of the lungs, some is lost in perspiration, and some leaves the body in the stool. The job of the kidneys is like that of a juggler. On the one hand, if large amounts of water are lost in other ways, they compensate by putting out less urine to conserve body water. On the other hand, when water intake is excessive, the kidneys excrete generous amounts of urine, and the anguish of a too-full bladder becomes very real.

Likewise, the proper concentrations of the various electrolytes must be present in both intracellular and extracellular fluids. Most electrolytes enter the body in foods and "hard" (mineral-rich) water. Although very small amounts are lost in perspiration and in feces, the major factor regulating the electrolyte composition of body fluids is the kidneys. Just how the kidneys accomplish their balancing act is explained in more detail next.

Reabsorption of water and electrolytes by the kidneys is regulated primarily by hormones. When blood volume drops for any reason (for example, as a result of hemorrhage or excessive water loss through sweating or diarrhea), arterial blood pressure drops, which in turn decreases the amount of filtrate formed by the kidneys. In addition, highly sensitive cells in the hypothalamus called **osmoreceptors** (oz"mo-re-sep'torz) react to the change in blood composition (that is, less water and more solutes) by becoming more active. The result is that nerve impulses are sent to the posterior pituitary (Figure 15.11), which then releases **antidiuretic hormone (ADH).** (The term *antidiuretic* is derived from *diuresis* [di"u-re'sis], which means "flow of urine from the kidney," and *anti,* which means "against.") As one might guess, this

How would the values shown here be affected by (1) drinking a six-pack of beer? (2) fasting (only water is ingested)?

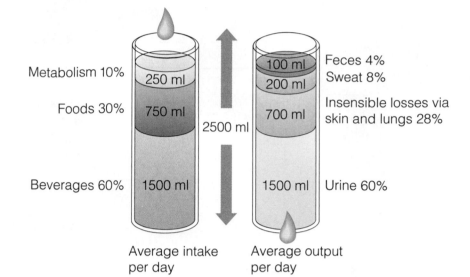

FIGURE 15.10 Water intake and output. Major sources of body water and routes of water loss from the body are shown. When intake and output are in balance, the body is adequately hydrated.

hormone prevents excessive water loss in the urine. ADH travels in the blood to its main target, the kidney's collecting ducts, where it causes the duct cells to reabsorb more water. As more water is returned to the bloodstream, blood volume and blood pressure increase to normal levels, and only a small amount of very concentrated urine is formed. ADH is released more or less continuously unless the solute concentration of the blood drops too low. When this happens, the osmoreceptors become "quiet," and excess water is allowed to leave the body in the urine.

HOMEOSTATIC IMBALANCE

When ADH is *not* released (perhaps because of injury or destruction of the hypothalamus or posterior pituitary gland), huge amounts of very dilute urine (up to 25 liters/day) flush from the body day after day. This condition, **diabetes insipidus** (in-sip'ĭ-dus),

can lead to severe dehydration and electrolyte imbalances. Affected individuals are always thirsty and have to drink fluids almost continuously to maintain normal fluid balance. ▲

A second hormone that helps to regulate blood composition and blood volume by acting on the kidney is **aldosterone** (al"dos'ter-on). Aldosterone is the major factor regulating sodium ion content of the ECF and in the process helps regulate the concentration of other ions (Cl^-, K^+, and Mg^{2+} [magnesium]) as well. Sodium ion (Na^+) is the electrolyte most responsible for osmotic water flows. When too little sodium is in the blood, the blood becomes too dilute. Consequently, water leaves the bloodstream and flows out into the tissue spaces, causing edema and possibly a shutdown of the circulatory system. Regardless of whether aldosterone is present or not, about 80 percent of the sodium in the filtrate is reabsorbed in the proximal convoluted tubules of the kidneys. When aldosterone concentrations are high, most of the remaining sodium ions are actively reabsorbed in the distal convoluted tubules and the collecting ducts. Generally speaking, for each sodium ion reabsorbed, a chloride ion follows and a potassium ion is secreted into the filtrate. Thus, as the sodium content of the blood increases, potassium concentration decreases, bringing these two ions back to their normal balance in the blood. Still another effect of

In case #1, the fluid ingested would greatly increase, as would the amount of urinary output. In case #2, there would be no fluid intake from ingested foods and less fluid resulting from metabolism. Fluid output would be severely curtailed—no output in feces and less in urine to conserve body water. Insensible losses would not change. Loss of water in perspiration would depend on body and ambient temperatures.

Which pathway would also stimulate thirst?

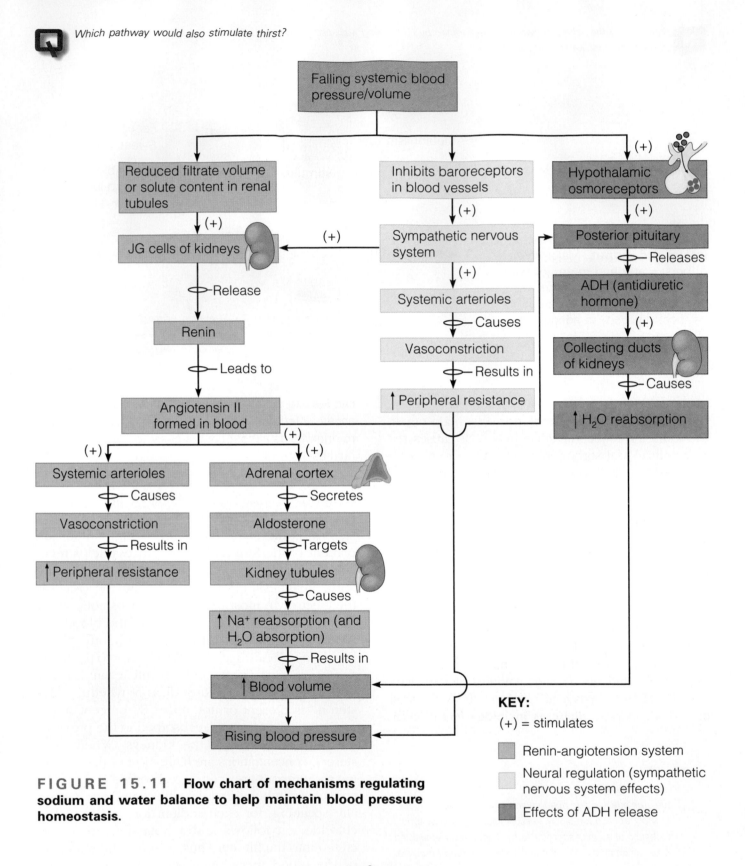

FIGURE 15.11 Flow chart of mechanisms regulating sodium and water balance to help maintain blood pressure homeostasis.

The pathway through the hypothalamus, which not only causes water retention, via the effect of ADH on the kidneys, but also stimulates thirst to increase water ingestion.

aldosterone is to increase water reabsorption by the tubule cells, because as sodium is reclaimed, water follows it passively back into the blood. A little rule to keep in mind here is: *water follows salt.*

Recall that aldosterone is produced by the adrenal cortex. Although rising potassium levels or falling sodium levels in the ECF directly stimulate the adrenal cells to release aldosterone, the most important trigger for aldosterone release is the **renin-angiotensin mechanism** (see Figure 15.11) mediated by the *juxtaglomerular (JG) apparatus* of the renal tubules. The juxtaglomerular apparatus (see Figure 15.3b) consists of a complex of modified smooth muscle cells (JG cells) in the afferent arteriole plus some modified epithelial cells forming part of the distal convoluted tubule. The naming of this cell cluster reflects its location close by *(juxta)* the glomerulus. When the cells of the JG apparatus are stimulated by low blood pressure in the afferent arteriole or changes in solute content of the filtrate, they respond by releasing the enzyme **renin** into the blood. (Notice the different spelling of this enzyme from *rennin,* an enzyme secreted by stomach glands.) Renin catalyzes the series of reactions that produce angiotensin II, which in turn acts directly on the blood vessels to cause vasoconstriction (and an increase in peripheral resistance) and on the adrenal cortical cells to promote aldosterone release. As a result, blood volume and blood pressure increase (see Figure 15.11). The renin-angiotensin mechanism is extremely important for regulating blood pressure.

The pressure drop also excites baroreceptors in the larger blood vessels. These baroreceptors alert sympathetic nervous system centers of the brain to cause vasoconstriction (via release of epinephrine and norepinephrine), which increases the peripheral resistance (see Figure 15.11). However, this neural mechanism's major focus is blood pressure regulation, not water and electrolyte balance.

HOMEOSTATIC IMBALANCE

People with **Addison's disease** (hypoaldosteronism) have **polyuria** (excrete large volumes of urine) and lose tremendous amounts of salt and water to urine. As long as adequate amounts of salt and fluids are ingested, people with this condition can avoid problems, but they are constantly teetering on the brink of dehydration. ▲

▶ DID YOU GET IT?

12. What are the four main functions of the kidneys?

13. What is the chief mechanism prompting water intake?

14. What is the role of aldosterone in water balance?

15. Where are osmoreceptors located, and to what stimulus do they respond?

For answers, see Appendix D.

Maintaining Acid-Base Balance of Blood

For the cells of the body to function properly, blood pH must be maintained between 7.35 and 7.45, a very narrow range. Whenever the pH of arterial blood rises above 7.45, a person is said to have **alkalosis** (al″kah-lo′sis). A drop in arterial pH to below 7.35 results in **acidosis** (as″ĭ-do′sis). Because a pH of 7.0 is neutral, 7.35 is not acidic, chemically speaking; however, it represents a higher-than-optimal hydrogen ion concentration for the functioning of most body cells. Therefore, any arterial pH between 7.35 and 7.0 is called **physiological acidosis.**

Although small amounts of acidic substances enter the body in ingested foods, most hydrogen ions originate as by-products of cellular metabolism, which continuously adds substances to the blood that tend to disturb its **acid-base balance.** Many different acids are produced (for example, phosphoric acid, lactic acid, and many types of fatty acids). In addition, carbon dioxide, which is released during energy production, forms carbonic acid. Ammonia and other basic substances are also released to the blood as cells go about their usual "business." Although the chemical buffers in the blood can temporarily "tie up" excess acids and bases, and the lungs have the chief responsibility for eliminating carbon dioxide from the body, the kidneys assume most of the load for maintaining acid-base balance of the blood. Before describing how the kidneys function in acid-base balance, let's take a look at how each of our other two pH-controlling systems, blood buffers and the respiratory system, works.

Blood Buffers

Chemical buffers are systems of one or two molecules that act to prevent dramatic changes in

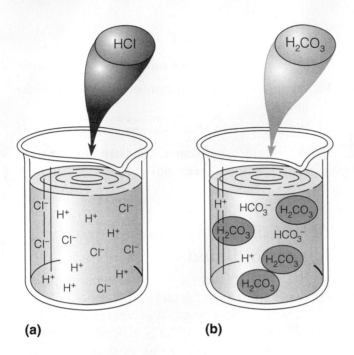

(a)　　　　　　**(b)**

FIGURE 15.12 **Dissociation of strong and weak acids. (a)** When HCl, a strong acid, is added to water it dissociates completely into its ions (H^+ and Cl^-). **(b)** By contrast, dissociation of H_2CO_3, a weak acid, is very incomplete, and some molecules of H_2CO_3 remain undissociated (symbols shown in green ovals) in solution.

hydrogen ion (H^+) concentration when acids or bases are added. They do this by binding to hydrogen ions whenever the pH drops and by releasing hydrogen ions when the pH rises. The chemical buffers act within a fraction of a second, so they are the first line of defense in resisting pH changes.

To better understand how a chemical buffer system works, let's review the definitions of strong and weak acids and bases. Recall that acids are proton (H^+) donors, and that the acidity of a solution reflects only the *free* hydrogen ions, not those still bound to anions. *Strong acids* dissociate completely and liberate all their H^+ in water. Consequently they can cause large changes in pH. By contrast, *weak acids* such as carbonic acid dissociate only partially and so have a much slighter effect on a solution's pH (Figure 15.12). However, weak acids are very effective at preventing pH changes since they are forced to dissociate and release more H^+ when the pH rises over the desirable pH range. This feature allows them to

play a very important role in the chemical buffer systems.

Also recall that bases are proton or hydrogen ion acceptors. *Strong bases* like hydroxides dissociate easily in water and quickly tie up H^+, but *weak bases* such as bicarbonate ion (HCO_3^-) and ammonia (NH_3) are slower to accept H^+. However, as pH drops, the weak bases become "stronger" and begin to tie up more hydrogen ions. Thus, like weak acids, they are valuable members of the chemical buffer systems.

The three major chemical buffer systems of the body are the *bicarbonate, phosphate,* and *protein buffer systems,* each of which helps to maintain the pH in one or more of the fluid compartments. They all work together, and anything that causes a shift in H^+ concentration in one compartment also causes changes in the others. Thus, drifts in pH are resisted by the entire buffering system. Because all three systems operate in a similar way, examining just one, the bicarbonate buffer system, which is so important in preventing changes in blood pH, should be sufficient.

The **bicarbonate buffer system** is a mixture of *carbonic acid* (H_2CO_3) and its salt, *sodium bicarbonate* ($NaHCO_3$). Carbonic acid is a weak acid, so it does not dissociate much in neutral or acidic solutions. Thus, when a strong acid, such as hydrochloric acid (HCl) is added, most of the carbonic acid remains intact. However, the *bicarbonate ions* (HCO_3^-) of the salt act as bases to tie up the H^+ released by the stronger acid, forming more carbonic acid:

$$HCl + NaHCO_3 \longrightarrow H_2CO_3 + NaCl$$

$\quad$strong$\qquad$weak$\qquad\qquad$weak$\qquad$salt
$\quad$acid$\qquad\quad$base$\qquad\qquad$acid

Because the strong acid is (effectively) changed to a weak one, it lowers the pH of the solution only very slightly.

Similarly, if a strong base such as sodium hydroxide (NaOH) is added to a solution containing the bicarbonate buffer system, $NaHCO_3$ will not dissociate further under such alkaline conditions. However, carbonic acid will be forced to dissociate further by the presence of the strong base—liberating more H^+ to bind with the OH^- released by NaOH.

$$NaOH + H_2CO_3 \longrightarrow NaHCO_3 + H_2O$$

$\quad$strong$\qquad$weak$\qquad\qquad$weak$\qquad$water
$\quad$base$\qquad\quad$acid$\qquad\qquad$base

The net result is replacement of a strong base by a weak one, so that the pH of the solution rises very little.

Respiratory System Controls

As described in Chapter 13, the respiratory system eliminates carbon dioxide from the blood while it "loads" oxygen into the blood. Remember that when carbon dioxide (CO_2) enters the blood from the tissue cells, most of it enters the red blood cells, where it is converted to bicarbonate ion (HCO_3^-) for transport in the plasma, as shown by the equation

$$\underset{\substack{\text{Carbon} \\ \text{dioxide}}}{CO_2} + \underset{\text{water}}{H_2O} \overset{\substack{\text{Carbonic} \\ \text{anhydrase}}}{\rightleftharpoons} \underset{\substack{\text{carbonic} \\ \text{acid}}}{H_2CO_3} \rightleftharpoons \underset{\substack{\text{hydrogen} \\ \text{ion}}}{H^+} + \underset{\substack{\text{bicarbonate} \\ \text{ion}}}{HCO_3^-}$$

The double-headed arrows reveal that an increase in carbon dioxide pushes the reaction to the right, producing more carbonic acid. Likewise, an increase in hydrogen ions pushes the equation to the left, producing more carbonic acid. In healthy people, carbon dioxide is expelled from the lungs at the same rate as it is formed in the tissues. Thus the H^+ released when carbon dioxide is loaded into the blood is not allowed to accumulate because it is tied up in water when CO_2 is unloaded in the lungs. So, under normal conditions, the hydrogen ions produced by carbon dioxide transport have essentially no effect on blood pH. However, when CO_2 accumulates in the blood (for example, during restricted breathing) or more H^+ is released to the blood by metabolic processes, the chemoreceptors in the respiratory control centers of the brain (or in peripheral blood vessels) are activated. As a result, breathing rate and depth increase, and the excess H^+ is "blown off" as more CO_2 is removed from the blood.

In contrast, when blood pH begins to rise (alkalosis), the respiratory center is depressed. Consequently, the respiratory rate and depth fall, allowing carbon dioxide (hence, H^+) to accumulate in the blood. Again blood pH is restored to the normal range. Generally, these respiratory system corrections of blood pH (via regulation of CO_2 content of the blood) are accomplished within a minute or so.

Renal Mechanisms

Chemical buffers can tie up excess acids or bases temporarily, but they cannot eliminate them from the body. And although the lungs can dispose of carbonic acid by eliminating carbon dioxide, only the kidneys can rid the body of other acids generated during metabolism. Additionally, only the kidneys have the power to regulate blood levels of alkaline substances. Thus, although the kidneys act slowly and require hours or days to bring about changes in blood pH, they are the most potent of the mechanisms for regulating blood pH.

The most important means by which the kidneys maintain acid-base balance of the blood are by (1) excreting bicarbonate ions and (2) conserving (reabsorbing) or generating new bicarbonate ions. Look back again at the equation showing how the carbonic acid–bicarbonate buffer system operates. Notice that losing a HCO_3^- from the body has the same effect as gaining an H^+ because it pushes the equation to the right (that is, it leaves a free hydrogen ion). By the same token, reabsorbing or generating new HCO_3^- is the same as losing H^+ because it tends to combine with a hydrogen ion and pushes the equation to the left. Renal mechanisms undertake these adjustments: As blood pH rises, bicarbonate ions are excreted and hydrogen ions are retained by the tubule cells. Conversely, when blood pH falls, bicarbonate is reabsorbed and hydrogen ions are secreted. Urine pH varies from 4.5 to 8.0, which reflects the ability of the renal tubules to excrete basic or acid ions to maintain blood pH homeostasis.

▶ DID YOU GET IT?

16. Why is blood pH in the range 7.0 to 7.35 considered acidic even though basic chemistry defines any pH above 7.0 as basic?

17. To minimize the pH shift that occurs when a strong acid is added to water, would it be better to add a strong base or a weak base? Why?

18. Brian's ultralight plane has crashed in the desert. It is hot, and he neglected to bring a canteen of water. Assume he is there all day. How would you expect this situation to affect the solute concentration of his blood?

19. What are the two main ways the kidneys maintain the acid-base balance of the blood?

For answers, see Appendix D.

Developmental Aspects of the Urinary System

When you trace the development of the kidneys in a young embryo, it almost seems as though they can't "make up their mind" about whether to come or go. The first tubule system forms and then begins to degenerate as a second, lower, set appears. The second set, in turn, degenerates as a third set makes its appearance. This third set develops into the functional kidneys, which are excreting urine by the third month of fetal life. It is important to remember that the fetal kidneys do not work nearly as hard as they will after birth, because exchanges with the mother's blood through the placenta allow her system to clear many of the undesirable substances from the fetal blood.

HOMEOSTATIC IMBALANCE

There are many congenital abnormalities of this system. Two of the most common are polycystic kidney and hypospadias.

Polycystic (pol"e-sis'tik) **kidney** is a degenerative condition that appears to run in families. One or both kidneys are enlarged and have many blisterlike sacs (cysts) containing urine. These cysts interfere with renal function by obstructing urine drainage. Currently, not too much can be done for this condition except to prevent further kidney damage by avoiding infection. Renal failure is the eventual outcome, but kidney transplants improve chances for survival.

Hypospadias (hi"po-spa'de-as) is a condition found in male babies only. It occurs when the urethral orifice is located on the ventral surface of the penis. Corrective surgery is generally done when the child is around 12 months old. ▲

Because the bladder is very small and the kidneys are unable to concentrate urine for the first 2 months, a newborn baby voids from 5 to 40 times per day, depending on fluid intake. By 2 months of age, the infant is voiding approximately 400 ml/day, and the amount steadily increases until adolescence, when adult urine output (about 1500 ml/day) is achieved.

Control of the voluntary urethral sphincter goes hand in hand with nervous system development. By 15 months, most toddlers are aware when they have voided. By 18 months they can hold urine in their bladder for about 2 hours, which is the first sign that toilet training (for voiding) can begin. Daytime control usually occurs well before nighttime control is achieved. It is generally unrealistic to expect that complete nighttime control will occur before the child is 4 years old.

During childhood and through late middle age, most urinary system problems are infectious, or inflammatory, conditions. Many types of bacteria may invade the urinary tract to cause urethritis, cystitis, or pyelonephritis. *Escherichia coli* (esh"er-i'ke-ah ko'li) are normal residents of the digestive tract and generally cause no problems there, but these bacteria act as pathogens (disease-causers) in the sterile environment of the urinary tract and account for 80 percent of urinary tract infections. Bacteria and viruses responsible for *sexually transmitted diseases (STDs),* which are primarily reproductive tract infections, may also invade and cause inflammation in the urinary tract, which leads to the clogging of some of its ducts.

HOMEOSTATIC IMBALANCE

Childhood streptococcal (strep"to-kok'al) infections, such as strep throat and scarlet fever, may cause inflammatory damage to the kidneys if the original infections are not treated promptly and properly. A common sequel to untreated childhood strep infections is **glomerulonephritis** (glo-mer"ŭ-lo-ne-fri'tis), in which the glomerular filters become clogged with antigen-antibody complexes resulting from the strep infection. ▲

As we age, there is a progressive decline in kidney size and function. By age 70, the rate of filtrate formation is only about half that of the middle-aged adult. This is believed to result from impaired renal circulation due to atherosclerosis, which affects the entire circulatory system of the aging person. In addition to a decrease in the number of functional nephrons, the tubule cells become less efficient in their ability to concentrate urine.

Another consequence of aging is bladder shrinkage and loss of bladder tone, causing many elderly individuals to experience **urgency** (a feeling that it is necessary to void) and **frequency** (frequent voiding of small amounts of urine). **Nocturia** (nok-tu're-ah), the need to get up during the night to urinate, plagues almost two-thirds of this population. In many, incontinence is the final

SYSTEMS IN SYNC

HOMEOSTATIC RELATIONSHIPS BETWEEN THE
URINARY SYSTEM AND OTHER BODY SYSTEMS

Endocrine System
- Kidneys dispose of nitrogenous wastes; maintain fluid, electrolyte, and acid-base balance of blood; produce the hormone erythropoietin; renal regulation of Na^+ and water balance essential for blood pressure homeostasis and hormone transport in the blood
- ADH, aldosterone, ANP, and other hormones help regulate renal reabsorption of water and electrolytes

Lymphatic System/Immunity
- Kidneys dispose of nitrogenous wastes; maintain fluid, electrolyte, and acid-base balance of blood
- By returning leaked plasma fluid to cardiovascular system, lymphatic vessels help maintain normal systemic blood pressure needed for kidney function; immune cells protect urinary organs from infection, cancer, and other foreign substances

Digestive System
- Kidneys dispose of nitrogenous wastes; maintain fluid, electrolyte, and acid-base balance of blood; also, metabolize vitamin D to the active form needed for calcium absorption
- Digestive organs provide nutrients needed for kidney cell health; liver synthesizes most urea, a nitrogenous waste that must be excreted by the kidneys

Urinary System

Muscular System
- Kidneys dispose of nitrogenous wastes; maintain fluid, electrolyte, and acid-base balance of blood; renal regulation of Na^+, K^+, and Ca^{2+} content in ECF crucial for muscle activity
- Muscles of pelvic diaphragm and external urethral sphincter function in voluntary control of micturition; creatinine is a nitrogenous waste product that must be excreted by the kidneys

Nervous System
- Kidneys dispose of nitrogenous wastes; maintain fluid, electrolyte, and acid-base balance of blood; renal regulation of Na^+, K^+, and Ca^{2+} content in ECF essential for normal neural function
- Neural controls involved in micturition; sympathetic nervous system activity triggers the renin-angiotensin mechanism

Respiratory System
- Kidneys dispose of nitrogenous wastes; maintain fluid, electrolyte, and acid-base balance of blood
- Respiratory system provides oxygen required by kidney cells; disposes of carbon dioxide; cells in the lungs convert angiotensin I to angiotensin II

Cardiovascular System
- Kidneys dispose of nitrogenous wastes; maintain fluid, electrolyte, and acid-base balance of blood; renal regulation of Na^+ and water balance essential for blood pressure homeostasis. Na^+, K^+, and Ca^{2+} regulation help maintain normal heart function
- Systemic arterial blood pressure is the driving force for glomerular filtration; heart secretes atrial natriuretic peptide; blood vessels transport nutrients, oxygen, etc. to urinary organs

Reproductive System
- Kidneys dispose of nitrogenous wastes; maintain fluid, electrolyte, and acid-base balance of blood

Integumentary System
- Kidneys dispose of nitrogenous wastes; maintain fluid, electrolyte, and acid-base balance of blood
- Skin provides external protective barrier; serves as site for vitamin D synthesis and water loss (via perspiration)

Skeletal System
- Kidneys dispose of nitrogenous wastes; maintain fluid, electrolyte, and acid-base balance of blood
- Bones of rib cage provide some protection to kidneys

outcome of the aging process. This loss of control is a tremendous blow to the pride of many aging people. Urinary retention is another common problem; most often it is a result of hypertrophy of the prostate gland in males. Some of the problems of incontinence and retention can be avoided by a regular regimen of activity that keeps the body as a whole in optimum condition and promotes alertness to elimination signals.

> **DID YOU GET IT?**

20. What is hypospadias?

21. What is urgency as related to the urinary system? What is frequency?

22. What accounts for these conditions in elderly people?

For answers, see Appendix D.

SUMMARY

Media study tools that provide additional review of key topics of Chapter 15 are referenced below.

> **IP** = *InterActive Physiology*
> **WEB** = The A&P Place

Kidneys (pp. 518–528)

1. The paired kidneys are retroperitoneal in the superior lumbar region. Each kidney has a medial indentation (hilum), where the renal artery, renal vein, and ureter are seen. Each kidney is enclosed in a tough fibrous capsule. A fatty cushion holds the kidneys against the body trunk wall.

   IP Urinary System Topic: Anatomy Review, page 4.

2. A longitudinal section of a kidney reveals an outer cortex, deeper medulla, and medial pelvis. Extensions of the pelvis (calyces) surround the tips of medullary pyramids and collect urine draining from them.

3. The renal artery, which enters the kidney, breaks up into segmental and then interlobar arteries that travel outward through the medulla. Interlobar arteries split into arcuate arteries, which branch to produce cortical radiate arteries, which serve the cortex.

   IP Urinary System Topic: Anatomy Review, pages 5–6.

4. Nephrons are structural and functional units of the kidneys. Each consists of a glomerulus and a renal tubule. Subdivisions of the renal tubule (from the glomerulus onward) are glomerular capsule, proximal convoluted tubule, loop of Henle, and distal convoluted tubule. A second (peritubular) capillary bed is also associated with each nephron.

WEB Exercise: Chapter 15, Anatomy and Function of the Nephron.

5. Nephron functions include filtration, reabsorption, and secretion. Filtrate formation is the role of the high-pressure glomerulus. Filtrate is essentially plasma without blood proteins. In reabsorption, done by tubule cells, needed substances are removed from filtrate (amino acids, glucose, water, some ions) and returned to blood. The tubule cells also secrete additional substances into filtrate. Secretion is important to rid the body of drugs and excess ions and to maintain acid-base balance of blood.

   WEB Exercise: Chapter 15, Nephron Activity; Early Filtrate Processing.

   IP Urinary System Topic: Anatomy Review, pages 7–9.

6. Urine is clear, yellow, and usually slightly acidic, but its pH value varies widely. Substances normally found in urine are nitrogenous wastes, water, various ions (always including sodium and potassium). Substances normally absent from urine include glucose, blood proteins, blood, pus (WBCs), bile.

Ureters, Urinary Bladder, and Urethra (pp. 528–531)

1. The ureters are slender tubes running from each kidney to the bladder. They conduct urine by peristalsis from kidney to bladder.

   IP Urinary System Topic: Anatomy Review, page 3.

2. The bladder is a muscular sac posterior to the pubic symphysis. It has two inlets (ureters) and one outlet (urethra). In males, the prostate gland surrounds its outlet. The function of the bladder is to store urine.

3. The urethra is a tube that leads urine from the bladder to the body exterior. In females, it is 3 to 4 cm long and conducts only urine. In males, it is 20 cm long and conducts both urine and sperm. The internal sphincter of smooth muscle is at the bladder-urethra junction. The external sphincter of skeletal muscle is located more inferiorly.

4. Micturition is emptying of the bladder. The micturition reflex causes the involuntary internal sphincter to open when stretch receptors in the bladder wall are stimulated. The external sphincter is voluntarily controlled, so micturition can ordinarily be temporarily delayed. Incontinence is the inability to control micturition.

Fluid, Electrolyte, and Acid-Base Balance   (pp. 531–537)

1. Blood composition depends on diet, cellular metabolism, and urinary output. To maintain blood composition, the kidneys must do the following:

   a. Allow nitrogen-containing wastes (urea, ammonia, creatinine, uric acid) to leave the body in the urine.

   b. Maintain water and electrolyte balance by absorbing more or less water and reclaiming ions in response to hormonal signals. ADH increases water reabsorption and conserves body water. Aldosterone increases reabsorption of sodium and water and decreases potassium reabsorption.

   c. Maintain acid-base balance by actively secreting bicarbonate ions (and retaining H^+) and by absorbing bicarbonate ions (and secreting H^+). Chemical buffers tie up excess H^+ or bases temporarily; respiratory centers modify blood pH by retaining CO_2 (decreases pH) or by eliminating more CO_2 from the blood (increases blood pH). Only the kidney can remove metabolic acids and excess bases from the body.

   IP Fluid Balance Topic: Introduction to Body Fluids, pages 3, 8–14, 18–22.

Developmental Aspects of the Urinary System   (pp. 538, 540)

1. The kidneys begin to develop in the first few weeks of embryonic life and are excreting urine by the third month.

2. Common congenital abnormalities include polycystic kidney and hypospadias.

3. Common urinary system problems in children and young to middle-aged adults are infections caused by fecal microorganisms, microorganisms causing, sexually transmitted disease, and *Streptococcus*.

4. Renal failure is an uncommon, but extremely serious, problem in which kidneys are unable to concentrate urine, and dialysis must be done to maintain chemical homeostasis of blood.

5. With age, filtration rate decreases and tubule cells become less efficient at concentrating urine, leading to urgency, frequency, and incontinence. In men, urinary retention is another common problem.

REVIEW QUESTIONS

Multiple Choice

More than one choice may apply.

1. Microscopic examination of a section of the kidney shows a thick-walled vessel with glomeruli scattered in the tissue on one side of the vessel but not on the other side. What vessel is this?
   a. Segmental vein
   b. Cortical radiate artery
   c. Interlobar vein
   d. Arcuate artery

2. What is the glomerulus?
   a. The same as the renal tubule
   b. The same as Bowman's capsule
   c. The same as the nephron
   d. Capillaries

3. Urine passes through the ureters by which mechanism?
   a. Ciliary action   c. Peristalsis
   b. Gravity alone   d. Suction

4. Effects of aldosterone include
   a. increase in sodium ion excretion.
   b. increase in water retention.
   c. increase in potassium ion concentration in the urine.
   d. higher blood pressure.

5. Which of the following is dependent on tubular secretion?
   a. Clearing penicillin from the blood
   b. Removal of nitrogenous wastes that have been reabsorbed
   c. Removal of excess potassium ions from the blood
   d. Control of blood pH

6. Which is a normal value for percentage of body weight that is water for a young to middle-aged man?

   a. 73%   c. 50%

   b. 45%   d. 60%

7. The smallest fluid compartment is the

   a. intracellular fluid.

   b. extracellular fluid.

   c. plasma.

   d. interstitial fluid.

8. In the carbonic acid–bicarbonate buffer system, strong acids are buffered by

   a. carbonic acid.

   b. water.

   c. bicarbonate ion.

   d. the salt of the strong acid.

Short Answer Essay

9. Name the organs of the urinary system, and describe the general function of each organ.

10. Describe the location of the kidneys in the body.

11. Make a diagram of a longitudinal section of a kidney. Identify and label the cortex, medulla, medullary pyramids, renal columns, and pelvis.

12. About 150 L of plasma filters into the renal tubules each day, but only 1–2 L of urine is formed. What happens to the rest of the plasma fluid?

13. Trace the pathway a uric acid molecule takes from a glomerulus to the urethra. Name every gross or microscopic structure it passes through on its journey.

14. What is the function of the glomerulus?

15. Besides ridding the body of wastes formed during cell metabolism, the kidney adjusts blood chemistry in other ways. What are these three other ways?

16. Explain the difference between filtrate and urine.

17. How does aldosterone modify the chemical composition of urine?

18. What hormone's name means "against urine flow"? What condition happens if it is not secreted?

19. Explain how Na$^+$ balance, ECF volume, and blood pressure are jointly regulated.

20. Explain how chemical buffer systems resist changes in pH.

21. Describe the role of the respiratory system in controlling acid-base balance.

22. Why is urinalysis a routine part of any good physical examination?

23. How do the internal and external urethral sphincters differ structurally and functionally?

24. Define *micturition*, and then describe the micturition reflex.

25. What sometimes happens when urine becomes too concentrated or remains too long in the bladder?

26. Define *incontinence*.

27. Why is cystitis more common in females?

28. What type of problem most commonly affects the urinary system organs?

29. Describe the changes that occur in kidney and bladder function in old age.

CRITICAL THINKING AND CLINICAL APPLICATION QUESTIONS

30. A 55-year-old woman is awakened by an excruciating pain that radiates from her right abdomen to her flank on the same side. The pain is not continuous, but it recurs every 3 to 4 minutes. Diagnose this patient's problem, and cite factors that might favor its occurrence. Explain why this woman's pain comes in "waves."

31. Mitchell's parents bring him to the clinic because his "wee-wee" (urine) is tinged with blood. Two days before, he was diagnosed with strep throat. His face and hands are swollen. What is the probable cause of Mitchell's current kidney problem?

32. A young woman has come to the clinic with dysuria and frequent urination. What is the most likely diagnosis?

33. Mrs. Gates exhibits excessive thirst and polyuria, with excessive blood levels of sodium. Will you check the pituitary or the adrenal glands? What hormone do you suspect is involved, and is hyposecretion or hypersecretion more likely to be occurring? What is the name of this condition?

34. B.J. has been diagnosed with a hypersecretory tumor of a parathyroid gland. What effect will this have on his renal tubule function?

35. What happens to the rate of RBC production in a patient on dialysis with total renal failure? What

could be given to the patient to counteract such a problem? (Hint: You might want to check Table 9.2 on page 333 for help with this one.)

36. Two physiology students are having a disagreement about renal function. Dan says that the kidneys work harder when you eat a high salt diet, whereas Peter says that they work harder when you drink lots of water. Who is right, and why?

37. Mr. Jessup, a 55-year-old man, is operated on for a cerebral tumor. About one month later, he complains that he is excessively thirsty and that he has been voiding almost continuously. A urine sample is collected, and its specific gravity is 1.001. What is your diagnosis of Mr. Jessup's problem, and what might its connection be to his previous surgery?

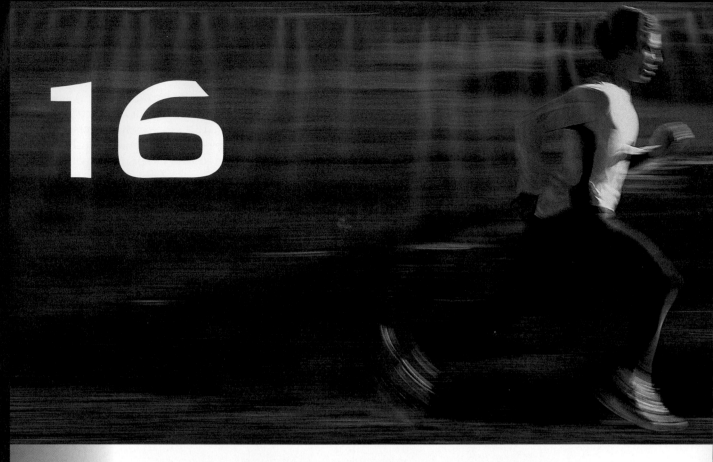

16

The Reproductive System

YOUR GOALS

After completing this chapter, you will have a working knowledge of the functions of the reproductive system and will have mastered the objectives below.

FUNCTION PREVIEW

- The reproductive system ensures continuity of the species by producing offspring.

OBJECTIVE CHECKLIST

Anatomy of the Male Reproductive System   (pp. 546–549)

➤ Discuss the common purpose of the reproductive system organs.

➤ When provided with a model or diagram, identify the organs of the male reproductive system, and discuss the general function of each.

➤ Name the endocrine and exocrine products of the testes.

➤ Discuss the composition of semen, and name the glands that produce it.

➤ Trace the pathway followed by a sperm from the testis to the body exterior.

➤ Define *erection*, *ejaculation*, and *circumcision*.

Male Reproductive Functions   (pp. 550–552)

➤ Define *meiosis* and *spermatogenesis*.

➤ Describe the structure of a sperm, and relate its structure to its function.

➤ Describe the effect of FSH and LH on testis functioning.

Anatomy of the Female Reproductive System (pp. 552–557)

➤ When provided with an appropriate model or diagram, identify the organs of the female reproductive system, and discuss the general function of each.

➤ Describe the functions of the vesicular follicle and corpus luteum of the ovary.

➤ Define *endometrium, myometrium,* and *ovulation.*

➤ Indicate the location of the following regions of the female uterus: cervix, fundus, body.

Female Reproductive Functions and Cycles (pp. 557–561)

➤ Define *oogenesis.*

➤ Describe the influence of FSH and LH on ovarian function.

➤ Describe the phases and controls of the menstrual cycle.

Mammary Glands (pp. 561–563)

➤ Describe the structure and function of the mammary glands.

Survey of Pregnancy and Embryonic Development (pp. 563–571)

➤ Define *fertilization* and *zygote.*

➤ Describe implantation.

➤ Distinguish between an embryo and a fetus.

➤ List the major functions of the placenta.

➤ Indicate several ways that pregnancy alters or modifies the functioning of the mother's body.

➤ Describe how labor is initiated, and briefly discuss the three stages of labor.

➤ List several agents that can interfere with normal fetal development.

Developmental Aspects of the Reproductive System (pp. 572–578)

➤ Describe the importance of the presence/absence of testosterone during embryonic development of the reproductive system organs.

➤ Define *menarche* and *menopause.*

➤ List common reproductive system problems seen in adult and aging men and women.

Most organ systems of the body function almost continuously to maintain the well-being of the individual. The reproductive system, however, appears to "slumber" until puberty. The **gonads** (go'nadz; "seeds"), or **primary sex organs,** are the *testes* in men and the *ovaries* in women. The gonads produce sex cells, or **gametes** (gam'ets; "spouses"), and secrete sex hormones. The remaining reproductive system structures are **accessory reproductive organs.** Although male and female **reproductive systems** are quite different, their joint purpose is to produce offspring.

The reproductive role of the man is to manufacture male gametes called **sperm** and deliver them to the woman's reproductive tract. The woman, in turn, produces female gametes, called **ova** (singular, *ovum*), or *eggs.* If the time is suitable, the sperm and egg fuse to produce a fertilized egg, which is the first cell of a new individual. Once fertilization has occurred, the female uterus provides a protective environment in which the *embryo,* later called the *fetus,* develops until birth.

The sex hormones play vital roles both in the development and function of the reproductive organs

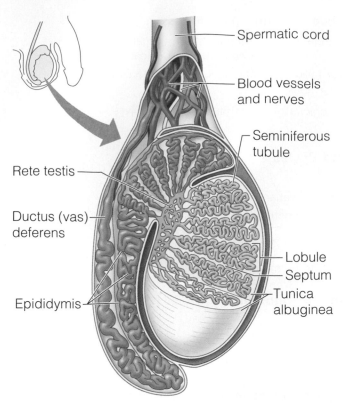

— Spermatic cord

— Blood vessels and nerves

— Seminiferous tubule

Rete testis —

Ductus (vas) deferens —

Epididymis —

— Lobule
— Septum
— Tunica albuginea

FIGURE 16.1 **Sagittal section of the testis and associated epididymis.**

and in sexual behavior and drives. These gonadal hormones also influence the growth and development of many other organs and tissues of the body.

Anatomy of the Male Reproductive System

As already noted, the primary reproductive organs of the male are the **testes** (tes′tēz), or *male gonads,* which have both an exocrine (sperm-producing) function and an endocrine (testosterone-producing) function. The accessory reproductive structures are ducts or glands that aid in the delivery of sperm to the body exterior or to the female reproductive tract.

Testes

Each plum-sized testis is approximately 4 cm (1½ inches) long and 2.5 cm (1 inch) wide. A fibrous connective tissue capsule, the *tunica albuginea* (tu′nĭ-kah al″bu-jin′e-ah; "white coat") surrounds each testis. Extensions of this capsule *(septa)* plunge into the testis and divide it into a large number of

wedge–shaped *lobules.* Each lobule contains one to four tightly coiled **seminiferous** (sem′in-if′er-us) **tubules,** the actual "sperm-forming factories" (Figure 16.1). Seminiferous tubules of each lobe empty sperm into another set of tubules, the *rete* (re′te) *testis,* located at one side of the testis. Sperm travel through the rete testis to enter the first part of the duct system, the *epididymis* (ep″ĭ-did′ĭ-mis), which hugs the external surface of the testis.

Lying in the soft connective tissue surrounding the seminiferous tubules are the *interstitial* (in″ter-stish′al) *cells,* functionally distinct cells that produce androgens—the most important of which is *testosterone.* Thus, the sperm-producing and hormone-producing functions of the testes are carried out by completely different cell populations.

Duct System

The accessory organs forming the male duct system, which transports sperm from the body, are the *epididymis, ductus deferens,* and *urethra* (Figure 16.2).

Epididymis

The cup-shaped **epididymis** is a highly coiled tube about 6 m (20 feet) long that caps the superior part of the testis and then runs down its posterolateral side (see Figure 16.1). The epididymis is the first part of the male duct system and provides a temporary storage site for the immature sperm that enter it from the testis. While the sperm make their way along the tortuous course of the epididymis (a trip that takes about 20 days), they mature, gaining the ability to swim. When a man is sexually stimulated and ejaculates, the walls of the epididymis contract to expel the sperm into the next part of the duct system, the ductus deferens.

Ductus Deferens

The **ductus deferens** (duk′tus def′er-enz; "carrying away"), or **vas deferens,** runs upward from the epididymis through the inguinal canal into the pelvic cavity and arches over the superior aspect of the urinary bladder. This tube is enclosed, along with blood vessels and nerves, in a connective tissue sheath called the **spermatic cord** (see Figure 16.1), which travels upward through the inguinal canal. The ductus deferens then loops medially over the ureter and descends along the posterior bladder wall. The end of the ductus deferens expands as the **ampulla** and then empties into

Looking at this diagram, it is easy to see how hypertrophy of the prostate gland might lead to urinary system problems. How so?

Ejaculatory duct
Prostatic urethra
Urinary bladder
Pubis
Ductus (vas) deferens
Erectile tissue of penis
Shaft of penis
Spongy (penile) urethra
Glans penis
Prepuce

Seminal vesicle
Ampulla of ductus deferens
Prostate
Membranous urethra
Rectum
Bulbourethral gland
Epididymis
Testis
Scrotum

(a)

Urinary bladder
Prostate
Bulbourethral gland
Erectile tissue of penis
Ductus deferens
Epididymis
Testis

Seminal vesicle (behind bladder)
Urethra
Scrotum
Glans penis

(b)

FIGURE 16.2 **Male reproductive organs. (a).** Sagittal view. **(b)** Frontal view.

Because the prostate gland encircles the superior part of the urethra, prostate hypertrophy would constrict the urethra in that region, impairing urination.

the **ejaculatory** (e-jak'u-lah-to"re) **duct,** which passes through the prostate gland to merge with the urethra. The main function of the ductus deferens is to propel live sperm from their storage sites, the epididymis and distal part of the ductus deferens, into the urethra. At the moment of **ejaculation** (*ejac* = to shoot forth), the thick layers of smooth muscle in its walls create peristaltic waves that rapidly squeeze the sperm forward.

As Figure 16.2 illustrates, part of the ductus deferens lies in the scrotum, which hangs outside the body cavity. Some men voluntarily opt to take full responsibility for birth control by having a *vasectomy* (vah-sek'to-me; "cutting the vas"). In this relatively minor operation, the surgeon makes a small incision into the scrotum and then cuts through and ligates (ties off) the ductus deferens. Sperm are still produced, but they can no longer reach the body exterior, and eventually they deteriorate and are phagocytized. A man is sterile after this procedure, but because testosterone is still produced, he retains the sex drive and secondary sex characteristics.

Urethra

The **urethra,** which extends from the base of the urinary bladder to the tip of the penis, is the terminal part of the male duct system. It has three named regions: (1) the **prostatic urethra,** surrounded by the prostate gland; (2) the **membranous urethra,** spanning the distance from the prostatic urethra to the penis; and (3) the **spongy (penile) urethra,** running within the length of the penis. As mentioned in Chapter 15, the male urethra carries both urine and sperm to the body exterior; thus, it serves two masters, the urinary and reproductive systems. However, urine and sperm never pass at the same time. When ejaculation occurs and sperm enter the prostatic urethra from the ejaculatory ducts, the bladder sphincter (internal urethral sphincter) constricts. This event not only prevents the passage of urine into the urethra but also prevents sperm from entering the urinary bladder.

▶ *DID YOU GET IT?*

1. What are the two major functions of the testes?

2. What is the role of the seminiferous tubules?

3. Name the organs of the male duct system, in order, from the scrotum to the body exterior.

For answers, see Appendix D.

Accessory Glands and Semen

The accessory glands include the paired *seminal vesicles,* the single *prostate,* and the *bulbourethral* (bul-bo-u-re'thral) *glands* (see Figure 16.2). These glands produce the bulk of *semen* (se'men), the sperm-containing fluid that is propelled out of the male's reproductive tract during ejaculation.

Seminal Vesicles

The **seminal** (sem'ĭ-nul) **vesicles,** located at the base of the bladder, produce about 60 percent of *seminal fluid,* the fluid volume of semen. Their thick, yellowish secretion is rich in sugar (fructose), vitamin C, prostaglandins, and other substances, which nourish and activate the sperm passing through the tract. The duct of each seminal vesicle joins that of the ductus deferens on the same side to form the ejaculatory duct (see Figure 16.2). Thus, sperm and seminal fluid enter the urethra together during ejaculation.

Prostate

The **prostate** is a single doughnut–shaped gland about the size of a peach pit (see Figure 16.2). It encircles the upper (prostatic) part of the urethra just below the urinary bladder. Prostate gland secretion is a milky fluid that plays a role in activating sperm. During ejaculation, the fluid enters the urethra through several small ducts. Because the prostate is located immediately anterior to the rectum, its size and texture can be palpated (felt) by digital (finger) examination through the anterior rectal wall.

⚖ HOMEOSTATIC IMBALANCE

The prostate has a reputation as a health destroyer. Hypertrophy of the gland, which affects nearly every older man, strangles the urethra. This troublesome condition makes urination difficult and enhances the risk of bladder infections **(cystitis)** and kidney damage. Traditional treatment has been surgery, but some newer options are becoming more popular. These include the following:

• Using drugs (finasteride) or microwaves to shrink the prostate

• Inserting a small inflatable balloon to compress the prostate tissue away from the prostatic urethra

• Inserting a tiny needle that emits bursts of radio-frequency radiation, which incinerate excess prostate tissue

Prostatitis, inflammation of the prostate, is the single most common reason for a man to consult a urologist, and **prostatic cancer** is the third most prevalent cancer in men. As a rule, prostatic cancer is a slow-growing, hidden condition, but it can also be a swift and deadly killer. ▲

Bulbourethral Glands

The **bulbourethral glands** are tiny, pea-sized glands inferior to the prostate gland. They produce a thick, clear mucus that drains into the penile urethra. This secretion is the first to pass down the urethra when a man becomes sexually excited. It cleanses the urethra of traces of acidic urine, and it serves as a lubricant during sexual intercourse.

Semen

Semen is a milky white, somewhat sticky mixture of sperm and accessory gland secretions. The liquid portion acts as a transport medium for nutrients and chemicals that protect the sperm and aid their movement. Mature sperm cells are streamlined cellular "missiles" containing little cytoplasm or stored nutrients. The fructose in the seminal vesicle secretion provides essentially all of their energy fuel. The relative alkalinity of semen as a whole (pH 7.2–7.6) helps neutralize the acidic environment (pH 3.5–4) of the female's vagina, protecting the delicate sperm. Sperm are very sluggish under acidic conditions (below pH 6). Semen also contains *seminalplasmin* (an antibiotic chemical that destroys certain bacteria), the hormone relaxin, certain enzymes that enhance sperm motility, and substances that inhibit an immune response in the female reproductive tract.

Semen also dilutes sperm; without such dilution, sperm motility is severely impaired. The amount of semen propelled out of the male duct system during ejaculation is relatively small, only 2 to 5 ml (about a teaspoonful), but there are between 50 and 150 million sperm in each milliliter.

HOMEOSTATIC IMBALANCE

Male infertility may be caused by obstructions of the duct system, hormonal imbalances, environmental estrogens, pesticides, excessive alcohol, and many other factors. One of the first series of tests done when a couple has been unable to conceive is *semen analysis.* Factors analyzed include sperm count, motility and morphology (shape and maturity), and semen volume, pH, and fructose content. A sperm count lower than 20 million per milliliter makes impregnation improbable. ▲

External Genitalia

The male **external genitalia** (jen"i-tal′e-ah) include the *scrotum* and the *penis* (see Figure 16.2). The **scrotum** (skro′tum; "pouch") is a divided sac of skin that hangs outside the abdominal cavity, between the legs and at the root of the penis. Under normal conditions, the scrotum hangs loosely from its attachments, providing the testes with a temperature that is below body temperature. This is a rather exposed location for a man's testes, which contain his entire genetic heritage, but apparently viable sperm cannot be produced at normal body temperature. The scrotum, which provides a temperature about 3°C (5.4°F) lower, is necessary for the production of healthy sperm. When the external temperature is very cold, the scrotum becomes heavily wrinkled as it pulls the testes closer to the warmth of the body wall. Thus, changes in scrotal surface area can maintain a temperature that favors viable sperm production.

The **penis** (pe′nis; "tail") is designed to deliver sperm into the female reproductive tract. The skin-covered penis consists of a **shaft,** which ends in an enlarged tip, the **glans penis.** The skin covering the penis is loose, and it folds downward to form a cuff of skin, the **prepuce** (pre′pus), or **foreskin,** around the proximal end of the glans. Frequently, the foreskin is surgically removed shortly after birth, by a procedure called *circumcision.*

Internally, the spongy urethra (see Figure 16.1) is surrounded by three elongated areas of **erectile tissue,** a spongy tissue that fills with blood during sexual excitement. This causes the penis to enlarge and become rigid. This event, called **erection,** helps the penis serve as a penetrating organ to deliver the semen into the female's reproductive tract.

▶ DID YOU GET IT?

4. What is the function of the erectile tissue of the penis?

5. What is an important function of each of the two components of semen?

6. Adolph, a 68-year-old gentleman, has trouble urinating and is given a rectal exam. What is his most probable condition, and what is the purpose of the rectal exam?

For answers, see Appendix D.

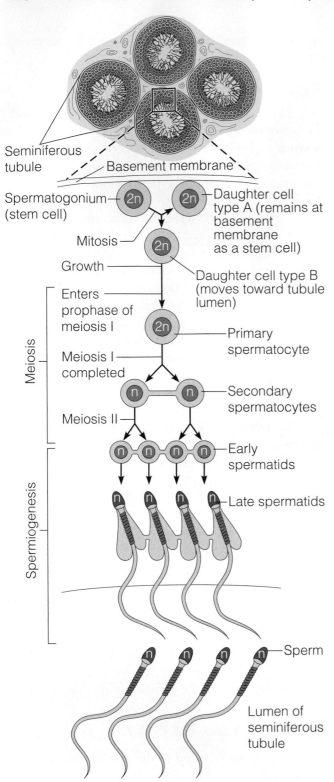

FIGURE 16.3   Spermatogenesis. Flow chart showing the relative position of the spermatogenic cells in the wall of the seminiferous tubule. Although the stem cells and the primary spermatocytes have the same number of chromosomes (46, designated as 2n) as other body cells, the products of meiosis (spermatids and sperm) have only half as many (23, designated as n).

Male Reproductive Functions

The chief role of the male in the reproductive process is to produce sperm and the hormone testosterone. These processes are described next.

Spermatogenesis

Sperm production, or **spermatogenesis** (sper″mah-to-jen′ĕ-sis), begins during puberty and continues throughout life. Every day a man makes millions of sperm. Only one sperm fertilizes an egg, so it seems that nature has made sure that the human species will not be endangered for lack of sperm.

Sperm are formed in the seminiferous tubules of the testis, as noted earlier. As shown in Figure 16.3, the process is begun by primitive stem cells called **spermatogonia** (sper″mah-to-go′ne-ah), found in the outer edge, or periphery, of each tubule. Spermatogonia go through rapid mitotic divisions to build up the stem cell line. From birth until puberty, all such divisions simply produce more stem cells. During puberty, however, *follicle-stimulating hormone (FSH)* is secreted in increasing

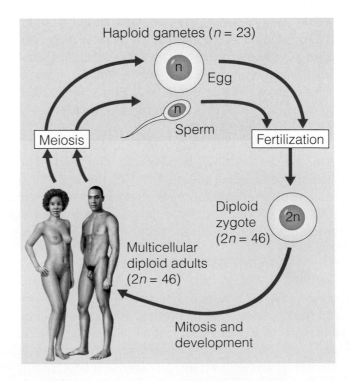

FIGURE 16.4   The human life cycle.

FIGURE 16.5 Structure of sperm. (a) Scanning electron micrograph of mature sperm (600×). **(b)** Diagrammatic view of a sperm.

amounts by the anterior pituitary gland, and, from this time on, each division of a spermatogonium produces one stem cell, called a *type A daughter cell,* and another cell, called a *type B daughter cell.* The type A cell remains at the tubule periphery to maintain the stem cell population. The type B cell gets pushed toward the tubule lumen, where it becomes a **primary spermatocyte,** destined to undergo *meiosis* (mi-o'sis) and form four sperm. **Meiosis** is a special type of nuclear division that occurs for the most part only in the gonads (testes and ovaries). It differs from *mitosis* (described in Chapter 3) in two major ways. Meiosis consists of two successive divisions of the nucleus (called meiosis I and II) and results in four (instead of two) daughter cells, or more precisely, four *gametes.* In spermatogenesis, the gametes are called **spermatids** (sper'mah-tidz). Spermatids have only half as much genetic material as other body cells. In humans, this is 23 chromosomes (or the so-called *n* number of chromosomes) rather than the usual 46 (2*n*). Then, when the sperm and the egg (which also has 23 chromosomes) unite, forming the fertilized egg, or zygote, the normal 2*n* number of 46 chromosomes is reestablished and is maintained in subsequent body cells by the process of mitosis (Figure 16.4).

As meiosis occurs, the dividing cells (primary and then secondary spermatocytes) are pushed toward the lumen of the tubule. Thus, the progress of meiosis can be followed from the tubule periphery to the lumen. The spermatids, which are the products of meiosis, are *not* functional sperm. They are nonmotile and have too much excess baggage to function well in reproduction. They must undergo further changes, in which their excess cytoplasm is stripped away and a tail is formed (see Figure 16.3). In this last stage of sperm development, called **spermiogenesis** (sper"me-o-gen'ĕ-sis), all the excess cytoplasm is sloughed off, and what remains is compacted into the three regions of the mature sperm—the *head, midpiece,* and *tail* (Figure 16.5). The mature sperm is a greatly streamlined cell equipped with a high rate of metabolism and a means of propelling itself, enabling it to move long distances in a short time to get to the egg. It is a prime example of the fit between form and function.

Sperm "pack" light. The sperm *head* contains compacted DNA, the genetic material. Essentially, it *is* the nucleus of the spermatid. Anterior to the nucleus is the helmetlike **acrosome** (ak'ro-sōm), which is produced by the Golgi apparatus and is similar to a large lysosome. When a sperm comes

What is the effect of negative feedback of testosterone on anterior pituitary and hypothalamic cells?

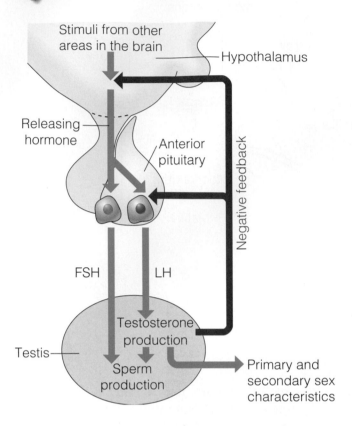

FIGURE 16.6 **Hormonal control of the testis.**

into close contact with an egg (or more precisely, an *oocyte*), the acrosomal membrane breaks down and releases enzymes that help the sperm penetrate through the follicle cells that surround the egg. *Filaments,* which form the long tail, arise from centrioles in the midpiece. *Mitochondria* wrapped tightly around these filaments provide the ATP needed for the whiplike movements of the tail that propel the sperm along its way in the female reproductive tract.

The entire process of spermatogenesis, from the formation of a primary spermatocyte to release of immature sperm in the tubule lumen, takes 64 to 72 days. Sperm in the lumen are unable to "swim" and are incapable of fertilizing an egg. They are moved by peristalsis through the tubules of the testes into the epididymis. There they undergo fur-

ther maturation, which results in increased motility and fertilizing power.

HOMEOSTATIC IMBALANCE

Environmental threats can alter the normal process of sperm formation. For example, some common antibiotics, such as penicillin and tetracycline, may suppress sperm formation. Radiation, lead, certain pesticides, marijuana, tobacco, and excessive alcohol can cause production of abnormal sperm (two-headed, multiple-tailed, and so on). ▲

Testosterone Production

As noted earlier, the interstitial cells produce **testosterone** (tes-tos′tĕ-rōn), the most important hormonal product of the testes. During puberty, as the seminiferous tubules are being prodded to produce sperm by FSH, the interstitial cells are being activated by **luteinizing hormone (LH),** which is also released by the anterior pituitary gland (Figure 16.6). From this time on, testosterone is produced continuously (more or less) for the rest of a man's life. The rising blood level of testosterone in the young man stimulates the adolescent growth spurt, prods his reproductive organs to develop to their adult size, underlies the sex drive, and causes the secondary male sex characteristics to appear. **Secondary sex characteristics** are features induced in *nonreproductive organs* by sex hormones. Male secondary sex characteristics include the following:

- Deepening of the voice as the larynx enlarges

- Increased hair growth all over the body, and particularly in the axillary and pubic regions and on the face (the beard and mustache)

- Enlargement of skeletal muscles to produce the heavier muscle mass typical of the male physique

- Increased heaviness of the skeleton due to bone growth and increase in density

Because testosterone is responsible for the appearance of these typical masculine characteristics, it is often referred to as the "masculinizing" hormone.

HOMEOSTATIC IMBALANCE

If testosterone is not produced, the secondary sex characteristics never appear in the young man, and his other reproductive organs remain childlike. This is **sexual infantilism.** Castration of the adult male (or the inability of his interstitial cells to produce

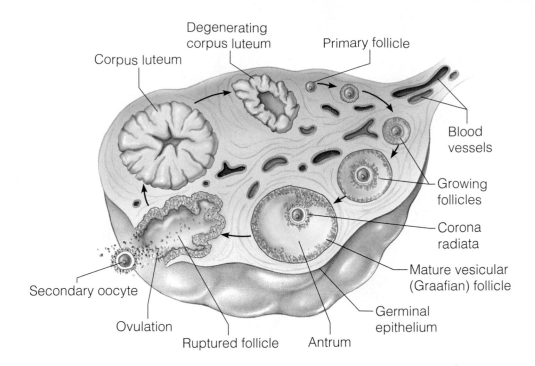

FIGURE 16.7 **Sagittal view of a human ovary showing the developmental stages of an ovarian follicle.**

testosterone) results in a decrease in the size and function of his reproductive organs, as well as a decrease in his sex drive. **Sterility** also occurs because testosterone is necessary for the final stages of sperm production. ▲

 DID YOU GET IT?

7. Which pituitary hormone stimulates spermatogenesis?

8. How does the final product of meiosis differ from the final product of mitosis?

9. How are nonmotile spermatids converted to functional sperm?

10. Which pituitary hormone prompts testosterone production?

For answers, see Appendix D.

Anatomy of the Female Reproductive System

The reproductive role of the female is much more complex than that of the male. Not only must she produce the female gametes (ova), but her body must also nurture and protect a developing fetus during 9 months of pregnancy. **Ovaries** are the primary female reproductive organs. Like the testes, ovaries produce both an exocrine product (eggs, or *ova*) and endocrine products (estrogens and progesterone). The other organs of the female reproductive system serve as accessory structures to transport, nurture, or otherwise serve the needs of the reproductive cells and/or the developing fetus.

Ovaries

The paired *ovaries* (o′vah-rēz) are pretty much the shape of almonds but are nearly twice as large. An internal view of an ovary reveals many tiny saclike structures called **ovarian follicles** (Figure 16.7). Each follicle consists of an immature egg, called an **oocyte** (o′o-sīt; *oo* = egg), surrounded by one or more layers of very different cells called **follicle cells.** As a developing egg within a follicle begins to ripen or mature, the follicle enlarges and develops a fluid-filled central region called an *antrum.* At this stage, the follicle, called a **vesicular,** or **Graafian** (graf′e-an), **follicle,** is mature, and the developing egg is ready to be ejected from the ovary, an event called **ovulation.** After ovulation, the ruptured follicle is transformed into a very

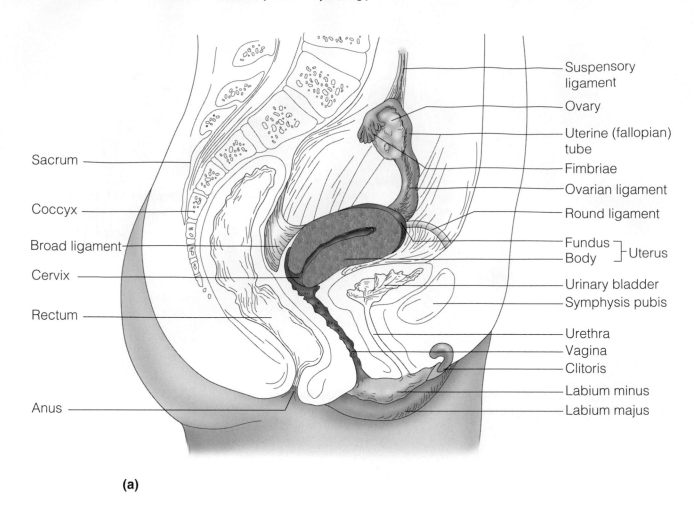

Sacrum

Coccyx

Broad ligament

Cervix

Rectum

Anus

Suspensory ligament

Ovary

Uterine (fallopian) tube

Fimbriae

Ovarian ligament

Round ligament

Fundus ⎤ Uterus
Body ⎦

Urinary bladder

Symphysis pubis

Urethra

Vagina

Clitoris

Labium minus

Labium majus

(a)

FIGURE 16.8 **The human female reproductive organs.**
(a) Sagittal section. (The plural of *labium minus* and *majus* is *labia minora* and *majora,* respectively.)

different-looking structure called a **corpus luteum** (kor'pus lu'te-um; "yellow body"), which eventually degenerates. Ovulation generally occurs every 28 days, but it can occur more or less frequently in some women. In older women, the surfaces of the ovaries are scarred and pitted, which attests to the fact that many eggs have been released.

The ovaries are secured to the lateral walls of the pelvis by the **suspensory ligaments.** They flank the uterus laterally and anchor to it medially by the **ovarian ligaments** (Figure 16.8). In between, they are enclosed and held in place by a fold of peritoneum, the **broad ligament.**

Duct System

The *uterine tubes, uterus,* and *vagina* form the duct system of the female reproductive tract (see Figure 16.8).

Uterine (Fallopian) Tubes

The **uterine** (u'ter-in), or **fallopian** (fal-lo'pe-an), **tubes** form the initial part of the duct system. They receive the ovulated oocyte and provide a site where fertilization can occur. Each of the uterine tubes is about 10 cm (4 inches) long and extends medially from an ovary to empty into the superior region of the uterus. Like the ovaries, the uterine tubes are enclosed and supported by the broad ligament. Unlike in the male duct system, which is continuous with the tubule system of the testes, there is little or no actual contact between the uterine tubes and the ovaries. The distal end of each uterine tube expands as the funnel-shaped *infundibulum,* which has fingerlike projections called **fimbriae** (fim'bre-e) that partially surround the ovary. As an oocyte is expelled from an ovary during ovulation, the waving fimbriae create fluid

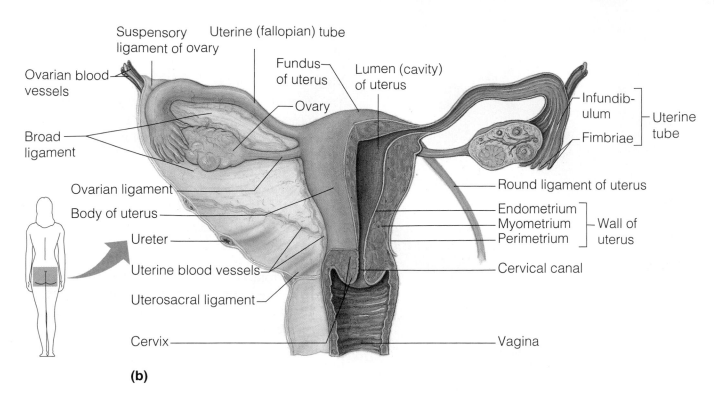

Suspensory
ligament of ovary

Uterine (fallopian) tube

Ovarian blood
vessels

Fundus
of uterus

Lumen (cavity)
of uterus

Ovary

Infundib-
ulum

Uterine
tube

Fimbriae

Broad
ligament

Ovarian ligament

Round ligament of uterus

Body of uterus

Endometrium
Myometrium
Perimetrium

Wall of
uterus

Ureter

Uterine blood vessels

Cervical canal

Uterosacral ligament

Cervix

Vagina

(b)

FIGURE 16.8 *(continued)* **The human female reproductive organs. (b)** Posterior view. The posterior organ walls have been removed on the right side to reveal the shape of the lumen of the uterine tube, uterus, and vagina.

currents that act to carry the oocyte into the uterine tube, where it begins its journey toward the uterus. (Obviously, however, many potential eggs are lost in the peritoneal cavity.) The oocyte is carried toward the uterus by a combination of peristalsis and the rhythmic beating of *cilia*. Because the journey to the uterus takes 3 to 4 days and the oocyte is viable for up to 24 hours after ovulation, the usual site of fertilization is the uterine tube. To reach the oocyte, the sperm must swim upward through the vagina and uterus to reach the uterine tubes. Because they must swim against the downward current created by the cilia, it is rather like swimming against the tide!

HOMEOSTATIC IMBALANCE

The fact that the uterine tubes are not continuous distally with the ovaries places women at risk for infections spreading into the peritoneal cavity from the reproductive tract. **Gonorrhea** (gon"o-re'ah) and other sexually transmitted bacteria sometimes infect the peritoneal cavity in this way, causing an extremely severe inflammation called **pelvic inflammatory**

disease (PID). Unless treated promptly, PID can cause scarring and closure of the narrow uterine tubes, which is one of the major causes of female infertility. ▲

Uterus

The **uterus** (u'ter-us; "womb"), located in the pelvis between the urinary bladder and rectum, is a hollow organ that functions to receive, retain, and nourish a fertilized egg. In a woman who has never been pregnant, it is about the size and shape of a pear. (During pregnancy, the uterus increases tremendously in size and can be felt well above the umbilicus during the latter part of pregnancy.) The uterus is suspended in the pelvis by the broad ligament and anchored anteriorly and posteriorly by the **round** and **uterosacral ligaments,** respectively (see Figure 16.8).

The major portion of the uterus is referred to as the **body.** Its superior rounded region above the entrance of the uterine tubes is the **fundus,** and its narrow outlet, which protrudes into the vagina below, is the **cervix.**

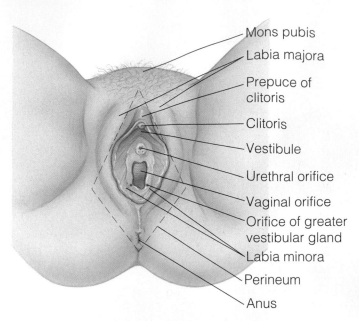

Mons pubis

Labia majora

Prepuce of clitoris

Clitoris

Vestibule

Urethral orifice

Vaginal orifice

Orifice of greater vestibular gland

Labia minora

Perineum

Anus

FIGURE 16.9   External genitalia of the human female.

The wall of the uterus is thick and composed of three layers. The inner layer or mucosa is the **endometrium** (en-do-me′tre-um). If fertilization occurs, the fertilized egg (actually the young embryo by the time it reaches the uterus) burrows into the endometrium (this process is called **implantation**) and resides there for the rest of its development. When a woman is not pregnant, the endometrial lining sloughs off periodically, usually about every 28 days, in response to changes in the levels of ovarian hormones in the blood. This process, called menstruation or *menses,* is discussed on pp. 559–561.

HOMEOSTATIC IMBALANCE

Cancer of the cervix is common among women between the ages of 30 and 50. Risk factors include frequent cervical inflammation, sexually transmitted diseases, multiple pregnancies, and many sexual partners. A yearly *Pap smear* is the single most important diagnostic test for detecting this slow-growing cancer. ▲

The **myometrium** (mi-o-me′tre-um), composed of interlacing bundles of smooth muscle, is the bulky middle layer of the uterus (see Figure 16.8b). The myometrium plays an active role during the delivery of a baby, when it contracts rhythmically to force the baby out of the mother's body. The outermost serous

layer of the uterus is the **perimetrium** (per-ĭ-me′tre-um), or the visceral peritoneum.

Vagina

The **vagina** (vah-ji′nah) is a thin-walled tube 8 to 10 cm (3 to 4 inches) long. It lies between the bladder and rectum and extends from the cervix to the body exterior (see Figure 16.8). Often called the *birth canal,* the vagina provides a passageway for the delivery of an infant and for the menstrual flow to leave the body. Because it receives the penis (and semen) during sexual intercourse, it is the female organ of copulation.

The distal end of the vagina is partially closed by a thin fold of the mucosa called the **hymen** (hi′men). The hymen is very vascular and tends to bleed when it is ruptured during the first sexual intercourse. However, its durability varies. In some women, it is torn during a sports activity, tampon insertion, or pelvic examination. Occasionally, it is so tough that it must be ruptured surgically if intercourse is to occur.

External Genitalia

The female reproductive structures that are located external to the vagina are the **external genitalia** (Figure 16.9). The external genitalia, also called the **vulva,** include the *mons pubis, labia, clitoris, urethral* and *vaginal orifices,* and *greater vestibular glands.*

The **mons pubis** ("mountain on the pubis") is a fatty, rounded area overlying the pubic symphysis. After puberty, this area is covered with pubic hair. Running posteriorly from the mons pubis are two elongated hair-covered skin folds, the **labia majora** (la′be-ah ma-jo′ra), which enclose two delicate, hair-free folds, the **labia minora.** The labia majora enclose a region called the **vestibule,** which contains the external openings of the urethra,* followed posteriorly by that of the vagina. A pair of mucus-producing glands, the **greater vestibular glands,** flank the vagina, one on each side. Their secretion lubricates the distal end of the vagina during intercourse.

Just anterior to the vestibule is the **clitoris** (kli′to-ris; "hill"), a small, protruding structure that

---

*The male urethra carries both urine and semen, but the female urethra has no reproductive function—it is strictly a passageway for urine.

corresponds to the male penis. Like the penis, it is hooded by a prepuce and is composed of sensitive erectile tissue that becomes swollen with blood during sexual excitement. The clitoris differs from the penis in that it lacks a reproductive duct. The diamond-shaped region between the anterior end of the labial folds, the anus posteriorly, and the ischial tuberosities laterally is the **perineum** (per″ĭ-ne′um).

DID YOU GET IT?

11. What is the exocrine product of the ovary?

12. Which organ of the female duct system serves as an "incubator" for fetal development? What is the most common site of fertilization?

13. What name is given to an ovarian follicle that is ready or nearly ready to ovulate?

For answers, see Appendix D.

Female Reproductive Functions and Cycles

Oogenesis and the Ovarian Cycle

As described earlier, sperm production begins at puberty and generally continues throughout life. The situation is quite different in women. Traditionally, it has been assumed that the total supply of eggs that a female can release is already determined by the time she is born. In addition, a female's reproductive ability (that is, her ability to release eggs) usually begins during puberty and ends in her fifties or before. The period in which a woman's reproductive capability gradually declines and then finally ends is called *menopause* (see pp. 576 and 578).

Meiosis, the special kind of cell division that occurs in the testes to produce sperm, also occurs in the ovaries. But in this case, gametes, or sex cells, are produced, and the process is called **oogenesis** (o″o-jen′ĕ-sis; "the beginning of an egg"). This process is shown in Figure 16.10 and described in more detail next.

In the developing female fetus, **oogonia** (o″o-go′ne-ah), the female stem cells, multiply rapidly to increase their number, and then their daughter cells, **primary oocytes,** push into the ovary connective tissue, where they become surrounded by a single layer of cells to form the *primary follicles*. By

birth, the oogonia no longer exist,* and a female's lifetime supply of primary oocytes (approximately 2 million of them) is already in place in the ovarian follicles, awaiting the chance to undergo meiosis to produce functional eggs. Because the primary oocytes remain in this state of suspended animation all through childhood, their wait is a long one—10 to 14 years at the very least.

At puberty, the anterior pituitary gland begins to release *follicle-stimulating hormone (FSH),* which stimulates a small number of primary follicles to grow and mature each month, and ovulation begins to occur each month. These cyclic changes that occur monthly in the ovary constitute the **ovarian cycle.** At puberty, perhaps 250,000 oocytes remain; and, beginning at this time, a small number of oocytes are activated each month. The reproductive life of a female is at best about 40 years (from the age of 11 to approximately 51), and there is typically only one ovulation per month; therefore, fewer than 500 ova out of her potential of 250,000 are released during a woman's lifetime. Again, nature has provided us with a generous oversupply of sex cells.

As a follicle prodded by FSH grows larger, it accumulates fluid in the central chamber called the *antrum* (see Figure 16.7), and the primary oocyte it contains replicates its chromosomes and begins meiosis. The first meiotic division produces two cells that are very dissimilar in size (see Figure 16.10). The larger cell is a **secondary oocyte** and the other, very tiny cell is a **polar body.** By the time a follicle has ripened to the mature (*vesicular follicle*) stage, it contains a secondary oocyte and protrudes like an angry boil from the external surface of the ovary. Follicle development to this stage takes about 14 days, and ovulation (of a secondary oocyte) occurs at just about that time in response to the burstlike release of a second anterior pituitary hormone, *luteinizing hormone (LH)*. As shown in Figures 16.7, 16.10, and 16.11, the ovulated secondary oocyte is still surrounded by its follicle-cell capsule, now called the *corona radiata* ("radiating crown"). Some women experience a twinge of abdominal pain in the lower abdomen when ovulation occurs. This phenomenon, called

---

*A recent study in mice indicated that germ stem cells are alive and exist in adult women. However, more studies are needed to overturn the "no new eggs" theory.

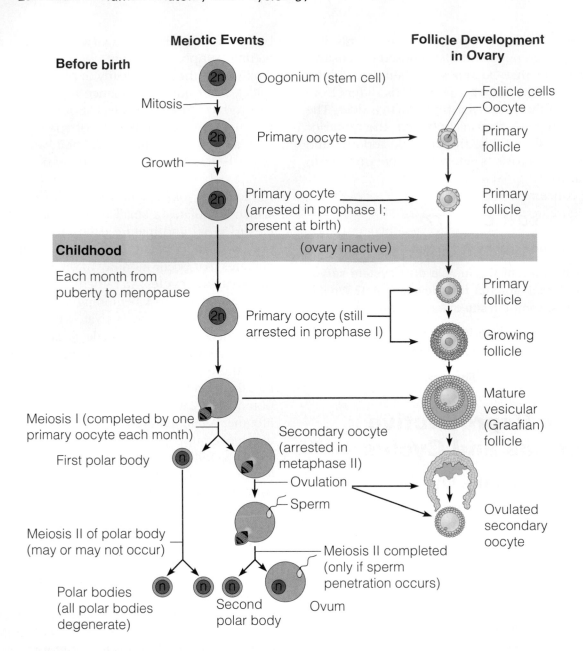

Meiotic Events

Follicle Development in Ovary

Before birth

2n — Oogonium (stem cell)

Mitosis

2n — Primary oocyte ——→ Primary follicle
Follicle cells
Oocyte

Growth

2n — Primary oocyte (arrested in prophase I; present at birth) ——→ Primary follicle

Childhood (ovary inactive)

Each month from puberty to menopause

2n — Primary oocyte (still arrested in prophase I) — Primary follicle

Growing follicle

Meiosis I (completed by one primary oocyte each month)

First polar body — n

Secondary oocyte (arrested in metaphase II)

Mature vesicular (Graafian) follicle

Ovulation

Sperm

Ovulated secondary oocyte

Meiosis II of polar body (may or may not occur)

Meiosis II completed (only if sperm penetration occurs)

Polar bodies (all polar bodies degenerate) — n n n

Second polar body — n

Ovum

FIGURE 16.10 Events of oogenesis. Left, flow chart of meiotic events. Right, correlation with follicular development and ovulation in the ovary.

mittelschmerz (mit'el-shmārts; German for "middle pain"), is caused by the intense stretching of the ovarian wall during ovulation.

Generally speaking, one of the developing follicles outstrips the others each month to become the dominant follicle. Just how this follicle is selected or selects itself is not understood, but the follicle that is at the proper stage of maturity when the LH stimulus occurs will rupture and release its oocyte into the peritoneal cavity. The mature follicles that are not ovulated soon become overripe and deteriorate.

In addition to triggering ovulation, LH also causes the ruptured follicle to change into a very different glandular structure, the *corpus luteum*. (Both the maturing follicles and the corpus luteum produce hormones, as will be described later.)

If the ovulated secondary oocyte is penetrated by a sperm in one of the uterine tubes, the oocyte undergoes the second meiotic division that produces another polar body and the **ovum.** Once the ovum is formed, its 23 chromosomes are combined with those of the sperm to form the fertilized egg, which

is the first cell of the yet-to-be offspring. However, if the secondary oocyte is not penetrated by a sperm, it simply deteriorates without ever completing meiosis to form a functional egg. Although meiosis in males results in four functional sperm, meiosis in females yields only one functional ovum and three tiny polar bodies. The polar bodies have essentially no cytoplasm, so they deteriorate and die quickly.

Another major difference between men and women concerns the size and structure of their sex cells. Sperm are tiny and equipped with tails for locomotion. They have little nutrient-containing cytoplasm; thus, the nutrients in seminal fluid are vital to their survival. In contrast, the egg is a large, non-motile cell, well stocked with nutrient reserves that nourish the developing embryo until it can take up residence in the uterus.

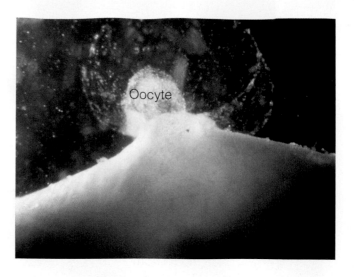

FIGURE 16.11 Ovulation. A secondary oocyte is released from a follicle at the surface of the ovary. The orange mass below the ejected oocyte is part of the ovary. The "halo" of follicle cells around the secondary oocyte is the *corona radiata*.

DID YOU GET IT?

14. Besides the one functional gamete (ovum), what other cell types are produced during oogenesis, and what happens to them?

15. Which anterior pituitary hormone promotes follicle development in the ovary?

16. Which anterior pituitary hormone causes ovulation?

For answers, see Appendix D.

Uterine (Menstrual) Cycle

Although the uterus is the receptacle in which the young embryo implants and develops, it is receptive to implantation only for a very short period each month. Not surprisingly, this brief interval coincides exactly with the time when a fertilized egg would begin to implant, approximately 7 days after ovulation. The events of the **uterine,** or **menstrual, cycle** are the cyclic changes that the endometrium, or mucosa of the uterus, goes through month after month as it responds to changes in the levels of ovarian hormones in the blood.

The cyclic production of estrogens and progesterone by the ovaries is, in turn, regulated by the anterior pituitary gonadotropic hormones, FSH and LH; therefore, it is important to understand how these "hormonal pieces" fit together. Generally speaking, both female cycles are about 28 days long (a period commonly called a *lunar month*), with ovulation typically occurring midway in the cycles, on or about day 14. Figure 16.12 illustrates the events occurring

both in the ovary (the ovarian cycle) and in the uterus (menstrual cycle) at the same time. The three stages of the menstrual cycle are described next.

- **Days 1–5: Menstrual phase.** During this interval, the superficial *functional layer* of the thick endometrial lining of the uterus is sloughing off (detaching) from the uterine wall. This is accompanied by bleeding for 3 to 5 days. The detached tissues and blood pass through the vagina as the menstrual flow. The average blood loss during this period is 50 to 150 ml (or about ¼ to ½ cup). By day 5, growing ovarian follicles are beginning to produce more estrogen.

- **Days 6–14: Proliferative phase.** Stimulated by rising estrogen levels produced by the growing follicles of the ovaries, the basal layer of the endometrium regenerates the functional layer, glands form in it, and the endometrial blood supply increases. The endometrium once again becomes velvety, thick, and well vascularized. (Ovulation occurs in the ovary at the end of this stage, in response to the sudden surge of LH in the blood.)

- **Days 15–28: Secretory phase.** Rising levels of progesterone production by the corpus luteum of the ovary act on the estrogen-primed endometrium and increase its blood supply even more. Progesterone also causes the endometrial

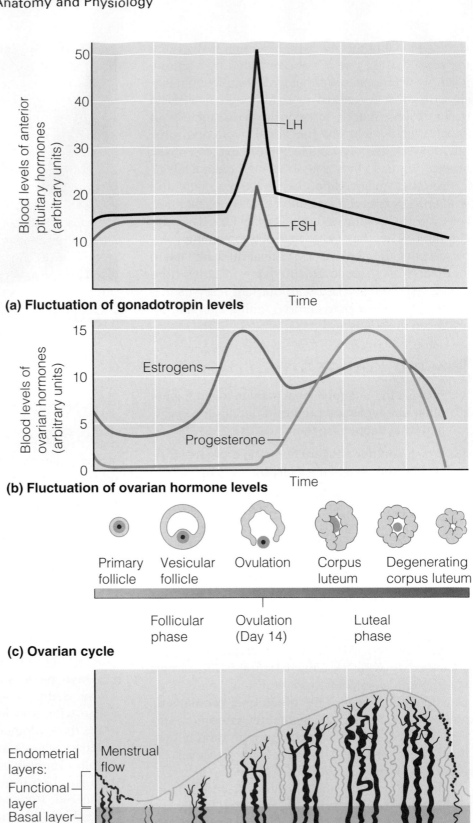

(a) **Fluctuation of gonadotropin levels**

(b) **Fluctuation of ovarian hormone levels**

(c) **Ovarian cycle**

FIGURE 16.12

Hormonal interactions of the female cycles. Relative levels of anterior pituitary gonadotropins correlated with hormonal and follicular changes of the ovary and with the menstrual cycle.

(d) **Uterine (menstrual) cycle**

glands to increase in size and to begin secreting nutrients into the uterine cavity. These nutrients will sustain a developing embryo (if one is present) until it has implanted. If fertilization does occur, the embryo produces a hormone very similar to LH that causes the corpus luteum to continue producing its hormones. If fertilization does not occur, the corpus luteum begins to degenerate toward the end of this period as LH blood levels decline. Lack of ovarian hormones in the blood causes the blood vessels supplying the functional layer of the endometrium to go into spasms and kink. When deprived of oxygen and nutrients, those endometrial cells begin to die, which sets the stage for menses to begin again on day 28.

Although this explanation assumes a classic 28-day cycle, the length of the menstrual cycle is quite variable. It can be as short as 21 days or as long as 40 days. Only one interval is fairly constant in all females; the time from ovulation to the beginning of menses is almost always 14 or 15 days.

Hormone Production by the Ovaries

As the ovaries become active at puberty and start to produce ova, production of ovarian hormones also begins. The follicle cells of the growing and mature follicles produce **estrogens,*** which cause the appearance of the *secondary sex characteristics* in the young woman. Such changes include the following:

- Enlargement of the accessory organs of the female reproductive system (uterine tubes, uterus, vagina, external genitals)
- Development of the breasts
- Appearance of axillary and pubic hair
- Increased deposits of fat beneath the skin in general, and particularly in the hips and breasts
- Widening and lightening of the pelvis
- Onset of menses, or the menstrual cycle

Beyond its promotion of secondary sex characteristics, estrogen also has metabolic effects. For example, it helps maintain low total blood cholesterol levels (and high HDL levels) and facilitates calcium uptake, which sustains bone density.

*Although the ovaries produce several different estrogens, the most important are *estradiol, estrone,* and *estriol.* Of these, estradiol is the most abundant and is most responsible for mediating estrogenic effects.

The second ovarian hormone, **progesterone,** is produced by the glandular *corpus luteum* (see Figure 16.7). As mentioned earlier, after ovulation occurs the ruptured follicle is converted to the corpus luteum, which looks and acts completely different from the growing and mature follicle. Once formed, the corpus luteum produces progesterone (and some estrogen) as long as LH is still present in the blood. Generally speaking, the corpus luteum has stopped producing hormones by 10 to 14 days after ovulation. Except for working with estrogen to establish the menstrual cycle, progesterone does not contribute to the appearance of the secondary sex characteristics. Its other major effects are exerted during pregnancy, when it helps maintain the pregnancy by inhibiting contraction of the myometrium of the uterus, and prepare the breasts for milk production. (However, the source of progesterone during pregnancy is the placenta, not the ovaries.)

Mammary Glands

The **mammary glands** are present in both sexes, but they normally function only in women. Because the biological role of the mammary glands is to produce milk to nourish a newborn baby, they are actually important only when reproduction has already been accomplished. Stimulation by female sex hormones, especially estrogens, causes the female mammary glands to increase in size at puberty.

Developmentally, the mammary glands are modified *sweat glands* that are part of the skin. Each mammary gland is contained within a rounded skin-covered breast anterior to the pectoral muscles. Slightly below the center of each breast is a pigmented area, the **areola** (ah-re′o-lah), which surrounds a central protruding **nipple** (Figure 16.13).

Internally, each mammary gland consists of 15 to 25 *lobes* that radiate around the nipple. The lobes are padded and separated from one another by connective tissue and fat. Within each lobe are smaller chambers called *lobules,* which contain clusters of **alveolar glands** that produce the milk when a woman is **lactating** (producing milk). The alveolar glands of each lobule pass the milk into the **lactiferous** (lak-tif′er-us) **ducts,** which open to the outside at the nipple.

HOMEOSTATIC IMBALANCE
Cancer of the breast is the second most common cause of death in American women.

Flat-chested women are perfectly able to nurse their newborn infants; hence, it is not glandular tissue that accounts for the bulk of the breast tissue. So, what does?

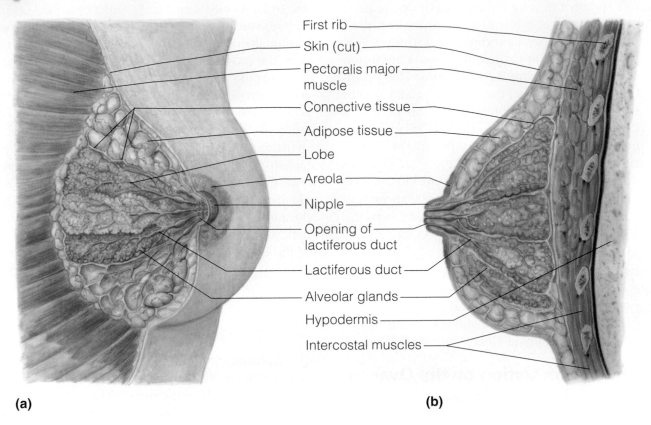

First rib

Skin (cut)

Pectoralis major muscle

Connective tissue

Adipose tissue

Lobe

Areola

Nipple

Opening of lactiferous duct

Lactiferous duct

Alveolar glands

Hypodermis

Intercostal muscles

(a)

(b)

FIGURE 16.13   Female mammary glands. (a) Anterior view.
(b) Sagittal section.

One woman in eight will develop this condition. Some 10 percent of breast cancers stem from hereditary defects, and half of these can be traced to dangerous mutations in a pair of genes (BRCA1 and 2). Eighty percent of women who carry the altered gene develop breast cancer. With the possible exception of family history, most risk factors reflect lifelong exposure to estrogen (early menses, late menopause, estrogen replacement therapy, and others).

Breast cancer is often signaled by a change in skin texture, puckering, or leakage from the nipple. Early detection by breast self-examination and mammography is unquestionably the best way to increase one's chances of surviving breast cancer. Because most breast lumps are discovered by women themselves in routine monthly breast exams, this simple examination should be a priority in every woman's life. Cur-

rently the American Cancer Society recommends scheduling **mammography**—X-ray examination that detects breast cancers too small to feel (less than 1 cm)—every 2 years for women between 40 and 49 years old and yearly thereafter (Figure 16.14). ▲

▶**DID YOU GET IT?**

17. Which ovarian hormone can be called a feminizing hormone because it promotes the formation of female secondary sex characteristics?

18. What happens during the proliferative stage of the uterine cycle?

19. What are three important functions of progesterone in women?

20. Why do mutations of the BRCA genes cause problems?

A *Adipose tissue.*

For answers, see Appendix D.

(a)   **(b)**   **(c)**

FIGURE 16.14   Mammograms. (a) Photograph of woman undergoing mammography. **(b)** Normal breast. **(c)** Breast with tumor.

Survey of Pregnancy and Embryonic Development

Because the birth of a baby is such a familiar event, we tend to lose sight of the wonder of this accomplishment. In every instance it begins with a single cell, the fertilized egg, and ends with an extremely complex human being consisting of trillions of cells. The development of an embryo is very complex, and the details of this process can fill a good-sized book. Our intention here is simply to outline the important events of pregnancy and embryonic development.

Accomplishing Fertilization

Before fertilization can occur, the sperm must reach the ovulated secondary oocyte. The oocyte is viable for 12 to 24 hours after it is cast out of the ovary, and sperm generally retain their fertilizing power within the female reproductive tract for 24 to 48 hours after ejaculation. Consequently, for fertilization to occur, sexual intercourse must occur no more than 2 days before ovulation and no later than 24 hours after, at which point the oocyte is approximately one-third of the way down the length of the uterine tube. Remember that sperm are motile cells that can propel themselves by lashing movements of their tails. If sperm are deposited in

a female's vagina at the approximate time of ovulation, they are attracted to the oocyte by chemicals that act as "homing devices," allowing them to locate the oocyte. It takes 1 to 2 hours for sperm to complete the journey up the female duct system into the uterine tubes even through they are only about 12 cm (5 inches) away. However, millions of sperm leak from the vagina, and of those remaining, millions more are destroyed by the vagina's acidic environment. Only a few hundred to a few thousand sperm finally make it to the egg's vicinity.

When the swarming sperm reach the oocyte, their cell surface hyaluronidase enzymes break down the "cement" that holds the follicle cells of the corona radiata together around the oocyte. Once a path has been cleared through the corona, thousands of sperm undergo the *acrosomal reaction* in which the acrosome membranes break down, releasing enzymes that digest holes in the oocyte membrane. Then, when the membrane is adequately weakened and a single sperm makes contact with the oocyte's membrane receptors, the head (nucleus) of the sperm is pulled into the oocyte cytoplasm. This is one case that does not bear out the adage "The early bird catches the worm" because it is sperm that come along after hundreds of sperm have undergone acrosomal reactions to expose the oocyte membrane, that are in

Q *Why is the multicellular blastocyst only slightly larger than the single-cell zygote?*

(a) Zygote (fertilized egg)

(b) Early cleavage 4-cell stage

(c) Morula

(d) Early blastocyst

Blastocyst cavity

(e) Late blastocyst (implanting)

Inner cell mass

Trophoblast

Fertilization

Uterine tube

Secondary oocyte

Ovary

Ovulation

Uterus

Endometrium

(a) (b) (c) (d) (e)

FIGURE 16.15   Cleavage is a rapid series of mitotic divisions that begins with the zygote and ends with the blastocyst. The zygote begins to divide about 24 hours after fertilization and continues to divide rapidly (undergo cleavage) as it travels down the uterine tube. Three to 4 days after ovulation, the preembryo reaches the uterus and floats freely for 2 to 3 days, nourished by secretions of the endometrial glands. At the late blastocyst stage, the embryo is implanting into the endometrium; this begins at about day 7 after ovulation. **(a)** Zygote (fertilized egg). **(b)** Four-cell stage. **(c)** Morula, a solid ball of blastomeres. **(d)** Early blastocyst; the morula hollows out, and fills with fluid. **(e)** Late blastocyst, composed of an outer sphere of trophoblast cells and an off-center cell cluster called the inner cell mass.

the best position to be *the* fertilizing sperm. Once a single sperm has penetrated the oocyte, the oocyte nucleus completes the second meiotic division, forming the ovum and a polar body.

After sperm entry, changes occur in the fertilized egg to prevent other sperm from gaining entry.

In humans, of the millions of sperm ejaculated, only *one* can penetrate an oocyte. **Fertilization** occurs at the moment the genetic material of a sperm combines with that of an ovum to form a fertilized egg, or **zygote** (zi′gōt). The zygote represents the first cell of the new individual.

A *Because as the zygote and then its descendants divide, little or no time is provided for growth between subsequent division cycles. As a result, the cells get smaller and smaller and the size of the cell mass stays approximately the same size as the initial zygote.*

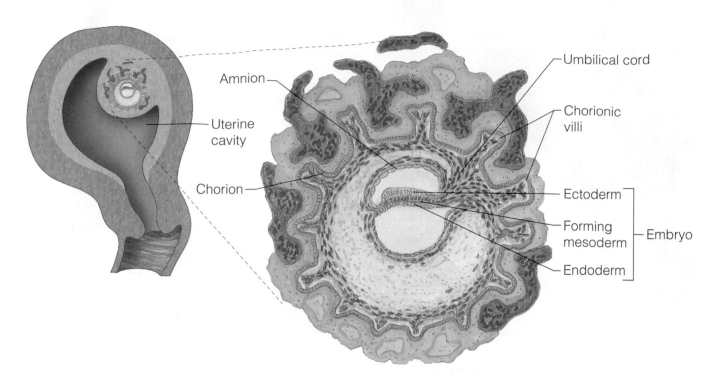

FIGURE 16.16 **Embryo of approximately 18 days.** Embryonic membranes present.

Events of Embryonic and Fetal Development

As the zygote journeys down the uterine tube (propelled by peristalsis and cilia), it begins to undergo rapid mitotic cell divisions—forming first two cells, then four, and so on. This early stage of embryonic development, called **cleavage,** is shown in Figure 16.15. Because there is not much time for cell growth between divisions, the daughter cells become smaller and smaller. Cleavage provides a large number of cells to serve as building blocks for constructing the **embryo** (developmental stage until the ninth week). Consider for a moment how difficult it would be to construct a building from one huge block of granite. If you now consider how much easier your task would be if you could use hundreds of brick-size granite blocks, you will quickly grasp the importance of cleavage. By the time the developing embryo reaches the uterus (about 3 days after ovulation, or on day 17 of the woman's cycle), it is a *morula,* a tiny ball of 16 cells that looks like a microscopic raspberry. The uterine endometrium is still not fully prepared to receive the embryo at this point, so the embryo floats free in the uterine cavity, tem-

porarily using the uterine secretions for nutrition. While still unattached, the embryo continues to develop until it has about 100 cells, and then it hollows out to form a ball-like structure called either a **blastocyst** (blas′to-sist) or a **chorionic** (ko″re-on′ik) **vesicle.** At the same time, it secretes an LH-like hormone called **human chorionic gonadotropin (hCG),** which prods the corpus luteum of the ovary to continue producing its hormones. (If this were not the case, the functional layer of the endometrium would be sloughing off shortly in menses.) It is hCG that many home pregnancy tests assay for in a woman's urine.

The blastocyst has two important functional areas: the **trophoblast,** which forms the large fluid-filled sphere, and the **inner cell mass,** a small cluster of cells displaced to one side (see Figure 16.15e). By day 7 after ovulation, the blastocyst has attached to the endometrium and has eroded away the lining in a small area, embedding itself in the thick velvety mucosa. All of this is occurring even while development is continuing and the three primary germ layers are being formed from the inner cell mass (Figure 16.16). The *primary germ layers* are the **ectoderm** (which gives rise to the nervous system and the epidermis of the skin), the

Amniotic sac Umbilical cord Umbilical vein

Chorionic villi

Yolk sac

Cut edge of chorion

FIGURE 16.17 The 7-week embryo.
A 7-week embryo, encased in its amniotic sac and the chorionic villi (to the right), which will cooperate with maternal uterine tissues to form the placenta.

endoderm (which forms mucosae and associated glands), and the **mesoderm** (which gives rise to virtually everything else). Implantation has usually been completed and the uterine mucosa has grown over the burrowed-in embryo by day 14 after ovulation—the day the woman would ordinarily be expecting to start menses. After it is securely implanted, the trophoblast part of the blastocyst develops elaborate projections, called **chorionic villi**, which combine with the tissues of the mother's uterus to form the **placenta** (plah-sen'tah (Figure 16.17). Once the placenta has formed, the platelike embryonic body, now surrounded by a fluid-filled sac called the **amnion** (am'ne-on), is attached to the placenta by a blood vessel–containing stalk of tissue, the **umbilical cord** (Figures 16.16 and 16.17). (The special features of the umbilical blood vessels and fetal circulation are discussed in Chapter 11.) Generally by the third week, the placenta is functioning to deliver nutrients and oxygen to and remove wastes from the embryonic blood. All exchanges are made through the placental barrier. By the end of the second month of pregnancy, the placenta has also become an endocrine organ and is producing estrogen, progesterone, and other hormones that help to maintain the pregnancy. At this time, the corpus luteum of the ovary becomes inactive.

By the eighth week of embryonic development, all the groundwork has been completed. All the organ systems have been laid down, at least in rudimentary form, and the embryo looks distinctly human. Beginning in the ninth week of development, the embryo is referred to as a **fetus.** From this point on, the major activities are growth and organ specialization, accompanied by changes in body proportions. During the fetal period, the developing fetus grows from a crown-to-rump length of about 3 cm (slightly more than 1 inch) and a weight of approximately 1 g (0.03 ounce) to about 36 cm (14 inches) and 2.7 to 4.1 kg (6 to 10 pounds) or more. (Total body length at birth is about 55 cm, or 22 inches.) As you might expect with such tremendous growth, the changes in fetal appearance are quite dramatic (Figure 16.18). The most significant of these changes are summarized in Table 16.1. By approximately 270 days after fertilization (the end of the tenth lunar month), the fetus is said to be "full-term" and is ready to be born.

Effects of Pregnancy on the Mother

Pregnancy (the period from conception to the birth of her baby) can be a difficult time for the mother. Not only are there obvious anatomical changes, but striking changes occur in her physiology as well.

Anatomical Changes

The ability of the uterus to enlarge during pregnancy is nothing less than remarkable. Starting as a fist-sized organ, the uterus grows to occupy most of the pelvic cavity by 16 weeks. As pregnancy continues, the uterus pushes higher and higher into the abdominal cavity. As birth nears, the uterus reaches the level of the xiphoid process and occupies the bulk of the abdominal cavity. The crowded abdominal organs press superiorly against the diaphragm, which intrudes on the thoracic cavity. As a result, the ribs flare, causing the thorax to widen.

The increasing bulkiness of the abdomen changes the woman's center of gravity, and many women develop an accentuated lumbar curvature (lordosis), often accompanied by backaches, during the last few months of pregnancy. Placental

(a)

(b)

FIGURE 16.18   **Photographs of a developing fetus.**
(a) Fetus in month 3, about 6 cm (2.5 inches) long. **(b)** Fetus late in
month 5, about 19 cm (8 inches) long.

production of the hormone **relaxin** causes pelvic ligaments and the pubic symphysis to relax, widen, and become more flexible. This increased motility eases birth passage, but it may also result in a waddling gait during pregnancy.

Obviously, good maternal nutrition is necessary throughout pregnancy if the developing fetus is to have all the building materials (proteins, calcium, iron, and the like) it needs to form its tissues and organs. The old expression "A pregnant woman is eating for two" has encouraged many women to eat *twice* the amount of food actually needed during pregnancy, which, of course, leads to excessive weight gain. Actually, a pregnant woman needs only about 300 additional calories daily to sustain proper fetal growth. The emphasis should be on high-quality food, not just more food.

HOMEOSTATIC IMBALANCE

Many potentially harmful substances can cross through the placental barrier into the fetal blood; therefore, the pregnant woman should be very much aware of what she is taking into her body. Substances that may cause life-threatening birth defects (and even

fetal death) include alcohol, nicotine, and many types of drugs (anticoagulants, antihypertensives, sedatives, and some antibiotics). Maternal infections, particularly German measles (rubella), may also cause severe fetal damage. Termination of a pregnancy by loss of a fetus during the first 20 weeks of pregnancy is called **abortion.** ▲

Physiological Changes

Gastrointestinal System   Many women suffer nausea, commonly called *morning sickness*, during the first few months of pregnancy, until their system adjusts to the elevated levels of progesterone and estrogens. *Heartburn* is common because the esophagus is displaced and the stomach is crowded by the growing uterus, which favors reflux of stomach acid into the esophagus. Another problem is constipation, because motility of the digestive tract declines during pregnancy.

Urinary System   The kidneys have the additional burden of disposing of fetal metabolic wastes, and they produce more urine during pregnancy. Because the uterus compresses the bladder, urination

16

TABLE 16.1	Development of the Human Fetus

Time	Changes/accomplishments
8 weeks (end of embryonic period)	Head nearly as large as body; all major brain regions present
	Liver disproportionately large and begins to form blood cells
	Limbs present; though initially webbed, fingers and toes are free by the end of this interval
	Bone formation begun
	Heart has been pumping blood since the fourth week
8 weeks	All body systems present in at least rudimentary form
	Approximate crown-to-rump length: 30 mm (3 cm; 1.2 inches); weight: 1 gram (0.03 ounce)
9–12 weeks (third month)	Head still dominant, but body elongating; brain continues to enlarge
	Facial features present in crude form
	Walls of hollow visceral organs gaining smooth muscle
	Blood cell formation begins in bone marrow
12 weeks	Bone formation accelerating
	Sex readily detected from the genitals
	Approximate crown-to-rump length at end of interval: 90 mm (9 cm)
13–16 weeks (fourth month)	General sensory organs are present; eyes and ears assume characteristic position and shape; blinking of eyes and sucking motions of lips occur
	Face looks human and body beginning to outgrow head
	Kidneys attain typical structure
16 weeks	Most bones are distinct and joint cavities apparent
	Approximate crown-to-rump length at end of interval: 140 mm (14 cm)

becomes more frequent, more urgent, and sometimes uncontrollable. (The last condition is called *stress incontinence*.)

Respiratory System The nasal mucosa responds to estrogen by becoming swollen and congested; thus, nasal stuffiness and occasional nosebleeds may occur. Vital capacity and respiratory rate increase during pregnancy, but residual volume declines, and many women exhibit *dyspnea* (difficult breathing) during the later stages of pregnancy.

Cardiovascular System Perhaps the most dramatic physiological changes occur in the cardiovascular system. Total body water rises and blood volume increases by 25 to 40 percent to accommodate the additional needs of the fetus. The rise in blood volume also acts as a safeguard against blood loss during birth. Blood pressure and pulse typically rise and increase cardiac output by 20 to 40 percent; this helps propel the greater blood volume around the body. Because the uterus presses on the pelvic blood vessels, venous return from the lower limbs may be impaired somewhat, resulting in varicose veins.

Time	Changes/accomplishments
17–20 weeks (fifth month)	Vernix caseosa (fatty secretions of sebaceous glands) covers body; silklike hair (lanugo) covers skin
	Fetal position (body flexed anteriorly) assumed because of space restrictions
	Limbs achieve near-final proportions
	Quickening occurs (mother feels spontaneous muscular activity of fetus)
	Approximate crown-to-rump length at end of interval: 190 mm (19 cm)
21–30 weeks (sixth and seventh months)	Substantial increase in weight (may survive if born prematurely at 27–28 weeks, but hypothalamus still too immature to regulate body temperature, and surfactant production by the lungs is still inadequate)
	Myelination of spinal cord begins; eyes are open
	Skin is wrinkled and red; fingernails and toenails are present
	Body is lean and well proportioned
	Bone marrow becomes sole site of blood cell formation
	Testes enter scrotum in seventh month (in males)
	Approximate crown-to-rump length at end of interval: 280 mm (28 cm)
30–40 weeks (term) (eighth and ninth months)	Skin whitish pink; fat laid down in subcutaneous tissue
At birth	Approximate crown-to-rump length at end of interval: 350–400 mm (35–40 cm; 14–16 inches); weight: 2.7–4.1 kg (6–10 pounds)

TABLE 16.1 *(continued)*

Childbirth

Childbirth, also called **parturition** (par″tu-rish′un; "bringing forth young"), is the culmination of pregnancy. It usually occurs within 15 days of the calculated due date (which is 280 days from the last menstrual period). The series of events that expel the infant from the uterus are referred to collectively as **labor.**

Initiation of Labor

Several events interlock to trigger labor. During the last few weeks of pregnancy, estrogens reach their highest levels in the mother's blood. This has two important consequences: it causes the myometrium to form abundant *oxytocin* receptors (so that it becomes more sensitive to the hormone oxytocin), and it interferes with progesterone's quieting influence on the uterine muscle. As a result, weak, irregular uterine contractions begin to occur. These contractions, called *Braxton Hicks contractions,* have caused many women to go to the hospital, only to be told that they were in **false labor** and sent home.

As birth nears, two more chemical signals cooperate to convert these false labor pains into the real thing. Certain cells of the fetus begin to produce oxytocin, which in turn stimulates the placenta to release *prostaglandins*. Both hormones stimulate more frequent and powerful contractions of the uterus. At this point, the increasing emotional and physical stresses activate the mother's hypothalamus, which signals for oxytocin release by the posterior pituitary. The combined effects of rising levels of oxytocin and prostaglandins initiate the rhythmic, expulsive contractions of true labor.

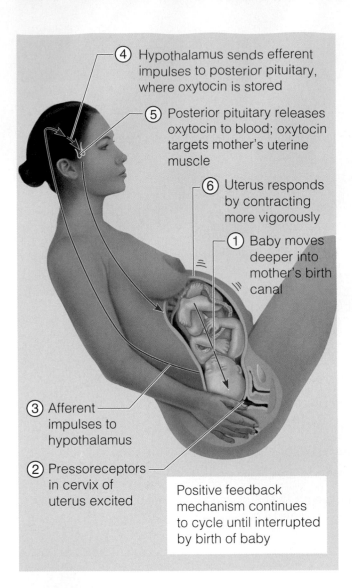

④ Hypothalamus sends efferent impulses to posterior pituitary, where oxytocin is stored

⑤ Posterior pituitary releases oxytocin to blood; oxytocin targets mother's uterine muscle

⑥ Uterus responds by contracting more vigorously

① Baby moves deeper into mother's birth canal

③ Afferent impulses to hypothalamus

② Pressoreceptors in cervix of uterus excited

Positive feedback mechanism continues to cycle until interrupted by birth of baby

FIGURE 16.19   The positive feedback mechanism by which oxytocin promotes labor contractions during birth.

Once the hypothalamus is involved, a positive feedback mechanism is propelled into action: Stronger contractions cause the release of more oxytocin, which causes even more vigorous contractions, forcing the baby ever deeper into the mother's pelvis, and so on (Figure 16.19).

Because both oxytocin and prostaglandins are needed to initiate labor in humans, anything that interferes with production of either of these hormones will hinder the onset of labor. For example, antiprostaglandin drugs such as aspirin and ibuprofen can inhibit labor at the early stages, and such drugs are used occasionally to prevent premature births.

Stages of Labor

The process of labor is commonly divided into three stages (Figure 16.20). These stages are described next.

Stage 1: Dilation Stage   The **dilation stage** is the time from the appearance of true contractions until the cervix is fully dilated by the baby's head (about 10 cm in diameter). As labor starts, regular but weak uterine contractions begin in the upper part of the uterus and move downward toward the vagina. Gradually, the contractions become more vigorous and more rapid, and, as the infant's head is forced against the cervix with each contraction, the cervix begins to soften, becomes thinner *(effaces)*, and dilates. Eventually, the amnion ruptures, releasing the amniotic fluid, an event commonly referred to as "breaking the water." The dilation stage is the longest part of labor and usually lasts for 6 to 12 hours or more.

Stage 2: Expulsion Stage   The **expulsion stage** is the period from full dilation to delivery of the infant. In this stage, the infant passes through the cervix and vagina to the outside of the body. During this stage, a mother experiencing natural childbirth (that is, undergoing labor without local anesthesia) has an increasing urge to push, or bear down, with the abdominal muscles. Although this phase can take as long as 2 hours, it is typically 50 minutes in a first birth and around 20 minutes in subsequent births.

When the infant is in the usual head-first *(vertex)* position, the skull (its largest diameter) acts as a wedge to dilate the cervix. The head-first presentation also allows the baby to be suctioned free of mucus and to breathe even before it has completely exited from the birth canal. Once the head has been delivered, the rest of the baby's body is delivered much more easily. After birth, the umbilical cord is clamped and cut. In *breech* (buttocks-first) presentations and other nonvertex presentations, these advantages are lost and delivery is much more difficult, sometimes requiring the use of forceps or a vacuum extractor.

HOMEOSTATIC IMBALANCE

During an extremely prolonged or difficult stage 2, a condition called **dystocia** (dis-to'se-ah) may occur. In dystocia, oxygen delivery to the infant is inadequate, leading to fetal brain damage (resulting in cerebral palsy or epilepsy) and decreased viability of the infant. To prevent these outcomes, a **cesarean** (se-zayr'e-an) **section,** also called a **C-section,** may be performed. A C-section is delivery of the infant through a surgical incision made through the abdominal and uterine walls. ▲

Stage 3: Placental Stage   The **placental stage,** or the delivery of the placenta, is usually accomplished within 15 minutes after birth of the infant. The strong uterine contractions that continue after birth compress uterine blood vessels, limit bleeding, and cause the placenta to detach from the uterine wall. The placenta and its attached fetal membranes, collectively called the **afterbirth,** are then easily removed by a slight tug on the umbilical cord. It is very important that all placental fragments be removed to prevent continued uterine bleeding after birth *(postpartum bleeding).*

DID YOU GET IT?

21. How does cleavage differ from cell divisions occurring during life after birth?

22. What are three roles of the placenta?

23. Explain how pregnancy affects a woman's respiratory and digestive processes.

24. What are the three stages of labor?

For answers, see Appendix D.

Developmental Aspects of the Reproductive System

Although the sex of an individual is determined at the time of fertilization (males have X and Y sex chromosomes and females have two X sex chromosomes), the gonads do not begin to form until about the eighth week of embryonic development. Prior to this time, the embryonic reproductive structures of males and females are identical and are said to be in the *indifferent stage.* After the gonads have formed, development of the accessory structures and external genitalia begins. Whether male or female structures will form depends entirely on whether testosterone is present or absent. The usual case is that, once formed, the embryonic testes produce testosterone, and the development

Placenta
Umbilical cord
Uterus
Cervix

① **Dilation of the cervix**

② **Expulsion: delivery of the infant**

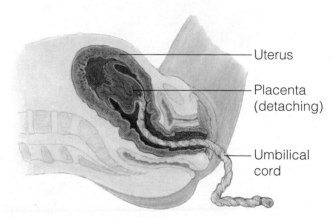

Uterus
Placenta (detaching)
Umbilical cord

③ **Delivery of the placenta**

FIGURE 16.20   The three stages of labor.

DOULA

Anatomy and physiology classes are central in the training of doulas, or labor support professionals.

"Why do I want to be a doula? Because I know how much one could have helped me when I gave birth," says Morgan Tharan. "I had a long labor that affected my baby's breathing and heart rate, so my midwife had to focus all her efforts on helping him. He turned out to be fine, but it was a really anxious time. It made me appreciate the importance of emotional

support during labor and delivery." Indeed, according to Doulas of North America (DONA), mothers who have doulas spend less time in labor, request less pain medication, and undergo 50 percent fewer cesarean sections than the national average.

Today Tharan is studying to become a doula, a professional who provides emotional and physical support to mothers during pregnancy, labor, birth, and the hours immediately

afterward. Sometimes called labor support professionals, doulas (from the Greek word for "servant") are a relatively new profession. Training requirements vary, but anatomy and physiology classes are always central. "I need to know about reproduction and fetal development to help the mother and answer questions," explains Tharan. "We study how the body changes during pregnancy and have a whole section on labor pain and the process of delivery. We learn the mechanics of breastfeeding and how the breast works, too."

Tharan loves the variety in her job and the rapport she develops with clients. "Like me, most doulas are 'birth junkies,'" she smiles. "We love participating in this wonderful life experience." Many doulas work on a freelance basis and contract directly with the expectant parents, initially meeting to discuss the mother's expectations and concerns about labor and delivery. Notes Tharan, "If there are difficult issues, such as a past miscarriage, a second prenatal visit is scheduled. We can also be a big help to the partner/father, because they often have questions and fears of their own. We facilitate communication and help them help the mother." A doula may also answer questions about medical procedures and offer suggestions about nutrition, exercise, and other ways to make pregnancy more comfortable.

When her client goes into labor, Tharan gets an urgent phone call. "Even if it's the middle of the night, if the mother wants me, I'm there," she says. "I meet her at the hospital or at home, depending on where she wants to give birth, and I stay

through labor. I may give a massage, help her change positions, coach the partner—whatever helps the mother the most. After birth, I can help her begin breastfeeding.

DONA, a national association, certifies many labor support professionals. It specifies a number of steps to acquire certification including the following:

> **"I need to know about reproduction and fetal development to help the mother."**

➤ Complete one of the following: training in childbirth education or midwifery; nursing work experience in labor and delivery; or observing a childbirth preparation series

➤ Complete an approved training course of 14 or more hours

➤ Provide continuous labor support at three births

For more information contact DONA:

P.O. Box 626
Jasper, IN 47547
(888) 788-3662
http://www.dona.org

For additional information on this career, click the Focus on Careers link at www.anatomyandphysiology.com.

of the male duct system and external genitalia follows. When testosterone is not produced, as is the case in female embryos that form ovaries, the female ducts and external genitalia result.

HOMEOSTATIC IMBALANCE

Any interference with the normal pattern of sex hormone production in the embryo results in abnormalities. For example, if the embryonic testes fail to produce testosterone, a genetic male develops the female accessory structures and external genitalia. If a genetic female is exposed to testosterone (as might happen if the mother has an androgen-producing tumor of her adrenal gland), the embryo has ovaries but develops male accessory ducts and glands, as well as a penis and an empty scrotum. Individuals having accessory reproductive structures that do not "match" their gonads are called **pseudohermaphrodites** (su"do-her-maf'ro-dītz) to distinguish them from true **hermaphrodites,** rare individuals who possess both ovarian and testicular tissues. In recent years, many pseudohermaphrodites have sought sex change operations to match their outer selves (external genitalia) with their inner selves (gonads).

Additionally, abnormal separation of chromosomes during meiosis can lead to congenital defects of this system. For example, males who have an extra female sex chromosome have the normal male accessory structures, but their testes atrophy, causing them to be sterile. Other abnormalities occur when a child has only one sex chromosome. An XO female appears normal but lacks ovaries; YO males die during development. Other, much less serious, conditions affect males primarily; these include **phimosis** (fi-mo'sis), which essentially is a narrowing of the foreskin of the penis, and misplaced urethral openings.

The male testes, formed in the abdominal cavity at approximately the same location as the female ovaries, descend to enter the scrotum about one month before birth. Failure of the testes to make their normal descent leads to a condition called **cryptorchidism** (krip-tor'ki-dizm). Because this condition results in sterility of a male (and also puts him at risk for cancer of the testes), surgery is usually performed during childhood to rectify this problem. ▲

Because the reproductive system organs do not function until puberty, there are few problems with this system during childhood. **Puberty** is the period of life, generally between the ages of 10 and 15 years, when the reproductive organs grow to their adult size and become functional under the influence of rising levels of gonadal hormones (testosterone in men and estrogen in women). After this time, reproductive capability continues until old age in men and menopause in women. The secondary sex characteristics and major events of puberty were described earlier, so these details will not be repeated here. It is important to remember, however, that puberty represents the earliest period of reproductive system activity.

The events of puberty occur in the same sequence in all individuals, but the age at which they occur varies widely. In boys, the event that signals puberty's onset is enlargement of the testes and scrotum, around the age of 13 years, followed by the appearance of pubic, axillary, and facial hair. Growth of the penis goes on over the next 2 years, and sexual maturation is indicated by the presence of mature sperm in the semen. In the meantime, the young man has unexpected, and often embarrassing, erections and frequent nocturnal emissions ("wet dreams") as his hormones surge and hormonal controls struggle to achieve a normal balance.

The first sign of puberty in girls is budding breasts, often apparent by the age of 11 years. The first menstrual period, called **menarche** (mĕ-nar'ke), usually occurs about 2 years later. Dependable ovulation and fertility are deferred until the hormonal controls mature, an event that takes nearly 2 more years.

HOMEOSTATIC IMBALANCE

In adults, the most common reproductive system problems are infections. Vaginal infections are more common in young and elderly women and in women whose resistance is low. Common infections include those caused by *Escherichia coli* (spread from the digestive tract); sexually transmitted microorganisms (such as gonorrhea, syphilis, and herpesvirus); and yeasts (a type of fungus). Untreated vaginal infections may spread throughout the female reproductive tract, causing pelvic inflammatory disease and sterility. Problems involving painful or abnormal menses may result from infection or hormone imbalance.

The most common inflammatory conditions in men are **urethritis, prostatitis,** and **epididymitis** (ep"ĭ-did-ĭ-mi'tis), all of which may follow sexual contacts in which sexually transmitted disease (STD) microorganisms are transmitted. **Orchiditis** (or"kĭ-di'tis), inflammation of

CONTRACEPTION: PREVENTING PREGNANCY

In a society such as ours, where many women opt for professional careers or must work for economic reasons, **contraception** (*contra* = against; *cept* = taking), or *birth control,* is often seen as a necessity. Thus far, much of the burden for birth control has fallen on women's shoulders, and most birth control products are directed toward women.

The key to birth control is dependability. As shown by the red arrows in the accompanying flow chart, the birth control techniques and products currently available have many sites of action for blocking the reproductive process. Let's examine the relative advantages of a few of these current methods more closely.

The most-used contraceptive product in the United States is the *birth control pill,* or simply, "the pill," a preparation taken daily that contains tiny amounts of estrogens and progestins (progesterone-like hormones), except that for the last 7 days of the 28-day cycle the tablets are hormone-free. The pill tricks the hypothalamic-pituitary control system and "lulls it to sleep" because the relatively constant blood levels of ovarian hormones make it appear that the woman is pregnant (both estrogen and progesterone are produced throughout pregnancy). Ovarian follicles do not mature, ovulation ceases, and menstrual flow is much reduced. However, because hormonal balance in the body is precisely con-

trolled, some women simply cannot tolerate the changes caused by the pill—they become nauseated and/or hypertensive.

The pill has adverse cardiovascular effects in a small number of users, and there is still debate about whether it increases the incidence of ovarian, uterine, and particularly breast cancer. However, it appears that the new, very low dose preparations may actually help protect against ovarian and endometrial cancer and may also have reduced the incidence of serious cardiovascular

> ## " *The key to birth control is dependability.* "

side effects, such as strokes, heart attacks, and blood clots, that occurred (rarely) with earlier forms of the pill.

Presently, the pill is one of the most widely used drugs in the world; well over 50 million women use these drugs to prevent pregnancy. The incidence of failure is less than 1 percent.

A different combination hormone pill, the *morning-after pill (MAP),* is the therapy of choice for rape victims. Marketed under various names, including Ovral, Tetragynon, and Trephasil, MAPs are becoming more

widely known. Taken within 3 days of unprotected intercourse, the concentrated estrogen-progesterone combination pills "mess up" the normal hormonal signals so much that fertilization is prevented altogether or a fertilized egg is prevented from implanting.

Other hormonal approaches are progestin-only products that cause cervical mucus to become thick, blocking sperm passage and making the endometrium inhospitable to implantation. These include *Minepill* (a tablet), *Norplant* (which consists of two, originally six, tiny silicon rods implanted just under the skin), which releases progestin over a 5-year period, and *Depo-Provera,* an injectable synthetic progesterone that lasts for 3 months. The failure rate of Norplant and Depo-Provera is even lower than that of the pill.

For several years, the second most used contraceptive method was the *intrauterine device (IUD),* a plastic or metal device inserted into the uterus that prevented implantation of the fertilized egg (see photo on p. 576). Although the failure rate of the IUD was nearly as low as that of the pill, IUDs were taken off the market in the United States because of problems with occasional contraceptive failure, uterine perforation, or pelvic inflammatory disease (PID). New IUD products that deliver sustained doses of synthetic progesterone to the endometrium are currently being recommended for women who have given birth and for women with a lower risk of developing PID in monogamous relationships.

Sterilization techniques, such as *tubal ligation* and *vasectomy* (cutting or cauterizing the uterine tubes or ductus deferens, respectively), are nearly foolproof and are the choice of approximately 33 percent of couples of childbearing age in the United States. Both procedures can be done in the physician's office. These changes are usually permanent, however, so they are not for individuals who plan to have children but want to choose the time.

Coitus interruptus, or withdrawal of the penis just before ejaculation, is simply against nature, and control of ejaculation is never assured. *Rhythm,* or *fertility awareness, methods* depend on avoiding intercourse during the period of ovulation or fertility. This may be accomplished by (1) recording daily basal body temperatures (body temperature drops slightly immediately prior to ovulation and then rises slightly after ovulation) or (2) recording changes in the pattern of salivary mucus with a lipstick-sized nonprescription instrument called an Ovulite Microscope. With a failure rate of 10 to 20 percent, rhythm techniques require accurate record-keeping for several cycles before they can be used with confidence. *Barrier methods,* such as diaphragms, cervical caps, condoms (see photo), spermicidal foams, gels, and sponges, are quite effective, especially when some agent is used by both partners. But many people

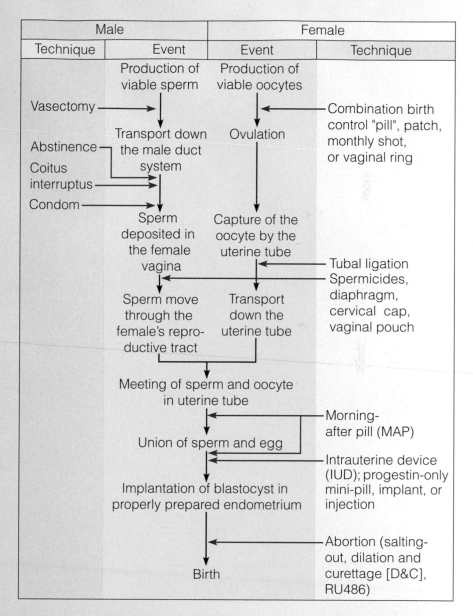

Flow chart of the events that must occur to produce a baby. Techniques or products that interfere with the process are indicated by red arrows at the site of interference; they act to prevent the next step.

A CLOSER LOOK   Contraception *(continued)*

avoid them because they can reduce the spontaneity of sexual encounters.

Abortion is the termination of a pregnancy that is in progress. Spontaneous abortion, also called *miscarriage,* is common and frequently occurs before a woman is aware she has conceived. Additionally, over 1 million women opt to terminate pregnancy in the physician's office. In this arena, *RU486,* the socalled *abortion pill* developed in France, is widely used in the United States. When taken during the first 7 weeks of pregnancy in conjunction with a tiny amount of prostaglandin to induce uterine contractions, it induces miscarriage by blocking progesterone's quieting effect on the uterus. RU486 has a 96 to 98 percent success rate with few side effects other than cramping and short-term spotting. However, a small number of deaths due to infection and sepsis prompted the FDA in July 2005 to issue a warning about using RU486. These incidents were very rare, but further studies on this drug are ongoing. Now approved by the FDA, it has become a topic of bitter controversy

Some contraceptive devices.

among pro-choice and pro-life groups in the United States.

This summary has barely touched on the large number of experimental birth control drugs now awaiting clinical trials; and other methods are sure to be developed in the near future. In the final analysis, however, the only 100 percent effective means of birth control is the age-old one—*total abstinence.*

---

the testes, is rather uncommon but is serious because it can cause sterility. Orchiditis most commonly follows STD or mumps (in an adult man).

As noted earlier, neoplasms represent a major threat to reproductive system organs. Tumors of the breast and cervix are the most common reproductive cancers in adult women, and prostate cancer (a common sequel to prostatic hypertrophy) is a widespread problem in adult men. ▲

Most women reach peak reproductive abilities in their late twenties. After that, a natural decrease in ovarian function occurs. As estrogen production declines, ovulation becomes irregular, and menstrual periods become scanty and shorter in length. Eventually, ovulation and menses cease entirely, ending childbearing ability. This event, called **menopause,** is considered to have occurred when a whole year has passed without menstruation.

Although estrogen production continues for a while after menopause, the ovaries finally stop functioning as endocrine organs. When deprived of the stimulatory effects of estrogen, the reproductive organs and breasts begin to atrophy. The vagina becomes dry; intercourse may become painful (particularly if infrequent), and vaginal infections become increasingly common. Other

SYSTEMS IN SYNC

HOMEOSTATIC RELATIONSHIPS BETWEEN THE
REPRODUCTIVE SYSTEM AND OTHER BODY SYSTEMS

Endocrine System
- Gonadal hormones exert feedback effects on hypothalamic-pituitary axis; placental hormones help to maintain pregnancy
- Gonadotropins help regulate function of gonads

Lymphatic System/Immunity
- Developing embryo/fetus escapes immune surveillance (not rejected)
- Lymphatic vessels drain leaked tissue fluids; transport sex hormones; immune cells protect reproductive organs from disease; IgA is present in breast milk

Digestive System
- Digestive organs crowded by developing fetus; heartburn, constipation common during pregnancy
- Digestive system provides nutrients needed for health

Urinary System
- Hypertrophy of the prostate inhibits urination; compression of bladder during pregnancy leads to urinary frequency and urgency
- Kidneys dispose of nitrogenous wastes and maintain acid-base balance of blood of mother and fetus; semen exits the body through the urethra of the male

Muscular System
- Androgens promote increased muscle mass
- Abdominal muscles active during childbirth; muscles of the pelvic floor support reproductive organs and aid erection of penis/clitoris

Nervous System
- Sex hormones masculinize or feminize the brain and influence sex drive
- Hypothalamus regulates timing of puberty; neural reflexes regulate sexual response

Respiratory System
- Pregnancy impairs descent of the diaphragm, causing difficult breathing
- Respiratory system provides oxygen; disposes of carbon dioxide; vital capacity and respiratory rate increase during pregnancy

Cardiovascular System
- Estrogens lower blood cholesterol levels and promote cardiovascular health in premenopausal women; pregnancy increases workload of the cardiovascular system
- Cardiovascular system transports needed substances to organs of reproductive system; local vasodilation involved in erection; blood transports sex hormones

Reproductive System

Integumentary System
- Male sex hormones (androgens) activate oil glands, which lubricate skin and hair; gonadal hormones stimulate characteristic fat distribution and appearance of pubic and axillary hair; estrogen increases skin hydration; enhances facial skin pigmentation during pregnancy
- Skin protects all body organs by enclosing them externally; mammary gland secretions (milk) nourish the infant

Skeletal System
- Androgens masculinize the skeleton and increase bone density; estrogen feminizes skeleton and maintains bone mass in women
- The bony pelvis encloses some reproductive organs; if narrow, the bony pelvis may hinder vaginal delivery of an infant

consequences of estrogen deficit include irritability and other mood changes (depression in some); intense vasodilation of the skin's blood vessels, which causes uncomfortable sweat-drenching "hot flashes"; gradual thinning of the skin and loss of bone mass; and slowly rising blood cholesterol levels, which place postmenopausal women at risk for cardiovascular disorders. At one time, physicians prescribed low-dose estrogen-progesterone preparations to help women through this often difficult period and to prevent the skeletal and cardiovascular complications. These seemed like great bonuses, and until July 2002, some 14 million American women were taking some form of estrogen-containing hormone replacement therapy (HRT). Then, on July 9, the Women's Health Initiative (WHI) abruptly ended a clinical trial of 16,000 postmenopausal women, reporting that in those taking a popular progesterone-estrogen hormone combination there was an increase of 51 percent in heart disease, 24 percent in invasive breast cancer, 31 percent in stroke, and a doubling of the risk of dementia compared to those taking placebos. The backlash of this finding is still spreading through physicians' offices and research labs, and it has dampened enthusiasm for HRT in both the medical community and postmenopausal women. A new and encouraging study in 2006 reported a significant drop in breast cancers, with the drop due nearly entirely to fewer women doing HRT.

There is no equivalent of menopause in males. Although aging men exhibit a steady decline in testosterone secretion, their reproductive capability seems unending. Healthy men well into their eighties and beyond are able to father offspring.

▶ *DID YOU GET IT?*

25. Which sex chromosome combination yields a boy—XX or XY? What hormone must be produced by an XY fetus during pregnancy to stimulate its formation of the male duct system?

26. What is cryptorchidism, and what results if it is not rectified?

27. What are the major health threats to the adult woman's reproductive system?

For answers, see Appendix D.

SUMMARY

Media study tools that provide additional review of key topics of Chapter 16 are referenced below.

IP = *InterActive Physiology*
WEB = The A&P Place

Anatomy of the Male Reproductive System (pp. 546–549)

1. The paired testes, the male gonads, reside in the scrotum outside the abdominopelvic cavity. Testes have both an exocrine (sperm-producing) and an endocrine (testosterone-producing) function.

2. The male duct system includes the epididymis, ductus deferens, and urethra. Sperm maturation occurs in the epididymis. When ejaculation occurs, sperm are propelled through duct passageways to the body exterior.

3. Male accessory glands include the seminal vesicles, prostate, and bulbourethral glands. Collectively, these glands produce a fluid that activates and nourishes sperm.

4. External genitalia:
   a. Scrotum—a skin sac that hangs outside the abdominopelvic cavity and provides the proper temperature for producing viable sperm.
   b. Penis—consists of three columns of erectile tissue surrounding the urethra. Erectile tissue provides a way for the penis to become rigid so it may better serve as a penetrating device during sexual intercourse.

   WEB Exercise: Chapter 16, Male Reproductive Anatomy: Sagittal View.

Male Reproductive Functions (pp. 550–552)

1. Spermatogenesis (sperm production) begins at puberty in seminiferous tubules in response to FSH. Spermatogenesis involves meiosis, a special nuclear division that halves the chromosomal number in resulting spermatids. An additional process that strips excess cytoplasm from the spermatid, called spermiogenesis, is necessary for production of functional, motile sperm.

2. Testosterone production begins in puberty in response to LH. Testosterone is produced by interstitial cells of the testes. Testosterone causes the appearance of male secondary sex characteristics and is necessary for sperm maturation.

Anatomy of the Female Reproductive System (pp. 552–557)

1. The ovaries, the female gonads, are located against the lateral walls of the pelvis. They produce female sex cells (exocrine function) and hormones (endocrine function).

2. The duct system:
   a. Uterine (fallopian) tubes extend from the vicinity of an ovary to the uterus. Ends are fringed and "wave" to direct ovulated oocytes into uterine tubes, which conduct the oocyte (embryo) to the uterus by peristalsis and ciliary action.
   b. The uterus is a pear-shaped muscular organ in which the embryo implants and develops. Its mucosa (endometrium) sloughs off each month in menses unless an embryo has become embedded in it. The myometrium contracts rhythmically during the birth of a baby.
   c. The vagina is a passageway between the uterus and the body exterior that allows a baby or the menstrual flow to leave the body. It also receives the penis and semen during sexual intercourse.

3. Female external genitalia include labia majora and minora (skin folds), clitoris, and urethral and vaginal openings.

Female Reproductive Functions and Cycles (pp. 557–561)

1. Oogenesis (production of female sex cells) occurs in ovarian follicles, which are activated at puberty by FSH and LH to mature and eject oocytes (ovulation) on a cyclic basis. The egg (ovum) is formed only if sperm penetrates the secondary oocyte. In females, meiosis produces only one functional ovum (plus three nonfunctional polar bodies), as opposed to the four functional sperm per meiosis produced by males.

2. Hormone production: Estrogens are produced by ovarian follicles in response to FSH. Progesterone, produced in response to LH, is the main hormonal product of the corpus luteum. Estrogens stimulate development of female secondary sex characteristics.

3. The menstrual cycle concerns changes in the endometrium in response to fluctuating blood levels of ovarian hormones. There are three phases:
   a. Menstrual phase. Endometrium sloughs off and bleeding occurs. Ovarian hormones are at their lowest levels.
   b. Proliferative phase. Endometrium is repaired, thickens, and becomes well vascularized in response to increasing levels of estrogens.
   c. Secretory phase. Endometrial glands begin to secrete nutrients, and lining becomes more vascular in response to increasing levels of progesterone.

4. If fertilization does not occur, the phases are repeated about every 28 days.

   WEB Exercise: Chapter 16, The Female Menstrual Cycle.

Mammary Glands (pp. 561–563)

1. Mammary glands are milk-producing glands found in the breasts. After the birth of a baby, they produce milk in response to hormonal stimulation.

Survey of Pregnancy and Embryonic Development (pp. 563–571)

1. An oocyte is fertilizable for up to 24 hours after release; sperm are viable within the female reproductive tract for up to 48 hours. Hundreds of sperm must release their acrosomal enzymes to break down the egg's plasma membrane.

2. Following sperm penetration, the secondary oocyte completes meiosis II. Then ovum and sperm nuclei fuse (fertilization), forming a zygote.

3. If fertilization occurs, embryonic development begins immediately. Cleavage, a rapid series of mitotic divisions without intervening growth, begins with the zygote and ends with a blastocyst.

4. By day 14 after ovulation, the young embryo (blastocyst) has implanted in the endometrium, and the placenta is being formed. Human chorionic gonadotropin (hCG) released by the blastocyst maintains hormone production of the corpus luteum, preventing menses, until the placenta assumes its endocrine role.

5. The placenta serves respiratory, nutritive, and excretory needs of the embryo and produces hormones of pregnancy.

6. All major organ systems have been laid down by eight weeks, and at nine weeks the embryo is called a fetus. Growth and tissue/organ specialization are the major events of the fetal period.

7. A pregnant woman has increased respiratory, circulatory, and urinary demands placed on her system by the developing fetus. Good nutrition is necessary to produce a healthy baby.

8. Childbirth (parturition) includes a series of events called labor. It is initiated by several factors but most importantly by rising levels of oxytocin and prostaglandins, which promote vigorous uterine contractions. The three stages of labor are dilation, expulsion, placental.

Developmental Aspects of the Reproductive System (pp. 571–578)

1. Reproductive system structures of males and females are identical during early development. Gonads begin to develop in the eighth week. The presence or absence of testosterone determines whether male or female accessory reproductive organs are formed.

2. Important congenital defects result from abnormal separation of sex chromosomes during sex cell formation.

3. The reproductive system is inactive during childhood. Reproductive organs mature and become functional for childbearing at puberty.

4. Common reproductive problems during young adulthood are infections of the reproductive tract. Neoplasms of breast and cervix are major threats to women. Prostate cancer is the most common reproductive system cancer seen in men.

   WEB Exercise: Chapter 16, Reproductive Case Study.

5. During menopause, female reproductive capabilities end, and reproductive organs begin to atrophy. Hot flashes and mood changes may occur. Reproductive capacity does not appear to decline significantly in aging men.

REVIEW QUESTIONS

Multiple Choice

More than one choice may apply.

1. Which of the following are accessory sex structures in the male?
   - a. Gonads
   - b. Gametes
   - c. Broad shoulders
   - d. Seminal vesicles

2. Which of these is mismatched?
   - a. Vagina—penis
   - b. Testis—ovary
   - c. Labia majora—scrotum
   - d. Oviduct—ductus deferens

3. The myometrium is the muscular layer of the uterus, and the endometrium is the _____ layer.
   - a. serosa
   - b. adventitia
   - c. submucosa
   - d. mucosa

4. All of the following are true of the gonadotropins except that they are
   - a. secreted by the pituitary gland.
   - b. LH and FSH.
   - c. hormones with important functions in both males and females.
   - d. the sex hormones secreted by the gonads.

5. The approximate area between the anus and clitoris in the female is the
   - a. peritoneum.
   - b. perineum.
   - c. vulva.
   - d. labia.

6. Which of the following attach to the ovary?
   - a. Fimbriae
   - b. Ovarian ligament
   - c. Suspensory ligaments
   - d. Broad ligament

7. Human ova and sperm are similar in that
   - a. about the same number of each is produced per month.
   - b. they have the same degree of motility.
   - c. they are about the same size.
   - d. they have the same number of chromosomes.

8. Select the false statement about the cervix of the uterus.
   - a. It is the superiormost part of the uterus.
   - b. It projects into the vagina.
   - c. Its cervical glands secrete mucus.
   - d. It contains the cervical canal.

9. Each month, typically only one
   - a. primary follicle is stimulated.
   - b. follicle secretes estrogen.
   - c. vesicular follicle undergoes ovulation.
   - d. ovary is stimulated.

10. After ovulation, the ruptured follicle
    - a. degenerates.
    - b. becomes a corpus luteum.
    - c. sloughs off as waste material.
    - d. mends and produces another oocyte.

11. The outer layer of the blastocyst, which attaches to the uterine wall, is the
    a. yolk sac.   c. amnion.
    b. inner cell mass.   d. trophoblast.

12. The usual and most desirable presentation for birth is
    a. vertex.   c. nonvertex.
    b. breech.   d. head first.

13. During human embryonic development, organogenesis occurs
    a. during the first trimester.
    b. during the second trimester.
    c. during the third trimester.
    d. during blastula formation.

Short Answer Essay

14. What are the primary sex organs, or gonads, of males? What are their two major functions?

15. What is the function of seminal fluid? Name the three types of glands that help produce it.

16. The penis contains erectile tissue that becomes engorged with blood during sexual excitement. What term is used to describe this event?

17. Define *ejaculation*.

18. Why are the male gonads not found in the abdominal cavity? Where are they found?

19. How does enlargement of the prostate interfere with a man's reproductive function?

20. When does spermatogenesis begin? What causes it to begin?

21. Testosterone causes the male secondary sex characteristics to appear at puberty. Name three examples of male secondary sex characteristics.

22. Explain why a man's sexual responsiveness and secondary sex characteristics generally remain unchanged after a vasectomy.

23. Name the female gonad, and describe its two major functions.

24. Why is the term *urogenital system* more applicable to males than females?

25. Name the structures of the female duct system, and describe the important functions of each.

26. Given that the uterine tubes are not continuous with the ovaries, how can you explain the fact that all ovulated "eggs" do not end up in the female's peritoneal cavity?

27. What is a follicle? What is ovulation?

28. The female cell that is ovulated is not a mature sex cell (ovum). When or under what conditions does it become mature?

29. What ovarian structures produce estrogens? Name the second hormone produced by the same structures.

30. List and describe the events of the menstrual cycle. Why is the menstrual cycle so important?

31. Define *menopause*. What does this mean to a woman?

32. Define *fertilization*. Where does fertilization usually occur? Describe the process of implantation.

33. How is body functioning of a pregnant woman altered by her pregnancy?

34. What events trigger labor?

35. Delivery of the infant occurs during which stage of labor?

36. What is the *indifferent stage* of embryonic development?

37. What are the major events of puberty?

38. Compare the effects of aging on the male and female reproductive systems.

CRITICAL THINKING AND CLINICAL APPLICATION QUESTIONS

39. A pregnant woman in substantial pain called her doctor and explained (between sobs) that she was about to have her baby "right away." The doctor calmed her and asked how she had come to that conclusion. She said that her water had broken and that her husband could see the baby's head. **(a)** Was she right to believe that birth was imminent? If so, what stage of labor was she in? **(b)** Do you think she had time to make it to the hospital 60 miles away? Why or why not?

40. Lucy had both her left ovary and her right uterine tube removed surgically at age 17 because of a cyst and a tumor in these organs. Now, at age 32, she remains healthy and is expecting her second child. How could Lucy conceive a child with just one ovary and one uterine tube, widely separated on opposite sides of the pelvis like this?

41. Some anatomy students were saying that the bulbourethral glands of men act like city workers who come around and clear parked cars from the street before a parade. What did they mean by this analogy?

42. A young woman visited her doctor for a premarital gynecological examination and requested information on contraception. She plans to have a large family but "not just yet." She reveals that her faith prevents her from using any drugs or mechanical means of birth control. What are the only options for this young woman?

43. Mrs. Montez is experiencing Braxton Hicks contractions in the sixth month of her pregnancy. Why did her doctor prescribe ibuprofen (with what mechanism does this drug interfere)?

44. In medieval times, young boys with beautiful soprano voices were sometimes castrated (had their testes removed) so that their singing voices would not change. Explain the cause and effect here.

45. Assume a sperm has penetrated a polar body and their nuclei fuse. Why is it unlikely that the resulting cell will form a healthy embryo?

Appendix A

WORD ROOTS, PREFIXES, AND SUFFIXES

Word element	Meaning
WORD ROOTS	
Circulatory system	
cardio	heart
angio, vaso	vessel
hem, hema, hemato	blood
vena, phlebo	vein
arteria	artery
lympho	lymph
thrombo	clot (of blood)
embolus	moving clot
Digestive system	
bucca	cheek
os, stomato	mouth
gingiva	gum
glossa	tongue
pharyngo	pharynx
esophago	esophagus
gastro	stomach
hepato	liver
cholecyst	gallbladder
pancreas	pancreas
entero	intestines
duodeno	duodenum
jejuno	jejunum
ileo	ileum
appendeco	appendix
colo	colon
recto	rectum
ano, procto	anus
Skeletal system	
skeleto	skeleton

Word element	Meaning
Respiratory system	
naso, rhino	nose
tonsillo	tonsil
laryngo	larynx
tracheo	trachea
bronchus, broncho	bronchus (pl. bronchi)
pulmo, pneuma, pneum	lung (sac with air)
Nervous system	
neuro	nerve
cerebro	brain; cerebrum
oculo, ophthalmo	eye
oto	ear
psych, psycho	mind
Urinary system	
urethro	urethra
cysto	bladder
uretero	ureter
reni, reno, nephro	kidney
pyelo	pelvis of kidney
uro	urine
Female reproductive system	
vulvo	vulva
perineo	perineum
labio	labium (pl. labia)
vagino, colpo	vagina
cervico	cervix
utero	womb; uterus
tubo, salpingo	fallopian tube
ovario, oophoro	ovary

Word element	Meaning
Male reproductive system	
orchido	testes
Regions of the body	
crani, cephalo	head
cervico, tracheo	neck
thoraco	chest
abdomino	abdomen
dorsum	back
Tissues	
cutis, dermato	skin
lipo	fat
musculo, myo	muscle
osteo	bone
myelo	marrow
chondro	cartilage
Miscellaneous	
cyto	cell
gene	formation, origin
gram	tracing or mark
graph	writing, description
kinesis	motion
lapar	through the abdominal wall
meter	measure
oligo	small, few
phobia	fear
photo	light
pyo	pus
roentgen	X ray
scope	instrument for visual examination

continued

WORD ROOTS, PREFIXES, AND SUFFIXES (CONTINUED)

Word element	Meaning	Word element	Meaning	Word element	Meaning
PREFIXES					
a, an, ar	without or not	extra	outside of, in addition to	ob	against, in front of
ab	away from			oculo	eye
acro	extremities	ferro	iron	odonto	tooth
ad	toward, to	fibro	fiber	ophthalmo	eye
adeno	glandular	fore	before, in front of	ortho	straight, normal
aero	air				
ambi	around, on both sides	gastro	stomach	os	mouth, bone
		glosso	tongue	osteo	bone
amyl	starch	glyco	sugar	oto	ear
ante	before, forward	hemi	half	pan	all
		hemo	blood	para	beside, accessory to
anti	against, counteracting	hepa, hepato	liver		
		histo	tissue	path	disease
bi	double	homo	same	ped	child, foot
bili	bile	hydro	water	per	by, through
bio	life	hygro	moisture	peri	around
bis	two	hyper	too much, high	pharyngo	pharynx
brachio	arm	hypo	under, decreased	phlebo	vein
brady	slow	hyster	uterus	photo	light
broncho	bronchus (pl. bronchi)	ileo	ileum	phren	diaphragm, mind
		in	in, within, into		
cardio	heart	inter	between		
cervico	neck	intra	within	pneumo	air, lungs
chole	gall or bile	intro	in, within, into	pod	foot
cholecysto	gallbladder	juxta	near, close to	poly	many, much
circum	around	lapar	abdomen	post	after
co	together	laryngo	larynx	pre	before
contra	against, opposite	latero	side	proct	rectum
		leuk	white	pseudo	false
costo	ribs	macro	large, big	psych	mind
cysto	bladder	mal	bad, poor	pyel	pelvis of the kidney
cyto	cell	mast	breast		
demi	half	medio	middle	pyo	pus
derma	skin	mega, megalo	large, great	pyro	fever, heat
dis	from	meno	menses	quadri	four
dorso	back	mono	single	radio	radiation
dys	abnormal, difficult	multi	many	re	back, again
		myelo	bone marrow, spinal cord	reno	kidney
electro	electric			retro	backward
en	into, in, within	myo	muscle	rhin	nose
encephal	brain	neo	new	sacro	sacrum
entero	intestine	nephro	kidney	salpingo	fallopian tube
equi	equal	neuro	nerve	sarco	fresh
eryth	red	nitro	nitrogen	sclero	hard, hardening
ex	out, out of, away from	noct	night	semi	half
		non	not		

WORD ROOTS, PREFIXES, AND SUFFIXES *(CONTINUED)*

Word element	Meaning	Word element	Meaning	Word element	Meaning
PREFIXES					
sex	six	syn	together	un	not, back reversal
skeleto	skeleton	tachy	fast	uni	one
steno	narrowing, constriction	thyro	thyroid, gland	uretero	ureter
		trache	trachea	urethro	urethra
sub	under	trans	across, over	uro	urine, urinary organs
super	above, excess	tri	three		
supra	above	ultra	beyond	vaso	vessel
SUFFIXES					
able	able to	graph	writing	otomy	to incise
algia	pain	ism	condition	pexy	fixation
cele	tumor, swelling	itis	inflammation	phage	ingesting
centesis	surgical puncture to remove fluid	ize	to treat	phobia	fear
		lith	stone, calculus	plasty	plastic surgery
		lithiasis	presence of stones	plegia	paralysis
cide	killing, destructive			rhage	to burst forth
		lysis	disintegration	rhea	excessive discharge
cule	little	megaly	enlargement		
cyte	cell	meter	instrument that measures	rhexis	rupture
ectasia	dilating, stretching	oid	likeness, resemblance	scope	lighted instrument for visual examination
ectomy	excision, surgical removal of	oma	tumor		
		opathy	disease of	scopy	to examine visually
emia	blood	orrhaphy	surgical repair		
esis	action	osis	disease, condition of	stomy	to form an opening
form	shaped like				
genesis, genetic	formation, origin	ostomy	to form an opening or outlet	tomy	incision into
				uria	urine
gram	tracing, mark			zyme	ferment

Sources: Courtesy of Margaret Ling, Director of Vocational Nursing, Santa Rosa Junior College, Santa Rosa, Calif.; Kozier, B., G. Erb, A. J. Berman, and K. Burke: *Fundamentals of Nursing: Concepts and Procedures,* sixth ed., Prentice Hall, 2000. Used by permission.

Appendix B

PERIODIC TABLE OF THE ELEMENTS

Representative (main group) elements

Representative (main group) elements

Periodic Table of the Elements

Transition metals

IA																	VIIIA
1 **H** 1.0079	IIA											IIIA	IVA	VA	VIA	VIIA	2 **He** 4.003
3 **Li** 6.941	4 **Be** 9.012											5 **B** 10.811	6 **C** 12.011	7 **N** 14.007	8 **O** 15.999	9 **F** 18.998	10 **Ne** 20.180
11 **Na** 22.990	12 **Mg** 24.305	IIIB	IVB	VB	VIB	VIIB	VIIIB		IB	IIB		13 **Al** 26.982	14 **Si** 28.086	15 **P** 30.974	16 **S** 32.066	17 **Cl** 35.453	18 **Ar** 39.948
19 **K** 39.098	20 **Ca** 40.078	21 **Sc** 44.956	22 **Ti** 47.88	23 **V** 50.942	24 **Cr** 51.996	25 **Mn** 54.938	26 **Fe** 55.845	27 **Co** 58.933	28 **Ni** 58.69	29 **Cu** 63.546	30 **Zn** 65.39	31 **Ga** 69.723	32 **Ge** 72.61	33 **As** 74.922	34 **Se** 78.96	35 **Br** 79.904	36 **Kr** 83.8
37 **Rb** 85.468	38 **Sr** 87.62	39 **Y** 88.906	40 **Zr** 91.224	41 **Nb** 92.906	42 **Mo** 95.94	43 **Tc** 98	44 **Ru** 101.07	45 **Rh** 102.906	46 **Pd** 106.42	47 **Ag** 107.868	48 **Cd** 112.411	49 **In** 114.82	50 **Sn** 118.71	51 **Sb** 121.76	52 **Te** 127.60	53 **I** 126.905	54 **Xe** 131.29
55 **Cs** 132.905	56 **Ba** 137.327	57 **La** 138.906	72 **Hf** 178.49	73 **Ta** 180.948	74 **W** 183.84	75 **Re** 186.207	76 **Os** 190.23	77 **Ir** 192.22	78 **Pt** 195.08	79 **Au** 196.967	80 **Hg** 200.59	81 **Tl** 204.383	82 **Pb** 207.2	83 **Bi** 208.980	84 **Po** 209	85 **At** 210	86 **Rn** 222
87 **Fr** 223	88 **Ra** 226.025	89 **Ac** 227.028	104 **Rf** 261	105 **Db** 262	106 **Sg** 263	107 **Bh** 264	108 **Hs** 265	109 **Mt** 266	110 **Uun** 269	111 **Uuu** 272	112 **Uub** 277			114		116	118

Rare earth elements

	58 **Ce** 140.115	59 **Pr** 140.908	60 **Nd** 144.24	61 **Pm** 145	62 **Sm** 150.36	63 **Eu** 151.964	64 **Gd** 157.25	65 **Tb** 158.925	66 **Dy** 162.5	67 **Ho** 164.93	68 **Er** 167.26	69 **Tm** 168.934	70 **Yb** 173.04	71 **Lu** 174.967
Lanthanides														
Actinides	90 **Th** 232.038	91 **Pa** 231.036	92 **U** 238.029	93 **Np** 237.048	94 **Pu** 244	95 **Am** 243	96 **Cm** 247	97 **Bk** 247	98 **Cf** 251	99 **Es** 252	100 **Fm** 257	101 **Md** 258	102 **No** 259	103 **Lr** 262

The periodic table arranges elements according to atomic number and atomic weight into horizontal rows called *periods* and 18 vertical columns called *groups* or *families*. The elements in the groups are classified as being in either A or B classes.

Elements of each group of the A series have similar chemical and physical properties. This reflects the fact that members of a particular group have the same number of valence shell electrons, which is indicated by the number of the group. For example, group IA elements have one valence shell electron, group IIA elements have two, and group VA elements have five. In contrast, as you progress across a period from left to right, the properties of the elements change in discrete steps, varying gradually from the very metallic properties of groups IA and IIA elements to the nonmetallic properties seen in group VIIA (chlorine and others), and finally to the inert elements (noble gases)

in group VIIIA. This change reflects the continual increase in the number of valence shell electrons seen in elements (from left to right) within a period.

Class B elements are referred to as *transition elements*. All transition elements are metals, and in most cases they have one or two valence shell electrons. (In these elements, some electrons occupy more distant electron shells before the deeper shells are filled.)

In this periodic table, the colors are used to convey information about the phase (solid, liquid, or gas) in which a pure element exists under standard conditions (25 degrees centigrade and 1 atmosphere of pressure). If the element's symbol is solid black, then the element exists as a solid. If its symbol is red, then it exists as a gas. If its symbol is dark blue, then it is a liquid. If the element's symbol is green, the element does not exist in nature and must be created by some type of nuclear reaction.

Appendix C

KEY INFORMATION ABOUT VITAMINS AND MANY ESSENTIAL MINERALS

Vitamin/ Mineral	Major dietary sources	Major functions	Signs of severe, prolonged deficiency	Signs of extreme excess
FAT-SOLUBLE				
A	Fortified milk, cheese, butter, eggs, liver, deep orange fruits and vegetables, dark green leafy vegetables.	Promotes healthy eyes, skin, and bones; hormone synthesis.	Night blindness; keratinization of epithelial tissues including the cornea of the eye (xerophthalmia) causing permanent blindness; dry, scaling skin; increased susceptibility to infection.	Joint pain, dry and itchy skin, cracked lips, nausea and vomiting, weight loss.
D	Fortified milk, eggs, liver (diet often not as important as sunlight exposure).	Promotes absorption and use of calcium and phosphorus (strong bones and teeth).	Rickets (bone deformities) in children; osteomalacia (bone softening) in adults.	Calcification of soft tissues, kidney stones, fatigue.
E	Vegetable oils, egg yolk, whole grain products, green leafy vegetables.	Antioxidant to prevent cell membrane damage.	Possible anemia and neurological effects.	Generally nontoxic; dizziness, weakness, may worsen clotting defect in vitamin K deficiency.
K	Green leafy vegetables, cabbage, cauliflower, liver.	Aids in formation of certain proteins, especially those for blood clotting.	Defective blood coagulation causing severe bleeding on injury.	Liver damage and anemia, interference with anticlotting medications.
WATER-SOLUBLE				
Thiamin (B_1)	Pork, organ meats, legumes, peanuts, enriched or whole-grain products.	Coenzyme used in energy metabolism.	Nerve changes, sometimes edema, heart damage; beriberi.	Rapid pulse, weakness, headache, insomnia.
Riboflavin (B_2)	Dairy products, whole and enriched grain products, green leafy vegetables.	Coenzyme used in energy metabolism.	Skin rash, eye sensitivity to the sun.	Generally nontoxic.
Niacin	Nuts, legumes, enriched and whole-grain products, meats, fish, all protein foods.	Coenzyme used in energy metabolism.	Weakness, dizziness, loss of appetite, confusion, diarrhea, rash.	Flushing of face, neck, hands; potential liver damage, swollen tongue, low blood pressure.
B_6	High-protein foods in general.	Coenzyme used in amino-acid metabolism.	Nervous, skin, and muscular disorders; anemia.	Damaged nerves, weakness, bloating.
Folate	Green leafy vegetables, orange juice, nuts, legumes, grain products.	Coenzyme used in DNA and RNA metabolism.	Megaloblastic anemia (large, immature red blood cells); digestive disturbances.	Masks vitamin B_{12} deficiency; interferes with drugs used to control epilepsy, diarrhea, insomnia.
B_{12}	Meat, fish, poultry, milk, cheese, eggs.	Coenzyme used in DNA and RNA metabolism; helps maintain nerve cells.	Megaloblastic anemia, fatigue.	Thought to be nontoxic.
Pantothenic acid	Meat, eggs; widely distributed in many foods.	Coenzyme used in energy metabolism.	Fatigue, vomiting.	Generally nontoxic; occasionally causes diarrhea.
Biotin	Liver, egg yolk, green vegetables, widely distributed in foods.	Coenzyme used in energy metabolism; fat synthesis.	Scaly dermatitis, loss of appetite, nausea.	Thought to be nontoxic.
C (ascorbic acid)	Citrus fruits and dark green leafy vegetables, broccoli, cabbage, cauliflower, strawberries, melons, tomatoes, potatoes.	Functions in synthesis of collagen; is an antioxidant; aids in detoxification; improves iron absorption.	Scurvy; petechiae (minute hemorrhages); weakness, delayed wound healing; impaired immune response.	GI upsets, fatigue; confounds certain lab tests.

KEY INFORMATION ABOUT VITAMINS AND MANY ESSENTIAL MINERALS *(CONTINUED)*

Vitamin/ Mineral	Major dietary sources	Major functions	Signs of severe, prolonged deficiency	Signs of extreme excess
Calcium	Milk products, dark green leafy vegetables, broccoli, shrimp, salmon, clams, fortified orange juice, legumes, tofu.	Bone and tooth formation; blood clotting; muscle function; nerve transmission; blood pressure.	Stunted growth in children; bone loss (osteoporosis) in adults.	Extra calcium usually excreted; possible depressed absorption of some other minerals and kidney damage.
Phosphorus	Milk products, meat, poultry, eggs, legumes, nuts.	Bone and tooth formation; acid-base balance; component of coenzymes.	Weakness; demineralization of bone.	Depressed absorption of some minerals. such as calcium.
Magnesium	Whole grains, nuts, legumes, dark green leafy vegetables.	Component of enzymes; bone and tooth formation.	Weakness, growth failure in children, confusion.	Unknown toxicity, but extreme amount can cause diarrhea.
Sulfur	Sulfur-containing amino acids in dietary proteins.	Component of cartilage, tendons, and proteins.	(Related to protein deficiency.)	Excess sulfur-containing amino acid intake leads to poor growth; liver damage.
Sodium	Salt in most foods: soy sauce, cured meats, pickles, canned soups, processed cheese.	Fluid balance, nerve impulse transmission.	Muscle cramps; reduced appetite, weakness.	High blood pressure in some people.
Potassium	Meat, milk, many fruits and vegetables, legumes, bananas.	Fluid balance; nerve and muscle function.	Muscular weakness; fatigue, confusion.	Muscular weakness; cardiac arrest.
Chloride	(Same as sodium)	Plays a role in acid-base balance; formation of gastric juice.	Muscle cramps; reduced appetite; poor growth in children.	Vomiting.
Iron	Red meat, organ meat, egg yolk, legumes, enriched cereals and breads, green leafy vegetables, dried fruits.	Components of hemoglobin and enzymes.	Anemia, weakness, infections, fatigue, pale eye membranes.	Acute: shock, death. Chronic: liver damage, cardiac failure.
Iodine	Seafood, iodized salt.	Component of thyroid hormones.	Enlarged thyroid, weight gain; retardation of infant both mentally and physically.	Iodide goiter.
Fluoride	Flouridated water and toothpastes; seafood.	Formation of bones and teeth.	Higher frequency of tooth decay.	Acute: Digestive distress. Chronic: mottling of teeth; skeletal deformation.
Zinc	Meat, fish, poultry, whole grain cereals and breads, legumes, nuts.	Component of enzymes; growth factor, production of insulin; making of sperm.	Growth failure; scaly dermatitis; reproductive failure; impaired immune function; taste and smell deficits.	Acute: nausea; vomiting; diarrhea. Chronic: Adversely affects copper metabolism, anemia, and immune function.
Selenium	Seafood, meat, whole grains.	Antioxidant properties; functions in close association with vitamin E.	Heart disease.	Nervous and digestive system disorders; hair loss.
Copper	Shellfish, nuts, legumes, organ meats.	Component of enzymes, production of hemoglobin.	Anemia; bone and cardiovascular changes.	Vomiting, diarrhea.
Chromium	Meat, vegetable oil, whole grain cereal.	Involved in glucose and energy metabolism; associated with hormone insulin.	Impaired glucose metabolism.	Lung and kidney damage (occupational exposures only).
Manganese	Nuts, whole grains, vegetables, and fruits.	Component of enzymes.		Central nervous system damage (occupational exposures).
Molybdenum	Organ meat, legumes, cereals.	Component of enzymes.	Disorder in nitrogen excretion.	Inhibition of enzymes; adversely affects copper metabolism.

Appendix D

ANSWERS TO DID YOU GET IT? QUESTIONS AND MULTIPLE CHOICE REVIEW QUESTIONS

CHAPTER 1

Did You Get It?

1. Anatomy and physiology are related. A given function can occur only if the corresponding structure allows it. **2.** The stomach exhibits the organ level of structural organization. Glucose is at the chemical level. **3.** These organs are part of the respiratory system. **4.** Survival also depends on the ability to maintain one's boundaries, to move, to respond to stimuli, and to reproduce. **5.** All the chemical reactions that occur in the body and release food energy require oxygen. **6.** No. We mean that they vary within a narrow and regulated range. **7.** Thirst is part of a negative feedback system. Thirst prods us to drink fluids (the response), which in turn causes the thirst sensation to decrease and end. Were it a positive feedback mechanism, we would become even more thirsty (the stimulus for drinking would increase). **8.** Most descriptions of the body using anatomical terminology refer to body regions as if the body is in the anatomical position regardless of its actual position. **9.** The axillary region is the armpit. The acromial region is the point of the shoulder. **10.** A coronal or frontal section would cut the brain into anterior and posterior parts. **11.** To separate the thoracic and abdominal cavities, you would make a transverse section (XS). **12.** Of these organs, only the spinal cord is in the dorsal body cavity.

Review Questions

1. d; **2.** a, b, c, d; **3.** c; **4.** superior, deep, proximal or lateral, proximal, medial, posterior; **5.** e, c, i, f, h, a, b, d, g; **6.** c; **7.** c; **8.** c

CHAPTER 2

Did You Get It?

1. Chemical changes involve bond formation or breakage. The result is a different substance. For example, when oxygen combines with iron, iron oxide (rust) is formed. A physical change does not produce a new substance; it just changes its physical properties (temperature, state, color, etc.). For example, cutting an iron bar into smaller pieces.

2. Matter is the substance of living and nonliving objects. Energy is the ability to do work or put matter into motion. **3.** Every time energy changes from one form to another, some heat is given off to the environment (is lost) and is unusable. **4.** Carbon, oxygen, hydrogen, and nitrogen. **5.** An atom is the smallest particle of an element that still retains the element's properties. **6.** The atom's atomic number (#p) is 4; its atomic mass number (#n + p) is 9. **7.** Radioisotope. **8.** A molecule is two or more atoms chemically bound together. **9.** A molecule of an element is a chemical combination of two or more atoms of the same kind. In a molecule of a compound, the atoms differ. **10.** In ionic bonds, electrons are completely transferred from one atom to another. In covalent bonds, the interacting atoms share one or more electron pairs. **11.** Hydrogen bonds. **12.** It is a decomposition reaction. **13.** A reversible reaction is shown by double reaction arrows. **14.** The high heat capacity of water prevents rapid changes in body temperature. **15.** Acids are proton donors. **16.** A pH of 11 is basic. **17.** All chemical reactions in the body take place in a watery environment. **18.** The structural units of carbohydrates are monosaccharides. Those of proteins are amino acids. **19.** Triglycerides are abundant in subcutaneous fat tissue. Phospholipids are most abundant in cellular membranes. **20.** DNA contains the bases A, T, G, and C, and the sugar deoxyribose. **21.** ATP is the immediately useful form of energy for all body cells.

Review Questions

1. a, c, d; **2.** a, c, e; **3.** a, b, c, d, e; **4.** c, e; **5.** b, c; **6.** d; **7.** a, b, c, d, e; **8.** c; **9.** a

CHAPTER 3

Did You Get It?

1. Oxygen and carbon. **2.** They are able to carry an electrical current and are essential to nervous system function and muscle activation. **3.** The generalized cell is a concept that describes organelles and functions common to all cells. **4.** It is the control center of the cell and is

continued

ANSWERS TO DID YOU GET IT? AND MULTIPLE CHOICE QUESTIONS *(CONTINUED)*

needed for cell division. **5.** The nuclear envelope is the double membrane barrier surrounding the nucleus. **6.** The phospholipids have both polar (heads) and nonpolar (tails) regions. Polar aligns with polar (water and other polar molecules inside and outside the cell). Nonpolar aligns with nonpolar in the membrane interior. **7.** They act as receptors, determine blood type, and play a role in cell-to-cell interactions. **8.** Communication and binding together, respectively. **9.** The cytosol is the liquid portion of the cytoplasm. Cytoplasm includes cytosol, organelles, and inclusions. **10.** Lysosomes break down ingested bacteria, worn-out organelles, and dead cells. Peroxisomes detoxify a number of harmful toxic substances and disarm free radicals. **11.** Mitochondria are the major site of ATP synthesis. **12.** Microtubules, intermediate filaments (help form desmosomes), and microfilaments (involved in cell motility). **13.** Fibroblasts and erythrocytes. **14.** Neurons gather information and control body functions. **15.** The transport process is active if cellular energy (ATP) is used to drive it. If kinetic energy is the energy source, the transport process is passive. **16.** The concentration gradient determines the direction that water and solutes move by diffusion. Movement is from high to low concentration of a given substance. **17.** Receptor mediated endocytosis. **18.** DNA is double stranded. When it is replicated, each strand serves as a template to build a complementary strand. Thus, if the template strand is ACT, the complementary strand formed at that site is TCA. **19.** If cytokinesis does not occur, the result is a binucleate cell. **20.** mRNA carries the coded information for building proteins from the DNA gene to the ribosome where protein synthesis occurs. **21.** Transcription and translation. Proteins are synthesized during translation. **22.** Cell shape and cell arrangement (layers) are the two criteria used to classify epithelium. **23.** Exocrine glands have ducts that carry their secretion (typically a protein-containing secretion other than hormones) to a free body surface. Endocrine glands produce only hormones and are ductless glands. **24.** Connective tissues differ from other tissues because of the nonliving matrix they produce and which surrounds their living cells. **25.** Skeletal and cardiac muscle are striated. Skeletal muscle is voluntary. **26.** Epithelium and some connective tissues remain mitotic. **27.** Neoplasm means "new growth." It is an abnormal growth or tumor. **28.** Endocrine activity tends to decline with age.

Review Questions

1. a; **2.** c; **3.** a, b, d; **4.** e; **5.** c; **6.** a, c; **7.** b; **8.** b; **9.** a; **10.** a; **11.** a, b, d, e; **12.** c; **13.** b

CHAPTER 4

Did You Get It?

1. Serous membranes line ventral body cavities closed to the exterior. Mucous membranes line body cavities open to the exterior (respiratory, digestive, urinary, and reproductive organ cavities). **2.** Parietal pleura, visceral pleura, (lung), visceral pleura, parietal pleura, parietal pericardium, visceral pericardium, (heart). **3.** Lining a fibrous capsule surrounding a joint. **4.** The skin is the epithelial membrane that covers the body surface. *Cutaneous membrane* is a synonym for skin, as is *integument*, which means covering. The integumentary system is the skin and its derivatives (nails, hair, glands). **5.** Any three of the functions listed in Table 4.1. **6.** Keratinocytes are the most abundant cell type in the epidermis. **7.** The stratum basale. **8.** The stratum corneum. **9.** Melanin, carotene, and hemoglobin all contribute to skin color. **10.** Cuticle, cortex, and medulla. **11.** Sebum is an oily secretion of the sebaceous glands. **12.** Both are dilute salt solutions containing vitamins and wastes. Apocrine secretion also contains proteins and fatty acids. **13.** No, the nail won't re-grow because the growth region (nail matrix) is torn off. **14.** Loss of body fluids containing needed proteins and electrolytes, resulting in circulatory shock, and overwhelming infection. **15.** First-degree burns are red and swollen but usually heal in 2–3 days; only epidermal damage. Second-degree burns damage the epidermis and some of the dermis; blisters appear but epithelial regeneration can occur. Third-degree burns destroy the entire skin thickness. The burn is gray and painless; must graft. **16.** Sun exposure. **17.** Because stratum corneum cells are dead. **18.** Loss of subcutaneous fat.

Review Questions

1. c; **2.** b, e; **3.** c, e; **4.** c; **5.** a, c, d; **6.** d; **7.** c; **8.** a; **9.** 1-e, 2-d, 3-f, 4-b, 5-g, 6-c

CHAPTER 5

Did You Get It?

1. Muscles use bones as levers to bring about body movements. **2.** Most long bones are found in the limbs. **3.** Shaft = diaphysis; bone ends = epiphyses. **4.** Compact bones appear solid and very dense with few holes. Spongy bone areas look like the cross-beams of a house with lots of space between the bone spicules. **5.** Membranes or cartilage. **6.** The hormonal stimulus (PTH) maintains blood calcium homeostasis. **7.** Bones will become thinner and weaker because osteoclasts are bone-destroying cells.

ANSWERS TO DID YOU GET IT? AND MULTIPLE CHOICE QUESTIONS *(CONTINUED)*

8. A fracture is a break in a bone. Compression and comminuted.   **9.** Skull, vertebral column, and bony thorax.   **10.** Eating or talking. These are the temporomandibular joints.   **11.** Maxillae.   **12.** Ethmoid bone.   **13.** Frontal joins with the parietals at the coronal suture. Parietals join one another at the sagittal suture.   **14.** Cervical, thoracic, lumbar, sacral, coccygeal.   **15.** All typical cervical vertebrae are small, have holes in their transverse processes, and a split spinous process. Lumbar vertebrae are large, block-like vertebrae with a blunt spinous process that projects directly back. They have a large body and no foramina in their transverse processes.   **16.** A true rib is attached directly to the sternum by its own costal cartilage. A false rib attaches indirectly (by the costal cartilage of a superior rib) or not at all.   **17.** The dens allows rotation of the skull on C1. Without the dens to secure its position the skull would move in many more directions.   **18.** The clavicle attaches medially to the sternum.   **19.** The humerus forms the skeleton of the arm.   **20.** Carpals are the short bones found in the wrist.   **21.** Radius and ulna.   **22.** Ileum, ischium, and pubis form the hipbone. The pelvic girdle is formed by the two hipbones.   **23.** The female pelvis is broader, lighter, has a less acute pubic angle, a wider inlet and outlet, and shorter ischial spines.   **24.** Tibia and fibula form the skeleton of the leg.   **25.** Flat feet.
26. The femur has those markings.   **27.** Joints connect bones together while allowing flexibility of the body.
28. The material between the articulating bone ends, which is connective tissue fibers in fibrous joints and cartilage in cartilaginous joints.   **29.** Lining a synovial joint capsule to provide a source of lubricating fluid in the joint.   **30.** The shoulder and hip joints are ball-and-socket joints. The carpometacarpal joint of the thumb is a saddle joint.
31. The thoracic and sacral curvatures are present.
32. At birth the newborn's spine is an arc (C-shaped), whereas an adult's spine has two additional curvatures and is S-shaped.   **33.** Compression fracture; osteoporosis.
34. Lower limbs and facial skeleton grow most rapidly during childhood.

Review Questions
1. a, b, d;   **2.** d;   **3.** b;   **4.** d;   **5.** a, b, c, d, e;   **6.** d;
7. d;   **8.** b, c, e;   **9.** b   **10.** b;   **11.** 1-a, b, 2-a, 3-a, 4-a, 5-b, 6-c, 7-c, 8-a, 9-c;   **12.** a-1, b-2, c-3, d-1, e-2, f-1.

CHAPTER 6
Did You Get It?
1. Skeletal muscle cells are long multinucleate cells with obvious striations. Cardiac cells are branching, typically uninucleate cells with less obvious striations but obvious junctions. Smooth muscle cells are spindle-shaped uninucleate cells, nonstriated.   **2.** Skeletal muscle.
3. Striped or having bands = striated.   **4.** Skeletal muscle movements can be very forceful and rapid, whereas smooth muscle movements tend to be slow and often rhythmic.   **5.** The alignment of the bands on the myofilaments is responsible for the banding pattern in skeletal muscle cells.   **6.** The axon ending of a motor neuron and the sarcolemma of the skeletal muscle cell.
7. Calcium ions trigger the sliding of the myofilaments.
8. Sodium ions enter the cells during action potential generation.   **9.** Pulling a bucket out of a well.
10. Phosphorylation of ADP by CP, stored ATP, and ATP generated by glucose oxidation.   **11.** Stored ATP.
12. Isometric contraction   **13.** Oxygen deficit occurs when a person is not able to take in oxygen fast enough to keep his/her muscles supplied with all the oxygen they need when working vigorously.   **14.** Resistance exercise leads to increased muscle size.   **15.** Abduction.   **16.** Flexion and extension.   **17.** Tibialis anterior—a muscle overlying the tibia anteriorly. Erector spinae—muscles that straighten the spine. Abdominis rectus—muscle that runs straight up the abdomen.   **18.** Circular.   **19.** They anchor or aid the activity of the prime mover.   **20.** Frontalis raises the eyebrows.   **21.** Masseter and temporalis are synergists in jaw closure.   **22.** Erector spinae.   **23.** It's like plywood. The various abdominal muscles run in different directions across the abdomen making the abdominal wall very strong.
24. Latissimus dorsi.   **25.** Triceps brachii.   **26.** Quadriceps on anterior thigh.   **27.** The medial gluteal site and the deltoid muscle of the shoulder.   **28.** Soleus and gastrocnemius. They plantar flex the foot.   **29.** Nerve fibers must be myelinated.   **30.** Exercise defers or reduces the natural loss in muscle mass and strength that occurs in old age.

Review Questions
1. c, e;   **2.** a;   **3.** c;   **4.** b;   **5.** a, b, c, d;   **6.** a, b;
7. a, b, d;   **8.** a, b, d

continued

ANSWERS TO DID YOU GET IT? AND MULTIPLE CHOICE QUESTIONS *(CONTINUED)*

CHAPTER 7

Did You Get It?

1. CNS = brain and spinal cord. PNS = nerves that extend to and from the CNS. **2.** Astrocytes are the most numerous glial cells. Oligodendrocytes produce myelin. **3.** Glial cells can divide. Most neurons cannot. A criterion of cancer cells is their uncontrolled division. **4.** A tract is a bundle of nerve fibers in the CNS. A nerve is a bundle of nerve fibers in the PNS. **5.** A ganglion is a cluster of nerve cell bodies in PNS; a nucleus is a cluster of nerve cell bodies in the CNS. **6.** Dendrites conduct impulses toward the nerve cell body; the axon terminal releases neurotransmitters. **7.** The fiber that conducts at 40M/sec. **8.** A graded potential is a local current that dies out with distance. An action potential is a current that is continuously regenerated along the length of the axon and does not die out. **9.** Chemically via the release of a neurotransmitter and binding of the neurotransmitter to the postsynaptic membrane. **10.** Dendrites. **11.** A reflex is a rapid, predictable, and involuntary response to a stimulus. **12.** Cerebral cortex, white matter, and basal nuclei. **13.** Myelinated nerve fibers. **14.** The brain stem controls vital activities. **15.** The cerebellum provides precise timing for skeletal muscle activity and helps control our balance and equilibrium. **16.** Diencephalon. **17.** Ventricles. **18.** Blood-brain barrier. **19.** Arachnoid mater. **20.** Contusion. **21.** Nerve cell bodies of interneurons and motor neurons. **22.** Sensory pathways are ascending pathways. **23.** Because the leash of nerve fibers there looks like a horse's tail, the literal translation of cauda equina. **24.** Around each nerve fiber. **25.** Vagus nerves. **26.** Plexus = complex network of nerves. **27.** Sciatic nerve of the sacral plexus. **28.** Visceral organs (smooth and cardiac muscle and glands) are served by the ANS. **29.** The ANS has a two-motor neuron pathway from the CNS to the organ to be served. The somatic nervous system has just one motor neuron in the motor pathway. **30.** Sympathetic division. **31.** They are unable to regulate their body temperature until the hypothalamus matures. **32.** It is a hypotension caused by a rapid change in position such as getting up quickly from a reclining position. The sympathetic nervous system, which regulates blood pressure, is less efficient in old age.

Review Questions

1. b; **2.** a, b, c; **3.** d; **4.** d; **5.** c; **6.** 1-d, 2-h, 3-e, 4-g, 5-b, 6-f, 7-i, 8-a; **7.** a; **8.** c; **9.** a,c; **10.** a, c; **11.** d; **12.** d

CHAPTER 8

Did You Get It?

1. The eyelids protect the eyes. **2.** Lacrimal glands produce tears. **3.** Tears are a dilute saline solution containing lysozyme and antibodies. **4.** They direct the eyeball toward what you wish to view. **5.** The blind spot contains no photoreceptors; it is the site where the optic nerve leaves the eyeball. **6.** Both contain pigment, which prevents light scattering in the eye. **7.** Rods have a rod-like outer segment containing the photopigment whereas cones have a shorter cone-shaped outer segment. Rods respond to low light conditions and produce black and white vision; cones need bright light and provide color vision. **8.** Refractory media include the cornea, aqueous humor, the lens, and vitreous humor. **9.** Accommodation. **10.** The optic nerves leave the eyeballs, and the medial half of the fibers of each optic nerve cross over to the opposite side, joining there with the fibers from the outside half of the opposite eye to form the optic tracts. **11.** It causes pupillary constriction in very bright light. Intense light stimulation can injure the photoreceptors. **12.** External and middle ears serve hearing only. **13.** The ossicles (hammer, anvil, and stirrup). **14.** Balance or equilibrium. **15.** Dynamic receptors located in the semicircular canals (crista ampullaris). **16.** Otoliths are tiny stiles made of calcium salts which are located in the maculae of the vestibule. They respond to static equilibrium cues relative to the position of the head in space. **17.** Tympanic membrane to bones of ossicles to fluids of the cochlear scalas. **18.** Cochlear nerve (division of VIII cranial nerve). **19.** Close to the oval window. **20.** Sensorineural deafness results from damage to neural structures involved in hearing (cochlear nerve, auditory region of the brain), whereas conductive deafness results from anything that prevents sound vibrations from reaching the cochlea (earwax, fusion of the ossicles, fluid in the middle ear). **21.** Chemoreceptors, because they respond to chemicals in solution. **22.** On the tongue. **23.** Odor receptors are located at the superior aspect of the nasal cavity. Sniffing brings the air upward. **24.** Presbyopia. **25.** Vision. **26.** Deafness of old age.

Review Questions

1. d; **2.** b, c; **3.** b, d; **4.** c; **5.** b; **6.** a, c; **7.** a, b, c, d; **8.** a, c; **9.** b; **10.** a, b, c

ANSWERS TO DID YOU GET IT? AND MULTIPLE CHOICE QUESTIONS *(CONTINUED)*

CHAPTER 9

Did You Get It?

1. The endocrine system delivers its commands via hormones carried by the blood; this is a slow process. The nervous system uses rapid electrical messages that are much faster, allowing you to raise your foot off the glass more quickly.   **2.** A hormone is a chemical messenger used by the endocrine system. The target organ of a hormone is the specific cells or tissues that the hormone affects.   **3.** Because it is not the initial messenger, a ligand that attaches to a receptor on the cell's plasma membrane and triggers the reactions leading to synthesis of the second messenger in the cell.   **4.** Endocrine organs are stimulated by hormones, by chemicals other than hormones, and by the nervous system.   **5.** The posterior pituitary is a storage and releasing area for hormones sent to it by the hypothalamus.   **6.** Endocrine glands are ductless and they release their hormone products directly into the intercelular fluid. Exocrine glands release their nonhormonal products to an epithelial surface via a duct. **7.** Tropic hormones stimulate certain endocrine organs to secrete their hormones.   **8.** Diabetes insipidus in which copious amounts of urine are voided due to hyposecretion of ADH.   **9.** The parathyroid glands reside on the thyroid gland. **10.** PTH produced by the parathyroid glands increases blood calcium levels.   **11.** Calcitonin, produced by the parafollicular cells of the thyroid gland, reduces blood calcium levels.   **12.** Functional thyroid hormone has iodine as part of its structure.   **13.** Aldosterone stimulates the kidneys to reabsorb more sodium.   **14.** Elevated because of her stress. When we are stressed, both glucocorticouds (adrenal cortical hormones) and epinephrine and norepinephrine (adrenal medullary hormones) are produced in increased amounts. Both sets of hormones promote a rise in blood glucose levels.   **15.** Sex hormones—mostly androgens.   **16.** Insulin stimulates cellular uptake of glucose. **17.** Melatonin, produced by the pineal gland.   **18.** Thymosin programs the T lymphocytes, which essentially direct our immune responses.   **19.** Estrogen   **20.** Stomach and small intestine.   **21.** Placenta.   **22.** Ovaries.

Review Questions

1. d;   **2.** b;   **3.** a, c;   **4.** c;   **5.** a, b, c, d;   **6.** a, b, c, d; **7.** a, b, c;   **8.** b;   **9.** b

CHAPTER 10

Did You Get It?

1. The liver is the major source of blood proteins. **2.** Erythrocytes, leukocytes, and platelets.   **3.** The color of blood varies with the amount of oxygen it is carrying. From most oxygen to least, the blood goes from scarlet to blue-red.   **4.** Hemoglobin transports oxygen in the blood as well as a small amount of carbon dioxide. **5.** Lymphocytes are the main actors in body immunity. **6.** Infection in the body causes an increase in WBC count, thus $15,000/mm^3$.   **7.** Anemia.   **8.** The hemocytoblast gives rise to all formed elements.   **9.** Lack of a nucleus; therefore, they cannot carry out transcription and translation to produce proteins (enzymes and others).   **10.** The stem cell (megakaryocyte) undergoes mitosis without cytokinesis many times, forming a large multinuclear cell, which then fragments into platelets.   **11.** Inactivity, leading to blood pooling, and anything that roughens or damages the lining of a blood vessel (laceration, atherosclerosis, physical trauma).   **12.** The self antigens (agglutinogens) the RBCs bear.   **13.** A transfusion reaction in which the RBCs are lysed and hemoglobin enters the bloodstream, which may lead to kidney shutdown.   **14.** O positive   **15.** An antigen is a substance foreign to the body which activates and is attacked by the immune system. An antibody is a protein released by immune cells that binds with a specific antigen and inactivates it in some way.   **16.** Fetal HbF has a greater ability to bind oxygen and binds it more strongly than adult HbA.   **17.** Leukemia, pernicious anemia, and clotting disorders are particularly common in the elderly.

Review Questions

1. a, b, d;   **2.** a, b, c, d;   **3.** d;   **4.** c;   **5.** a, d;   **6.** a; **7.** b, c;   **8.** c;   **9.** b, c, d;   **10.** a, d;   **11.** a;   **12.** b

CHAPTER 11

Did You Get It?

1. The heart is in the mediastinum between the lungs. **2.** Pulmonary circulation strictly serves gas exchange. Oxygen is loaded and carbon dioxide is unloaded from the blood in the lungs. Systemic circulation provides oxygen-laden blood to all body organs.   **3.** Heart valves keep blood flowing forward through the heart.   **4.** The coronary arteries supply the myocardium (cardiac muscle) with oxygen. If that circulation fails, the heart fails.   **5.** The intrinsic

continued

ANSWERS TO DID YOU GET IT? AND MULTIPLE CHOICE QUESTIONS *(CONTINUED)*

conduction system of the heart coordinates the action of the heart chambers and causes the heart to beat faster than it would otherwise. **6.** Left ventricle **7.** The operation of the heart valves. **8.** CO = amount of blood pumped out by each side of the heart in one minute. **9.** Fever increases the heart rate because the rate of metabolism of the cardiac muscle increases. **10.** It is a vein. **11.** Blood pressure in veins is much lower than that in arteries because veins are farther along in the circulatory pathway. Hence, veins need extra measures to force blood back to the heart. **12.** Capillary walls consist only of the innermost intima layer which is very thin. Capillaries are the exchange vessels between the blood and tissue cells, thus thin walls are desirable. **13.** Lower limb. **14.** Upper limb. **15.** Hepatic portal vein. **16.** Blood pressure in the pulmonary circulation is much lower. Pulmonary arteries carry oxygen-depleted/carbon dioxide rich blood whereas the pulmonary veins carry oxygen rich/carbon dioxide depleted blood. The opposite is true of the arteries and veins of the systemic circulation. **17.** The ductus venosus is a liver bypass in the fetus. Since the mother's liver is working for the fetus as well, the entire liver need not be continuously perfused with blood. **18.** Radial artery at the wrist; femoral at the groin; common carotid at the side of the neck. **19.** It decreases from heart to venae cavae. **20.** Hemorrhage reduces blood pressure initially because blood volume drops. **21.** Fluid enters the capillary bed at its venous end.

Review Questions

1. d; **2.** b; **3.** c; **4.** a, c; **5.** c; **6.** a, c; **7.** d; **8.** a, c; **9.** d; **10.** a; **11.** b; **12.** a, c, d; **13.** b; **14.** a, b, c; **15.** c; **16.** b; **17.** d; **18.** b; **19.** b

CHAPTER 12

Did You Get It?

1. Lymphatic vessels pick up fluid and proteins leaked from the blood into the interstitial space. **2.** Lymphatic capillaries are blind-ended and not fed by arteries as blood capillaries are. They also have flaplike minivalves that make them more permeable than blood capillaries. **3.** Particularly large collections of lymph nodes occur in the axillary, inguinal, and cervical regions. **4.** The number of afferent lymphatic vessels entering the node is greater than the number of efferent vessels leaving the node at the hilum. Therefore, lymph flow stagnates somewhat. **5.** The spleen destroys worn out RBCs. **6.** The lymphoid tissue associated with the mucosa—tonsils in the throat, and Peyer's patches in the intestinal walls—which acts to prevent pathogens from entering the body through the

mucosa. **7.** Innate defenses are nonspecific and always ready to protect the body. They include intact membranes (mucosa, skin), inflammatory response, and several protective cell types and chemicals. Adaptive defenses must be programmed and specifically target particular pathogens or antigens. **8.** Redness, heat, swelling (edema), and pain. **9.** It attaches to foreign cells and when it is activated, membrane attack complexes (MAC) are inserted in the foreign cell's membrane and produce lesions that allow water entry and cause lysis. **10.** Viruses elicit interferon formation. **11.** A self-antigen is a body protein, typically displayed in the plasma membrane, that is foreign to anyone but yourself. An antigen is a foreign substance in the body. **12.** B lymphocytes mount a humoral response by producing antibodies. T lymphocytes mount the cellular response by activating B cells and cytotoxic T cells and stimulating the inflammatory response. **13.** In the thymus. **14.** They are antigen presenters to the T cells. **15.** This is the region that binds to the antigen. **16.** IgA, a dimer. **17.** Antibodies attach to viruses or bacterial toxins, thereby blocking the virus or toxin from injuring the body. **18.** Plasma cells make up the bulk of antibodies made; their number would be increased. **19.** T cells have to bind to both an antigenic particle and to a self protein on the antigen presenting cell. **20.** The cytotoxic T cell inserts perforins (toxic chemicals) into the foreign antigen's plasma membrane, which then develops holes. Then granzymes, enzymes from the T cell's cytoplasmic granules, enter and kill the foreign cell. **21.** To slow or stop it once the "enemy" has been conquered. **22.** Allograft. **23.** Inefficient lymphocyte programming, appearance of self proteins in the circulation that were not previously exposed to the immune system, or antibodies that cross-react with antibodies produced against foreign antigens. **24.** An overzealous immune response against an otherwise harmless substance that causes injury to the body. **25.** In anaphylactic shock, released histamine causes constriction of the bronchioles, sudden vasodilation, and fluid loss. **26.** Abnormal production or functioning of immune cells or complement.

Review Questions

1. c; **2.** a; **3.** b; **4.** a, c; **5.** a, d; **6.** b, d; **7.** c; **8.** a, c; **9.** b; **10.** b, d; **11.** d; **12.** a, b, c, d; **13.** a

CHAPTER 13

Did You Get It?

1. Because the respiratory mucosa rests on thin-walled veins that warm the incoming air, mucus produced by the

ANSWERS TO DID YOU GET IT? AND MULTIPLE CHOICE QUESTIONS (CONTINUED)

mucous glands moistens the air and traps dust and bacteria. The oral mucosa performs none of these functions. **2.** Ciliated cells of the mucosa move the sheet of contaminated mucus away from the lungs and toward the throat for swallowing. **3.** Nasal cavity, pharynx, larynx, trachea, bronchi, bronchioles, alveoli. **4.** The right because it's wider and straighter. **5.** The passageways conduct air. The elastic tissue allows lungs to recoil passively when exhaling, saving energy. **6.** Respiratory bronchiole, alveolar duct, alveolar sac, and individual alveoli. **7.** To exchange gases between the external environment and the blood—oxygen in, carbon dioxide out. **8.** Increased air pressure in the lungs as they recoil. **9.** VC is largest; TV is smallest. **10.** About 350 ml reaches the alveoli. **11.** His left lung collapsed because the pressure in the intrapleural space (normally negative) became equal to atmospheric pressure. **12.** Diffusion. **13.** As bicarbonate ion. **14.** Cyanosis is a bluish cast to the skin and nails due to inadequate oxygenation of the blood. **15.** The medulla. **16.** He has COPD, emphysema. **17.** The lung alveoli will collapse after every breath; IRDS. **18.** Possible causes include a problem with neural control; viral infection; heart rhythm abnormality, which means a genetic component might be involved.

Review Questions
1. d; **2.** d; **3.** b; **4.** b; **5.** b, c; **6.** c, d; **7.** b

CHAPTER 14

Did You Get It?
1. Mouth, pharynx, esophagus, stomach, small intestine, large intestine, anus. **2.** Protein digestion begins in the stomach. **3.** Alkaline mucus protects the stomach wall. Intrinsic factor is needed for intestinal absorption of vitamin B_{12}. **4.** The pyloric sphincter. **5.** Water absorption and absorption of some vitamins made by resident bacteria. **6.** Villi are extensions of the mucosa of the small intestine. They increase the surface area of the small intestine tremendously for nutrient absorption. **7.** Starch. Saliva contains salivary amylase. **8.** 32 permanent teeth. **9.** Bile, secreted by the liver, acts as a detergent to mechanically break up large fat masses into smaller ones for enzymatic digestion. **10.** The pancreas. **11.** Mechanical digestion breaks food down physically by squeezing and pummeling it. Chemical digestion uses enzymes to break the chemical bonds of the food molecules and release the units.

12. Amino acids **13.** Ingestion, digestion, absorption, and defecation. **14.** Pepsin, the main enzyme of the stomach, needs acidic conditions to work. **15.** Food went down the air passageway (trachea) instead of the digestive passage (esophagus). **16.** Fruits, vegetables, and grains. **17.** It provides fiber, which is important for moving feces along the colon and defecation. **18.** Oils are unsaturated lipids. **19.** Most are coenzymes that work with enzymes to bring about metabolic reactions. **20.** Cellular respiration **21.** Carbon dioxide and reduced coenzymes. **22.** Water and ATP. **23.** Making glucose from noncarbohydrate molecules, e.g., fats and proteins. **24.** HDLs because they are headed back to the liver for breakdown and elimination from the body. **25.** Fats **26.** Large surface area relative to volume. **27.** Vasoconstriction of blood vessels serving the skin and shivering. **28.** It decreases body temperature. **29.** Because it clogs the pancreatic ducts so that pancreatic enzymes cannot reach the small intestine, cystic fibrosis impairs food digestion, and fat digestion is virtually stopped, resulting in fatty stools and an inability to absorb fat-soluble vitamins. **30.** No phenylalanine-containing foods in the diet. **31.** You gain weight (fat).

Review Questions
1. a, c, d; **2.** b; **3.** c; **4.** 1-e, 2-h, 3-c, 4-b, 5-g, 6-a, 7-f, 8-d; **5.** d; **6.** d; **7.** c, d; **8.** d; **9.** d; **10.** a; **11.** b; **12.** b; **13.** c

CHAPTER 15

Did You Get It?
1. Retroperitoneal = "behind or in back of the peritoneum." **2.** Fat helps keep the kidneys anchored against the body trunk wall. When she lost weight, the fat decreased and the kidneys fell to a lower position causing the ureter(s) to kink (ptosis) and inhibit urine flow. **3.** Cortex, medulla, pelvis. **4.** The nephron **5.** Renal tubule carries out tubular reabsorption and secretion. The peritubular capillaries receive the fluid, nutrients, and needed ions to be returned to the general circulation. **6.** It decreases it. **7.** The specific gravity of urine is higher because it contains more solutes than water. **8.** The bladder **9.** It allows the cavity of the bladder to be increased in volume to store more urine. **10.** It is longer (8″ vs. 1½″) and it transports both urine and semen. The female urethra transports urine only. **11.** Voiding or urination. **12.** Excreting nitrogenous wastes,

continued

ANSWERS TO DID YOU GET IT? AND MULTIPLE CHOICE QUESTIONS *(CONTINUED)*

maintaining acid-base, water, and electrolyte balance of the blood. **13.** Thirst. **14.** Aldosterone increases sodium ion reasbsorption by the kidney tubules, and water follows (if able). **15.** Osmoreceptors are in the brain (hypothalamus) and they respond to changing (increasing) osmolarity of the blood. **16.** The homeostatic pH of blood in the body varies between 7.35 and 7.45. Any blood pH below 7.35 is considered to acidic for normal body function. **17.** A weak base because a weak base will neutralize it by tying up only enough hydrogen ions to maintain a physiological pH, and there is no chance of overshoot and making the pH strongly basic. **18.** It will increase because water will be lost in sweat (and urine). **19.** Acid-base balance is maintained by excreting hydrogen ions and reabsorbing hydroxide ions. **20.** A condition in a newborn baby boy in which the urethral opening is on the ventral surface of the penis. **21.** Urgency is the urgent feeling that you have to urinate. Frequency is the condition in which you urinate small amounts of urine frequently. **22.** Shrinking of the urinary bladder and loss of bladder tone.

Review Questions

1. d; **2.** d; **3.** b; **4.** b, c, d; **5.** a, b, c, d; **6.** d; **7.** c; **8.** c

CHAPTER 16

Did You Get It?

1. The testes produce male gametes (sperm) and secrete sex hormones, mainly testosterone. **2.** The seminiferous tubules produce sperm. **3.** Epididymis, ductus deferens, ejaculatory duct, and urethra (prostatic, membranous, and spongy regions). **4.** To make the penis firm by allowing it to fill with blood, so that it can serve as a penetrating device during sexual activity. **5.** Sperm are male gametes that fertilize the female's "eggs." Seminal fluid serves as a transport medium for sperm and various substances that nourish and protect the sperm or aid their movement. **6.** His prostate is probably hypertrophied. The prostate is immediately anterior to the rectum and can be examined through the anterior rectal wall. **7.** FSH stimulates

spermatogenesis. **8.** The final product of mitosis is two diploid cells that are genetically identical to each other and to the mother cell. The final product of meiosis is four cells each with half the normal (diploid) number of chromosomes. Variation is introduced by meiosis. **9.** Excess cytoplasm is discarded and what remains is compacted into the head, midpiece, and tail regions. **10.** Luteinizing hormone stimulates testosterone production. **11.** Female gametes (eggs or ova). **12.** The uterus serves as an incubator. The fallopian tubes are the most common site of fertilization. **13.** Graafian or vesicular follicle. **14.** Polar bodies are also produced. They deteriorate and die because they lack sustaining cytoplasm. **15.** FSH promotes follicle development. **16.** LH stimulates ovulation. **17.** Estrogen **18.** The functional layer of the endometrium is rebuilt. **19.** Progesterone (1) causes the secretory phase of the menstrual cycle, (2) helps prepare the breasts for lactation, and (3) helps quiet the uterine muscle to maintain pregnancy. **20.** A large percentage (80%) of those who carry the altered gene(s) develop breast cancer. **21.** Successive divisions not separated by growth of the cells, so the cells get smaller with each division. **22.** The placenta produces hormones of pregnancy, delivers nutrients and oxygen to the fetus, and removes wastes from the fetal blood. **23.** During pregnancy, many women have heartburn because the stomach is crowded by the uterus. Constipation is another problem because mobility of the digestive tract decreases. Nasal stuffiness and difficulty breathing are common. **24.** Dilation, expulsion, and placental stages. **25.** XY; testosterone. **26.** Cryptorchidism is failure of the testes to descend into the scrotum; infertility. **27.** Vaginal infections (E. coli, STDs, and fungal infections) may lead to PID. Abnormal or painful menses.

Review Questions

1. d; **2.** a; **3.** d; **4.** d; **5.** c; **6.** c, d; **7.** d; **8.** a; **9.** c; **10.** b; **11.** d; **12.** a, d; **13.** a, d

Photographic Credits

Chapter 1 1.1: Corbis. 1.6a–c top: Jenny Thomas, Pearson Benjamin Cummings. 1.6a middle: CNRI/SPL/Photo Researchers. 1.6b middle: Petit Format/Photo Researchers. 1.6c middle; A Closer Look, a: Howard Sochurek. A Closer Look, b: Custom Medical Stock Photography. Focus on Careers: Elena Dorfman, Pearson Benjamin Cummings.

Chapter 2 2.4 left: Chip Clark. 2.4 middle, right: Pearson Benjamin Cummings. 2.9b: George Bernard/Animals Animals. A Closer Look: Geoff Tomkinson/SPL/Photo Researchers. Focus on Careers: Pearson Benjamin Cummings.

Chapter 3 3.7a: J. V. Small and G. Rinnerthaler, Austrian Academy of Sciences. 3.12b: Birgit H. Satir, Department of Anatomy and Structural Biology, Albert Einstein College of Medicine. 3.18a: G. W. Willis/Visuals Unlimited. 3.18b,e,f; 3.19a,c,g; 3.20c: Allen Bell, University of New England; Pearson Benjamin Cummings. 3.18c: Cabisco/Visuals Unlimited. 3.18d: R. Calentine/Visuals Unlimited. 3.19b,e,h; 3.20b: Ed Reschke. 3.19d: Ed Reschke/Peter Arnold. 3.19f: Carolina Biological/Visuals Unlimited. 3.20a: Eric Graves/Photo Researchers. 3.21: Biophoto Associates/Photo Researchers. A Closer Look 1: David M. Philips/Photo Researchers.

Chapter 4 4.3: From *Gray's Anatomy*, Henry Gray, © Churchill Livingstone, UK. 4.5: Kozier, Erb, and Olivieri, *Fundamentals of Nursing*, 4e, © Pearson Benjamin Cummings, 1991. 4.6a: Cabisco/Visuals Unlimited. 4.6b: John D. Cunningham/Visuals Unlimited. 4.8: CNRI/SPL/Photo Researchers. 4.10a: Rotker/Phototake. 4.10b,c: NMSB/Custom Medical Photography. 4.11b top: Myrleen Ferguson/PhotoEdit. 4.11b middle: P. Marazzi/SPL/Photo Researchers. 4.11b bottom: John Meyer/Custom Medical Stock Photography. 4.12a: Bart's Medical Library/Phototake. 4.12b: P. Marazzi/SPL/Photo Researchers. 4.12c: Zeva Oelbaum/Peter Arnold. A Closer Look: Phanie/Photo Researchers. Focus on Careers: Elena Dorfman, Pearson Benjamin Cummings.

Chapter 5 5.3c: Allen Bell, University of New England; Pearson Benjamin Cummings. 5.15: Reik/age fotostock. 5.20b: Shawn Miller (dissection), Mark Nielsen and Alexa Doig (photography). 5.31: CNRI/SPL/Photo Researchers. 5.32: Carolina Biological Supply. 5.34: P. Motta, Department of Anatomy, University "La Sapienza," Rome/SPL/Photo Researchers. A Closer Look 1: John Wilson White, Pearson Benjamin Cummings.

Chapter 6 6.4b: Eric Graves/Photo Researchers. 6.11a: B. Daemmrich/The Image Works. 6.11b: Vandystadt Agence De Presse/Photo Researchers. 6.13: John Wilson White, Pearson Benjamin Cummings. A Closer Look: Thinkstock/PictureQuest. Focus on Careers: Elena Dorfman, Pearson Benjamin Cummings. Table 6.1 left: Eric Graves/Photo Researchers. Table 6.1 center: Ed Reschke. Table 6.1 right: Allen Bell, University of New England; Pearson Benjamin Cummings.

Chapter 7 7.4: Biophoto Associates/Photo Researchers. 7.11d: Jim Selby/SPL/Custom Medical Stock Photo. 7.13b, 7.17b: From *A Stereoscopic Atlas of Human Anatomy* by David Bassett. 7.19: Carroll H. Weiss. A Closer Look 1: Toby Talbot/Associated Press. A Closer Look 2: Hank Morgan/Photo Researchers.

Chapter 8 8.1: Richard Tauber, Pearson Benjamin Cummings. 8.4b: From *A Stereoscopic Atlas of Human Anatomy* by David Bassett. 8.7: NMSB/Custom Medical Stock Photography. 8.8: Custom Medical Stock Photography. 8.13b: John Wilson White, Pearson Benjamin Cummings.

Chapter 9 9.5a: Bill Pugliano/Getty Images. 9.5b: Chris Pizzello/AP Photo. 9.7b: Ed Reschke. 9.8, 9.9: Photo Researchers. 9.14b: Victor Eroschenko, Pearson Benjamin Cummings. A Closer Look: Lisa Pines/Getty Images.

Chapter 10 10.2: Victor Eroschenko, University of Idaho; Pearson Benjamin Cummings. 10.3: Stan Flegler/Visuals Unlimited. 10.7: Lennart Nilsson, Boehringer Ingelheim International GmbH. 10.8: Jack Scanlon, Holyoke Community College. A Closer Look: Ed Eckstein/Phototake. Focus on Careers: Daniel M. Grossman/Phototake.

Chapter 11 11.8: Robert Brenner/PhotoEdit. 11.9a: Gladden Willis/Visuals Unlimited. A Closer Look: Carolina Biological Supply/Phototake. Focus on Careers: Elena Dorfman, Pearson Benjamin Cummings.

Chapter 12 12.7a: Lennart Nilsson, *The Body Victorious*, New York: Dell, © Boehringer Ingelheim International GmbH. 12.15a: Computer modeling and photography, A. J. Olson © The Scripps Institute. 12.CL: Eye of Science/Photo Researchers.

Chapter 13 13.3b: SPL/Photo Researchers. 13.4a: Richard Tauber, Pearson Benjamin Cummings. 13.5b: CNRI/SPL/Photo Researchers. A Closer Look: Martin M. Rotker. Focus on Careers: Elena Dorfman, Pearson Benjamin Cummings.

Chapter 14 14.4b: From *Color Atlas of Histology* by Leslie P. Garner and James L. Hiatt, © Williams and Wilkins, 1990. 14.5: From *A Stereoscopic Atlas of Human Anatomy*, by David L. Bassett. 14.20b: Stephen Frisch. A Closer Look 1, a: Javier Domingo/Phototake. A Closer Look 1, b: Oliver Meckes/Photo Researchers. A Closer Look 2: Mary Ann Chastain/AP Photo.

Chapter 15 15.1b: Richard Tauber, Pearson Benjamin Cummings. 15.2a, 15.3d: From *A Stereoscopic Atlas of Human Anatomy*, by David L. Bassett. A Closer Look: AJ Photos/Photo Researchers.

Chapter 16 16.5a: Manfred Kage/Peter Arnold. 16.11: C. Edleman/La Vilette/Photo Researchers. 16.14a: Spencer Grant/Stock Boston. 16.14b,c: Richard D'Amico/Custom Medical Stock Photography. 16.17: From *A Stereoscopic Atlas of Human Anatomy* by David L. Bassett. 16.18: Lennart Nilsson/Albert Bonniers Forlag. A Closer Look 2: Anthony Loveday, Pearson Benjamin Cummings. Contraceptive devices courtesy of Planned Parenthood. Focus on Careers: Elena Dorfman, Pearson Benjamin Cummings.

Art Credits

All illustrations are by Imagineering STA Media Services unless noted below.

Chapter 1 1.3: Adapted from Campbell, Reece, and Mitchell, *Biology*, 5e, F40.10a, © Pearson Benjamin Cummings, 1999. 1.6: Precision Graphics/Imagineering.

Chapter 3 3.2: Carla Simmons/Kristin Mount. 3.3, 3.4, 3.7: Tomo Narashima. 3.15: Adapted from Campbell, Mitchell, Reece, Taylor, *Biology: Concepts and Connections*, 3e, F8.6, © Pearson Benjamin Cummings, 2000.

Chapter 4 4.1: Precision Graphics/Imagineering. 4.4: Tomo Narashima. 4.6: Precision Graphics/Imagineering.

Chapter 5 5.3, 5.5: Carla Simmons/Imagineering. 5.7–5.9, 5.11: Kristin Mount. A Closer Look 2: Adapted from Ranier I. Kotz, Reinhard Windhager, et al., *Nature*, Fig 1, Vol 406: 143, 13 July 2000, © Macmillan Publishers, Ltd.

Chapter 6 6.1: Raychel Ciemma. 6.2b: Carla Simmons/Kristin Mount.

Chapter 7 7.20, 7.21: Laurie O'Keefe/Kristin Mount. 7.23: Charles W. Hoffman/Kristin Mount.

Chapter 8 8.2a: Adapted from Campbell, Mitchell, Reece, Taylor, *Biology: Concepts and Connections*, 4e, F29.9d, © Pearson Benjamin Cummings, 2003. 8.2b: Charles W. Hoffman.

Chapter 11 11.1: Wendy Hiller Gee/Kristin Mount. 11.2, 11.4: Barbara Cousins. 11.5: Barbara Cousins/Imagineering. 11.6: Barbara Cousins/Kristin Mount. 11.9: Adapted from Tortora and Grabowski, *Principles of Anatomy and Physiology*, 9e, F21.1, New York: Wiley, © Biological Sciences Textbooks and Sandra Reynolds Grabowski, 2000. 11.14, 11.16, 11.17: Kristin Mount.

Chapter 14 14.3: Adapted from Seeley, Stephens, Tate, *Anatomy & Physiology*, 4e, F24.2, New York: WCB/McGraw Hill, © The McGraw Hill Companies, 1998. 14.5: Kristin Otwell/Kristin Mount. 14.17: USDA. 14.20: From Campbell, Mitchell, Reece, *Biology: Concepts and Connections*, 3e, © Pearson Benjamin Cummings.

Chapter 15 15.6: Linda McVay/Imagineering.

Chapter 16 16.3, 16.5: Precision Graphics/Imagineering. 16.8: Martha Blake/Kristin Mount.

Glossary

Pronunciations in the text and this glossary use the following rules:

1. Accent marks follow stressed syllables. The primary stress is shown by ′ and the secondary stress by ″.

2. Unless otherwise noted, assume that vowels at the ends of syllables are long and vowels followed by consonants are short. Exceptions to this rule are indicated by a bar (¯) over the vowel, which indicates a long vowel, or a breve sign (˘) over the vowel, indicating that the vowel is short.

For example, the phonetic spelling of "thrombophlebitis" is *throm″bo-flĕ-bi′tis*. The next-to-last syllable (*bi*) receives the greatest stress, and the first syllable (*throm″*) gets the secondary stress. The vowel in the second syllable comes at the end of the syllable and is long. The vowel that comes at the end of the third syllable is short because it has a breve sign.

Abdomen *ab′do-men* the portion of the body between the diaphragm and the pelvis.

Abduct *ab-dukt′* to move away from the midline of the body.

Abortion *ab-bor′shun* termination of a pregnancy before the embryo or fetus is viable outside the uterus.

Absorption *ab-sorp′shun* passage of a substance into or across a blood vessel or membrane.

Accommodation (1) adaptation in response to differences or changing needs; (2) adjustment of the eye for seeing objects at close range.

Acetabulum *as″ĕ-tab′u-lum* the cuplike cavity on the lateral surface of the hip bone that receives the head of the femur.

Acetylcholine *as″ĕ-til-ko′lēn* a chemical transmitter substance released by certain nerve endings.

Achilles tendon *ah-kil′ēz ten′don* the tendon that attaches the calf muscles to the calcaneus, or heel bone; also called the calcaneal tendon.

Acid a substance that liberates hydrogen ions when in an aqueous solution; (compare with *base*.

Acidosis *as″ĭ-do′sis* a condition in which the blood has an excess hydrogen ion concentration and a decreased pH.

Acne inflammatory disease of the skin; infection of the sebaceous glands.

Acromion *ah-kro′me-on* the outer projection of the spine of the scapula; the highest point of the shoulder.

Acrosome *ak′ro-sōm* an enzyme-containing structure covering the nucleus of the sperm.

Actin *ak′tin* a contractile protein of muscle.

Action potential an electrical event occurring when a stimulus of sufficient intensity is applied to a neuron or muscle cell, allowing sodium ions to move into the cell and reverse the polarity.

Active immunity immunity produced by an encounter with an antigen; provides immunologic memory.

Active transport net movement of a substance across a membrane against a concentration or electrical gradient; requires release and use of cellular energy.

Adaptation (1) any change in structure or response to suit a new environment; (2) decline in the transmission of a sensory nerve when a receptor is stimulated continuously and without change in stimulus intensity.

Adduct *ah-dukt′* to move toward the midline of the body.

Adenosine triphosphate (ATP) *ah-den″o-sin tri-fos′fāt* the compound that is the important intracellular energy source; cellular energy.

Adipose *ad′ĭ-pōs* fatty.

Adrenal glands *ah-dre′nal glanz* hormone-producing glands located superior to the kidneys; each consists of a medulla and cortex areas.

Adrenergic fibers *ad″ren-er′jik* nerve fibers that release norepinephrine.

Aerobic *a-er-o′bik* requiring oxygen to live or grow.

Aerobic respiration respiration in which oxygen is consumed and glucose is broken down entirely; water, carbon dioxide, and large amounts of ATP are the final products.

Afferent *af′er-ent* carrying to or toward a center.

Afferent neurons *nu′ronz* nerve cells that carry impulses toward the central nervous system.

Agglutination *ah-gloo″tin-a′shun* clumping of (foreign) cells, induced by cross-linking of antigen-antibody complexes.

Agglutinins *ah-gloo′tĭ-ninz* antibodies in blood plasma that cause clumping of corpuscles or bacteria.

Agglutinogens *ag″loo-tin′o-jenz* (1) antigens that stimulate the formation of a specific agglutinin; (2) antigens found on red blood cells that are responsible for determining the ABO blood group classification.

Agonist *ag′o-nist* a muscle that bears the primary responsibility for causing a certain movement; a prime mover.

AIDS acquired immuno deficiency syndrome; caused by human immunodeficiency virus (HIV); symptoms include severe weight loss, night sweats, swollen lymph nodes, opportunistic infections.

Albumin *al-bu′min* a protein found in virtually all animal, the most abundant plasma protein.

Albuminuria *al″bu-mĭ-nu′re-ah* presence of albumin in the urine.

Alimentary *al″ĭ-men′tar-e* pertaining to the digestive organs.

Alkalosis *al″kah-lo′sis* a condition in which the blood has a lower hydrogen ion concentration than normal, and an increased pH.

Allergy *al′er-je* overzealous immune response to an otherwise harmless antigen; also called hypersensitivity.

Alopecia *al″o-pe′she-ah* baldness, condition of hair loss.

Alveolus *al-ve′o-lus* (1) a general term referring to a small cavity or depression; (2) an air sac in the lungs.

Amino acid *ah-me′no* an organic compound containing nitrogen, carbon, hydrogen, and oxygen; the building block of protein.

Amnion *am′ne-on* the fetal membrane that forms a fluid-filled sac around the embryo.

Amphiarthrosis *am″fe-ar-thro′sis* a slightly movable joint.

Anabolism *an-nab′o-lizm* the energy-requiring building phase of metabolism in which simpler substances are combined to form more complex substances.

Anaerobic *an-a′-er-ōb-ik* not requiring oxygen.

Anatomy the science of the structure of living organisms.

Anemia *ah-ne′me-ah* reduced oxygen-carrying capacity of the blood caused by a decreased number of erythrocytes or decreased percentage of hemoglobin in the blood.

Aneurysm *an′u-rizm* blood-filled sac in an artery wall caused by dilation or weakening of the wall.

Angina pectoris *an-ji′nah pek′tor-is* severe, suffocating chest pain caused by brief lack of oxygen supply to heart muscle.

Anorexia *an′o-rek′se-ah* loss of appetite or desire for food.

Anoxia *ah-nok′se-ah* a deficiency of oxygen.

Antagonists *an-tag′o-nists* muscles that act in opposition to an agonist or prime mover.

Antecubital anterior surface of the elbow.

Anterior *an-ter′e-er* the front of an organism, organ, or part; the ventral surface.

Antibody *an′tĭ-bod′e* a specialized substance produced by the body that can provide immunity against a specific antigen.

Antigen *an′tĭ-jen* any substance—including toxins, foreign proteins, or bacteria—that, when introduced to the body, is recognized as foreign and activates the immune system.

Anus *a′nus* the distal end of the digestive tract; the outlet of the rectum.

Aorta *a-or′tah* the major systemic artery; arises from the left ventricle of the heart.

Aortic body a receptor in the aortic arch sensitive to changing oxygen, carbon dioxide, and pH levels of the blood.

Apocrine gland *ap′o-krin* the less numerous type of sweat gland. Produces a secretion containing water, salts, and proteins.

Aponeurosis *ap″o-nu-ro′sis* fibrous or membranous sheet connecting a muscle and the part it moves.

Appendicular skeleton *ap″en-dik′u-lar* bones of the limbs and limb girdles that are attached to the axial skeleton.

Appendix *ah-pen′diks* a wormlike extension of the large intestine.

Aqueous humor *a′kwe-us hu′mer* the watery fluid in the anterior chambers of the eye.

Arachnoid *ah-rak′noid* weblike; specifically, the weblike middle layer of the three meninges.

Areola *ah-re′o-lah* the circular, pigmented area surrounding the nipple.

Arrector pili *ah-rek′tor pi′li* tiny, smooth muscles attached to hair follicles, which cause the hair to stand upright when activated.

Arteriole *ar-tēr′e-ol* minute artery.

Arteriosclerosis *ar-tēr′e-o-skler-o′sis* any of a number of proliferative and degenerative changes in the arteries leading to their decreased elasticity.

Artery a vessel that carries blood away from the heart.

Arthritis *ar-thri′tis* inflammation of the joints.

Articulation joint; point where two bones meet.

Asthma *az′mah* disease or allergic response characterized by bronchial spasms and difficult breathing.

Astigmatism *ah-stig′mah-tizm* a visual defect resulting from irregularity in the lens or cornea of the eye causing the image to be out of focus.

Atherosclerosis *a′ther-o″skler-o′sis* changes in the walls of large arteries consisting of lipid deposits on the artery walls. The early stage of arteriosclerosis and increased rigidity.

Atlas the first cervical vertebra; articulates with the occipital bone of the skull and the second cervical vertebra (axis).

Atom *at′um* the smallest part of an element; indivisible by ordinary chemical means.

Atomic mass number the sum of the number of protons and neutrons in the nucleus of an atom.

Atomic number the number of protons in an atom.

Atomic symbol a one- or two-letter symbol indicating a particular element.

Atomic weight average of the mass numbers of all of the isotopes of an element.

Atrioventricular node (AV node) *a′tre-o-ven-trik′u-lar* a specialized mass of conducting cells located at the atrioventricular junction in the heart.

Atrium *a′tre-um* a chamber of the heart receiving blood from the veins; superior heart chamber.

Atrophy *at′ro-fe* a reduction in size or wasting away of an organ or cell resulting from disease or lack of use.

Auditory *aw′dĭ-to″re* pertaining to the sense of hearing.

Auditory ossicles *aw′sih-kulz* three tiny bones, the malleus, incus, and stapes, located within the middle ear that serve as transmitters of sound vibrations.

Auscultation *aws″kul-ta′shun* the act of examination by listening to body sounds.

Autoimmune response the production of antibodies or effector T cells that attack a person's own tissue.

Automaticity *aw-to″mah-tis′ĭ-te* the ability of a structure, organ, or system to initiate its own activity.

Autonomic *aw″to-nom′ik* self-directed; self-regulating; independent.

Autonomic nervous system the division of the nervous system that functions involuntarily; innervates cardiac muscle, smooth muscle, and glands.

Axial skeleton *ak′se-al* the bones of the skull, vertebral column, thorax, and sternum.

Axilla *ak-sih′lah* armpit.

Axis (1) the second cervical vertebra; has a vertical projection called the dens around which the atlas rotates; (2) the imaginary line about which a joint or structure revolves.

Axon *ak′son* neuron process that carries impulses away from the nerve cell body; efferent process; the conducting portion of a nerve cell.

B cells lymphocytes that oversee humoral immunity; their descendants differentiate into antibody-producing plasma cells; also called B lymphocytes.

Bacteria any of a large group of microorganisms, generally one-celled; found in humans and other animals, plants, soil, air, and water; have a broad range of functions.

Basal metabolic rate *met″ah-bol′ik* the rate at which energy is expended (heat produced) by the body per unit time under controlled (basal) conditions: 12 hours after a meal, at rest.

Basal nuclei *nu′kle-i* gray matter areas deep within the white matter of the cerebral hemispheres; also called basal ganglia.

Base a substance that accepts hydrogen ions; proton acceptor; compare with *acid*.

Basement membrane a thin layer of extracellular material to which epithelial cells are attached in mucosa surfaces.

Basophils *ba′zo-filz* white blood cells whose granules stain deep blue with basic dye; have a relatively pale nucleus and granular-appearing cytoplasm.

Benign *be-nīn′* not malignant.

Biceps *bi′seps* two-headed, especially applied to certain muscles.

Bicuspid *bi-kus′pid* having two points or cusps.

Bile a greenish-yellow or brownish fluid produced in and secreted by the liver, stored in the gallbladder, and released into the small intestine.

Biopsy *bi′ŏp-se* the removal and examination of live tissue; usually done to detect or rule out the presence of cancerous cells.

Blastocyst *blas′to-sist* a stage of early embryonic development.

Blood-brain barrier a mechanism that inhibits passage of materials from the blood into brain tissues.

Bolus *bo′lus* a rounded mass of food prepared by the mouth for swallowing.

Bony thorax *bōn′e tho′raks* bones of the thorax, including ribs, sternum, and thoracic vertebrae.

Brachial *bra′ke-al* pertaining to the arm.

Bradycardia *brad″e-kar′de-ah* slow heart beat, usually defined as a rate under 60 beats per minute.

Brain stem the portion of the brain consisting of the medulla, pons, and midbrain.

Bronchitis *brong-ki′tis* inflammation of the mucous membranes of the bronchi.

Bronchus *brong′kus* one of the two large branches of the trachea leading to the lungs.

Buccal *buk′al* pertaining to the cheek.

Buffer a substance or substances that help to stabilize the pH of a solution.

Bundle branch block a blocking of heart action resulting from damage to one of the bundle branches; delayed contraction of one ventricle.

Bursa *ber′sah* a small sac filled with fluid and located at friction points, especially joints.

Calculus *kal′ku-lus* a stone formed within various body parts.

Calorie *kal′o-re* unit of heat; the large calorie (spelled with a capital letter C) is the amount of heat required to raise 1 kg of water 1°C; also used in metabolic and nutrition studies as the unit to measure the energy value of foods.

Calyx *ka′liks* a cuplike extension of the pelvis of the kidney.

Canal a duct or passageway; a tubular structure.

Canaliculus *kan′ah-lik′u-lus* extremely small tubular passage or channel.

Cancer a malignant, invasive cellular neoplasm that has the capability of spreading throughout the body or body parts.

Capillary *kap′ĭ-lar″e* a minute blood vessel connecting arterioles with venules.

Carbohydrate *kar″bo-hi′drāt* organic compound composed of carbon, hydrogen, and oxygen; includes starches, sugars, cellulose.

Carcinogen *kar-sin′o-jen* cancer-causing agent.

Carcinoma *kar″sĭ-no′mah* cancer; a malignant growth of epithelial cells.

Cardiac *kar′de-ak* pertaining to the heart.

Cardiac cycle sequence of events encompassing one complete contraction and relaxation of the atria and ventricles of the heart.

Cardiac muscle specialized muscle of the heart.

Cardiac output the blood volume (in liters) ejected per minute by the left ventricle.

Cardioesophageal sphincter *kar″de-o-ĕ-sof″ah-je′al sfingk′ter* valve between the stomach and esophagus.

Cardiovascular system organ system that distributes blood to all parts of the body.

Carotid *kah-rot' id* the main artery in the neck.

Carotid body a receptor in the common carotid artery sensitive to changing oxygen, carbon dioxide, and pH levels of the blood.

Carotid sinus *si'nus* a dilation of a common carotid artery; involved in regulation of systemic blood pressure.

Carpal *kar'pal* one of the eight bones of the wrist.

Cartilage *kar'tĭ-lij* white, semiopaque connective tissue.

Cartilaginous joint *kar"ti-laj' ĭ-nus* bones united by cartilage; no joint cavity is present.

Catabolism *kah-tab'o-lizm* the process in which living cells break down substances into simpler substances; destructive metabolism.

Cataract *kat' ah-rakt* partial or complete loss of transparency of the crystalline lens of the eye.

Catecholamines *kat"ĕ-kol' ah-menz* epinephrine and norepinephrine.

Caudal *kaw' dal* toward the tail; in humans, the inferior portion of the anatomy.

Cecum *se' kum* the blind-end pouch at the beginning of the large intestine.

Cell the basic biological unit of living organisms, containing a nucleus and a variety of organelles enclosed by a limiting membrane.

Cell membrane see *plasma membrane.*

Cellular immunity *sel' u-lar ĭ-mu' nĭ-te* immunity conferred by lymphocytes called T cells; also called cell-mediated immunity.

Cellular respiration metabolic processes in which ATP is produced.

Cementum *se-men' tum* the bony connective tissue that covers the root of a tooth.

Central nervous system (CNS) the brain and the spinal cord.

Centriole *sen' tre-ō-l* a minute body found near the nucleus of the cell composed of microtubules; active in cell division.

Cerebellum *ser"ĕ-bel' um* part of the hindbrain; involved in producing smoothly coordinated skeletal muscle activity.

Cerebral aqueduct *ser' ĕ-bral ak' we-dukt"* the slender cavity of the midbrain that connects the third and fourth ventricles; also called the aqueduct of Sylvius.

Cerebrospinal fluid the fluid produced by choroid plexi; fills the ventricles and surrounds the central nervous system.

Cerebrum *ser' ĕ-brum* the largest part of the brain; consists of right and left cerebral hemispheres.

Cerumen *sĕ-roo' men* earwax.

Cervical *ser' vĭ-kal* refers to the neck or the necklike portion of an organ or structure.

Cervix *ser' viks* the inferior necklike portion of the uterus leading to the vagina.

Chemical bond an energy relationship holding atoms together; involves the interaction of electrons.

Chemical energy energy form stored in chemical bonds.

Chemical reaction process in which molecules are formed, changed, or broken down.

Chemoreceptors *ke" mo-re-sep' torz* receptors sensitive to various chemicals in solution.

Chiasma *ki-as' mah* a crossing or intersection of two structures, such as the optic nerves.

Cholecystokinin *ko'le-sis" to-kin' in* an intestinal hormone that stimulates gallbladder contraction and pancreatic juice release.

Cholesterol *ko-les' ter-ol* a steroid found in animal fats as well as in most body tissues; made by the liver.

Cholinergic fibers *ko' lin-er' jik* nerve endings that, upon stimulation, release acetylcholine.

Chondrocyte *kon' dro-sīt* a mature cartilage cell.

Chorion *ko' re-on* the outermost fetal membrane; helps form the placenta.

Choroid *ko' roid* the pigmented nutritive layer of the eye.

Chromatin *kro' mah-tin* the structures in the nucleus that carry the hereditary factors (genes).

Chromosome *kro' ma-sōm* barlike body of tightly coiled chromatin; visible during cell division.

Chyme *kīm* the semifluid stomach contents consisting of partially digested food and gastric secretions.

Cilia *sil' e-ah* tiny, hairlike projections on cell surfaces that move in a wavelike manner.

Ciliary zonule suspensory ligament that attaches the lens to the ciliary body in the anterior eye.

Circle of Willis a union of arteries at the base of the brain.

Circumduction *ser" kum-duk' shun* circular movement of a body part.

Cirrhosis *sĭ-ro' sis* a chronic disease of the liver, characterized by an overgrowth of connective tissue or fibrosis.

Cleavage *klev' ij* an early embryonic phase consisting of rapid cell divisions without intervening growth periods.

Clitoris *kli' to-ris* a small, erectile structure in the female, homologous to the penis in the male.

Clonal selection *klo' nul* the process during which a B cell or T cell becomes sensitized through binding contact with an antigen.

Clone descendants of a single cell.

Coagulation clotting (of blood).

Cochlea *kok' le-ah* a cavity of the inner ear resembling a snail shell; houses the hearing receptor.

Coitus *ko' ĭ-tus* sexual intercourse.

Coma *ko' mah* unconsciousness from which the person cannot be aroused.

Complement a group of plasma proteins that normally circulate in inactive forms; when activated by complement fixation, causes lysis of foreign cells and enhances phagocytosis and inflammation.

Compound substance composed of two or more different elements, the atoms of which are chemically united.

Concave *kon' kāv* having a curved or depressed surface.

Conductivity *kon' duk-tiv' ĭ-te* ability to transmit an electrical impulse.

Condyle *kon' dīl* a rounded projection at the end of a bone that articulates with another bone.

Cones one of the two types of photoreceptor cells in the retina of the eye. Provides for color vision.

Congenital *kon-jen' ĭ-tal* existing at birth.

Congestive heart failure (CHF) condition in which the pumping efficiency of the heart is depressed so that circulation is inadequate to meet tissue needs.

Conjunctiva *kon' junk-ti' vah* the thin, protective mucous membrane lining the eyelids and covering the anterior surface of the eyeball.

Connective tissue a primary tissue; form and function vary extensively. Functions include support, storage, and protection.

Contraception *kon' trah-sep' shun* the prevention of conception; birth control.

Contraction *kon-trak' shun* to shorten or develop tension, an ability highly developed in muscle cells.

Contralateral *kon" trah-lat' er-al* opposite; acting in unison with a similar part on the opposite side of the body.

Convergence *kon-ver' jens* turning toward a common point from different directions.

Convoluted *kon' vo-lūted* rolled, coiled, or twisted.

Cornea *kor' ne-ah* the transparent anterior portion of the eyeball.

Coronal plane see *frontal plane.*

Corpus *kor' pus* body; the major portion of an organ.

Cortex *kor' teks* the outer surface layer of an organ.

Costal *kos' tal* pertaining to the ribs.

Covalent bond *ko-va' lent* a bond involving the sharing of electrons between atoms.

Coxal pertaining to the leg.

Cramp painful, involuntary contraction of a muscle.

Cranial *kra' ne-al* pertaining to the skull.

Cranial nerves the 12 pairs of nerves that arise from the brain.

Crenation *kre-na' shun* the shriveling of a cell, for example an erythrocyte, resulting from loss of water.

Crural pertaining to the leg.

Cryptorchidism *krip-tor' kĭ-dizm* a developmental defect in which the testes fail (or one testis fails) to descend into the scrotum.

Cupula *ku' pu-lah* a domelike structure.

Cushing's syndrome *koosh' ingz sin' drōm* a disease produced by excess secretion of adrenocortical hormone; characterized by adipose tissue accumulation, weight gain, and osteoporosis.

Cutaneous *ku-ta'ne-us* pertaining to the skin.

Cutaneous membrane the skin; composed of epidermal and dermal layers.

Cyanosis *si"ah-no'sis* a bluish coloration of the mucous membranes and skin caused by deficient oxygenation of the blood.

Cystitis *sis-ti'tis* an inflammation of the urinary bladder.

Cytokinesis *si"to-ki-ne'sis* division of cytoplasm that occurs after the cell nucleus has divided.

Cytology *si-tol'o-je* the science concerned with the study of cells.

Cytoplasm *si'to-plazm"* the substance of a cell other than that of the nucleus.

Cytotoxic T cell see *killer T cell*.

Deciduous *de-sid'u-us* temporary.

Deciduous (milk) teeth the 20 temporary teeth replaced by permanent teeth; "baby" teeth.

Decomposition reaction a destructive chemical reaction in which complex substances are broken down into simpler ones.

Defecation *def"ih-ka'shun* the elimination of the contents of the bowels (feces).

Deglutition *deg"loo-tish'un* the act of swallowing.

Dehydration *de"hi-dra'shun* a condition resulting from excessive loss of water.

Dehydration synthesis process by which a larger molecule is synthesized from smaller ones by removal of a water molecule at each site of bond formation.

Dendrites *den'drits* the branching extensions of neurons that carry electrical signals to the cell body; the receptive portion of a nerve cell.

Dentin *den'tin* the calcified tissue forming the major part of a tooth; deep to the enamel.

Deoxyribonucleic acid (DNA) *de-ok'se-ri"bo-nu'kla'ik* nucleic acid found in all living cells: carries the organism's hereditary information.

Depolarization *de-po"lar-i-za'shun* the loss of a state of polarity; the loss of a negative charge inside the plasma membrane.

Dermatitis *der"mah-ti'tis* an inflammation of the skin; nonspecific skin allergies.

Dermis *der'mis* the deep layer of the skin; composed of dense, irregular connective tissue.

Diabetes mellitus *di"ah-be'tez mel-li'tus* a disease caused by deficient insulin release or inadequate responsiveness to insulin, leading to inability of the body cells to use carbohydrates at a normal rate.

Diapedesis *di"ah-pĕ-de'sis* the passage of blood cells through intact vessel walls into the tissues.

Diaphragm *di'ah-fram* (1) any partition or wall separating one area from another; (2) a muscle that separates the thoracic cavity from the abdominopelvic cavity.

Diaphysis *di'af'ĭ-sis* elongated shaft of a long bone.

Diarthrosis *di"ar-thro'sis* a freely movable joint.

Diastole *di-as'to-le* a period (between contractions) of relaxation of the heart during which it fills with blood.

Diencephalon *di"en-sef'ah-lon* that part of the forebrain between the cerebral hemispheres and the midbrain including the thalamus, the third ventricle, and the hypothalamus.

Diffusion *dĭ-fu'zhun* the spreading of particles in a gas or solution with a movement toward uniform distribution of particles.

Digestion *di-jest'jun* the bodily process of breaking down foods chemically and mechanically.

Digestive system system that process food into absorbable units and eliminates indigestible wastes.

Digital pertaining to the digits; fingers, toes.

Dilate *di'lāt* to stretch; to open; to expand.

Disaccharide *di-sak'ĭ-rīd* literally, double sugar; examples include sucrose and lactose.

Distal *dis'tal* farthest from the point of attachment of a limb or origin of a structure.

Diverticulum *di"ver-tik'u-lum* a pouch or sac in the walls of a hollow organ or structure.

Dorsal *dor'sal* pertaining to the back; posterior.

Dorsiflexion up and down movement that includes lifting the foot so that its superior surface approaches the shin (standing on your heels).

Duct *dukt* a canal or passageway.

Duodenum *du'o-de'num* the first part of the small intestine.

Dura mater *du'rah ma'ter* the outermost and toughest of the three membranes (meninges) covering the brain and spinal cord.

Dynamic equilibrium sense that reports on angular or rotatory movements of the head in space.

Dyspnea *disp'ne-ah* labored, difficult breathing.

Ectopic *ek-top'ik* not in the normal place; for example, in an ectopic pregnancy the egg is implanted at a place other than the uterus.

Edema *ĕ-de'mah* an abnormal accumulation of fluid in body parts or tissues; causes swelling.

Effector *ef-fek'tor* an organ, gland, or muscle capable of being activated by nerve endings.

Efferent *ef'er-ent* carrying away or away from.

Efferent neurons neurons that conduct impulses away from the central nervous system.

Ejaculation *e-jak"u-la'shun* the sudden ejection of semen from the penis.

Electrical energy energy form resulting from the movement of charged particles.

Electrocardiogram (ECG) *e-lek"tro-kar'de-o-gram"* a graphic record of the electrical activity of the heart.

Electroencephalogram (EEG) *e-lek"tro-en-sef'ah-lo-gram"* a graphic record of the electrical activity of nerve cells in the brain.

Electrolyte *e-lek'tro-līt* a substance that breaks down into ions when in solution and is capable of conducting an electric current.

Electron negatively charged subatomic particle; orbits the atomic nucleus.

Electron transport chain metabolic pathway within the mitochondria in which energy harvested from high-energy hydrogen atoms is used to make ATP. Final delivery of H to molecular oxygen produces water.

Element *el'ĕ-ment* any of the building blocks of matter; oxygen, hydrogen, carbon, for example.

Embolism *em'bo-lizm* the obstruction of a blood vessel by an embolus (blood clot, bubble of air, or fatty mass floating in the blood).

Embryo *em'bre-o* an organism in its early stages of development; in humans, the first 2 months after conception.

Emesis *em'ĕ-sis* vomiting.

Emmetropia the eye that focuses images correctly on the retina is said to have this "harmonious vision."

Emphysema *em"fĭ-se'mah* a condition caused by overdistension of the pulmonary alveoli and fibrosis of lung tissue.

Enamel the hard, calcified substance that covers the crown of a tooth.

Endocarditis *en'do-kar-di'tis* an inflammation of the inner lining of the heart.

Endocardium *en'do-kar'de-um* the endothelial membrane lining the interior of the heart.

Endocrine glands *en'do-krin* ductless glands that empty their hormonal products directly into the blood.

Endocrine system body system that includes internal organs that secrete hormones.

Endometrium *en-do-me'tre-um* the mucous membrane lining of the uterus.

Endomysium *en"do-mis'e-um* the thin connective tissue surrounding each muscle cell.

Endoneurium a delicate connective tissue sheath that surrounding each fiber in a nerve.

Endoplasmic reticulum *een"do-plas'mik rĕ-tik'u-lum* a membranous network of tubular or saclike channels in the cytoplasm of a cell.

Endothelium *en"do-the'le-um* the single layer of simple squamous cells that line the walls of the heart and the vessels that carry blood and lymph.

Energy the ability to do work.

Enzyme *en'zīm* a substance formed by living cells that acts as a catalyst in bodily chemical reactions.

Eosinophils *e"o-sin'o-filz* granular white blood cells whose granules readily take up a stain called eosin.

Epicardium a serous membrane that tightly hugs the external surface of the heart and is actually part of the heart wall; also called visceral pericardium.

Epidermis *ep'ĭ-der'mis* the outer layers of the skin; epithelium.

Epididymis *ep'ĭ-did'ĭ-mis* that portion of the male duct system in which sperm mature. Empties into the ductus, or vas, deferens.

Epiglottis *ep'' ĭ-glot' is* the elastic cartilage at the back of the throat; covers the glottis during swallowing.

Epimysium *ep'' ĭ-mis' e-um* the sheath of fibrous connective tissue surrounding a muscle.

Epineurium a tough, fibrous sheath that binds together the fascicles in a nerve.

Epiphysis *ĕ-pif' ĭ-sis* the end of a long bone.

Epithelium *ep'' ĭ-the' le-um* one of the primary tissues; covers the surface of the body and lines the body cavities, ducts, and vessels.

Equilibrium *e'' kwĭ-lib' re-um* balance; a state when opposite reactions or forces counteract each other exactly.

Erythrocytes *ĕ-rith' ro-sĭts* red blood cells.

Erythropoiesis *ĕ-rith'' ro-poi-e' sis* the process of erythrocyte formation.

Estrogens *es' tro-jenz* hormones that stimulate female secondary sex characteristics; female sex hormones.

Eupnea *ŭp-ne' ah* easy, normal breathing.

Eversion special movement of the foot achieved by turning the sole laterally.

Exchange reaction a chemical reaction in which bonds are both made and broken; atoms become combined with different atoms.

Excretion *ek-skre' shun* the elimination of waste products from the body.

Exocrine glands *ek' so-krin* glands that have ducts through which their secretions are carried to a body surface (skin or mucosa).

Expiration *eks'' pĭ-ra' shun* the act of expelling air from the lungs; exhalation.

Extension movement that increases the angle of a joint, e.g., straightening a flexed knee.

External respiration the actual exchange of gases between the alveoli and the blood (pulmonary gas exchange).

Extracellular *eks'' trah-sel' u-lar* outside a cell.

Extracellular matrix nonliving material in connective tissue consisting of ground substance and fibers that separate the living cells.

Extracellular fluid fluid within the body but outside the cells.

Fallopian tube *fal-lo' pe-an* see *uterine tube*.

Fascia *fash' e-ah* layers of fibrous tissue covering and separating muscles.

Fascicle *fas' ĭ-kul* a bundle of nerve or muscle fibers bound together by connective tissue.

Fatty acid a building block of fats.

Feces *fe' sēz* material discharged from the bowel composed of food residue, secretions, and bacteria.

Femoral pertaining to the thigh.

Fertilization *fer' tĭ-lĭ-za' shun* fusion of the nuclear material of an egg and a sperm.

Fetus *fe' tus* the unborn young; in humans the period from the third month of development until birth.

Fibrillation *fi-brĭ-la' shun* irregular, uncoordinated contraction of muscle cells, particularly of the heart musculature.

Fibrin *fi' brin* the fibrous insoluble protein formed during the clotting of blood.

Fibrinogen *fi-brin' o-jen* a blood protein that is converted to fibrin during blood clotting.

Fibrous joint bones joined by fibrous tissue, no joint cavity is present.

Fibrous protein a strandlike protein that appears most often in body structures. They are very important in binding structures together and for providing strength in certain body tissues.

Fibular pertaining to the area of the fibula, the lateral bone of the leg.

Filtration *fil-tra' shun* the passage of a solvent and dissolved substances through a membrane or filter.

Fissure *fis' zher* (1) a groove or cleft; (2) the deepest depressions or inward folds on the brain.

Fixators *fiks-a' torz* muscles acting to immobilize a joint or a bone; fixes the origin of a muscle so that muscle action can be exerted at the insertion.

Flaccid *flak' sid* soft; flabby; relaxed.

Flagella *flah-jel' ah* long, whiplike extensions of the cell membrane of some bacteria and sperm; serve to propel the cell.

Flexion *flek' shun* bending; the movement that decreases the angle between bones.

Focus *fo' kus* creation of a sharp image by a lens.

Follicle *fol' lĭ-kul* (1) structure in an ovary consisting of a developing egg surrounded by follicle cells; (2) colloid-containing structure in the thyroid gland.

Fontanels *fon'' tah-nelz'* the fibrous membranes in the skull where bone has not yet formed; babies' "soft spots."

Foramen *fo-ra' men* a hole or opening in a bone or between body cavities.

Formed elements cellular portion of blood.

Fossa *fos' ah* a depression; often an articular surface.

Fovea *fo-ve' ah* a pit.

Frontal (coronal) plane a longitudinal plane that divides the body or an organ into anterior and posterior parts.

Fundus *fun' dus* the base of an organ; that part farthest from the opening of the organ.

Gallbladder the sac beneath the right lobe of the liver used for bile storage.

Gallstones particles of hardened cholesterol or calcium salts that are occasionally formed in gallbladder and bile ducts.

Gamete *game' ēt* male or female sex cell (sperm/egg).

Gametogenesis *gam'' ē-to-jen' ĕ-sis* the formation of gametes.

Ganglion *gang' gle-on* a group of nerve cell bodies located in the peripheral nervous system.

Gastrin *gas' trin* a hormone that stimulates gastric secretion, especially hydrochloric acid release.

Gene *jēn* biological units of heredity located in chromatin; transmits hereditary information.

Genetics *je-net' iks* the science of heredity.

Genitalia *jen'' ĭ-ta' le-ah* the external sex organs.

Germ layers the initial or primary tissues formed in the embryo (ectoderm, mesoderm, endoderm) from which all body tissues arise.

Gingiva *jin-ji' vah* the gums.

Gland an organ specialized to secrete or excrete substances for further use in the body or for elimination.

Glaucoma *glaw-ko' mah* an abnormal increase of the pressure within the eye.

Glia *gli' ah* see *neuroglia*.

Globular protein a protein whose functional structure is basically spherical . Also referred to as functional protein; includes hemoglobin enzymes and some hormones.

Glomerular capsule *glō-mer' yoo-ler* double-walled cuplike end of a renal tubule; encloses a glomerulus; also called Bowman's capsule.

Glomerulus *glo-mer' u-lus* a knot of coiled capillaries in the kidney; forms filtrate.

Glottis *glot' is* the opening between the vocal cords in the larynx.

Glucose *gloo' kōs* the principal sugar in the blood; a monosaccharide.

Glycerol *glis' er-ol* a sugar alcohol; one of the building blocks of fats.

Glycogen *gli' ko-jen* the main carbohydrate stored in animal cells; a polysaccharide.

Glycogenesis *gli'' ko-jen' ĕ-sis* formation of glycogen from glucose.

Glycogenolysis *gli'' ko-jē-nol' ĭ-sis* breakdown of glycogen to glucose.

Glycolysis *gli-kol' ĭ-sis* breakdown of glucose to pyruvic acid; an anaerobic process.

Goblet cells individual cells (simple glands) that produce mucus.

Goiter *goi' ter* a benign enlargement of the thyroid gland.

Gonads *go' nadz* organs producing gametes; ovaries or testes.

Graafian follicle *graf' e-an fol' lĭ-kul* see *vesicular follicle*.

Graded potential a local change in membrane potential that varies directly with the strength of the stimulus, declines with distance.

Graded response a response that varies directly with the strength of the stimulus.

Gray matter the gray area of the central nervous system; contains unmyelinated nerve fibers and nerve cell bodies.

Groin the junction of the thigh and the trunk; the inguinal area.

Gustation *gus-ta' shun* taste.

Gyrus *ji' rus* an outward fold of the surface of the cerebral cortex.

Hamstring muscles the posterior thigh muscles: the biceps femoris, semimembranosus, and semitendinosus.

Haversian system *ha-ver' shan* see *osteon*.

Heart block impaired transmission of impulses from atrium to ventricle.

Heart murmur an abnormal heart sound (usually resulting from valve problems).

Heat stroke the failure of the heat-regulating ability of an individual under heat stress.

Helper T cell the type of T lymphocyte that orchestrates cellular immunity by direct contact with other immune cells and by releasing chemicals called lymphokines; also helps to mediate the humoral response by interacting with B cells.

Hematocrit *he-mat' o-krit* the percentage of erythrocytes to total blood volume.

Hematopoiesis *he″mato-poi-e' sis* formation of blood cells.

Hemiplegia *hem' e-ple' je-ah* paralysis of one side of the body.

Hemocytoblasts *he″mo-si' to-blastz* stem cells that give rise to all the formed elements of the blood.

Hemoglobin *he″mo-glo' bin* the oxygen-transporting pigment of erythrocytes.

Hemolysis *he-mol' ĭ-sis* the rupture of erythrocytes.

Hemophilia *he″mo-fil' e-ah* an inherited clotting defect caused by absence of a blood-clotting factor.

Hemorrhage *hem' or-ij* the loss of blood from the vessels by flow through ruptured walls; bleeding.

Hepatic portal system *he-pat' ik* the circulation in which the hepatic portal vein carries dissolved nutrients from the digestive tract to the liver for processing.

Hepatitis *hep' ah-ti' tis* inflammation of the liver.

Hilum, hilus *hi' lum, hi' lus* a depressed area where vessels enter and leave an organ.

Histamine *his' tah-mēn* a substance that causes vasodilation and increased vascular permeability.

Histology *his-tol' o-je* the branch of anatomy dealing with the microscopic structure of tissues.

Homeostasis *ho″me-o-sta' sis* a state of body equilibrium or stable internal environment of the body.

Homologous *ho-mol' o-gus* parts or organs corresponding in structure but not necessarily in function.

Hormones *hor' mōnz* chemical messengers secreted by endocrine glands; responsible for specific regulatory effects on certain parts or organs.

Humoral immunity *hu' mor-al* immunity provided by antibodies released by sensitized B cells and their plasma cell progeny. Also called antibody-mediated immunity.

Hyaline *hi' ah-lin* glassy; transparent.

Hydrochloric acid *hi″dro-klo' rik* HCl; aids protein digestion in the stomach; produced by parietal cells.

Hydrogen bond weak bond in which a hydrogen atom forms a bridge between two electron-hungry atoms. An important intramolecular bond.

Hydrolysis *hi-drol' ĭ-sis* the process in which water is used to split a substance into smaller particles.

Hyperopia *hi″per-o' pe-ah* farsightedness.

Hypertension *hi″per-ten' shun* an abnormally high blood pressure.

Hypertonic *hi″per-ton' ik* excessive, above normal, tone or tension.

Hypertrophy *hi-per' tro-fe* an increase in the size of a tissue or organ independent of the body's general growth.

Hypotension low blood pressure.

Hypothalamus *hi″po-thal' ah-mus* the region of the diencephalon forming the floor of the third ventricle of the brain.

Hypothermia *hi″po-ther' me-ah* subnormal body temperature.

Hypotonic *hi-po-ton' ik* below normal tone or tension.

Hypoxia *hi-pok' se-ah* a condition in which inadequate oxygen is available to tissues.

Ileum *il' e-um* the terminal part of the small intestine; between the jejunum and the cecum of the large intestine.

Immune response antigen-specific defenses mounted by activated lymphocytes (T cells and B cells).

Immunity *ĭ-mu' nĭ-te* the ability of the body to resist many agents (both living and nonliving) that can cause disease; resistance to disease.

Immunocompetence *im″mu-no-kom' pĕ-tents* the ability of the body's immune cells to recognize (by binding) specific antigens; reflects the presence of plasma membrane–bound receptors.

Immunodeficiency disease *im″mu-no-de-fish' en-se* disease resulting from the deficient production or function of immune cells or certain molecules (complement, antibodies, and so on) required for normal immunity.

Immunoglobulin *im″mu-no-glob' u-lin* a protein molecule, released by plasma cells, that mediates humoral immunity; an antibody.

Infarct *in' farkt* a region of dead, deteriorating tissue resulting from a lack of blood supply.

Inferior (caudal) pertaining to a position near the tail end of the long axis of the body.

Inflammation *in″flah-ma' shun* a physiological response of the body to tissue injury; includes dilation of blood vessels and increased vessel permeability.

Inguinal *ing' gwĭ-nal* pertaining to the groin region.

Inner cell mass a cluster of cells in the blastocyst from which the embryo develops.

Innervation *in″er-va' shun* the supply of nerves to a body part.

Inorganic compound a compound that lacks carbon; for example, water.

Insertion *in-ser' shun* the movable attachment of a muscle as opposed to its origin.

Inspiration *in″spĭ-ra' shun* the drawing of air into the lungs; inhalation.

Integumentary system *in-teg-u-men' tar-e* the skin and its accessory organs.

Intercellular *in″ter-sel' u-lar* between the body cells.

Intercellular matrix *ma' triks* the material between adjoining cells; especially important in connective tissue.

Internal respiration the use of oxygen by body cells; also called *cellular respiration.*

Interneurons completes the pathway between afferent and efferent neurons; also called *association neurons.*

Interstitial fluid *in″ter-stish' al* the fluid between the cells.

Intervertebral disks *in″ter-ver' tĕ-bral* the disks of fibrocartilage between the vertebrae.

Intracellular *in' trah-sel' u-lar* within a cell.

Intracellular fluid fluid within a cell.

Intrinsic factor *in-trin' sik* a substance produced by the stomach that is required for vitamin B_{12} absorption.

Invert to turn inward.

Ion *i' on* an atom with a positive or negative electric charge.

Ionic bond bond formed by the complete transfer of electron(s) from one atom to another (or others). The resulting charged atoms, or ions, are oppositely charged and attract each other.

Ipsilateral *ip″sĭ-lat' er-al* situated on the same side.

Iris *i' ris* the pigmented, involuntary muscle that acts as the diaphragm of the eye.

Irritability *ir″ ĭ-tah-bil' ĭ-te* ability to respond to a stimulus.

Ischemia *is-ke' me-ah* a local decrease in blood supply.

Isometric *i″so-met' rik* of the same length.

Isotonic *i″so-ton' ik* having a uniform tension; of the same tone.

Isotope *i' sĭ-tōp* different atomic form of the same element. Isotopes vary only in the number of neutrons they contain.

Jaundice *jawn' dis* an accumulation of bile pigments in the blood producing a yellow color of the skin.

Jejunum *je-joo' num* the part of the small intestine between the duodenum and the ileum.

Joint the junction of two or more bones; an articulation.

Keratin *ker' ah-tin* a tough, insoluble protein found in tissues such as hair, nails, and epidermis of the skin.

Killer T cell effector T cell that directly kills foreign cells; also called a cytotoxic T cell.

Kilocalories (kcal) unit used to measure the energy value of food.

Kinetic energy energy of motion.

Kinins *ki' ninz* group of polypeptides that dilate arterioles, increase vascular permeability, and induce pain.

Krebs cycle the aerobic pathway occurring within the mitochondria, in which energy is liberated during metabolism of carbohydrates, fats, and amino acids and CO_2 is produced.

Labia *la' be-ah* lips.

Labyrinth bony cavities and membranes of the inner ear that house the hearing and equilibrium receptors.

Lacrimal *lak' rĭ-mal* pertaining to tears.

Lactation *lak-ta' shun* the production and secretion of milk.

Lacteal *lak′ te-al* special lymphatic capillaries of the small intestine that take up lipids.

Lactic acid *lak′ tik* the product of anaerobic metabolism, especially in muscle.

Lacuna *lah-ku′ nah* a little depression or space; in bone or cartilage, lacunae are occupied by cells.

Lamina *lam′ ĭ-nah* (1) a thin layer or flat plate; (2) the portion of a vertebra between the transverse process and the spinous process.

Laryngitis *lar″in-ji′ tis* an inflammation of the larynx.

Larynx *lar′ inks* the cartilaginous organ located between the trachea and the pharynx; voice box.

Lateral *lat′ er-al* away from the midline of the body.

Lens the elastic, doubly convex structure in the eye that focuses the light entering the eye on the retina.

Lesion *le′ zhun* a tissue injury or wound.

Leukemia *lu-ke′ me-ah* a cancerous condition in which there is an excessive production of immature leukocytes.

Leukocyte *lu′ ko-sīt* white blood cell.

Ligament *lig′ ah-ment* a cord of fibrous tissue that connects bones.

Lipid *lip′ id* organic compound formed of carbon, hydrogen, and oxygen; examples are fats and cholesterol.

Lumbar *lum′ bar* the portion of the back between the thorax and the pelvis.

Lumen *lu′ men* the space inside a tube, blood vessel, or hollow organ.

Lymph *limf* the watery fluid in the lymph vessels collected from the tissue spaces.

Lymph node a mass of lymphatic tissue

Lymphatic system *lim-fat′ ik* a system of lymphatic vessels, lymph nodes, and other lymphoid organs and tissues.

Lymphocytes *lim′ fo-sītz* agranular white blood cells formed in the bone marrow that mature in the lymphoid tissue.

Lymphoid organs refers to organs in the lymphatic system including lymphatic vessels, lymph nodes, spleen, and tonsils; see *lymphatic system.*

Lymphokines *lim′ fo-kīnz* proteins involved in cells-mediated immune responses that enhance the immune and inflammatory responses.

Lysosomes *li′ so-sōmz* organelles that originate from the Golgi apparatus and contain strong digestive enzymes.

Lysozyme *li′ so-zīm* an enzyme found in sweat, saliva, and tears that is capable of destroying certain kinds of bacteria.

Macrophage *mak′ ro-fāj″* cell particularly abundant in lymphatic and connective tissues; important in the immune response as an antigen-presenter to T cells and B cells.

Malignant *mah-lig′ nant* life threatening; pertains to neoplasms that spread and lead to death, such as cancer.

Mammary glands *mam′ mer-e* milk-producing glands of the breasts.

Mastication *mas″tĭ-ka′ shun* the act of chewing.

Matter anything that occupies space and has mass.

Meatus *me-a′ tus* the external opening of a canal.

Mechanical energy energy form directly involved in putting matter into motion.

Mechanoreceptors *mek″ah-no-rē-sep′ terz* receptors sensitive to mechanical pressures such as touch, sound, or contractions.

Medial *me′ de-al* toward the midline of the body.

Mediastinum *me″de-as-ti′ num* the region of the thoracic cavity between the lungs.

Medulla *mĕ-dul′ ah* the central portion of certain organs.

Meiosis *mi-o′ sis* the two cell successive cell divisions in gamete formation producing nuclei with half the full number of chromosomes (haploid).

Melanin *mel′ ah-nin* the dark pigment synthesized by melanocytes; responsible for skin color.

Melanocyte a cell that produces melanin.

Memory cell member of T cell and B cell clones that provides for immunologic memory.

Menarche *mĕ-nar′ ke* establishment of menstrual function; the first menstrual period.

Meninges *mĕ-nin′ jēz* the membranes that cover the brain and spinal cord.

Meningitis *men″in-ji′ tis* inflammation of the meninges of the brain or spinal cord.

Menopause *men′ o-pawz* the physiological end of menstrual cycles.

Menses *men′ sēz* monthly discharge of blood from the uterus. Menstruation.

Menstruation *men″stroo-a′ shun* the periodic, cyclic discharge of blood, secretions, tissue, and mucus from the mature female uterus in the absence of pregnancy.

Mesentery *mes′ en-ter″e* the double-layered membrane of the peritoneum that supports most organs in the abdominal cavity.

Metabolic rate *met″ah-bol′ ik* the energy expended by the body per unit time.

Metabolism *mĕ-tab′ o-lizm* the sum total of the chemical reactions that occur in the body.

Metabolize *mĕ-tab′ o-līz* to transform substances into energy or materials the body can use or store by means of anabolism or catabolism.

Metacarpal *met″ah-kar′ pal* one of the five bones of the palm of the hand.

Metastasis *mĕ-tas′ tah-sis* the spread of cancer from one body part or organ into another not directly connected to it.

Metatarsal *met″ah-tar′ sal* one of the five bones between the tarsus and the phalanges of the foot.

Microvilli *mi″kro-vil′ i* the tiny projections on the free surfaces of some epithelial cells; increase surface area for absorption.

Micturition *mik″tu-rish′ un* urination, or voiding; emptying the bladder.

Midsagittal (median) section specific sagittal plane that lies exactly in the midline.

Minerals the inorganic chemical compounds found in nature.

Mitochondria *mi″to-kon′ dre-ah* the rod-like cytoplasmic organelles responsible for ATP generation.

Mitosis *mi-to′ sis* the division of the cell nucleus; often followed by division of the cytoplasm of a cell.

Mixed nerves nerves containing the processes of motor and sensory neurons; their impulses travel to and from the central nervous system.

Molecule *mol′ ĕ-kyool* particle consisting of two or more atoms held together by chemical bonds.

Monoclonal antibodies *mon″o-klōn′ ul* pure preparations of identical antibodies that exhibit specificity for a single antigen.

Monocyte *mon′ o-sīt* large single-nucleus white blood cell; agranular leukocyte.

Monosaccharide *mon″o-sak′ ĭ-rīd* literally, one sugar; the building block of carbohydrates; examples include glucose and fructose.

Mons pubis *monz pu′ bis* the fatty eminence over the pubic symphysis in the female.

Motor unit a motor neuron and all the muscle cells it supplies.

Mucous membrane (mucosa) membrane that forms the linings of body cavities open to the exterior (digestive, respiratory, urinary, and reproductive tracts).

Mucus *myoo′ kus* a sticky, thick fluid, secreted by mucous glands and mucous membranes, that keeps the free surface of membranes moist.

Muscle fibers muscle cells.

Muscle spindle encapsulated sensory receptor found in skeletal muscle that is sensitive to stretch.

Muscle tone sustained partial contraction of a muscle in response to stretch receptor inputs; keeps the muscle healthy and ready to react.

Muscle twitch a single rapid contraction of a muscle followed by relaxation.

Muscular dystrophy *dis′ tro-fe* a progressive disorder marked by atrophy and stiffness of the muscles.

Muscular system organ system consisting of skeletal muscles and their connective tissue attachments.

Myelin *mi′ ĕ-lin* a white, fatty lipid substance.

Myelinated fibers *mi′ ĕ-lĭ-nat″ed* axons (projections of a nerve cell) covered with myelin.

Myocardial infarction *mi″o-kar′ de-al in-fark′ shun* a condition characterized by dead tissue areas in the myocardium caused by interruption of blood supply to the area.

Myocardium *mi″o-kar′ de-um* the cardiac muscle layer of the heart wall.

Myofibrils *mi″o-fi′ brilz* contractile organelles found in the cytoplasm of muscle cells.

Myofilament *mi″o-fil′ ah-ment* filaments composing the myofibrils. Of two types: actin and myosin.

Myometrium *mi″o-me′ tri-um* the thick uterine musculature.

Myopia *mi-ō'pe-ah* nearsightedness.

Myosin *mi'o-sin* one of the principal contractile proteins found in muscle.

Nares *na'rēz* the nostrils.

Nasal pertaining to the nose.

Necrosis *nĕ-kro'sis* the death or disintegration of a cell or tissues caused by disease or injury.

Negative feedback feedback that causes the stimulus to decline or end.

Neoplasm *ne'o-plazm* an abnormal growth of cells. Sometimes cancerous.

Nephrons *nef'ronz* structural and functional units of the kidney.

Nerve bundle of neuronal processes (axons) outside the central nervous system.

Nerve fiber axon of a neuron.

Nerve impulse a self-propagating wave of depolarization; also called an *action potential.*

Nervous system fast-acting control system that employs nerve impulses to trigger muscle contraction or gland secretion.

Neuroglia *nu-rog'le-ah* the nonneuronal tissue of the central nervous system that performs supportive and other functions; also called glia.

Neuromuscular junction *nu'ro-mus'ku-lar* the region where a motor neuron comes into close contact with a skeletal muscle cell.

Neurons *nu'ronz* cells of the nervous system specialized to transmit messages throughout the body.

Neurotransmitter chemical released by neurons that may, upon binding to receptors of neurons or effector cells, stimulate or inhibit them.

Neutralization *nu'tral-i-za'shun* (1) a chemical reaction that occurs between an acid and a base; (2) blockage of the harmful effects of bacterial exotoxins or viruses by the binding of antibodies to their functional sites.

Neutron *nu'tron* uncharged subatomic particle; found in the atomic nucleus.

Neutrophils *nu'tro-filz* the most abundant of the white blood cells.

Nucleic acid *nu-kle'ic* class of organic molecules that includes DNA and RNA.

Nucleoli *nu-kle'o-li* small spherical bodies in the cell nucleus; function in ribosome synthesis.

Nucleotide *nu'kle-o-tīd* building block of nucleic acids.

Nucleus *nu'kle-us* a dense central body in most cells containing the genetic material of the cell.

Occipital *ok-sip'ĭ-tal* pertaining to area at the back of the head.

Occlusion *ŏ-kloo'zhun* closure or obstruction.

Olfaction *ol-fak'shun* smell.

Oogenesis *o'o-jen'ĕ-sis* the process of formation of the ova.

Ophthalmic *of-thal'mik* pertaining to the eye.

Opposition the action by which the thumb is used to touch the tips of the other fingers on the same hand. This unique action makes the human hand such a fine tool for grasping and manipulating things.

Optic *op'tik* pertaining to the eye.

Optic chiasma *op'tik ki-as'mah* the partial crossover of fibers of the optic nerves.

Oral relating to the mouth.

Orbital eye area.

Organ a part of the body formed of two or more tissues that performs a specialized function.

Organ system a group of organs that work together to perform a vital body function; e.g., nervous system.

Organelles *or"gan-elz'* specialized structures in a cell that perform specific metabolic functions.

Organic compound a compound containing carbon; examples include proteins, carbohydrates, and fats.

Organism an individual living thing.

Origin attachment of a muscle that remains relatively fixed during muscular contraction.

Osmoreceptor *oz"mo-re-cep'tor* a structure sensitive to osmotic pressure or concentration of a solution.

Osmosis *oz-mo'sis* the diffusion of a solvent through a membrane from a dilute solution into a more concentrated one.

Ossicles *os'sĭ-kulz* the three bones of the middle ear: hammer, anvil, and stirrup.

Osteoblasts *os'te-o-blasts"* bone-forming cells.

Osteoclasts *os'te-o-klasts"* large cells that resorb or break down bone matrix.

Osteocyte *os'te-o-sīt"* a mature bone cell.

Osteon *os'te-on* a system of interconnecting canals in the microscopic structure of adult compact bone; unit of bone.

Osteoporosis *os"te-o-po-ro'sis* an increased softening of the bone resulting from a gradual decrease in rate of bone formation; a common condition in older people.

Otic *o'tik* pertaining to the ear.

Otolith *o'to-lith* one of the small calcified masses in the utricle and saccule of the inner ear.

Ovarian cycle *o-va're-an* the monthly cycle of follicle development, ovulation, and corpus luteum formation in an ovary.

Ovary *o'var-e* the female sex organ in which ova (eggs) are produced.

Ovulation *ov"u-la'shun* the release of an ovum (or oocyte) from the ovary.

Ovum *o'vum* the female gamete (germ cell); an egg.

Oxidation *ok's ĭ-da'shun* the process of substances combining with oxygen or the removal of hydrogen.

Oxygen debt *ok's ĭ-jen* the volume of oxygen required after exercise to oxidize the lactic acid formed during exercise.

Oxyhemoglobin *ok"s ĭ-he"mo-glo'bin* hemoglobin combined with oxygen.

Palate *pal'at* roof of the mouth.

Palpation *pal-pa'shun* examination by touch.

Pancreas *pan'kre-as* gland posterior to the stomach, between the spleen and the duodenum, produces both endocrine and exocrine secretions.

Pancreatic juice *pan"kre-at'ik* a secretion of the pancreas containing enzymes for digestion of all food categories.

Papilla *pah-pil'ah* small nipplelike projection.

Papillary muscles *pap'ĭ-ler"e* cone-shaped muscles found in the heart ventricles.

Paralysis *pah-ral'ĭ-sis* the loss of muscle function.

Paraplegia *par"ah-ple'je-ah* paralysis of the lower limbs.

Parasympathetic division *par"ah-sim"pah-thet'ik* a division of the autonomic nervous system; also referred to as the craniosacral division.

Parathyroid glands *par"ah-thi'roid* small endocrine glands located on the posterior aspect of the thyroid gland.

Parathyroid hormone (PTH) hormone released by the parathyroid glands that regulates blood calcium level.

Parietal *pah-ri'ĕ-tal* pertaining to the walls of a cavity.

Parotid *pah-rot'id* located near the ear.

Passive immunity short-lived immunity resulting from the introduction of "borrowed antibodies" obtained from an immune animal or human donor; immunological memory is not established.

Passive transport membrane transport processes that do not require cellular energy (ATP); e.g., diffusion, which is driven by kinetic energy.

Patella *pah-tel'ah* the kneecap.

Pathogen disease-causing microorganism (e.g., some bacteria, fungi, viruses, etc).

Pathogenesis *path'o-jen'ĕ-sis* the development of a disease.

Pectoral *pek'to-ral* pertaining to the chest.

Pectoral girdle see *shoulder girdle.*

Peduncle *pe-dung'kul* a stalk of fibers, especially that connecting the cerebellum to the pons, midbrain, and medulla oblongata.

Pelvic girdle incomplete bony basin formed by the two coxal bones that secures the lower limbs to the sacrum of the axial skeleton.

Pelvis *pel'vis* a basin-shaped structure; lower portion of the skeleton of the body trunk.

Penis *pe'nis* the male organ of copulation and urination.

Pepsin an enzyme capable of digesting proteins in an acid pH.

Pericardium *per"ĭ-kar'de-um* the membranous sac enveloping the heart.

Perimysium *per"ĭ-mis'e-um* the connective tissue enveloping bundles of muscle fibers.

Perineum *per"i-ne'um* that region of the body extending from the anus to the scrotum in males and from the anus to the vulva in females.

Perineurium coarse connective tissue wrapping that binds groups of fibers in a nerve, forming fascicles, or fiber bundles.

Periosteum *per"e-os'te-um* double-layered connective tissue that covers and nourishes the bone.

Peripheral nervous system (PNS) *pĭ-rif'er-al* a system of nerves that connects the outlying parts of the body with the central nervous system.

Peripheral resistance the resistance to blood flow offered by the systemic blood vessels; a measure of the amount of friction encountered by blood.

Peristalsis *per"ĭ-stal'sis* the waves of contraction seen in tubelike organs; propels substances along the tract.

Peritoneum *per"ĭ-to-ne'um* the serous membrane lining the interior of the abdominal cavity and covering the surfaces of the abdominal organs.

Peritonitis *per"ĭ-to-ni'tis* an inflammation of the peritoneum.

Permeability *per"me-ah-bil'ĭ-te* that property of membranes that permits passage of molecules and ions.

Peroneal *per"o-ne'al* pertaining to the lateral aspect of the leg.

pH the symbol for hydrogen ion concentration; a measure of the relative acidity or alkalinity of a solution.

Phagocyte *fag'o-sīt* a cell capable of engulfing and digesting particles or cells harmful to the body.

Phagocytosis *fag"o-si-to'sis* the ingestion of solid particles by cells.

Phalanges *fah-lan'jēz* the bones of the finger or toe.

Pharyngotympanic (auditory) tube tube that connects the middle ear and the pharynx; allows pressure to be equalized on both sides of the ear drum; also called the Eustachian tube.

Pharynx *far'inks* the muscular tube extending from the posterior of the nasal cavities to the esophagus.

Phospholipid *fos'fo-lip"id* a modified triglyceride containing phosphorus.

Photoreceptors *fo"to-re-sep'torz* specialized receptor cells that respond to light energy.

Physiology *fiz"e-ol'o-je* the science of the functioning of living organisms.

Pinocytosis *pi"no-si-to'sis* the engulfing of extracellular fluid by cells.

Pituitary gland *pĭ-tu'ĭ-tār"e* the neuroendocrine gland located beneath the brain that serves a variety of functions including regulation of the gonads, thyroid, adrenal cortex, water balance, and lactation.

Placenta *plah-sen'tah* the temporary organ that provides nutrients and oxygen to the developing fetus, carries away wastes, and produces the hormones of pregnancy.

Plantar *plan'tar* pertaining to the sole of the foot.

Plasma *plaz'mah* the fluid portion of the blood.

Plasma cell member of a B cell clone; specialized to produce and release antibodies.

Plasma membrane membrane that encloses cell contents; outer limiting membrane.

Platelet *plāt'let* one of the irregular cell fragments of blood; involved in clotting.

Pleura *ploor'ah* the serous membrane covering the lungs and lining the thoracic cavity.

Pleurisy *ploor'ĭ-se* inflammation of the pleurae, making breathing painful.

Plexus *plek'sus* a network of interlacing nerves, blood vessels, or lymphatics.

Plica *pli'kah* a fold.

Pneumothorax *nu"mo-tho'raks* the presence of air or gas in a pleural cavity.

Polar body a minute cell produced during meiosis in the ovary.

Polar molecules nonsymmetrical molecules that contain electrically unbalanced atoms.

Polarized *po'lar-īzd* the state of an unstimulated neuron or muscle cell in which the inside of the cell is relatively negative in comparison to the outside; the resting state.

Polycythemia *pol"e-si-the'me-ah* presence of an abnormally large number of erythrocytes in the blood.

Polypeptide *pol"e-pep'tīd* a chain of amino acids.

Polysaccharide *pol"e-sak'ĭ-rīd* literally, many sugars; a polymer of linked monosaccharides; examples include starch and glycogen.

Pons (1) any bridgelike structure or part; (2) the brain area connecting the medulla with the midbrain, providing linkage between upper and lower levels of the central nervous system.

Positive feedback feedback that tends to cause a variable to change in the same direction as the initial change; enhances the stimulus.

Postganglionic (postsynaptic) neuron *pōst"gang-gle-on'ik* a neuron of the autonomic nervous system having its cell body in a ganglion and its axon extending to an organ or tissue.

Precipitation formation of insoluble complexes that settle out of solution.

Preganglionic (presynaptic) neuron *pre"gang-gle-on'ik* a neuron of the autonomic nervous system having its cell body in the brain or spinal cord and its axon terminating in a ganglion.

Pressoreceptor *pres"o-re-sep'tor* a nerve ending in the wall of the carotid sinus and aortic arch sensitive to vessel stretching.

Pressure gradient difference in hydrostatic (fluid) pressure that drives filtration.

Primary (immune) response the initial response of the immune system to an antigen; involves clonal selection and establishes immunological memory.

Prime mover muscle whose contractions are primarily responsible for a particular movement; agonist.

Process (1) a prominence or projection; (2) a series of actions for a specific purpose.

Pronation *pro-na'shun* the inward rotation of the forearm causing the radius to cross diagonally over the ulna—palms face posteriorly.

Prone refers to a body lying horizontally with the face downward.

Proprioceptor *pro"pre-oh-sep'tor* a receptor located in a muscle or tendon; concerned with locomotion, posture, and muscle tone.

Protein *pro'tēn* a complex nitrogenous substance; the main building material of cells.

Proteinuria *pro"te-in-u're-ah* the passage of proteins in the urine.

Proton *pro'ton* subatomic particle that bears a positive charge; located in the atomic nucleus.

Proximal *prok'sĭ-mal* toward the attached end of a limb or the origin of a structure.

Puberty *pu'ber-te* the period at which reproductive organs become functional.

Pubic pertaining to the genital region.

Pulmonary *pul'mo-ner"e* pertaining to the lungs.

Pulmonary circulation system of blood vessels that carry blood to and from the lungs for gas exchange.

Pulmonary edema *ĕ-de'mah* a leakage of fluid into the air sacs and tissue of the lungs.

Pulmonary ventilation breathing; consists of inspiration and expiration.

Pulse the rhythmic expansion and recoil of arteries resulting from heart contraction; can be felt from the outside of the body.

Pupil an opening in the center of the iris through which light enters the eye.

Purkinje fibers *pur-kin'je* the modified cardiac muscle fibers of the conduction system of the heart.

Pus the fluid product of inflammation composed of white blood cells, the debris of dead cells, and a thin fluid.

Pyelonephritis *pi"ĕ-lo-nĕ-fri'tis* an inflammation of the kidney pelvis and surrounding kidney tissues.

Pyloric region *pi-lor'ik* the final portion of the stomach; joins with the duodenum.

Pyramid any cone-shaped structure of an organ.

Pyrogen *pi'ro-jen* an agent or chemical substance that induces fever.

Quadriplegia *kwod"rĭ-ple'je-ah* the paralysis of all four limbs.

Radiant energy energy of the electromagnetic spectrum, which includes heat, light, ultraviolet waves, infrared waves, and other forms.

Radiate *ra'de-āt* diverge from a central point.

Radioactivity the process of spontaneous decay seen in some of the heavier isotopes, during which particles or energy is emitted from the atomic nucleus; results in the atom becoming more stable.

Radioisotope *ra"de-o-i'sĭ-tōp* isotope that exhibits radioactive behavior.

Ramus *ra'mus* a branch of a nerve, artery, vein, or bone.

Receptor *re-sep'tor* (1) a peripheral nerve ending specialized for response to particular types of stimuli; (2) molecule that binds specifically with other molecules, e.g., hormones and neurotransmitters.

Reduction restoring broken bone ends (or a dislocated bone) to its original position.

Reflex automatic reaction to a stimulus.

Reflex arc neural pathway for reflexes.

Refract bend; usually refers to light.

Refractory period *re-frak' to-re* the period of unresponsiveness to threshold stimulation.

Renal *re' nal* pertaining to the kidney.

Renal calculus *re' nal kal' ku-lus* a kidney stone.

Renin *re' nin* a substance released by the kidneys that is involved with raising blood pressure.

Repolarization restoration of the membrane potential to the initial resting (polarized) state.

Reproductive system organ system that functions to produce offspring.

Respiratory system organ system that carries out gas exchange; includes the nose, pharynx, larynx, trachea, bronchi, and lungs.

Responsiveness the ability to sense changes (stimuli) in the environment and then to react to them; see also *irritability*.

Reticulum *re-tik' u-lum* a fine network.

Retina *ret' ĭ-nah* light sensitive layer of the eye; contains rods and cones.

Ribonucleic acid (RNA) *ri" bo-nu-kle' ic* the nucleic acid that contains ribose; acts in protein synthesis.

Ribosomes *ri' bo-sōmz* cytoplasmic organelles at which proteins are synthesized.

Rods one of the two types of photosensitive cells in the retina.

Rotate to turn about an axis.

Rugae *roo' je* elevations or ridges, as in the mucosa of the stomach.

Sacral *sa' kral* the lower portion of the back, just superior to the buttocks.

Sagittal section (plane) *sa' jih-tul* a longitudinal (vertical) plane that divides the body or any of its parts into right and left portions.

Saliva *sah-li' vah* the secretion of salivary gland which is ducted into the mouth.

Salt ionic compound that dissociates into charged particles (other than hydrogen or hydroxyl ions) when dissolved in water.

Sarcomere *sar' ko-mēr* the smallest contractile unit of muscle; extends from one Z disc to the next.

Sclera *skle' rah* the firm white fibrous outer layer of the eyeball; protects and maintains eyeball shape.

Sebaceous glands *se-ba' shus* glands that empty their sebum secretion into hair follicles.

Sebum *se' bum* the oily secretion of sebaceous glands.

Second messenger intracellular molecule generated by binding of a chemical to a membrane receptor; mediates intracellular responses.

Secondary (immune) response second and subsequent responses of the immune system to a previously met antigen; more rapid and more vigorous than the primary response.

Secondary sex characteristics anatomical features that develop under influence of sex hormones (male or female pattern of muscle development, bone growth, body hair, etc.)

that are not directly involved in the reproductive process.

Secretion *se-kre' shun* (1) the passage of material formed by a cell to its exterior; (2) cell product that is transported to the cell exterior.

Semen *se' men* fluid mixture produced by male reproductive structures; contains sperm, nutrients, and mucus.

Semilunar valves *sem" e-lu' nar* valves that prevent blood return to the ventricles after contraction.

Seminiferous tubules *se" mĭ-nif' er-us* highly convoluted tubes within the testes that form sperm.

Sensory nerve a nerve that contains processes of sensory neurons and carries nerve impulses to the central nervous system.

Sensory nerve cell an initiator of nerve impulses following receptor stimulation.

Serous fluid *ser' us* a clear, watery fluid secreted by the cells of a serous membrane.

Serous membrane membrane that lines a cavity without an opening to the outside of the body (except for joint cavities); serosa.

Sex chromosomes chromosomes that determine genetic sex; the X and Y chromosomes.

Shoulder girdle composite of two bones, scapula and clavicle, that attach the upper limb to the axial skeleton; also called the pectoral girdle.

Sinoatrial node *si" no-a' tre-al* the mass of specialized myocardial cells in the wall of the right atrium; pacemaker of the heart.

Sinus *si' nus* (1) a mucous membrane– lined, air-filled cavity in certain cranial bones; (2) a dilated channel for passage of blood or lymph.

Skeletal muscle muscle composed of cylindrical multinucleate cells with obvious striations; the muscle(s) attached to the body's skeleton; also called *voluntary muscle*.

Skeletal system system of protection and support composed primarily of bone and cartilage.

Skull bony enclosure for the brain.

Smooth muscle muscle consisting of spindle-shaped, unstriped (nonstriated) muscle cells; involuntary muscle.

Solute *sol' yoot* the dissolved substance in a solution.

Solution a homogenous mixture of two or more components.

Somatic nervous system *so-mat' ik* a division of the peripheral nervous system; also called the voluntary nervous system.

Sperm mature male germ cell.

Spermatogenesis *sper" mah-to-jen' ĕ-sis* the process of sperm production in the male; involves meiosis.

Sphincter *sfink' ter* a circular muscle surrounding an opening; acts as a valve.

Spinal nerves the 31 pairs of nerves that arise from the spinal cord.

Squamous *skwa' mus* (1) flat, scalelike; (2) pertaining to flat, thin cells that form the free surface of some epithelial tissues.

Stasis *sta' sis* (1) a decrease or stoppage of flow; (2) a state of nonchange.

Static equilibrium *stat' ik e" kwĭ-lib' re-um* balance concerned with changes in the position of the head.

Stenosis *stĕ-no' sis* abnormal constriction or narrowing.

Sternal breastbone area.

Steroids *stĕ' roidz* a specific group of chemical substances including certain hormones and cholesterol.

Stimulus *stim' u-lus* an excitant or irritant; a change in the environment producing a response.

Stratum *stra' tum* a layer.

Stressor any stimulus that directly or indirectly causes the hypothalamus to initiate stress-reducing responses, such as the fight-or-flight response.

Striated muscle *stri' āt-ed* muscle consisting of cross-striated (cross-striped) muscle fibers; includes cardiac and skeletal muscle.

Stroke a condition in which brain tissue is deprived of a blood supply, as in blockage of a cerebral blood vessel.

Stroke volume a volume of blood ejected by a ventricle during systole.

Subcutaneous *sub" ku-ta' ne-us* beneath the skin.

Sudoriferous glands *su' do-rif' er-us* see *sweat glands*.

Sulcus *sul' kus* a furrow on the brain, less deep than a fissure.

Summation *sum-ma' shun* the accumulation of effects, especially those of muscular, sensory, or mental stimuli.

Superficial (external) located close to or on the body surface.

Superior refers to the head or upper body regions.

Supination *su" pĭ-na' shun* the outward rotation of the forearm causing palms to face anteriorly.

Supine refers to a body lying with the face upward.

Suppressor T cells regulatory T lymphocytes that suppress the immune response.

Surfactant *sur-fak' tant* a chemical substance coating the pulmonary alveoli walls that reduces surface tension, thus preventing collapse of the alveoli after expiration.

Sutures *soo' churz* immovable fibrous joints that connect the bones of the adult skull.

Sweat glands the glands that produce a saline solution called sweat; also called sudoriferous glands.

Sympathetic division a division of the autonomic nervous system; opposes parasympathetic functions; called the fight-or-flight division.

Synapse *sin' aps* the region of communication between neurons.

Synaptic cleft *sĭ-nap' tik* the fluid-filled space at a synapse between neurons.

Synarthrosis *sin" ar-thro' sis* an immovable joint.

Synergists *sin' er-jists* muscles cooperating with another muscle or muscle group to produce a desired movement.

Synovial fluid *sĭ-no′ve-al* a fluid secreted by the synovial membrane; lubricates joint surfaces and nourishes articular cartilages.

Synovial joint freely movable joint exhibiting a joint cavity enclosed by an articular (fibrous) capsule lined with synovial membrane.

Synovial membrane membrane that lines the capsule of a synovial joint.

Synthesis reaction chemical reaction in which larger molecules are formed from simpler ones.

System a group of organs that function cooperatively to accomplish a common purpose; there are eleven major systems in the human body.

Systemic *sis-tem′ik* general; pertaining to the whole body.

Systemic circulation system of blood vessels that carries nutrient and oxygen-rich blood to all body organs.

Systemic edema *ĕ-de′mah* an accumulation of fluid in body organs or tissues.

Systole *sis′to-le* the contraction phase of heart activity.

Systolic pressure *sis-tol′ik* the pressure generated by the left ventricle during systole.

T cells lymphocytes that mediate cellular immunity; include helper, killer, suppressor, and memory cells. Also called T lymphocytes.

Tachycardia *tak″e-kar′de-ah* an abnormal, excessively rapid heart rate; over 100 beats per minute.

Tarsal *tahr′sal* one of the seven bones that form the ankle and heel.

Taste buds receptors for taste on the tongue, roof of mouth, pharynx, and larynx.

Tendon *ten′dun* cord of dense fibrous tissue attaching a muscle to a bone.

Testis *tes′tis* the male primary sex organ that produces sperm.

Testosterone *tes′tos′tĕ-rōn* male sex hormone produced by the testes; during puberty promotes virilization and is necessary for normal sperm production.

Tetanus *tet′ah-nus* (1) the tense, contracted state of a muscle; (2) an infectious disease.

Thalamus *tha′luh-mis* a mass of gray matter in the diencephalon of the brain.

Thermoreceptor *ther″mo-re-sep′ter* a receptor sensitive to temperature changes.

Thoracic *tho-ras′ik* refers to the chest.

Thorax *tho′raks* that portion of the body trunk above the diaphragm and below the neck.

Threshold stimulus the weakest stimulus capable of producing a response in an irritable tissue.

Thrombin *throm′bin* an enzyme that induces clotting by converting fibrinogen to fibrin.

Thrombophlebitis *throm″bo-fle-bi′tis* an inflammation of a vein associated with blood clot formation.

Thrombus *throm′bus* a fixed clot that develops and persists in an unbroken blood vessel.

Thymus gland *thi′mus* an endocrine gland active in the immune response.

Thyroid gland *thi′roid* one of the largest of the body's endocrine glands; straddles the anterior trachea.

Tidal volume amount of air inhaled or exhaled with a normal breath.

Tissue a group of similar cells specialized to perform a specific function; primary tissue types are epithelial, connective, muscle, and nervous tissues.

Trachea *tra′ke-ah* The windpipe; the respiratory tube extending from larynx to bronchi.

Tract a collection of nerve fibers in the CNS having the same origin, termination, and function.

Transverse plane plane that divides the body or its parts into superior and inferior portions; also called a cross section.

Trauma *traw′mah* an injury, wound, or shock; usually produced by external forces.

Triglycerides *tri-glis′er-īdz* compounds composed of fatty acids and glycerol; fats and oils; also called neutral fats.

Trochanter *tro-kan′ter* a large, somewhat blunt process.

Tropic hormone *trōp′ik* a hormone that regulates the function of another endocrine organ.

Tubercle *tu′ber-kul* a nodule or small rounded process.

Tuberosity *tu″bĕ-ros′ĭ-te* a broad process, larger than a tubercle.

Tunica *too′nĭ-kah* a covering or tissue coat; layer.

Tympanic membrane *tim-pan′ik* the eardrum.

Ulcer *ul′ser* a lesion or erosion of the mucous membrane, such as gastric ulcer of stomach.

Umbilical cord *um-bĭ′lĭ-kul* a structure bearing arteries and veins connecting the placenta and the fetus.

Umbilicus *um-bĭ′lĭ-kus* navel; marks site of the umbilical cord in the fetal stage.

Urea *u-re′ah* the main nitrogen-containing waste excreted in the urine.

Ureters *u-re′terz* tubes that carry urine from kidney to bladder.

Urethra *u-re′thrah* the canal through which urine passes from the bladder to the outside of the body.

Urinary system system primarily responsible for water, electrolyte, and acid-base balance and the removal of nitrogenous wastes from the blood.

Urine filtrate containing waste and excess ions excreted by the kidneys.

Uterine tube the oviduct. The tube through which the ovum is transported to the uterus; also called fallopian tube.

Uvula *u′vu-lah* tissue tag hanging from soft palate.

Valence shell *va′lens* the outermost energy level of an atom that contains electrons; the electrons in the valence shell determine the bonding behavior of the atom.

Vas *vas* a duct; vessel.

Vascular *vas′ku-lar* pertaining to blood channels or vessels.

Vasoconstriction *vas″o-kon-strik′shun* narrowing of blood vessels.

Vasodilation *vas″o-di-la′shun* relaxation of the smooth muscles of blood vessels producing dilation.

Vasomotor nerve fibers *vas-o-mo′tor* the nerve fibers that regulate the constriction or dilation of blood vessels.

Vein *vān* a vessel carrying blood away from the tissues toward the heart.

Venae cavae two large blood vessels that drain oxygen-poor blood from the veins into the right side of the heart.

Ventral anterior or front.

Ventricles *ven′tri-kulz* (1) discharging chambers of the heart; (2) cavities within the brain.

Venule *ven′ūl* a small vein.

Vertebral column the spine, formed of a number of individual bones called vertebrae and two composite bones (sacrum and coccyx).

Vesicular follicle a mature ovarian follicle.

Villi *vil′i* fingerlike projections of the small intestinal mucosa that tremendously increase its surface area for absorption.

Viscera *vis′era* the internal organs.

Visceral *vis′er-al* pertaining to the internal part of a structure or the internal organs.

Viscosity *vis-kos′ĭ-te* the state of being sticky or thick.

Visual acuity *ah-ku′ĭ-te* the ability of the eye to distinguish detail.

Vital capacity the volume of air that can be expelled from the lungs by forcible expiration after the deepest inspiration; total exchangeable air.

Vitamins organic compounds required by the body in minute amounts for physiological maintenance and growth.

Vitreous humor a gel-like substance that helps prevent the eyeball from collapsing inward by reinforcing it internally.

Voluntary muscle muscle under control of the will; skeletal muscle.

Vulva *vul′va* female external genitalia.

White matter white substance of the central nervous system; the myelinated nerve fibers.

Zygote *zi′gōt* the fertilized ovum; produced by union of two gametes.

Index

NOTE: A *t* following a page number indicates tabular material, and *f* a page number indicates a figure, and a *b* following a page number indicates a boxed feature.

A bands (dark bands), 187, 188*f*, 192*f*
ABCD(E) rule for recognizing melanoma, 126
Abdominal aorta, 378, 379*f*
    arterial branches, 378, 379f
Abdominal cavity, 20, 20*f*
Abdominal organs
    alimentary canal wall structure, 472, 473*f*
    peritoneal attachments, 475*f*
Abdominal region of body, 16, 16*f*
Abdominal wall muscles, 208–209, 208*f*
    posterior, 209*f*, 210
Abdominopelvic cavity, 20, 20*f*
    nerve supply, 264*t*, 268, 268*f*
    peritoneal attachments, 472, 475*f*
    quadrants, 20–21, 21*f*
    regions, 21, 21*f*
Abducens nerve (cranial nerve VI), 259*t*, 261*f*, 284*f*
Abduction (body movement), 199, 201*f*
ABO blood groups, 353, 353*t*
Abortion, 567, 576*b*
Abscess, 413
Absorption of food, 481, 482*f*, 483, 484*f*, 485
    in small intestine, 489–492, 490*t*, 491*f*
    in large intestine 482*f*, 492–493
Absorptive cells of small intestine, 476–477, 477*f*
Accessory digestive organs, 470*f*, 479–481
Accessory nerve (cranial nerve XI), 260*t*, 261*f*
Accessory pancreatic duct, 476*f*
Accessory reproductive organs, 545
Accessory structures of eye, 281–283, 282*f*, 283*f*
Accommodation, 290, 290*f*
Accommodation pupillary reflex, 293–294
Acetabulum, 163*f*, 164
Acetic acid, 43, 190, 191*f*, 500
Acetoacetic acid, 500
Acetylcholine (ACh), 189–190, 191*f*
    ANS innervation/effects, 266*f*, 269
    somatic nervous system and, 266*f*
Acetylcholinesterase (AChE), 190, 191*f*
ACh. *See* Acetylcholine
AChE. *See* Acetylcholinesterase
Achilles (calcaneal) tendon, 214, 215*f*
Acid-base balance, 535–537, 536*f*
    changes in pH and, 44–45
Acid group (COOH) in amino acids, 49, 50*f*
Acidic solutions, 44, 44*f*
Acid mantle of skin, 114*t*, 408*f*, 409, 414*t*
Acid mantle of vagina, 409, 414*t*

Acidosis, 326, 342, 460, 461, 498, 535–537
    physiological, 535
Acids, 43–45
    acid-base concentrations and, 44–45, 44*f*
    strong, 43, 536–537, 536*f*
    weak, 43, 536–537, 536*f*
Acne, 119
Acoustic meatus
    external, 145, 146*f*, 294, 295*f*
    internal, 145, 146*f*
Acoustic nerve. *See* Vestibulocochlear nerve
Acquired immune deficiency syndrome (AIDS), 431, 432–433*b*
    growth hormone therapy and, 317*b*
Acquired immunity, 420–421, 420*f*
Acromegaly, 315
Acromial region of body, 16, 16*f*
Acromioclavicular joint, 159*f*, 160
Acromion of scapula, 159*f*, 160, 171*f*
Acrosome, 551–552, 551*f*
ACTH (adrenocorticotropic hormone), 315–316, 315*f*, 330*t*, 331*t*
    glucocorticoids and, 323–324, 324*f*
    in stress response, 325, 325*f*
Actin, 73, 74*f*, 192*f*, 193*f*
Actin (thin) filaments, 188*f*, 189
Action potential. *See also* Nerve impulse
    in muscle contraction, 190, 191*f*, 192*f*
    in nerve impulse, 237–239, 238*f*
Active immunity, 420–421, 420*f*
Active sites, 51, 52*f*
Active transport processes, 76, 78–79, 79*f*
Acute (immediate) hypersensitivity, 430, 430*f*
AD (Alzheimer's disease), 253*b*
Adam's apple (thyroid cartilage), 443*f*, 444
Adaptation
    auditory, 300
    olfactory, 302
Adaptive body defenses, 408*f*, 409, 415–431
    cells of (overview), 416–418
    cellular (cell-mediated), 425–429
        summary flowchart, 428*f*
    humoral (antibody-mediated), 418–425
        summary flowchart, 428*f*
    inflammatory response and, 412
A (dark) bands, 187, 188*f*
Addison's disease, 324, 535
Adduction (body movement), 199, 201*f*
Adductor magnus muscle, 212*f*
Adductor muscles, 213*f*, 214, 216*f*, 217*t*, 218*f*
Adenine (A), 54*f*, 55
Adenoid (pharyngeal tonsil), 443*f*, 444
Adenosine diphosphate (ADP), 55, 56*f*, 195, 196*f*
Adenosine triphosphate. *See* ATP
ADH. *See* Antidiuretic hormone

Adhesions, pericardial layers and, 363
Adipose tissue (fat), 96*f*, 97
    ANS innervation/effects, 269*t*
    hormones produced by, 333*t*
    in hypodermis of skin, 116*f*
    resistin and, 333*t*
    in subcutaneous tissue, 115, 116*f*
ADP. *See* Adenosine diphosphate
Adrenal cortex, 331*t*
    ANP and, 333*t*
    stress response and, 325–326, 325*f*
Adrenal cortex hormones (corticosteroids), 322–323, 323*f*, 324*f*
    location/functions in body, 47*t*
Adrenal glands, 313, 314*f*, 322–326, 331*t*
    ACTH, 315, 315*f*, 330*t*
    ANS innervation/effects, 267*f*, 269*t*, 270
    disorders, 324
    kidneys in relation to, 519, 519*f*
    location, 314*f*, 322, 323*f*
    microstructure of, 322, 323*f*
Adrenaline. *See* Epinephrine
Adrenal medulla, 323*f*, 324, 331*t*
    ANS innervation/effects, 267*f*, 269*t*
    homeostatic imbalance, 326
    hormones of, 324–326, 325*f*
    stress response and, 325–326, 325*f*
Adrenergic fibers, norepinephrine released by, 266*f*, 269
Adrenocorticotropic hormone. *See* ACTH
Aerobic exercise, 197–198, 197*f*
Aerobic respiration, 195, 196*f*
Afferent arterioles, glomerular, 522*f*, 523*f*
Afferent lymphatic vessels, 406, 407*f*
Afferent pathway, in homeostatic control mechanism, 12–13, 13*f*
Afferent (sensory) division of PNS, 229, 230*f*
Afferent (sensory) nerves, 258
Afferent (sensory) neurons, 235–236, 235*f*
Afterbirth, 571
Aging
    Anti-aging growth hormone injections and 317*b*
    blood disorders and, 356*b*
    body membranes and 127
    cellular changes and 101, 104
    cardiovascular changes and 372–373, 392–393*b*, 397
    digestive system and 507
    endocrine system and 332, 335
    hair changes and 127
    hearing and 300
    metabolic rate and, , 503, 507
    muscular system and 221
    nervous system and 273
    postural changes and, 391
    reproductive systems and 576, 578
    respiratory system and 464
    skeletal system and 174–176
    skin and 101, 104, 127
    smell sense and 305

taste sense and 305
    tissues and, 101, 104
    urinary system and 538, 540
    vision and, 304
Agglutination, 351, 423–424, 423*f*
Agglutinins, 351
Agglutinogens (RBC antigens), 351, 353, 353*t*
Agranulocytes, 345, 346*t*
AIDS (acquired immune deficiency syndrome), 431, 432–433*b*
    growth hormone therapy and, 317*b*
Air-blood barrier (respiratory membrane), 447, 449*f*
Air hunger, 461
Air sacs (alveoli), 441, 447, 448*f*
Alae
    of ilium, 162
    sacral, 157, 157*f*
Albumin, 341*f*, 342, 501
Albuminuria, 528*t*
Alcohol drinking
    blood-brain barrier and, 252
    blood pressure and, 391
    brain size and, 273
    dehydrating effect of, 319
Aldosterone, 322–323, 323*f*, 324*f*
    location/functions in body, 47*t*
    mechanisms controlling release, 323, 324*f*
    in water/electrolyte balance, 533, 534*f*, 535
Alimentary canal (gastrointestinal tract), 469, 470, 470*f*. *See also* Digestive system
    organs of, 469–479, 470*f*
    wall structure, 472, 473*f*
Alkaline (basic) solutions, 44, 44*f*
Alkalosis, 342, 460, 535–537
Allergic contact dermatitis, 431
Allergies (hypersensitivities), 430–431, 430*f*
    delayed, 431
    eosinophils and, 346*t*
    rhinitis and, 443
    skin, 123, 127, 431
Allografts, 427
All-or-none response/law
    of muscle physiology, 194
    of nerve impulses, 238*f*, 239
Alopecia, 127
Alpha radiation, 33
Alveolar ducts, 447, 448*f*
Alveolar epithelium at respiratory membrane, 449*f*
Alveolar glands, 561, 562*f*
Alveolar macrophages, 447
Alveolar margins (teeth), 146*f*, 148, 148*f*, 149
Alveolar pores, 447, 448*f*, 449*f*
Alveolar sacs, 447, 448*f*
Alveoli (air sacs), 441, 447, 448*f*, 449*f*
Alveoli (tooth sockets), 149
Alzheimer's disease (AD), 253*b*
    PET scans to diagnose, 271*b*
Ameboid motion of white blood cells, 345
Amine group in amino acids, 49, 50*f*
Amine hormones, 330*t*, 331*t*
Amino acids, 49–50
    essential, 495
    hormones derived of (nonsteroidal), 310–311, 312*f*

Amino acids (*continued*)
  protein synthesis and,
    86–88, 87*f*
  structure (generalized), 50*f*
Amitotic tissue, 101
Amnion, 566, 566*f*
Amphiarthroses, 166, 170*t*
Ampulla
  of ductus (vas) deferens,
    546, 547*f*
  of semicircular canal, 297, 297*f*
Anabolic steroids, 203–204*b*
Anabolism, 495
Anaerobic glycolysis, 195, 196*f*
Anal canal, 470*f*, 477, 478*f*
Anal sphincters, 478, 478*f*
Anaphase stage of mitosis, 84, 85*f*
Anaphylactic shock, 430–431
Anatomical neck of humerus,
    160, 161*f*
Anatomical position, 15, 16*f*
Anatomical terminology, 15–22
  body cavities, 17, 20–22,
    20*f*, 21*f*
  body planes, 17, 19*f*
  body sections, 17, 19*f*
  directional, 15, 18*f*, 18*t*
  orientational, 15, 18*f*, 18*t*
  regional, 16–17, 16*f*
Anatomy, 2–3
  gross, 2
  microscopic, 2
Anchoring junctions
    (desmosomes), 69, 69*f*, 89
Androgens, 324, 329, 331*t*
  apocrine glands and, 120–121
Androstenedione, 203–204*b*
Anemia, 343, 344*t*
  age-related changes and, 356*b*
  iron-deficiency, 344*t*, 356*b*
  pernicious, 344*t*, 356
Anencephaly, 272
Anesthetics, blood-brain barrier
    and, 252
Angina pectoris, 368
Angiography, 8–9*b*
Angiotensin II, 323, 324*f*, 390–391
Anion, 36
Ankle, bone (talus), 166, 166*f*
Ankle joint muscles 211, 214, 215*f*
Ankylosis, 173, 173*f*
Anosmias, 302
ANP (atrial natriuretic peptide),
    323, 324*f*
  as non-endocrine
    hormone, 333*t*
ANS. *See* Autonomic nervous system
Antagonist muscle, 202
Antebrachial region of body, 16, 16*f*
Antecubital region of body, 16, 16*f*
Anterior (aqueous) segment of
    eye, 289
Anterior border of tibia, 165, 165*f*
Anterior cardiac vein, 363*f*
Anterior cerebral artery, 383, 383*f*
Anterior communicating artery,
    383, 383*f*
Anterior fontanel, 150, 150*f*
Anterior inferior iliac spine,
    162, 163*f*
Anterior interventricular artery,
    363*f*, 367
Anterior segment of eye, 285*f*
Anterior superior iliac spine, 162,
    163*f*, 213*f*
Anterior tibial artery, 378, 379*f*
Anterior tibial vein, 380, 381*f*
Anterior (ventral) body landmarks,
    16–17, 16*f*
Anterior (ventral) direction/
    orientation, 18*f*, 18*t*
Anterior (ventral) horns, 256, 256*f*

Anti-aging growth hormone injec-
    tions, 317*b*
Antibodies (immunoglobulins/Igs),
    351, 415, 421–425, 421*f*, 422*t*
  classes of, 422–423, 422*t*
  functions, 51*t*, 423–424,
    423*f*, 426*t*
  lymphocytes and, 346*t*,
    416–418, 417*f*
  mechanisms of action,
    423–424, 423*f*
  structure, 421–422, 421*f*
  transfusion reactions and, 353
Antibody-mediated (humoral)
    immunity, 416,
    418–425, 428*f*
Anticoagulants, 346*t*, 350
Anticodons, in protein synthesis,
    87*f*, 88
Antidiuretic hormone (ADH),
    318–319, 318*f*, 330*t*,
    532–533, 534*f*
Antigen-antibody complexes,
    423*f*, 424
Antigen-binding site, 421*f*, 422
Antigen presentation, 425, 426*t*
Antigen-presenting cells, 425,
    426*t*, 428*f*
Antigens, 416, 427*t*
  antibody mechanisms against,
    423–424, 423*f*
  summary flowchart, 428*f*
  RBC (agglutinogens), 351,
    353, 353*t*
  T cell activation and, 417,
    424*f*, 425
Antigravity muscles, posterior,
    207–208, 209*f*
Antihistamines, 430
Antimicrobial proteins, in body
    defense, 413, 414*t*, 415
Antioncogene (tumor suppressor
    gene), 102*b*
Antrum of ovary, 553, 553*f*
Anucleate cells, 342
Anuria, 524
Anus, 470*f*, 475*f*, 478, 478*f*,
    482*f*, 554*f*
Anvil (incus) bone, 295,
    295*f*, 299*f*
Aorta, 362, 364*f*, 365, 365*f*,
    378, 379*f*
  abdominal, 378, 379*f*
  ascending, 363*f*, 378, 379*f*
  blood pressure in, 388*f*
  fetal, 384*f*
  kidneys in relation to, 519*f*
  thoracic, 378, 379*f*
Aortic arch, 363*f*, 378, 379*f*
  arterial branches, 378, 379*f*
Aortic semilunar valve, 364*f*,
    366, 367*f*
Apex
  of heart, 362, 362*f*, 363*f*
  of lung, 445, 446*f*, 447
  of renal pyramids, 521
Aphasias, 254
Apical surface of simple epithelia,
    89, 89*f*
Aplastic anemia, 344*t*, 349
Apnea, 460
  sleep, 464
Apocrine glands, 119, 120–121
Aponeuroses, 185
Aponeurosis (abdominal wall), 208*f*
Appendages of skin, 116*f*,
    119–122
  cutaneous glands, 119–121, 120*f*
  hairs/hair follicles, 121–122,
    121*f*, 122*f*
  nails, 122, 123*f*
Appendicitis, 478, 507

Appendicular skeleton, 134, 144*f*,
    158–166
  lower limbs, 144*f*, 158
  pectoral girdle, 144*f*,
    158–160, 159*f*
  pelvic girdle, 144*f*, 158,
    162–164, 163*f*
  upper limbs, 144*f*, 158
Appendix, 470*f*, 477, 478, 478*f*
Appetite, leptin and, 333*t*
Appositional growth of long
    bones, 140, 141*f*
Aquaporins, 77, 78*f*
Aqueous humor, 289
  in anterior segment, 285*f*
Arachnoid mater
  cerebral, 249*f*, 251
  spinal, 255, 255*f*, 256*f*
Arachnoid villi, 249*f*, 250*f*, 251
Arches of foot, 166, 166*f*
  "fallen," 166
Arcuate arteries
  of foot, 378, 379*f*, 380
  of kidneys, 520*f*, 521, 522*f*
Arcuate veins, 520*f*, 521, 522*f*
Areola of breast, 561, 562*f*
Areolar tissue, 96*f*, 97
Arm
  blood vessels of, 378, 379*f*,
    380, 381*f*
  bone, 160, 161*f*
  muscles, 208, 208*f*, 209*f*, 210,
    210*f*, 211, 216*f*, 217*t*,
    218*f*, 219*t*
  nerves serving, 264*t*
  veins draining, 380, 381*f*
Arrector pili muscles, 116*f*,
    121*f*, 122
  ANS innervation/effects, 269*t*
Arteries, 374, 375*f*
  blood pressure in, 388*f*
  capillaries *vs.*, 376–377, 377*f*
  fetal, 383–384, 384*f*
  lymphatic vessels in relation to,
    403–404, 404*f*
  major, of systemic circulation,
    378, 379*f*, 380
  microscopic structure,
    374–377, 375*f*
  pulse and pressure points,
    387, 387*f*
  veins *vs.*, 376, 388*f*
Arterioles, 374, 375*f*
  blood pressure in, 388*f*
  glomerular, 522*f*, 523
  terminal, 377, 377*f*
  venules and, 377, 377*f*
Arteriosclerosis, 273, 332, 393*b*
Arthritis, 173
  gouty, 174
  osteoarthritis, 173
  rheumatoid, 173–174, 173*f*, 429
Articular capsule, fibrous, 112*f*,
    169*f*, 170, 171*f*
Articular (hyaline) cartilage, 136,
    137*f*, 169*f*, 170, 171*f*
Articular processes, vertebral, 155,
    155*f*, 156*f*
Articulations. *See* Joints
Artificial blood substitutes,
    355–356*b*
Artificial heart valves, 366
Artificial pacemaker, 369
Ascending aorta, 363*f*, 378, 379*f*
  arterial branches, 378, 379*f*
Ascending colon, 470*f*, 478, 478*f*
Ascending general sensory
    tracts, 247*f*
Aspartic acid, structure of, 50*f*
Association fiber tracts, 245
Association neuron (interneuron),
    235*f*, 236

Asthma, 451, 464
Astigmatism, 292*b*
Astrocytes, 230–231, 231*f*
Ataxia, 248
Atelectasis, 451–452
Atherosclerosis, 391, 392–393*b*, 397
Athlete's foot (tinea pedis), 123
Atlas (C1), 151*f*, 155, 156*f*
Atmospheric pressure as survival
    factor, 12
Atomic decay, 33
Atomic mass, 32, 32*f*, 33*t*
Atomic number, 32, 33*t*
Atomic symbol, 29
Atomic weight, 33, 33*t*
Atoms, 3*f*, 4, 29–34
  models of, 29, 31, 31*f*
  structure of, 29, 31, 31*f*
  subatomic particles, 29–31, 31*f*,
    31*t*, 33, 41, 41*t*
ATP (adenosine triphosphate), 55
  aerobic respiration and,
    195, 196*f*
  dietary nutrients and, 493,
    496–500, 499*f*
  energy form conversions
    and, 28
  erythrocytes and, 342–343
  as an exchange reaction,
    40*f*, 41
  how it drives cellular work, 56*f*
  hydrolysis of, 56*f*
  mitochondria as supplier of, 71
  in muscle contraction, 193*f*,
    195, 196*f*
  oxidative phosphorylation and,
    195, 196*f*
  regeneration pathways, 56*f*,
    195, 196*f*
  sodium-potassium pump and,
    79, 79*f*, 239
  structure of, 55, 56*f*
  synthesis
    by carbohydrate metabolism,
      46, 496–497, 497*f*,
      498*f*, 499*f*
    by fat metabolism,
      497–498, 499*f*
    by protein metabolism, 498,
      499*f*, 500
Atria/atrium of heart, 363–364*f*,
    365, 365*f*
  intrinsic conduction system
    and, 369*f*
Atrial natriuretic peptide (ANP),
    323, 324*f*, 333*t*
Atrioventricular (AV) bundle (bun-
    dle of His), 368–369, 369*f*
Atrioventricular (AV) node,
    368–369, 369*f*
Atrioventricular (AV) valves
  left (bicuspid valve), 364*f*,
    366, 367*f*
  operation of, 366, 367*f*
  right (tricuspid valve), 364*f*,
    366, 367*f*
Atrioventricular groove (coronary
    sulcus), 363*f*, 367
Atrophy, 104, 197, 256
Attenuated vaccines, 420, 420*f*
Auditory area of brain,
    243, 244*f*
Auditory canal/acoustic meatus
  external, 145, 146*f*, 294, 295*f*
  internal, 145, 146*f*
  route of sound waves through,
    298, 299*f*, 300
Auditory ossicles, 295, 295*f*
Auditory (pharyngotympanic) tube,
    294–295, 295*f*
Auditory receptors, adaptation to
    sounds and, 300

Auricle, heart, 363f
Auricle (pinna), of ear, 294, 295f
Auricle (pinna) of ear, 299f
Auscultatory method of measuring blood pressure, 388, 389f
Auto-antibodies, 429
Autografts, 427
Autoimmune diseases, 123, 124f, 429–430
Autonomic behaviors for survival, 247–248
Autonomic nervous system (ANS), 262, 266–270. See also specific division
  aging effects, 273
  anatomy, 266–268, 267f
  blood pressure and, 389–390, 390f
  definition, 230, 230f, 262
  functions/physiology, 268–270, 269t
  heart rate and, 372–373, 373f
  somatic nervous system compared to, 262, 266, 266f
Autonomic reflexes, 240
AV (atrioventricular) bundle (bundle of His), 368–369, 369f
AV (atrioventricular) node, 368–369, 369f
AV (atrioventricular) valves
  left (bicuspid valve), 364f, 366, 367f
  operation of, 366, 367f
  right (tricuspid valve), 364f, 366, 367f
Axial skeleton, 134, 144f
  bony thorax, 145
  skull, 145–150, 146f–150f
  vertebral column, 145
Axillary artery, 378, 379f
Axillary lymph nodes, 406f
Axillary nerve, 264t, 265f
Axillary region of body, 16f, 17
Axillary vein, 380, 381f
Axis (C2), 151f, 155, 156f
Axon hillock, 232, 233f
Axon (nerve fiber), 189, 190f, 232, 233f
  in PNS, 234, 234f
Axon terminals, 189, 190f, 191f, 232, 233f
Azygos vein, 380

Baby/milk teeth (deciduous teeth), 479, 479f
Back
  exercises for, 152–154b
  spine (vertebral column), 150–157, 151f
Backache prevention, 152–154b
Back muscles, 209–210, 209f, 218f
Bacterial damage, skin's protective acid mantle and, 114f
Bacterial infections, hemolytic anemia and, 344t
Balance sense. See Equilibrium
Baldness, male pattern, 127
Ball-and-socket joint, 170t, 171–172, 172f
Balloon angioplasty, 393b
Bare zone, 188f, 189
Baroreceptors (pressoreceptors), 389–390, 390f
Barrier methods of contraception, 575–576b
Basal cell carcinoma, 125–126, 126f
Basal cells (stem cells), taste bud cells replaced by, 302, 303f
Basal metabolic rate (BMR), 502–503, 503t
Basal nuclei (basal ganglia), 245, 246f

Base
  of heart, 362, 362f
  of lung, 446f
  of renal pyramids, 521
Basement membrane, 89, 91f, 92f
Bases, 43–45
  complementary, 55
Basic (alkaline) solutions, 44, 44f
  blood alkalosis and, 342
Basilar artery, 383, 383f
Basilar membrane, 298, 299f, 300
Basilic vein, 380, 381f
Basophils, 341f, 345, 346t
B cells (B lymphocytes), 416
  in adaptive immune response (summary), 428f
  differentiation and activation of, 416–418, 417f
  functions in immune response, 426t
  helper T cells and, 424f
  lymph nodes and, 406, 417f, 418, 426t
Bed, nail, 122, 123f
Bedsores (decubitus ulcers), 118, 118f
Benign neoplasm, 102b
Beta amyloid peptide, 253b
Beta cells of pancreatic islets, 326, 327f
Biaxial movement of saddle and condyloid joints 171, 172f
Bicarbonate buffer system, 536–537
Bicarbonate ions, 454, 455f, 456
  in blood plasma, 341f, 454
  as weak base, 43, 536–537
Biceps brachii muscle, 205, 205f, 208f, 211, 216f, 217t
Biceps femoris muscle, 212f, 214, 218f, 219t
Biceps muscle, tendon, 171f
Bicuspid (premolar) teeth, 479–480, 479f
Bicuspid valve (mitral valve/left AV valve), 364f, 366, 367f
Bile, 476, 481, 491
Bile duct, 476, 476f, 481
Bile pigment, in urine, 528t
Bile salts, 47t
Biliopancreatic diversion for obesity, 510b
Bilirubinuria, 528t
Bimolecular lipid layer of plasma membrane, 67–68, 68f
Binocular vision, 291, 291f
Binucleate cells, 85
Biochemistry, 41–58
  inorganic compounds, 41–45
  organic compounds, 45–58
Biopsy, bone marrow, 349
Biorhythms, melatonin and, 329, 330t
Bipennate muscle structure, 205, 205f
Bipolar cells of retina, 284, 286, 286f
Bipolar neuron, 237, 237f
Birth canal, 556
Birth control, 574–576b
Bitter taste receptors, 302
Blackhead, 119
Blanching of skin, 119
Blastocyst, 564f, 565
"Bleaching of the pigment," 287–288b
Bleeding disorders, 350–351
Blindness
  color, 288
  congenital, 304
  night, 286
Blind spot (optic disc), 285f, 286f

Blister
  fever, 123, 124f
  friction, 115
  in second-degree burns, 124
Blood, 97, 98f, 339–359
  age-related changes and, 356b
  artificial, 355–356b
  cells (formed elements), 341f, 342–347
  components, 340, 341f
  as connective tissue, 97, 98f, 339
  developmental aspects of, 354, 356
  disorders, 356
  homeostatic imbalances, 343–344, 343f, 344t, 345, 350–351
  pH of, 340
    variations and, 44–45
  physical characteristics, 340
  substances transported by, 341f
  viscosity, 343, 344, 390f
  volume, 340
    of average adult, 372
    blood pressure and, 389–390, 390f
    cardiac output influenced by, 373f
    kidneys' role in, 390–391, 390f
Blood-brain barrier, 252
Blood buffer systems, 342, 454, 535–537, 536f
Blood cell formation (hematopoiesis), 4, 347–349, 347f, 348f
  bone marrow as site of, 135, 347
  of platelets, 349
  of RBCs, 347–348, 348f
  of WBCs, 348–349
Blood clotting
  disorders, 350
  platelets and, 341f, 346t, 347
  in tissue repair, 100–101
Blood groups, 351, 353–354, 353t, 354f
  ABO, 353, 353t
    blood typing and, 354, 354f
  Rh, 353–354, 353t
Blood pressure, 387–391, 394
  arterial pulse, 387, 387f
  brain stem and, 248
  cardiac output influenced by, 373f
  factors affecting
    chemical/diet/temperature, 390f, 391
    neural, 389–390, 390f
    renal, 390–391, 390f
  measuring, 388, 389f
  sodium/water balance and, 532–535, 534f
  osmotic pressure and, 394–395, 395f
  peripheral resistance and, 388–389, 390f
  in pregnancy, 568
  pressure gradients and, 387–388, 388f
  renin-angiotensin mechanism and, 534f, 535
  sympathetic vasoconstriction and, 389–390, 390f
  variations in, 391
  in various blood vessels, 387, 388f
Blood pressure cuff, 388, 389f
Blood substitutes, 355–356b
Blood sugar (glucose), 496. See also Glucose

Blood typing of ABO blood groups, 354, 354f
Blood vessels, 374–395
  adrenal glands and, 331t
  aging and, 372–373, 392–393b, 397
  anatomy
    gross, 378–386
    microscopic, 374–377, 375f
  ANS innervation/effects, 267f, 269t
  arteries, 374, 375f. See also Arteries
    major, of body, 378, 379f, 380
    structure of, 374–377, 375f
  arterioles, 374, 377, 377f, 388f
    microcirculation of, 377, 377f
  blood pressure and, 387–391, 394. See also Blood pressure
  capillaries, 374, 375f. See also Capillaries
  capillary beds, 374, 375f. See also Capillary beds
  circulation and, 387–394. See also Circulation
  in compact bone, 139–140, 139f
  coronary artery disease and, 397
  cutaneous, 116f
  damaged, platelets and, 346t, 347
  in dermal papillae, 116f, 117, 121f
  developmental aspects of, 395, 397
  homeostatic imbalances and, 377, 391, 392–393b, 394
  lymphatic vessels in relation to, 403–404, 404f
  tunics of, 374, 375f, 376
  veins, 374, 375f. See also Veins
    major, of body, 380, 381f
    structure of, 374–377, 375f
  venules, 374, 375f, 377, 377f
B lymphocytes. See B cells
BMI (body mass index), 508b
BMR (basal metabolic rate), 502–503, 503t
Body cavities, 17, 20–22, 20f, 21f
Body defenses, 408–431, 408f
  adaptive, 415–431
    antibody-mediated, 416, 418–425
    cell-mediated, 416, 425–429
    summary flowchart, 428f
  cells of, 340, 341f, 344, 346t, 408f, 409, 416–418, 426–427t
  developmental aspects of, 431, 435
  first line of defense, 409, 414t
  innate, 408, 409–415
    cells/chemicals, 409–415
    surface membrane barriers, 408f, 409, 414t
  second line of defense, 409–415
  third line of defense, 415–431
  white blood cells and, 340, 341f, 344
Body fluids. See Fluids
Body heat
  blood plasma's distribution of, 342
  production, metabolic rate and, 502–503, 503t
  skin's protective functions in, 114t, 115
  skin's sweat glands and, 114t, 115
  sweat and, 120

... (BMI), 508b
... s for proper lifting,
...53b
... branes, 109–112, 111f.
... See also specific type
... ng process and, 127
... evelopmental aspects of, 127
epithelial, 110, 111f
mucous, 90, 110, 111f, 112f
serous, 90, 110, 111f, 112
Body movements. See Movement
Body of bone
of hyoid, 149, 149f
of mandible, 146f, 149
of pubis, 163f
of sternum, 157, 158f
of vertebra, 154, 155f, 156f
of nail, 122, 123f
of stomach, 473, 474f
of uterus, 554f, 555, 555f
Body planes, 17, 19f
Body posture, skeletal muscles
and, 187
Body proportions over time,
174–176, 175f, 176f
Body salts, 43
Body sections, 17, 19f
Body temperature regulation,
504–506, 505f
dermal capillaries and, 118
heat-loss mechanisms and, 504
heat-promoting mechanisms
and, 504
mechanisms of, 505f
muscle contraction's role in, 187
as survival factor, 12
water's high heat capacity
and, 42
Body tissues. See Tissues
Boils and carbuncles, 123
Bolus of food, 480
Bonds
covalent, 36–38, 38f
intramolecular, 39
ionic, 35–36, 37f
Bone fractures, 142–143,
142t, 143f
advances in repair of, 167–168b
Bone grafts, 167b
Bone implants, 167b
Bone markings, 136–137, 138t
Bone marrow
B cells and, 417f, 418
erythropoietin and, 333t
red, 136, 137f
blood cell formation and,
347–349, 347f
yellow, 136, 137f
Bone marrow biopsy, 349
Bone matrix, 139–140
in ossification, 140
Bone (osseous tissue), 94, 94f
aging and, 104
compact, 135, 137, 137f,
139–140, 139f
formation/growth/remodeling,
140, 141f, 142
spongy, 135, 137, 137f
Bone remodeling, 140, 141f, 142
in fracture healing, 143, 143f
Bones
blood supply, 137, 137f
classed by shape, 135, 136f
flat, 135, 136f
formation/growth/remodeling,
140, 141f, 142
fractures of, 142–143,
142t, 143f
functions, 134–135

homeostatic imbalances 142–143,
175–176
importance of weight-bearing
exercise, 175
injuries to, 140
irregular, 135, 136f
long, 135, 136f
as mineral storehouse, 135
movement and, 135
osteoporosis , 175–176
protection of body organs, 135
short, 135, 136f
storage functions, 135
support functions, 134–135
surface markings on,
136–137, 138t
Bone spurs, 173
Bone substitutes, 168b
Bony callus in bone fracture
healing, 143, 143f
Bony (osseous) labyrinth,
295–296, 295f
Bony pelvis, 162–164, 163f
Boundary maintenance, as
necessary life function, 10
Bowman's (glomerular) capsule,
521, 522f
"Boxer's" muscle, 211
Boxing, brain damage and, 273
Brachial artery, 378, 379f
as pulse point, 387f
Brachialis muscle, 208f, 211, 216f,
217t, 218f
Brachial plexus, 263f, 264t
distribution of nerves, 265f
Brachial region of body, 16f, 17
Brachial vein, 380, 381f
Brachiocephalic artery, 363f
Brachiocephalic trunk, 378, 379f
Brachiocephalic vein, 380, 381f
Brachioradialis muscle, 208f,
216f, 218f
Bradycardia, 369
Brain, 229, 230f, 242–248
arterial supply and Circle of
Willis, 378, 379f,
383, 383f
brain stem, 242, 243f
cerebellum, 242, 243f
cerebral hemispheres, 242–246,
243f, 244f
developmental aspects, 174–175,
175f, 242, 243f
13 weeks vs. adult, 243f
diencephalon, 242, 243f
disorders, 252–255
homeostatic imbalances,
245–246, 248, 251–252,
251f, 253–254b
leptin and, 333t
major regions, 242, 243f, 244f
medical imaging techniques and,
8–9b
protection of, 248–252,
249f, 250f
reflexes and, 240, 242f
traumatic injuries to, 252
tumors, 232, 254–255
Brain stem, 242, 243f, 244f,
247–248, 247f, 257f
ANS innervation/effects,
267f, 269t
Brain waves, electroencephalography and, 271–272b
Braxton Hicks contractions, 569
Breastbone. See Sternum
Breast cancer, 561–562, 563f
Breastfeeding
oxytocin and, 318, 318f, 330t
prolactin and, 318, 318f, 330t
Breathing, 448
aging and, 464

body temperature and, 456
brain stem and, 248
chemical factors affecting, 457,
457f, 460
conscious control and, 456
emotions and, 457
forced, 209
homeostatic imbalances, 451–452
hyperventilation, 460
hypoventilation, 460
mechanics of, 449–452
expiration, 450f, 451, 451f
inspiration, 450f, 451, 451f
medulla and, 248, 456, 457f
muscles of, 158, 208, 208f, 209,
216f, 450f, 451
neural regulation of, 456–457,
457f, 460
physical factors affecting, 456
pons and, 248, 456, 457f
Brittle diabetes (Type 1), 327
Broad ligament of ovary, 554,
554f, 555f
Broca's area, 243, 244f
Bronchi
mucosa of, 111f
primary, 442f, 445, 446f
right vs. left, 445
Bronchial arteries, 378
Bronchial (respiratory) tree,
447, 448f
Bronchial sounds, 453
Bronchioles, 447, 448f
terminal, 447, 448f
Bronchitis, chronic, 451,
460–461, 461f
Bruises, 119
Brush border, 477
Brush border enzymes, 476, 489
Buccal phase of swallowing,
485, 486f
Buccal region of body, 16f, 17
Buccinator muscle, 206f, 207,
216f, 217t
Buffer systems, 44, 535–537
Buffy coat, 340
Bulbourethral glands, 547f, 549
Bundle branches, 368–369, 369f
Bundle of His, 368–369, 369f
Burns, 123–125, 125f
classification, 124, 125f
definition, 124
regeneration and, 124
selective permeability of plasma
membrane and, 76
when considered critical,
124–125
Bursae, 112, 112f, 170, 171f
Bursitis, 172–173
Bypass surgery, 393b

Cadaver bone to repair
fractures, 168b
Calcaneal (Achilles) tendon,
214, 215f
Calcaneal region of body, 16f, 17
Calcaneus bone of foot, 166, 166f
Calcitonin, 319, 320–321, 320f,
322f, 331t
Calcium
atomic structure, 33t
bones as storage site, 135
osteoporosis and, 175
percentage of body mass, 30t
rickets and, 142
role of, 30t
vitamin D, intestines and, 333t
Calcium ions
blood clotting and, 350
blood levels of, 140, 142, 311,
321, 322f, 331t
found in blood plasma, 341f

cardiac output affected by,
373, 373f
in muscle contraction, 191f,
193, 193f
Calcium salts, 94, 135, 140
otoliths and, 297
Callus
bony, 143, 143f
fibrocartilage, 143, 143f
Calories, food, 493
Calyces, 520f, 521
cAMP, 311, 312f
Canaliculi, 139–140, 139f
Canal of Schlemm (scleral venous
sinus), 285f, 289
Cancer, 102–103b, 103f
breast, 561–562, 563f
cervical, 556
colon, 102b
current treatments, 103b
lung, 458–459b, 460, 464
prostate, 549
screening procedures, 103b
skin, 117, 125–126, 126f
vaccine, 103b
Canine teeth, 479, 479f
Canthus of eye, 281–282, 282f
Capillaries, 374, 375f, 376–377
blood pressure in, 388f
fenestrated, 394, 394f
leaky, 394–395, 411, 411f
lymphatic, 404, 404f, 405f
postcapillary venules and,
377, 377f
precapillary sphincters and,
377, 377f
at respiratory membrane, 449f
in tissue repair, 100–101
true, 377, 377f
vs. arteries/veins, 376–377, 377f
Capillary beds, 374, 375f, 377, 377f
fluid movements at,
394–395, 395f
gases/nutrient exchanges at,
365, 365f, 394, 394f,
454, 454f
of hepatic portal system,
385–386, 385f
Capitate bone, 162f
Capitulum, 160, 161f
Capsule of lymph node, 406, 407f
Carbohydrates
dietary sources of, 494, 494t
digestion/absorption of,
483, 484f
glucose and, 496
metabolism of, 496–497, 496f,
497f, 498f, 499f
as organic compounds,
45–46, 45f
structure, 45–46, 45f
Carbon
atomic structure, 33t
as chemically reactive element,
35, 36f
percentage of body mass, 30t
role of, 30t
Carbon dioxide
chronic lung diseases and, 460
formation of, 37
in gas exchanges
in body tissues, 365, 365f,
394, 394f, 455f, 456
in lungs, 448–449, 453,
454f, 455f
hypoventilation/hyperventilation
and, 460
in muscle contraction, 195, 196f
respiratory rate/depth and, 457,
457f, 460
Carbon dioxide transport, 340,
341f, 346t, 454–455, 455f

Carbonic acid, 43, 454–455, 455f, 456
Carbon monoxide poisoning, 455
Carboxypeptidase, 490
Carbuncles and boils, 123
Carcinogens, 102b
   in tobacco smoke, 458b
Carcinoma
   adenocarcinoma, 458b
   basal cell, 125–126, 126f
   small cell, 458b
   squamous cell, 126, 126f, 458b
Cardiac cycle, 369, 371–372, 371f
   homeostatic imbalances, 371–372
   summary of events during, 371, 371f
Cardiac muscle
   blood supply impaired and, 369
   bundles, 186, 186f
   cell shape/appearance, 184t, 186, 186f
   contraction of, 186
      regulation, 184t
   regenerative ability of, 101
   skeletal muscle vs., 184t
   smooth muscle vs., 184t
   as type of body tissue, 98, 99f
Cardiac output , 372–374, 373f
   blood pressure and, 388–389, 390f
Cardiac physiology, 2
Cardiac region of stomach, 472, 474f
Cardiac veins, 367–368
   anterior, 363f
   great, 363f
   small, 363f
Cardinal signs of inflammation, 410–411, 411f
Cardioesophageal sphincter, 472, 474f, 486, 486f
Cardiovascular system, 360–401
   aging and, 372–373, 397
   atherosclerosis, 392–393b, 392f
   blood vessels, 374–395. See also Blood vessels
   congenital heart defects, 395, 397
   definition/overview, 5f, 7, 361–362
   developmental aspects of, 395, 397
   heart, 360–374. See also Heart
   homeostatic imbalances, 363, 366, 369, 371–372, 374, 377, 391, 392–393b, 394
   homeostatic relationships, 396b
   in pregnancy, 568
Career focus
   dental hygienist, 14b
   doula, 572b
   food technologist, 53b
   licensed practical nurse, 462b
   massage therapist, 220b
   medical transcriptionist, 128b
   phlebotomy technician, 352b
   surgical technologist, 382b
Carotid arteries, 363f, 378, 379f
Carotid canal, 145, 147f
Carpal bones (carpus/wrist), 144f, 162, 162f
Carpal region of body, 16f, 17
Carpometacarpal joints of thumb, 171, 172f
Carpus (carpal bones/wrist), 144f, 162, 162f
Carrier-mediated facilitated diffusion, 77, 78f
Cartilage, 94, 95f
   articular, 136, 137f, 169f, 170, 171f
   of the skeletal system, 134

Cartilaginous joint, 168, 169f
   pubic symphysis as, 164, 169f
   structural features/types/ mobility, 170t
Castration of adult males, 552–553
Catabolism, 495
Catalase, 73
Catalysts, 52
   chemical reactions and, 41t
   enzymes and, 51t, 52, 54
Cataracts, 289, 289f
   congenital, 304
CAT (computerized axial tomography). See Computed tomography
Catecholamines, 325–326, 325f
   hypersecretion and, 326
Catheter, urinary, 530
Cation, 36
Cauda equina, 255f, 256
Caudal (inferior) direction/ orientation, 18f, 18t
Cavities (bone markings), 137, 138t
Cavities of body, 17, 20–22, 20f, 21f
CCK (cholecystokinin), 333t, 490t, 491, 491f
Cecum, 470f, 477–478, 478f
   peritoneal attachments and, 475f
Celiac ganglia, 268, 268f
Celiac trunk, 378, 379f
Cell body of neurons, 190f, 232, 233f
Cell diversity, 74–75, 75f
Cell division, 83–86
   cytokinesis, 83, 84–85
   DNA replication prior to, 83, 84f
   mitosis, 83–84, 85f
"Cell drinking" (pinocytosis), 82, 82f
"Cell eating" (phagocytosis), 82, 82f
Cell junctions (membrane junctions), 68–69, 69f, 89
Cell life cycle, 83
Cell-mediated (cellular) immune response, 416, 425–429
Cell membrane. See Plasma membrane
Cell (membrane) junctions. See Cell junctions
Cell physiology, 76–88
   cell division, 83–86
   membrane transport, 76–83
   protein synthesis, 86–88
Cells, 3f, 4, 65–88. See also specific structures
   aging process and, 101, 104
   anatomy of a generalized, 66–76, 66f
   binucleate, 85
   chemical makeup of, 65
   developmental aspects, 101–104
   diversity of, 74–75, 75f
   membrane of. See Plasma membrane
   multinucleate, 85
Cellular (cell-mediated) immune response, 416, 425–429
Cellular respiration, 449, 496–497, 497f
   electron transport chain and, 496, 498f
   events of, 496–497, 497f
   summary equation of, 496f
Cellulose, 483
Cementum, 480, 480f
Central artery of retina, 285f, 286f
Central canal of bone cell, 94f
Central canal of spinal cord, 242, 250f
   gray matter surrounding, 256, 256f

Central (Haversian) canals, 139, 139f
Central nervous system (CNS), 229, 230f, 242–258. See also Brain; Spinal cord
   aging effects, 273
   brain, 229, 230f, 242–248
   cerebrospinal fluid pathway, 250f
   developmental aspects, 272–273, 275
   diagnostic tests, 271–272b
   integration centers, 240, 241f
   protection of, 248–252, 249f, 250f
   spinal cord, 229, 230f, 255–258
   supporting cells of, 230–232, 231f
Central sulcus, 242, 244f
Central vein of retina, 285f, 286f
Centrioles, 70f, 73, 85f
Centromeres, 84, 85f
Centrum (body), of vertebrae, 154, 155f
Cephalad (superior, cranial) direction/orientation, 18f, 18t
Cephalic region of body, 16f, 17
Cephalic vein, 380, 381f
Cephalin, 47t
Cerebellum, 242, 243f, 244f, 247f, 248
   cerebrospinal fluid in relation to, 250f
   dura mater in relation to, 249f
   equilibrium and, 297–298
Cerebral angiography, CNS disorders and, 271b
Cerebral aqueduct, 247f, 248, 250f
Cerebral arterial circle, 383, 383f
Cerebral cortex, 242–243, 244f
   gray matter of, 242, 244f
   pathways between spinal cord and, 256–257, 257f
Cerebral edema, 252
Cerebral embolus, 350
Cerebral hemispheres (cerebrum), 242–246, 243f, 244f
   ascending/descending pathways, 256–257, 257f
   cortex, 242–243, 244f
   gray matter of basal nuclei, 245–246, 246f
   white matter, 244f, 245, 246f
Cerebral palsy, 272
Cerebral peduncles of midbrain, 247f, 248
Cerebrospinal fluid (CSF), 250f, 251–252
   circulatory pathway, 250f
   homeostatic imbalance, 251–252, 251f
   testing, 251
Cerebrovascular accident (CVA)/ stroke, 252, 254–255
   hemianopia and, 291
Cerebrum (cerebral hemispheres), 242–246, 243f, 244f
Certified surgical technologist (CST), 382b
Cerumen (earwax), 294
Ceruminous glands, 295
Cervical canal, 555f
Cervical curvature, 151, 151f
Cervical enlargement of spinal cord, 255, 255f
Cervical lymph nodes, 406f
Cervical plexus, 263f, 264t
Cervical region of body, 16f, 17
Cervical spinal nerves, 255f, 263f, 267f
Cervical vertebrae, 150, 151f, 155, 156f

Cervix, 554f, 555, 555f
Cesarean section (C-section), 5
CF (cystic fibrosis), 461, 464, 506–507
cGMP (cyclic guanosine monophosphate), 311
Chambers of heart, 363–364f, 365, 365f
Channel-mediated facilitated diffusion, 77, 78f
Cheekbones (zygomatic bones), 146f–148f, 149
Cheeks, 471, 471f
Chemical bonds, 35–39
   covalent, 36–38, 38f
   electron's role in, 35, 36f
   hydrogen, 39, 39f
   ionic, 35–36, 37f
Chemical buffer systems, 535–537
Chemical digestion of food, 482f, 483f, 484
   small intestine as starting point for, 476
Chemical energy, 28
   ATP as, 55, 56f
Chemical equation, 34
Chemical level of body's structural organization, 3–4, 3f
Chemically inert elements, 35, 36f
Chemical reactions, 35, 40–41
   factors increasing rate of, 41, 41t
   patterns of, 40–41, 40f
   reactivity rule, 35, 36f
   reversibility of, 41
   water's role in, 42
Chemical senses, 301–303, 301f
   aging effects, 305
Chemistry, 26–63
   bonds and, 35–39
   chemical reactions and, 35, 40–41
   compounds and, 34–35
   energy and, 27–28
   of living matter, 41–58. See also Biochemistry
   matter and, 27–28
      composition of, 29–34
      molecules and, 34–35
Chemoreceptors, 301–303, 301f
Chemotactic factors of immune response molecules, 426t
Chemotaxis, 413
   in inflammatory response, 411, 412f
   positive, 345
Chewing (mastication), 479
   muscles, 206, 206f, 207
CHF (congestive heart failure), 372–373, 374
Chief cells, 474f, 475
Childbirth, 569–571
   homeostatic imbalances in, 570–571
   hormonal effects during, 318, 318f, 330t
   labor stages, 569–571, 571f
Chin (mandibular body), 146f, 149
Chloride ions, in blood plasma, 341f
Chlorine
   atomic structure, 33t
   percentage of body mass, 30t
   properties, 34–35, 34f
   role of, 30t
Cholecystokinin (CCK), 333t, 490t, 491, 491f
Cholesterol, 47t, 49, 501–502
   liver and, 501–502
   metabolism and, 501–502
   in plasma membrane, 67, 68, 68f

...ived

...f
...ers, 266f, 269
..., 95f
...endineae, 364f, 366
...ic vesicle, 564f, 565
...onic villi, 565f, 566, 566f
...roid, 283, 285f, 286f
...noroid plexuses, 247, 247f, 250f
   CSF formation and, 247, 251
Chromatids, 84, 85f
   sister, 85f
Chromatin, 66f, 67, 70f, 85f
Chromosomes, 67, 84, 85f
Chronic bronchitis, 451,
   460–461, 461f
Chronic obstructive pulmonary disease (COPD), 458b,
   460–461, 461f, 464
   carbon dioxide retention in, 460
Churning of food by stomach, 482f
Chyme, 475, 487, 487f, 490, 491f
Chymotrypsin, 490
Cilia, 73
   in body defense, 414t
   smoking and, 445
   tracheal, 445f
   of uterine tube, 555
Ciliary body, 283, 285f
Ciliary glands, 282
Ciliary muscle, ANS
   innervation/effects,
   267f, 269t
Ciliary zonule, 283, 285f
Circle of Willis, 383, 383f
Circular folds (plicae circulares) of
   small intestine, 477, 477f
Circular layer of smooth muscle,
   186, 186f
Circular muscle structure, 204, 205f
Circulation
   blood pressure and, 387–391,
   394. See also Blood pressure
   capillary bed microcirculation,
   377, 377f
   cardiac, 367–368
   cerebral, 383, 383f
   fetal, 383–385, 384f, 395
   hepatic portal, 385–386,
   385f, 386f
   physiology, 387–394
      arterial pulse, 387, 387f
      blood pressure, 387–391, 394
      capillary exchanges, 394–395
   pulmonary, 365, 365f
   systemic
      arteries of, 378, 379f
      veins of, 380, 381f
Circulatory shock, 391
   skin burns and, 124
Circumcision, 549
Circumduction (body movement),
   199, 201f
Circumflex artery, 363f, 367
Circumvallate papillae, 302, 303f
Cirrhosis, 481
Cisterna, 72f
Cisterna chyli, lymphatic vessels in
   relation to, 406f
Clavicle (collarbone), 144f, 158,
   159f, 160, 208f
Clavicular notch, 158f
Cleavage, 564f, 565
Cleavage furrow, 84–85, 85f
Cleft lip, 506
Cleft palate, 149, 442, 461, 506
Clitoris, 554f, 556–557, 556f
Clonal selection, 418, 419f
Clone, 418, 419f

Closed fracture reduction, 143
Clot-dissolving agent, 393b
Clotting, blood, 100–101
Clotting cascade, 350
Clotting proteins, 350, 501
   found in plasma, 341f, 342
CNS. See Central nervous system
Coagulation (blood clotting), 349f,
   350, 350f
CO (cardiac output), 372–374, 373f
Coccyx, 150, 151f, 157, 157f, 163f
   female reproductive organs in
   relation to, 554f
Cochlea, 295, 295f, 298, 298f,
   299f, 300
Cochlear branch, vestibulocochlear
   nerve, 260t, 261f
Cochlear duct, 298, 298f, 299f
Cochlear nerve, 298f, 300
Codon, 86, 87f, 88
Coenzymes, 495
Coitus interruptus, 575b
Cold sores (fever blisters), 117,
   123, 124f
Cold temperature
   blood pressure and, 391
   cardiac output influenced
   by, 373t
Cold viruses, rhinitis and, 443
Colic (hepatic) flexure, 478, 478f
Colic (splenic) flexure, 478, 478f
Collagen, 50
   in dermis, 118
Collagen fibers, 95f, 140
Collarbone. See Clavicle
Collateral branch of axon, 232, 233f
Collateral ganglion, 268, 268f
Collecting ducts of kidneys, 521,
   522f, 523
Colloids, 42
Colon, 477, 478f
Colon cancer, 102b
Colony stimulating factors (CSFs),
   348–349
Color blindness, 288
Color vision, 304
Columnar epithelium
   pseudostratified, 90, 92f
   pseudostratified ciliated,
   80, 92f
   simple, 90, 91f
Coma, 248
Comminuted fracture, 142f, 142t
Commissural fibers (corpus callo-
   sum), 245, 246f, 250f
Commissure (canthus) of eye,
   281–282, 282f
Commissures, anterior, 247f
Common carotid arteries, 363f,
   378, 379f
   as pulse point, 387f
Common fibular nerve, 264t, 265f
Common hepatic artery, 378, 379f
Common hepatic duct, 476f, 480
Common iliac artery, 378, 379f
   fetal, 384f
Communicating (gap) junctions,
   69, 69f
Compact bone, 135, 137, 137f,
   139–140, 139f
Complement, 413, 413f, 414t, 427t
   fixation, 413, 413f,
   423–424, 423f
Complementary bases, 55
   DNA replication and, 83, 84f
   in protein synthesis,
   86–88, 87f
Complement fixation, 413, 413f,
   423–424, 423f
Complete (fused) tetanus,
   194, 194f
Complicated plaques, 393b

Compounds (chemical), 34–35, 34f
   inorganic, 41–45
   organic, 45–58
Compression fracture, 142f, 142t
Computed tomography (CT),
   overview, 8–9b
Computerized axial tomography
   (CAT). See Computed
   tomography
Concentration gradients, 77–79, 79f
Conchae (nasal), 148f, 149, 442, 443f
Concussion, 252
Conducting zone structures, 447
Conduction deafness, 300
Conductivity of neurons, 98
   factors that impair, 239
   nerve impulse and,
   237–239, 238f
Condyle (bone marking), 138t
Condyles of femur, 164, 165f
Condyles of tibia, 164, 165f
Condyloid joint, 170t, 171, 172f
Cones, 284, 286, 286f, 287–288b,
   287f, 288, 288f
Congenital eye disorders, 303–304
Congenital heart defects, 395, 397
Congenital malformations
   (neural), 272
Congestive heart failure (CHF),
   372–373, 374
Conjunctiva, 282, 282f, 283f, 284f
Conjunctivitis, 282
   ophthalmia neonatorum, 304
Connective tissue, 93–97
   aging process and, 104
   blood supply of, 93
   bone, 94, 94f
   of cardiac/skeletal/smooth mus-
   cle, compared, 184t
   common characteristics, 93
   functions, 93
Connective tissue membranes, 112
Connexons, 69, 69f
Constant (C) region of antibodies,
   421f, 422
Constipation, 493
Contact dermatitis, 123
   allergic, 431
Contraception, 574–576b
Contractile filaments, 75f
Contractility of muscle cells, 189
Contraction of muscle. See Muscle
   contraction
Control center, in homeostatic
   mechanisms, 12, 13f
Contusion, brain, 252
Convergence, 291, 293
Convergent muscle structure,
   205, 205f
COPD (chronic obstructive
   pulmonary disease), 458b,
   460–461, 461f, 464
Coracoid process of scapula,
   159f, 160
Cornea, 282f, 283, 285f
Cornified (horny) skin cells,
   115, 117
Cornua (horns) of hyoid bone,
   149, 149f
Coronal (frontal) plane or section,
   17, 19f
Coronal suture, 145, 146f, 148f
Corona radiata, 553f, 557, 559f
Coronary arteries, 363f, 367,
   378, 379f
Coronary artery bypass
   surgery, 393b
Coronary artery disease, 397
Coronary atherosclerosis, 374
Coronary (heart attack/myocardial
   infarction), 368
   fibrillation and, 369

Coronary sinus, 368
Coronary sulcus (atrioventricular
   groove), 363f, 367
Coronary thrombosis, 350
Coronoid fossa, 160, 161f
Coronoid process, ulna, 161, 161f
Corpora quadrigemina, 247f, 248
Corpus callosum (commissural
   fibers), 245, 246f, 247f, 250f
Corpus luteum, 553f, 554, 558, 561
Cortex
   of hair, 121, 121f
   of lymph node, 406, 407f
Cortical nephrons, 522f, 523
Cortical radiate arteries, 520f, 521,
   522f, 523f
Cortical radiate veins, 520f,
   521, 522f
Corticospinal (pyramidal) tract, 243
Corticosteroids. See Adrenal cortex
   hormones
Cortisol, 47t, 323
Cortisone, 323
Costal cartilages, 158, 158f
Coughing, 452t
Cough reflex, 444
Covalent bonds, 36–38, 38f
Coxal bones (hip bones), 144f,
   158, 162–164, 163f
Coxal region of body, 16f, 17
CP (creatine phosphate), 195, 196f
Crackles (respiratory sounds), 453
Cranial aponeurosis, 206f, 207
Cranial cavity, 20, 20f
Cranial nerves, 258–262
   definition, 229, 258
   distribution of, 261f, 267f
   extrinsic eye muscles supplied
   by, 284f
   name/number/origin/course/
   function, 259–260t
   in nervous system
   organization, 230f
   testing of, 258, 259–260t
Cranial (superior, cephalad) direc-
   tion/orientation, 18f, 18t
Craniosacral division. See Parasym-
   pathetic division of ANS
Cranium, 144f, 145–148, 146f
   developmental aspects,
   174–175, 175f
Creatine phosphate in muscle
   contraction, 195, 196f
Creatinine, 524
Crenate, hypertonic solutions caus-
   ing cells to, 81b
Crepitus, 173
Crest (bone marking), 138t
Cretinism, 319–320
Cribriform plates, 146f, 148,
   301f, 443f
Cricoid cartilage, 443f
Crista ampullaris (crista),
   297–298, 297f
Cristae (mitochondrial), 71
Crista galli, 146f, 148
Cross bridges, 188f, 189, 192–193
Cross matching in blood
   typing, 354
Cross (transverse) section, 17, 19f
Crown region of tooth, 480, 480f
Crural region of body, 16f, 17
Crying, 452t
Cryptorchidism, 573
C-section (Cesarean section), 571
CSFs (colony stimulating factors),
   348–349
CT (computed tomography)
   CNS disorders and, 271–272b
   overview, 8–9b
Cubital vein, median, 380, 381f
Cuboidal epithelium, 90, 91f

Cuboid bone of foot, 166f
Cuneiform bone of foot, 166f
Cupula of crista ampullaris, 297, 297f
Curvatures
  spinal, 151, 151f, 154
  stomach, 473, 474f
Cushing's syndrome, 324
Cushioning function of water, 42
Cutaneous glands, 119–121, 120f
Cutaneous membrane, 110, 111f. See also Skin
Cutaneous sense organs, 235, 236f
Cutaneous sensory receptors, protective functions of, 114f, 115
Cuticle
  hair, 121, 121f, 122f
  nail, 122, 123f
CVA (cerebrovascular accident/stroke), 252, 254–255
  aging and, 273
Cyanosis, 119, 460
Cyanotic body tissues, 455
cyclic AMP, 311, 312f
Cyclic guanosine monophosphate, 311
Cysteine, 50f
Cystic duct, 476f, 481
Cystic fibrosis (CF), 461, 464, 506–507
Cystitis, 530, 548
Cytokines, 418, 424f, 426t
Cytokinesis, 83, 84–85
Cytomegalovirus retinitis, 432b
Cytoplasm, 66, 66f, 69–74, 70f
  organelles, 69–74, 70f. See also specific type
Cytosine, 54f, 55
Cytoskeleton, 73, 74f
Cytosol, 69, 70f
Cytotoxic T cells, 424f, 425, 425f, 426t, 428f

Dandruff, 117
Dark bands (A bands), 187, 188f, 192f
Daughter cells, 83, 85, 85f
Daughter chromosomes, 85f
DCT (distal convoluted tubule), 521, 522f
Dead space volume, 453
Deafness, 300
  conduction, 300
  maternal rubella and, 272
  sensorineural, 300
Deciduous teeth (baby/milk teeth), 479, 479f
Decomposition reactions, 40, 40f
Decubitus ulcers (bedsores), 118, 118f
Deep artery of the thigh, 378, 379f
Deep (internal) direction/orientation, 18f, 18t
Deep palmar arch, 379f
Defecation, 482f, 483, 492
Defecation reflex, 492
Deglutition (swallowing), 481–482, 482f, 484f, 485, 486f
Dehydration, hypotonic solutions to treat, 81b
Dehydration synthesis, 45–46, 46f
Delayed hypersensitivities, 431
Deltoid muscles, 208f, 209f, 210, 210f, 216f, 217t, 218f, 219t
  as injection site, 210, 210f
  multipennate structure of, 205, 205f
Deltoid region of body, 16f, 17
Deltoid tuberosity, 160, 161f

Dementia, in AIDS patients, 432–433b
Denatured proteins, 51, 52f
Dendrites, 232, 233f
Dens, of axis (C2), 155, 156f
Dense (fibrous) connective tissue, 95f, 97
  of skin's dermis, 117–118
Dental hygienist, 14b
Dentin, 480, 480f
Deoxyribonucleic acid. See DNA
Deoxyribose, 45, 55
Depolarization, 238f, 239
Deprenyl, to treat Parkinson's disease, 253–254b
Depressed fracture, 142f, 142t
Depressions (bone markings), 137, 138t
Depth perception, 291
Dermal papillae, 116f, 117–118
Dermal sheath, of hair follicles, 122
Dermatitis, 127
  contact, 123, 431
Dermis, 115, 115f, 116f, 117–118
Descending colon, 470f, 478, 478f
Descending motor projections, 247f
Desmosomes (anchoring junctions), 69, 69f, 89
Detoxification, cellular, 73
Detrusor muscle, 529
Deuterium, as hydrogen isotope, 32f
Developmental aspects. See under each body system
Diabetes insipidus, 319, 533
Diabetes mellitus, 326–327, 429
Diagnosis, imaging techniques, 8–9b
Dialysis of kidneys, 526–527b
Diapedesis, 344, 412, 412f
Diaphragm
  blood vessels of, 378
  in breathing, 450f, 451, 456, 457f
  heart in relation to, 362, 362f
  lungs in relation to, 446f
  nerve supply, 264f
  peritoneal attachments and, 475f
  respiratory organs in relation to, 442f
Diaphysis, 135, 137f
Diarrhea, 493
Diarthroses, 166
Diastole, 369
  mid-to-late and early periods of 371, 371f
Diastolic pressure, 388, 389f
Diencephalon (interbrain), 242, 243f, 246–247, 247f
Diet
  blood pressure and, 391
  cardiovascular diseases and, 393b, 397
Diet drugs, 509–510b
Diffusion, 76–77, 77f, 78f
  capillary transport mechanisms, 394, 394f
  exchanges of respiratory gases by, 453–454, 454f
Digestion, 11, 481
  autonomic reflex control of, 483
  chemical, 483, 484f
  hormones that act in, 490t
  in large intestine, 492–493
  mechanical, 483
  in mouth/pharynx/esophagus, 484f, 485
  as necessary life function, 11
  propulsion and. See Propulsion in food

in small intestine, 489–492, 490t, 491f
in stomach, 484f, 485–487
Digestive cavity, 22
Digestive system, 6f, 7, 468–493, 470f
  aging and, 507
  anatomy, 469–481, 470f
    accessory organs, 479–481
    GI tract organs, 469–479
  ANS innervation/effects, 269t
  congenital disorders, 506–507
  developmental aspects, 506–507
  functions, 481–493
    flow chart, 484f
    schematic summary, 482f
  homeostatic imbalances, 471, 472, 479, 481, 486, 487, 490, 492, 493, 506
  homeostatic relationships, 511b
  in pregnancy, 567
Digital arteries, 379f
Digitalis, 373
Digital region of body, 16f, 17
Digital subtraction angiography (DSA), 8–9b
Digital veins, 381f
Dilation stage of labor, 570, 571f
Dimers, 423
Direct gene activation by hormones, 311, 312f
Directional terms in anatomy, 15, 18f, 18t
Disaccharides 45–46, 45f, 483
Discharging chambers of heart, 365
Discs
  herniated, 151
  intervertebral, 151, 151f
Disease, homeostatic imbalances and, 15
Dislocation, shoulder girdle and, 160
Dissociation of salts, 42, 43f, 536, 536f
Distal convoluted tubule (DCT), 521, 522f
Distal direction/orientation, 18f, 18t
Distal tibiofibular joint, 165f
Disulfide bonds, 421–422, 421f
Diuresis, 318
Diuretics, 319, 509b
Diverticula, 492
Diverticulitis, 492
Diverticulosis, 492
DNA (deoxyribonucleic acid), 55
  location in cell, 67
  replication, 83, 84f
  structure, 54f, 55
  synthesis, 83, 84f
DNA fingerprinting, 57–58b
DNA gel electrophoresis, 57–58b
DNA probe, 57–58b
Donor organs/tissues, 427, 429
Dorsal body cavity, 20, 20f
Dorsal columns of spinal cord, 256–257
Dorsal digital veins of foot, 381f
Dorsalis pedis artery, 378, 379f, 380
  as pulse point, 387f
Dorsal (posterior) body landmarks, 16f, 17
Dorsal (posterior) direction/orientation, 18f, 18t
Dorsal (posterior) horns, 256, 256f
Dorsal rami, 262, 263f
Dorsal root ganglion, 256, 256f, 263f
Dorsal root of spinal nerve, 256, 256f, 263f
Dorsal venous arch, 380, 381f
Dorsiflexion (body movement), 201f, 202

Double helix, 55, 83, 84f
Double sugars (disaccharides), 45–46, 45f, 483
Doula, 572b
Dowager's hump. See Kyphosis
Drugs
  blood pressure effects, 391
  Integrase, 433f
  Diet 509b
Dry membranes, 110
DSA (digital subtraction angiography), 8–9b
DSR (dynamic spatial reconstruction), 8–9b
Duchenne's muscular dystrophy, 221
Ductless glands, 314
Duct systems
  female, 554–556, 554f, 555f
  male, 546, 547f, 548
Ductus arteriosus, 384f, 385
Ductus (vas) deferens, 546, 547f, 548
Ductus venosus, 384, 384f
Duodenal papilla, 476, 476f
  CCK and, 333t
Duodenum, 470f, 474f, 476, 476f
  CCK and, 333t
  hormones secreted by, 333t, 490t
  intestinal gastrin and, 333t
  peritoneal attachments and, 475f
  secretin and, 333t
Dural sinuses, 249
  veins draining, 380, 381f
Dura mater
  cerebral, 249, 249f, 251f
  spinal, 249, 255, 255f, 256f
Dwarfism, pituitary, 314–315, 316f
Dynamic equilibrium, 12, 297–298, 297f
Dynamic spatial reconstruction (DSR), 8–9b
Dyspnea, 460–461, 461f, 568
Dystocia, 570–571
Dysuria, 530

Ear, 299–300. See also Hearing
  anatomy, 294–296, 295f
  congenital abnormalities and 304
  external, 294, 295f
  homeostatic imbalances and, 294–295
  internal, 295–296, 295f
  equilibrium mechanisms, 296–298, 296f, 297f
  middle, 22, 294–295, 295f
Eardrum (tympanic membrane), 294, 295f
  route of sound waves, 298, 299f, 300
Earwax (cerumen), 294
Eccrine glands, 116f, 119–120, 120f
ECG (electrocardiogram), 370b
Ectoderm, 565, 565f
Edema, 81b, 97, 319, 323
  in acute hypersensitivity response, 430f
  cerebral, 252
  lymphatic vessels and, 403–404
  of peripheral congestion, 374
  pulmonary, 374
EEG (electroencephalogram), 271b
Effectors, 229, 229f
  in homeostatic control mechanism, 12–13, 13f
  organs in reflex arcs, 240, 241f
Efferent arterioles, glomerular, 522f, 523
Efferent lymphatic vessels, 406, 407f

of PNS,
...s, 258
...urons,
...y, in homeostatic
...l mechanism, 13, 13f
..., 545
...on, 548
...atory duct, 547f, 548
...tic cartilage, 94
...astic fibers, dermal, 118
Elasticity of muscle cells, 189
Elastic laminae of blood vessel
 walls, 375f, 376
Elbow joint muscles, 208f, 211,
 216f, 217t
Electrical energy, 28
Electrical stimulation at fracture
 sites, 167b
Electrocardiogram (ECG), 370b
Electrocardiography, 368, 370b
Electroencephalogram (EEG), 271b
 flat, clinical death and, 271b
Electrolyte balance, 531–535, 534f
 aldosterone in regulating,
 323, 324f
 effects on heart activity, 373
 hypothalamus and, 330t
Electrolytes, 43
 in plasma, 340, 341f
Electromagnetic energy, 33
Electromagnetic spectrum, 28
Electron, 29, 31–32, 31f, 31t
Electron cloud, 31, 31f
Electron shells (energy levels),
 35–36, 36f
Electron transport chain, 496,
 497f, 498f
Elements, 29–34
 atomic structures, 33t
 chemically inert/reactive,
 35, 36f
 common to human body, 30t
 inert, 35, 36f
 periodic table of, 29
 reactive, 35, 36f
 trace, 30t
Elephantiasis, 431
Embolism, pulmonary, 377
Embolus, cerebral, 350
Embryo, 545, 565, 565f, 566f
Embryonic development,
 565–566, 566f
 bone growth, 140, 141f
Emesis (vomiting), 487
Emmetropia, 292b, 304
"Emotional-visceral brain" (limbic
 system), 246
Emotions, influencing skin
 color, 119
Emphysema, 460–461, 461f
Emulsification of fats, 481
Enamel of tooth, 480, 480f
Encephalitis, 251
Endocarditis, 366
Endocardium, 364, 364f
Endocrine glands, 93
 major, of body, 313–329, 314f
 actions of/regulated by (sum-
 mary chart), 330–331t
 types of stimuli that activate,
 311–312, 313f
Endocrine system, 5f, 7, 309–338.
 See also Hormones
 age-related changes in, 332, 335
 definition, 310
 developmental aspects, 332, 335
 function overview, 5f, 7, 310
 homeostatic imbalances,
 314–315, 316f, 319–320,
 321f, 324, 326–327

homeostatic relationships
 of, 334b
 major organs of, 313–329, 314f
 summary chart, 330–331t
 as regulating system, 229
 structure overview, 5f, 7
Endocrinology, 310
Endocytosis, 81–83, 82f
 receptor-mediated, 82–83, 82f
Endoderm, 565f, 566
Endolymph, 296, 297f, 298f
Endometrium, 555f, 556
Endomysium, 185, 185f
 of cardiac/skeletal/smooth
 muscle, 184t
Endoneurium, 258, 258f
Endoplasmic reticulum (ER),
 71–72, 71f
 rough, 66f, 70f, 71–72, 71f
 smooth, 70f, 72
 sarcoplasmic reticulum of
 skeletal muscle, 189
Endosteum, 137f
Endothelial cell, in respiratory
 membrane, 449f
Endothelium
 of blood vessel walls, 375f
 capillary, 449f
Endurance exercise, 197–198, 197f
Energy, 27–28
 conversions, 28
Energy balance of body, 502–506
Energy intake, 502
Energy levels (electron shells),
 35–36, 36f
Energy output, 502
Energy sources for muscle
 contraction, 195–197, 196f
Enteroendocrine cells, 474f, 475
Enterogastric reflex, 487
Enzyme-producing acinar tissue of
 pancreas, 326, 327f
Enzymes, 50, 52, 54
 as catalysts, 51t, 52
 denatured, 52, 52f
 hormones and, 311, 312f
 importance of, 86
 restriction, 57–58b
 trace elements and, 30t
Eosinophils, 341f, 345, 346t
Ependymal cells, 231–232, 231f
Epicardium, 363, 364f
Epicondyle (bone marking), 138t
Epicranius muscle, 207
Epidermal sheath, of hair
 follicles, 122
Epidermis, 115, 115f, 116f
 avascularity of, 115
Epididymis, 546, 546f, 547f
Epididymitis, 573
Epigastric region of
 abdominopelvic cavity,
 21–22, 21f
Epiglottis, 303f, 443f, 444, 471f
 in swallowing, 485, 486f
Epimysium, 184t, 185, 185f
Epinephrine (adrenaline), 325–326,
 325f, 331t
 anaphylactic shock treated
 by, 431
 blood pressure and, 391
 effects on heart activity, 373
 heart rate and, 391
 sympathetic fibers and, 266f,
 269, 270
Epineurium, 258, 258f
Epiphyseal line, 136, 137f
Epiphyseal plate, 136, 137f
 in adolescence, 140, 174
Epiphyses, 136, 137f
Epithalamus, 247
Epithelial cells, 74–75, 75f

Epithelial membranes, 110, 111f
Epithelial tissue (epithelium),
 88–93. See also specific type
 aging and, 101, 104
 alimentary canal wall, 473f
 avascularity of, 89
 classes, 89–93, 89f, 91f, 92f
 functions, 89
 glandular, 93
 regenerative ability of, 89
 special characteristics, 89f
Epithelium. See Epithelial tissue
Equilibrium, 294, 296–298,
 296f, 297f
 dynamic, 12, 297–298, 297f
 homeostatic imbalances
 Ménière's syndrome, 300
 vertigo, 300
 receptors, 296–298, 296f, 297f
 static, 296–297, 296f
ER. See Endoplasmic reticulum
Erectile tissue of penis, 547f, 549
Erection, 549
Erector spinae muscles, 209f,
 210, 219t
ERV (expiratory reserve volume),
 452, 453f
Erythema (redness), skin, 119
Erythrocytes (red blood cells), 74,
 75f, 340, 341f, 342–344,
 342f, 346t
Erythropoietin, 348, 348f, 518
 as non-endocrine
 hormone, 333t
Esophageal sphincter, 486f
Esophagitis, 486
Esophagus, 443, 443f, 444, 446f,
 470f, 471f
 blood vessels of, 378, 379f,
 380, 381f
 GI tract activities in, 482f
 mucosa lining, 111f, 472, 473f
 stomach in relation to, 472, 474f
Essential (primary) hypertension,
 391, 394
Estrogens, 47t, 324, 329, 331t, 561
 bone density and, 175–176
 nutritional performance
 enhancers and, 204b
 in ovarian cycle, 560f, 561
Ethmoid bone, 146f, 147–148, 148f
Ethmoid sinuses, 147f
Eupnea, 456, 457f
Evaporation, heat loss via, 504
Eversion (body movement),
 201f, 202
Exchange reactions, 40–41, 40f
Exchange vessels of capillary
 beds, 377, 377f
Excitability
 (responsiveness/irritability),
 of muscle cells, 189
Excreta, 11
Excretion, 11
Excretory system, 7. See also
 Urinary system
Exercise
 aerobic, 197–198, 197f
 backache prevention, 152–154b
 benefits to back/spine,
 152–154b
 breathing patterns during, 456
 cardiac output influenced by,
 373, 373f
 endurance, 197–198, 197f
 isometric, 197f, 198
 resistance, 197f, 198
 sympathetic nervous system
 activity and, 390, 390f
 venous return and, 372
Exocrine (enzyme-producing) part
 of pancreas, 326, 327f

Exocrine glands, 93, 314
Exocytosis, 70f, 72f, 81, 81f
Exophthalmos, 320, 321f
Exotoxins, 423f, 424
Expiration (exhalation), 450f,
 451, 451f
 forced, 451
 neural controls, 456, 457f
Expiratory reserve volume (ERV),
 452, 453f
Expulsion stage of labor,
 570, 571f
Extensibility of muscle cells, 189
Extension (body movement),
 199, 200f
Extensor carpi muscle, 211
Extensor carpi radialis longus
 muscle, 218f
Extensor carpi radialis
 muscle, 219t
Extensor carpi ulnaris
 muscle, 218f
Extensor digitorum longus muscle,
 205, 205f, 214, 215f,
 216f, 217t
Extensor digitorum muscle, 211,
 218f, 219t
External acoustic meatus (auditory
 canal), 145, 146f, 294, 295f
External anal sphincter, 478, 478f
External carotid arteries, 378, 379f
External eye muscles, 281,
 282, 284f
External genitalia
 female, 556–557, 556f
 male, 547f, 549
External iliac artery, 378, 379f
External iliac vein, 380, 381f
External jugular vein, 380, 381f
External oblique muscles, 208f,
 209, 216f, 217t
External (outer) ear, 294, 295f
External respiration, 448–449, 453,
 454f, 455f
External (superficial) direction/
 orientation, 18f, 18t
Extracellular fluid (ECF), 531,
 531f, 532f
Extracellular matrix, 93–94
Extrinsic eye muscles, 281, 282,
 284f, 291, 293
 eye reflexes and, 291–294
Eye, 281–294. See also under
 Visual
 anatomy
 accessory structures, 281–283,
 282f, 283f
 external, 281–283, 282f
 internal, 283–290, 285f
 extrinsic muscles, 281, 282,
 284f, 291, 293
 intrinsic, 283–284, 285f, 291
 ANS innervation/effects,
 267f, 269t
 homeostatic imbalances, 282,
 286, 288, 289, 291, 292b
 eye-focusing, 292–293b
 pathway of light through,
 290, 290f
 reflexes, 291–294
Eyeball, 283–288, 285f
Eyebrows, 282f
 muscles acting on, 206f, 207,
 216f, 217t
Eyelashes, 282, 282f, 283f
Eyelids, 281–282, 282f, 283f
Eyestrain, 293–294

Face, superficial muscles of,
 206–207, 206f
Facet (bone marking), 138t
 vertebral, 155f, 156f

Facial artery, as pulse point, 387f
Facial bones, 144f, 145, 146f, 148–150, 148f
Facial burns, 125
Facial muscles, 206–207, 206f, 216f, 217t
Facial nerve (cranial nerve VII), 260t, 261f, 281, 282, 284f, 291, 293
taste impulses and, 302
Facilitated diffusion, 77, 78f
Fad diets, 510b
Falciform ligament, 475f, 481
Fallopian (uterine) tubes, 554–555, 554f, 555f
False labor, 569
False pelvis, 163f, 164
False ribs, 158, 158f
Falx cerebri, 249f, 251
Farsightedness (hyperopia), 292b, 293f
Fascicles, nerve, 258, 258f
Fascicles of skeletal muscles, 185, 185f
arrangement patterns, 204–206, 205f
Fasting state, insulin secretion in, 326
Fat (adipose tissue), 96f, 97
ANS effects on, 269t
kidneys surrounded by, 519–520
stored in bone cavities, 135, 136, 137f
resistin and 333t
in subcutaneous tissue, 115, 116f
Fat cells, 75, 75f, 96f, 97
Fatigue, muscle, 195–197
Fats (neutral, triglycerides), 46, 47t, 49
dietary sources of, 494, 494t
digestion/absorption of, 483, 484f
formation/structure of, 48f
metabolism of, 497–498, 499f
Fat-soluble vitamins, 47t
Fatty acids
in muscle contraction, 196f
omega-3, 48f, 49
prostaglandins derived from, 333t
saturated, 48f, 49
triglycerides and, 46, 47t, 48f, 49
unsaturated, 48f, 49
Fatty streak stage of atherosclerosis, 392–393b
Fear, sympathetic nervous system activity and, 390
Feces, 482f, 483, 492
Fed state, insulin secretion during, 326
Feedback mechanisms. See Negative feedback mechanisms; Positive Feedback mechanisms
Female reproductive system, 6f, 7, 553–563
aging and, 576, 578
anatomy, 552–557
developmental aspects, 571, 573, 576, 578
homeostatic imbalances, 555, 556, 561
homeostatic relationships, 577b
physiology, 557–563
Female sex hormones, 329, 561
Femoral artery, 378, 379f
as pulse point, 387f
Femoral cutaneous nerves, 265f
Femoral nerve, 264t, 265f

Femoral region of body, 16f, 17
Femoral vein, 380, 381f
Femur, 144f, 164, 165f
Fenestra, 394, 394f
Fenestrated capillaries, 394, 394f
Fertility
male, 332
melatonin and, 329
Fertility awareness methods of contraception, 575b
Fertilization, 563–564
Fetal circulation, 383–385, 384f
Fetal development, 566–567, 567f, 568f
bone growth, 140, 141f
developmental timeline, 568–569t
skeleton ossification centers, 174, 174f
Fetal skull, 149–150, 150f
Fetal umbilicus, 384f
Fetus, 545, 566
Fever, 414f, 414t, 415
as controlled hyperthermia, 506
heart rate increased by, 373, 373f
Fever blisters (cold sores), 117, 123, 124f
Fiber, dietary, 483
Fibrillation
cardiac, 369
ECG pattern and, 370b
Fibrin clot, 349f, 350, 350f
Fibrinogen, 349f, 350
as plasma protein, 341f
Fibroblasts, 74, 75f, 95f, 97
Fibrocartilage, 94, 95f
Fibrocartilage callus, in bone fracture healing, 143, 143f
Fibrosis, in tissue repair/wound healing, 100–101
cystic. See Cystic fibrosis
of lungs 461, 461f
Fibrous articular capsule, 112f, 169f, 170, 171f
Fibrous atherosclerotic plaques, 392–393b
Fibrous capsule of kidneys, 519, 520, 521f, 522f
Fibrous joints, 168, 169f
characteristics/types/mobility, 170t
Fibrous layer of eyeball, 283, 285f
Fibrous pericardium, 362–363, 362f, 364f
Fibrous (structural) proteins, 50, 51f
synthesis of, 86–88
Fibula, 144f, 165, 165f
Fibularis brevis muscle, 214, 215f, 217t
Fibularis longus muscle, 214, 215f, 216f, 217t, 218f
Fibularis tertius muscle, 214, 215f, 217t, 218f
Fibular nerves, 265f
Fibular region of body, 16f, 17
Fibular vein, 380, 381f
Fight-or-flight response, 270, 325–326, 325f
"Fight-or-flight"/"rest-and-digest" systems, 270, 483
Filaments, of sperm, 551f, 552
Filtrate, 77–78
Filtration, 77–78
Filtration slits, 521, 522f
Fimbriae, 554, 554f, 555f
Fingerprints, 117–118
Fingers
bones, 144f, 162, 162f
muscles that move, 211
First-degree burns, 124, 125f
Fissure (bone marking), 138t

Fissures, cerebral hemispheres, 242, 244f
Five Golden Rules of skeletal muscle activity, 198t
Fixator muscle, 202
Flaccid paralysis, 197, 256, 262
Flagella, 73, 75f
Flat bones, 135, 136f
Flexion (body movement), 199, 200f
plantar, 201f, 202
Flexor carpi muscle, 211
Flexor carpi radialis muscle, 216f, 219t
Flexor carpi ulnaris muscle, 218f, 219t
Flexor digitorum muscle, 211
Flexor digitorum superficialis muscle, 219t
Flexor (withdrawal) reflex, 240, 241f, 242
Floating ribs, 158, 158f
Fluid balance, 531–535, 531f
Fluid (hydrostatic) pressure, 77–78
Fluids (body)
continuous mixing of, 532, 532f
extracellular, 531, 531f
interstitial, 76, 189, 394, 394f, 403–405, 404f, 531f
intracellular, 76, 531, 531f
maintaining balance in blood, 531–535, 531f, 532f
major compartments, 531, 531f
pH concentrations and, 44–45, 44f
selective permeability of plasma membrane and, 76
serous, 112
water and electrolyte balance, 531–535, 531f
fMRI (functional MRI), 9b
Follicle cells of ovaries, 553, 553f
Follicle cells of thyroid gland, 319, 320f
Follicles of lymph nodes, 406, 407f
Follicle-stimulating hormone (FSH), 315f, 316, 330t, 331t, 550–551, 552, 552f
in ovarian cycle, 557, 558f, 560f, 561
Fontanels, 150, 150f, 174
Food
basic food groups, 494t, 495f
GI tract activities and (summary), 482f
major nutrients in, 493–495, 494t
Food digestion
chemical, 482f, 483
ingestion, 484f, 485
mechanical, 482f, 483
propulsion in. See Propulsion of food
Food Guide Pyramid, 493, 495f
Food intake regulation, 402
Food technologist, 53b
Foot
arches, 166, 166f
blood vessels of, 378, 379f
bones, 165–166, 166f
muscles that move, 214, 215f, 216f, 217t
nerves serving, 264t
Foot processes of podocytes, 521, 522f
Foramen/foramina (bone marking), 138t
Foramen magnum, 145, 146f, 147f
Foramen ovale, 145, 146f, 147f, 384f, 385

Forearm
blood vessels of, 378, 379f, 380, 381f
bones of, 160–161, 161f
muscles of, 210–211, 216f, 218f, 219t
nerves serving, 264t
Foreskin (prepuce)
male, 547f, 549
female, 556
Formed elements of blood, 340, 341f, 342–347, 342f
summary table, 346t
Fornix, 246f
Fossa (bone marking), 138t
Fossa ovalis, 364f
Fourth ventricle, 247f, 248, 250f
Fovea centralis, 285f, 286, 289f
Fractures, 142–143
advances in repair of, 167–168b
pathologic, 175–176
stages in healing, 143, 143f
types of, 142f, 142t
Freckles, 117
Free edge of nail, 122, 123f
Free nerve endings (pain receptors) in dermal papillae, 117
Free radicals, 73
Free vascular fibular graft technique, 167b
Frontal association area, 244f
Frontal bone, 145, 146f, 148f
Frontal (coronal) plane or section, 17, 19f
Frontalis muscle, 206f, 207, 216f, 217t
Frontal lobe of cerebral hemisphere, 243, 244f, 247f
Frontal region of body, 16f, 17
Frontal sinuses, 147f, 443f
Frostbite, 504
Fructose, 45, 46f
in foodstuffs, 483
FSH. See Follicle-stimulating hormone
Functional (globular) proteins, 50–52
denaturation process, 52f
examples/roles in body, 51t
structure, 51f
synthesis of, 86–88
Functional MRI (fMRI), 9b
Fundus of eye, 289, 289f
Fundus of stomach, 472–473, 474f
Fundus of uterus, 554f, 555, 555f
Fungiform papillae, 302, 303f
Fused (complete) tetanus, 194, 194f
Fusiform muscle structure, 205, 205f

Galactose, 45
dietary, 483
Gallbladder, 470f, 481
ANS innervation/effects, 267f, 269t
CCK and, 333t
duodenum in relation to, 476f
Gallstones, 481
Gametes, 545, 550f, 551
Gamma interferon, 427t
Gamma radiation, 33
Gamma rays, 33
Ganglia, 234
Ganglion cells of retina, 284, 286, 286f
Gap (communicating) junctions, 69, 69f
Gases, 27
Gas exchanges
in lungs, 448–449, 453, 454f, 455f
in body tissues, 365, 365f, 394, 394f, 455f, 456
respiratory membrane and, 447, 448–449, 449f

…9,

…378, 379f
…74f, 475
…tion/effects,
…269t
…ibitory peptide
…GIP), 490t
…c juice, 475, 485–486
…l body defense, 409, 414t
Gastric pits, 474f, 475
Gastric vein, left, 386, 386f
Gastrin, 333t, 485, 490t
Gastrocnemius muscle, 212f, 214, 216f, 218f, 219t
Gastroenteritis, 507
Gastrointestinal (GI) tract, 469–479, 470f. See also Digestive system
  organs of, 469–479, 470f
  wall structure, 472, 473f
Gel electrophoresis, DNA, 57–58b
General (common) interpretation area of brain, 244f
Generalized cell, definition of, 66
Genes, 54
  DNA replication and, 83, 84f
  location in cell, 67
  protein synthesis and, 86
Genitalia
  ANS innervation/effects, 267f, 269t
  female external, 556–557, 556f
  male external, 547f, 549
Germinal centers, 406, 407f
Germinal epithelia of ovaries, 553f
GH. See Growth hormone
Gigantism, 314–315, 316f
Gingivae (gums), 471f, 480, 480f
GIP (gastric inhibitory peptide), 490t
GI tract. See Gastrointestinal (GI) tract
Glands, 93
  accessory, male, 548–549
  ANS innervation/effects, 262, 267f, 269t
  apocrine, 120–121
  cutaneous, 116f, 119–121, 120f
  ductless, 314
  eccrine, 119–120, 120f
  endocrine, 93, 313–331
  exocrine, 93, 116f, 119–121, 120f, 313
  oil, 116f, 119, 120f
  sebaceous, 116f, 119, 120f
  sudoriferous, 119–121, 120f
  sweat, 119–121, 120f
Glandular epithelium, 93
Glans penis, 547f, 549
Glaucoma, 289
Glenoid cavity, 159f, 160
Glial cells (glia/neuroglia) in CNS, 230–232, 231f
Gliomas, 232
Globular proteins. See Functional (globular) proteins
Globulins, as plasma protein, 341f
Glomerular (Bowman's) capsule, 521, 522f, 523f
Glomerular capillaries, 522f, 523, 523f
Glomerular filtration, 523, 523f, 524, 525f
Glomerulonephritis, 429, 538
Glomerulus, 521
Glossopharyngeal nerve (cranial nerve IX), 260t, 261f
  taste impulses and, 302
Glottis of larynx, 444, 486f

Glucagon, 326–327, 327f, 328f, 331t
Glucocorticoid hormones, 47t, 323–324, 323f, 330t, 331t
  in stress response, 325f, 326
Gluconeogenesis, 500, 501f
Glucose
  blood level regulation, 326–327, 328f
    adrenal glands and, 331t
    liver's role in, 500, 501f
    pancreatic hormones and, 331t
  in foodstuffs, 483
  metabolism and, 496–497, 496f, 498f, 499f
    to fuel muscle activity, 195, 196f
  as universal cellular fuel, 45, 46f
  in urine, 528t
Gluteal nerves, 264t, 265f
Gluteal region of body, 16f, 17
Gluteal tuberosity of femur, 164, 165f
Gluteus maximus muscle, 211, 212f, 218f, 219t
Gluteus medius muscle, 211–212, 212f, 218f, 219t
Glycerol, triglycerides and, 46, 48f
Glycine, 50f
Glycocalyx, 68
Glycogen, 46, 500, 501f
  in muscle contraction, 195, 196f
Glycogenesis, 500, 501f
Glycogenolysis, 500, 501f
Glycolipids, skin's waterproofing and, 114t, 117
Glycolysis, 195, 196f, 496, 497f
  anaerobic, 195, 196f
Glycoproteins, 68
Glycosuria, 528t
Goblet cells, 90, 92f, 478
Goiters, 319, 321f
Golgi apparatus, 70f, 72–73, 72f, 75f
Golgi tendon organs, 236f
Gomphoses, 170t
Gonadal arteries, 378, 379f
Gonadal veins, 380
Gonadotropic hormones, 315f, 316
Gonads, 315f, 316, 329, 331t, 545
  female. See Ovaries
  male. See Testes
Gonorrhea, 304, 555
"Goose bumps, ," 122
Gout (gouty arthritis), 174
Graafian (vesicular) follicle, 553, 553f
Gracilis muscle, 216f
Graded potential, 238f, 239
Graded responses in muscle contraction, 194–195, 194f
Gradients
  concentration, 77
  pressure, 77–78
Graft rejection, 416
  T lymphocytes and, 346t
Grafts of bone to heal non-union fractures, 167b
Graft/transplant rejection, 416, 427, 429
Granulation tissue in wound healing, 100–101
Granulocytes, 345, 346t
Granzymes, 425, 425f, 427t
Graves' disease, 320, 321f, 429
Gravity
  adductor muscles and, 214
  antigravity muscles, 207–208, 209f
  body's center of, 152b, 164

equilibrium and, 296–298, 296f, 297f
  hip joints and, 211
Gray hair, 127
Gray matter, 234–235
  brain stem, 247
  cerebral, 243, 244f, 246f
  spinal, 256, 256f, 257f
Great cardiac vein, 363f, 381f
Greater curvature of stomach, 473, 474f
Greater omentum, 473, 474f, 475f
Greater sciatic notch, 163f, 164
Greater trochanter of femur, 164, 165f
Greater tubercle, humerus, 160, 161f
Greater vestibular glands, 556, 556f
Greater wing, sphenoid bone, 147f
Great saphenous veins, 380, 381f
Greenstick fracture, 142f, 142t
Groove (bone marking), 138t
Gross anatomy, 2
Ground substance of matrix, 93
Growth
  defined, 11
  as necessary life function, 11
Growth hormone (GH), 51t, 314–315, 315f, 330t
  as anti-aging drug, 317b
  as functional protein, 51t
  homeostatic imbalances, 314–315, 316f
  long bones and, 140
  potential uses for, 317–318b
Growth zone (matrix) of hair, 121, 121f
Guanine, 54f, 55
Gullet. See Esophagus
Gums (gingivae), 471f, 480, 480f
Gustatory area of brain, 244f
Gustatory hairs, 302
Gustatory (taste) cells, 302, 303f
Gyri, 242, 244f

Hair, 121–122, 121f, 122f
  blood supply, 116f, 121f, 122
  color, 121
  developmental aspects and, 127
  graying, 127
  homeostatic imbalances and, 127
  nasal, 409, 414t
  thinning, 127
Hair bulb, 121, 121f
Hair cells
  equilibrium, 296f, 297, 297f
  hearing, 298, 298f, 299f, 300
Hair cortex, 121, 121f
Hair follicles, 116f, 121–122, 121f, 122f
  inflammation of (boils), 123
  smooth muscle cells of, 122
Hair root, 116f, 121, 121f
Hair shaft, 116f, 121, 121f, 122f
Hamate bone, 162f
Hammer (malleus) bone, 295, 295f, 299f
Hamstring muscles, 212f, 214, 218f, 219t
Hand
  bones of, 160, 161–162, 162f
  nerves serving, 264t
Haptens (incomplete antigens), 416, 430
Hard palate, 147f, 149, 442, 443f, 471, 471f
Haustra, 478f, 479
Haustral contractions, 492
Haversian (central) canals, 139, 139f
Haversian system (Osteon), 139, 139f

Hb. See Hemoglobin
hCG (human chorionic gonadotropin), 332, 565
HDL (high-density proteins), 502
Head. See also Skull
  injuries to, 252
  muscles of, 206–207, 206f, 209–210, 209f, 216f, 217t
  veins draining, 380, 381f
Headache, sinus, 443
Head (bone marking), 138t
  of femur, 164, 165f
  of fibula, 165f
  of humerus, 161f
  of radius, 161f
Head of sperm, 551f, 552
Hearing, 294, 298–300
  aging effects, 304–305
  developmental aspects, 304–305
  mechanism of, 298–300, 298f, 299f
  route of sound waves, 298, 299f
Hearing loss, 300
Heart, 362–374
  aging and, 372–373, 397
  as a "muscular pump," 361, 372
  anatomy, 362–368
  ANS innervation/effects, 267f, 269t
  blood supply (cardiac circulation), 367–368
  cardiac output, 372–374, 373f
  chambers, 363–364f, 365, 365f
  conduction system of, 368–369, 369f
  congenital defects and, 395, 397
  coverings, 362–363, 362f, 363f
  developmental aspects of, 395, 397
  heart rate and, 369, 372–374, 373f
  homeostatic imbalances, 363, 366, 368, 369, 371–372, 374
  hormone produced by, 333t
  location of, 362, 362f
  lungs in relation to, 446f
  pacemaker of, 368, 369f
    artificial, 369
  physiology, 368–374
  in pregnancy, 568
  size of, 362
  "skeleton of," 364
  valves, 363f, 366, 367f
  wall layers, 363–364, 364f
Heart attack (myocardial infarction/coronary), 368
  fibrillation and, 369
Heart block, 369
Heartburn, 486
  in pregnancy, 567
Heart rate (HR)
  blood pressure and, 390f
  cardiac output and, 372–374, 373f
  factors modifying basic, 372–374, 373f
  fast/slow, 369
  in females vs. males, 373
Heart sounds, 371
  abnormal, 371–372
Heart valves, 363f, 366, 367f
  artificial/mechanical, 366
  incompetent, 366
  operation of, 367f
  stenosis of, 366
Heat exhaustion, 506

Heat (external)
blood pressure and, 391
heart rate increased by, 373, 373f
water's capacity to absorb, 42
Heat-loss mechanisms of body, 504
Heat-promoting mechanisms of body, 504
Heat stroke, 506
Heelbone (calcaneus), 166, 166f
Heimlich maneuver, 444
Helicobacter pylori, peptic ulcers and, 488–489b, 489f
Helium
atomic structure, 31, 32f
as chemically inert element, 35, 36f
Helix, double, 55, 83, 84f
Helper T cells, 424f, 425, 426t, 427, 428f
HIV virus and, 432–433b
Hematocrit, 340
Hematoma, 119
in bone fractures, 143, 143f
Hematopoiesis (blood cell formation), 4, 135, 347–349, 347f, 348f
Hematuria, 528t
Hemianopia, 291
Hemiplegia, 254
Hemodialysis, 526–527b
Hemoglobin, 51, 51f, 342
fetal vs. newborn/adult, 356
normal, 343, 343f
problems with/substitutes for, 355–356b
sickle cell, 343–344, 343f, 344t
in urine, 528t
Hemoglobinuria, 528t
Hemolysis, 353
Hemolytic anemia, 344t
Hemolytic disease of the newborn, 354, 356b
Hemophilia, 119, 351
HIV virus and, 433b
Hemorrhage
anemia and, 344t
blood pressure and, 389–390, 390f
intracranial, 252
spleen and liver's reaction to, 407
Hemorrhagic anemia, 344t
Hemostasis, 349–351, 349f, 350f
disorders, 350–351
Heparin, 527b
basophils and, 346t
Hepatic arteries, 378, 379f
Hepatic (colic) flexures, 478, 478f
Hepatic ducts, 476f
Hepatic portal circulation, 385–386, 385f, 386f
Hepatic portal vein, 380, 381f, 385, 385f, 386f
fetal, 384f
Hepatic vein, 380, 381f, 385, 385f
fetal, 384f
Hepatic veins, 519f
Hepatitis, 481
Hepatitis C infection, tattoos and, 113b
Hepatopancreatic ampulla, 476, 476f
Hermaphrodites, 573
Hernia, hiatal, 486
Herniated discs, 151
Herpes simplex infection, cold sores and, 117, 123, 124f
Herpes simplex virus, 117
Hiatal hernia, 486
Hiccups, 452t

High blood pressure (hypertension), 391, 394
diet and, 391, 394
High-density lipoproteins (HDLs), 502
High-energy phosphate bonds, 55, 56f
Hilum
lung, 445, 446f
lymph node, 406, 407f
renal, 519, 519f
Hinge joint, 170t, 171, 172f
Hip bones (coxal bones), 144f, 158, 162–164, 163f
Hip joint
ligaments, 162
muscles, 211–212, 212–213f, 214, 216f, 217f
nerve supply, 264t, 267, 267f
Hip muscles, 218f, 219t
Hip (pelvic) girdle
bones, 144f, 158, 162–164, 163f
muscles, 211–212, 212–213f, 214, 218f, 219t
nerve supply, 264t, 267, 267f
Histamine, 345, 346t
acting in digestion, 490t
in acute hypersensitivity, 430, 430f
in inflammatory response, 411, 411f
HIV (human immunodeficiency virus), 432–433b
Homeostasis, 12–13, 13f, 15
Homeostatic relationships
of cardiovascular system, 396b
of digestive system, 511b
of endocrine system, 334b
of integumentary system, 129b
of lymphatic system, 433b
of muscular system, 222b
of nervous system, 274b
of reproductive system, 577b
Homeostatic set point for blood sugar levels, 328f
Horizontal fissure, of lung, 446f
Hormonal stimuli
pituitary hormones regulated by, 314
of endocrine organs, 311–312, 313f
Hormone replacement therapy (HRT), 578
Hormones
anabolic steroids, 203–204b
chemistry of, 310–311
control of release of, 311–313, 313f
definition, 310
endocrine gland stimuli
hormonal, 311–312, 313f
humoral, 312, 313f
neural, 312, 313f
of endocrine organs, 313–329
summary table, 330–331t
as functional proteins, roles in body, 51t
mechanisms of action, 311, 312f
of non-endocrine organs, 332, 333t
overview, 310–313
as plasma constituent, 341f
regulating blood levels of, 311
sex. *See* Sex hormones
steroid. *See* Steroid hormones
Horns (cornua) of hyoid bone, 149, 149f
Horny (cornified) skin cells, 115, 117
Hospice care, 462b
"Hot flashes" of menopause, 332

hPL (human placental lactogen), 332
HR. *See* Heart rate
HRT (hormone replacement therapy), 578
Human blood groups, 351, 353, 353t
Human body
elements commonly found in, 30t, 33t
levels of structural organization, 3–7, 3f, 10
necessary life functions, 10–11, 10f
survival factors, 11–12
Human chorionic gonadotropin (hCG), 332, 565
Human life cycle, 550f
Human placental lactogen (hPL), 332
Humerus, 144f, 160, 161f, 171f, 210, 210f
muscles of, 208f, 211, 216f
muscles that move, 208, 208f, 209f, 210
Humoral (antibody-mediated) immune response, 416, 418–425
primary, 418–419, 419f, 420f, 428f
secondary, 419, 419f, 428f
Humoral stimuli of endocrine glands, 312, 313f
Hunger, excessive, 326
Huntington's disease/chorea, 245–246, 254b
Hyaline cartilage, 94, 95f
as articular cartilage, 136, 137f, 169f, 170, 171f
bone formation and, 140
tracheal wall, 444, 445f
Hydrocephalus, 251–252, 251f, 272
Hydrochloric acid (HCL)
in gastric juice, 409, 414t
release of, 333t
Hydrogen bonds, 39, 39f
Hydrogen gas formation, 34, 36, 38f
Hydrogen
atomic structure, 31, 32f, 33t
bonds, 39, 39f
as chemically reactive element, 35, 36f
isotopes, 32f, 33
percentage of body mass, 30t
role of, 30t
as simplest atom, 31, 32f
Hydrogen ions
acids and 43
pH units and, 44, 44f
Hydrolases, 52
Hydrolysis reactions, 42, 46, 46f, 56f, 483
Hydronephrosis, 520
Hydrophilic molecules, 67
Hydrophobic molecules, 67
Hydrostatic (fluid) pressure in filtration process, 77–78
Hydroxides, 43
Hydroxyl ions, 43
pH units and, 44, 44f
Hymen, 556
Hyoid bone, 149, 149f, 166, 443f, 471f
Hyperaldosteronism, 324, 535
Hypercalcemia, 140
Hypercalcemic hormones, 321
Hyperextension (body movement), 200f
Hyperglycemia, 496
Hyperglycemic hormones, 323, 326
Hyperopia, 292b, 293f, 304
Hyperplasia, 104
prostate gland, 530

Hyperpnea, 456
Hypersensitivities (allergies), 430–431, 430f
delayed, 431
eosinophils and, 346t
rhinitis and, 443
skin, 123, 127, 431
Hypertension (high blood pressure), 391, 394, 397
diet and, 391, 394
Hyperthermia, 504, 506
Hyperthyroidism, 320, 321f, 503
Hypertonic solutions, 80–81b
Hypertrophy, prostatic, 548–549
Hyperventilation, 460
Hypoaldosteronism, 324, 535
Hypocalcemic hormones, 321
Hypochondriac regions of abdominopelvic cavity, 21–22, 21f
Hypodermis (subcutaneous tissue), 116f
Hypogastric (pubic) region of abdominopelvic cavity, 21–22, 21f
Hypoglossal nerve (cranial nerve XII), 260t, 261f
Hypoglycemia, 496–497
Hypoglycemic hormones, 326
Hypospadias, 538
Hypotension, 391
orthostatic, 273, 391
Hypothalamic neurosecretory cells, 318, 318f
Hypothalamus, 246, 247f, 330t
as body's thermostat, 13, 504–506, 505f
developmental aspects, 273
as endocrine organ, 313, 314f
hormones of, 311–312, 313f, 318, 318f, 330t
neurosecretory cells of, 318, 318f
pituitary relationship, 316, 318, 318f, 330t
releasing/inhibiting hormones of, 315f, 316, 330t
role in stress response, 325–326, 325f
Hypothermia, 504
Hypothyroidism, 319–320, 321f, 335, 503
Hypotonic solutions, 81b
Hypoxia, 455, 461
H zone, 187, 188f, 192f

I bands (light bands), 187, 188f, 192f
ICF (intracellular fluid), 76, 531, 531f, 532f
IgA, 422–423, 422t
in saliva, 480
secretory, 423
IgD, 422–423, 422t
IgE, 422–423, 422t
in acute allergy response, 430, 430f
IgG, 422–423, 422t
IgM, 422–423, 422t
Igs (immunoglobulins), 51t, 421–425, 422t, 426t. *See also* Antibodies
Ileocecal valve, 476, 478f
Ileum, 470f, 476f, 478f
Iliac arteries, 378, 379f
Iliac crest, 162, 163f, 212f, 213f, 519f
Iliac (inguinal) regions of abdominopelvic cavity, 21–22, 21f
Iliac spines, 162, 163f
Iliacus muscle, 212, 213f

210
213f,

218f
mus and, 211
3f, 164
chniques, medical, 8–9b
.e (acute) hypersensitivity,
430, 430f
une response/immunity, 415
acquired, 420–421, 420f
active, 420, 420f
burn injury and, 124
cellular (cell-mediated), 416,
425–429
summary flowchart, 428f
functions of cells/molecules
involved in, 426–427t
humoral (antibody-mediated),
416, 418–425
summary flowchart, 428f
lymphocytes and, 345, 346t,
416–418, 417f
passive, 420–421, 420f
WBCs' role in, 340, 341f, 344
Immune system, 408–431, 408f.
See also Immune response/
immunity
body defenses
adaptive, 415–431
innate, 409–415
cells/molecules of, 346t, 408f,
409, 416–418, 426–427t
developmental aspects of,
431, 435
disorders of, 416, 429–431
organ transplants and, 427, 429
overview chart, 408f
Immunocompetency, lymphocyte
differentiation and,
416–418, 417f
Immunodeficiencies, 431
Immunoglobulins (Igs), 421–425,
422t, 426t. See also
Antibodies
Immunological memory, 419
Immunology, 415
Immunosuppressive therapy, 429
Impacted fracture, 142f, 142t
Impacted teeth, 479
Impetigo, 123, 124f
Implantation, 556
Incisor teeth, 479, 479f
Incompetent heart valve, 366, 372
Incomplete antigens (haptens),
416, 430
Incontinence, 530
stress, 568
urinary, 538, 540
Incus (anvil) bone, 295, 295f, 299f
Inert elements, 35, 36f
Infancy
skull in, 149–150, 150f
spinal curvatures during, 154
Infant respiratory distress
syndrome (IRDS), 461
Infarct, 368
Infections
skin, 123, 124f
white blood cells and, 346t
Inferior articular processes of
vertebrae, 155, 155f, 156f
Inferior (caudal) direction/orienta-
tion, 18f, 18t
Inferior meatus of nasal cavity, 283f
Inferior mesenteric artery, 378, 379f
Inferior mesenteric vein, 381f,
386, 386f
Inferior nasal conchae, 148f, 149
Inferior oblique muscle of eye, 284f
Inferior ramus of pubis, 163f, 164

Inferior rectus muscle of eye, 284f
Inferior vena cava, 363–364f, 519f
fetal, 384f
Infertility, male, 549
Inflammation, cardinal signs of,
410–411, 411f
Inflammatory response,
410–413, 414t
abscesses and, 413
flowchart, 411f
pus and, 413
Infundibulum, 554, 555f
Ingestion of food, 481, 482f
Inguinal (iliac) regions of
abdominopelvic cavity,
21–22, 21f
Inguinal ligament, 213f
Inguinal lymph nodes, 406f
Inguinal region of body, 16f, 17
Inhibiting hormones, hypothalamic,
315f, 316, 330t
Injection sites
buttock, 164
deltoid, 210, 210f
gluteus medius, 212, 212f
Inlet, pelvic, 163f, 164
Innate (non-specific) body
defenses, 408–409, 408f,
409–415, 414t
Inner cell mass, 564f, 565
Inner (internal) ear, 295–296, 295f
Inorganic compounds, 41–45
acids and bases, 43–45
salts, 42–43, 43f
water, 42
Insertion (muscle attachment),
199, 199f
Inspiration (inhalation), 450f,
451, 451f
neural controls, 456, 457f
Inspiratory reserve volume (IRV),
452, 453f
Insulin, 326–327, 327f, 328f, 331t
as functional protein, 51t
Insulin resistance, 327
Integrase drugs, 433b
Integration center, CNS, in reflex
arcs, 240, 241f
Integration of sensory input by
nervous system, 229, 229f
Integument. See Skin
Integumentary system, 4, 5f,
114–127. See also Skin
in body defense, 408f, 409,
414f, 414t
boundary maintenance role, 10
functions of, 4, 5f, 114–115, 114t
homeostatic imbalances, 117,
118, 119, 123–126, 127
homeostatic relationships, 129b
Interatrial septum, 365
Intercalated discs of cardiac muscle, 98, 99f, 186
Intercellular clefts, 394, 394f
Intercondylar eminence of tibia,
164, 165f
Intercondylar fossa of femur,
164, 165f
Intercostal arteries, 378, 379f
Intercostal muscles, 158, 208,
216f, 446f
in breathing, 450f, 451,
456, 457f
external, 450f, 451
internal, 451
Intercostal nerves, 262, 263f
breathing muscles controlled by,
456, 457f
Intercostal spaces, 158, 158f
Interferon, to treat multiple
sclerosis, 234
Interferons, 413, 414t, 415

Interleukins, 348–349, 426t
Interlobar arteries, 520f, 521
Interlobar veins, 520f, 521
Intermediate filaments, 70f, 73,
74f, 75f
Internal acoustic meatus, 145, 146f
Internal anal sphincter, 478
Internal capsule, 246f
Internal carotid arteries, 378, 379f,
383, 383f
Internal (deep) direction/orientation,
18f, 18t
Internal iliac artery, 378, 379f
fetal, 384f
Internal iliac vein, 380, 381f
Internal (inner) ear, 295–296, 295f
route of sound waves through
298, 299f
Internal jugular vein, 380, 381f
lymphatic vessels in relation
to, 406f
Internal oblique muscles, 208f,
209, 216f
Internal respiration, 440
Internal urethral orifice, 528, 529f
Internal urethral sphincter, 529, 529f
Interneuron (association neuron)
cerebral, 235f, 236
spinal cord, 256–257, 257f
Interosseous membranes
of forearm, 160, 161f
of leg, 164, 165f
Interphase period in cell life
cycle, 83
Interstitial cells of testes, 546,
552–553
Interstitial fluid (tissue fluid), 76,
97, 531, 531f
capillary exchanges and,
394, 394f
lymphatic vessels and,
403–405, 404f
in synaptic cleft, 189
Intertrochanteric crest of femur,
164, 165f
Intertrochanteric line of femur,
164, 165f
Intertubercular sulcus of humerus,
160, 161f
Interventricular arteries, 363f, 367
Interventricular septum, 364f, 365,
366f, 369f
Intervertebral discs, 151, 151f
fibrocartilage of, 94, 95f
Intervertebral foramen, 151f
Intervertebral joints, 168, 169f
Intestinal gastrin, 333t, 490t
Intestinal juice, 489
Intestines. See Large intestine;
Small intestine
Intracellular fluid (ICF), 76, 531,
531f, 532f
Intracranial hemorrhage, 252
Intramolecular bonds, 39
Intraocular pressure, 289
Intrapleural pressure, 451
Intrapulmonary pressure, 450f,
451, 451f
Intrapulmonary volume, 451
Intrauterine device (IUD), 574–575b
Intravenous (IV) solutions, tonicity
and, 80–81b
Intrinsic conduction (nodal) sys-
tem of heart, 368–369, 369f
ECG patterns and, 370b
Intrinsic factor, 475
age-related changes and, 356
deficiency and, 344t
Intrinsic (internal) eye muscles, 291
Intrinsic nerve plexuses, 472, 473f
Inversion (body movement),
201f, 202

Involuntary muscle, 98, 184t,
185, 186
Involuntary nervous system, 230,
230f, 262
Involuntary sphincters, 478
Iodine
atomic structure, 33t
deficiencies, 319–320, 321f
hormones containing, 319
percentage of body mass, 30t
role of, 30t
Ionic bonds, 35–36, 37f
Ionic compounds, salts, 42–43, 43f
Ions, 28, 29, 36
bonding and, 35–36, 37f
IRDS (infant respiratory distress
syndrome), 461
Iris, 282f, 283–284, 285f
ANS innervation/effects,
267f, 269t
Iron deficiency anemia, 344t, 356b
Iron
atomic structure, 33t
dietary, anemia and, 344t
percentage of body mass, 30t
role of, 30t
Irregular bones, 135, 136f
of spine, 150, 151f
Irritability (responsiveness), 11. See
also Nerve impulse
muscle cell and, 189
as necessary life function, 11
neuron, 98, 237–239, 238f
IRV (inspiratory reserve volume),
452, 453f
Ischemia, 369
ECG pattern and, 370b
Ischial ramus, 163f, 164
Ischial spine, 162, 163f
Ischial tuberosity, 162, 163f
Ischium, 162, 163f, 164f
body of, 163f
Islets of Langerhans (pancreatic
islets), 326–327, 327f
Isografts, 427
Isometric muscle contractions, 197
Isotonic muscle contractions, 197
Isotonic solutions, 80–81b
Isotopes, 33
radioisotopes, 33
Isthmus of thyroid gland, 319, 320f
IUD (intrauterine device),
574–575b

Jaundice, physiologic, 356b
Jaundiced skin, 119
Jaundiced tissues, 481
Jaw bone
lower. See Mandible
muscles acting on, 216f, 217f
upper. See Maxillae
Jejunum, 470f, 476f
duodenum in relation to, 476f
Joint cavity, 112f, 170, 171f
Joint injuries, burns and resulting
scar tissue, 125
Joints, 166–174
cartilaginous, 168, 169f
fibrous, 168, 169f
functions, 166
homeostatic imbalances,
172–173, 176, 173–174,
173f, 429
immovable, 145, 166
intervertebral, 168, 169f
stabilizing role of skeletal
muscles, 187
synovial, 168, 169f, 170–172,
170t, 171f, 172f
synovial membranes lining,
112, 112f
types of, 166, 168, 169f

Jugular foramen, 145, 146f, 147f
Jugular notch, 157, 158f
Jugular veins, 380, 381f
Juvenile diabetes (Type 1), 327
Juvenile (Type 1) diabetes
    mellitus, 327
Juxtaglomerular (JG) apparatus,
    522f, 534f, 535
Juxtamedullary nephron, 522f

Kaposi's sarcoma, 432b
kcal (kilocalories), 493, 502
Keratin, 50, 114t, 115, 117
    in body defense, 409, 414t
Keratinization, 115
Keratinocytes, 116
Ketoacidosis, 498
Ketosis, 326
Kidneys, 518–528
    in acid-base balance, 537
    ADH effects on, 318–319,
        318f, 330t
    adrenal glands and, 331t
    ANP and, 333t
    ANS innervation/effects,
        267f, 269t
    artificial, 526–527b
    blood pressure and,
        390–391, 390f
    blood vessels serving, 378, 379f,
        380, 381f
    erythropoietin and, 333t
    homeostatic imbalances,
        519–520, 524
    hormones produced by, 333t
    location, 518, 519f
    pathway of renal blood
        vessels, 520f
    provitamin D activated by, 333t
    renal failure and, 526–527b
    structure, 518–521, 520f
    transplants, 527b
Kidney stones (renal calculi), 528
Killer macrophages, 418
Killer T cells, 424f, 425, 425f,
    426t, 428f
Kilocalories (kcal), 493, 502
Kinetic energy, 28
    diffusion and, 76–77, 77f
Kinins, in inflammatory response,
    411, 411f
Knee-jerk (patellar) reflex, 240, 241f
Knee joint, 165
    muscles moving, 211, 213f, 214,
        216f, 217f
Knuckle (metacarpophalangeal)
    joints, 171, 172f
Knuckles (metacarpals), 162, 162f
Krebs cycle, 496, 497f
Kyphosis, 154, 154f, 175

Labia (lips), 471, 471f
Labia majora, 554f, 556, 556f
Labia minora, 554f, 556, 556f
Labor of childbirth, 569
    doula and, 572b
    false labor, 569
    initiation of, 569–570, 570f
    stages, 570–571, 571f
Lacrimal apparatus, 282, 283f
Lacrimal bones, 146f, 148f, 149
Lacrimal canaliculi, 282, 283f
Lacrimal caruncle, 282f
Lacrimal fluid, lysozyme in, 409
Lacrimal glands, 282, 283f
    ANS innervation/effects, 262,
        267f, 269t
Lacrimal sac, 282, 283f
Lacrimal secretions (tears),
    lysozyme in, 409, 414t
Lactation, 561
Lacteal, 477, 477f

Lactic acid, in muscle contraction,
    195–197, 196f
Lactiferous ducts, 561, 562f
Lactose, 45–46, 483
Lacunae, 94, 94f, 139, 139f
Lambdoid suture, 145, 146f
Lamellae, 94f, 139, 139f
Laminae, vertebral, 155, 155f, 156f
Lamina propria, 96f, 97, 110,
    111f, 473f
Language comprehension area of
    brain, 244f
Lanugo, 127
Large intestine, 470f, 477–479, 478f
    defecation and, 492
    food breakdown/absorption in,
        482f, 492–493
    peritoneal attachments
        and, 475f
    propulsion of residue in, 492
    small intestine and, 475
Laryngopharynx, 443, 443f,
    471f, 472
Larynx, 442, 443f, 444
    hyaline cartilage of, 94, 444
Lateral columns of spinal cord,
    256–257
Lateral commissure (canthus) of
    eyelid, 281–282, 282f
Lateral condyle of femur, 164, 165f
Lateral condyle of fibula, 164, 165f
Lateral condyle of tibia, 164, 165f
Lateral cuneiform bone of
    foot, 166f
Lateral direction/orientation,
    18f, 18t
Lateral epicondyle of humerus,
    160, 161f
Lateral horns, 256f, 268f
Lateral longitudinal arch of foot,
    166, 166f
Lateral malleolus, 165, 165f, 215f
Lateral rectus muscle, 284f
Lateral sulcus, 243, 244f
Lateral ventricle of brain,
    246f, 250f
Latissimus dorsi muscles, 209f,
    210, 218f, 219t
Laughing, 452t
LDLs (low-density
    lipoproteins), 502
L-dopa, to treat Parkinson's
    disease, 253b
Left common carotid artery, 363f,
    378, 379f
Left common iliac vein, 380, 381f
Left external carotid artery,
    378, 379f
Left gastric artery, 378, 379f
Left gastric vein, 386, 386f
Left gonadal vein, 380
Left hypochondriac region,
    21–22, 21f
Left iliac (inguinal) region of
    abdominopelvic cavity,
    21–22, 21f
Left internal carotid artery,
    378, 379f
Left lower quadrant (LLQ), 21, 21f
Left lumbar regions, 21–22, 21f
Left subclavian artery, 363f,
    378, 379f
Left upper quadrant (LUQ), 21, 21f
Leg
    blood vessels of, 378, 379f
    bones of, 164–165, 165f
    muscles of, 211, 214, 215f, 216f,
        217t, 218f, 219t
    nerves serving, 264t
Lens, 285f, 288–290
    cataracts, 288–289
    focusing and, 290, 290f

Leptin, as non-endocrine
    hormone, 333t
Lesser curvature of stomach,
    473, 474f
Lesser omentum, 473, 474f
    peritoneal attachments and, 475f
Lesser trochanter of femur,
    164, 165f
Lesser tubercle of humerus,
    160, 161f
Let-down reflex, 318, 330t
Lethal hit, 425
Leukemia, 349, 356b
Leukocytes (white blood cells),
    98f, 340, 341f, 342f,
    344–345, 346t
    summary table, 346t
    thymus and, 329
Leukocytosis, 345
Leukopenia, 345
LH. See Luteinizing hormone
Licensed practical nurse, 462b
Life
    cellular basis of, 65–66
    cycle of, for humans, 550f
    functions necessary to maintain,
        10–11, 10f
Lifting, to protect spine, 152–153b
Ligaments, 112f
    dense connective (fibrous) tissue
        of, 95f, 97
    of foot, 166
    hip joint and, 162
    ovarian, 554, 554f
    periodontal, 170t
    reinforcing synovial joints,
        170, 171f
    shoulder joint and, 160
    of the skeletal system, 134
Ligamentum arteriosum, 363f, 385
Light, pathway through eye,
    290, 290f
Light absorption, visual pigments
    and, 287–288b
Light (I) bands, 187, 188f, 192f
Light refraction, 290, 290f
Limbic system, 246
Limbs. See Lower limbs; Upper
    limbs
Line (bone marking), 138t
Lingual frenulum, 471, 471f
Lingual tonsil, 303f, 443f, 444,
    471f, 472
Lipases, 490
Lipid bilayer of plasma membrane,
    67, 68f
    diffusion processes and,
        77–78, 78f
Lipid metabolism, smooth ER
    and, 72
Lipids, 46–49. See also Fats
    dietary sources of, 494, 494t
    digestion/absorption of,
        483, 484f
    formation/structures of, 48f
    found in body, 46, 47t
    transport, 341f
Lipoid substances, 47t
Lipoproteins, 47t, 501–502
Liposuction, 510b
Lips (labia), 471, 471f
Liquids, 27
Lithium, atomic structure of, 31, 32f
Lithotripsy, 528
Liver, 470f, 475f, 481
    ANS innervation/effects,
        267f, 269t
    arterial supply, 378, 379f
    hepatic portal circulation and,
        385–386, 385f, 386f
    metabolic functions of,
        500–502, 501f

pancreatic hormones and,
    327, 327f
resistin and, 333t
secretin and, 333t
Liver sinusoids, 385f
LLQ (left lower quadrant), 21, 21f
Lobes
    of brain, 242, 244f
    of lungs, 446f
    of mammary glands, 561, 562f
Lobules, of testes, 546, 546f
Lockjaw (tetanus), 194
Long bones, 135–137, 136f, 137f
    formation/growth/remodeling,
        140, 141f, 142
    hormones controlling, 140
    structure, 135–137, 137f,
        139–140, 139f
Longissimus muscle, 209f, 210
Longitudinal arches of foot,
    166, 166f
Longitudinal fissure of brain,
    242, 246f
    falx cerebri in relation to, 249f
Longitudinal layer of smooth
    muscle, 186, 186f
Loop of Henle, 521, 522f
Loose connective tissue, 96f, 97
    of blood vessel walls, 375f
Lordosis, 154, 154f
Low-density lipoproteins
    (LDLs), 502
Lower jaw. See Mandible
Lower limbs
    anterior (ventral) landmarks,
        16–17, 16f
    bones, 144f, 158, 164–166,
        165f, 166f
    developmental aspects,
        175, 175f
    nerves serving, 265f
    posterior (dorsal) landmarks,
        16f, 17
    veins draining, 380, 381f
LPN. See Licensed practical nurse
Lumbar arteries, 378
Lumbar curvature, 151, 151f
Lumbar enlargement of spinal
    cord, 255, 255f
Lumbar plexus, 263f, 264t
    distribution of nerves, 265f, 267f
Lumbar region of body, 16f, 17
Lumbar regions of abdominopelvic
    cavity, 21–22, 21f
Lumbar spinal nerves, 255f,
    263f, 267f
Lumbar (spinal) tap, 251
Lumbar vertebrae, 150, 151f,
    155, 156f
Lumen
    of alimentary canal, 473f
    of arteries/veins, 375f
    of uterus, 555f
Lunate bone, 162f
Lung cancer, 458–459b, 460, 464
Lungs, 362f, 442f, 445–447, 446f
    aging and, 464
    ANS innervation/effects and,
        267f, 269t
    arterial supply, 378
    base, 442f
    capillary beds of, 365, 365f
    disorders, 460–461, 461f, 464
    during breathing, 450f, 451
    fetal, 384–385
    fibrosis of, 461, 461f
    healthy vs. cancerous, 459f
    heart in relation to, 362, 362f
Lunula, nail, 122, 123f
LUQ (left upper quadrant) of
    abdominopelvic cavity,
    21, 21f

315f,
...t,

557, 558f,

404f
...capillaries, 404, 404f
...capillaries in relation to,
   404, 405f
...stribution/structural
   features, 405f
Lymphatic collecting vessels,
   404, 404f
Lymphatic duct, right, 404, 406f
Lymphatic system, 7, 403–408
   developmental aspects of, 431
   function overview, 6f, 7
   homeostatic relationships, 433b
   lymphatic vessels, 403–405, 404f
   structure overview, 6f, 7
Lymphatic vessels (lymphatics),
   403–405, 404f
   afferent, 406, 407f
   blood vessels in relation to,
      403–404, 404f
   distribution in body, 405, 406f
   efferent, 406, 407f
   GI tract activities and, 482f
Lymph duct, 404f
Lymph nodes, 404f, 405–407,
   406f, 407f
   in alimentary canal wall, 473f
   B cells, T cells and, 406, 417f,
      418, 426t
   capsule surrounding, 406, 407f
   distribution in body, 405, 406f
   HIV virus and, 432–433b
Lymphocytes, 341f, 345, 346t
   in lymph nodes, 405, 406f
Lymphoid organs, 407–408, 407f
Lymphoid stem cell, 347, 347f
Lymph trunk, 404f
Lyse, hypotonic solutions causing
   cells to, 81b
Lysine, structure of, 50f
Lysosomes, 70f, 72f, 73, 75, 75f
   in body defense, 410, 410f
   rupture of, 73
Lysozyme, 282, 409, 442
   in saliva, 480

MAC (membrane attack
   complexes), 413, 413f
Macrophage (phagocytic cell),
   75, 75f
Macrophages, 405, 406f
   alveolar, 447, 449f
   in body defenses, 408f, 409–410,
      410f, 418, 428f
   killer, 418
   T cell activation and, 424f
Maculae, 289f, 296–297, 296f
Magnesium ions, 341f
Magnesium
   atomic structure, 33t
   percentage of body mass, 30t
   role of, 30t
Magnetic resonance imaging
   (MRI), 9b
   functional, 9b
Magnetic resonance spectroscopy
   (MRS), 9b
Male gonads, 313, 314f, 331t, 546,
   546f, 547f
Male pattern baldness, 127
Male reproductive system, 6f, 7
   anatomy, 546–549, 547f
      accessory glands and semen,
         547f, 548–549
      duct system, 546, 547f, 548
      external genitalia, 547f, 549

developmental aspects, 571, 573,
   576, 578
homeostatic imbalances,
   548–549, 549, 552–553
homeostatic relationships, 577b
physiology, 550–553
   spermatogenesis, 550–552
   testosterone production,
      552–553
sterility and, 316
Male sex hormones, 120–121, 329
Malignant melanoma, 126, 126f
Malignant neoplasm, 102b
Malleolus
   lateral, 165, 165f, 215f
   medial, 165, 165f, 215f
Malleus (hammer) bone, 295,
   295f, 299f
MALT (mucosa-associated
   lymphatic tissue), 408
Maltose, 45–46, 483
Mammary glands, 561–562,
   562f, 563f
   oxytocin, nursing mothers and,
      318, 318f
Mammillary bodies, 246–247, 247f
Mammogram/mammography,
   562, 563f
Mandible, 148f, 149
Mandibular body (chin), 146f, 149
Mandibular fossa, 147f
Mandibular rami, 146f, 149
Manubrium, 157, 158f
MAP (morning-after-pill), 574b
Marginal artery, 363f, 367
Masculinization, 324
Massage therapist, 220b
Masseter muscle, 206f, 207,
   216f, 217t
Mass movements, 492
Mast cells, 430, 430f
Mastication (chewing), 472, 479
Mastoiditis, 145
Mastoid process, 145, 146f, 147f
Maternal rubella, congenital abnor-
   malities and, 272, 304
Matrix
   bone, 139–140
   extracellular, 93–94
   of hair bulb, 121, 121f
   nail, 122, 123f
Matter, 27–28
   chemical vs. physical changes
      in, 27
   composition of, 29–34
Maxillae (maxillary bones), 146f,
   147f, 148–149, 148f
Maxillary sinuses, 147f
Meatus (bone marking), 138t
Mechanical digestion of food,
   482f, 483
Mechanical energy, 28
Mechanoreceptors, 294
Medial commissure (canthus) of
   eyelid, 281–282, 282f
Medial condyle of femur,
   164, 165f
Medial condyle of tibia, 164, 165f
Medial direction/orientation,
   18f, 18t
Medial epicondyle, of humerus,
   160, 161f
Medial longitudinal arch of foot,
   166, 166f
Medial malleolus, 165, 165f, 215f
Medial rectus muscles of
   eye, 284f
Median cubital vein, 380, 381f
Median (midsagittal) plane or sec-
   tion, 17, 19f
Median nerve, 264t, 265f
Median sacral crest, 157, 157f

Mediastinum, 362, 445, 446f
Medical imaging, 8–9b
Medical transcriptionist, 128b
Medicine, nuclear, 8–9b
Medulla
   of hair, 121, 121f
   of lymph node, 406, 407f
Medulla oblongata, 244f, 246f,
   247, 247f, 248
   arachnoid mater in relation
      to, 249f
   breathing centers in, 456, 457f
Medullary cavity, 136, 137f, 139f
   in ossification, 140, 141f
Medullary (renal) pyramids,
   520f, 521
Megakaryocytes, 347
Meiosis, 551
   in ovaries, 557, 558f
   in sperm production, 550f, 551
Meissner's corpuscles, 116f,
   117, 236f
Melanin, 117, 118
   hair color and, 121
   graying, 127
   protective effects of, 114t, 117
Melanocytes, 117, 121f
Melanoma, malignant, 126, 126f
Melanosomes, 117
Melatonin, 329, 330t
Membrane
   nuclear, 66f, 67
   plasma. See Plasma membrane
Membrane attack complexes
   (MAC), 413, 413f
Membrane (cell) junctions,
   68–69, 69f
Membranes of body, 110–112, 111f
   cutaneous, 110, 111f. See
      also Skin
   dry, 110
   mucous (mucosa), 110,
      111f, 112
   serous (serosae), 90
   wet or moist, 110
Membrane transport, 76–83
   active, 76, 78–79, 79f
   passive, 76–78, 77f, 78f
   vesicular, 79, 81–83
Membranous labyrinth, 296
Membranous urethra, 530,
   547f, 548
Memory cells, 419, 419f, 426t,
   427, 428f
Menarche, 573
Ménière's syndrome, 300
Meningeal layer of dura mater,
   249, 249f, 250f
Meninges
   cerebral, 249, 249f, 251
   spinal, 255, 255f, 256f
Meningitis, 251
Menopause, 332, 557, 576, 578
Menses. See Menstruation
Menstrual (uterine) cycle, 329,
   556, 559–561, 560f
   hormonal interactions of, 560f
   iron-deficiency anemia
      and, 344t
Menstruation (menses), 556,
   559–561, 560f
Mental foramen, 146f
Mesenteric arteries, 378, 379f
Mesenteric ganglia, 268, 268f
Mesenteric vein, 381f
Mesenteries, 472, 473f, 475f,
   476, 478f
Mesoderm, 565f, 566
Messenger RNA (mRNA), 55,
   86–88, 87f
Metabolic phase, in cell life
   cycle, 83

Metabolic rate, 502–504
   basal, 502–503, 503t
   total, 503–504
Metabolism, 11, 495–502
   adrenal glands and, 331t
   aging and, 507
   of carbohydrates, 496–497, 497f,
      498f, 499f
   cellular, ANS effects on, 269t
   of cholesterol, 501–502
   developmental aspects, 506–507
   of fat, 497–498, 499f
   homeostatic imbalances, 503,
      504, 506
   hormonal stimuli of, 330t
   inborn errors of, 506–507
   liver's role in, 500–502, 501f
   as necessary life function, 11
   of protein, 498, 499f, 500
Metacarpal bones/metacarpals,
   144f, 162, 162f
Metaphase plate, 84, 85f
Metaphase stage of mitosis,
   84, 85f
Metastasis, 102b
Metatarsals (metatarsal bones),
   144f, 166, 166f
Methane gas, 38
Microcirculation of capillary beds,
   377, 377f
Microfilaments, 70f, 73, 74f
Microglia/microglial cells,
   231, 231f
Microscopic anatomy, 2
Microtubules, 70f, 73, 74f
Microvilli, 68, 69f, 70f
   of small intestine, 476–477, 477f
Micturition (voiding), 530
Midbrain, 243f, 247, 247f, 248
Middle cerebral artery, 383, 383f
Middle ear (tympanic cavity), 22,
   294–295, 295f
   route of sound waves through,
      298, 299f
Middle nasal conchae, 148, 148f
Midsagittal (median) plane or sec-
   tion, 17, 19f
Midsternal line, 362f
Mid-to-late diastole of heart,
   371, 371f
MIF (migration inhibiting
   factor), 426t
Migration inhibiting factor
   (MIF), 426t
Milia, 127
Milk/baby teeth (deciduous teeth),
   479, 479f
Milk let-down reflex, 318, 330t
Mineralocorticoid hormones,
   322–323, 323f, 324f, 331t
   regulation of water/electrolyte
      balance and, 323
   role in stress response, 325f
Minerals
   bones as storage site for, 135
   as nutrients, 495
Minivalves of lymph capillaries,
   404, 405f
Miscarriage, 576b
Mitochondria, 70–71, 70f, 191f
   of sperm, 551f, 552
   of typical motor neuron, 233f
Mitosis, meiosis vs., 551
Mitotic spindle, 73, 84, 85f
Mitral valve (bicuspid/left AV
   valve), 364f, 366, 367f
Mittelschmerz, 558
Mixed nerves, 258, 262
M line, 187, 188f
Molar teeth, 479f, 480
Mole (concentration unit), 44
Molecular formula, 34

Molecules, 3f, 4, 34–35, 34f
  covalent, 36
  nonpolar, 37
  nonpolar covalently bonded, 37
  polar, 37–38, 38f
Moles (skin), 117
Monocyte, 341f
Monocytes, 98f, 345, 346t, 418
  in inflammatory response,
    411f, 412
Monomers, 94, 423
Monosaccharides (simple sugars),
    45, 45f, 483
Monounsaturated fatty acids,
    48f, 49
Mons pubis, 556, 556f
Morning-after pill (MAP), 574b
Morning sickness, 567
Motion, energy of, 28
Motor aphasia, 254
Motor area/cortex, primary,
    243, 245f
Motor (efferent) division of PNS,
    230, 230f
Motor (efferent) nerves, 258
Motor (efferent) neurons, 190f,
    191f, 235f, 236
  descending pathways/tracts and,
    257, 257f
  in muscle contraction, 189–198
  in reflex arcs, 240, 241f
Motor homunculus, 243, 245f
Motor neuron, typical structure
    of, 233f
Motor output, 229, 229f
Motor speech (Broca's area) of
    brain, 243, 244f
Motor unit, 189, 190f
Mouth (oral cavity), 22, 442f, 470f,
    471–472, 471f
  food digestion/absorption in,
    482f, 484f, 485
  mucosa of, 111f
  muscles acting on, 216f, 217t
  taste buds of, 302
Movement, body, 10
  bones and, 135
  as necessary life function, 10–11
  skeletal muscles and, 183,
    198–202, 200–201f
  skeletal system and, 134
  types of, 186, 198–202
MRI (magnetic resonance
    imaging), 9b
  functional (fMRI), 9b
MRI scans, CNS disorders and,
    271–272b
mRNA (messenger RNA), 55,
    86–88, 87f
MRS (magnetic resonance
    spectroscopy), 9b
MS (multiple sclerosis), 234, 429
Mucosa, of alimentary canal wall,
    472, 473f
Mucosa-associated lymphatic tissue
    (MALT), 408
Mucous membranes (mucosae),
    90, 110, 111f, 112
  alimentary canal wall, 472, 473f
  in body defense, 408f, 409,
    414t, 443
  nasal, 441–442
  tracheal, 444–445, 445f
Mucous neck cells, 474f, 475
Mucus, in body defense, 409, 414t
Multiaxial movement of ball-and-
    socket joints, 171–172, 172f
Multinucleate cells, 85
  of skeletal muscle, 187, 188f
Multipennate muscle structure,
    205, 205f
Multiple sclerosis (MS), 234, 429

Multipolar neuron, 236–237, 237f
Mumps, 480
Murmurs, heart, 371–372
Muscle atrophy, declining growth
    hormone output and, 332
Muscle attachments, 199, 199f
Muscle cells
  functional properties, 189
  skeletal, 75f
Muscle contraction
  body heat as by-product of, 187
  cardiac, 184t
  energy sources for, 195, 196f
  graded, 194–195, 194f
  isotonic, 197
  skeletal, 184t
  sliding filament theory,
    192–193, 193f
  in smooth muscle, 184t
  tension and, 197
  twitches, 194, 194f
Muscle fatigue, 195–197
Muscle fibers/cells, 183
  skeletal, 98, 99f
  smooth, 75f, 98, 99f
Muscle insertions, 198t
Muscle response, to nerve stimuli,
    194–195, 194f
Muscles, 4, 183
  essential functions of, 183
  major superficial, anterior sur-
    face, 216f, 217t
  resistin and, 333t
  skeletal, 4, 5f
Muscle spindle, 236f
Muscle tendons, role in reinforc-
    ing/stabilizing joints, 187
Muscle tissue, 97–98, 99f,
    183–187
  skeletal, 98, 99f
  types, 183–186
    comparison chart, 184t
Muscle tone, 197
Muscle twitches, 194, 194f
Muscular dystrophy, 221
Muscularis externa of alimentary
    canal wall, 472, 473f, 474f
  circular muscle layer, 473f, 474f
  large intestine, 478–479
  longitudinal muscle layer,
    473f, 474f
  stomach, 473, 474f, 475
"Muscular pump" of skeletal mus-
    cles, 376, 376f
  blood pressure and, 387
  lymph transport and, 404
Muscular system, 4, 5f, 182–266.
    See also Skeletal muscle
  aging effects, 221
  developmental aspects, 221
  function overview, 4, 5f
  homeostatic imbalances, 197,
    207, 221
  homeostatic relationships, 222b
  structure overview, 4, 5f
Musculocutaneous nerve, 264t, 265f
Mutations in DNA, 102b
Myasthenia gravis, 221, 429
Myelin, 232, 234, 234f
Myelinated axon of motor
    neuron, 191f
Myelinated nerve fibers
  in CNS, 231f, 234
  in PNS, 232, 233f, 234
Myelin sheaths, 231f, 232, 233f,
    234, 234f
Myeloid stem cell, 347, 347f
Myeloid tissue, 347
Myenteric nerve plexus, 472, 473f
Myocardial infarction (heart
    attack/coronary), 368
  arteriosclerosis and, 393b

electrocardiogram and, 370b
  fibrillation and, 369
Myocardium, 363–364, 364f
  as cardiac muscle tissue,
    186, 186f
Myofibrils, 187, 188f, 191f
Myofilaments, 183, 187, 188f, 189,
    193, 193f
Myometrium, 555f, 556
Myopia, 292b, 293f
Myosin, 73, 192f, 193f
Myosin heads, 188f, 189
Myosin (thick) filaments, 188f, 189
Myringotomy, 294–295
Myxedema, 320

Nails, 122, 123f
Naked nerve endings, 236f
Nares (nostrils), 283f, 441,
    442f, 443f
Nasal aperture, posterior, 443f
Nasal bone, 146f, 148f, 149
Nasal cavity, 22, 441–443,
    442f, 443f
  inferior meatus of, 283f
  mucosa of, 111f, 442–443
Nasal conchae, 442, 443f
  inferior, 148f, 149, 443f
  middle, 148, 148f, 443f
  superior, 148, 148f, 443f
Nasal hairs, in body defense,
    409, 414t
Nasal mucosa, 441–442
  rhinitis and, 443
Nasal region of body, 16f, 17
Nasal septum, 441, 442f
  bony, 149
Nasolacrimal ducts, 282, 283f, 443
Nasopharynx, 443, 443f, 471f
Natural killer (NK) cells, 410, 414t
Navicular bone of foot, 166f
Nearsightedness (myopia),
    292b, 293f
Neck
  anatomical, 160, 161f
  muscles, 206f, 207, 209–210,
    209f, 216f, 217t,
    218f, 219t
  nerves serving, 264t
  vertebrae, 150, 151f, 155, 156f
Neck (bone marking)
  of femur, 164, 165f
  of radius, 161f
Neck region of tooth, 480, 480f
Negative feedback mechanisms,
    13, 311
  in blood glucose regulation,
    326, 328f
  pituitary hormones and, 314
  in regulating blood levels of
    hormones, 13, 311
  regulating calcium blood levels
    and, 321, 322f
Neon, as chemically inert element,
    35, 36f
Neoplasm, 102–103b, 104
Nephrons, 521–523, 522f, 523f
  cortical, 522f, 523
  juxtamedullary, 522f, 523
  urine formation and, 521–524
Nerve cell (neuron), 74f, 75, 75f.
    See also Neurons
Nerve fiber (axon) of neuron,
    189, 190f
Nerve fibers, supporting cells and,
    230–232, 231f
Nerve growth factor, as functional
    protein, 51t
Nerve impulse, 4, 28, 232,
    237–239, 238f, 240f
  in muscle contraction, 189–191,
    190f, 191f, 194–198, 194f

saltatory conduction of, 23
  transmission as an
    electrochemical event, 2.
  multiple sclerosis and, 234
Nerve plexuses, 262, 265f
  intrinsic, 472, 473f
Nerves, 234
  afferent, 258
  cranial, 258, 259–260t, 261f
  efferent, 258
  mixed, 258
  motor, 258
  sensory, 258
  spinal, 262, 263f, 264t, 265f
  structure of, 258, 258f
Nerve stimulus, action potential
    and, 189–191, 190f, 191f
Nerve tracts, 234
  between brain and spinal cord,
    256–257, 257f
Nervous system, 4, 5f, 227–279.
    See also Nervous tissue
  aging effects, 273
  autonomic, 230f, 262–270. See
    also Autonomic nervous
    system
  central, 229, 230f, 242–258
  congenital disorders, 272–273
  developmental aspects of,
    272–273, 275
  functional classification,
    229–230, 229f
  functions, 4, 5f, 228–229, 229f
  homeostatic imbalances, 234,
    245–246, 248, 253–254b,
    272–273
  homeostatic relationships, 274b
  homeostatic regulating role
    of, 229
  organization of, 229–230, 230f
  peripheral, 230f, 258–270. See
    also Peripheral nervous
    system
  structural classification, 229–230,
    230f
Nervous tissue, 98, 100f,
    230–242
  homeostatic imbalances,
    234, 239
  neuroglia (supporting cells),
    230–232
  neurons, 232–242. See also
    Neurons
  protection of, 248–252,
    249f, 250f
  regenerative ability of,
    101, 234
Neural layer of retina, 284, 286f
Neural stimuli of endocrine
    glands, 312, 313f
Neural tube, 242
Neurilemma, 234f
Neurofibrils, 232, 233f
Neuroglia (glia/glial cells/support-
    ing cells), 230–232, 231f
Neuromuscular disorders, 272
Neuromuscular junctions, 189,
    191, 191f
Neurons (nerve cells)
  definition, 75, 75f, 98, 100f,
    232, 233f
  in muscle contraction
    of single muscle cell, 189–194
    of whole muscle, 194–198
  physiology, 237–242, 238f,
    240f, 241f
    nerve impulses, 237–239,
      238f, 240f
    reflexes, 240–242, 241f
  sensory (afferent), 235–236, 235f
  in spinal gray matter, 256, 256f
  structure, 232–235, 233f

, 237f
236,
236–237, 237f
258, 258f
gy, science of, 2
ory cells of hypothala-
us, 318, 318f
ransmitters, 180
etylcholine and, 189–190, 191f
axon terminals and, 232, 233f
norepinephrine acting as, 325
synapses and, 239, 240f
Neutral fats. See Triglycerides
Neutralization by antibodies, 423–424, 423f
Neutralization reaction, 44
Neutron, 29, 31–32, 31f, 31t
Neutrophils, 98f, 341f, 346, 346t
in body defense, 410
in inflammatory response, 411f, 412, 412f
Newborn
skull in, 149–150, 150f
spinal curvature of, 151, 151f
Nicotine
addictive nature of, 458–459b
blood-brain barrier and, 252
blood pressure and, 390f, 391
Night blindness, 286
Nipple, breast, 561, 562f
Nissl substance, 232, 233f
Nitrogen
atomic structure, 33t
percentage of body mass, 30f
role of, 30f
Nitrogenous waste products, 524
Nitroglycerin, 585
Nitrosamine, 458b
NK (natural killer) cells, 410
Nocturia, 538
Nodal (intrinsic) conduction system, 368–369, 369f
Node of Ranvier, 233f, 234
Nonaxial movements of plane joints, 171, 172f
Nonpolar covalently bonded molecules, 37
Nonpolar tails of phospholipids, 67, 68f
Nonrespiratory air movements, 452, 452t
Nonself antigens, 416
Non-specific (innate) body defenses, 408–409, 408f, 409–415, 414t
Nonsteroidal (amino acid-based) hormones, 310
mechanisms of action, 311, 312f
Nonstriated muscle, 184t, 185
Noradrenaline. See Norepinephrine
Norepinephrine (noradrenaline), 325–326, 325f, 331t
sympathetic fibers and, 266f, 269, 270
Norian SRS, 168b
Nose, 441–443, 442f
Nosebleeds, 441
Nostrils (nares), 283f, 441, 442f, 443f
Nuclear envelope/membrane, 66f, 67, 70f, 85f
Nuclear medicine, 8–9b
Nuclear pores, 66f, 67
Nuclei, 234
Nucleic acids, 45, 54–55, 54f
protein synthesis, 86–88, 87f
Nucleoli, 67
Nucleolus, 66f, 70f, 85f
Nucleoplasm, 67
Nucleotides, 54–55, 54f, 83

Nucleus, 66–67, 66f, 70f, 75f
of typical motor neuron, 233f
Nutrients
capillary exchanges, 365, 365f, 394, 34f
definition, 493
major
dietary sources of, 494–495
food groups that supply, 494t
minor nutrients vs., 493
as metabolic fuel, 493
minerals as, 495
as survival factor, 11
vitamins as, 495
Nutrition, 493–495
Food Guide Pyramid, 493, 495f
Nutritional performance enhancers, 203–204b

OA (osteoarthritis), 173
Obesity, 508–510b
Oblique fissure, lung, 446f
Oblique muscles
external, 208f, 209, 216f
internal, 208f, 209, 216f
Oblique muscles of eye, 284f
Obturator foramen, 163f, 164
Obturator nerve, 264t, 265f
Occipital bone, 145, 146f, 147f, 209f
Occipital condyles, 145, 147f
Occipitalis muscle, 206f, 207, 218f
Occipital lobe of cerebral hemisphere, 243, 244f, 247f
dura mater in relation to, 249f
Occipital region of body, 16f, 17
Oculomotor nerve (cranial nerve III), 259t, 261f
extrinsic eye muscles supplied by, 284f
Odors, psychological reactions to, 301–302
Oil (sebaceous) glands, 116f, 119, 120f
Olecranal region of body, 16f, 17
Olecranon fossa of humerus, 160, 161f
Olecranon process of ulna, 161, 161f, 209f, 211
Olfactory area of brain, 243, 244f
Olfactory bulb, 301f
Olfactory filaments, 301, 301f
Olfactory hairs, 301, 301f
Olfactory mucosa, 301f
Olfactory nerve (cranial nerve I), 259t, 261f
olfactory filaments and, 301, 301f
Olfactory receptor cells, 301, 301f
Olfactory receptors, 301–302, 301f
of nasal cavity, 441
Olfactory sense, 247
Olfactory tract, 301f
Oligodendrocytes, 231f, 232, 234
Oliguria, 524
Omentum, greater/lesser, 473, 474f, 475f
Oncogens, 102b
Oocytes, 75, 552, 553, 553f, 554–555
primary, 557, 558f
secondary, 557, 558f
Oogenesis, 553f, 557–559, 558f, 559f
Oogonia, 557, 558f
Open fracture reduction, 143
Ophthalmoscope, 289
Opposition (body movement), 201f, 202
Opsin, 287–288b, 287f
Opsonization, 413
Optic canal, 146f, 147, 148f

Optic chiasma, 247f, 291, 291f
Optic disc (blind spot), 285f, 286f, 289f
Optic nerve (cranial nerve II), 259t, 261f, 284f, 285f, 286f
pathways to brain, 290–291, 291f
Optic radiation, 291, 291f
Optic tracts, 291, 291f
Oral cavity (mouth), 22, 442f, 470f, 471–472, 471f
food digestion/absorption in, 484f, 485
mucosa of, 111f
muscles acting on, 216f, 217t
taste buds of, 302
Oral cavity proper, 471, 471f
Oral region of body, 16f, 17
Orbicularis muscles, 204, 205f, 216f, 217t
Orbicularis oculi muscle, 206f, 207, 216f, 217t
Orbicularis oris muscle, 204, 205f, 206f, 207, 216f, 217t
Orbital cavities (orbits), 22
Orbital fissures, superior, 147, 148f
Orbital model of atomic structure, 29, 31, 31f
Orbital region of body, 16f, 17
Orbitals (atomic), 29
Orbits (orbital cavities), 22
Orchiditis, 573, 576
Organ, 3f, 4
Organelles, 69, 70–74, 70f. See also specific type
Organic compounds, 45–58
Organism, 3f, 4
Organismal level, 3f, 4
Organ level, 3f, 4
Organ systems, 3f, 4
contributing to necessary life functions, 10–11, 10f
interrelationships among, 10, 10f
overview, 4–7, 5–6f
Organ transplants, rejection and, 427, 429
Orientation terms, 18t
Origin (muscle attachment), 199, 199f
Oropharynx, 443, 443f, 471f, 472
GI tract activities in, 482f
Orthostatic hypotension, 273, 391
Osmoreceptors, 532
Osmosis, 77, 78f
Osmotic balance, 341f
Osmotic pressure, blood pressure and, 394–395, 395f
Ossa coxae (hip bones), 162, 163f
Osseous tissue (bone), 94, 94f
Ossicles, auditory, 295, 295f
Ossification, 140, 141f
Osteoarthritis (OA), 173
Osteoblasts, 140
Osteoclasts, 140
Osteocytes, 137, 139, 139f
Osteon (Haversian system), 139, 139f
Osteoporosis, 175–176, 176f, 332
Otitis media, 294–295, 444
Otolithic hair membrane, 296f, 297
Otoliths, 296f, 297
Otosclerosis, 300, 304
Outer (external) ear, 294, 295f
Outlet, pelvic, 163f, 164
Ova (eggs), 330t, 545
in fertilization, 563–564, 563f
production of, 557–559, 558f, 559f
Oval window, 294, 295f, 299f
Ovarian arteries, 378, 379f
Ovarian cycle, 553f, 557–559, 558f, 559f

hormonal interactions of, 560f
Ovarian follicles, 553, 553f
Ovarian ligament, 554, 554f, 555f
Ovaries, 313, 314f, 315f, 316, 330t, 331t, 553–554, 553f, 554f, 555f
hormone production by, 329, 561
Ovulation, 553–554
Ovum. See Ova
Oxidases, 52
Oxidative phosphorylation, 195, 196f, 496, 497f
Oxygen
atomic structure, 33t
breathing mechanics and, 449–452
as chemically reactive element, 35, 36f
deficit, muscle fatigue and, 195–197
formation of, 36–37, 38f
in gas exchanges
body tissues, 365, 365f, 394, 394f, 455f, 456
pulmonary, 448–449, 453, 454f, 455f
in muscle contraction, 195–197, 196f
percentage of body mass, 30t
respiratory rate/depth and, 457, 457f, 460
role of, 30t
as survival factor, 11
Oxygen transport, 340, 341f, 342, 346t, 454–456, 455f
artificial blood and, 355–356b
impaired, 455
Oxyhemoglobin, 454, 455f
Oxytocin, 318, 318f, 330t, 569
in labor and childbirth, 569–571, 570f
p16 gene, 102b
p53 gene, 102b

Pacemaker (SA node), 368, 369f
artificial, 369
Pacinian corpuscles, 116f, 118, 236f
Pain
glucocorticoids and, 323
lower back, 210
stimuli causing, withdrawal reflex and, 240, 241f, 242
Pain receptors, 114t, 115, 117, 235, 236f
"hot" foods and, 303
Palate, 442
cleft, 149, 442, 461
hard, 442, 443f, 471, 471f
soft, 442, 443f, 471, 471f
Palatine bones, 147f, 149
Palatine processes, 147f, 149
Palatine tonsils, 303f, 443f, 444, 471f, 472
Pallor, 119
Palmar arches, 379f
Palm of hand, 162, 162f
Palpebral fissure of eye, 282, 282f
Pancreas, 313, 326–328, 331t, 470f, 476f, 480. See also Pancreatic islets
ANS innervation/effects, 267f, 269t
CCK and, 333t
diabetes mellitus and, 326–327
digestive functions, 326, 470f, 476f, 480
duodenum in relation to, 476f
endocrine functions, 326–327, 327, 328
endocrine (islets) areas of, 326, 327f

exocrine areas of, 326, 327f
glucose regulation by, 326–327, 328f
hormones of, 326–327, 327f, 328f
location, 314f, 326, 327f
peritoneal attachments and, 475f
secretin and, 333t
Pancreatic amylase, 490
Pancreatic ducts, 476, 476f
Pancreatic islets (islets of Langerhans), 326–327, 327f
alpha cell hormones, 327, 327f
beta cell hormones, 326, 327f
in blood glucose regulation, 326, 327, 328f
Pancreatic juice, 490, 491, 491f
Pancreatitis, 490
Pannus, 173
Papillae
dermal, 116f, 117–118, 121f
of hair follicles, 121f, 122
tongue, 302, 303f, 472
Papillary layer of dermis, 116f, 117–118, 121f
Pap smear, 556
Parafollicular cells of thyroid gland, 320, 320f
Parallel muscle structure, 205, 205f
Paralysis
cerebrovascular accident and, 254
flaccid, 197, 256
Paranasal sinuses, 147f, 149, 442–443, 443f
Paraplegics, 258
Parasites, eosinophils and, 346t
Parasympathetic division of ANS
anatomy, 266–267, 267f
blood pressure and, 389
definition, 230, 230f, 266
functions/physiology, 268–270, 269t
heart rate and, 372–373, 373f
organs served by, 267f, 269t
somatic nervous system vs., 266f
summary of major effects of, 269t
sympathetic division vs., 269t, 270
Parathormone. See Parathyroid hormone
Parathyroid glands, 140, 313, 314f, 321, 322f, 331t
blood calcium levels and, 322f, 331t
Parathyroid hormone (PTH), 321, 331t, 333t
blood calcium levels and, 140, 142, 321, 322f, 331t
Parietal bones, 145, 146f, 147f, 148f
Parietal cells, 474f, 475
Parietal layer of serous membranes, 111f, 112
of serous pericardium, 364f
Parietal lobe, 242, 244f
Parietal lobe of cerebral hemisphere, 247f
Parietal pericardium, 111f, 362f
Parietal peritoneum, 111f, 475f
Parietal pleura, 111f, 362f, 446f, 447
Parieto-occipital sulcus, 244f
Parkinson's disease, 246, 253–254b
Parotid glands, 470f, 480
Partial-thickness burns, 124
Particles (subatomic), 29, 31–32, 31f, 31t
alpha, 33
beta, 33

size and chemical reactions, 41, 41t
Parturition. See Childbirth
Passive immunity, 420–421, 420f
Passive transport processes, 76–78, 77f, 78f
Patella, 144f, 213f
as sesamoid bone, 135
Patellar (kneecap) ligament, 165
Patellar (knee-jerk) reflex, 240, 241f
Patellar ligament, 213f
Patellar region of body, 16f, 17
Patellar surface of femur, 164, 165f
Pathogens, 409
PCT (proximal convoluted tubule), 521, 522f
Pectoralis major muscle, 205, 205f, 208, 208f, 216f, 217t
Pectoralis minor muscle, 216f
Pectoral (shoulder) girdle
bones of, 144f, 158–160, 159f
muscles of, 206f, 208f, 209–210, 209f, 216f, 217t
Pedicles, vertebral, 155, 155f, 156f
PEG (polyethylene glycol), 355b
Pelvic brim, 163f, 164
Pelvic cavity, 20, 20f
nerves serving, 267, 267f
Pelvic (hip) girdle
bones of, 144f, 158, 162–164, 163f
muscles, 211–212, 212–213f, 214, 218f, 219t
nerve supply, 264t, 267, 267f
Pelvic inflammatory disease (PID), 555
Pelvic inlet, 163f, 164
Pelvic nerves (pelvic splanchnic nerves), 267, 267f, 530
Pelvic outlet, 164
Pelvic region of body, 16f, 17
Pelvic splanchnic nerves (pelvic nerves), 267, 267f, 530
Pelvis
false, 164
in female vs. male, 163f, 164, 175
muscles, 216f
true, 164
Penicillin reaction, 416
Penile (spongy) urethra, 530, 547f, 548
Penis, 547f, 549
ANS innervation/effects, 267f, 269t
Pennate muscle structure, 205, 205f
Pentamers, 423
Pepsin, 474f, 484f, 486
pH values and, 51–52
Pepsinogen, 474f, 486
Peptic ulcers, 488–489b
Peptide hormones, 330t, 331t
Perforated hydrocarbon chains (PFCs), 356b
Perforating (Sharpey's) fibers, 135, 137f, 139f
Perforating (Volkmann's) canals, 139f, 140
Perforins, 410, 425, 427t, 525f
Pericardial cavity, 364f
lungs in relation to, 446f
Pericarditis, 363
Pericardium, 111f, 112, 362–363, 362f, 364f
fibrous, 111f, 362, 364f
serous, 111f, 362f 363, 364f,
Periodontal ligament/membrane, 480, 480f
Perilymph, 296, 298f, 299f
Perimetrium, 555f, 556

Perimysium, 184t, 185, 185f
Perineum, 556f, 557
Perineurium, 258, 258f
Periodontal ligaments, 170t
Periosteal layer of dura mater, 249, 249f, 250f
Periosteum, 135, 137f, 139f, 249, 249f
Peripheral congestion, 374
Peripheral nervous system (PNS), 229–230, 230f, 258–270
aging effects, 273
cranial nerves, 229, 230f, 258–262
developmental aspects, 272–273, 275
spinal nerves, 229, 230f
Peripheral resistance, 388
blood pressure and, 388–389, 390f
Perirenal fat capsule, 519
Peristalsis, 98, 472, 482, 482f, 484f, 485, 486, 487, 487f, 492
in newborns, 507
Peritoneal attachments of abdominal organs, 472, 475f
Peritoneum, 112
parietal, 111f, 472, 473f
visceral, 111f, 472, 473f
Peritonitis, 472
Peritubular capillaries, 522f, 523, 523f
Permanent teeth, 479–480, 479f
Permeability, selective, 76
Pernicious anemia, 344t, 356
Peroxisomes, 70f, 73
Petechiae, 351
PET (positron emission tomography) scan, 8–9b
PET scans, CNS disorders and, 271–272b
Peyer's patches, 407f, 408, 477
PF3, in coagulation events, 349f, 350
PFCs (perfluorinated hydrocarbon chains), 356b
PGs. See Prostaglandins
pH, 44–45
acid-base balance and, 535–537
of blood, 44–45, 340, 535–537
electrolytes in blood and, 341f
functional proteins and, 51–52
scale, 44f
of semen, 549
of sweat, 120
of urine, 525
Phagocytes, 75, 97, 346t
in body defense, 408f, 409–410, 410f, 414t
Phagocytosis, 82, 82f, 410f
in inflammatory response, 411f, 412
Phalanges
finger bones, 144f, 162, 162f
of foot, 166, 166f
toe bones, 166, 166f
Pharyngealesophageal phase of swallowing, 485, 486f
Pharyngeal tonsil (adenoid), 443f, 444
Pharyngotympanic (auditory) tube, 294–295, 295f, 443f, 444
Pharynx, 442f, 443–444, 443f, 470f, 472
GI tract activities in, 482f, 485
muscles of, 472
in swallowing, 482f, 485, 486f
Phenylketonuria (PKU), 506–507
Phimosis, 573
Phlebotomists, 352b
Phlebotomy technician, 352b

Phosphate bonds, high-energy, 55, 56f
Phosphate buffer system, 536
Phospholipids, 47t, 49
hydrophilic, 67
hydrophobic, 67
of plasma membrane, 67–68, 68f
structure, 48f
Phosphorus
atomic structure, 33t
bones as storage site for, 135
percentage of body mass, 30t
role of, 30t
Phosphorylation
direct, 195, 196f
oxidative, 195, 196f
Photopupillary reflex, 293
Photoreceptors, 284, 286, 286f, 287–288b
Phrenic arteries, 378
Phrenic nerve, 264t
breathing muscles controlled by, 456, 457f
Physical factors influencing heart rate, 373, 373f
Physiological acidosis, 535
Physiologic jaundice, 356b
Physiology, 2
Pia mater, 249f, 250f, 251, 256f
PID (pelvic inflammatory disease), 555
Pigmented layer of retina, 284, 286f, 287f
Pigments, tattoo, 113b
Pineal body/gland, 247, 247f, 313, 314f, 329, 330t
developmental aspects, 332
Pinkeye, 282
Pinna (auricle) of ear, 294f, 295f, 299f
Pinocytosis, 82, 82f
Pisiform bone, 162f
Pituitary dwarfism, 314–315, 316f
Pituitary gland, 246, 247f, 250f, 313, 314–319, 314f, 330t
anterior lobe hormones, 314–316, 315f, 317–318b, 330t
developmental aspects, 332
homeostatic imbalances, 314–315, 316f, 319
hypothalamic relationship, 316, 318
posterior lobe hormones, 318–319, 318f, 330t
Pivot joint, 170t, 171, 172f
PKU (phenylketonuria), 506–507
Placenta, 332, 384f, 566, 566f
hormones produced by, 332
substances that cross, 567
Plane joint, 170–171, 170t, 172f
Planes/sections of body, 17, 19f
Planetary model of atomic structure, 29, 31, 31f
Plantar branch of tibial nerve, 264t, 265f
Plantar flexion (body movement), 201f, 202
Plantar nerves, 265f
Plantar region of body, 16f, 17
Plaques
atherosclerotic, 392–393b
complicated, 393b
Plasma, 340, 342
constituents, 340, 341f
as extracellular fluid, 531, 531f
plasma proteins, 341f, 342
Plasma cells, 406, 418–419, 419f, 420f, 426t, 428f
Plasma membrane, 66, 66f, 67–69, 68f, 70f

...ed)
...rest, 237,
...by, 333t
...69f
...s and,
...238f
...237, 238f
...andins of, 333t
...ive permeability of, 76
...cializations of, 68–69, 69f
...sma proteins. *See under* Plasma
Platelet plug, 350
  formation, 349–350, 349f
Platelets, 340, 341f, 346t, 347, 347f
Platysma muscle, 206f, 207, 216f, 217t
Pleura, 112
  parietal, 111f, 362f, 446f, 447
  visceral, 111f, 446f, 447
Pleural cavity, 446f
Pleural fluid, 447
Pleural space, 447
Pleurisy, 447
Plexuses, nerve, 262, 265f
Plicae circulares (circular folds) of small intestine, 477, 477f
Pneumocystis pneumonia, 432b
Pneumonia, 451
Pneumothorax, 452
PNS. *See* Peripheral nervous system
Podocytes, 521, 522f
Polar body, 557, 558f
Polar heads of phospholipids, 67, 68f
Poles, molecular, 37
Polycystic kidney, 538
Polycythemia, 344
  secondary, 344
Polycythemia vera, 344
Polydipsia, 326
Polyethylene glycol (PEG), 355b
Polypeptides, 49
Polyphagia, 327
Polyps, colorectal, 507
Polysaccharides, 45f, 46, 483
Polyunsaturated fatty acids, 49
Polyuria, 326, 535
Pons, 244f, 246f, 247, 247f, 248
  breathing centers in, 456, 457f
Popliteal artery, 378, 379f
  as pulse point, 387f
Popliteal region of body, 16f, 17
Popliteal vein, 380, 381f
Pore, sweat, 116f, 120f
Portal circulations, 316
Positive chemotaxis, 345
Positive feedback mechanism, 13
Positive feedback mechanisms
  oxytocin and labor contractions, 570, 570f
Positron emission tomography (PET), 8–9b
Postcapillary venule, 377, 377f
Postcentral gyrus, 244f
Posterior communicating artery, 383, 383f
Posterior (dorsal) body landmarks, 16f, 17
Posterior (dorsal) horns, 256, 256f
Posterior inferior iliac spine, 162, 163f
Posterior interventricular artery, 367
Posterior nasal aperture, 443f
Posterior sacral foramina, 157, 157f
Posterior segment of eye, 285f
Posterior superior iliac spine, 162, 163f, 212f
Posterior tibial artery, 378, 379f
  as pulse point, 387f
Posterior tibial vein, 380, 381f
Posterior (vitreous) segment, 289

Postganglionic axons, 266, 266f, 268
Postural changes
  blood pressure and, 389, 390f
  orthostatic hypotension and, 391
Posture, proprioceptors and, 236
Posture, body, role of skeletal muscles in, 187
Potassium ions
  blood level regulation of, 323, 324f
  in blood plasma, 341f
  cardiac output affected by, 373
  mineralocorticoids and, 331t
  in muscle contraction, 190–191, 191f
  in nerve impulse, 237–239, 238f
Potassium
  percentage of body mass, 30t
  role of, 30t
  in sodium-potassium pump, 79, 79f
Potential energy, 28
Practical nurse. *See* Licensed practical nurse
"Prayer" muscles, 207
Precapillary sphincters, 377, 377f
Precentral gyrus, 244f
Precipitation, 423–424, 423f
Preganglionic axons, 262, 266, 266f, 267–268
Pregnancy
  childbirth and, 569–571
  effects on mother, 566–568
  embryonic/fetal development during, 565–566, 565f, 566f, 568t
  events of (overview), 563–568
  events required to produce a baby, 575b
  homeostatic imbalances, 567
  hormones that support, 331t
  oxytocin and, 330t, 331t
  progesterone, 329, 561
Premolar (bicuspid) teeth, 479–480, 479f
Premotor area, 244f
Prepuce (foreskin)
  female, 557
  male, 547f, 549
Presbycusis, 304
Presbyopia, 304
Pressoreceptors (baroreceptors), blood pressure and, 389–390, 390f
Pressure gradient, 77–78
  blood pressure and, 387–388, 388f
Pressure points, to stop bleeding, 387
Pressure receptors, 236f
  Pacinian corpuscles of dermis, 118, 236f
Pressure sensory receptors, 114t, 115
Primary curvatures of spine, 151, 151f
  developmental aspects, 175
Primary (essential) hypertension, 391, 394
Primary germ layers, 565–566, 565f
Primary humoral response, 418–419, 419f, 420f, 428f
Primary motor area, 243, 244f, 245f
Primary oocytes, 557, 558f
Primary sex organs (gonads), 315f, 316, 329, 331t, 545
Primary somatic sensory area, 242, 244f, 245f
Primary spermatocyte, 550f, 551
Prime mover muscle, 202

PRL (prolactin), 315, 315f, 330t
Processes (bone markings), 137, 138t
Processes (neuron), 75, 75f, 98, 100f, 232, 233f
Product, 34
Progesterone, 47t, 329, 331t, 561
Projection fibers/fiber tracts, 245, 246f
Projections (bone markings), 137, 138t
Prolactin (PRL), 315, 315f, 330t
Pronation (body movement), 201f, 202
ProOsteon, 168b
Prophase stage of mitosis, 83–84, 85f
Proportions, body, 174–176, 175f, 176f
Proprioceptors, 116f, 235, 236f
Propulsion of food, 481–482, 482f
  in large intestine, 492–493
  in mouth/pharynx/esophagus, 484f, 485
  in small intestine, 492
  in stomach, 487, 487f
  by swallowing/peristalsis, 98, 472, 482, 482f, 484f, 485, 486, 487, 487f, 492
Prostaglandins (PGs), 47t, 311
  derivation, 333t
  in labor and childbirth, 569–570
  as non-endocrine hormone, 333t
  as pain-causing molecules, 323, 333t
  target organ/effects, 333t
Prostate gland, 528–529, 547f, 548–549
Prostatic cancer, 549
Prostatic urethra, 530, 547f, 548
Prostatitis, 549, 573
Protease inhibitors, 433b
Protective functions
  of bones, 135
  of skin, 114–115, 114t
Protein buffer system, 536
Protein digestion, 484f
Protein hormones, 330t, 331t
Proteins, 49–52, 54
  in blood plasma, 341f
  as carriers, 68
  channels formed by, 68
  denatured, 51, 52f
  dietary sources of, 494–495, 494t
  digestion/absorption of, 483, 484f
  DNA as blueprint for building, 67
  fibrous (structural), 50, 51f
  globular (functional), 50–52, 51f, 51t, 52f
  Golgi apparatus and, 72–73, 72f
  iron-bearing. *See* Hemoglobin
  metabolism of, 498, 499f, 500
  "sugar-proteins" (glycoproteins), 68
  transport of, 68, 71, 71f, 72f
  in urine, 528t
Protein synthesis, 86–88, 87f
  ribosomes as site of, 71
  RNA's role, 86
  rough ER and, 71–72, 71f
  transcription phase, 86, 87f
  translation phase, 86, 87f, 88
Proteinuria, 528t
Prothrombin, 349f, 350, 491
Prothrombin activator, 349f, 350
Proton acceptors, 43
Protooncogenes, 102b

Proton donors, 43
Protons, 29, 31–32, 31f, 31t
Proximal convoluted tubule (PCT), 521, 522f
Proximal direction/orientation, 18f, 18t
Proximal tibiofibular joint, 165f
Pseudohermaphrodites, 573
Pseudopods, 75, 75f, 82, 82f
Pseudostratified ciliated columnar epithelium, 90, 92f
Pseudostratified columnar epithelium, 90, 92f
Psoas major muscle, 212, 213f
Psoriasis, 123, 124f
Psychiatric disorders, steroid users and, 203–204b
PTH (parathyroid hormone/parathormone), 140, 142, 321, 333t
Ptosis, kidney, 519–520
Puberty, 101, 329, 573
  apocrine glands and, 120–121
  female pelvis during, 175
Pubic arch, 163f, 164
  in female vs. male, 163, 164f
Pubic bone (pubis), 163f, 164
Pubic (hypogastric) region of abdominopelvic cavity, 21–22, 21f
Pubic region of body, 16f, 17
Pubic symphysis, 163f, 164, 168, 169f
Pubis (pubic bone), 163f, 164
  male, 547f
Pulmonary artery, 363f, 364f, 365, 365f, 446f
  fetal, 384f
Pulmonary circulation/circuit, 365, 365f
Pulmonary congestion, 374
Pulmonary edema, 374
Pulmonary embolism, 377
Pulmonary gas exchange (external respiration), 448–449, 454, 454f
Pulmonary semilunar valve, 364f, 366, 367f
Pulmonary trunk, 362f, 363f, 365, 446f
Pulmonary vein, 446f
Pulmonary veins, 363–364f, 365, 365f
  fetal, 384f
Pulmonary ventilation (breathing), 448, 449–452, 450f, 451f
Pulmonary (visceral) pleura, 446f, 447
Pulp cavity of tooth, 480, 480f
Pulp of tooth, 480, 480f
Pulse, 387, 387f
  apical, 362
Pupil, 282f, 284, 285f
Purkinje fibers, 368–369, 369f
Pus, 413
  in urine, 528t
P wave, 370b
Pyelitis, 530
Pyelonephritis, 527, 530
Pyloric antrum, 473, 474f
Pyloric sphincter (valve), 473, 474f, 476, 487, 487f
Pylorus, 473, 474f
Pyramidal (corticospinal) tract, 243
Pyrogens, 415, 506
Pyruvic acid, in muscle contraction, 195, 196f
Pyuria, 528t

QRS complex, 370b
Quadrants of abdominopelvic cavity, 20–21, 21f

Quadratus lumborum muscles, 209f, 210, 219t
Quadriceps muscles, 213f, 214, 216f, 217t
Quadriplegics, 258
Quickening, 221

Radial artery, 378, 379f
  as pulse point, 387f
Radial fossa, 161f
Radial groove, 160, 161f
Radial nerve, 264t, 265f
Radial tuberosity, 160, 161f
Radial vein, 380, 381f
Radiant energy, 28
Radiation, heat loss via, 504
Radioactivity, 33
Radioisotopes, 33–34
Radioulnar joints, distal/proximal, 160, 161f
Radius, 144f, 160, 161f, 162f
Ramus (bone marking)
  definition, 138t
  of pubis, 163f, 164
Ramus communicans, 268, 268f
Range of motion, 205–206
RA (rheumatoid arthritis), 173–174, 173f, 429
RAS (reticular activating system), 248
RBC antigens (agglutinogens), 351, 353, 353t
RBCs. See Red blood cells
Reactants, 34
Reactive elements, 35, 36f
Real image, retina and, 290, 291f
Receiving chambers of heart, 365
Receptor, in homeostatic control mechanism, 12–13, 13f
Receptor-mediated endocytosis, 82–83, 82f
Rectum, 470f, 477, 478f, 519f
  female, 554f
  male, 547f
  peritoneal attachments and, 475f
Rectus abdominis muscle, 208f, 209, 216f, 217t
Rectus femoris muscle, 205, 205f, 213f, 214, 216f, 217t
Rectus muscles of eye, 284f
Red blood cells (erythrocytes), 74, 75f, 98f, 340, 341f, 342–344, 342f, 346t
  antigens, 351, 353
Red bone marrow, 136, 137f
  blood cell formation in, 347–349, 347f, 348f
Reddened skin, 119
Reduction of fractures, 143
Reflex arcs, 240, 241f
Reflexes, 240–242, 241f
  digestive activity, 483
  skeletal muscles activated by, 185
Refraction of light, 290, 290f
Regeneration
  of nerve fibers in CNS, PNS, 234
  in tissue repair/wound healing, 100–101
Regional terms in anatomy, 16–17, 16f
Regions of abdominopelvic cavity, 21, 21f
Regulatory T cells, 426t, 427
Reinforcing ligaments of synovial joints, 170
Relaxin, 332, 567
Releasing hormones, hypothalamic, 315f, 316, 330t

Remodeling of bone, 140, 141f, 142
  in fracture healing, 143, 143f
Renal arteries, 378, 379f, 519f, 520f, 521
Renal calculi (kidney stones), 528
Renal columns, 520f, 521
Renal cortex, 520, 520f, 522f
Renal fascia, 519
Renal mechanisms in acid-base balance, 537
Renal medulla, 522f
Renal (medullary) pyramids, 520f, 521
Renal pelvis, 520f, 521, 522f
Renal tubule, 521
Renal veins, 380, 381f, 519f, 520f, 521
Renin, 323, 324f, 390, 390f, 518, 534f, 535
Renin-angiotensin mechanism, 534f, 535
Rennin, 486, 535
Repolarization, 238f, 239
Reproduction, 11
  as necessary life function, 11
Reproductive system, 6f, 7, 544–582
  developmental aspects, 571, 573, 576, 578
  female, 6f, 7. See also Female reproductive system
  homeostatic imbalances, 573, 576
  homeostatic relationships, 577b
  male, 6f, 7. See also Male reproductive system
Residual volume, 452, 453f
Resistin, 333t
Respiration, 448
  aerobic, 195, 196f
  cellular. See Cellular respiration
  control of, 456–457, 457f
  events of
    breathing, 448, 449–452, 450f, 451f
    gas exchange, 448–449
    gas transport, 449
  external, 448–449
  internal, 449
Respiratory (bronchial) tree, 447, 448f
Respiratory capacities, 452–453, 454f
Respiratory failure, 221
Respiratory gases
  exchanges. See Gas exchanges
  as plasma constituent, 341f
Respiratory membrane (air-blood barrier), 447, 449f
Respiratory mucosa of nasal cavity, 441–442
Respiratory paralysis, phrenic nerve damage and, 264f
"Respiratory pump," 373f, 376, 404
Respiratory rate, aging and, 464
Respiratory sounds, 453
Respiratory system, 7, 440–467, 442f
  in acid-base balance, 537
  aging and, 464
  anatomy of, 441–448
  cardiovascular system and, 396b
  developmental aspects of, 461, 464
  disorders
    COPD, 460, 460–461, 461f, 464
    lung cancer, 458–459b, 460, 464
  function overview, 6f, 7
  homeostatic imbalances, 442, 443, 444, 445, 447, 451–452, 453, 456, 460–461, 464

homeostatic relationships, 463b
nonrespiratory air movements, 452, 452t
physiology, 448–460
  breathing mechanics, 449–452
  control of respiration, 456–457, 460
  gas exchanges, 453–454
  gas transport, 454–455
  respiratory sounds, 453
  volumes and capacities, 452–453
  in pregnancy, 568
  skeletal system and, 177b
  structure overview, 6f, 7
Respiratory volumes, 452–453, 454f
Respiratory zone structures, 447, 448f
Response to injury hypothesis, atherosclerosis and, 392b
Responsiveness, 11, 98, 189. See also Irritability
"Rest-and-digest" nervous system, 270, 483
Restriction enzymes, 57–58b
Rete testis, 546f
Reticular activating system (RAS), 248
Reticular cells/fibers, 96f, 97
Reticular connective tissue, 96f, 97
Reticular formation, 247f, 248
Reticular layer of dermis, 116f, 118
Reticulocytes, 347–348
Retina, 284–288, 285f, 286f, 287f, 289f
  neurons composing, 284, 286, 286f
  posterior wall (fundus) of, 289, 289f
Retinal, 287–288b
Retroperitoneal organs, 480
Reverse transcriptase inhibitors, 433b
R-group in amino acids, 49, 50f
Rh blood groups, 353–354, 353t
Rheumatic fever, 430
Rheumatoid arthritis (RA), 173–174, 173f, 429
Rhinitis, 443
Rhodopsin, 287–288b
Rhythm method, 575b
Rib cage
  muscles that move, 158, 208, 216f
  position during breathing, 450f, 451
Ribonucleic acid (RNA), 55
  protein synthesis and, 86–88, 87f
Ribosomal RNA (rRNA), 55, 71, 86–88, 87f
Ribosomes, 67, 70f, 71, 71f
Ribs, 144f, 157–158, 158f, 446f
  heart in relation to, 362, 362f, 446f
  intercostal muscles and, 158, 208, 216f
  vertebral facets for, 156f
Rickets, 142
Right common iliac vein, 380, 381f
Right gonadal vein, 380
Right hypochondriac region, 21–22, 21f
Right iliac (inguinal) region, 21–22, 21f
Right lower quadrant (RLQ), 21, 21f
Right lumbar regions, 21–22, 21f
Right lymphatic duct, 404, 406f
  subclavian vein and, 406f
Right upper quadrant (RUQ), 21, 21f

Renal hilum, 519, 519f
RLQ (right lower quadrant), 2.
RNA (ribonucleic acid), 55
  protein synthesis and, 86–88, 87f
  ribosomal, 71
Rods, 284, 286, 286f, 287b, 287f
'roid rage (steroid rage), 203b
Root
  lung, 446f
  nail, 122, 123f
Root canal region of tooth, 480, 480f
Rooting reflex, 507
Root region of tooth, 480, 480f
Rotation (body movement), 199, 200f
  lateral or medial, 200f
Rough ER (rough endoplasmic reticulum), 66f, 70f, 71–72, 71f, 72f, 75f
  protein synthesis and, 71–72, 71f
Round ligament of uterus, 554f, 555, 555f
Round window, 294, 295f, 299f
rRNA (ribosomal RNA), 55, 71, 86–88, 87f
RU486 (abortion pill), 576b
Rubella (measles), maternal blindness and, 304
  deafness and, 272, 304
Rugae, of stomach, 473, 474f
Rule of eights, 35
Rule of nines, 124, 125f
RUQ (right upper quadrant), 21, 21f

Sacral canal, 157, 157f
Sacral crest, median, 157, 157f
Sacral curvature, 151, 151f
Sacral foramina, posterior, 157, 157f
Sacral hiatus, 157, 157f
Sacral plexus, 263f, 264t
  distribution of nerves of, 265f
Sacral region of body, 16f, 17
Sacral spinal nerves, 255f, 263f, 267f
Sacroiliac joints, 162, 163f
Sacrum, 144f, 150, 155, 157, 157f, 163f, 554f
Saddle joint, 170t, 171, 172f
Sagittal section of body, 17, 19f
Sagittal sinus, superior, 249f, 250f
Sagittal suture, 145, 146f
Saliva, 480, 484f, 485
  lysozyme in, 409, 414t
Salivary amylase, 480, 484f, 485
Salivary glands, 470f, 480
  ANS innervation/effects, 262, 267f, 269t
Saltatory conduction of nerve impulse, 239
Salts, 36, 42–43, 43f
  body, 43
  as electrolytes, 43
  formation of, 36, 37f
Salty taste receptors, 302
Saphenous veins, 380, 381f
Sarcolemma, 187, 188f, 191f
  during muscle contraction, 190–191, 191f
  at neuromuscular junction, 190–191, 191f
Sarcomeres, 187, 188f
Sarcoplasm, 183
Sarcoplasmic reticulum (SR), 189
Sartorius muscle, 205, 205f, 213f, 214, 216f, 217t
SA (sinoatrial) node (pacemaker), 368–369, 369f

...232
...49
...ng/tissue
..., 298f, 299f
...298f, 299f
...249t
...one, 162f
...(shoulder blades), 144f,
...58, 159f, 160
...scles that move,
209–210, 209f
scapular region of body, 16f, 17
Scar tissue, 100–101
burns and joint mobility, 125
normal organ functioning
and, 101
SCA (sickle cell anemia), 343–344,
343f, 344t
Schwann cells, 231f, 232, 233f
axons in relation to in PNS,
234, 234f
Sciatic nerve, 212, 212f, 264t, 265f
Sciatic notch, greater, 163f, 164
SCID (severe combined immunodeficiency disease), 431
Sclera, 282f, 283, 285f, 286f
Scleral venous sinus (canal of
Schlemm), 285f, 289
Scleroses, nerve fiber myelin
sheaths and, 234
Scoliosis, 154, 154f
Scrotum, 329, 547f, 549
SCT (sickle cell trait), 344
Sebaceous (oil) glands, 116f, 119,
120f, 121f
inflammation of, 123
Seborrhea, 119
Sebum, 119
Secondary humoral response, 419,
419f, 420f, 428f
Secondary sex characteristics
female, 561
male, 552–553
Second-degree burns, 124, 125f
Second-messenger systems,
311, 312f
pituitary hormones and, 314
Secretin, 333t, 490t, 491, 491f
Secretion, 93
Secretory IgA, 423
Secretory vesicles, 72, 72f
Sections/planes of body, 17, 19f
Segmental arteries, 520f, 521
Segmentation of food, 482, 482f
Selective permeability, 76
Self-antigens, 416, 417
Self-exciting inspiratory center,
456, 457f
Self-extending leg implant, 167b
Self-tolerance, 417
Sella turcica (Turk's saddle),
145, 146f
Semen, 548, 549
Semen analysis, 549
Semicircular canals, 295, 295f,
297–298, 297f
Semilunar valves, 366
aortic, 364f, 366, 367f
pulmonary, 364f, 366, 367f
Semimembranosus muscle, 212f,
214, 218f, 219t
Seminal fluid, 548
Seminalplasmin, 549
Seminal vesicles, 547f, 548
Seminiferous tubules of testes,
546, 546f
Semitendinosus muscle, 212f, 214,
218f, 219t
Senile plaques, 253b
Senility, 273
"reversible," 273

Sense organs, cutaneous,
235, 236f
Senses. See Special senses
Sensorineural deafness, 300, 304
Sensory (afferent) division of PNS,
229, 230f
Sensory (afferent) nerves, 258, 262
Sensory (afferent) neurons,
235–236, 235f
Sensory (afferent) tracts,
256–257, 257f
Sensory aphasia, 254
Sensory areas of cerebral cortex,
242–243, 245f
Sensory homunculus,
242–243, 245f
Sensory input, 229, 229f
Sensory layer of eyeball, 284–288,
285f–287f
Sensory nerve fibers, in skin, 116f
Sensory neurons
in reflex arcs, 240, 241f
in spinal cord pathways,
256–257, 257f
Sensory receptor, 4, 5f
in homeostatic control mechanism, 12–13, 13f
Sensory receptors, 235–236, 236f
cutaneous, 235, 236f
in reflex arcs, 240, 241f
for special senses, 281
in spinal cord pathways/tracts,
256–257, 257f
Septum
interventricular, 364f, 365, 366f
of testes, 546f
Seromucous glands, 445f
Serosa/serosae. See Serous
membranes
Serous fluid, 112
Serous membranes (serosae), 90,
110, 111f, 112
of alimentary canal wall,
472, 473f
of stomach, 474f
Serous pericardium, 363, 364f
Serratus anterior muscle, 216f
Serum, 350
Sesamoid bones, 135
Set point, homeostatic, 328f
Severe combined
immunodeficiency disease
(SCID), 431
Sex characteristics
development of, 329
female secondary 561
hormones and, 331t
male secondary, 552–553
Sex hormones, 47t, 323f, 324,
545–546
female, 324
growth of long bones and, 140
male, 324
Sexual infantilism, 552–553
Shaft of penis, 547f, 549
Sharpey's (perforating) fibers, 135,
137f, 139f
Shells
electron, 35, 36f
valence, 35, 36f
Shinbone (tibia), 144f,
164–165, 165f
Shivering, as heat-promoting
mechanism, 504
Short bones, 135, 136f
Shortening of muscle. See
Contraction
Shoulder muscles, 206f, 208f,
209–210, 209f, 210f, 216f,
217t, 218f, 219f
Shoulder (pectoral) girdle
bones, 144f, 158–160, 159f

muscles, 206f, 208f, 209–210,
209f, 210f, 216f, 217t,
218f, 219f
nerves serving, 264t
Sickle cell anemia (SCA), 343–344,
343f, 344t
Sickle cell trait (SCT), 344
SIDS (sudden infant death
syndrome), 464
Sigmoid colon, 470f, 478, 478f
Signet ring cells (fat cells), 97
Simple columnar epithelium, 90, 91f
Simple cuboidal epithelium, 90, 91f
Simple diffusion, 77, 78f
Simple epithelium, 89–90, 89f, 91f
columnar, 90, 91f
cuboidal, 90, 91f
Simple squamous epithelium, 90, 91f
Simple sugars (monosaccharides),
45, 45f, 483
Sinoatrial (SA) node (pacemaker),
368–369, 369f
Sinus, transverse, 249f
Sinus (bone marking), 138t
Sinuses, 149
lymph node, 406, 407f
maxillary, 147f, 149
paranasal, 147f, 149,
442–443, 443f
Sinus headache, 443
Sinusitis, 149, 443
Sister chromatids, 85f
Skeletal muscle fiber/cell, 183,
184t, 185, 185f
as cells that move organs/body
parts, 75, 75f
contraction of, 189–194, 190f,
191f, 192f, 193f
functional properties of, 189
microscopic anatomy,
187–189, 188f
nerve impulse/stimulus and
action potential, 189–191,
190f, 191f
as type of body tissue, 98, 99f
Skeletal muscles, 183, 185
activity of, 189–198
Five Golden Rules, 198t
aging effects, 221
atrophy, 197
body movements and, 186,
198–202, 200–201f
cardiac muscle compared to,
184t, 187
connective tissue wrappings of,
184f, 185, 185f
contraction of
energy sources for, 195, 196f
graded responses,
194–195, 194f
muscle fatigue/oxygen deficit,
195–197
muscle tone and, 197
regulation of, 184t
single muscle cell, 189–194,
190f, 191f, 192f, 193f
whole muscle, 194–198,
194f, 196f
developmental aspects of, 221
exercise's effects on,
197–198, 197f
fascicle arrangement patterns,
204–206, 205f
functions of, 187
gross anatomy of, 206–219
head and neck,
206–207, 206f
lower limbs, 211–215,
212–213f, 215f
trunk, 207–210, 208f, 209f
upper limbs, 208f, 209f,
210–211

heat generated by, 187
homeostatic imbalances, 197,
207, 221
insertion/origin of, 199, 199f
interactions of, 198, 202
microscopic anatomy,
187–189, 188f
naming criteria, 202, 204
origin/insertion of, 199, 199f
paralysis, 197
power of, 205–206
range of motion and, 205–206
smooth muscles compared to,
184t, 187
somatic nervous system and,
262, 266, 266f
superficial (major), 206–219
body views, 216f, 218f
summary tables, 217t, 219t
Skeletal system, 4, 133–181. See
also specific component
appendicular skeleton, 158–166
axial skeleton, 144–158
bones (overview), 134–144
developmental aspects,
174–176
functions (overview), 4, 5f, 134
homeostatic imbalances,
151, 154, 154f, 170,
172–173, 174
homeostatic relationships, 177b
joints, 166–174
movement and, 10, 134. See
also Movement
structure (overview), 4, 5f, 134
Skeleton, 134, 144f. See also
Skeletal system
appendicular, 144f, 158–166
axial, 144–158, 144f
developmental aspects,
174–176
embryonic, 140
Skin cancer, 117, 125–126, 126f
Skin (cutaneous membrane/integu-
ment), 114–127
acidic secretions of, 408f, 409
aging process and, 101,
104, 127
as a membrane, 110, 111f
ANS innervation/effects,
267f, 269t
appendages, 119–122, 120f–123f
blood supply, 115, 116f, 118
as body's first defense,
408f, 409
boundary maintenance role
of, 10
cancer, 117, 125–126, 126f
color, 118–119
developmental aspects, 127
functions, 114–115, 114t
homeostatic imbalances, 117,
118, 119, 123–126, 127
homeostatic relationships, 129b
nerve supply, 116f, 118
nervous system structures
of, 116f
pain receptors, 235, 236f
structure, 115–118, 116f
surface membrane barriers of,
408f, 409, 414t
tattoos and, 113b
Skull, 144f
cranium, 145–148, 146f
developmental aspects,
174–175, 175f
facial bones, 144f, 145, 146f,
148–150, 148f
fetal, 149–150, 150f
joints of, 145
meninges in relation to, 249,
249f, 251

Sleep, melatonin and, 329
Sleep apnea, 464
SLE (systemic lupus erythematosus), 429
Sliding filament theory, 192–193, 193f
Small cardiac vein, 363f
Small intestine, 470f, 475–477, 476f
  blood supply, 477, 477f
  digestion/absorption in, 476, 482f, 484f, 489–492, 491f
  hormones produced by, 333t, 490t
  pancreas in relation to, 326, 327f, 476f
  peritoneal attachments and, 475f
  stomach in relation to, 476f
Smell sense, 247, 301–302, 301f
  aging effects, 305
  homeostatic imbalances
    anosmias, 302
    olfactory auras, 302
Smoking, 175. See also Nicotine
  ciliated mucosa damage from, 445
  disorders related to, 460–461, 461f
  lung cancer and, 458–459b
Smooth ER (smooth endoplasmic reticulum), 70f, 72
Smooth muscles
  autonomic nervous system and, 262, 266f, 269t
  in blood vessel walls, 376
  cell shape/appearance, 75, 75f, 184t, 185–186, 186f
  circular layer, 186, 186f
  connective tissue components, 184t
  contraction of, 184t, 186
  longitudinal layer, 186, 186f
  as type of body tissue, 98, 99f
Sneeze, 452t
Sodium
  atomic structure, 33t
  as chemically reactive element, 35, 36f
  percentage of body mass, 30t
  properties, 34–35, 34f
  role of, 30t
  in sodium-potassium pump, 79, 79f
Sodium chloride (NaCl), properties, 34f, 35
Sodium hydroxide (NaOH), 43
Sodium ions
  blood level regulation of, 323, 324f
  in blood plasma, 341f
  cardiac output affected by, 373
  link between water/salt, 531–532
  mineralocorticoids and, 331t
  in muscle contraction, 190–192, 191f, 192f
  in nerve impulse, 237–239, 238f
Sodium-potassium pump, 79, 79f, 191, 191f, 239
Soft palate, 147f, 149, 442, 443f, 471, 471f
Soleus muscle, 214, 215f, 216f, 218f, 219t
Solids, 27
Solute pumps, 76, 78–79, 79f
Solutes, 42, 76
Solutions, 42, 76
  acidic, 44, 44f
  alkaline (basic), 44, 44f, 342
  hypertonic/hypotonic/isotonic, 80–81b
  pH units and, 44, 44f

Solvents, 42, 76
  water as, 42, 341f
Somatic nervous system, 230, 230f
  ANS compared to, 262, 266, 266f
Somatic reflexes, 240
Somatic sensory (afferent) fibers, 229, 230f
Somatic sensory area/cortex, primary, 242, 244f, 245f
Somatostatin, 490t
Sound waves
  auditory canal and, 294
  route through ear, 298, 299f, 300
Sour taste receptors, 302
Special circulations, 383–387
  cerebral arterial supply/Circle of Willis, 383, 383f
  fetal, 383–385, 384f
  hepatic portal, 385–386, 385f, 386f
Special sense receptors, 281
Special senses, 280–308. See also specific sense
  cortical interpretation areas for, 243, 244f
  definition, 281
  developmental aspects, 303–305
  equilibrium, 299–300
  hearing, 299–300
  smell, 301–303
  taste, 301–303
  vision, 281–294
Specific (adaptive) defense system, 408f, 409. See also Adaptive body defenses
Specific gravity of urine, 525
Speech area (Broca's area) of brain, 243, 244f
Sperm, 75, 75f, 545
  in fertilization, 563–564, 563f
  hormonal stimulation of production of, 330t, 331t
  motility, semen and, 549
  production, 550–552, 550f
  structure, 551–552, 551f
Spermatic cord, 546, 547f
Spermatids, 550f, 551
Spermatocytes, primary, 550f, 551
Spermatogenesis, 550–552, 550f, 551f
Spermatogonia, 550, 550f
Spermiogenesis, 550f, 551
Sphenoid bone, 145, 146f, 147, 148f
  greater wing, 147f
Sphenoid sinuses, 147, 147f, 443f
Sphincter muscles, 204, 205f
  ANS effects on, 269t
Sphincters
  anal, 478, 478f
  involuntary/voluntary, 478
  precapillary, 377, 377f
Spina bifida, 272–273
Spinal cavity, 20, 20f
Spinal cord, 229, 230f, 255–258
  anatomy, 255–256, 255f
  brain stem in relation to, 247f, 255
  gray matter, 256, 256f, 257f
  homeostatic imbalances
    flaccid paralysis, 256
    spastic paralysis, 257–258
  injuries to, 257–258
  meninges and, 255, 255f, 256f
  pathways between brain and, 256–257, 257f
  protection of, 248–252, 249f, 250f
  vertebral column and, 150, 255

white matter, 256–257, 256f, 257f
Spinalis muscle, 209f, 210
Spinal (lumbar) tap, 251
Spinal nerve plexuses, 262, 263f, 264t, 265f
  results of damage to, 264t
Spinal nerves, 262, 263f, 264t, 265f
  definition of, 229, 230f, 262
  distribution of, 255f, 263f
  in nervous system organization, 229, 230f
  plexuses, 262, 263f, 264t, 265f
  spinal cord and, 255–256, 255f, 256f
  vertebrae and, 263f
Spinal reflexes, 240, 242
Spine (bone marking), 138t
Spine (vertebral column), 144f, 150–157, 151f
  herniated discs, 151
Spinous processes, vertebral, 151f, 155, 155f, 156f
Spiral fracture, 142f, 142t
Spiral organ of Corti, 298, 298f, 299f
Spirometer, 453
Splanchnic nerves, 267, 267f, 268, 268f
Spleen, 407–408, 407f, 470f, 475f
  lymphatic vessels in relation to, 406f
Splenic artery, 378, 379f
Splenic vein, 381f, 386, 386f
Spongy bone, 135, 137, 137f, 139f
Spongy (penile) urethra, 530, 547f, 548
Sprains, 173
Squamous cell carcinoma, 126, 126f, 458b
Squamous epithelial cells of alveolar wall, 449f
Squamous sutures, 145, 146f
SR (sarcoplasmic reticulum), 189
Stapes (stirrup) bone, 295, 295f, 299f
Starch, 45–46, 45f, 46
  digestion of, 483
Starling's law of the heart, 372
Static equilibrium, 296–297, 296f
Stem cells
  basal cells, 302, 303f
  hemocytoblast, 347, 347f
  of immune system, 431
  lymphoid, 347, 347f
  myeloid, 347, 347f
Stenosis of heart valves, 366
Sterility, 47t, 316, 553, 573
  by vasectomy, 548
Sterilization techniques in contraception, 575b
Sternal angle, 157, 158f
Sternal puncture, 157
Sternal region of body, 16f, 17
Sternoclavicular joint, 160
Sternocleidomastoid muscle, 206f, 207, 209f, 216f, 217t, 218f
Sternum, 144f, 157, 158f, 208f, 446f
  relationship of heart to, 362, 362f
Steroid diabetes, 324
Steroid hormones, 47t, 48f, 49, 310, 310–311, 331t
  anabolic, 203–204b
  corticosteroids, 322–324
  mechanism of action, 311, 312f
Stimuli, 229
  endocrine gland, 311–313, 313f
  in homeostatic control mechanism, 12, 13f
  muscle, graded responses and, 194–195, 194f
  types that excite neurons, 237

Stirrup (stapes) bone, 295, 295f, 299f
Stomach, 470f, 472–474, 474f
  ANS innervation/effects, 267f, 269t
  arterial supply, 378, 379f
  digestion/absorption in, 482f, 484f, 485–487
    food propulsion, 487, 487f
  digestive activities, 482f
  duodenum in relation to, 476f
  hormones produced by, 333t, 485, 490t
  hydrochloric acid secretion and, 333t
  pancreas in relation to, 326, 327f
  peptic ulcers and, 488–489b
Storage functions, of bones, 135
Strabismus, 303–304
Stratified columnar epithelium, 90
Stratified cuboidal epithelium, 90
Stratified epithelium, 89f, 90, 92f
Stratified squamous epithelium, 90, 92f
Stratum basale (stratum germinativum), 115, 115f, 116, 123f
Stratum corneum, 115, 115f, 117
Stratum germinativum. See Stratum basale
Stratum granulosum, 115, 115f, 117
Stratum lucidum, 115, 115f, 117
Stratum spinosum, 115, 115f, 117
Stress response
  cardiac output influenced by, 373, 373f
  long-term, 325–326, 325f
  short-term, 325–326, 325f
Stretch sensory receptors, 235–236
Striated muscle, 98, 184t, 185, 186
Striations
  of cardiac muscle, 184t, 186
  of skeletal muscle, 98, 184t, 185
Stroke (cerebrovascular accident), 252, 254–255
  aging and, 273
  embolus and, 350
  hemianopia and, 291
Stroke volume (SV), 372, 373f
  blood pressure and, 390f
Stroma, 97
Stroma of lungs, 447
Strong acids, 43, 536–537, 536f
Strong bases, 43, 536–537, 536f
Structural (fibrous) proteins, 50, 51f
  synthesis of, 86–88
Styloid process
  radius, 160, 161f
  temporal bone, 145, 146f, 147f
  ulna, 161f
Subarachnoid space, 250f, 251
Subatomic particles, 29, 31–32, 31f, 31t
  alpha, 33
  beta, 33
  size and chemical reactions, 41, 41t
Subclavian artery, left, 363f, 378, 379f
Subclavian vein, 380, 381f
  right lymphatic duct, 406f
  thoracic duct in relation to, 406f
Subcutaneous tissue (hypodermis), 115, 116f
  adipose tissue forming, 96f, 97, 115
Sublingual glands, 470f, 480

, 480

, tary canal
, 3f

, 507
46, 46f, 483
fant death syndrome
(SIDS), 464
iferous glands (sweat
glands), 119–121, 120f, 561
ugars
double (disaccharides),
45–46, 45f
simple (monosaccharides),
45, 45f
Sulci, 242, 244f
Sulfur
atomic structure, 33t
in cysteine, 50f
percentage of body mass, 30t
role of, 30t
Sunburn, 124
Sun exposure
cold sore eruptions and,
117, 123
excessive, 114f, 117
Superficial (external) direction/
orientation, 18f, 18t
Superior articular processes of vertebrae, 155, 155f, 156f
Superior (cranial, cephalad) direc-
tion/orientation, 18f, 18t
Superior mesenteric artery,
378, 379f
Superior mesenteric vein, 381f,
386, 386f
Superior nasal conchae, 148, 148f
Superior oblique muscle of
eye, 284f
Superior orbital fissure, 147, 148f
Superior rectus muscle of eye, 284f
Superior sagittal sinus, 249f, 250f
Superior vena cava, 362f, 363f,
364f, 369f
fetal, 384f
veins draining into, 380, 381f
Supination (body movement),
201f, 202
Support functions of bones,
134–135
Supporting cells
in CNS, 98, 100f,
230–232, 231f
in PNS, 98, 100f, 231f, 232
Suppressor T cells. See Regulatory
T cells
Suprascapular notch, 159f, 160
Sural nerve, 264t, 265f
Sural region of body, 16f, 17
Surface membrane barriers, in
body defense, 408f, 409,
414f, 414t
Surfactant, 447, 449f, 461
Surgical neck, 160
Surgical technician/
technologist, 382b
Surgical therapies for
obesity, 510b
Survival needs of human body,
11–12
autonomic behaviors supporting,
247–248
Suspensions, 42
Suspensory ligament of ovary,
554, 554f, 555f
Sutures, 145, 146f, 168, 169f, 170t
SV (stroke volume), 372,
373f, 390f
Swallowing (deglutition), 481–482,
482f, 484f, 485, 486f

Sweat, 120
Sweat glands (sudoriferous
glands), 119–121, 120f
ANS innervation/effects,
267f, 269t
mammary glands as, 561
Sweet taste receptors, 302
"Swollen glands," 405
Sympathetic chain ganglion,
268, 268f
Sympathetic chain/trunk, 268, 268f
Sympathetic division of ANS
aging and, 391
aging effects, 273
anatomy, 267–268, 267f, 268f
blood pressure and,
389–390, 390f
definition, 230, 230f, 266
excessive stimulation by, 270
functions/physiology,
268–270, 269t
heart rate and, 372–373, 373f
organs served by, 267f, 269t
parasympathetic division vs.,
269t, 270
pathways, 267–268, 268f
somatic nervous system
vs., 266f
summary of major effects
of, 269t
Sympathetic ganglia, 267f
organs serving, 267f
Symphysis joint, 170t
Symphysis pubis, 554f
Synapses, 232
neurotransmitters and,
239, 240f
Synaptic cleft, 189, 191f, 232
Synaptic vesicle, 191f
Synarthroses (immovable joints),
145, 166, 168, 170t
Synchondroses, 170t
Syndesmoses, 168, 169f, 170t
Synergist muscle, 202
Synovial fluid, 170, 171f
in joint cavity, 112f
Synovial joints, 168, 169f, 170–172
distinguishing features,
170, 171f
structure/types/mobility, 170t
types, based on shape,
170–172, 172f
Synovial membrane, 112, 112f,
170, 170t, 171f
Synthesis reactions, 40, 40f
dehydration, 45–46, 46f
Systemic circulation, 365–366, 365f
arteries of, 378, 379f
veins of, 380, 381f
Systemic lupus erythematosus
(SLE), 429
Systole, 369
ventricular, 371, 371f
Systolic pressure, 388, 389f

T3 (triiodothyronine), 319–320,
321f, 330t
T4 (thyroxine), 319–320,
321f, 330t
Tachycardia, 369
Tailbone. See Coccyx
Tail of sperm, 551f, 552
"Tailor's" muscle, 214
Talus, 166, 166f
Talus bone (ankle), 166, 166f
Target cells/organs, of hormone
action, 311, 312f
Tarsal bones (tarsals/tarsus), 144f,
165–166, 166f
Tarsal glands, 282, 283f
Tarsal region of body, 16f, 17
Tarsus, 165–166, 166f

Taste buds, 302–303, 303f, 472
Taste pores, 302, 303f
Taste sensations, 302
Taste sense, 302–303, 303f
aging effects, 305
aromas and, 302–303
Taste sense area of brain, 244f
Tattoos, 113b
Tau protein, 253b
T cells (T lymphocytes), 416
cytotoxic (killer), 424f, 425, 425f
differentiation and activation of,
416–418, 417f
interactions with other immune
response cells, 424f, 425,
426t, 427
lymph nodes and, 406,
417f, 418
thymus gland and, 329, 331t,
416, 417f
TCP (bone substitute), 168b
Tears, lysozyme in, 409, 414t
Tectorial membrane, 298,
299f, 300
Teeth, 479–480, 479f
Telophase stage of mitosis,
84, 85f
Temperature, body. See Body
temperature
Temperature (external)
blood pressure and, 391
chemical reactions influenced
by, 41, 41t
Temperature sensory receptors,
114t, 115, 236f
Template, nucleotide, 83, 84f
Temporal artery, as pulse
point, 387f
Temporal bones, 145, 146f,
147f, 148f
bone markings of, 145, 146f
dura mater in relation to, 249f
Temporalis muscle, 206f, 207,
216f, 217t
Temporal lobe, 243, 244f
Temporal lobe of cerebral hemisphere, 247f
Tendons, 97, 185, 185f
dense fibrous connective tissue
of, 95f, 97
functions, 185
role in reinforcing/stabilizing
joints, 187
Tendon sheath, 112, 112f, 170, 171f
Teniae coli, 478f, 479
Tension, muscle, 197
Tentorium cerebelli, 249f,
250f, 251
Terminal arterioles, 377, 377f
Terminal bronchioles, 447, 448f
Terminal ganglion, 266–267, 266f
Testes, 313, 314f, 331t, 546,
546f, 547f
blood supply, 546f
hormonal control of, 315f, 316,
329, 330t, 552–553, 552f
Testicular arteries, 378, 379f
Testosterone, 47t, 329
developmental disorders
and, 573
interstitial cells and, 546
production of, 546,
552–553, 552f
steroid abuse and, 203–204b
Tetanic muscle contraction,
194, 194f
Tetanus
fused (complete), 194, 194f
unfused (incomplete),
194f, 195
Tetanus (lockjaw), 194
Tetany, 321

TF (tissue factor), 349f, 350
Thalamus, 246, 246f, 247f, 257f
Thermal damage, skin's protective
receptors and, 114t
Thermal energy, 28
Thick (myosin) filaments, 188f, 189
Thigh
blood vessels of, 378, 379f
bone (femur), 164, 165f
muscles of, 211, 212–213f, 214,
216f, 217t, 218f, 219t
nerves serving, 264t
Thin (actin) filaments, 188f, 189
Third-degree burns, 124, 125f
Third ventricle of brain, 246, 246f,
247f, 250f
Thirst center of hypothalamus, 532
Thirst mechanism, 532–533, 533f
disorders, 326
Thoracic aorta, 378, 379f
arterial branches, 378, 379f
Thoracic cage (bony thorax), 144f,
157–158, 158f
Thoracic cavity, 20, 20f
heart location in, 362, 362f, 446f
muscles, 208–209, 208f, 216f
nerves serving, 264t
organs of, 446f
pressure changes in, blood
pressure and, 387
Thoracic curvature, 151, 151f
Thoracic duct, 404, 406f
Thoracic region of body, 16f, 17
Thoracic spinal nerves, 255f,
263f, 267f
Thoracic vertebrae, 150, 151f, 155,
156f, 446f
Thoracolumbar division. See Sym-
pathetic division of ANS
Thorax, bony. See Thoracic cage
Throat. See Pharynx
Thrombin, 349f, 350
Thrombocytopenia, 351
Thrombophlebitis, 377
Thrombopoietin, 349
Thrombosis, coronary, 350
Thrombus, 350
TH (thyrotropic hormone),
315–316, 315f
Thumb, joints of, 171, 172f
Thymine (T), 54f, 55
Thymosin, 329, 331t, 408, 416
Thymus gland, 313, 314f, 329,
331t, 407f, 408, 446f
T cells arising from,
416–418, 417f
Thyroid cartilage, 443f, 444
Thyroid gland, 313, 319–321,
330–331t
blood calcium levels and, 322f
hormones produced by,
319–321, 321f, 330–331t
location, 314f, 319, 320f
TSH and, 315–316, 315f, 330t
Thyroid hormone, 319–320, 321f
mechanism of action, 311, 312f
Thyroid-stimulating hormone
(TSH), 315–316, 315f,
319, 330t
Thyrotropic hormone (TH). See
Thyroid-stimulating
hormone
Thyroxine (T4), 319–320,
321f, 330t
basal metabolic rate and, 503
effects on heart activity, 373
TIA (transient ischemic
attack), 255
Tibia, 144f, 164–165, 165f, 215f
Tibial arteries, 378, 379f
Tibialis anterior muscle, 214, 215f,
216f, 217t

Tibial nerve, 264t, 265f
Tibial tuberosity, 165, 165f
Tibial vein, 380, 381f
Tibiofibular joint
    distal, 165f
    proximal, 165f
Tidal volume (TV), 452, 453f
Tight junctions, 68–69, 69f, 89
Tinea pedis (athlete's foot), 123
Tinodr, 45
Tissue factor (TF), 349f, 350
Tissue fluid. See Interstitial fluid
Tissue level, in body's structural
    hierarchy, 3f, 4
Tissue plasminogen activator
    (t-PA), 393b
Tissue repair (wound healing),
    100–101
Tissues, 4, 88–101. See also
    specific type
    aging process and, 101, 104
    benefits of studying, 88
    connective, 93–97
    developmental aspects, 101, 104
    epithelial, 88–93
    gas exchanges and, 365, 365f,
        394, 394f, 454, 454f
    injury to/repair of, 100–101
    repair (wound healing), 100–101
    scar, 100–101
    types, 4
T lymphocytes. See T cells
TMR (total metabolic rate),
    503–504
TNF (tumor necrosis factor), 427t
"Toe dancer's" muscle, 214
Toe joints, muscles acting on, 211
Tongue, 443f, 470f, 471, 471f
    taste sense and, 302–303, 303f
Tonicity of solutions, 80–81b
Tonometer, 289
Tonsillitis, 408, 444
Tonsils, 303f, 407f, 408, 443f, 444,
    471f, 472
Torticollis (wryneck), 207
Total metabolic rate (TMR),
    503–504
Touch receptors, 114t, 115, 116f,
    117, 236f
t-PA (tissue plasminogen
    activator), 393b
Trabeculae of lymph node,
    406, 407f
Trace elements, 30t
Trachea, 442f, 444–445, 446f
    esophagus in relation to,
        444, 445f
    hyaline cartilage of, 94, 95f,
        444, 445f
    obstructions, Heimlich maneuver
        and, 444
    in swallowing, 485, 486f
Tracheoesophageal fistula, 506
Tracheostomy, 444
Tracts (nerve), 234
    between brain and spinal cord,
        256–257, 257f
Transcription phase of protein
    synthesis, 86, 87f
Trans fats, 49
Transfer RNA (tRNA), 55,
    86–88, 87f
Transfusions, 351, 353–354,
    353t, 354f
    HIV virus and, 433b
    human blood groups, 351,
        353, 353t
    reactions to, 353
Transient ischemic attack
    (TIA), 255
Transitional epithelium, 90, 92f, 93
    of urinary bladder, 529

Translation phase of protein
    synthesis, 86–88, 87f
Transplant/graft rejection, 416,
    427, 429
Transport, membrane. See
    Membrane transport
Transport proteins, as functional
    proteins, roles in body, 51t
Transport vesicles, 71, 71f
Transverse arch of foot, 166, 166f
Transverse colon, 470f, 478, 478f
    peritoneal attachments and, 475f
Transverse (cross) plane or
    section, 17, 19f
Transverse mesocolon, 478f
Transverse processes, vertebral,
    151f, 155, 155f, 156f
Transversus abdominis muscle,
    208f, 209, 216f
Transverse sinus, 249f
Trapezium bone, 162f
Trapezius muscle, 206f, 209–210,
    209f, 216f, 218f, 219t
Trapezoid bone, 162f
Tremors, of Parkinson's disease,
    253–254b
Triceps brachii muscle, 209f, 211,
    216f, 218f, 219t
Tricuspid valve (right AV valve),
    364f, 366, 367f
Trigeminal nerve (cranial nerve V),
    259t, 261f
Triglycerides (neutral fats), 46,
    47t, 49
    formation/structure of, 48f
Trigone, 528, 529f
Triiodothyronine (T3), 319–320,
    321f, 330t
Triplet, in protein synthesis, 86,
    87f, 88
Triquetrum bone, 162f
Tritium, as hydrogen isotope, 32f
tRNA (transfer RNA), 55,
    86–88, 87f
Trochanter (bone marking), 138t
    femoral, 164, 165f
Trochlea, 284f
    humerus, 160, 161f
Trochlear nerve (cranial nerve IV),
    259t, 261f
    extrinsic eye muscles supplied
        by, 284f
Trochlear notch of ulna, 161, 161f
Trophoblast, 564f, 565
Tropic hormones, 314
True pelvis, 163f, 164
True ribs, 157–158, 158f
True vocal cords (vocal folds),
    443f, 444
Trunk, nerves serving, 264t
Trunk muscles, 207
    anterior, 208–209, 208f,
        216f, 217t
    posterior, 209–210, 209f,
        218f, 219t
Trypsin, 490
TSH (thyroid-stimulating
    hormone), 315–316, 315f,
    319, 330t
T tubule, 191f
Tubal ligation, 575b
Tubercle (bone marking), 138t
Tuberosity (bone marking), 138t
Tubular reabsorption, 523f,
    524, 525f
Tubular secretion, 523f, 524, 525f
Tubulin, 74f
Tumor necrosis factor (TNF), 427t
Tumor (neoplasm), 102–103b, 104
Tumor suppressor genes
    (antioncogenes), 102b
Tunica albuginea, 546, 546f

Tunica externa, 375f, 376
Tunica intima, 374, 375f, 376
Tunica media, 375f, 376
Turk's saddle (sella turcica), 145,
    146f, 314
TV (tidal volume), 452, 453f
T wave, 370b
Tympanic cavity (middle ear), 22,
    294–295, 295f
Tympanic membrane (eardrum),
    294, 295f
Type 1 (juvenile, brittle) diabetes,
    327, 429
Type 2 (adult-onset) diabetes,
    326–327
Type 2 diabetes mellitus, elderly
    and, 335
Type A daughter cells, 550f, 551
Type A individuals, 270
Type B daughter cells, 550f, 551

Ulcer
    bleeding, 344t
    decubitus, 118, 118f
    peptic, 488–489b
Ulna, 144f, 160, 161, 161f, 162f
Ulnar artery, 378, 379f
Ulnar nerve, 264t, 265f
Ulnar vein, 380, 381f
Ultrasound
    CNS disorders and, 271b
    to speed fracture repair, 167b
Ultrasound imaging (ultrasonogra-
    phy), 8–9b
Umami (taste sensation), 302
Umbilical arteries, 383–384, 384f
Umbilical cord, 383, 384f, 565f,
    566, 566f
Umbilical region of body, 16f, 17
    of abdominopelvic cavity,
        21–22, 21f
Umbilical veins, 383, 384f
Unconsciousness (coma), 248
Uniaxial movement of hinge
    joints, 171, 172f
Unipennate muscle structure,
    205, 205f
Unipolar neurons, 237, 237f
Universal solvent, 42
Unsaturated fatty acids, 48f, 49
Upper limbs
    anterior landmarks, 16–17, 16f
    blood vessels of, 378, 379f,
        380, 381f
    bones of, 144f, 160–162,
        161f, 162f
    developmental aspects,
        175, 175f
    factors affecting
        movement, 160
    nerves serving, 264t, 265f
    posterior landmarks, 16f, 17
Uracil, 55
Urea, 114t, 341f, 500, 524
Ureters, 519f, 520f, 522f,
    528, 529f
    female, 555f
    transitional epithelium of, 90,
        92f, 93
Urethra, 519f, 529–530, 529f
    ANS innervation/effects,
        267f, 269t
    female, 554f
    male, 530, 548
Urethral orifices, 528, 529f
Urethral sphincters, 529, 529f
Urethritis, 530, 573
Uric acid, 114t, 341f, 524
Urinary bladder, 519f, 528, 529,
    529f, 530f
    ANS innervation/effects,
        267f, 269t

    female, 554f
    fetal, 384f
    male, 547f
    peritoneal attachments and, 47
    transitional epithelium of, 90,
        92f, 93, 529
Urinary incontinence, 538, 540
Urinary retention, 530
Urinary system, 6f, 7, 517–543. See
    also specific structures
    aging and, 538, 540
    developmental aspects of,
        538, 540
    function overview, 6f, 7
    homeostatic imbalances,
        519–520, 524, 528, 529–530,
        530, 533,
        535, 538
    homeostatic relationships, 539
    kidneys, 518–528. See also
        Kidneys
    organs of, 518, 519f
    in pregnancy, 567–568
    structure overview, 6f, 7
Urine
    abnormal constituents, 527, 528t
    acidic pH as body
        defense, 414t
    characteristics, 524–525,
        527, 528t
    formation of, 523–524,
        523f, 524f
Urochrome, 524
USDA Food Guide Pyramid,
    493, 495f
Uterine (fallopian) tubes, 554–555,
    554f, 555f
Uterine (menstrual) cycle, 329,
    556, 559–561, 560f
    hormonal interactions of, 560f
    iron-deficiency anemia
        and, 344t
Uterosacral ligament, 555, 555f
Uterus, 554f, 555–556
    blood supply, 555f
    peritoneal attachments and, 475f
    wall of, 555f
UV radiation
    cold sore eruptions and,
        117, 123
    melanin and skin's protection
        from, 114t
Uvula, 443f, 471, 471f

Vaccines, 420, 420f
    cancer, 103b
Vagina, 554f, 555f, 556
Vagus nerve (cranial nerve X),
    260t, 261f
    cardiac output and, 372, 373f
    pancreatic juice secretion
        and, 491f
    taste impulses and, 302
Valence shell, 35, 36f
Valve incompetency, heart
    murmurs and, 372
Valves
    in heart. See Heart valves
    in lymphatic collecting vessels,
        404, 405f
    in lymph capillaries
        (minivalves), 404, 405f
    in veins, 375f, 376, 376f
        blood pressure and, 387
Valvular stenosis, 366
Variable, in homeostatic controls,
    12–13, 13f
Variable (V) region of antibodies,
    421f, 422
Varicose veins, 377
Vascular endothelial growth factor
    (VEGF), 167–168b

...349f
...4–395. *See also* ...els; Circulation ... *See* Blood ...deferens, 546, ...f, 548 ...ny, 548, 575b ...onstriction, 389 ...ood pressure and, 389–390, 390f
cold temperatures and, 391
in flight-or-fight response, 390
as heat-promoting mechanism, 504
in hemostasis, 349

Vasodilation
alcohol drinking and, 391
hot temperatures and, 391

Vasopressin, 319. *See also* Antidiuretic hormone

Vastus intermedius muscle, 214, 217t

Vastus lateralis muscle, 213f, 216f, 217t

Vastus medialis muscle, 213f, 216f, 217t

Vastus muscles, 213f, 214, 216f, 217t

VC (vital capacity), 452, 453f

VEGF (vascular endothelial growth factor), 167–168b

Veins, 374, 375f
arteries *vs.*, 376
blood pressure in, 388f
lymphatic vessels in relation to, 403–404, 404f
major, of systemic circulation, 380, 381f
thrombophlebitis, 377
valves in, 376, 376f
varicose, 377

Vellus hairs, 127

Venae cavae
blood pressure in, 388f
inferior, 363–364f, 365, 381f
veins draining into, 380, 381f
superior, 362f, 363–364f, 365, 369f, 380, 381f

Venous return
cardiac output and, 372–374, 373f
exercise and, 372
hemorrhage and, 389–390, 390f
skeletal muscle activity and, 376, 376f

Venous system, lymphatic vessels in relation to, 404, 404f

Venous valves, 375f, 376, 376f

Ventilation, liquid, 356b

Ventral (anterior) body landmarks, 16–17, 16f

Ventral (anterior) direction/orientation, 18f, 18t

Ventral (anterior) horns, 256, 256f

Ventral body cavity, 20–22, 20f

Ventral columns of spinal cord, 256–257

Ventral rami, 262, 263f

Ventral root of spinal nerve, 256, 256f, 263f

Ventricles of brain, 242, 247f, 250f

Ventricles of heart
anatomical differences in, 365–366, 366f
as discharging chambers/pumps, 365, 365f
left, 363–364f, 365–366, 365f, 366f
right, 363–364f, 365–366, 365f, 366f

Ventricular systole of cardiac cycle, 371, 371f

Venules, 374, 375f
blood pressure in, 388f
flow of blood from arterioles to, 377, 377f
postcapillary, 377, 377f

Vernix caseosa, 127

Vertebrae, 144f, 150
cervical, 150, 151f
collapse of, 175, 176f
herniated discs, 151
lumbar, 150, 151f
structural features, 154–155, 155f
thoracic, 150, 151f

Vertebral arch, 155, 155f, 156f

Vertebral artery, 378, 379f, 383, 383f

Vertebral column (spine), 144f, 150–157, 151f
herniated discs, 151
muscles that move, 209f, 210, 216f, 217t
vertebral collapse, 175, 176f

Vertebral foramen, 155, 155f, 156f

Vertebral region of body, 16f, 17

Vertebral vein, 380, 381f

Vertigo, 300

Vesicles, 394, 394f

Vesicular breathing sounds, 453

Vesicular (Graafian) follicle, 553, 553f

Vesicular transport, 79, 81–83, 81f, 82f

Vestibular membrane, 298f

Vestibular nerve, 260t, 261f, 296f, 297, 297f

Vestibule
of bony labyrinth, 295, 295f, 297f
of female external genitalia, 556, 556f
of oral cavity, 471, 471f

Vestibulocochlear nerve (cranial nerve VIII), 260t, 261f, 295f, 297, 297f, 300

Villi of small intestine, 476–477, 477f

Visceral afferents (visceral sensory fibers), 229, 230f

Visceral layer of serous membranes, 111f, 112, 364f, 446f, 447, 473f, 475f

Visceral muscle, 98, 99f, 185. *See also* Smooth muscle

Visceral pericardium, 111f, 364f

Visceral peritoneum, 111f, 473f, 475f, 556

Visceral pleura, 111f, 446f, 447

Visceral sensory fibers (visceral afferents), 229, 230f

Visceral (smooth) muscle, 98, 99f, 185

Visible light, 288, 288f

Vision
aging and, 304
developmental aspects, 304
focusing disorders, 292–293b, 293f
homeostatic imbalances, 286, 288, 289
night blindness, 286

Visual acuity, 286

Visual area of brain, 243, 244f

Visual fields, 290–291, 291f

Visual pathways, 290–291, 291f

Visual pigments, 287–288b

Vital capacity (VC), 452, 453f

Vital signs, 387

Vitamin A, 47t
night blindness and, 286
retinal and, 287–288b

Vitamin B12
deficiency, 344t
intrinsic factor and, 475

Vitamin D, 47t, 333t
rickets and, 142
skin synthesis of, 114t, 115

Vitamin E, 47t

Vitamin K, 47t, 491
in blood clotting, 350

Vitamins, 47t
as coenzymes, 495
as nutrients, 495

Vitreous body, 289

Vitreous humor, 285f, 289

Vocal folds (true vocal cords), 443f, 444

Voice box. *See* Larynx

Volkmann's (perforating) canals, 139f, 140

Voluntary muscle, 98, 99f, 184t, 185

Voluntary nervous system, 230, 230f

Voluntary sphincters, 478

Vomer bone, 147f, 148f, 149

Vomiting (emesis), 487

Vulnerable plaque hypothesis, 393b

Vulva, 556–557, 556f

Walking, 211, 212, 214

Water
heat absorbing quality in blood, 341f
diffusion of (osmosis), 77, 78f
fluid balance and, 531–535, 531f, 532f
molecular structure, 37, 39, 39f, 42
in plasma, 340, 341f
polarity of, 37, 39, 39f, 42
properties of, 42
protective cushioning function of, 42
as survival factor, 12
as universal solvent, 42

Water balance, 531–535, 531f
intake/output, 532–535, 533f

WBCs. *See* White blood cells

Weak acids, 43, 536–537, 536f

Weak bases, 43, 536–537, 536f

Weight lifting exercise, 197f, 198

Weight-loss drugs, 509–510b

Wheezing (respiratory sounds), 453

White blood cells (leukocytes), 98f, 340, 341f, 342f, 344–345
summary table, 346t
thymus and, 329

Whitehead, 119

White matter, 234–235
cerebral, 242, 244f, 246f
spinal cord, 256–257, 256f, 257f

White thrombus. *See* Platelet plug

Windpipe. *See* Trachea

Wisdom teeth, 479, 479f

Withdrawal (flexor) reflex, 240, 241f, 242

Wound healing (tissue repair), 100–101

Wrist (carpal bones/carpus), 144f, 162, 162f
muscles that move, 211

Wryneck (torticollis), 207

Xenografts, 427

Xiphisternal joint, 157, 158f

Xiphoid process, 157, 158f

X rays, imaging techniques *vs.*, 8–9b

Yawning, 452t

Yellow bone marrow, 136, 137f

Yellow marrow (medullary) cavity, 136, 137f

Yellow skin tone, 119

Z discs, 187, 188f, 192f

Zygomatic bones, 146f, 147f, 148f, 149

Zygomatic processes, 145, 146f, 147f

Zygomaticus muscle, 206f, 207, 216f, 217t

Zygote, 564, 564f